Manufacturing Management

THE IRWIN SERIES IN INDUSTRIAL ENGINEERING AND MANAGEMENT

EDITORIAL COMMITTEE

M. R. LOHMANN
Dean, College of Engineering
Oklahoma State University

JOHN F. MEE
Chairman, Department of Management
Indiana University

MANUFACTURING MANAGEMENT
Revised Edition, by FRANKLIN G. MOORE, *University of Michigan*

ANALYSIS FOR PRODUCTION MANAGEMENT
By EDWARD H. BOWMAN, *Massachusetts Institute of Technology,*
and ROBERT B. FETTER, *Yale University*

MOTION AND TIME STUDY
Revised Edition, by BENJAMIN W. NIEBEL, *Pennsylvania State University*

ORGANIZATION FOR PRODUCTION
By E. S. ROSCOE, *Pennsylvania State University*

PERSONNEL MANAGEMENT
Third Edition, by MICHAEL J. JUCIUS, *The Ohio State University*

CASES IN MANAGEMENT
By HENRY M. CRUICKSHANK, *Stonehill College*
and KEITH DAVIS, *Indiana University*

INDUSTRIAL MANAGEMENT IN TRANSITION
Revised Edition, by GEORGE FILIPETTI, *University of Minnesota*

THE WRITINGS OF THE GILBRETHS
Edited by WILLIAM R. SPRIEGEL, *University of Texas*
and CLARK E. MYERS, *Ohio University*

PRINCIPLES OF MANAGEMENT
Revised Edition, by GEORGE R. TERRY, *Northwestern University*

PRODUCTION CONTROL: Text and Cases
By WILLIAM VORIS, *Los Angeles State College*

SAFETY MANAGEMENT: Accident Cost and Control
By ROLLIN H. SIMONDS, *Michigan State University, and*
JOHN V. GRIMALDI, *General Electric Company*

EXECUTIVE DECISION MAKING
By MANLEY HOWE JONES, *Illinois Institute of Technology*

DESIGNING FOR PRODUCTION
By BENJAMIN W. NIEBEL, *Pennsylvania State University, and*
EDWARD N. BALDWIN, *Westinghouse Electric Corporation*

JOB EVALUATION: Text and Cases
Revised Edition, by JOHN A. PATTON, *John A. Patton Management*
Engineers, Inc., and C. L. LITTLEFIELD, *North Texas State College*

SELECTED READINGS IN MANAGEMENT
Edited by FREMONT A. SHULL, JR., *Indiana University*

MANUFACTURING MANAGEMENT

by

FRANKLIN G. MOORE, Ph.D.

Professor of Industrial Management
University of Michigan

REVISED EDITION

1958

RICHARD D. IRWIN, INC.

HOMEWOOD, ILLINOIS

REVISED EDITION
First Printing, January, 1958
Second Printing, July, 1958
Third Printing, December, 1958

Library of Congress Catalogue Card No. 58–5804

PRINTED IN THE UNITED STATES OF AMERICA

PREFACE

Several new managerial developments have taken place since the first edition of *Manufacturing Management* came out. More attention is being given to planning for the future. Companies ask, what will the nation be like in ten years?, in twenty years? What should our company be like in ten years and in twenty years? What should we do now in order to get to the place where we should be?

Answers to these and other questions have brought greater emphasis on several areas in manufacturing. More money is being spent for research, nearly twice as much as when the first edition of this book was printed. So, more attention is put on research in this revision.

Also capital expenditures, the money spent for buildings, equipment, and machines, are now more tightly controlled than they used to be. These set the course of a business for the years ahead. Companies now watch to see that today's spending will lead to tomorrow's goals. One whole new chapter has been added to cover this development.

Along with closer control over activities that have long-range effects has come more interest in cost control. There is little in writing on this subject for the student to turn to. So we have added a "how-to-do-it" chapter on how to control costs.

Operations research and linear programming, outgrowths of World War II, have come of age. The attempt to use a mathematical approach to solving business problems has proved to be somewhat controversial. Men argue back and forth about whether you can use formulas to get answers to business problems. A chapter has been added explaining these procedures and pointing out the strong and weak points of operations research and linear programming.

Electronic computers have also appeared since the first edition. We hear fabulous stories of what they can do. What they are, what they do, and how they do it, and their good and bad points are described in a new chapter.

Besides these specific areas where whole chapters have been added, all of the other chapters in the book have been completely rewritten to incorporate new material and to make the text more readable. The writing style is now more conversational and streamlined. And, to make them more accessible, the study cases have been put at the ends of chapters instead of at the end of the book.

This edition, like the first, is, indirectly, the work of many people. Ideas are where you find them; they come from talking with other people, from reading what others have written, from classroom discussions, from plant visits, and from personal experience. I am indebted also, for ideas to the many users of the first edition, who sent in letters about the ways we could improve this revised edition.

I am indebted also to the several businessmen who read parts of the revised manuscript to check its technical correctness and to the many companies which furnished pictures. I want particularly to thank Wallace G. Gardner for suggestions in the area of operations research. And I want to thank Charles E. Palmer, who read the whole manuscript, and the several students who read parts of it and made suggestions to improve readability. I am also grateful to Mrs. Esther Rentschler and Mrs. Elaine Palmer for their help in typing.

FRANKLIN G. MOORE

ANN ARBOR, MICHIGAN
October, 1957

TABLE OF CONTENTS

TABLE OF CASE PROBLEMS

Chapter 1

INTRODUCTION

The president of a manufacturing company is responsible for making, financing, and selling products. Our interest is in the "making" end of the work. What products should we make? How are they designed? How are they made? How many should we make of each kind? When should we make them? What machines do we need? What materials? How many men? How do we direct their work? This book deals with answers to these and related questions.

We are interested in how all of this work is done, how it is directed and controlled, the decisions that have to be made, and the pros and cons of different ways of doing things.

ORIGINS OF THE FACTORY SYSTEM

Our Western industrialized civilization seems so firmly rooted that it is hard to believe it is less than 200 years old. In the long history of men that is but yesterday. It has been said that George Washington would fit better into the world of Julius Caesar than into today's world—so great has been the change since his time and so little before.

The Great Inventions. What caused this great change? How and when did it all start? The Industrial Revolution, for that is what it is called, started in England. It was an outgrowth of changes that had been going on slowly for centuries. Trade had increased, wealth had increased, roads had been improved, agriculture flourished. The stage was set. Then came the immediate causes that triggered the rapid change. Between 1764 and 1785 came five inventions: (1) the *spinning jenny*, (2) the *water frame*, (3) the *mule-spinner*, (4) the *power loom*, and (5) the *steam engine*. They set off the Industrial Revolution. The time is easy to fix in mind because it happens also to cover the period of the American Revolutionary War.

During the early 1700's England's trade in woolen and cotton cloth flourished. English cloth was exported all over the world. But both spinning thread and weaving cloth were done by hand—by methods not

1

much different from those used a thousand years earlier. Because the trade was so profitable, merchants tried to figure out how to spin and weave faster and with less work. They even offered money prizes to anyone who might improve the processes.

Kay's Flying Shuttle. In 1733, James Kay introduced the flying shuttle. With it a weaver could weave wider cloth and could weave faster. The flying shuttle is not usually listed as one of the immediate causes of the Industrial Revolution, and it is not in the list above. Perhaps it should be; it certainly helped set the stage because it upset the balance between spinning and weaving. Now, weaving was so much faster that the weavers easily used all the yarn and thread the spinners could make.

The Science Museum, London

FIG. 1–1. Hargreaves' spinning jenny, 1764.

Hargreaves' Spinning Jenny. Great effort then went into trying to spin faster. James Hargreaves' spinning jenny solved the problem. Patented in 1764, it was a manually operated machine for spinning several threads at one time. Figure 1–1 shows that it was not much of a machine by today's standards. It was clumsy and hard to operate, but it greatly increased the spinners' output.

Arkwright's Water Frame.   Improvements in the jenny were soon made. In 1769, Richard Arkwright patented his water frame. It made threads of greater strength than the jenny, and it saved labor by using animal or water power instead of men.

Crompton's Mule-Spinner.   By 1779, Samuel Crompton developed his mule-spinner. It spun threads both better and with less effort than either the jenny or the water frame. Although still cumbersome, it worked well enough to make threads of finer and more even quality than had ever been made before by hand.

Cartwright's Power Loom.   Improvements in spinning turned the pendulum the other way. Now, spinning outran weaving. So there was great pressure to speed up weaving. In 1785, Edmund Cartwright patented a power loom which ultimately broke the bottleneck in weaving. Although his early models didn't work very well, improvements were soon made and the power loom came into common use.

Watt's Steam Engine.   Spinning and weaving machines could hardly have started the Industrial Revolution by themselves. Power to run them was necessary, and man, animal, water, and wind power all have too many limitations. While textile machines were being developed, James Watt was developing a workable steam engine. He took out his first patent in 1769, but it was not until 1785 that one of his engines was satisfactorily used in a cotton mill. Thereafter, its use spread rapidly. By 1802, Trevithick had put a steam engine on wheels, and the railroad was born, although it was a few more years before Stephenson developed a really practical railroad engine.

Whether we regard the inventions in the textile industry and Watt's steam engine as merely important events in the early stages of the Industrial Revolution, as some historians do, or whether we consider them its main cause is not too important. The early days of the Industrial Revolution showed that machines could do the work of skilled craftsmen —and do it faster and cheaper and often better. After machines proved themselves in the textile industry, other machines were developed in other fields.

Transfer of Skill to Machines.   Before going on we should note a fundamental change that occurred with the coming of machines. Skill was transferred from worker to machine. Woolen yarn and cotton threads could be made of unvarying thickness and strength on machines operated (or really tended) by relatively unskilled workers. Cloth, better than the best craftsman made, could be woven by a machine plus its operator, who was not a skilled weaver. Truly the skill was transferred to the machine.

Skill is only partly the ability to do things with your hands. It is partly a matter of knowing what to do. Knowing what to do is mental skill. This skill too went over to the machine. Weaving machines could automatically make designs in cloth, getting the right threads in the right places. In a very real sense, mental skill, you might even say thought, was transferred to the machine. At least, once set up, the machines did the work, without the operator having to know how to do it by hand.

Early Machine Tool Industry.   In the early days of the Industrial Revolution there was no machine tool industry. Most of the machines did not work very well because the parts fit so poorly. Wooden parts were common, and the metal parts were crude. There was no good way to make parts for a close fit. James Watt had great difficulty with his early steam engines because he couldn't, with the equipment available, make close-fitting parts.

Better machines to make better parts which in turn made better machines developed only slowly at first. Improvement came faster after

The Science Museum, London

FIG. 1–2.   Maudslay's lathe, 1797.

1797 when Henry Maudslay introduced the power-driven lead-screw toolholder (shown in Fig. 1–2) for lathes. With it, all parts made on lathes could be made much more accurately.

"Interchangeable" Parts.   Within a few years, in the United States, Eli Whitney and Simeon North succeeded in making "interchangeable" parts by machine and at reasonable cost.[1] Earlier both the French and the Russians had made simple assembled products with interchangeable parts. But, because the parts were made largely by hand, they were so costly that the idea didn't take hold in either country.

Effects on Employees.   By 1800, machines were the rule in textile factories in England, and they were becoming common in other industries. By 1825, when production by machines was the rule in most industries

---

[1] "Interchangeable" parts do not have to be hand fitted to a particular assembly to operate. Thus triggers and frames for pistols are made to size so exactly that any trigger will fit and operate smoothly in any frame.

in England, far-reaching social changes had occurred. Production had increased remarkably, and the prices of many manufactured goods were lower. The new class of factory workers, however, participated very little in the gains. Many women and children were employed. Their wages were low and work hours long. In parts of England and Scotland four out of five employees in the textile industry were women and children. In fact even as late as 1900 three out of every four employees still were women and children.[2]

Working conditions got so bad in many industries in the early 1800's that they were investigated by the English Parliament. What it found (14- to 16-hour workdays, children starting to work as a rule before they were 10 years old, unhealthy working conditions, very low pay) caused Parliament to pass laws limiting the hours and conditions of work of women and children. Parliament also repealed its centuries-old anti-union laws. Further regulations, always in the direction of more protection for employees, were passed in succeeding years. Helped by such laws and by continuing increases in output from using machines, the standard of living of factory workers improved steadily though slowly.

EARLY DEVELOPMENT OF FACTORIES IN THE UNITED STATES

What about the rest of the world? Was the Industrial Revolution an all-English affair? In its early days—yes—pretty largely. It started in England, and it started in the textile industry, and in that industry England dominated the world. From England and from the textile industry the Industrial Revolution spread rapidly, *but only to western Europe and the United States.* The rest of the world still slept on. And even in western Europe long-established ways of doing things yielded only slowly to new methods.

But the seed found fertile soil in the United States. Before the American Revolutionary War the American colonies were not allowed to develop their own industries. After the war (by that time the great inventions had been made), and no longer held down by mother country restrictions, American industry quickly started to develop. An expanding economy, free lands in the West, the need for industry, and a shortage of workers—all contributed to rapid industrial development. The pace was speeded by knowledge of English and European methods brought by immigrant workers. Nor was it held back by a long heritage of "we have always done it that way."

Early Mechanization.   Right from the start American manufacturers turned to machines. They had to, because they could never hire as many employees as they wanted. A French observer, traveling in the United States in the early 1830's, commented that the Americans adopted "every

---

[2] Abbott P. Usher, *The Industrial History of England* (New York: Houghton Mifflin Co., 1920), pp. 357–63.

new method which leads by a shorter road to wealth, every machine which spares labor, every instrument which diminishes the cost of production."[3]

Whitworth-Wallis Report.   By the middle of the nineteenth century American factories were, in many cases, more highly mechanized than factories in England and Europe. A report made by the English observers Whitworth and Wallis in 1854 states:

The Bettmann Archive

FIG. 1–3.   Calico printing in the early 1800's.

In the States the labour-market is higher than with ourselves, especially as respects skilled labour. It has, therefore, been a principal aim as much as possible to apply machinery for the purpose of supplying this want, and, as the consequence, it will be seen that some of the principal achievements of American inventions have been acquired in this department. To this very want of human skill, and the absolute necessity for supplying it, may be attributed the extraordinary ingenuity displayed in many of their labour-saving machines, where automatic action so completely supplies the place of the more abundant hand-labour of older manufacturing countries.[4]

Both Whitworth and Wallis described many automatic machines which they saw on their visit to the United States. Wallis reported seeing an automatic button-making machine which made buttons from sheet metal and wire at the rate of 200 a minute. The attendant had only to feed a tube with blanks and occasionally put another coil of wire in the ma-

---

[3] Alexis de Tocqueville, *Democracy in America* (1840) (New York: Colonial Press, 1900), Vol. II, p. 46.

[4] *The Industry of the United States*, compiled from the official reports of Sir Joseph Whitworth and Mr. George Wallis (London: George Routledge & Co., 1854), p. v.

chine. Whitworth reported that American workers, spinning yarn by improved machinery, turned out over *three thousand times as much per man* as did skilled spinners using hand methods in India.

The Whitworth-Wallis report and other records show that the persistent labor shortage in this country stimulated the invention of labor-saving machines more here than abroad. Even by the 1850's some machines had upped output remarkably.

American Shop Conditions in 1850. In the early years both the number and size of factories increased rapidly. Compared to England and Europe the pay was good, though certainly not by today's standards. And the hours were long. Here are reports made in 1850 of the work practices of two companies. The first one made cloth, and the second one shoes.

1. The cloth manufacturer:
   Labour begins, or the gate closes, at five o'clock A.M. from May 1 to September 1, and at ten minutes before sunrise the remainder of the year. A first bell is rung about forty minutes before, to allow time to prepare for work. *Labour ends* at half-past seven P.M. from September 20 to March 20; at seven from May 1 to September 1; and at fifteen minutes after sunset for the remainder of the year.
   The principal part of the operatives work by the job, the males earning on the average about $5.80 per week, and the females about $2.75 per week, besides board, which is $1.50 to $2 per week for males, and $1.25 for females.
2. The shoe manufacturer:
   All the labour is paid for by the piece. Idle time here receives no compensation, and none need be spent. Full employment can always be obtained by competent workmen. The binders earn from $3 to $4, and the workmen from $3 to $9 per week, according to inclination, ability and time employed (the latter averaging about $5), out of which they pay their board, which in Lynn is $2 to $2.50 for males, and $1.25 to $1.75 for females. The net earnings of the females are about half as great as those of the males.[5]

EARLY INTEREST IN MANAGEMENT

Interest in *how to manage* an organization came late rather than early. There is almost nothing about management in books and magazines published before 1850.

In 1776 Adam Smith, in his *Wealth of Nations*, called attention to the benefits of specialization of labor. He reported that in the manufacture of pins one man cut them to length, another put points on, and another heads and that their total output far exceeded what three other men each making pins complete could turn out. Specialization was, however, practiced in the armor factories of Rome and Greece, so we can hardly say that Smith's observations were new.

Two generations later Charles Babbage wrote a book, *On the Economy*

---

[5] *Report of the Sanitary Commission of the State of Massachusetts* (1850), describing the practices of the Bay State Mills, Lawrence, Mass., and an unidentified shoe manufacturer.

of Manufactures (1832), in which he added two more ideas. (1) He pointed out that cutting jobs up into parts and assigning each part to a different worker (specialization) allowed the employer to buy just the right kind and quality and amount of labor for the job. And (2) Babbage described a method of timing jobs used by a French manufacturer. (Frederick W. Taylor is usually credited with having originated time study in the 1880's.)

Other references to early interest in how to do things better are few and far between. One early writer, Andrew Ure, said that Arkwright (the water-frame inventor) had contributed more as a manager than as an inventor because he trained men "to renounce their desultory habits of work, and to identify themselves with the unvarying regularity of the complex automaton."[6] He also gave Arkwright credit for devising and administering a "successful code of factory discipline." We could wish that Ure had told us just what Arkwright did, but he doesn't.

George Stephenson, who developed the early locomotive, also recognized the existence of managerial problems. In a speech made in 1841, he described some of the difficulties he had while developing the locomotive 30 years earlier. But those troubles were, he said, "little compared with the difficulty I have had in the management of men."[7] He, too, fails to tell us what he did about it.

The Last Half of the Century. During the last half of the 1800's the United States expanded rapidly to the West and American industry grew by leaps and bounds. The demands of the Civil War for enormous quantities of standardized guns, ammunition, uniforms, and so on helped develop larger, more efficient, and more highly mechanized manufacturing companies in the industrial North. Following the Civil War there was a serious depression, but after it was over industry surged ahead to new highs. By 1900, over 6 million people worked in factories. We were still primarily an agricultural country but were fast becoming industrialized.

Not until the 1870's was there any general awakening of interest in management as such. In the 1850's, factories employing hundreds of men were numerous, a few employed over a thousand. Yet—no interest in management. All interest and attention centered on the machines themselves. There must have been many well-run companies, but no one thought of management as a specialized job.

William Gregg, the manager of a southern textile mill, seems to have expressed the typical view when, in 1855, he told the stockholders of his company: "With the perfection of our machinery, any sensible man can carry on your affairs successfully. I could select from among our stockholders many gentlemen who would, with a little practice, conduct our affairs quite as successfully as they have ever been conducted and prob-

---

[6] Andrew Ure, *Philosophy of Manufactures* (London: C. Knight, 1835), p. 15.

[7] Samuel Smiles, *The Life of George Stephenson, Railway Engineer* (4th London ed.; Boston: Ticknor & Fields, 1858), p. 374.

ably more so."[8] Of course, maybe Gregg was just being overly modest when he said that, but what he said seems to be what everyone thought about management's job.

The Idea of "Progress."   After the Civil War and through the 1870's there awakened interest in better management. Maybe it grew out of the difficulties of running bigger factories. But also a new philosophical idea had caught the fancy of Western civilization—the idea of "progress." It certainly speeded the interest in management.

People began to think that we live in a world governed by physical laws. Once we knew the laws we could apply them and direct the world so we would all be better off. This idea grew out of important discoveries in chemistry and physics—discoveries which did reveal underlying laws. Most of these laws came to light as a result of experiments—consciously directed experiments aimed at finding nature's laws. People began to have confidence in science and scientific inquiry into problems.

"Progress" is the end idea of a three-step analysis: (1) there are natural laws for everything, (2) we can learn nature's laws by experimentation, and (3) we can apply the laws and improve our well-being. Step 3 is the progress idea. We will always go forward. Always we will know as much as we knew yesterday plus what we have learned today, so every new day should be an improvement over the day before.

But we must use step 2 to get to step 3. We must have an inquiring mind; we must experiment and search for nature's laws. If we do so we can expect to improve our lot. These ideas took hold in manufacturing—first in product design and process and machine development and then in management.

Even before the Civil War many companies, particularly machinery manufacturers, were applying scientific investigation to factory problems. Whitworth's 1854 report describes an experiment made by a Philadelphia chandelier manufacturer to solve a manufacturing difficulty.[9] Lacquers made by the English formula streaked in the hot Philadelphia summers and did not hold their colors. Experiments with different formulas were carried on until the trouble was eliminated.

After the Civil War.   Right after the Civil War interest in what we now call motion and time study picked up, if we may judge from magazines of the time. In 1866, Mr. Lines Yale invented a vise which closed faster than older types. He developed it after finding that 12 per cent of his workers' time was spent opening and closing their vises.[10] Studying the job, finding that certain work took 12 per cent of the time, and

---

[8] William Gregg, "Practical Results of Southern Manufacturers," *De Bow's Review*, June, 1855, p. 779.

[9] Whitworth, *op. cit.*, p. 127.

[10] The vise was shown at a meeting of the Franklin Institute by Mr. William Sellers, who 12 years later hired Frederick Taylor (see p. 11) and helped him in his early career (*The Journal of the Franklin Institute*, April, 1866, p. 283).

figuring out how to reduce the time we now call motion and time study. C. R. Tompkins, writing at a later date, said that in 1865 by locating toilets closer to the work area he saved 10 minutes per day per worker for 60 machinists under his direction. He clocked the lost time before and after the relocation to arrive at this figure.[11]

In 1868 a writer described the operations (observed several years earlier) performed by the Colt Patent Fire-Arms Company in the manufacture of pistols. Fifteen hundred separate machines were used by the company, so the operations were on a large scale. The description given below of the operations required to make the rotating cylinder shows that a thorough job of subdividing the work and planning the individual operations was done:

> The rotating chambered cylinder is turned out of cast-steel bars, manufactured expressly for the purpose. The machines, after getting them the desired length, drill center holes, square up ends, turn for ratchet, turn exterior, smooth and polish, engrave, bore chambers, drill partitions, tap for nipples, cut pins for hammer-rest and ratchet, and screw in nipples. In all there are thirty-six separate operations before the cylinder is ready to follow the lock-frame to the inspector.[12]

Besides the operations listed, the cylinders were inspected after several of the operations by inspectors who were supplied with specialized gages and measuring devices.

The *Journal* of the Franklin Institute provides many evidences of the increased interest in better methods of shop management. Several articles on belt drives for machinery were published in 1860's and 1870's. During the 1870's the *Journal* published articles on plant layout, transporting and handling material, and a whole series of articles on how best to perform such operations as turning, boring, drilling, etc. In the July, 1876, issue an article on educating engineers discusses the need to observe and record data and adapt the findings to practical use—in short, to develop a science.

The American Society of Mechanical Engineers. The American Society of Mechanical Engineers was organized in the late 1870's. Annually thereafter it published its *Transactions*, containing the speeches delivered at its meetings. The 1881 issue contained articles on indexing drawings and patterns, the identifications of machine parts, the development of manufacturing and purchasing specifications, and the use of inspection and tests.

At the 1886 meeting of the A.S.M.E., Henry Metcalfe read a paper on "The Shop Order System of Accounts," and Oberlin Smith read one on "Inventory Valuation of Machinery Plant." The discussion that fol-

---

[11] C. R. Tompkins, "Machine Shop Economy," *Mechanics Magazine,* January, 1889.

[12] J. Leander Bishop, *A History of American Manufacturers, 1608 to 1860* (Philadelphia: Edward Young & Co., 1868), Vol. III, p. 409.

lowed these papers indicates that many companies were using procedures similar to those described by the speakers. Frederick Taylor, 30 years old at the time, took part in the discussion and reported that his company, the Midvale Steel Company, had been employing similar methods for 10 years.

Besides the publications already referred to, there were at least two early books on the subject of shop management. Frederic Smith's *Workshop Management* was published in England in 1878 and ran through several editions. It contained chapters on "Economy of Time," "Economy of Labor," "Economy of Material," "Economy of Power," "The Foreman and His Duties," "Arrangement of the Workshop," "Payment of Wages," and other subjects. In this country, Henry Metcalfe wrote *Cost of Manufacturers* in 1885, and it also went into several editions.

The developments in the period following the Civil War have been treated at some length here to give proper perspective to the work of Frederick Taylor, who, in later years, did much to develop the study of management. By 1886, when Taylor was 30 years old, many industrial leaders were already thinking and writing in the field in which Taylor later became an authority. The thinking of those years was well summarized by Henry R. Towne when he said that ". . . shop management is of equal importance to that of engineering, as affecting the successful conduct of most, if not all, of our great establishments, and that the *management of works* has become a matter of such great and far reaching importance as perhaps to justify its classification also as one of the modern arts."[13] Towne went on to say that there ought to be an organization devoted just to ideas about management and that someone ought to put the unorganized knowledge on this subject together into a scientfic body of knowledge.

The time was ripe and the stage set for just such a man as Frederick W. Taylor. With him came the period of rapid development in the emerging science of industrial management.

FREDERICK W. TAYLOR

Frederick W. Taylor was probably the most important man in the development of shop management techniques. Born in 1856, he died in 1915. After having served a machinist's apprenticeship at the Cramp Shipyard in Philadelphia, he came to the Midvale Steel Company in 1878, where he worked for the next 12 years.

Many of Taylor's ideas grew out of practices he observed at Midvale. William Sellers, Midvale's president, was also owner of William Sellers and Company, manufacturers of machinery, and was at that time the leading machine designing engineer in the country. Sellers' machines were among the best in the world and were noted for the precise work

---

[13] *Transactions of the American Society of Mechanical Engineers* (1886), p. 427.

they could do and for being designed to save the time of the machine operators. An English writer, seeing them exhibited at the Vienna machinery exhibition in 1873, said: "No opportunity is lost to save a useless step, an unnecessary motion. Writers on this subject remark that Americans [as evidenced by the Sellers' machines] try to arrange their machines so as to make them the most convenient for the workmen."[14]

Taylor was fortunate in having an opportunity to work at Midvale. He gave Sellers credit for much of what he learned there. The ideas of experimentation, of finding better methods, of saving human movements, all were favored at Midvale before Taylor's arrival, having been introduced by Sellers in 1873 when he came to head what was then virtually a bankrupt company. The friendship between Taylor's family and the E. W. Clark family, who owned a majority of the Midvale stock, probably helped his early advancement in the company. Though he started as a laborer, he was made a gang boss 2 years later, and after 4 more years, when he was 28 years old, he was appointed chief engineer.

Taylor is sometimes referred to as the father of scientific management, but to credit him with originating it is claiming too much. He certainly did a great deal to develop the field of management into a scientific study, but his greatest contribution was to develop and dramatically publicize the field of management. He was the movement's catalytic agent. His imagination and zeal in carrying through his investigations were perhaps equal to the task of originating the ideas. The fact is, however, that he arrived too late on the scene to be credited with the whole job. He himself said: "Hardly a single piece of original work was done by me in Scientific Management. Everything that we have has come from a suggestion by someone else."[15]

Taylor's Contributions. Taylor's contributions to scientific management were nonetheless of utmost importance. He probably deserves credit for originating what is today considered the best practice in time study, i.e., timing jobs in small parts rather than in an over-all way. He was the first to emphasize, in speeches and in writing, the need to select men to fit the jobs for which they were hired. He was the first to stress that it is an *obligation of management* to find the best way of doing jobs and to train the workers to work in that way. He was by no means the first to emphasize that employees should do their jobs in a manner most economical of time and effort, but he was the first to insist that management should study and analyze alternative methods, select the best, and then train the workers to do the work that way.

Curiously Taylor seems to have had little part in the development of

---

[14] Quoted from *The Engineering Magazine* (London) in the *Journal of the Franklin Institute*, November, 1873, p. 352.

[15] Quoted in Harlow S. Person, "Frederick W. Taylor," *Advanced Management, Quarterly Journal of The Society for the Advancement of Management*, January–March, 1945, p. 3.

the line and staff form of organization.[16] Its application to manufacturing enterprises appears to have been the contribution of Harrington Emerson more than of any other man. Taylor developed a functional form of shop control which eliminated the line form of organization and substituted functional specialists. In its complete form, this type of organization was never successful. It is described on page 50.

Taylor did not follow the general thinking of his times on the subject of wages, although he was not alone in his views. He held that high wages should be paid to workmen if their high productivity made it possible to keep unit costs low. In other words, in so far as was reasonable and possible, they should share, in the form of higher wages, if their efforts to produce more goods were successful.

Nation's Business

FIG. 1–4. Workers laboring for $1 a day eyed Fred Taylor with suspicion when he appeared among them and made many notes on a pad.

The Shoveling Experiment. Taylor had a flair for the dramatic and received widespread attention for some of the things he did. In the late 1890's, while working for the Bethlehem Steel Company, he conducted two historic experiments with the yard labor gang. Taylor was not the first to study shoveling, but his study made the headlines. He found that each man in the gang furnished his own shovel and that the shovels were of various sizes. Sometimes the yard laborers had to shovel coal, sometimes iron ore, sometimes ashes. Hence the weight per shovelful

---

[16] See page 52.

varied considerably, depending on the material lifted. By experiment he found that the most work was done when a load of about 21.5 pounds was moved per shovelful. He had the company buy a stock of shovels of various sizes. No matter what the material shoveled, the appropriate size shovel could be furnished to the workers. Large shovels were used for ashes, small shovels for iron ore, etc. In that way the load was always about 21.5 pounds. As a result, the work done per worker increased and costs were reduced.

Pig Iron Handling. His second experiment, which became a classic example of job improvement, was with a pig iron handler named Schmidt. Taylor decided after watching his men load pig iron into freight cars from the storage yard that they were not doing it right. He thought that they used the wrong motions and that they worked too hard and too long, became overtired, and then had to rest too long. He believed that the work would be less tiring if the workers did the work differently and took frequent short rest periods.

The men made $1.15 a day. They loaded an average of 12½ tons of pig iron per man per day. Schmidt, one of the group, was offered the opportunity to earn more money if he would follow directions on how to pick up, carry, and put down the pigs of iron, and if he would take frequent short rests. Taylor believed that in this way Schmidt could load more pig iron. Schmidt followed the directions, loaded 47 tons in one day, and earned $1.85, and continued to do so thereafter. Some of the workers could not handle that much pig iron, but the company soon had many applicants for the $1.85 job.

In speeches and articles Taylor later described both the shoveling and the pig iron handling incidents. They created considerable interest and comment (not all favorable) and caused many industrial leaders to become interested in his methods.

High-Speed Steel. Outside the field of shop management Taylor, in collaboration with Maunsel White, working at the Bethlehem Steel Company in the late 1890's, developed high-speed cutting steel. This development revolutionized metal-cutting procedures all over the world because, with high-speed steel, metalworking machines could run twice as fast and turn out twice as much work. The old-style carbon steel tool would heat up and lose its cutting edge much faster than the new, high-speed steel tool. In 1894, while experimenting at another company, Taylor had also discovered that the cutting speeds of carbon steel tools could be stepped up nearly 40 per cent if a stream of water were directed at the point of cutting.[17]

At Bethlehem, Taylor also directed experiments to determine the best speeds, feeds, and depth of cut for running metal-cutting machinery.

---

[17] Frank B. Copley, *Frederick W. Taylor* (New York: Harper & Bros., 1923), Vol. II, p. 83.

It proved to be a complex problem which was finally worked out by Taylor's old colleague from Midvale, Carl Barth. Taylor brought Barth to Bethlehem to work on the experiments. Barth's mathematical ability enabled him to reduce the several variables involved to mathematical formulas. He then devised several slide rules with which anyone, even a person with no mathematical training whatever, could compute the proper speed, feed, and depth of cut. These slide rules for many years had widespread use as guides in metalworking companies. After leaving Bethlehem in 1901, Taylor set himself up as a consultant specializing in shop management procedures. He seems to have been the first industrial engineer to go into the consulting business.

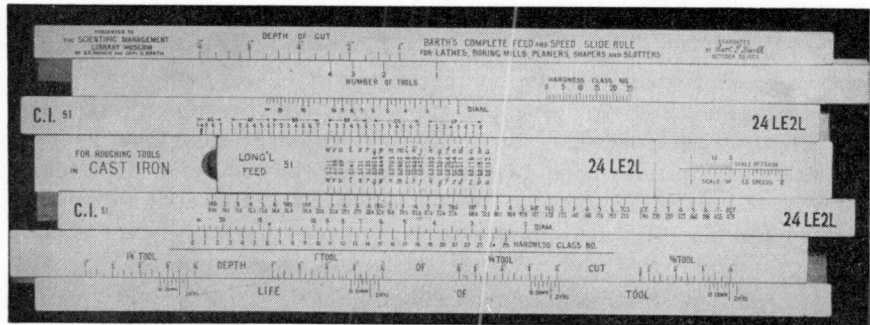

Stevens Institute of Technology

FIG. 1–5. A Barth slide rule.

Taylor's Writings. At the turn of the century there was a growing interest in improved shop management techniques, and they were used more frequently after 1900. During this time Taylor was prominent in management activities. In 1906, he was president of the American Society of Mechanical Engineers. He wrote numerous articles, most noteworthy of which were "A Piece Rate System" (1895) and "On the Art of Cutting Metals" (1906). His two books, *Shop Management* (1903) and *The Principles of Scientific Management* (1911), are classics in the literature of management.

Eastern Railroads Case. In spite of the growing interest in better management techniques, the new practices were used in only a small minority of manufacturing companies until two events occurred which gave great publicity to them. The first was the Railroad Rate hearings in 1910 and the second was the House of Representatives hearings in 1911 and 1912.

In 1910 the eastern railroads asked the Interstate Commerce Commission to approve rate increases. In the public hearings on the question the shippers who were affected objected to the increased rates, claiming that no increase would be necessary if the railroads practiced better and more efficient methods. Louis D. Brandeis, later a justice of the Supreme

Court of the United States, was the counsel for the shippers. He had a number of men in the management field testify, among them Harrington Emerson. All testified to the savings that could be made by better procedures. Emerson stated that the railroads could save $1 million a day if they used new methods. Among the several terms then used to refer to the new methods, Brandeis selected the term "scientific management." Both the term "scientific management" and the million-dollar figure caught the fancy of the newspapers. The resulting publicity caused many companies to adopt some of the procedures, principally time study.

Congressional Investigation. In 1911 an attempt to take time studies[18] in a government arsenal was objected to by the union, and later in the year the House of Representatives appointed a committee to investigate the situation. Taylor and others testified in the committee hearings, and again considerable publicity followed. The union objected to time study on the grounds that the pace set might injure the workers' health. The argument found some sentimental support, but the investigating committee found no evidence that time study had, in any specific case, resulted in setting an injurious pace. In 1912, however, the House of Representatives passed an appropriations bill to which was attached a rider prohibiting the use of time study in government arsenals and post offices. This provision was attached to all succeeding appropriation bills until 1948.

It is difficult to evaluate Taylor's contribution to the development of the study of management. Had Taylor never been born, progress certainly would have come anyway, for he was a product of his times. Even though he cannot be considered its originator, his untiring energy and his flair for the dramatic undoubtedly speeded up the growth of the management movement. He himself was concerned primarily with shop management, but others were quick to apply the ideas, where applicable, to the higher echelons of management and to organizations other than manufacturing enterprises.

OTHER PIONEERS IN THE MANAGEMENT MOVEMENT

Some pioneers in the management movement, such as Henry L. Gantt, Carl B. Barth, and Dwight V. Merrick, worked with Taylor. Others, such as Henry R. Towne and Frederick A. Halsey, were active contributors before and, to some extent, during Taylor's time. Still others, among them, Harrington Emerson and Frank B. and Lillian M. Gilbreth worked independently and into a later period.

Gantt is best known as an author and an engineer. An early colleague of Taylor's, he later installed scientific management procedures in several companies. He developed an incentive wage payment plan which was used by some companies and developed a chart which helped control

---

[18] Time study men always say they "take" a time study rather than "make" a time study.

manufacturing operations. Such charts, known as "Gantt Charts," are still used occasionally today. As already mentioned, Barth is best remembered as the inventor of slide rules with which the proper machine speeds, feeds, and depth of cut for metal-cutting machines could be calculated. Merrick was the first well-known time study man. Towne installed efficient procedures in his plant while Taylor was yet in his teens. His papers before the Franklin Institute and the A.S.M.E. were outstanding and undoubtedly strongly influenced the younger Taylor. Halsey is remembered today for his gain-sharing wage incentive plan presented in a paper before the A.S.M.E. in 1891.

Harrington Emerson was a contemporary (but not a colleague) of Taylor's and an engineering consultant with a western railroad. He was mainly responsible for introducing the line and staff form of organization into manufacturing concerns. Emerson put less emphasis on exact time study methods in setting time standards than did Taylor. His standards, in some instances, were reported to have been both inaccurate and unsatisfactory.

Frank B. and Lillian M. Gilbreth did important pioneer work in motion study. Taylor and his predecessors had made some progress in motion study but did not carry it as far as the Gilbreths did. They introduced charts and moving pictures (or "micromotion" study) to help analyze, study, and improve jobs. Gilbreth, a bricklayer by trade, became an outstanding industrial engineer in the decade before his death in 1924. Mrs. Gilbreth, a psychologist by training, worked with her husband during his lifetime and after his death continued the practice of industrial engineering.

The two Gilbreths did very important pioneer work in fatigue analysis as well as motion study. They also developed the idea that all human work is composed of various combinations of basic human movements which they called "therbligs." Although their work was done many years ago, only since World War II has their therblig idea been taken up by industrial engineers generally. Today many leading industrial engineers think it offers a valuable approach both to improving jobs and to setting time standards.

STATE OF MANAGEMENT SCIENCE AT CLOSE OF PIONEER PERIOD

World War I marked the close of the pioneer era. During the war everyone went all out for production. New methods were used more widely than ever.

Here are the accomplishments of the pioneer period:

1. The "inquiring frame of mind" became common. Not only factory problems but administrative problems as well were made subject to inquiry to see if they could be improved.

2. "Scientific" investigation was rather widely accepted as the way to tackle both shop and nonshop problems. Briefly, you first recognize a

problem, then investigate it and collect data, analyze the data, draw conclusions, and lastly, apply them.

3. "Principles" of management were thought to exist. No one was yet quite sure what they were. One, the "exception principle," had some acceptance. It holds that rules to guide the decisions of subordinates should be set up. Apply a rule to all usual cases, but refer exceptions to the rule to a higher official for decision.

4. There was some interest in delegation of responsibility and authority and how best to make the delegation.

5. The line and staff form of organization was widely used.

6. In the shop the use of staff departments, such as time study and production control, was common.

7. Personnel was recognized as a staff function, dealing largely with hiring and training.

THE MIDDLE PERIOD

The middle period between World War I and World War II saw the earlier techniques become more commonly used. More interest was shown in developing a body of principles and a genuine philosophy of management. Quite a few books were written, but no generally accepted body of principles resulted. Much was written on how to delegate responsibility, the use of authority, the selection and training of new men, motivating them, and so on.

Many other areas of knowledge also expanded. Time study grew into industrial engineering. In inventory control, the subject of economic lot sizes (explained on pages 743–45) received much attention. Personnel work expanded, and industrial psychologists came on the scene. Formal job evaluation and merit rating techniques began to appear in the 1930's. In the late 1930's personnel became more important than ever as big unions came into being. In the teaching area, the Harvard Business School introduced the case method. It de-emphasized principles and purported to "teach by doing." Its supporters felt that students should learn to make their own generalizations, using factual or near-factual situations instead of accepting generalizations made by others.

WORLD WAR II AND AFTER

What with big unions and the labor shortage of World War II, all companies became even more personnel conscious than they had been. Employees became people—became individuals—to be treated and handled as individuals. The Western Electric Company had in the late 1920's and early 1930's carried on extensive research into the behavior of factory employees.[19] Not much attention was paid to it by industry

---

[19] The Western Electric Company experiments are described in F. J. Roethlisberger, W. J. Dickson, and H. A. Wright, *Management and the Worker* (Cambridge, Mass.: Harvard University Press, 1939).

for years, but only since the late 1940's has the idea that people respond in different ways according to their nature become popular.

After years of giving only lip service to the idea, nearly all companies now try to pick good men for their jobs and to train them. Some companies had done that for years, but now nearly all do.

"Organization" departments are becoming more common. Uncommon even in the late 1940's, new ones now appear frequently. Organization departments chart the organization, study departmental arrangements, and recommend new arrangements.

Committees are common at high levels in industry. This is not really new, but they seem to be more common than formerly. There is also more "consultative" management. Underlings are given an opportunity to be heard. Their suggestions and ideas about proposals are asked. Formerly this was less common.

Today's company officials are more conscious of public relations than were their predecessors. Also, today's executives feel a greater social responsibility to employees, customers, and their communities. Probably it has been forced by laws and labor unions. But, whatever the cause, the feeling of responsibility exists.

The 1950's have seen companies grow larger and larger. Along with growth in size has come decentralization of operations. Several small factories in different parts of the country are preferred to one large one. Decentralization has forced attention to managerial techniques. You can't control decentralized operations in the same way as operations centralized in one large plant.

We still have no widely accepted set of principles of organization. Books and magazines on how to organize and run companies are added daily to library shelves. But they don't agree on what is important. The gist of their ideas is in Chapters 3 to 5.

The inquiring frame of mind and scientific method of investigation have, in the factory, taken the form of well-organized industrial engineering departments. But more important is the movement toward organized research—research to improve the product, the process, to find new products—or basic research intended to unlock more of nature's secrets. Organized research is the order of the day.

In spite of the early work of Taylor and Gilbreth, most factories did little motion study work before World War II. During the war, motion study was rediscovered and has since been widely used. Closely related to motion study, the analysis of office procedures has been a growing field, particularly since 1950.

Time study and incentive pay plans, on the other hand, although widely used, are perhaps losing some ground. They are not used in the airplane industry and, partly because of union opposition, seem to be less common than years ago in automobile manufacture.

Systematic job evaluation and, to a lesser extent, merit rating became established during World War II. Today they are commonly accepted practices.

The trend toward mechanization continues unabated. In fact, new electronic devices have made more nearly automatic production possible. We now call our most extreme mechanization by a new word "automation." The appearance of electronic data handling computors in the mid-1950's opens new doors to still more mechanization.

"Operations research," "linear programming," and "cybernetics" are coming over the horizon and will be more important in the future. They are closely related, and all aim at better management decisions by using mathematics and electronic computors.

Although we come back to these terms later, brief definitions are appropriate here. *Operations research* is a broad term referring to the study of problems by taking an over-all view. It looks at problems as a whole—not from the point of view of one department or one kind of scientist. A team of specialists in diverse fields may need to be set up to solve a problem. For example, solving a problem having to do with the product's quality may require a team consisting of a lubrication specialist, a mathematician, a cost accountant, and a buyer from the purchasing department.

Linear programming is one technique sometimes used in operations research. Linear programming expresses relationships in mathematical formulas—often complicated formulas. In fact, they were too complicated to solve until electronic computors came along. The computors, which now solve complex problems in minutes, have made linear programming a practical tool. Linear programming requires everything to be in numbers. You have to "quantify" everything. Linear programming does not solve problems having nonquantifiable factors.

Cybernetics refers to the "feed-back" part of the "circuit" idea. A machine (or a man) does something. You check to see what was done, compare with what should have been done, and where they differ, issue new directions. This is a "circuit." Now start around again. The "feedback" idea is getting the report, comparing actual to desired, and issuing instructions to get back in line. More and more "feedback" is being built into automatic machines in factory operations and in electronic computors handling office procedures formerly done by hand.

MANUFACTURING TODAY

Manufacturing industries today employ over one fourth of all gainfully employed persons in the United States. No other economic activity employs nearly so many. Sixteen million employees, of whom 13 million are hourly paid factory workers, work for manufacturing establishments. Only 7 million persons, including owners, are now employed in agriculture. The United States has changed in the last century from a primarily agricultural society to a highly industrialized one.

Today many manufacturing companies count their assets in the hundreds of millions of dollars, and many of them have over 10,000 employees. Enormous investments of money are required. A typical manufacturing plant needs perhaps $12,000 of investment *per employee*.[20] Half of that is needed for plant and equipment. Land costs come to over $1,000, while inventories and accounts receivable each require nearly $2,000 per employee. Bank accounts and other investments make up the rest.

Giant companies never do all of their manufacturing in one extremely large factory. All large, and many small, companies divide their operations among several small factories rather than concentrating them in a single large establishment. There are transportation, marketing, and other advantages in decentralization. Large-scale operations, particularly multi-plant operations, have created difficult managerial problems. Their successful solution requires managerial skill of a far higher caliber than was needed by yesterday's captains of industry.

MANAGEMENT LITERATURE AND ASSOCIATIONS

No one today need lack reading material on all aspects of management. Libraries are full of books and magazines, and more arrive daily. Students interested in manufacturing will find two magazines, *Factory Management Maintenance* and *Mill and Factory*, helpful. Then there are magazines for almost every kind of work done in a factory—on purchasing, traffic, accounting, and so on.

Besides these the student should know of the American Management Association, the American Society of Mechanical Engineers, and the Society for the Advancement of Management. All of them publish the speeches given at their conventions, and they all publish other special articles. Company and labor organizations nearly all publish magazines. Many universities have Institutes of Industrial Relations and Bureaus of Business Research which publish bulletins and research reports.

However, you really should discount what you read. Companies and labor unions don't tell everything. They avoid washing their dirty linen in public. When one of their men gives a speech or writes an article, he must usually get it reviewed (censored?) first. Also, companies tell lots about their successful innovations but say nothing about things that fail to work out.

Nor can you rely wholly on people outside of industry—even teachers. Outsiders often write about how to manage a company and how to handle labor relations. But outsiders don't know as much about it as insiders and can't tell the whole story because they don't know it. Students should realize that they can hardly ever find the whole story in print.

---

[20] From *Capital Goods Review* (Washington, D.C.: Machinery and Allied Products Institute, August, 1955).

STUDY QUESTIONS

1. When did the Industrial Revolution start? Why there and not elsewhere?
2. Explain how the early inventions in the textile industry provided the setting for the Industrial Revolution.
3. What part did the United States play in the early days of the Industrial Revolution?
4. What is meant by "interchangeable" parts?
5. It has been said that the Industrial Revolution transferred thought to machines. Did it? Justify your answer.
6. What part did the machine tool industry play in the early days of the Industrial Revolution?
7. Why did mechanization become popular more rapidly in the United States than elsewhere in the 1800's?
8. Trace the history of interest in management up to 1900.
9. Explain the idea of "progress." Show how it is important in the history of management.
10. Frederick W. Taylor has been called the father of scientific management. What did he do to justify that title?
11. Was there any interest in management before Taylor? If so, how far had it developed? If not, how did companies get along?
12. Describe Taylor's pig iron experiment. Why was it important?
13. What part did the Eastern Railroads case play in the history of management?
14. What did H. L. Gantt, Harrington Emerson, and the Gilbreths contribute to industrial management?
15. Where did management science stand at the close of the pioneer period?
16. How has the management movement grown since World War II?
17. As a student, what sources (in print) can you go to to find out what goes on in industry?

Chapter 2

MANAGEMENT PRINCIPLES

A PRINCIPLE is a basic rule—it must be valid everywhere and for all time. To be a principle, a rule must be true in Europe as well as in the United States—it must be true in business, government, armies, churches, everywhere—and it has to have been true a thousand years ago, be true today, and still be true a thousand years from now.

A stiff test? Yes—so stiff that some people say that none of our management rules qualify as principles. Their objection is more than a mere quibble. If there are principles, we can learn them and do a better job of managing than if we didn't know them. But if nothing is enduring, then all we have are "currently useful generalizations." Learning them is helpful only for today. We had better spend our time learning how to do our own generalizing and not much time on learning rules. But if there really are principles, we can save a lot of time by not having to figure them all out for ourselves. They are the wisdom of the ages boiled down for us. We should learn what we can from the past and then go on from there.

We could make up a long list of rules (or principles?) of good practice to follow in business. Here is a list of ten that seem to be of top importance:

1. The proper form of organization depends on what it has to do.
2. Every organization needs one single head man.
3. Since he can't do all the work himself, he must assign work to others.
4. He must give others *authority* to do things.
5. He can't decide every minor matter himself. He must let underlings decide some things.
6. He ought, now and then, to consult with his subordinates.
7. He must check up on what his subordinates do.
8. The head man can't supervise directly the work of very many subordinates.
9. He must set up departments and choose department heads.
10. Specialization usually pays dividends.

Are these ten statements fundamental? Does knowing them help? Or are they just common-sense observations? Yes, they are just common sense, but if we know about them we will do things differently than if we had never heard or thought of them. Many business troubles come from men not knowing them. Take number 5, for example. Too often top men will not let underlings decide enough things, and this makes trouble for everyone.

Let's test to see if they are principles. Are they true everywhere? In all kinds of activities? And for all time? They certainly seem to be. Can you think of any kind of organization, any time, anywhere, where they don't apply?

You probably noticed that our principles say that the "head man" does this and that. Everyone except those at the bottom is a head man. The president is the head of everything. A vice-president reporting to him is not a head man in the president's immediate organization but he is the head of his own major division. What is said about a head man applies to him as he runs his division. Similarly a factory foreman is the head of his department. Much of what is said about a head man applies to his work too.

Some people think that it is important to distinguish between a company's "administration" and its "management." If we must say that they are different, we can call vice-presidents and above, the "administration." Below that is the "management." The top men spend most of their time on major policies and on long-range planning. Lower men carry out plans and policies—theirs is more a job of doing than it is of planning, although there is some minor planning and policy making even low in the organization.

THE PROPER FORM OF ORGANIZATION DEPENDS ON WHAT IT HAS TO DO

A manufacturing company makes and sells products. To do this it must design products, buy materials, and use men and machines to change them into products. After that it must sell and get the product to the customer. Departments must be set up to do all of this work.

Nonmanufacturing organizations have to do different things and have to set up different departments. A bank, for example, needs a loan department to approve lending money to borrowers. A church needs no machines to make products. A railroad has to direct its main attention to operating transportation equipment. Transportation is less important in a manufacturing company.

Manufacturing companies have about the same general objectives, yet they use different organizational setups. Shouldn't they—having similar objectives—have similar organizational arrangements? Yes—and they do as far as major patterns go. They all have manufacturing, sales, purchasing, engineering, personnel, accounting, and various other departments not always found in nonmanufacturing companies.

But manufacturing companies are like people. They are alike in many respects, yet every one is different. Each one should have an organization best suited to *its* needs. Its goal (to make money) may be the same as its competitors', but each one already has certain established products and customers. Boeing makes large airplanes. North American makes small airplanes and missiles. Continental Can makes tin cans. Sherwin-Williams makes paint. Florsheim makes shoes. Each is established. Each already has factories located in certain places and equipped with certain machines. And every one is different—different even from its direct competitors. So each one has to have its own unique organization.

Objectives and Policies.   Actually one might ask, what should a company try to do? What should its officers be trying to do? The minimum objectives are clear: (1) to stay in business, and (2) to make some money. Many companies publish high-sounding lists of objectives as their goals, but if they fail to stay in business, the other objectives don't matter. And if any set of officers loses money for very long, they are out and others are in.

But beyond the first two objectives lie some others. Managers should ask themselves: Where should our company be in 10 years? In what businesses? How much volume? Where located? When they answer these questions, they set objectives for themselves. Some years ago National Distillers went into the chemical business, Schenley did not. Their officials decided on different objectives—one to diversify—the other not to diversify. Some years ago General Tire bought RKO. What would a tire company want with a moving-picture company? Certainly General Tire's objectives are different from Firestone's. Firestone has bought no movie companies. In the decade after World War II, Sears, Roebuck and Co. and Montgomery Ward chose different objectives: Sears—to grow and expand; Montgomery Ward—to conserve cash and expand at the bottom of the depression it expected.

Some companies set up high-sounding objectives. They say that they have responsibilities to the public, to customers, and to employees. And, of course, today, their objectives really must be in line with the community good. Look at Figure 2–1, Johnson & Johnson's published list of objectives. There is nothing in it about staying in business, and even making money is low on the list.

Some people say that objectives and policies (rules to follow to reach objectives) ought to be put in writing. Perhaps, but not certainly so, particularly if their being in writing tends to freeze them very much. You need to be opportunistic at times. Maybe General Tire made a lot of money buying RKO and selling old films to TV. The Olin-Mathieson chemical merger came in part because Mr. Olin was getting old. Merging to get a good president (a man already with Mathieson) for the years

Our Credo

WE BELIEVE THAT OUR FIRST RESPONSIBILITY IS TO OUR CUSTOMERS
OUR PRODUCTS MUST ALWAYS BE GOOD, AND
WE MUST STRIVE TO MAKE THEM BETTER AT LOWER COSTS.
OUR ORDERS MUST BE PROMPTLY AND ACCURATELY FILLED.
OUR DEALERS MUST MAKE A FAIR PROFIT.

OUR SECOND RESPONSIBILITY IS TO THOSE WHO WORK WITH US —
THE MEN AND WOMEN IN OUR FACTORIES AND OFFICES.
THEY MUST HAVE A SENSE OF SECURITY IN THEIR JOBS.
WAGES MUST BE FAIR AND ADEQUATE.
MANAGEMENT JUST, HOURS SHORT, AND WORKING CONDITIONS CLEAN AND ORDERLY.
WORKERS SHOULD HAVE AN ORGANIZED SYSTEM FOR SUGGESTIONS AND COMPLAINTS.
FOREMEN AND DEPARTMENT HEADS MUST BE QUALIFIED AND FAIR MINDED.
THERE MUST BE OPPORTUNITY FOR ADVANCEMENT — FOR THOSE QUALIFIED
AND EACH PERSON MUST BE CONSIDERED AN INDIVIDUAL
STANDING ON HIS OWN DIGNITY AND MERIT.

OUR THIRD RESPONSIBILITY IS TO OUR MANAGEMENT
OUR EXECUTIVES MUST BE PERSONS OF TALENT, EDUCATION, EXPERIENCE AND ABILITY.
THEY MUST BE PERSONS OF COMMON SENSE AND FULL UNDERSTANDING.

OUR FOURTH RESPONSIBILITY IS TO THE COMMUNITIES IN WHICH WE LIVE.
WE MUST BE A GOOD CITIZEN — SUPPORT GOOD WORKS AND CHARITY,
AND BEAR OUR FAIR SHARE OF TAXES.
WE MUST MAINTAIN IN GOOD ORDER THE PROPERTY WE ARE PRIVILEGED TO USE.
WE MUST PARTICIPATE IN PROMOTION OF CIVIC IMPROVEMENT,
HEALTH, EDUCATION AND GOOD GOVERNMENT,
AND ACQUAINT THE COMMUNITY WITH OUR ACTIVITIES.

OUR FIFTH AND LAST RESPONSIBILITY IS TO OUR STOCKHOLDERS.
BUSINESS MUST MAKE A SOUND PROFIT.
RESERVES MUST BE CREATED, RESEARCH MUST BE CARRIED ON,
ADVENTUROUS PROGRAMS DEVELOPED, AND MISTAKES MADE AND PAID FOR.
BAD TIMES MUST BE PROVIDED FOR, HIGH TAXES PAID, NEW MACHINES PURCHASED,
NEW FACTORIES BUILT, NEW PRODUCTS LAUNCHED, AND NEW SALES PLANS DEVELOPED.
WE MUST EXPERIMENT WITH NEW IDEAS.
WHEN THESE THINGS HAVE BEEN DONE THE STOCKHOLDER SHOULD RECEIVE A FAIR RETURN.
WE ARE DETERMINED, WITH THE HELP OF GOD'S GRACE,
TO FULFILL THESE OBLIGATIONS TO THE BEST OF OUR ABILITY.

FIG. 2–1. Johnson & Johnson's statement of objectives. Not all companies would agree that profits should come fifth in a list of five.

ahead was surely not a part of any long-range objective set up years earlier. If writing out objectives and major policies tends to keep them from changing, perhaps they shouldn't be put in writing.

There is more need to put minor policies in writing. How else can men down in the organization find out about them and carry them out? When you get verbal instructions about a great many things, you are likely to forget some of them or get them mixed up. Figure 2–2 shows one policy from International Harverster's policy manual for foremen. The whole manual is a booklet of over 100 pages. There are other manuals for higher executives. Having it all written out does not insure that everyone will follow the policies, but no one has to depend on his memory. Certainly it is easier to get men to carry out consistent policies if they can readily check to see what the policies are.

INTERNATIONAL HARVESTER COMPANY
APPROVED COMPANY POLICIES

DATE IN EFFECT	NEW OR REVISED POLICY: Revised	REPLACES POLICY DATED	SHEET 1 OF 1 SHEETS	FILE NO. E-006-1

Fran L. Willis

VICE PRESIDENT

SHOULD ANY STATEMENT OF GENERAL POLICY CONTAINED ON THIS PAGE OR APPLICATION THEREOF BE IN CONFLICT WITH ANY STATE OR LOCAL LAWS OR SPECIFIC AGREEMENTS, SUCH LAWS OR AGREEMENTS MUST BE OBSERVED.

SUBJECT   EMPLOYMENT

An applicant is required to complete normal employment processing before he is assigned work and before he commences to earn wages. This processing includes the interview, physical examination, initiation of routine personnel forms and preliminary orientation.

An employe's service and pay will begin immediately upon the termination of such processing if he starts to work promptly during the current shift. In all other cases, the employe's service and pay will commence as soon as he has reported for work at the employment office (or other specified activity) in accordance with authoritative instructions.

FIG. 2–2.   International Harvester's policy on employment, a page from its foremen's manual.

EVERY ORGANIZATION NEEDS A HEAD MAN

We all know that nothing gets done when no one is responsible for doing anything. Activity may occur, but co-ordinated work by several people toward a common goal is more likely to occur when one person —*and only one*—has charge. Someone needs to make over-all decisions, to choose objectives and to make plans, and to assign work to carry out objectives and plans. Someone needs to set up departments and to select people to do the work. Someone needs to find out what is being done and to give new directions from time to time. The organization needs control. And it can best be gotten by having a "unity of command" centralized in a head man—one at the head of the company and one at the head of each department.

As we work down through the organization it becomes more difficult to keep a complete unity of command. Subordinates sometimes get directions from two bosses instead of only one. Having two or more superiors is said to be bad, but it sometimes happens. The problems of multiple bosses are discussed on page 34.

THE HEAD MAN MUST ASSIGN WORK TO OTHERS

Since the top man can't do everything himself, he has to assign work —delegate work—to others. There are tricks to proper delegation; it is not as simple as it sounds at first.

First, decide what you want someone to do. Decide as exactly as you can because that will keep him from wasting time doing things you don't want done. You see the over-all picture and can tell him what he ought to do. He doesn't see the over-all picture. If he tries to figure out for himself what to do, he isn't too likely to end up doing the right things. Work assignments can't always be precise, but they ought to be reasonably so.

Second, make the work assignment. Watch out for danger points here. Tell the man who is to be responsible what his job is. Tell him what he is to accomplish, what are the limits of his authority, what he can do, and what he cannot do. Be *sure* to be clear.

Some superiors do a poor job of delegation. They don't tell their men exactly what is wanted. Often they assign work verbally—not in writing —and they are vague about the full extent of the assignment. Verbal assignments are not always bad, but they are sometimes misunderstood or later forgotten. Better put them in writing. A man who gets vague assignments is not likely to be very decisive nor is he likely to do the best job. Actually many directions are given verbally. Middle-level officials don't really need written lists of their duties. They know what they are supposed to get done. Written job descriptions, listing regular duties, are becoming more common, however, partly because they are a by-product of job evaluation—which is now common for middle-level jobs.

Care should be taken not to overdo written directions. They tend to limit flexibility. Some employees think that they should do only the things written out and no more. This weakness is particularly noticeable at the lowest levels. Even if verbal instructions are a little vague, they are flexible and may keep employees doing more than the bare minimum. Written instructions also tend to develop complex procedures; employees on all levels feel that, in the case of anything unusual, their hands are tied until written authorizations reach them through proper channels. Much red tape, therefore, can often be avoided if written instructions are used sparingly.

Since assignments are often made carelessly, it is small wonder that there are sometimes gaps in assignments—work which gets assigned to no one or at least no one knows that it is his job. Maybe the boss never thought about it needing to be done. Maybe he thought of it but forgot to assign it, or maybe he told one man to do it and that man forgot. Or there may be overlaps—two men think that they have been told to do the same thing. Neither situation, gaps or overlaps, is common, yet each sometimes occurs and makes trouble. Either work remains undone or there is wasteful duplication or even friction between two men, each of whom thinks that someone else is trying to do his work.

Assignments of top jobs do not have to be quite so exact and detailed. The president doesn't need to tell a vice-president every little thing about how to get a job done. He just tells him the results or conditions he wants the vice-president to bring about, then lets the vice-president decide how to do the job. But even this means that the president has to, himself, get a good mental picture of what he wants.

It is the style today not to order people around—particularly those near the top. A president *can* order a vice-president to do something, but today that isn't what he does. Instead he tries to win the support of his subordinates to his programs. The difference is important. *Orders* don't generate much enthusiasm or strong support. But subordinates will pitch in and work hard to try to fulfill a program they like—particularly if they helped develop it.

Don't misunderstand what you do when you delegate work. When you delegate work, you get rid (if all goes well) of doing the detailed work yourself, but *you don't get rid of the responsibility for getting it done.* Delegating responsibility for work is not like giving a man a five-dollar bill. When you give a man a five-dollar bill, he now has it and you don't have it. When you give a man a work assignment, you delegate to him the responsibility for doing it. But—to your superiors—*you* still have that responsibility. It is a little like imparting knowledge. First, you have the knowledge; then you pass it on to someone else. But you still have it yourself. You still have responsibility even after you have passed responsibility down to someone below you. Passing out responsibility differs, however, from passing out knowledge in that you can take it back. You can relieve a subordinate of responsibility.

THE HEAD MAN MUST GIVE OTHERS AUTHORITY TO DO THINGS

Responsibility and authority should go hand in hand. When you tell a man that it is his job to do something, he can't do it unless you give him authority—probably authority to spend money or authority to tell other people to do things. If responsibility and authority always went hand in hand, we wouldn't need to mention it. But, unfortunately, they can be separated, and sometimes they are. And when they are not about equal, the work usually suffers.

Granting Too Little Authority.   Almost always the trouble is too little authority. The boss tells you to do certain things but holds back on authority. Often he doesn't realize that he has not given authority. He tells you that you do have authority, but he asks that you "keep him informed." He expects you to run in and ask him before making even minor decisions. And he criticizes you if you don't. Sometimes he goes around you. He gives orders (that you don't know about) directly to your subordinates. Or he listens to their complaints and fixes them up—again without consulting you. Or he doesn't back you up and reverses your decisions. Your subordinates soon learn that you don't count for much —you have no real authority.

Sometimes he tells you to do something that requires your getting information or help from other departments. But he doesn't tell the other departments! Small wonder that you have trouble carrying out the assignment. Or he changes the extent of your authority. He tells you about it but he doesn't tell anyone else. That is not likely to make trouble if he cuts your authority, but it is likely to cause trouble if he extends it and doesn't tell others.

Some bosses take away authority by oversupervising. If a man is new on a job, the boss probably knows better than the new man how to do it well. In fact it may be his old job. It is easier and quicker for him just to do some of the work himself—or at least make many of the decisions —than it is to stop and explain it all to his new man or to take the chance that the man will make a mistake. The end result is that he has not really delegated authority. Now, that is all right when a man is new on the job. He should be supervised closely. But the boss should let a new man go more and more on his own as he learns the job. The trouble is that some bosses never do let their men go ahead on their own.

Some bosses never seem to learn really how to delegate responsibility and authority. They believe that "the best way to get a job done is to do it yourself." So they try to do everything—particularly deciding everything—themselves. Some men seem to feel that they are indispensable if no decisions can be made without them. They get bogged down in detail, work long hours, work themselves to death, and keep their subordinates from developing.

Of course your superior has his problems, too. When he gives you authority to do things and to make decisions, he is stuck with what you do. When you make a mistake, it is on his shoulders as well as yours. He can't go to his superior and disclaim responsibility because you made the mistake. Your chief's future success rests on how good a job he does. And, since he doesn't do it all himself, that means how good a job you and his other subordinates do. Naturally, then, he is vitally interested in how good a job all of you do—it is his future as well as yours. He may oversupervise you (and, in effect, take away your authority) without realizing it.

Bosses have to set some limit on your decisions. Usually you can't, without asking them, make promotions, give raises, or spend money for machines. Even factory managers have to get approval (from the board of directors in some companies) to buy a $10,000 machine. One billion-dollar company requires the president's approval for all purchases over $2,500 and all salary increases over $6,000! It is one thing to admit that you can't let subordinates decide everything, but that doesn't have to mean that they are not to decide anything!

Authority-of-Position and Authority-of-Knowledge. Authority is the right to give orders. A department head who knows nothing about his job can give orders—he can have *authority-of-position*—but it takes more than that to run a department. It takes know-how—technical and administrative. Men respect superiors who know all about the kind of work they are supervising. But, even more important, administrative know-how is needed too. Department heads need to know how to direct other people's work. A department head's authority-of-position is much stronger if it is backed up with the *authority-of-knowledge*. Position can command compliance, but knowledge commands respect. A man with both has real authority.

Don't overlook this when putting men in management jobs. Too, you can give a man positional authority but not knowledge. No? Yes you can —over a period of time—through training; but not overnight. Don't forget, though, that positional authority is only half-authority. You need to give your men the other half too.

Lack of Equality of Responsibility and Authority. Having made quite a point of the need to delegate authority to go along with responsibility, we now have to backtrack a little. *You can never give any man all of the authority needed to carry out his work.* A company's president is responsible for its well-being and for its making profits. But he has no control over what his competitors or his customers do—nor can he control laws, tax rates, labor unions, or the national prosperity. Yet all of these bear upon the company's well-being and its profits.

In a smaller way the same applies to every department head. You tell the foreman to run his department efficiently, but he has full control over very few things. He has to make the products you tell him to make and do it with the materials, men, and machines you furnish him. The foreman, just like the president, can never have as much authority as he would like to have to carry out his responsibility. That is no excuse, however, for your not giving him and every department head as much authority as you can.

THE HEAD MAN CAN'T DECIDE EVERY MINOR MATTER HIMSELF

In every organization of any size many, many decisions must be made. Some are major decisions. What products should you make? Should you buy or make parts? Should you spend much or little on research? Some are minor decisions. Should you work the drill-press department overtime this Saturday? Should you make this part from a casting or a forging? What will you do with Joe Smith who came to work drunk this morning?

Decide at Low Levels.   Major decisions need to be made high in the organization. Minor decisions can be made lower down. So we have a rule: *Make all decisions as far down in the organization as you can,* **provided,** *that the man deciding has enough knowledge, information, and ability to make an intelligent decision.*

Doing this frees top men from deciding minor matters. It gives lower officials experience in making decisions and helps them to learn to stand on their own feet. It makes them feel more important because they really

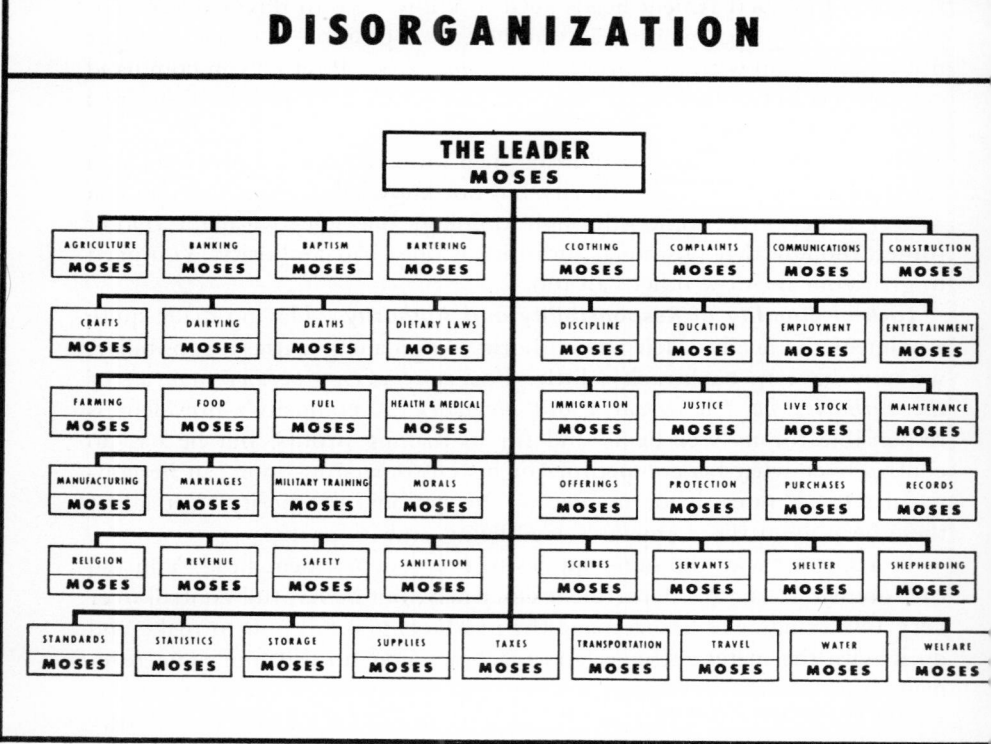

U. S. Steel Co.

FIG. 2–3. Even Moses found that he couldn't decide every minor matter himself.

are more important. It produces quick and, usually, good decisions because they are made by men who understand the situation. Decisions are less costly, too, because fewer and lower-paid men decide.

Making decisions at lower levels runs the risk that different people deciding will not all decide the same way. To avoid this trouble, higher officials should lay down policies or rules to guide subordinates. The foreman should have no problem knowing what to do with his drunk man. Shop rules cover that.

Formulating policies is not quite enough. Everyone must know them. So it is necessary (1) to formulate them, and (2) to tell everyone what they are. That still is not quite enough. You need to (3) check up every now and then and straighten out anyone who is not following them.

Deciding at low levels risks mistakes. Subordinates don't have rules to cover every situation. When they decide things outside the framework of the rules laid down, and having neither the background nor experience of higher officials, they will sometimes make unwise decisions.

FIG. 2–4. Jethro tells Moses to delegate work and decision making to others.

The Exception Principle. You can usually make most decisions at low levels yet avoid the possibility of serious error by using the "exception" principle. You lay down rules to cover all usual situations. Your subordinates decide all routine cases by applying the rules. *But* exceptions —nonroutine situations—are *not* decided by the subordinate. All of the exceptions go up to you for decision.

Making decisions at low levels and using the exception principle are far from new ideas. Fifteen hundred years before Christ, Jethro told an overburdened Moses to relieve himself of detail by delegating to others power to decide minor matters.[1]

"Exceptions" should not be the same as "crises," however. Don't

---

[1] The Bible. Exodus, chap. 18.

let your subordinates have so much freedom that problems get to the crisis stage before you spot them or before they come to you. It is well, too, to get summary reports telling how often rules are used. Suppose that foremen, for example, have the right to impose penalties for minor infractions of shop rules without asking the shop superintendent. This is reasonable. But it is a good idea for the superintendent to know how many infractions there are. It gives him a clue as to how things are going.

Many companies use the exception idea in accounting and production control. Standard costs are set up to cover making products the usual way. As long as production goes smoothly you say that products are costing the standard amounts—as they are. You cut out a great deal of cost accounting work. But if things go wrong, they show up as deviations from standard. Detailed records are kept of the deviations from standard; but they are not very numerous, and you end up with fewer records and reports than if you kept individual cost records of everything.

Production control can also be simplified by using exceptions. You start raw materials in at one end of the factory but cut out most of the record keeping needed to keep track of exactly where everything is while it is being made in the factory. If nothing goes wrong, the products will come out on schedule. If something does go wrong (as often happens), the foreman knows it and *reports it*. The exception is reported. Again the total effect is to reduce paper work.

NO ONE SHOULD HAVE TWO BOSSES

Picture yourself working for two or more bosses each telling you what to do. Even two superiors is one too many. With two or more, the day is bound to come when, together, they ask for more than you can do or they give you conflicting orders. Dissatisfaction all the way round results. Having two bosses is called "divided accountability."

How does a two-boss situation arise? Usually it comes from the need to consult with, or get advice from, someone other than your main boss. Suggestions and advice sometimes sound like (and are) orders. Usually, unless you have good reason not to, you accept suggestions. But when you do, as far as you are concerned, there is not one chain of command but two (or more). You are getting directions ("suggestions?") from others besides your main boss.

For example, a foreman is responsible for running his department. But he gets schedules from production control, specifications from engineering, and instructions about how to handle people from the personnel department.

Actually, some people do have two superiors in spite of the disadvantages. When you need specialized help on some part of your work, your regular boss may need to call in a staff specialist to tell you how to do that part of your work. It is good to have specialists help out but bad to have two bosses. Sometimes, however, it is better to put up with two men telling you what to do than it is to be without staff help.

Another type of divided accountability arises in multiplant companies. It concerns the relationship of home office staff specialists to individual plant staff specialists. Time and motion study men, for example, are employees of an individual plant and report to its manager. They are, however, in some companies, told *how* to do their work by a central time and motion study department in the home office, which does no time and motion study itself but only explains and directs the methods used in individual plants. The central office staff may select new men for the plants, train them, or transfer them. Usually these things are done only with the permission of the plant managers, but the individual time study men in the various plants may actually have two bosses.

The same thing occurs in purchasing, personnel, traffic and shipping, and other areas. There seems to be no good way to give specialized staff advice from a central office without putting someone in the position of working for two people. The situation is the same in any factory where the staff is allowed to tell the line how to do things. Foremen and other line officers are, in fact, accountable to two or more bosses when that occurs.

Divided accountability is often found in secretarial work. Two or more minor executives must share a secretary. Together they can keep her busy. As long as they are reasonable, there is no trouble. But trouble is always possible if both men get in a hurry for their work at the same time.

A particularly objectionable form of divided accountability, fortunately rarely found, exists when a subordinate is asked by his supervisor's boss to judge his supervisor's work. The subordinate is indeed in a bad spot.

THE HEAD MAN OUGHT, NOW AND THEN, TO CONSULT WITH HIS SUBORDINATES

Asking your subordinates what they think makes them feel important and produces some good ideas. Of course, you must not ask them and then never pay attention to their ideas. If you pay no attention, they soon see that you are not sincere in wanting their ideas.

You also find out more about what is going on down through the organization if you listen now and then. You learn things that help you make more intelligent decisions. And by having allowed subordinates to speak, you will find them more ready to accept programs. We are all more enthusiastic about programs we help develop. We work harder to make them successful.

You can even work in some training along with supervision while asking a subordinate for his ideas. Training done this way is less painful than when done directly. Ask your subordinate what goes on, ask him what he plans to do, look over his proposals, tell him to do certain things. If he is a production official, ask him how the ABC Company order is coming. Behind time? What can we do to speed it up? What products are we to make next September? Too many for our capacity? How can we increase our capacity? You ask the questions; let the man come up with his answers. Then you add your own. He gets to think over the problems, yet you work in a little guidance too.

THE HEAD MAN MUST CHECK UP ON WHAT HIS SUBORDINATES DO

"Interest begets interest." Whatever the boss always checks up on gets done. What he usually leaves unchecked is less likely to get done. If he asks for reports on what you have gotten done and what is still to be done, you try harder. Besides, by checking, the boss can find out sooner if things aren't going right. Maybe he can do something about it. Periodic checking up is a must.

Lawrence Appley once told this story about what happened in one company. Every year all the presidents of subsidiary companies met with the board of directors to answer three questions: (1) Did you meet your this-year's budget? (2) What budget have you set for next year? (3) What budget changes do you see ahead for the next 5 years? The subsidiary presidents were always well prepared. But they didn't seem to be much interested in developing future executive talent. So at one meeting the board added three more direct questions: (4) What is your present organization structure, who fills key jobs, and what are your personnel practices? (5) What changes in key people and in personnel policies do you see for next year? (6) What changes do you see in the next 5 years? No subsidiary president could answer the last three questions. No directions were given, but at the next meeting the questions were repeated. This time every man was ready with answers. After the board asked directly about organization planning, the presidents took care of it. Before that, when the board didn't check, it wasn't done.

Being interested is a good way to get subordinates to carry out the programs you want. Ask them what progress they have made on a project. Ask them how much more they expect to get done in the next month and how they propose to do it. Then ask again next month. Ask them if they got as far as they expected on the program. If not, what held it up and what they did to move it faster. Just asking makes them know that you are interested and that they have to show progress or explain why not.

Some people call checking up "accountability." You give a man responsibility, you give him authority, then you hold him accountable. Budgets are the most common and most concrete method for holding people accountable. Budgets set goals—production and cost goals—to be achieved; then you can compare actual to planned. Differences between actual and planned are high lighted.

However you plan to hold a subordinate accountable, it is only fair that he know what you expect so that he can tell, all the while, how he is doing. Then he can try harder if he sees he is not measuring up.

THE HEAD MAN CAN'T SUPERVISE DIRECTLY THE WORK OF VERY MANY SUBORDINATES

Every department head must spend part of his time supervising his men. He must give them directions, tell them what he wants done, find out the trouble they are having, help straighten them out, show them how to do things, and give them new directions.

The "Span of Control." How many men can one man supervise? The answer is called the "span of control." At high levels in a company the responsibilities are great and the work assignments are broad and general. At lower levels responsibilities are less and work assignments detailed and specific. At the top, the span is small (6 to 12); at the bottom, it is wide (15 to 30).

Most authorities recommend spans of 3 to 7 at the top, not 6 to 12. But a survey of actual practice in 100 large companies showed that 6 to 12, with an average of 8 or 9, was far more common.[2]

Actual practice is not a wholly reliable guide as to what is best. Everyone likes to report directly to the president—it is a sign of status and may help bring a promotion. Besides some top men feel more important if they have a large number of people reporting directly to them. Or they try to keep their finger in all the pies and so have lots of people report to them. It all adds up to more people reporting high up than should. Probably the *best* number is a little smaller than the actual count found.

At the bottom of the organization the span of control is wider. Men working on detailed and specific jobs need directions only when they start on a job. Once he learns his job, an elevator operator, for example, needs little supervision. Nor does a machine operator, *except* when he finishes one job and gets another. The foremen will probably have to tell him what to do next and may have to explain the job to him. So how many men one foreman can supervise depends upon both (1) the complexity of the work, and (2) the frequency of new work assignments.

Besides these two conditions, there are at least two more things that affect how many he can supervise: (3) the ability of his men, and (4) how much time he spends on nonsupervisory work. The maintenance department foreman rarely has to tell his electricians how to put up a light fixture or his roofers how to repair a leaky roof. They know how. Factory

---

[2] See Ernest Dale, *Planning and Developing the Company Organization Structure,* Research Report No. 20 (New York: American Management Association, 1952), pp. 49–60.

foremen often do not have to explain jobs to their experienced men because they are skilled and can themselves figure out how to do them.
Their being skilled lessens the amount of supervision and allows their boss
to supervise more men.

How many men a foreman can supervise depends, in part, then, on
how good a trainer he is. If he trains his men well, he can supervise more
men. It also depends on labor turnover. If his men are always coming and
going, he has lots more training to do and so can't supervise so many.

A foreman's span of control (or any one else's) depends also on his
nonsupervisory duties. Nearly always he must keep records, make reports, attend meetings, confer with his superior, with staff men, and with
other department heads. All of this takes time. The more time he spends
on nonsupervisory work, the less he has for supervising and the fewer
people he can supervise.

Some companies claim much higher ratios at the bottom than 30 to 1
(and 30 to 1 is high). A foreman can supervise 50 employees or more if
they are all doing the same thing in the same work area. Usually he does
not, in fact, supervise so many even when it looks as if he does. He always
has assistant foremen, group leaders, setup men, job dispatchers, or
others who do part of the supervision. If you count them as part-time
supervisors, you will find most factory departments have between 15
and 25 men per supervisor.

Now, returning to the matter of the importance of work and the complexity and frequency of work assignments made to subordinates: Top
jobs are more responsible and difficult than bottom jobs. Also, a much
greater proportion of the time must be spent in nonsupervisory ways.
Remember, too, that every executive spends part of his time *receiving*
supervision. These things cut into supervisory time and limit the span
of control to smaller numbers than at the bottom.

Not all companies go along with small numbers at the top. Some exceed
the usual spans. Sears, Roebuck and Company and Johnson & Johnson each
use a wider span. Sears has thirteen vice-presidents reporting to its president, Johnson & Johnson has more. These two companies are almost alone,
however, in favoring wide spans at the top.

Wide spans at the top result in fewer layers of management. If one
president supervises 15 division heads, who each supervise 20 at the next
level, who in turn each supervise 25, you have an organization with
7,500 men at the bottom level, or 7,816 altogether (including 316 supervisors); yet there are only two levels of supervision between the president and the 7,500 bottom-level employees.

Wide spans reduce layers and need fewer executives. If we cut the
spans to 10, 15, and 20, we could supervise only 3,000 bottom workers
with three intermediate layers of supervision. It would take 161 supervisors and executives. But to supervise 7,500 men at the bottom we would
have to introduce another layer of supervision and go up to 551 super-

visors and executives. This way it takes 235 more supervisors. Saving 235 supervisors is a big payroll savings.

Payroll savings is not the whole story of span of control. If it were, everyone would go in for wide spans. But before we get to the disadvantages of wide spans, there is another advantage. Wide spans prevent oversupervising. A subordinate in a wide-span company just has to make his own decisions because his boss doesn't have much time to spend with him. Making his own decisions helps him to develop. It is essentially a sink or swim situation. Each man goes it on his own and stands or falls on his own performance. Men who succeed are better men for the experience. Those that fail are shunted off into less demanding jobs.

Actually it isn't that bad. Companies using wide-span or "flat" organizations usually set up policies to guide (even to bind) minor executives. This cuts the decision-making area. Besides, the home office lays out accounting procedures, purchasing methods, and so on so that the men who are supposedly on their own do not have to figure such things out for themselves. Also the home office has special trainers to show plant managers or store managers how to do their jobs well. This helps new men get off to a good start.

Flat spans lessen the levels between bottom and top, which helps cut red tape. Every added level seems to make it harder to get information up and down and to get decisions quickly.

Flat-span companies claim that they have higher morale. Why? Department heads have real decision-making authority. They are not themselves overspecialized nor are they hampered by the interference of specialists. Distances from top to bottom, organization-wise, are short. Communication is easier; top officials understand work-level problems better. It may not be so, however. If you are one of twenty reporting to a vice-president, he isn't going to have time to hear much about your problems.

The arguments favoring flat organizations seem good. Why aren't such organizations common? First, you lose a degree of control. You don't know what your subordinates are doing when you have so many that you can't keep track of them. Some do their work well—some not so well. By the time you find out, they have lost considerable money for the company.

Next, if you are the boss, even though you can't supervise many subordinates well, you can try. Probably you will try—and get so swamped in detail that you have no time for the nonsupervisory parts of your own job.

Third, when subordinates have to sink or swim, some of them sink. When you find out that they aren't doing well, you can replace them, but replacing is costly and hurts everyone's morale. Besides, some of them learn to swim but not well. Self-made men don't always make a very good product.

THE HEAD MAN MUST SET UP DEPARTMENTS AND CHOOSE HEADS FOR THEM

No president ever gets to set up the organization from scratch. He inherits a going concern. It already has departments. But it is easier to explain departments and how they *should* be set up if we talk about it as if he did start from scratch. So we will start that way and then come back later (in Chapter 4) to the going-concern idea.

The question is how to divide and how to combine work into departmental work groups. Several guides are available. Most of them are alternatives, however. Using one precludes the others at the same level in the organization. You should:

1. Group work requiring similar knowledge, skills, or equipment.
2. Group work that is closely related.
3. Group work geographically.
4. Group work by type of product.
5. Group work by type of customer.
6. Separate one department's work from another's wherever there is a natural break in activities.
7. Separate doing from checking up.
8. Consider competition between departments. Some is good. Some is bad. Use the good; avoid the bad.
9. Let new developments grow at the start under the direction of the executive who is interested.

Group Work Requiring Similar Knowledge, Skills, or Equipment. This gives you the advantage of specialization. The work is always done by men who know the subject, and it is all done under the direction of your best man in that subject. You might, for example, group all purchasing, and do it centrally to get better knowledge of markets as well as to get the best quantity discounts. Grouping work requiring the same equipment allows its fullest use and so saves on equipment expense. This idea applies more at lower levels than at high. Presidents and vice-presidents don't operate machines—expensive or inexpensive.

Group Work That Is Closely Related. Sometimes several steps in a procedure, although unlike in themselves, need to be tied closely together. They need to be closely co-ordinated. You can best get co-ordination by assigning all of the closely related steps to one department head. You might, for example, put the raw materials stock room and the receiving department under the production control department because it knows what materials are required today and what will be required tomorrow.

Group Work Geographically. If your headquarters are in the Northeast and you have factories and sales agencies all over the country, you may want to group certain work geographically. A southwestern division can head up all activities in the southwest states. Many questions can be settled on a regional basis and not have to go back to the home office for decision.

Group Work by Type of Product. General Electric makes household appliances. It also makes electric generating equipment and many other items. General Motors makes autos, refrigerators, and railroad locomotives. Du Pont makes explosives, chemicals, and fabrics. In all three companies, the company's *major* subdivisions are by product group. Each product group has its own manufacturing plants and sales organization. It certainly seems more logical to do it this way than for GE to make automatic toasters and power plant generators in the same plant, or for GM to make autos, refrigerators, and locomotives in the same plant, or for Du Pont to make explosives, chemicals, and fabrics in the same plant. Also, imagine selling locomotives and refrigerators in the same sales department!

Group Work by Type of Customer. General Foods Company has recently set up a division to sell to hotels, hospitals, the Armed Forces, and other institutional buyers of food. This division sells the same foods that you and I buy at the grocery, but it will be able to sell better to institutional buyers than can the separate product group sales departments.

Auto tire companies have separate sales organizations to sell tires to automobile manufacturers, truck, bus and taxi companies, and service stations. They specialize by type of customers.

Specializing by type of customer is most common in selling—not in the manufacturing end. It is effective because it sets up ways to get to the customer ("channels of distribution") that are best for each kind of customer.

Separate One Department's Work from Another's Wherever There Is a Natural Break in Activities. Every department's work is related to the work of one or several other departments. You have to cut apart the activities, assigning some work to one and other work to another. It is easy if there is a natural break in the things done. Draw the cut-off line there. Then there will be little confusion as to which does what work; nor will co-ordination suffer much because not so much co-ordination is needed where natural breaks occur.

This idea is called the "clean-break." There is almost never a truly "clean-break." The engineering department is a fairly good clean-break example in many companies. It designs the product; the factory makes it. Things having to do with design belong to the engineering department; things having to do with making products are the factory's. Admittedly our example is not perfect because a product's design is dependent on how you will make it. Yet it is usually possible to draw a rather clear line between the duties of the two departments.

In practice you may see the clean-break idea used more negatively than positively. Some things that you would like to separate and give to different departments you can't very well separate because there is no good breaking point. So they are left together in one department.

Separate Doing from Checking Up. Don't let anyone be his own final judge. Everyone should know how you judge him and for that he needs to be able to judge his own work. But final judgment should be in someone else's hands. Auditing of accounts should be done separately and by people other than those who keep the accounts. The auditors should report through a separate chain of command to a high official. The same with inspection in the factory. You can let the foreman have his own inspectors (or let his men do their own inspecting) to check work and be sure that things are being made right. But let the inspectors who approve work leaving the department work for a chief inspector, not for the foreman. Most companies go farther and have all inspectors (not just department final inspectors) report to a chief inspector rather than to foremen.

Why separate doing from checking up? Why not tell a man that it is his job to do something and that you expect him to do it well? Then allow him to do it, taking his word for it that it is well done. Most of us are honest, so why not do it that way? Well, not quite everyone is honest. Besides, and much more important, it is our tendency to be uncritical of our own work—especially when, by being critical, we would make our record look bad. No, it is safer to have someone else check up and pass judgment.

Consider Competition. Most everyone likes competition. Put us into competition with someone else and we try harder. Such a driving force should not be overlooked. GM's Chevrolet competes against GM's Pontiac as well as against Ford and Plymouth. General Electric's GE line of appliances competes with its Hotpoint line. Sales departments often have contests pitting sales territories against each other. In factories, safety campaigns pit departments against each other.

Of course, there is always considerable competition between heads of departments trying to make the best showing. Each must try to operate more efficiently than the others so as to be promoted.

An organization can be set up to increase or to decrease competition between divisions or departments. If you want to increase it—set departments up so that they can be compared easily—let departments have about the same things to do. Keep the records in a comparable way when you can. Probably you should give each department considerable freedom of action—let them each make many of their decisions. Then they can really compete.

You won't want to carry this competition idea too far. It makes for duplication. GE has to advertise its GE appliances. GE's Hotpoint division has to advertise its line. Chevrolet and Pontiac each must advertise. Certainly some waste is involved. Some duplication is also probably involved in manufacturing. You have to offset the losses from competition against the gains. Be sure the losses don't outweigh the gains. Choose the degree of competition that seems best for your organization.

Let New Things Grow under Interested Persons.   Most companies grow all the time. In small companies there aren't many departments, yet most of the things done in large companies have to be done—at least occasionally. Departments in small companies combine activities which, when the company gets large, will belong to separate departments. One man may run the raw materials stockroom and also do all the purchasing. Foremen may do all of their work planning and set production standards.

At the start some of the activities that will later grow into departments are done by whoever has the greatest interest in them. You don't need to worry about that. And as the company grows, let those activities grow under the man who has been interested. Maybe you get an illogical combination of duties, but an interested man won't shuffle them off to one side and neglect them. Ultimately, the time to separate out the now matured department will come. Then you can try for a better over-all arrangement. But in the growing stage there is much to be said for putting it where the interest is. A corollary to this idea is: don't let growing activities stay under men not interested in them.

Applying Guides for Setting Up Departments.   How would you apply our rules for setting up departments? Can you follow all of them at once? If you set up major divisions on a product-line basis, can you also set them up on a geographical basis? If you set up major divisions either of these ways, then how do you handle sales and manufacturing? Are you going to have several sales and manufacturing subdivisions—one in each major division?

Usually you can't apply more than one guide at a time. Automobile companies all set up their major divisions on a product basis. Ford, Chrysler, and GM are all without a company-wide sales or manufacturing department. So are Continental Can, Du Pont, General Foods, Lockheed Aircraft, and many others.

Our guides are often alternatives; if you choose one you can't at the same time use the others—*at the same level*. But you can, as Du Pont does, have as a major division the "explosives Department"—and then subdivide it into sales and manufacturing—and then subdivide sales into geographical units and manufacturing into geographical units. Or you could subdivide the manufacture of explosives on a particular product basis. The fact that you have once used product groups as a basis for setting up major divisions does not stop you from using the idea again lower down.

Notice, too, that if you do subdivide the manufacture of explosives on a particular product basis, you probably *at the same time* are applying the idea of joining together things that take the same equipment. You are also joining together work of similar and related nature. You end up applying several of our guides at once. Our guides are, then, not always alternatives. Sometimes you would set up about the same departments, whichever guide was uppermost in your mind.

SETTING UP DEPARTMENTS IN GOING CONCERNS

At the start of our discussion of how to set up departments (page 40) we said that going concerns already have departments. Then we put aside the going-concern idea and discussed setting up departments as if the company president had a basketful of activities to be sorted out and put into piles (departments) any way that he wanted.

Of course, he never gets to do it that way. The president inherits a going concern. He can do a little reshuffling of activities between departments (and so can every department head reorganize lesser departments reporting to him), but the going concern restricts the freedom to change.

Suppose, for example, that a large concern decides that it is time to reorganize on a product-line basis. The present job of vice-president in charge of sales will disappear. So will the job of vice-president of manufacturing. But you are going to have a vice-president in charge of household appliances, a vice-president in charge of farm equipment, a vice-president in charge of guided missiles, and so on. Each new vice-president will have under him a sales manager and a production manager.

What happens to our present two vice-presidents? Will they be demoted and work under one of the new V.P.'s? Or will they become product-line V.P.'s themselves? And if they do, how well fitted are they to have charge of both sales and production in their new area?

The point is that you have to work forever at reaching an ever-receding goal—the ideal organization structure. Unless you are in financial trouble, you seldom make wholesale changes. You keep working at changing the organization all the time, but you probably have to do it bit by bit. This means that you have some idea of what the ideal setup ought to be and then make changes here and there toward the ideal when opportunity arises (as when a man retires). But you are never done; you always have an organization with many good features and some bad. Our rules for setting up departments are guides to use when you make changes.

A top executive at Lever Brothers (soaps and detergents) took a good company in 1947 ($14 million profits) and, in 3 years, ran it down hill to a $7 million loss in 1949. He did it by making wholesale departmental rearrangements and firing officials right and left. He lost his own job in 1950. This doesn't prove that making changes wholesale is bound to work out badly, but it did that time, and it is usually a poor way to make changes.

SPECIALIZE WHERE POSSIBLE

Specialization usually pays any time a whole job takes two or more people. Divide the job into parts and let one man specialize in each part

of it. Each gets good at his task and together, because they have specialized, they turn out more products than if each man did the whole job
himself.

Specialization saves training time. Anyone can learn a small part of a
big job quickly; if he had to learn a big job, it would take longer. Specialization allows you to use less skillful men. Men who never would do
well on a complicated job can get very good if given only a part of it
to do over and over again. You have many niches into which men of
limited ability can fit. Even physically handicapped persons can be given
jobs where they are at no disadvantage.

Specialization would seem to limit flexibility. Men on small specialized
tasks can't transfer their skills readily. But actually such men can easily
be transferred, not because they already know other jobs but because
the other jobs are just as simple as their own and can be learned quickly.

With specialization, employers can buy just the right amount of skill
for the work, and workers perform at their highest skill all the time.
Without specialization you have complex tasks, parts of which take lots
of skill, while other parts do not. You have to have a good man on the
job, yet he is spending part of his time on low-skill work. Using a good
machine setup man to set up *and operate* a machine is an example. Once
set up, machines can be operated with unskilled labor. Let the skilled
setup man spend all his time setting up jobs. Use lower-skilled operators
to tend the machines, once they are set up.

Specialized workers performing only one task do not lose time, as does
an employee doing a whole job when changing from one part of the job
to another. They do not have to get out and put away different tools or
change from one workplace to another.

Specialization requires volume and standardization. If fifty workers
each perform separate tasks, there must be enough work of each kind
to keep them busy. Some people get concerned about specialization increasing monotony, which they believe causes workers to lose interest
in their jobs. Fortunately some men and women like highly repetitive
jobs. Companies rarely have trouble keeping employees on such jobs.

Specialization also increases interdependence in that the activities of
one person are completely dependent on those of others. Specialization,
therefore, makes co-ordination very important. When a worker does a
whole complex job himself, he co-ordinates the minor parts of the job
himself. But if those minor parts of the job are divided up among many
employees, you have to get each man to make the right quantity at the
right time and you must move materials from operation to operation.
In a word, you do a lot of co-ordination that is unnecessary when one
man does the whole thing himself.

Specialization occurs at high as well as low levels in an organization,
but at the top levels extreme specialization should give way to "generalization." Since the president and the heads of the major divisions of the

company must administer diverse activities, they should have broad training and experience.

Machinery, factories, companies, and even industries are specialized. In fact, can you think of activity of any kind which is not, to some extent, specialized? Factories probably should not specialize so much that they can't change if they some day have to make different products. Specialized factories and companies can't swing over immediately to new activities.

STUDY QUESTIONS

1. What difference does it make whether you call a rule a principle or a generalization? Support your position.
2. Start with this statement: "The proper organization to do anything depends on what it has to do." If it is so, can you justify two companies in the same industry having unlike organizations?
3. Should job assignments be put in writing? Justify your answer.
4. "It is not my fault," said the vice-president to the president. "My plant manager made that mistake." Discuss.
5. What is meant by delegation of responsibility? Can you really delegate responsibility? Explain.
6. Should authority and responsibility be equal? Explain.
7. How does the "exception" principle work? Discuss its pros and cons.
8. Though the "exception principle" saves considerable time, it is not used everywhere? Why not?
9. Is there ever a time for having two bosses? Answer fully.
10. Can you justify a wider span of control at bottom than at top levels?
11. What conditions hold down the span of control? What conditions increase it?
12. Explain what is meant by organizing on a "flat" basis.
13. When would you ever group work by type of customer?
14. How does the "clean-break" idea work?
15. What should you do about competition between departments? Why?
16. Why is specialization so good? Are there any bad features? Discuss.

Case 2–1. Gibson Toy Company

The Gibson Toy Company (600 employees) makes toys of many varieties but has its biggest volume in toy musical instruments. Gibson holds patents to the use of a loop of rubber tape with bumps on it to play tunes on music box type toys. Some income comes from royalties from other toy manufacturers, but Gibson itself is the biggest maker of such toys.

Gibson does all the metal work, woodwork, assembly, and painting on its toys. But it buys the rubber tape and all plastic parts.

The company is family-owned with no stock outstanding. The Board Chairman, Bill Gibson, is 68 years old and is not active in the company (he is a great outdoor man and isn't around the factory much) except that sometimes he feels that the younger men are pushing him into the background. When he gets these notions, he usually makes a big fuss about something they did without asking him and insists that it be changed.

Jack Gibson, 66, his brother, is president. He, too, is not very active (although he is a director in six other companies) and is inclined to let Earl Johnson, executive vice-president, run things the way he wants. Johnson and the two Gibsons constitute the Board of Directors, although the stock is owned 50–50 by the Gibsons.

Johnson found that Gibson's plastics and rubber purchases mounted every year. When they passed the million-dollar mark, he decided to go into the plastics and rubber business. Accordingly he bought the necessary equipment to make nearly all of the plastic and rubber parts. The manufacturing equipment for plastics and rubber were put in a wing of the factory that had formerly been used for storage.

After a few initial difficulties with the new machines, production began to pick up. And although they showed a loss the first 3 months, they were clearly "over the hump" and were going to make money. It was at that time that the neighborhood residents circulated a petition, claiming that the odors caused by the new process were obnoxious.

Bill Gibson, on hearing of the petition, was quite upset since he did not know about the plastics and rubber manufacture. He railed about Johnson putting the company into money-losing businesses, spending his money without authority, and making the company a nuisance in the neighborhood. Johnson didn't think it wise to argue with him, but he reminded Jack Gibson that this had been discussed for over 2 years and that he, Johnson, thought that they had agreed that he should "try out, on a small scale, making our own plastics and rubber."

What, if any, principles of good management (or good organization) have been violated here? What is the real problem here? Recommend a course that will avoid problems of this nature in the future.

Chapter 3

ORGANIZATION STRUCTURES

THE way you finally group activities into departments and set up chains of command determines your organization structure. The structure is the organization's framework.

It is popular to say that "organization is people." But to neglect structure is like neglecting bones in a study of human anatomy. Bones aren't the whole body, but you don't find tall men with short bones or vice versa. And dogs can't walk upright because their bones aren't hooked up right. Structure is important in men, dogs, and organizations.

Of course, an organization *is* people. But one of the people is president, another is vice-president, another is janitor. Each one has a job to do. The *job* (but not the man) is indispensable. Can you get along without Bigdome, the president?—or Littledome, the vice-president?—or Schmaltz, the janitor? Yes. But can you get along without their jobs being done? Maybe Schmaltz' job, but not the others. In this chapter we admit that people are important but spend our time on organization structure.

Flaws in the organization structure make lots of trouble. One management consultant said that three fourths of his business was solving problems coming from defects in organization structure of his client companies. In most companies, particularly single-plant companies, the departmental arrangement in use is not too logical, being in part the result of the way the departments happened to be set up historically and in part the result of the careful grouping of responsibilities. Probably all old companies were originally organized on a line basis. In the last 50 years, most of them, by adding staff departments with special work assignments, have changed to the line and staff form. *In the typical company there has never been an over-all review of departmental groupings.* Illogical arrangements often exist.

All large manufacturing organizations are "line and staff" organizations. There are two other kinds: (1) "line" organization, and (2) "functional" organization. Neither is important today, but discussing them first helps us understand line and staff organizations.

48

LINE ORGANIZATIONS

"Line" organizations use no staff specialists and have no staff departments,[1] but they do have departments doing different things. Going down from the top, line organizations divide into departments—but only into "operational" departments, not staff departments. Figure 3–1 shows how this works.

Below the president, line organizations usually split into three major departments: sales, manufacturing, and finance. Each in turn is divided into several small departments. Figure 3–1 shows the smaller departments

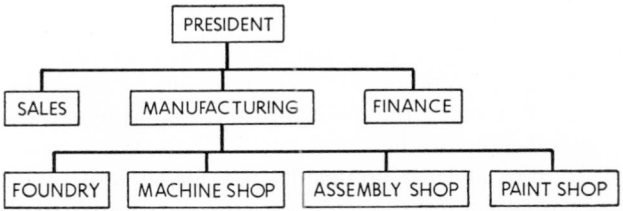

FIG. 3–1. A line organization with manufacturing departments divided on an *operational* basis.

only for manufacturing, but sales and finance divide into smaller departments too.

Figures 3–1 and 3–2 show two line organizations with different subdivisions in manufacturing. You have one or the other—not both. Notice

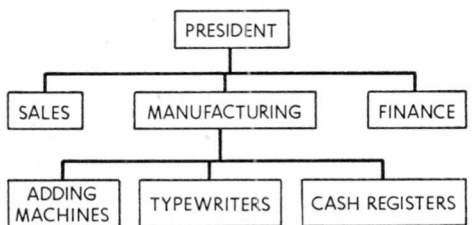

FIG. 3–2. A line organization with manufacturing departments divided on a *product* basis.

in Figure 3–1 that the foundry, machine shop, assembly shop, and paint shop are all separate departments; the basis for setting them apart is that they do different *operations*. In Figure 3–2 each department makes a different *product*.

But, where—in the charts—are personnel, production control, and industrial engineering? They don't show because they are not, in line organizations, separate departments. Whenever they exist, they are staff departments—but they don't exist in line organizations.

Of course, someone has to do personnel and other kinds of staff work. But who? The operating departments themselves do it. Each line depart-

---

[1] The "line" form is sometimes improperly called the "military" form.

ment head hires and trains his own men. Each head plans and schedules his own work, sets piece rates, quality standards, and so on. Each head has nearly complete authority to decide things himself, except that he must get his work out so the next department won't be held up and he must operate efficiently.

One advantage of line organizations is the elimination of buck passing. The line form places responsibilities squarely on department heads' shoulders. Quick decisions are also claimed. The direct chain of command—with no need to consult outside staff departments—allows quick decisions. You get quick decisions, that is, unless line officials are bogged down with too much work.

You may wonder how a big company can operate with line organization. It can't. Line structures were once used by most companies and are still used today in small companies. We don't really know how the big companies of a century ago operated. Mostly, we believe, they tried, but not too successfully, to use the line form.

Line organizations in large companies overload minor executives with too many and too varied duties. And when they get overloaded, the work suffers because (1) they can't be expert at everything, and (2) they don't have time for everything. So some work just doesn't get done. The line form is said to make or break executives.

A caution about the word "function." Some people would say that the line departments (such as sales and manufacturing) we have used as examples are functional departments—that each operating division has charge of a "function." If a function is a specialized activity (and that is one meaning you will find listed in the dictionary), then they are right. But in organization talk "function" is used so often to refer to the work of staff departments that, to some people, it refers *only* to staff departments. You have to watch the context to see what it means. Most of the time, it means staff work.

TAYLOR'S "FUNCTIONAL" ORGANIZATION

If department heads have to do too many things to be able to do them all well, why not take part of the work away from them? Both "functional" and "line and staff" organizations do just that.

Actually there is, today, no such thing as a "functional" organization. But there was one once, and it is of historical interest. Back in the 1880's, Frederick Taylor became a foreman and found himself swamped by the variety and amount of work he had to do.

His solution to his problem was to remove parts of the foreman's job and give those duties to specialists. Taylor didn't stop halfway though. He wanted to eliminate completely the old foreman's job and put *all* supervision in the hands of functional specialists. Of course Taylor couldn't make all of these changes when he was only a foreman. He tried it out later after he was an official.

Figure 3–3 shows Taylor's functional organization. Notice the two groups of functional supervisors. The four on the upper level—the time and cost clerk, instruction card clerk, order of work and route clerk, and the disciplinarian—were primarily office men. The four on the lower level —the gang boss, speed boss, repair boss, and the inspector—worked largely in the shop. The old "foreman" job is nowhere to be found. Each of Taylor's eight specialists dealt directly with the workers *as far as his own function was concerned*. Every factory worker had eight bosses.

This did not mean that there were eight times as many supervisors as before, but there were some more. Remember, Taylor was trying to relieve overburdened foremen, and he couldn't do it without adding supervisors. He would have his eight functional specialists doing the work that perhaps as many as four line foremen had been trying to do.

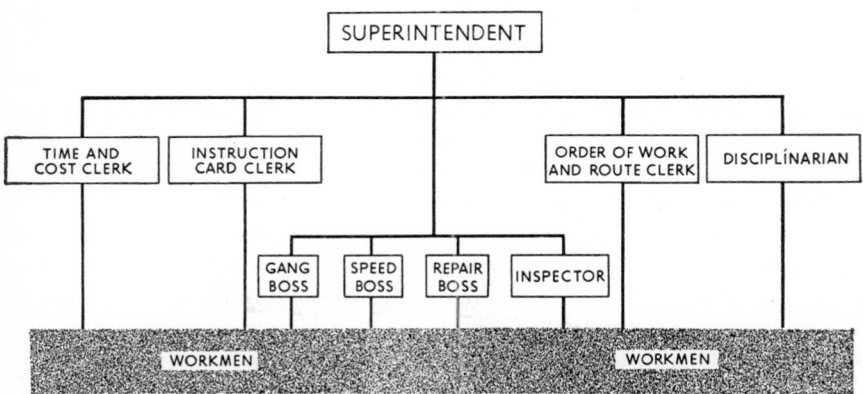

FIG. 3–3. Taylor's functional organization as he set it up for factory use.

Taylor's functional organization didn't work. With eight bosses, the men surely must have been frustrated at times trying to satisfy them all. Taylor claimed for the functional form these advantages: (1) great use of specialists, (2) getting rid of one-man control, and (3) developing of co-operation. Disadvantages seem to have been: (1) no one wanted it because it upset existing arrangements, (2) hard to divide responsibilities and make a clear assignment of some to one man and some to another, (3) too many bosses, and (4) buck passing arising from 2 and 3.

Why bother studying about a failure? How was Taylor's functional organization important? It was important because it came at the time the line and staff form was beginning to shape up, though without any push from Taylor. But Taylor was dynamic. He got around. He made speeches, wrote books, and was a consultant. He spread the gospel of his ideas, one of which was functional organization. His listeners didn't adopt functional organization but they did adopt its first cousin—the line and staff form. They got, in the line and staff form, all the advantages of Taylor's functional form with only a few of the disadvantages. Taylor's missionary work for his form surely helped speed the other.

LINE AND STAFF ORGANIZATION

Today you find line and staff organization everywhere but in the smallest organizations.[2] You keep the line (just as in line organizations) so that you can fix responsibility and get unity of command. One man is responsible, and everyone knows who he is. But you avoid overloading line officers by relieving them of certain functions which you give to specialized staff departments. The staff departments report to the line officers. This way you lighten line officers' loads, put functions in charge of specialists, yet preserve unity of command.

Line and staff forms have weaknesses however: (1) Staff men give line men advice which often borders on orders. This keeps line men from having real authority to run their departments as they think best. (2) Except in very large companies, staff departments are sometimes so small that inside their own department they cannot specialize and be efficient. They have so little of any one kind of work that specialists have to spend part of their time on nonspecialized work. They hire a specialist and pay him a good salary, then use him on odd jobs half the time.

Small Companies. Figure 3–4 is the line and staff organization used by one company (1,000 employees). Notice the "line"—President, Vice-President, Works Manager, General Superintendent, General Foreman, Foreman. From the bottom—where the product is made—right up to the top there is no question of who is the next higher in command. (Later on we have to qualify this a little, but you need to accept it here.)

Looking at the chart, you see that it branches out at almost every level, but the branches don't grow into anything. That is partly because the chart is simplified (part of it is left out—if it were all there it would take a very large sheet of paper) and partly because some branches do stop where the chart shows.

Before we go on, let us note that the line, from Foreman A's point of view goes, Foreman A, General Foreman, General Superintendent, and so on. From Foreman B's point of view it goes Foreman B, General Foremen, General Superintendent, and so on. Foremen C, D, and E each sees himself as the first step. All are correct. The line part of the organization has branched into five parts at the bottom.

The line could have branched up higher also. There could have been General Foremen A and General Foreman B—each with several

---

[2] Line and staff organization came from the military. The German Army used it as early as 1860. Harrington Emerson introduced it into the business world in the United States around the 1900's. See *Efficiency* by Harrington Emerson, published by the *Engineering Magazine*, New York, in 1909, pp. 40–41; and Thompson, C. B., *The Theory and Practice of Scientific Management* (New York: Houghton Mifflin Co., 1917), p. 49.

foremen reporting to him. Or it could have branched out still higher. You could have several superintendents as you do have in a very large factory. Yet each superintendent would be a line officer, and each would have under him a line organization. Actually, the line branches out at any or every level up to the President. You probably have noticed that there is, in Figure 3–4, branching out at the high levels. Our chart shows three people reporting to the President, three to the Vice-President and General Manager, six to the Works Manager, and three to the General Superintendent.

We have been using the manufacturing chain of command to illustrate the line idea. But it is not, alone, the whole line organization. The sales department is another important line chain of command. The block in the chart "Vice-President—Sales" is actually the head block of another chart (not shown here).

The organization form we are looking at is line and staff. Where is

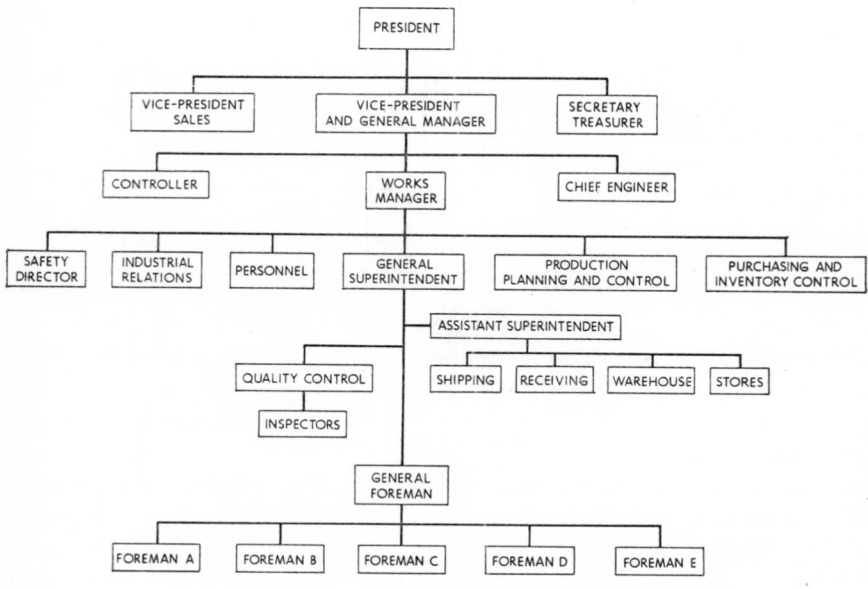

FIG. 3–4. A line and staff organization.

the staff? In Figure 3–4 the staff departments are the Controller, Chief Engineer, Safety Director, Industrial Relations, Personnel, Production Planning and Control, and Purchasing and Inventory Control. Some people would also call the Secretary-Treasurer a staff department.

What do staff departments do that is different from what line departments do? And how are line and staff departments related to each other? Answers are not simple; books have been written on line and staff relationships. But it is easy to give oversimplified answers. Here are several quickies: Lines *do;* staffs *think.* Line officers say "do"; staff officers say "if and when you do, do it this way." The line does something to or with the product; the staff advises or performs services for the line. More about these relationships later.

Departments are line or staff depending on *what they **do** not how they are themselves set up. Within* nearly every department—staff and line

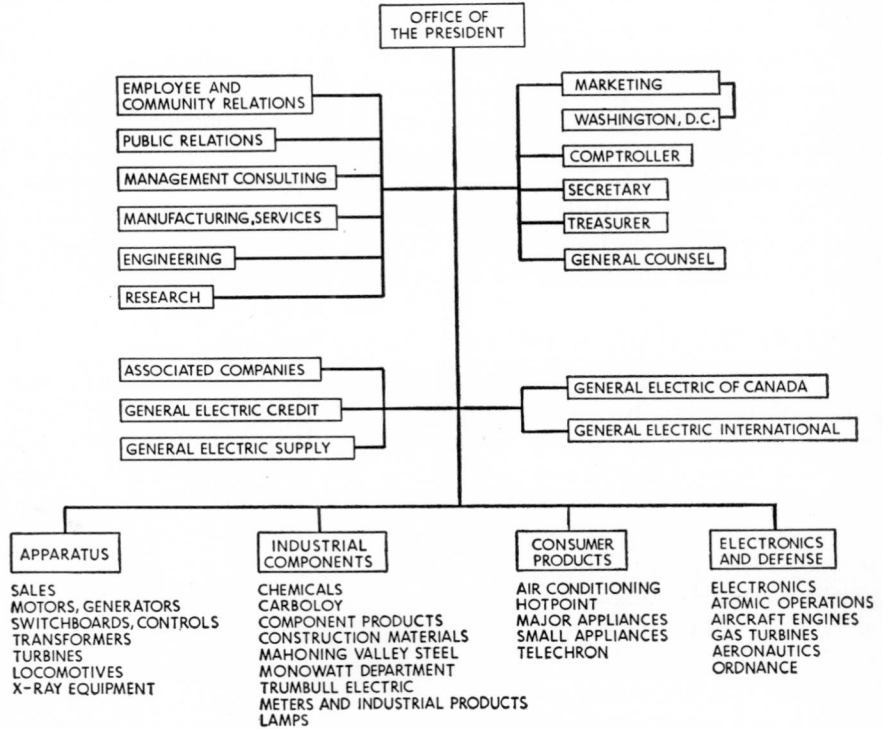

FIG. 3–5. General Electric's organization.

alike—there is probably a line organization. *Being itself organized on the line (or line and staff) form does not make a department into either line or staff.*

Large Companies. Figure 3–4 is a chart for a company with 1,000 employees, small compared to the giants. General Motors has 600,000 employees; General Electric, 250,000; and so on. Giant companies, such as GM and GE, use line and staff organizations. Size makes their charts different in many ways, but you find line departments and staff departments there just as in our small company example.

Look at GE's top-level organization chart, Figure 3–5. Most of what you see is line—in fact, everything below the top dozen blocks directly below the President is line. Most staff departments would appear on more detailed charts for each bottom block of Figure 3–5. For example, the Vice-President in charge of the apparatus group has, under him, a large organization. He would have, below him, both line and staff departments —as would every other man at the head of each department shown in Figure 3–5.

GE does have some staff departments (GE calls them service departments) set apart right up at the top: Employee and Community Relations, Public Relations, Management Consulting, and so on. On a chart you can't show just how they tie in with the rest of the organization. Figure 3–5 shows them reporting to the President but that is all. Actually they are responsible for giving help in their specialties everywhere in the company—and they do not have to clear every minor detail through the President. They sometimes deal directly with similar staff departments in the company's various divisions. Usually they deal directly with lower line officers. In most companies that sometimes makes questions as to who is the lower line officer's boss. These questions are discussed later. Here we want to learn about the form of line and staff structure.

PLACE OF THE STAFF IN ORGANIZATION STRUCTURE

Perhaps you noticed that, in the GE chart, certain staff departments report directly to the company president. Looking at the chart you might think that the man in charge of employee and community relations is superior in status to the man in charge of the apparatus group. His block is higher on the chart than the head of the apparatus group.

The man in charge of employee relations is by no means that important. He has only a handful of employees, where the apparatus group head has tens of thousands. Then why put him (and the other staff heads) so high on the chart? It is so that he can serve all of the chains of command. He has to report to the same man who heads up all the chains of command that he serves.

If he does not report that high, he cannot serve the whole organization without crossing into chains of command beyond his superior's sphere, and that would make trouble. Suppose, for example, that the head of Industrial Relations worked for the head of the apparatus group. He can easily serve the departments making motors, generators, transformers, and locomotives because they belong to his superior.

But let him try to serve the departments making lamps, carbaloy, Hotpoint, or air conditioners! They don't belong to his boss. Their group heads could very properly tell him to keep out. If they need help, they'll get it from their own Industrial Relations departments. Staff departments should always report to the man who has charge of all the departments they serve.

RELATIONSHIPS OF LINE AND STAFF—SINGLE PLANTS

It is axiomatic: "The line should *do*, the staff should *advise*." But, on examination, this turns out to be only partly true. Are engineering drawings of a product's design advice? Is production control's schedule advice? Is purchasing materials only advice? Is accounting just advice giving? Is it advice when maintenance fixes a leak in the roof? No one would say yes in every case. Maybe we have asked the wrong question. Maybe we should ask: Are all of the departments doing these things staff? Or are some line? Or are there in-between departments?

We don't ask these last three questions because nearly everyone agrees that they are all staff departments. So we go back to the earlier questions. Studying them we find that the staff is doing more than advising.

Kinds of Staff Departments. Staff departments are not all alike. There seem to be four kinds: those which (1) advise, (2) control, (3) serve, and (4) co-ordinate.[3] Few staff departments turn out to be just *advisory*. Some which are just advisory are the legal, economic, public relations, and the labor relations part of personnel. Other staff departments have more real authority. Also there is certainly an element of service in the work of all staff departments.

Control departments include industrial engineering, personnel, credit, costs and budgets, and accounting and auditing. *They have authority* to see that their functions are properly executed everywhere in the organization.

Service departments include research and development, engineering and construction, purchasing, traffic, tax, insurance, and maintenance. They are called staff more because they don't work on the product than for any other reason. If we hold to the idea that staffs advise, they just don't belong.

Co-ordinating departments include order and distribution and production planning. Here we have departments that do give "advice," but it is written down, and the line accepts it because the advice really amounts to orders. Production planning, for example, makes up production schedules for the factory departments. Such schedules are genuine orders to the plant.

Nature of Staff's Authority over the Line. If you are a purist, you may want to object to all of this and stick to the staff-advice idea. You object because the acid test of authority is the right to fire a man. Can one of the above staff men fire a line officer who refuses to follow one of his orders? No—never.

But if a line man wants to refuse a staff order, he should be very sure that he has a good reason, because *each of these semiadvisory staff departments is acting for its boss, who is a high line officer.* Look at Figure 3–7. It is part of Figure 3–4 on page 53. Notice that Production Planning and Control reports to the Works Manager, a line officer. He has dele-

---

[3] For a more complete discussion of these, see Paul E. Holden, Lounsbury S. Fish, and Herbert L. Smith, *Top Management Organization and Control* (New York: McGraw-Hill Book Co., Inc., 1949).

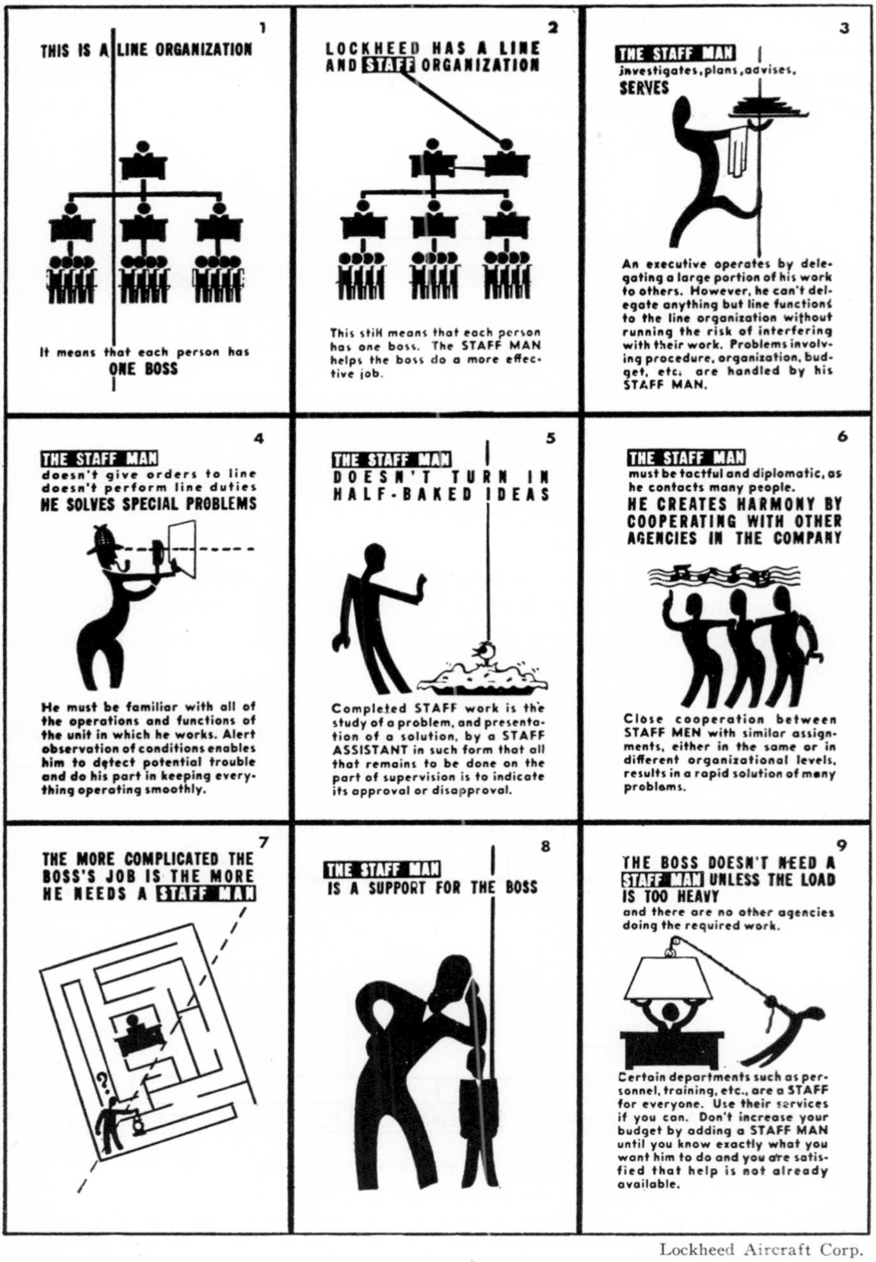

Lockheed Aircraft Corp.

FIG. 3–6. Relationship of staff to line.

gated to Planning the job of making up work schedules for the factory
—that means for Foremen A, B, C, and so on. You don't find any direct
lines going from Planning to the foremen only because the chart would
get too complicated. You might picture the relationship as in Figure 3–8.

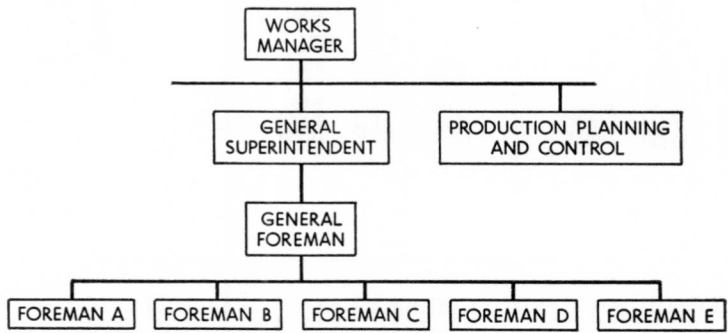

FIG. 3–7. Production planning and control in its staff position.

Other staff departments work the same way. Their advice carries
weight beyond mere advice because above and behind them stands a high
line officer. Everyone knows that he has told the staff to do certain things.
Line as well as staff men know—so the line obeys.

Staff domination over line officers is hard to avoid. Staff men are specialists. They know more about their specialty than line men. Most staff

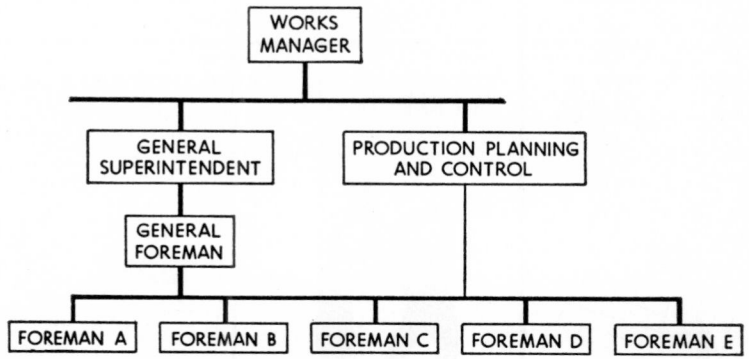

FIG. 3–8. Production planning and control's authority over the line.

men have been to college and are self-possessed. They are encouraged to
belong to associations and to go (at company expense) to conventions.
What foreman ever gets to do this? Staff men work in offices and
come to work on the office work schedule. They dress well, know the
boss by his first name, and eat with him at noon. Staff men don't punch
time clocks. And they don't have to meet schedules and run their de-

partments to suit other departments. Small wonder that self-possessed and assured staff men dominate the line men, who are on the short end of everything.

Top bosses should try not to let staff men dominate the line too much because it makes weak line officers. But confining staffs wholly to advice-giving means allowing line men to refuse the advice. Big companies just have to give staff departments certain real authority over the line.

Bad Features of Staff Authority over Line. Having staff men tell line men what to do is fine for getting everything supervised by experts, but it creates some problems.

First, single accountability is upset. Foremen (and other line officers) get orders from too many sources, have too many bosses. Divided accountability does not have to be bad, but it is unhealthy and certainly is bad when you get too many orders from too many places. It can be irritating and frustrating.

Second, line officers end up with smaller jobs. Their decision-making areas are cut down. Some of them tend to rely on staff assistance when they shouldn't. They don't learn to stand on their own feet. In a word—they become weak line officers.

Third, your staff groups go too far, actually usurping the line's power. Some people say that staffs always do this—that a staff man feels insecure. And why? Because the *line* is the solid thing. The line makes products, the lifeblood of the company. So, goes the reasoning, staff men try to horn into the line and get command authority over line officers.[4] When they try this and the line men object, there are arguments. Remember point two above, though. Some foremen don't object—but they should.

Fourth, staff men think narrowly, in terms of their own specialty. They give orders, unaware of their effects outside their specialty. Engineering, for example, may call for such high quality as to increase costs heavily. Or time study may set production standards that ask for so much production that, to get it, quality has to be forgotten. Such things don't happen often, but when they do, line men should object. If the staff man still insists, the line men should carry the objection up to the big boss. He can see both sides and can decide which he wants—high quality and a lot of scrap or less of each.

Staff Authority over Other Staffs. So far we have talked about staff departments and their relation only to line departments. But staff departments receive, as well as give, advice and instructions from each other. Personnel, for example, serves all other staff departments. So does accounting. Every problem listed above for line officers applies to staff men, too, whenever they are on the receiving end.

[4] For more on this, see Ernest Dale, *Planning and Developing the Company Organization Structure*, Research Report No. 20 (New York: American Management Association, 1952), pp. 73–83.

LINE AND STAFF RELATIONSHIPS—MULTIPLANT COMPANIES

Giant companies always operate several or many plants. Decentralizing operations forces decentralizing some of the decision making. Companies vary as to the amount of autonomy they give to individual operating units, but if there is a trend, it is in the direction of giving more, rather than less, responsibility to the heads of individual plants.

Common practice gives a plant manager authority to operate his plant but provides guidance from the home office for his functional staff departments. His staff departments are accountable to him for *what* they do but to home office superstaff departments for *how* it is done. A certain amount of divided accountability results, but you get consistent company-wide practices.

Some companies give plant managers more authority. Their staff departments do not have to ask or follow home office advice. That advice is available to them, but they don't have to ask for advice nor follow any but the broadest company-wide policy. With this plan central staff departments have to be very good and stay very good, so that the staffs of the individual plants will come to them and not go somewhere else when they want help.

Some large companies go even farther in giving plant managers authority over their staffs. There are no centralized staffs of functional specialists at all. The staff departments of individual plants operate independently.

While the trend is toward more local autonomy, it hasn't touched two areas. One is capital expenditures (buying machines and buildings). The company's money needs to be spent where it can produce the most. Only the company's top officials can decide where that is.

The second area is labor negotiations. Individual plants in a multiplant company usually are not allowed to do their own union contract negotiating. Often industry-wide, union-wide, or company-wide patterns must be considered, so centralization is desirable. Otherwise concessions and contracts will differ, and in every plant the company will be caught in a cross fire of union claims of greater liberality in its other plants. Even in union matters, however, some companies still permit distant plants to act on their own authority. Many nation-wide companies, for example, permit their West Coast plants to handle their own labor relations.

LINE AND LINE RELATIONSHIPS

We have been discussing line and *staff* relationships. The relationships between different *line* chains of command also create problems.

Giant companies usually subdivide, at the top, on a product-line basis. There are usually a few top staff departments that serve all product-line divisions. But there are few cross relationships between product-line divisions.

General Dynamics makes submarines and airplanes, but there is practically no tie-in between these divisions except at the very top. National Distillers makes liquor and chemicals—again no tie-in except at the top. Du Pont makes paint and explosives—same story. There are practically no relationships between these main line chains of command. Each operates as if the other didn't exist, although they have the same top financial control.

But the picture is different sometimes. Suppose you compete with sister divisions as do Buick and Oldsmobile? Not so much problem there, you almost go your own way. Neither division is boss, but a superboss higher up holds a check rein on both of you. He keeps you both in line.

But suppose you buy from or sell to other divisions as do Buick and Fisher Body? Each division has its own line chain of command. Then what are your relations—which is boss? Every big company has some divisions which supply parts to other divisions. They have different line chains of command, but when one makes products for the other, they have to work together. Buick's needs become Fisher Body's work schedules.

Here problems do arise between different *line* chains of command. At what *price* are things transferred? Remember, each division head is trying to make a good showing—to show that he is operating his division or department profitably. Fisher Body's head can make a fine showing *if* he can charge Buick (as well as Cadillac, Oldsmobile, Pontiac, and Chevrolet) as much as he'd like for automobile bodies. But Buick's head can't make a good showing if car bodies cost too much. So what should the price be? And who should decide? You can see how arguments arise.

Price problems aren't the only ones. Closely related are such questions as: *Must* we buy from a sister plant (let's say that our example now is storage batteries or engine parts, not bodies)? Are we allowed to make our own? Are we allowed to buy outside? Or if we are on the selling end, must we accept orders from a sister plant? Or can we turn them down and take on more profitable business from other customers? Do we give sister plants better service than others—or poorer? Can we charge sister plants for our research? How about co-operation? Do we try our best to help a sister plant? Or do we tell people from sister plants to paddle their own canoes and we will paddle ours? Do we show men from sister plants all our little secret ways of getting more output? Or do we hold out?

Relations between Line Departments in Every Plant Make Similar Problems in a Smaller Way. Top management finds that it often has real problems getting line departments to take the over-all view. Time and again, department heads try to make a good showing *at the expense* of the over-all good.

CO-ORDINATION

One of the most important and difficult jobs of administrators is to co-ordinate the activities of the various parts of their organization. First of all they must have *over-all programs* so that detailed plans co-ordinating work assignments can be made. In a factory, at the operating level, most of the co-ordination is done by the production control department. Besides plans, adequate *procedures* are also essential if activities are to be co-ordinated. Plans must be made showing when and where certain work is to be done. Procedures must be set up to get directions out to the departments concerned. A system of reports must be devised to show accomplishment. In case of failure there must be some procedure for drawing up a new program.

Plans, procedures, reports, and comparisons by themselves may still fall short of producing co-ordination if the all-important ingredient, co-operation, is lacking. A co-operative attitude can make up for many deficiencies in planning, while its lack hurts co-ordination. Willingness to co-operate can be fostered by having department heads meet together now and then. They get to know each other's problems. Committee service also helps. So do conferences on subjects of common interest. Consultative management also helps build a co-operative attitude, and so does the tactful settling by a superior of differences between subordinates. Conflicts between line and staff, mentioned earlier, can cause trouble, and management must be particularly alert to keep them down.

Obviously plans, procedures, reports, and comparisons must be appropriate to their purpose and not overly complex. They can easily be overdone to the point of wastefulness. Likewise, management should not, simply because it encourages and promotes co-operation, rely on a friendly attitude to offset a lack of plans, inadequate procedures, and defects in organizational structures.

STAFF ASSISTANTS

Neither of our charts, the one for the small company or GE's, shows any staff assistants. Probably there are none in the small company. GE surely has some, but it is against its policy so that even a big chart would not show many.

Staff assistants (often titled "assistant to—") relieve their bosses of burdensome detail—minor things which don't fit exactly into the work of regular departments. Any official from, say, the superintendent up may have a staff assistant.

Don't confuse an "assistant to" and an "assistant." An assistant general manager acts for his boss, makes decisions, and issues instructions in the boss's name; and he acts in his place when the boss is absent. Usually he is the heir apparent to the boss's job. An "assistant" has an important job.

But an "assistant to" the general manager is a legwork man. He does lots of little things but does not make decisions, issue instructions in the boss's name, or act in his place in the boss's absence. He has no executive duties. He investigates, researches, analyzes, recommends, and helps his chief get things done. The assistant-to idea comes from the military. It is a recent transplant and, though yet uncommon, is growing more common.

"Assistants to" have disadvantages as well as advantages. They can make trouble; some overstep their authority and act for their bosses. They make trouble too if they keep the boss from seeing people he should see. Assistants to executives are often young, and older line officers resent it if they, the oldsters, have to get orders through the staff assistant.

COMMITTEES

Committees are useful at times in all organizations. They work best when they only *discuss and recommend*. And they aren't so bad when they *investigate, evaluate,* and *report* without making recommendations. But they are weak when it comes to *making decisions* and *taking action*.

In recent years there has been a trend toward having, at the top level of the company, a policy-making and planning committee. It is made up of the company's major executives. Generally it holds short meetings every week. This top committee is, in many companies, asked to make decisions. Companies using such a management committee report that it helps to provide co-ordination of long- and short-term company objectives and to develop co-operation between departments and consistency in policy formation.

. Committees are usually directly responsible to a high line officer, although they may be responsible to a staff officer. Sometimes, but not often, they operate at lower levels in the organization. Some committees are permanent and meet regularly; others are set up for special purposes and dissolved when their work is done.

An executive who appoints a committee to look into a problem does not have to take its advice; but, having asked for help, he usually follows its recommendations. The fact that he acted on committee advice in no way relieves him, though, if things go wrong.

Committee recommendations help executives because they are based on a variety of expert knowledge and a more thorough consideration than any one person can give to a problem. Committee service helps to develop co-operation among committee members and wins their acceptance of the recommended programs. Members accept decisions more willingly when they help make them. Through committee work they learn the reasons for certain policies and their over-all effects. Members,

over a period of time, generally develop more objectivity in their thinking as a result of committee service. Administrators, for their part, are
spared a certain amount of criticism if their decisions are recommended
by committees.

Some large companies consider the educational value of committee
service to be nearly as important, in the long run, as the accomplishments
of the committee itself. Such service is almost sure to broaden the view
of its members because they are drawn from different departments.
They get a better grasp of company-wide problems and the interrelationships of departments. Committee service is particularly helpful to younger
men, who learn from those with experience. In committee work they
also develop and improve their ability to express themselves. When the
membership of a committee is determined, its educational value should
not be forgotten. One or more young men should be appointed, so as to
learn by taking part.

Committees have some bad points. They waste time and are expensive.
They should, therefore, be kept small. Because of this, only important
matters and particularly complex problems involving several departments
should be given to committees. If speed is important, a committee is
likely to be a hindrance rather than a help. Generally committees are
loath to come to a conclusion, and their recommendations are often compromises which by no means always give the right solutions to problems. You don't even get the educational advantages of committee work
unless everybody takes part in the discussions—something that doesn't
happen if a few members dominate the group.

One management consultant says that committees weaken future executives. It reports that executives raised in an atmosphere of committees
are reluctant to take individual responsibility and rely on committees
too much.

A committee chairman should be chosen for his ability to lead a group.
He should see that all members take part. He should save the group's
time by advance planning and by giving the members an agenda of the
meeting ahead of time so that they can think over the subjects to be
discussed. Time can also be saved by the appointment of one-man sub-
committees to investigate and report on certain topics. Factual material
can often be prepared by staff assistants and given to committee members to study in advance of the meeting.

In the meeting the chairman should keep the discussion from going
too far afield and should break it off if it degenerates into argument; better yet, he should channel it into the next subject of discussion. He should
also sum up the views expressed by the committee members in his report
to the executive to whom the committee is responsible.

OUTSIDE CONSULTANTS

Almost all companies need outside help of a specialized nature from
time to time. The profession of industrial consulting has come into ex-

istence to meet such needs. The staff of a good consulting firm is generally composed of high-caliber men with varied backgrounds and wide experience in other companies. Consequently, a consulting firm can assign top-flight specialists to any of a variety of jobs. Often the work a client company requires is of such a nature that no one on the company's staff is qualified to do it. Consultants can provide specialists to do the job and to train and supervise company employees until they are ready to carry on the work alone.

Consultants are often used to install or to oversee the installation of job evaluation programs or wage incentive systems, or to set time standards by time study methods in companies instituting such programs for the first time. They may also help companies develop employee training programs, psychological tests for hiring, or procedures for statistical quality control. Sometimes they conduct employee attitude studies. In recent years they have frequently made executive inventories for companies, interviewing all major and minor executives and making recommendations for their future training and, perhaps, promotions. They make market surveys, recommending changes in merchandising methods, products, or design. They may recommend plant layouts, equipment needs, or even plant locations.

In short, consultants stand ready to help in any situation where considerable extra technical help is needed for a short time. Some large companies retain outside specialists to "check over" their organization periodically and make recommendations. In some companies they review the operations of individual departments at regular intervals and make suggestions directly to the head of the department rather than to the higher officers.

Consultants have several advantages over inside specialists in the same field. They have time to study a client's problem, and they are unhampered by routine. Wide experience has made them acquainted with almost every kind of problem; they have seen many solutions tried and know the pitfalls to be avoided. Having seen similar problems in varied settings, they learn to strip off nonessentials and get to the heart of the matter. Insiders with less varied experience are not so good at that.

Having laid bare a problem, outsiders are better able to set goals for achievement, after which they can lay out and carry through a program designed to reach the goals set. Outsiders are more free than insiders to plan the best program for solving problems, because they work under the authority of the top administration of the company and are beholden to no one. They do not need to go through channels. When they recommend a course of action, the chips fall where they may. They are free from favoritism and prejudice; they can say and do things that cannot always be said or done from within. Naturally, their recommendations should be made as tactfully as possible; but, being outsiders, they have more freedom in this respect than do inside staff specialists, who must continue to live and work with those who may be affected. The prestige of outside consultants helps them get at problems involving the work of officers high in the organization, problems which, perhaps, no one inside the organization could tackle. Their prestige also helps them win acceptance for their recommendations by both administrators and subordinates.

But consultants have their disadvantages. Sometimes men set themselves up as consultants when they don't know much about the subject. Sometimes they are too salesminded and try to sell their clients on work that they don't need. Most consultants are, however, ethical, reputable, and qualified.

Their fees ($100 to $250 a day) are another disadvantage. Because the cost is high, the client wants quick service (he wants quick service anyway but the fees put more pressure on speedy action). But good work often cannot be done quickly, and the company which insists on quick results may be disappointed in the quality. Reputable consultants refuse to take jobs unless they are assured of sufficient time to produce dependable results.

The high charges made by outside consultants may be resented by the company's inside specialists. They sometimes feel that calling in a consultant is a reflection on their work. They may even not co-operate with him. The consultant is doubly resented because he is known to be expensive and because the inside staff specialist feels that if he could spend the same money for more help or equipment he could produce noteworthy improvements also.

Inside specialists do not always resent the outsiders. Sometimes they have problems beyond their ability to handle, and they know it. In such cases consultants are welcomed. Outside specialists should not be brought into an organization until the inside staff has utilized and exhausted all its own resources in trying to handle a problem. When an outsider is introduced, both the administration and the consultant himself must be tactful in order to win the inside specialist's support for the consultant's work.

The perfectly natural desire of consultants to get more business proves a temptation even for the most ethical firm. It is easy to recommend programs requiring the maximum rather than the minimum of its services in the future. This is a danger and a disadvantage in using outside consultants.

Some one officer or some group inside the company should always be an integral part of any project supervised by consultants. It gives the inside group training, lets someone in the organization know exactly what is being done, and curbs any tendency the consultant may have to stretch out the job.

ORGANIZATION DEPARTMENTS

Rare in the 1940's, organization departments are now common. They make organization charts, work out changes in organization structure, and plot the course, organization-wise, of the company. Years ago, no one did such work in most companies. What was done was done by the president's secretary or by the personnel department. It is too important to handle that way. Because the work is high level, the organization department reports to a vice-president or higher.

Organization departments try to get answers to such questions as: What departments should we have 5 years from now? What changes must we make? Who heads up today's departments? Who will head up tomorrow's departments? What grooming do today's middle executives need for tomorrow's top echelon jobs? All of this is top-drawer information and is confidential. It can be done only in a department close to the top.

Organization departments also prepare policy manuals to guide middle- and high-level officials. In multiplant companies the central office organization department directs similar departments in each major operating division. The main job, however, is usually the one done at the top.

ORGANIZATION CHARTS

Organization charts are useful tools for management because they show departments and lines of direct authority. They might seem to be unnecessary, since the executives of any company ought to know what departments it has and the responsibilities of each one. A popular cliche says that charts are bad because there is a danger that people will mistake an organization chart for an organization. Charts are not perfect tools, and, actually, there are some companies that do not use them. But almost all large manufacturing companies do, and they don't seem to have any trouble mistaking charts for organizations.

Charts show the organization structure graphically, and often when they are first introduced, they show up a few organizational weaknesses. Organization analysts, making charts for companies which have had none, sometimes find that some employees do not know exactly what they are supposed to do or for whom they work. Sometimes certain work has never been specifically assigned; in other cases two or more people think they have been assigned the same work. Sometimes subordinates believe they are accountable to one superior when, in fact, they are accountable to another. In other cases a supervisor thinks certain people work for him when they don't, nor do they think they do. Such organizational weaknesses as these are by no means the rule, but they are common enough to justify the effort needed to check the organizational structure and draw up a chart.

Look back to the charts on pages 53 and 54. Notice that they show only departments and direct lines of authority. Sometimes charts show department titles, and sometimes the names of the men in charge. Company officials often want more information than a chart shows; perhaps they want to know the duties and requirements of a job, the training and experience of the incumbent, the number of subordinates he supervises, and so on. This information is usually put in text rather than chart form. One page, or more, of typewritten information may cover each job. The flow of information from department to department and the procedures for issuing instructions and getting reports are not shown on organization charts either. They can be shown graphically if desired, but ordinarily separate procedure charts and diagrams are used for that.

Charts are not perfect devices for showing the organization's structure because smooth operation depends so much on the co-operation between departments on the same level and between the different chains of command in the organization. On a chart there is no good way to depict such co-operation and informal interrelationships or to show the give and take and exchange of ideas which are so important to smooth functioning and good morale.

QUESTIONS

1. How can work be divided up in line organizations? Who does the work normally done by the personnel department?
2. Compare line and Taylor's functional organizations. Give strong and weak points of each.
3. Tell what happened to Taylor's functional form of organization. Why?
4. Why is the line and staff form so popular today?
5. Give examples of line departments; of typical staff departments. How do you tell them apart?
6. Discuss the relationships between line and staff departments in a one-plant company.
7. Lines *do;* staffs *advise.* Expand on this theme.
8. Some people say that staffs naturally tend to dominate the line. Do you agree? Support your position.
9. Suppose staffs do give orders to the line, what difference does it make?
10. Discuss the relationship between staff departments in the central office and staff departments in individual divisions in multiplant companies.
11. Compare "assistants" and "assistants to—."
12. In what areas do committees seem to work best? Worst? Why?
13. When would you recommend using an outside consultant? When not?
14. The head of an organization department reporting to a works manager claims that he should report to the president. Should he? Justify your answer.
15. Although they are probably in the minority among big companies, some big companies do not use organization charts. What reason could they have for that?

CASE 3–1.   GIGANTIC OIL COMPANY

The Board of Directors of the Gigantic Oil Company sought a change in the plan of organization that would relieve the President of some of the duties he had assumed. Accordingly the following statement of organization policy was written into the minutes:

"The pattern of organization will be that the *staff* departments will report primarily to the Chairman of the Board of Directors, and that the *line* or operating departments will report primarily to the President." The organization was divided into eleven main departments as follows:

1. Finance Department
2. Corporation Secretary's Department
3. Legal Department
4. Research and Development Department
5. Industrial Relations Department
6. Public Relations Department
7. Sales Department
8. Procurement Department
9. Transportation Department
10. Production Department
11. Refining Department

Set up the organization in such a way as to carry out the Board's wishes. Which departments did you find it hard to classify? Why? How does the new arrangement fit in with your understanding of good organizational principles?

CASE 3–2.   BUTLER BROS. MOTOR CAR COMPANY

Three years ago, the Butler Bros. Motor Car Company added a division to make its own frames for automobiles. The frames had formerly been bought. J. D. Gunnison had been brought in from the outside to be in charge of the work. He had previously worked for a frame manufacturing company and also for another automobile manufacturer. In the Butler company his division, numbering 7,000 employees, made not only the frames but certain other parts made from heavy stamped sheet steel.

Under Gunnison's direction the frame division turned out products of satisfactory quality and in sufficient quantity. In the third year of the division's operation, however, the company still had netted only 6 per cent on the capital invested in that department, whereas other divisions of the company averaged 13 per cent. No other division earned less than 10 per cent, and one earned 21 per cent.

Viewing the record, Gunnison decided that he did not have enough control over operations. He decided to set up an "organization department" to survey the organization and the procedures used. He proposed to give this new department authority to investigate, recommend changes, and to approve or disapprove all changes in organization or procedure. There was no other similar department in the whole company.

Should the Butler Bros. company allow him to set up such a department? How much authority should it be given? Should it be permanent? If so, what should its permanent duties be?

Chapter 4

THE LIVING ORGANIZATION

IN CHAPTER 3 we agreed that "organization is people," and then talked about fundamentals and for the most part left people out. Now we must put people back in. People do (or don't do) the things we have been talking about. No one is perfect, and no one perfectly fits the job he holds. But, he holds down the job anyway, and the way he does it is the way it is done. The things he is best at he does well; what he is weak at he does poorly. You have to make your organization out of imperfect people. Your whole organization works only as well as the limitations of your men permit.

Even the men at the top are imperfect. Good management is always a goal to strive for but one you don't always reach and hold. Students going into industry will find poor management as well as good. Our discussion tries to explain good management—not poor management—so it is at odds with some companies' practices.

How can you improve an organization if it must always be limited to the abilities of its people? In several ways. You can *pick good men* to start with. You can *train them*, showing them how to do better. And you can *motivate them*, getting them to try harder. Do all these things—*and* have a logical organization structure too—and you should have a good organization.

PERSONAL OBJECTIVES OF OFFICIALS

To most people a company's officials are the "company." They decide the company's objectives and policies and make its long-range plans. Probably most people do not realize that nearly all executives are hired men, not main owners. Sometimes they act just like other hired men and put their own interests first.

Ideally, perhaps, every official should have a "nose-for-profit." If he is in sales he should *sell* in spite of every obstacle; if sales are good he should try to boost them higher. If he is in production he should be very cost conscious; he should always try to cut costs to the bone and then

70

some more (but of course not hurt quality). If he is a staff official he should always think of how much added profits or lower costs will come from his services.

Although stockholders would like its officials to be profit minded at all times, this is not the case. Officials act more like employees in their reluctance to take chances than in other ways. Top men like their jobs and want to keep them. Mistakes can be serious, and no executive wants to make them—they may cost him his job. After World War II Argus Camera Company went into the household appliance business and promptly lost $1 million. The officials lost their jobs, and Argus went out of the appliance business. Such things don't happen often, but they happen often enough to give venturesome officials something to think about.

Officials are not always too happy when business is exceptionally good. When profits are high, stockholders want dividends raised and employees want pay raises, and both of them want you to keep up the fine performance. Keeping it up is the hard part. A while back a large equipment making company's president said his company used "administered" prices. That meant, he said, that prices were set to yield a 15 per cent return on invested capital. This was when times were good and higher prices could have been gotten. "But," said the president, "why put prices up? True, we would make more profits this year, but income taxes would take most of it, and stockholders and employees would want more. Then next year they wouldn't like it when things got back to normal. This way everyone, including customers, is happy, and we help hold down inflation and make it easier for ourselves next year."

Officials sometimes decide things on a "decent survival" basis. Another term is "dynamic status-quoism." Both mean: keep things on an even keel. The officials are satisfied to do as well (or a little better) today and tomorrow as they did yesterday; keep the same profits and dividends. But what happens if profits dip? That is where the dynamic part comes in. Management really goes to work then to try to increase sales and cut costs and get back to where they were profit-wise. Mostly they get back—then relaxation sets in again, and business goes on as before.

Relaxing is not a good way to the top, however. Men on their way up and even many top men are not relaxers—particularly the not-yet-arrived. Their goal is: bigger and better. They may "empire-build"—try to make their departments grow bigger and do more things. Such ambition is fine, but top men may have to keep upcoming expansionists in line—their empire building is not always economical. You don't want to discourage hard-working subordinates, but they need to be kept in line. Middle- and upper-level executives are usually ambitious to move higher —where there are better (but fewer) jobs. Rivalry is often intense, and there is "jockeying for position" just as in politics.

Struggle for advancement may go beyond the office and even into executives' home lives. Wives can help or hinder young executives' advancements. Wives should observe protocol—such as, never invite wives of superiors first, but let them make the first move. Wives should not be disagreeable to other wives, lest the other's husband pass her own on the way up. If you are a minor executive, never outdo the big boss in houses, automobiles, mink coats, grand pianos, golf-club memberships, or exclusive schools for children.

INFORMAL GROUPS

Every organization has its cliques and little groups. They exist at all levels—top to bottom. Some authorities on management think that such "informal groups" are very important. They say that the group attitudes mold individual attitudes and that group views are sometimes at odds with company objectives. This is important because you don't want company objectives to come second.

Cliques often have their own informal rules about things. They have codes of behavior for their members. Factory pieceworkers often limit their output and will not let anyone produce more than the quota they set. Another thing they do is not to inform on workers who cheat the company. Pieceworkers often say that they do more work than they actually do. Small-scale stealing is also not unknown. Most workers don't falsify reports or steal, but since the group has its code, they don't tell on those who do, nor do they cold-shoulder them.

Probably there is more cliquishness at low levels than at top levels. Vice-presidents don't work together all day long. Their offices are not all next door to each other. Some even live in different cities. When you don't see each other very often, cliques aren't strong. They are even less strong when you go down another level to factory managers. Factory managers live where their plants are and almost never see managers of the company's other plants. And going on down, superintendents and general foremen over different areas in the same plant don't see each other for days so there aren't many "informal groups" in their ranks.

But cliques are common at low levels. Newcomers often find it hard to break in and get accepted (and nonaccepted newcomers sometimes quit). Foremen can usually smooth the way for new men by introducing them around.

Companies can't do much about informal organizations, but they ought not to forget them when making decisions. Groups sometimes get upset about what the company does, and when they do, they don't do what the company wants or expects. Companies should not make sudden, unannounced changes, nor should they let the grapevine carry the first news of things to come. Changes in hours of work, workplaces, and workers (particularly if outsiders are brought in) are upsetting. All such changes are better received if men are told ahead and the way prepared. Otherwise—men are hostile to change.

THE PRESIDENT'S JOB

The president should set up long-range goals for his company and make long-range plans for their fulfillment. He should implement his plans and set in action whatever activities are necessary to work toward the goals. He should check periodically and see what progress the company is making. If things aren't moving as they should, he must try to get them going, starting new activities if they are needed.

Of course, the president doesn't do all this by himself, nor does he alone make all the decisions. Presidents of most large companies act more as committee chairmen or council chairmen than as independent leaders. Major executives work more as team members than as separate individuals taking orders from a common superior. Important decisions are likely to be group decisions, or at least they are arrived at after group discussions. Some problems are so technical that you have to ask your staff specialists about them. Top administrators may know so little about the subjects that they can't really tell what to do. It amounts to the staff deciding some matters.

All of this consulting doesn't in fact relieve the president from making decisions. There are times when the president should not follow the recommendations of his subordinates. Group recommendations are often compromises which may not point to the proper course of action. The president should see the over-all picture. He has the final responsibility. He must be the final judge as to action. He should not claim that his subordinates' decisions are not his responsibilities.

Although a president is but one level above the other major executives, his situation is very different from theirs. They recommend, but he decides, so he must be surer than they; he can't afford to be overhasty. He must always question figures and doubt the impossibility of doing things differently. He must ask incisive and discerning questions. If his staff overlooks a weakness in a plan, he must catch it because he is the last review. If he too overlooks it, the plan may be adopted; only too late will the weakness be found.

The president's decisions often have far-reaching effects, and there is no appeal; he must weigh his decisions more carefully than others in the organization. Sometimes what seem to be minor decisions involve major points. Changes in old policies may have to be made, but he should be quite sure that they are wise if they change long-established practices. In spite of the greater care that he must exercise, he still has to decide. Indecision or inaction does not relieve him. The consequences of indecision are the same as if he had decided not to act.

The president must see that the work is properly divided, that departments are set up, that individuals are assigned their work, and that they have appropriate tools, equipment, and facilities. He should remove "road

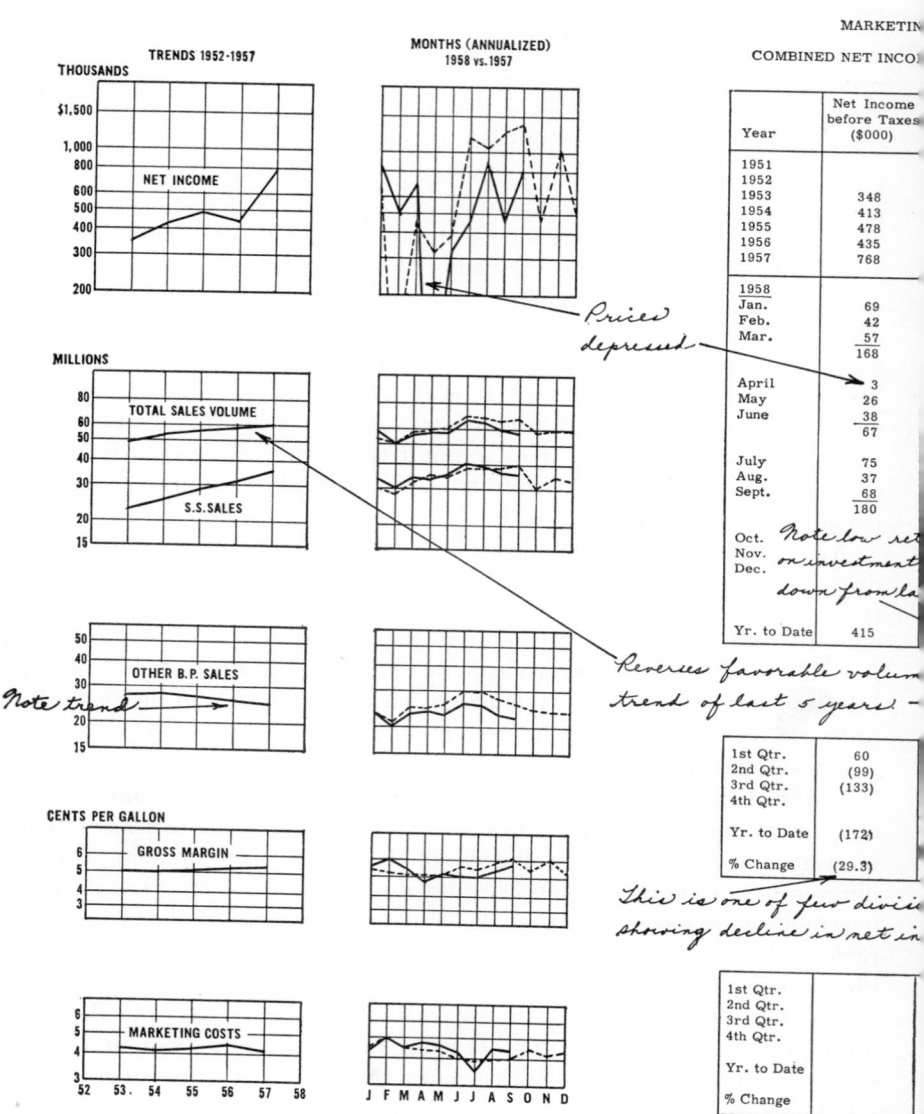

FIG. 4–1.   A control report that highlights pertinent information for management. The figures are hypothetical.

"blocks" and "dead wood" from the organization without damaging its morale.

He must remember that underlings ape their bosses. Autocratic bosses make autocratic underlings. If the president is a good leader, he will be fair in his decisions and forward looking in his plans for the future of the business and the future of individuals in his organization.

"A"

NATURAL GASOLINE PLANTS

BULK PLANT AND SERVICE STATION BUSINESS

S/S Volume (000 Gals.)	Other Bulk Plant Sales (000 Gals.)	Gross Margin per Gal.	Marketing Costs per Gal.	Net Income per Gal.
22,416	27,035	.0497	.0427	.0070
25,551	27,164	.0494	.0425	.0069
28,243	27,410	.0507	.0421	.0086
30,719	27,177	.0522	.0447	.0075
34,544	25,937	.0552	.0425	.0127
2,799	1,963	.0571	.0426	.0145
2,545	1,677	.0600	.0500	.0100
2,769	1,964	.0570	.0451	.0119
8,113	5,604	.0580	.0458	.0122
2,810	2,006	.0481	.0474	.0007
2,856	1,934	.0523	.0469	.0094
3,339	2,178	.0499	.0431	.0068
9,005	6,118	.0501	.0457	.0044
3,197	2,186	.0500	.0360	.0140
3,056	1,917	.0525	.0451	.0074
2,928	1,857	.0585	.0444	.0141
9,181	5,960	.0535	.0416	.0119
26,299	17,682	.0537	.0443	.0094

Net income per gallon lower than .0101 in jobber channel

NCE FROM LAST YEAR

490	(272)	.0047	.0005	.0042
117	(749)	(.0032)	.0030	(.0062)
(471)	(1,022)	(.0046)	.0023	(.0069)
136	(2,043)	(.0013)	.0021	(.0034)
0.5	(10.4)	(2.4)	5.0	(26.6)

ine in net income per gallon due arily to rising unit costs

Continues down trend of last 3 years

NCE FROM FORECAST

Unit costs up because volume well below forecast

Decline in gross margin due primarily to volume; secondarily to prices

ANALYSIS OF CHANGE IN NET INCOME: 9 MONTHS

Causes of Variation	($000)	Per Gal.
Gross Margin Inc.-(Dec.) from change in:		
Volume	(128)	
Price	(23)	
Mdse. Cost	(11)	
Net Change-Gross Margin	(162)	(.0013)
Marketing Costs Inc.-(Dec.) from change in:		
Over. & Oper. Expense	7	.0020
Taxes	–	.0001
Depreciation	19	.0006
Misc. Income	–	(.0001)
T.B.A. Commissions	4	–
Subtotal	30	.0026
Loss (Gain) on Assets	(20)	(.0005)
Net Change-Mktg. Costs	10	.0021
Net Income Inc.-(Dec.)	(172)	(.0034)

MONTHLY AVERAGES

	Number of Service Station	Total Gasoline Gallons Per S.S.	Total Motor Oil Per S.S.	Ratio of Total Motor Oil to Gasoline
1958	239	11,990	176	1.47
1957	232	12,247	216	1.76
Change	7	(257)	(40)	(0.29)
% Change	3.0	(2.1)	(18.5)	

MONTHLY AVERAGES - BULK PLANT SALES (EXCLUDING SERVICE STATION SALES)

	Number Bulk Plants	Total Gasoline Per B.P.	Total Other Light Oil Per B.P.	Total Lube Oils Per B.P.
1958	99	17,083	2,017	722
1957	104	18,352	1,906	739
Change	(5)	(1,269)	111	(17)
% Change	(4.8)	(6.9)	5.8	(2.3)

Note decline in gasoline and motor oil sales per service station and in gasoline sales per bulk plant.

Continental Oil Co.

A good president will consult frequently with his subordinates both to get suggestions and to win support for his plans. He will recognize that attitudes toward changes are influenced by personal considerations, particularly if a man's status is going to go up or down as a result of the change. He will see to it that a new generation of minor executives is given training and broad experience so that they will be good major executives when their day comes. He will see to it that they are properly paid for their work. He must try to develop the characteristics of an effective organization, such as dollar consciousness throughout the company, good morale, co-operation between departments, capable people in all jobs, capable replacements available when needed, and adequate, but not unduly complex, procedures for directing and controlling operations.

CONTROLLING THE ORGANIZATION

Management's job is to manage, yet managers cannot know personally all that goes on. How can the president of an organization of 10,000 men know what they are all doing, or even what each one ought to be doing? Of course he can't, nor does he need to, know what every single person does or ought to do.

His control over the organization is indirect—not direct. He controls his vice-presidents; they control their plant managers, and so on. But just how does this "control" operate? What information does a top man get by which to judge what goes on? He gets reports, many of them and of many kinds. They show numbers—totals, group totals, averages, ratios. They report sales, production, costs, employment, and so on—reports of what is going on.

But if that is all they show, the reports are not worth much. What do you learn from a report that tells you that last month the organization sold 20,000 power lawn mowers which cost $50 each to make? Is that good? Or is it bad? You can't tell without other figures for comparison. You have to know also how many were sold month by month in recent months, also last year, as well as what they cost to make last month and last year, and also how much money you made on them.

Reports always need to show *comparisons* so you can judge whether today's performance is good or bad. And they need to be by *department* —then you can judge the work of its head. Even the arrangement of reports is important; figures that are to be compared should be set next to each other. Charts help too. Obviously, reports must be up to date. It is of no help to learn today that we did poorly on something we did two months ago.

Really worth-while reports do even more than compare yesterday to the day before yesterday. *They compare yesterday's actual performance with yesterday's planned performance.* You see, yesterday's production may be different from that of all previous yesterdays because of variations in product mix or of total volume.

We should *plan* (probably set up a budget) for each department and each division of the company. The plan should set forth what is supposed to be done—then actual performances can be compared. If actual and planned differ, the reports should *high light the variances* so that they can be looked into. Good variances (say, something cost less than expected) you want to continue; bad ones you look into to see if you can't get rid of them in the future. The real purpose of reports is, of course, forward looking. You look to the past only to learn where you made mistakes so that you will do better tomorrow.

Reports are the eyes of management. It sees what goes on only through reports. Here is a list of only a few of the reports you need:

WEEKLY REPORT

Type of Report	Who Gets It
Production, major items.	Plant managers, top management, foremen.
Order backlogs.	President, sales management, plant managers.
Inventories, raw materials, and finished goods.	Top management, sales management.
Budget comparisons, overhead, sales, direct and indirect labor, etc.	President, top management.
Manufacturing efficiency.	Plant manager.
Payroll, hourly, incentive, overtime.	Controller, personnel.
Employment, numbers employed.	Personnel management, plant foremen.

MONTHLY REPORT

Type of Report	Who Gets It
Shipments per man-hour.	Controller, plant foremen.
Orders booked.	President, sales management, plant management.
Production, comparative and cumulative, against budget.	All top management.
Inventories, finished, in process, raw materials.	President, sales management, manufacturing management, plant foremen.
Costs by functions, purchasing, accounting, etc.	Top management, middle management.
Profit margins by product.	Top management.
Product profit and loss.	All executives, directors.
Cost trends.	President, controller, manufacturing management.
Budget comparisons: budget and variance, purchases to budget, sales to budget, purchases to gross sales, etc.	All top management, board of directors, middle management, plant foremen, plant supervisors.
Interpretive comment (graphs, oral briefings, etc.) by controller.	Top and middle management.

SPECIAL REPORTS

Type of Report	Who Gets It
Break-even points.	President, directors, all top managers, middle managers.
Capital equipment on order.	President, directors.
Merit ratings of nonunion employees.	Personnel management.
Tax effects.	President, controller.
Industry comparisons.	President, sales, and plant management.
Overhead.	President, controller, top management.
Price and cost trends.	President, controller, top management.

LEADERSHIP AT LOWER LEVELS

Over the years more and more emphasis is being put on the quality of the leadership in the lower levels of an organization. Knowing how to run machines used to be the principal qualification for jobs from the superintendent down. Now nearly everyone agrees that these jobs can be well done only by supervisors properly qualified to handle people. This emphasis has been heightened by mechanization. Factory jobs require less technical skill than they used to because much of that skill has been transferred to and built into machines. Where complicated jobs still exist, they have been cut into small segments, each requiring but little skill. The bulk of work in manufacturing is done by large numbers of semiskilled workers.

This changes a foreman's job from supervising work to supervising people. It isn't quite so important now that he be able to run machines. The jobs of general foremen and superintendents have also become largely matters of supervising people. More use of staff departments, such as research, engineering, production control, and others, has further reduced the need for technical ability in supervisory personnel. Over the years the job of managing an enterprise has become more and more one of managing people at all levels in the organization.

ORGANIZATIONAL STABILITY

Key men sometimes retire, resign, or die. Can the organization take it in stride? Or will everything be upset? If you have organizational stability, all goes well. A well-qualified junior is moved up. It didn't just happen that you had him ready though. He is well qualified because you made him so.

Stability is bought at a price. You have to do certain things to get it, and they are not things that you can do overnight. You have to lay out a program and keep working at it. A good way to go about it is to, first, list your executive jobs—present and future. Then, list today's executives. Note how old they are. Then draw a schedule of executive jobs to be filled in the next 5 years. Show all the vacancies that will be caused by retirement and all new executive jobs to be caused by the company growing. Remember, too, the chain effect of promotions. When a man is promoted, his old job is vacant. If you plan to fill it by promoting someone, that will make another vacancy, and so on. If one man retires you may have to fill several jobs, one after the other.

Now compare future job openings and men. Do you have enough men or will you need more? Which men will most likely get the future top jobs? Next, how do their present abilities stack up with jobs ahead? Maybe they need more training or experience along certain lines so that they will fit the top jobs. So, go ahead, plan the training, then carry out the plan, give them one or two job assignments to let them get the training they need. Then, finally, when the time comes, they should be ready. You have organizational stability.

But planned vacancies aren't the only reason for vacancies. What about death, poor health, and resignations? They sometimes make emergency openings. You can't tell when or where they will hit. Usually they don't make as many openings as regular retirements for old age, but they make *all* the unexpected openings.

Whatever the number of executives you know you will need, *always train too many too soon*. Get a few more men ready than you are sure you will need and have them ready before you think you will need them. Emergency openings—from death, poor health, resignations, and unforeseen expansion—will find you ready. Don't overdo it though. If you groom ten men for one job and do it 10 years before an opening, you will have a lot of disappointed men around.

Stability can't come overnight. It takes long-range planning and training. It is also largely a high-level matter. No low-level official is so important that his sudden loss can hurt the company seriously.

ORGANIZATION FLEXIBILITY

Short-term ups and downs in a company's business ought not make operations inefficient. Most companies have these ups and downs. How can you stay efficient when you expand and contract operations all the time? Develop a flexible organization.

Flexibility is a bottom-level and near-bottom-level matter. To expand rapidly, move some of your better bottom-level workers up to group leaders and assistant foremen. Present group leaders and assistant foremen move up a notch too. To contract rapidly, put them back on their regular jobs. Lay off men from the bottom and demote others all along the line. Of course no one likes demotion, but when customers quit buying products you have to cut production and employment.

You can have a flexible organization if you want it. But, like stability, you have to train for it. Unlike stability, however, it does not have to be a long-range training matter. If you had to, you could do it quickly. You could, in a matter of weeks, give some of your good hourly paid men enough training to get by as assistant foremen and assistant foremen enough to get by as foremen. Or, on the down side, most assistant foremen and group leaders have come from the ranks and need no training to go back to their old jobs. In the ranks themselves, you could train workers to do two jobs so that they could double up, leaving no job undone, when the work force is reduced.

No one wants to train others to do his job when layoffs are coming. The problem is not serious though. Most bottom jobs can be learned readily, and vacations and day-to-day absenteeism mean someone else learning to do the absentee's work.

ADMINISTRATORS' USE OF STAFF SPECIALISTS' ADVICE

How do top line men know when to take and when not to take their staff specialists' advice? The staff specialists are the experts, so why not just take their advice? Executives can't do this in every case because too many people ride their hobbies too hard. Some recommendations have to be turned down. Specialists get overly enthusiastic about their fields or want to "empire-build." The personnel director may want to hire psychiatrists and psychologists. The head of the metallurgy department may recommend an elaborately equipped laboratory. The industrial engineers may want expensive equipment for taking and showing moving pictures of jobs.

All these things may be worth while in the largest companies, but generally they can't be justified in smaller companies. Any specialist worth his salt wants to do a good job and make the greatest possible contribution to the organization. The administration of the company, seeing the over-all situation, including the relationship between departments, and knowing the sales and financial condition of the company, must keep the organization in balance and, now and then, turn down recommendations.

There seems to be no way to avoid having administrators pass judgment on the recommendations of specialized staff men. If they accept all the staff recommendations, they will probably make more mistakes than if they reject some, even though they run the risk of vetoing the wrong suggestions. A top executive's view of the over-all operation of the whole enterprise and his general knowledge of the specialized fields should permit him, in most cases, to know when to reject staff recommendations. Top men, however, should guard against the temptation to assume that just because they have prestige and authority they are superspecialists in everything.

TWO-WAY COMMUNICATION

Does the president know what really goes on in a company? Does he know what the man at the bottom thinks about what the company does? If he knows these things he can make better decisions than if he doesn't know them. And do men at the bottom know why the company does what it does? If they do, they will try to help and not to hinder what the company does. If you can answer "yes" to these questions, you have good two-way communication. If the answer is "no," your communication is poor.

Many top men assume that they know how workers think about things because they came up from the ranks. Having once been hourly paid men, they really do understand their workers fairly well. But a well-paid and comfortable official, now 60 years old, has come a long way from the ranks. Maybe it was 30 years ago. In 30 years his memory plays tricks on him. Besides, times and men have changed, and today's men at the bottom don't think as they did 30 years ago when the president was just starting out.

Of course two-way communication doesn't always mean that *all* information goes *all the way* from bottom to top or top to bottom. But it means that information flows up and down as far as it needs to—that everyone at every level understands how things are working out at lower levels and how future actions will be received. And it means that directions and information flow down to middle and to lower levels.

Communications up and down are often poor. Ideas starting down from the top ought to get down to the last link in the chain of command, unscathed by the journey. But this isn't easy. Same thing going up. Ideas get twisted and warped. Particularly on the upward flow department heads will cover up bad things and report only the good. Also, they don't pass ideas upward if they are not asked or if they do get asked and no one pays any attention to what they say.

Subordinates often keep things from the top man even if he is open minded. When a man is moved up to a top job, he is no longer "one of the boys," even though he might want to be; the relationship between superior and subordinate cuts down the free flow of information, ideas, suggestions, and questions. The top man is no longer in on the give-and-take of everyday "bull sessions." Lawrence A. Appley says the top man is "wrapped in cellophane." Subordinates tell him what they think he wants to hear or what they want him to hear. Subordinates also tend to accept the wishes of their bosses without a question. They get to be "yes men" even when the boss tries to keep them from being so. There are, of course, administrators who want this kind of treatment, but some don't, and the practice keeps both kinds from knowing what goes on and prevents them from making the best decisions.

There seems to be no sure way of insuring an upward flow of ideas. It is hard to tell if you are really getting a true picture of things down the line. And if you think that you are not, it is hard to go around the road block without making someone mad. It makes trouble if you go around a subordinate and talk to his men. You undermine his authority and make him suspicious.

The best thing to do is to try to avoid surrounding yourself with "yes men" and impress upon your subordinates your desire for the truth. You ought, of course, to learn to be a good listener and to express your own ideas last rather than first. This gives subordinates a chance to talk. Let them present their problems and their suggestions as to what to do, and if you can, follow their suggestions. This magnifies the men in their own eyes and encourages more suggestions. Never belittle or ignore their suggestions, no matter how inconsequential or unpalatable they may seem. Belittle or ignore them, and you get no more suggestions.

In the lower levels of the organization the company suggestion system and the grievances filed are additional sources of information about the company policies.

Many companies now conduct occasional attitude or morale surveys to find out what employees—hourly paid and salaried alike—think of various company practices and policies. Any attempt on the part of management to learn and keep informed about worker attitudes is distinctly helpful.

Communicating down is a little different from communicating up. First, the administration should adopt only policies it thinks are fair. Then it should tell everyone what they are. Explanations can get to the employees through the company newspaper, occasional direct letters sent to employees' homes, bulletin board notices, and verbally in meetings with workers and by the foremen talking directly to the workers. Of these methods, the face-to-face method seems to be much the best at every level in the organization. Printed material is too often unread or misunderstood.

In spite of the obvious importance of maintaining two-way communication, many companies pay little attention to it. Others give it lip service but do very little about it. The number of companies seriously interested in it, however, is growing.

CONSULTATIVE MANAGEMENT

Some companies try to improve teamwork, particularly at middle levels of management, by using what they call "consultative" management (some of them call it "multiple" or "group" management). What they

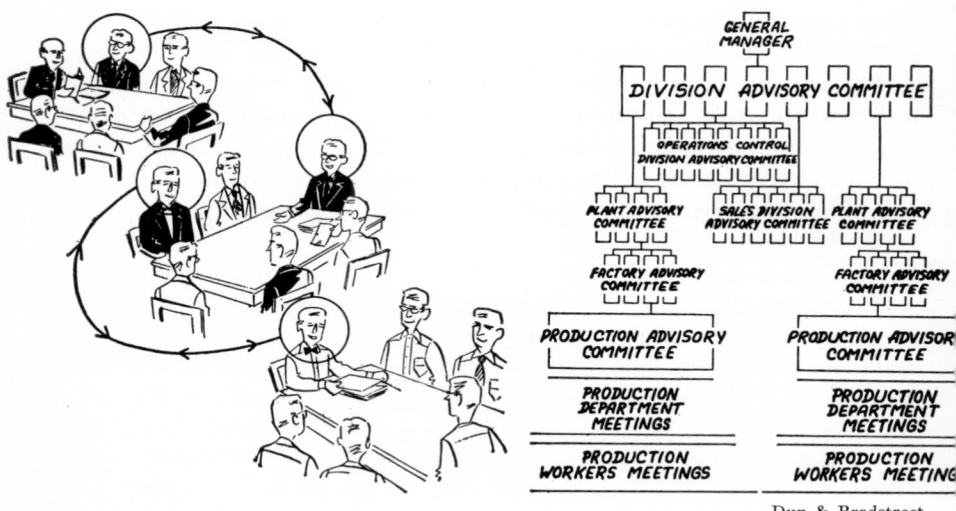

Dun & Bradstreet

FIG. 4–2. How information flows under multiple management at Calumet & Hecla, Wolverine Tube Division.

do is ask all lesser executives for suggestions and let them help decide on policies and how to handle problems.

Now, many companies do this, but they don't call it consultative management. What is different about it? First, consultative management sets up regular committees or councils of middle-level department heads, whereas in other companies the top men consult with subordinates informally. And when it is done informally, it often isn't done at all. And, second, consultative management companies say that they let middle-level men discuss even top-level matters. Good ideas come out of the discussions, and it is great training for middle-level men. They develop "management thinking" habits. In other companies middle-level men do not have much chance to learn about top-level problems.

Only courageous executives should go in for consultative management. Many things formerly kept private will have to be talked over with subordinates, and reasons given for the policies adopted. Also, if you ask subordinates for ideas about problems, you must be willing to accept and follow their suggestions or explain why you don't. Doing otherwise makes them feel that you lack sincerity and that consultative management is only a gimmick to get them to work harder.

Probably the best-known "multiple" management program is that of McCormick & Company, packagers of spices and food products. It was a pioneer plan started in 1932.[1] It sets up several boards to which a number of young men in the organization are elected. One board, the Junior Board of Directors, passes on matters of general company interest; another, the Factory Executive Board, deals with factory matters. Members of the boards are elected to the office by their colleagues and serve for a definite term. Every 6 months, six of the sixteen members are replaced.

Multiple management, of the McCormick type, has been adopted by some, but not many, other companies. Other companies must feel that the gains of consultative management can be realized better if it is not restricted to small, elected boards because not very many have adopted the McCormick plan. Probably some companies feel that competition for membership on the board and possible jealousy of and between board members reduce its over-all value.

MORALE

Morale is a man's attitude—his frame of mind. It is important because when he feels good—thinks the company is swell—he usually does more work. But if he is down on the company he usually turns out less. Sometimes he doesn't develop this attitude all by himself. He gets it from fellow workers. If they like the company, he does; if they don't, he doesn't.

Don't mistake the importance of morale. Poor morale doesn't mean no work. If you are ruthless enough you can get work out of men who

---

[1] The plan is described in Charles P. McCormick, *The Power of People* (New York: Harper & Bros., 1949).

hate you. Germany did it with factory workers in captured countries in World War II. Russia does it in slave labor camps today. We can't compare our operations to those. Our employers can't exert much pressure. Even fear of losing a job is small when jobs are plentiful.

"High morale = high production" has been accepted for years as axiomatic. Today's experts are not so sure of that now. Some researchers have found that you can have high morale and low production. A country club atmosphere can produce country club production. Sometimes you find low morale and high production. A worker may hate the boss, but be held by him to high production.

You usually get high production from pieceworkers—regardless of their morale. After all, low production = low pay, so production stays up. Also, hourly paid employees paced by machines have to keep up, no matter what their morale, or be taken off the job. On the other hand, many hourly paid employees are not on piecework, nor are they paced, and their morale affects their output. If an hourly paid employee is dissatisfied enough he can quit, thus increasing costs by labor turnover.

We miss the point, though, when we talk about how much work we can force out of a man. The point is that enthusiastic men usually turn out more work and do it with less supervision. Output is usually higher, and costs are lower.

The morale of foremen is probably more important than the morale of bottom-level workers. The whole department's work is good or bad depending on the foreman's work. Besides, morale is catching—the men get to feeling the same way the foreman does.

Unfortunately the costs of poor morale are not measurable and do not show, as such, on the profit and loss statement. They are probably real, however, and the usual gains from good morale are great enough to justify some effort on the part of the company to try to create it. It can usually be achieved if the company sincerely tries to be fair and reasonable in wages, promotions, grievance handling, and the like.

Two warnings should, however, be given. First, the company must try to be fair all the time. Most of the time won't do. Just a few instances of favoritism or unfairness in grievance handling will tear down good morale even where a sincere attempt has been made to develop it. And, second, labor unions sometimes put a great deal of effort into trying to get workers to feel that they are being mistreated and that management cannot be trusted. The union may be successful in building up an anticompany feeling when there is little actual reason for it, but the union's job is made easier when real causes exist.

DISCIPLINE

Members of every organization have to obey its rules. Employees have to come to work regularly and on time, and they have to take orders and do their work. On the job they must not fight, get drunk, gamble, or steal from the company or fellow workers. Most of these things are covered by shop rules or company policies.[2] *In all organizations, however, there will be men who won't do their work properly or who violate the rules, so you have to have penalties.* At the hourly paid level the rules and penalties for their violation ought always to be written out so that everyone knows them; sometimes they are written into the labor contract with the union. On the higher levels in the organization there are few violations; when they occur, they are handled individually.

Historically, discipline has been a negative thing: "don't do this," "don't do that"—"if you do, here's the penalty." It is much better psychologically to go at it positively (some people call it "constructive discipline") and to try to get men to accept rules because they understand them and agree to their fairness. Then they will obey them. But they obey because they want to, and not because there is any reward for complying or not just to avoid a penalty. You don't "jaywalk" in busy traffic because you don't want to get hurt—not just because there is a law against it.

Unfortunately, you can't always avoid using negative discipline. When rules are violated, you have to do something or the rules are meaningless, and you get more violations. Negative discipline, if carefully administered, need not cause undue employee dissatisfaction. It is important, however, to be sure that the rules are fair, that the penalties are appropriate to the seriousness of the violation, and that the rules are administered consistently. You ought, also, to have a grievance procedure through which appeals from decisions concerning penalties can be heard. Union contracts always contain provisions for such appeals by the employees covered.

You sometimes have to criticize a subordinate. Criticism is a minor kind of discipline. No one likes to be criticized, and you should make very sure it is justified before you do it. If a criticism is necessary, make it privately if possible and certainly not in front of other employees of equal or lower rank. Try to make it in such a way that the criticized subordinate can save face in his own thinking and before others. On the other hand, though, if a subordinate has been flagrantly insubordinate, maybe you ought to reprimand him publicly to be sure that other workers know that he is reprimanded.

Normally you should try to "soft pedal" a criticism and emphasize a suggestion as to how to avoid the situation in the future, making it a positive rather than a negative matter. Some administrators like the "sandwich" approach, in which the subordinate is first praised for a good deed, then criticized for something bad, and finally praised again for some-

---

[2] Shop rules and their enforcement are discussed on page 249.

thing else good, all in the same interview. By using courtesy and tact it is possible to criticize when necessary, yet help rather than hurt the confidence of the man criticized.

NEPOTISM

"From office boy he worked his way to the presidency by age 35." It happens—but only if your father owns the company. There is at least some nepotism in almost every company. What is more natural than for bosses to take care of their sons, sons-in-law, and nephews? Of course nonrelatives don't like it and perhaps their work suffers.

Nepotism is said to be bad because the best men don't always get the top jobs. It is bad when this happens. But nepotism is not all bad. When

George Lichty, used by permission of Chicago Sun-Times Syndicate

FIG. 4–3.   "This is the boss' son, Gus! He's going to start at the bottom for a few days! . . . ."

a top job opens up, who has better training and experience to take over than the boss's son, particularly if he is also the owner's son? The owner's son is sometimes the best-qualified man for the job. He has been groomed for the job at home and at work for years. Besides, no hired employee—even a president—has a greater personal interest in the company's future than its future owner. It is nepotism to give him the job, but it is also good to have the best man in it. Nepotism is not all bad. Remember, though, that nepotism is the unusual, not the usual, thing.

OUTSIDE CONTACTS

Most companies say that it is a fine idea for their men to participate in activities outside the company. Staff men are encouraged to belong to professional organizations and to take part in their activities. Some companies are, however, loath to give employees time off from their duties to go to professional meetings. Many companies will not pay professional organization membership dues; nor will they pay the expenses of employees going to meetings.

Many companies like to have their men write magazine articles and make speeches at conventions. Most of them, however, want to approve articles prior to publication. Most companies require approval of speeches before they are given. But there are some companies which do not allow their employees to take part in outside professional activities. It it hard for a man to divorce himself from his organization when speaking professionally on the outside, and there is danger that employees making public appearances will say things that embarrass the company.

As for participation in community affairs, many companies, particularly multiplant companies with plants in small towns, encourage their employees to be active. They recognize that the employees' interest and leadership in civic affairs build good will for the company in the community.

STUDY QUESTIONS

1. What do you think of the "decent survival" or "status-quoism" philosophy? What is meant? Do you favor it? Why?
2. Why are "informal groups" sometimes important? What, if anything, should management do about them?
3. "It is the president's job to decide things." Discuss thoroughly.
4. Is it true that today's foreman doesn't have to know as much about running the machines in his department as foremen 50 years ago? Explain your answer.
5. "All large companies must control operations by indirect means." Explain.
6. How can you have organizational stability so long as you cannot foresee death and resignations?
7. How do organization stability and flexibility differ? How can you develop each?
8. How can a high line officer judge the recommendations of his staff specialists? What problems are involved? How can he be sure of being right?
9. Why are there any problems in two-way communication? How can you avoid them?
10. Why two-way communication? What good is it? Can't we get along without it?
11. What is "consultative" management? Is it good? If so, why isn't it used more? If not, what is the matter with it?
12. "High morale = high production." Discuss this axiom.
13. Why is middle management morale likely to be more important than bottom-level morale? Explain.
14. Nearly everyone agrees that positive discipline is better than negative. So, why not do away with negative discipline? Explain fully.
15. Write out instructions for a newly promoted foreman telling him how to criticize one of his men when he thinks that it must be done.

CASE 4–1.   AMERICAN MALLEABLE IRON CO.

The American Malleable Iron Co., makers of plumbing fittings, tees, ells, etc., has been located about one mile from the center of a large city for over 75 years. Along one side of the factory lies a railroad, beyond which is a radio factory. Adjacent to another side of the plant is a manufacturer of electric fans and other electrical products. On the other two sides are streets across which lies an old and poor residential neighborhood.

The company employs 1,500 persons, most of whom work in the foundry, which is one of two manufacturing departments, the other being the threading department, where threads are cut onto the fittings. Over the years, the neighborhood in which the company is located has deteriorated. Most of the foundry employees are colored, and many of them live nearby. Like most foundries, American Malleable's foundry is dirty and is housed in very old buildings. The threading departments and even the offices are housed in buildings at least 50 years old. For years the company has not been very profitable.

The company has never had any formal training programs for anyone. All of the foremen and the plant superintendent have come up through the ranks. The present employment manager (there is no personnel director) had previously been the union president. The only college-trained men in the organization are the works manager and the foundry testing-laboratory engineer.

Because Mr. Winkelman, the company treasurer and a large stockholder, is nearing retirement, he is thinking of the company's future. The company has, over the years, made a few halfhearted attempts to recruit employees who might be long-range executive material, but its attempts have been unsuccessful. The company's location and its physical appearance have hampered its efforts. The fact that it has not been a particularly profitable company played a part too.

What do you think of the company's future? What action should be taken? Should the company have made the union president its employment manager?

Chapter 5

OVER-ALL POLICIES

Top management sets a company's major policies and makes its important decisions. What products are we to make and sell? What departments should we have? What prices will we charge? Do we buy or rent a factory? Where?

Can top management really decide these things? In a limited way and in the long run, yes. But there are many limitations. A new administrator inherits a going concern—an organization already in existence. If his organization is not as good as he thinks it ought to be, he can't change it overnight for the better. The reverse isn't true, though. Anyone can tear down a good organization fast.

But, can't management change nonhuman things? Usually not very fast. Again you run up against the going-concern idea. The company is already in business—in a particular business. It is known and its products are known, and people buy them. It makes things in plants already located. Can management change this? Well—no and yes. Can Studebaker-Packard take over General Motors' car market? Leaving out dreams—no. Could U.S. Steel successfully make and sell automobiles? Well, maybe, but it would be a big undertaking, even for U.S. Steel. Can Avco go out of the airplane business? Yes—it sold Consolidated-Vultee. Can General Tire make moving pictures? It can now, since it bought RKO.

In a book on manufacturing management we can't get into buying and selling whole companies. We deal with policies and decision making *inside* the company, and we stress the manufacturing aspects of policies and decisions.

Nearly always management has to change inside things slowly. New products, for example, take time and effort to develop. But even after developing good products, a market has to be found for them. Management doesn't always succeed because other companies are in there competing too. Jack and Heintz Company was a fabulous manufacturing company in World War II. It made only war products. After the war its try at making electric motors bumped into the giants, General Electric, Westinghouse, and others. Small wonder Jack and Heintz had trouble. It is now finding a place for itself in the specialty motor business, but it has been a long pull. Its manufacturing has had to be adapted to its market.

How about plant location? Can management decide that? If it doesn't like its location can it move the company? Yes—but it will cost one third to one half of a year's payroll to build a new plant. Companies without the money don't move. This is another area where management can make decisions only some of the time.

Administrative decisions deal with all of these subjects—subjects that management can't always do very much about. But they also deal with subjects management can do more about: management can try to make the company into a leader in the industry or it can be content to follow; management can decide to make or buy its materials, parts, and supplies. Ford makes its own glass for windshields. General Motors doesn't. Management can add new products or cut off products that don't sell, and it can decide between buying and renting machines and plants. It can try for government defense products or not. It can decide to manufacture things lot by lot or continuously, and it can mechanize or not. If it makes things in lots, it can choose between frequent small lots or infrequent large lots. Mostly these are internal questions—and they are questions that management must answer.

Management can also do long-range planning—planning for 5 years hence. It can decide where it wants the company to be—what products, what sale volume, where it will put new plants. And after it plans where it wants to be, it can do things to get there. The president can steer his ship and not let it drift rudderless.

LEADERS AND FOLLOWERS

Most industries have leaders and followers. Any company can be a follower if it chooses, but would-be leaders don't always succeed in becoming leaders. Some of them end up being followers.

Leader and follower companies usually do different things and have different organizations. Leaders spend more money on research and are always working on new products. Their research departments are relatively large. Followers spend little on research. When a leader brings out something that catches on, the followers jump on the bandwagon and imitate the new product as closely and quickly as they can. Probably you see more of this in clothing than in other industries. But you see it everywhere; remember when "king size" and "filter-tip" cigarettes came out? First one company, then all.

Most companies both lead and follow. They try to be first but don't always make it. Some companies (generally the big ones) nearly always lead. They (1) do research, (2) develop new products, (3) make high-quality products, (4) usually charge higher prices, and (5) are not always low-cost producers. Companies that end up following do less research and new product development. Their products are usually lower priced; they have to be to sell. Sometimes they are of lower quality. Successful followers are usually quite efficient producers—they run their factories well, produce at low costs and sell with low profit margins.

SIZE CONSIDERATIONS

A company's size is important in policy and decision making. The bigger you are the better you can solve most business problems. General Foods, General Electric, and General Motors have plants all over the country so they are near both raw materials and markets. That lets them get good service from suppliers, give good service to customers, and keep freight costs low—all at the same time.

Location. Multiplant companies can usually stay well located all the time. If southern California or Florida, for example, grows into a major market area, a multiplant company can do its expanding there. It doesn't move—it migrates. As it grows it has to put in new facilities somewhere, so it just puts a new plant or expands an existing one in the area not well served by old plants. Or if New England slows down, the company doesn't have to close down plants there (although it could do that too). All it needs to do is *not* to put in new machines or plants there. Operations are never much upset in the old location, yet over the years the company has really moved.

Cost Comparisons. Multiplant companies can compare the cost of production of one plant with that of another doing the same work. If there are differences, then they adopt the procedures of the efficient plant in the less efficient one. Or they can move some of their efficient managers into inefficient plants. Or operations can be expanded in the efficient plants and cut in the inefficient ones.

Executive Trainees. Big companies have distinct advantages over little ones in the development of future executives. Their prestige draws good young men. They get the "pick of the crop." Over the years these men can be given the necessary training and varied experience to develop them into good executives. They virtually assure the company's future good management. Trainees who prove incapable of becoming top administrators can be kept on jobs in line with their ability or weeded out. Note, though, that unless large companies consciously provide training and varied experience for junior executives, even the best trainees will not automatically develop into good major executives.

Small companies find it harder to attract good young men, and they can't provide formal training or the varied experience necessary for the development of well-rounded top-flight executives. Many people, however, believe that small companies often develop first-class executives because their young men, having less guidance and staff help, have to be self-reliant. Because they can see the enterprise in its entirety, they get a better understanding of the over-all effects of their decisions than can be obtained in large companies.

Union Relations.   Large companies have some advantages over small ones in union contract negotiations. Contract negotiation has become so technical it takes specialists to do the job. They need to know all about economic matters, industry wage patterns, wording of contract provisions, etc. Large companies can afford to hire specialists and so do a better job of bargaining. Small companies, however, have an advantage in the closer day-to-day relations existing between top management and factory workers. Often a fuller appreciation on the part of each for the other's problems reduces the number of disputes.

Use of Waste.   Large companies can utilize the wastes from manufacture better than can small companies. In large companies there is often enough waste to justify its manufacture into by-products. Meat packers, for example, no longer throw away the viscera from slaughtered animals. Much of it is now sold to pharmaceutical companies which extract insulin from the pancreas, pituitrin from the pituitary glands, and adrenal and thyroid extracts from other glands. But the meat packers have to spend some money to separate out the valuable waste. If they weren't large, it would not be worth while to do this. Small companies don't have enough waste material to make by-products profitable.

Engineering.   Large companies ordinarily have a big advantage over small companies in the amount and quality of engineering and other technical knowledge that is available to them. A company with 50,000 employees, 1 per cent of whom are technical experts, has 500 specialists. A company with 500 employees, 1 per cent of whom are engineers, has 5 experts. The large group can carry specialization to a degree far beyond what is possible in small companies, and yet the financial burden on the company is proportionally no greater.

Research.   Very large companies have a near-monopoly on basic research and a virtual monopoly, therefore, on the fruits of such work. Laboratory projects inquiring into the laws of physics, chemistry, and metallurgy are very expensive. A $10,000 budget will unlock few of nature's secrets. Millions of dollars may be needed to conduct one basic research project. For a company counting its sales in billions of dollars, the cost of such a project is within reason, but that cost is prohibitive even to companies with millions of dollars of sales annually.

Machines.   Large companies have a similar advantage in the use of large, expensive, but fast-producing laborsaving machinery. They have the engineers to design such machines, the money to buy them, and the volume necessary to allow them to operate at low unit costs. This advantage tends to increase over the years because the characteristic practice of depreciating equipment rapidly on the company's books recovers the cost of such machines long before they wear out.

Disadvantages of Being Big.   Being big makes good management a must; it is a big job to control far-flung empires. But even with good managers, big companies have some disadvantages. They can't adjust quickly to changed conditions. Often they can't give quite such good service as small companies. Usually they can't make exactly what the customer wants so quickly or at as low a cost. But these disadvantages rarely offset the long list of advantages to being big.

Social Responsibilities.   Big companies are also in the limelight. They must be very sure to toe the line as far as all laws are concerned. And they must watch out for public opinion and not do things that irritate the public. The bigger the company, the greater its social responsibilities. Big company managements can't always make the last dollar of profit nor cut costs to the last penny.

MULTIPLANT OPERATIONS

America's largest manufacturing companies have, for the most part, steadily grown larger for many years. During the last 20 years, however, there has been a trend away from enormous individual plants. Most of our biggest companies have become convinced that several small separate plants can operate more efficiently than a few large plants. Giant plants (say 10,000 employees and up) require a high degree of managerial skill and are more vulnerable to shutdowns caused by strikes or material shortages. Multiplant companies generally try to divide their work so that few individual plants employ more than 5,000 workers. Lots of the plants of giant companies employ less than 1,000 persons, though there are generally some plants considerably bigger than that.

Administrators of large companies must determine the degree to which their operations will be centralized. If they choose to decentralize, they must decide how to do it. Some companies decentralize by having each plant specialize in making *a particular product line* but serve a wide geographic area. Another plan calls for each individual plant to make the company's *whole line of products* but serve only its own territory. Sometimes decentralization is accomplished by having certain plants concentrate on making *parts* for other plants.

Multiplant operations introduce managerial problems different from those of single large or small plants. In general, the individual plant managers of multiplant companies are given wide authority to run their plants in their own way. Home office direction is to a great extent a matter of setting over-all policies and furnishing specialized staff help where it is needed.

Some very perplexing problems can come up. Plant managers of the company's different divisions are judged and given pay raises and promotions based on how efficiently they run their plants or, put differently, how much money they make. But (and here is one difficult problem) when you buy parts from sister plants, the price is important to both

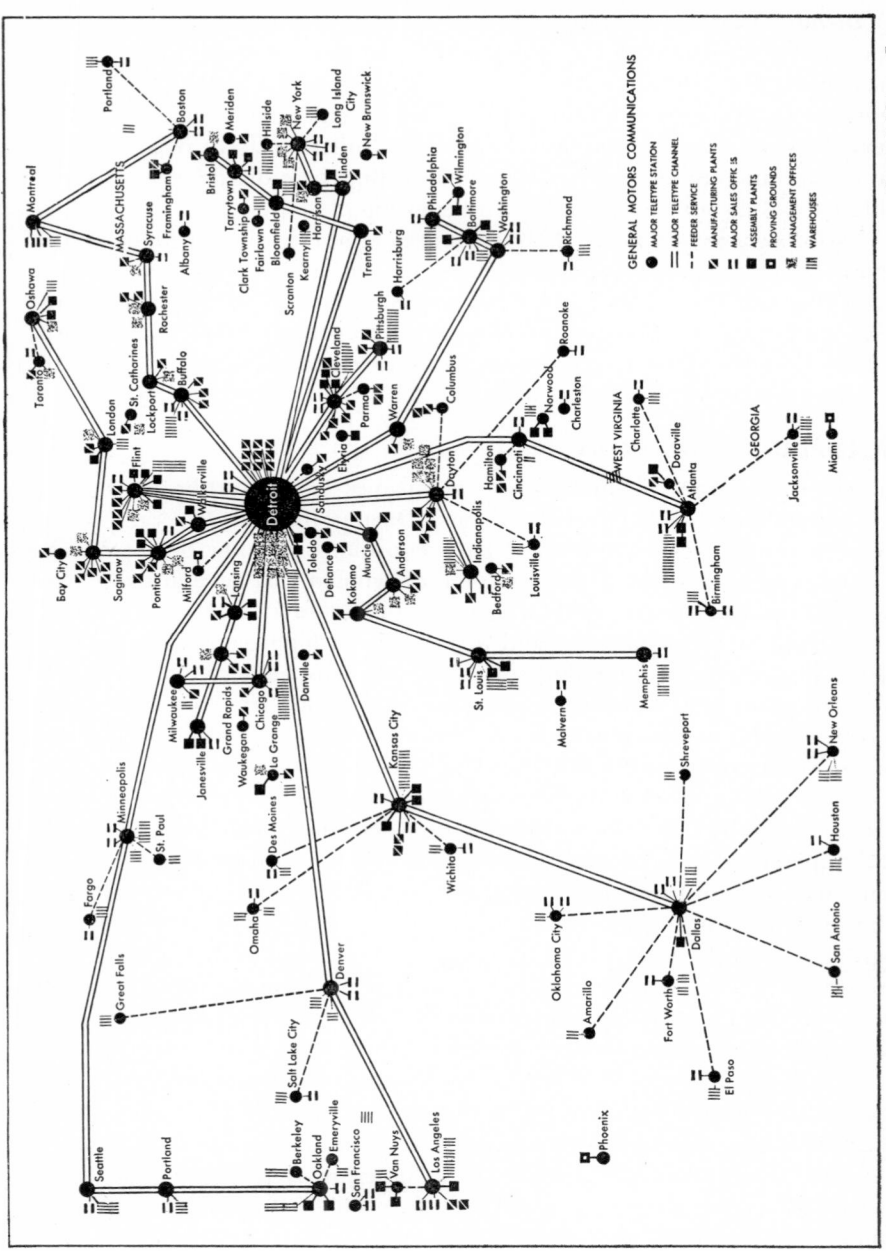

GENERAL MOTORS COMMUNICATIONS

● MAJOR TELETYPE STATION
▬ MAJOR TELETYPE CHANNEL
▬ ▬ FEEDER SERVICE
◤ MANUFACTURING PLANTS
■ MAJOR SALES OFFICES
◧ ASSEMBLY PLANTS
▣ PROVING GROUNDS
☒ MANAGEMENT OFFICES
▥ WAREHOUSES

General Motors Corp.

Mail the Corporation's 126 or more offices and assembly plants are spread all over the United States and Canada.

you and the selling plant manager. Your costs are low if you pay a low price—but in that case the selling plant manager's income is low. So he makes a poor profit showing. But if he charged you more, it would be the other way around. Your costs would be high, and you would make less profit. This problem is so troublesome at Ford Motor Company that it has set up an arbitration department just to settle arguments over pricing between divisions.

Another problem is: Which customer do you take care of first? If your plant makes products for outside sale (at a high price) and also products sold to a sister plant (at a lower price), you don't want sister-plant business as long as you can keep busy on outside jobs. You'd like to turn down low-price sister-plant business, but will you be allowed to?

Another problem: Must you buy from a sister plant when you think you can get as good a product on the outside for less money? Most companies allow outside buying in such a case—but not on big items.

Another: Suppose a division serves one territory. What happens when its sales department gets a great many orders—will part of them be taken away and sent to a plant with fewer orders? Usually some orders will be transferred if the first plant is very busy and sister plants are not. But if this is done, why try so hard to get lots of orders?

Still another problem: Suppose you work hard and develop new products. The costs all go on your record. You make less profit than if you hadn't researched. Then when it comes time to go into production and make money on the new product, the administration takes the product away from you and puts it in a new division!

We could go on. You can see that multiplant company administrations have some problems over and above those faced by single-plant company administrators. It is all very well to say that the top administrators are not fools and can see who is doing the best job, but middle-level officials aren't always convinced.

INTEGRATION

Everything you buy is someone else's *finished* product. Probably you could make those products yourself—conceivably you could produce nearly all of the things you buy. It is for management to decide. Actually, nearly all companies that make assembled products (typewriters, washing machines, autos, and so on) make many of the parts they use—maybe half or more. But, on the other hand, they *buy, not make*, the other half of the things they need. An auto company *can* make its own pig iron, sheet metal, plate glass, upholstery fabric, and paint, but usually they do not. A newspaper *can* own its own paper mills; some do.

Vertical Integration.   Pushing ownership back into raw materials making is called *vertical integration.* Pushing the other way toward the customer is also vertical integration, as when a steel company makes steel wire and then makes it into steel fences, or a shoe factory which owns its own retail stores. No matter where you start—on the finished goods end and work back or on the raw materials end and work forward—it is vertical integration if you own *successive stages of manufacture.*

Vertical integration gives a company control over its source of supply —it gets what it wants in the way of quality, quantity, time of delivery, control of research and development, and, usually, it gets lower costs. Integrating towards the customer—making finished products and selling them through the company's own stores—gives it a market for its products.

Vertical integration is a little dangerous, and you can't always make it pay. It takes plenty of money and good management to run all the different businesses and make them all pay. Besides, companies that make your raw materials are often efficient and can make products for less than you can make them yourself. Also they do quite a bit of research that no one of their customers has to wholly pay for. If you buy their products you get the benefit of their research. We think of the auto industry as being integrated, but GM buys 50 per cent of the parts it uses; Ford buys 60 per cent; Chrysler, 65 per cent.

Horizontal Integration.   Some integration is called *"horizontal."* This means that the company has several plants doing the same thing. Continental Can and American Can are examples. Mostly they make tin cans in all their factories. They are not examples of vertical integration. They don't run steel mills and they don't can foods. They just make the cans; but they make cans in factories all over the country.

Horizontal integration advantages are: good customer service, low freight costs, good protection against production stopping everywhere at once, and often lower labor costs and low property tax costs. You get these low costs by having plants near the customers and by putting plants in low-cost areas. Usually, with horizontal integration, you have many not-so-large plants instead of a few large ones. You might think that running a number of not-so-large plants would be less efficient than running a few large ones. Some executives don't think so. Sylvania Electric, Johnson & Johnson, and many others think smaller plants are more efficient. They do all their manufacturing in many small plants, not in a few large ones.

Like vertical integration, horizontal integration won't pay without good managerial skill. This time, though, you don't run a large number of *different kinds* of factories but many *scattered* factories. You don't need managers with the skill to run *diverse* activities, but it takes good managers to control things in plants scattered all over the country.

Not all integration can be classified as either vertical or horizontal. For example, Armour and Company, meat packers, makes cushioning material for furniture from hair and foam rubber. Both General Motors and American Motors make automobiles and refrigerators. General Mills makes automatic assembly equipment for sale to other companies. General Foods sells coffee and corn flakes. There are all kinds of odd combinations.

Sometimes a company takes on a product to fill out its line, so its customers can buy all their needs from it. Sometimes by-products need marketing so companies go into side businesses. Sometimes research people come up with something good, but not in the regular line. Rather than let go of it, the company keeps the idea and goes into a new business with it. Sometimes a merged or bought company has odds and ends. After the merger you find yourself in businesses you hadn't thought much about.

Diversification is another reason for integration. You don't have all of your eggs in one basket. Parts makers, in particular, often go in for diversification. Companies making parts for other manufacturers are in a more vulnerable position than are manufacturers of finished products, since the companies to which they sell can, at any time, start to make their own parts. Parts manufacturing companies and processors of basic raw materials must operate so efficiently that they can carry on a profitable business and yet sell their goods at a price below that at which the customer would be able to produce them himself. Parts companies can't be sure that they can always do that, so most of them try to diversify.

OWNERSHIP OF ASSETS

Manufacturing companies usually own all the assets needed to carry on their business, but they don't have to own them all. Buildings, machinery, and even inventories need not be owned by the company.

Buildings. Young and growing companies often rent their quarters. In most cities there are large old factory buildings located near the downtown area in which as much or as little space as is wanted can be rented. Ordinarily, the management of the building furnishes all the services required, including building maintenance, window cleaning, elevator service, receiving and shipping facilities, power, water, heat, etc. In a few cities, buildings have been erected for the express purpose of providing rented quarters for small businesses, for example, Philadelphia's Budd Terminal.

Although rented quarters hold down the investment in fixed assets, they have disadvantages. Ordinarily you can't find a building to rent just where you would like to have it. Besides, the building itself is generally old and poorly arranged for the kind of work you do. Some costs, such as fire insurance, may be higher if other renters have fire hazards. Renting space in a building with other companies may require common labor policies on the part of all neighboring companies. This could be a disadvantage. Also additional space might not be available if you wished to expand.

The worst thing about a rented building, however, is the rent itself and the uncertainty of long-time possessions. Landlords are noteworthy for charging all that the traffic will bear. If they raise the rent, a renter has no alternative but to pay or move. Leases give both renter and building owner a certain amount of security during the life of the lease, but sometimes difficulties arise over the maintenance of the premises and such things. Generally, lessee and lessor get along well together during the period of the lease, but the owner sometimes ups the rent for the next lease period.

In recent years many large companies, particularly department stores and chain mail-order outlets, have changed from owned to leased quarters to raise capital (at very low interest rates) for expansion. The practice is less common in manufacturing but is not unknown. You count the rent you pay as cost of operation and that lowers your income taxes. The money you get from selling your buildings is costing you whatever you pay in rent but reduced by the income tax saving. It amounts to using borrowed money at only about 2 per cent net interest. Of course, you don't do this if you don't need money for expansion.

Equipment.   The assets of a manufacturing company, other than land and buildings, are generally owned rather than rented. Equipment for most factories, however, can be bought on an installment plan. Or it can be leased, with an option to buy and apply the rent on the purchase price. Or it can be leased without anyone expecting a sale to follow. Leasing equipment is the rule in a few industries. In the shoe industry, for example, the United Shoe Machinery Company owns many patents on up-to-date shoe manufacturing equipment and will rent machines on a royalty basis to manufacturers. Mechanical tabulation equipment and electronic computors are usually rented or leased rather than bought. Tabulating equipment is highly complex and is widely used in sales, accounting, payroll, statistical, production control, and other departments of manufacturing companies. For many years the International Business Machines Company wouldn't sell its equipment, only leasing it. The Federal Trade Commission got it to change that policy. Now, like other companies making similar machines, it will sell or lease, whichever you prefer.

Inventories.   Inventories of stock must nearly always be owned by manufacturing companies themselves. They may get help in financing inventories by means of liberal credit terms from the vendor, or they may borrow from a bank. Sometimes a bank will lend money on raw materials by "field warehousing," an arrangement by which the mortgaged materials are set apart in the company's own stockroom and kept under lock and key. As they are issued and used by the company, a part of the loan, corresponding to the proportion of the materials used, must be paid.

Accounts Receivable.   The practice of "factoring" accounts receivable is common in some industries (shoe manufacturing, for example). Ordinarily, a manufacturing company has to extend credit to its customers (which may be other manufacturing companies) for a short time. Some companies need the money at once, so they "factor," or sell, at a slight discount, their accounts receivable as a regular practice to get their money sooner.

DEFENSE CONTRACTS

The government spends some 15 billions of dollars a year for defense products. Probably all large companies get some government business. But some companies do not want government orders very badly because they can't make much money on them and there is endless red tape and forms and reports to fill in. On the other hand, some contracts are so big (millions and even hundreds of millions of dollars) that it pays to go after them even with low profit margins. Besides if war comes the contracts will go to the companies that know how to make the products.

Defense contracts are the lifeblood of the nation's biggest industry. Our biggest industry is not autos, foods, textiles, or steel, it is airplanes. When we add airplanes and the associated electronics industry (such as radar and automatic fire controls) to it, we have a combination that is far bigger than any other industry. The United States government buys almost the whole output. Defense work is not all airplanes, guided missiles, and electronics, but most of it is. And the problems are much alike in other defense products manufacture.

Airplanes and electronics (and other defense products) are heavily "researched." Millions and millions of dollars pour into research all the time. Nor is it wasted. It produces knowledge of how to make better and better products.

But that makes manufacturing problems. Airplanes take a long time to make—4 to 6 years from first ideas to production on a volume basis. Even after you go on a volume basis, it still takes up to a year to make an airplane. The problem is how can you make an up-to-date airplane? If you design an airplane in 1957 for 1963 production, it is out of date design-wise before it is made, yet it can't be made any quicker. What happens in practice is that you keep changing the design all the time and put in all the new things you can clear up to the last minute. You end up with a partly outdated airplane.

The continual change while production goes on makes a great deal of extra work. Paper work and the number of directions given are multiplied. Designs are redesigned. Work plans are made, torn up, and re-made. Purchase orders are placed, canceled, and new ones placed.

Defense production differs from other manufacturing in still other important ways. Sales contracts give the government the right to go over your books—to see how your accounts are kept. In fact, the government tells you how you have to keep your accounts and how much overhead charge the government will pay and which items are overhead. (Before the government made such rules, companies charged it with overhead having nothing to do with its contract.) The government will help carry expenses by paying for materials and labor as you go along, but it won't pay *all* your operating costs before getting its product.

Pricing, too, is different. The price is intended to allow a maximum profit of about 7 per cent of the sales dollar. But some products are so different and so new that no one really knows what it will cost to make them. Maybe the government will give you a cost-plus-fixed-fee contract. Then you won't lose if costs are higher than you expected. Or maybe the government will guarantee to pay you for your costs. If they are higher than everyone expected, you lose part or all of your profits. If it is so bad that the costs go above the total contract price, the government will up the price enough to cover all the costs. With this kind of a contract you can never actually lose money. Government contracts usually work the other way too. If your costs are way below expectations, the government "renegotiates" (cuts) the price.

Because the business is precarious, airplane companies don't try to raise enough money to finance all the buildings and machines that they need. The government puts up most of the money for airplane factories; it owns them and it assigns them to particular companies to operate. Probably most airplane companies own, in their own right, less than one third of the factories and the machinery that they operate.

Government ownership of assets makes pricing problems. Particularly, it raises questions of profit margins. If airplane companies are allowed to make normal rates of profits on their products—say 15 per cent of the sales dollar—that is too high considering the small amount of assets owned. Yet, if a smaller rate, say, 5 per cent of the sales dollar, is allowed for profits, there is only a very thin margin between profits and losses.

Defense work has other peculiarities. Research costs are high, and the money must be spent *before* you get results. But if you do research work *before* you get a government contract, the government doesn't want to pay for the research because it didn't authorize it. You really need two contracts, one to pay for research and another to make products. Sometimes you can get a government research contract and sometimes not. It is fine if you can because then the government not only pays for the research but pays you a profit as well.

Defense companies, too, sometimes see their new developments handed to their competitors. A company may carry research through successfully only to have the government allow a competitor to make the product, say it is a fire control system, and put it in *his* airplane. Of course switching around contracts for improvements is a two-way street. Defense product companies may lose sole control over something they develop, but they get some contracts to make things that someone else developed.

Still another oddity about defense work is that the government usually won't pay for advertising, sales commissions, insurance, and fancy buildings. This is logical from the taxpayers' point of view, but it makes you run your business differently.

Subcontracting is also different on government contracts. Our Congress is dedicated to helping small businessmen. So airplane companies *must* farm out the making of many minor items. The government doesn't say which, but it does tell you how much money must be spent on subcontract work. Often it would be better all the way around not to bother with little companies that only make headaches for you, but there is no alternative on government contracts.

In summary, defense work is big business, very big. Yet its very nature creates a different setting for management decision making. Ordinary, business practice sometimes has to be modified to suit these conditions.

MECHANIZATION

American industry becomes more mechanized every year. More and more things are done mechanically instead of by hand, and things formerly done mechanically are done faster and better. All of this costs money for new machines—money which it is hoped will be returned out of savings in the future.

How to select projects to go ahead with and how to figure which will pay and which will not are discussed in Chapter 8. Here we are concerned with general policies—not specific cases.

Mechanization decisions depend in part on your forecast of the future. You want to be as sure as you can that business will be good enough to keep the machines busy after you buy them—particularly in the near future. It is a serious matter if business declines before the new equipment has had an opportunity to return very much of its cost.

An administrator's philosophy also plays a part. Often he won't get, from any calculations, a clear answer as to whether to buy a new machine or not. He can't be sure whether it will pay for itself in 2 years, 3 years, or when. If he is cautious he won't mechanize. A less cautious person might go ahead and buy the machines. In the years right after 1929, companies that had followed cautious policies in the preceding year or two were better off than those which had invested heavily in new machines. Since 1939 the reverse has been true.

Deciding to mechanize is an important step because the investment raises fixed costs. After a company raises its fixed costs, it has to do more business than it did before in order not to lose money. Then why do it? Why mechanize and raise fixed costs and the break-even point? Look at Figures 6–1 and 6–2, page 110. They give you the answer. True, mechanizing makes you lose money at levels that used to produce a profit, and at low levels you stand to lose much more. *But at high levels you make* much more. Keep the volume up and you are way ahead by mechanizing.

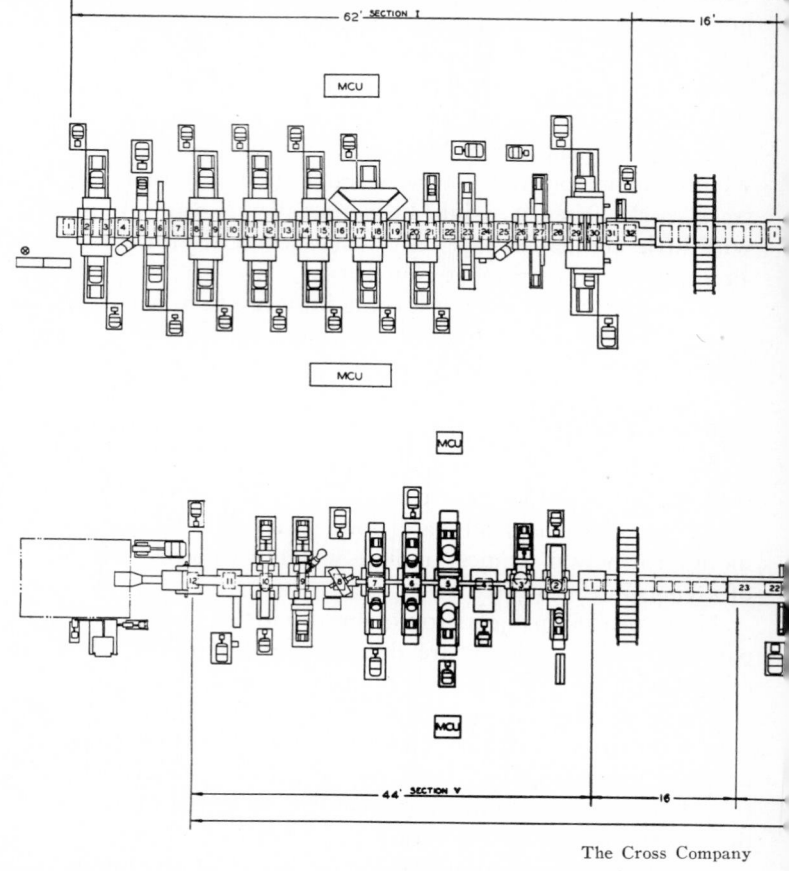

The Cross Company

FIG. 5–2.   Drawing of an 8-cylinder automobile engine block production line.

Actually, it isn't quite as hard to keep sales up as you might think. Normally, year by year, the company grows and so naturally will do more and more business.

When automation or continuous production is adopted as the method of manufacture, equipment is selected and the plant is laid out as if it were one gigantic, special purpose machine. That is discussed elsewhere. The main thing here is to recognize that an important administrative decision is made when the manufacturing method is selected. A great deal of money has to go into machinery.

Borderline Decisions.   If, in the long run, it appears to be a "tossup" as to whether to mechanize or not, it might be better to mechanize. There are several reasons for this.

First, the quality of the product is usually improved. Because that gain is not measurable, though real, it is usually left out when figuring savings.

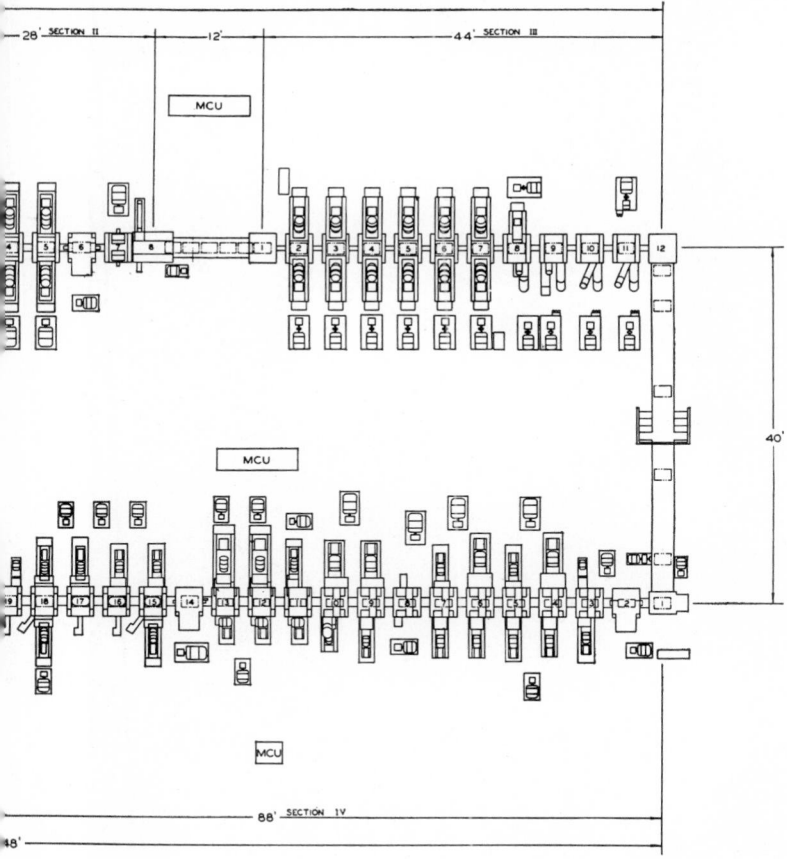

Second, mechanization makes jobs simpler, reducing the skill required and simplifying employee training. That, too, is not in the calculations.

Third, if wages go up during the life of a machine, you save more than you figured. Laborsaving machinery bought in the 1940's with the expectation of saving of labor at $1.00 an hour, for example, actually saved labor at more than $2.00 an hour less than 10 years later. The fact that when the machine wears out its replacement will cost more doesn't take away the extra savings already in pocket.

Maybe it is unwise to expect wages to go up every year when figuring how much a machine will save in the years ahead. But if wages do keep going up and we never figure on it, we won't mechanize sometimes when we should. Actually wages have been increasing since 1932 almost without a break. Machines bought any time since then have probably all saved far more than was expected when they were bought. If wages

FIG. 5-3. Picture of the automobile cylinder line shown in Figure 5-2.

keep going up every year—and who thinks they won't?—leaving wage increases out of the figures gives us a wrong answer. We will end up thinking that a new machine will save less than it really will.

There is a fourth reason for mechanizing, even when the figures show it to be a tossup. That is the short life of a machine assumed in the calculations. Most factory machines are assumed to have but a short life, often 10 years. Actually, nearly all machines last much longer than 10 years, and very few have to be thrown away sooner because of obsolescence.

The arguments in favor of mechanizing when the figures show it to be of questionable merit seem strong. How about the negative side? Three of the bad things—the money needed, raising fixed costs, and the danger of loss if sales fall off—have been mentioned. But there is still another bad thing.

New machines have a way of not coming up to expectations. Of course no one expects them to do as well as the selling company says they should. But even so new machines often produce less than expected. They are out of order, producing nothing too much of the time. They turn out too many poor products. They need more repairs, wear out tools faster, and so on, than we truly expected. Particularly at the beginning there is likely to be trouble. This all adds to the costs. Such extra costs should be put into estimates, but often not enough is allowed for.

Knowing this, officials sometimes turn thumbs down on many projects that—on paper—show great promise. They don't always go ahead and mechanize in tossup situations.

EXPANSION

Most well-established companies grow along with our national economy so a company's administration must decide, from time to time, whether to expand operations and, if so, how, when, and where.

It seems logical to expand when costs are low. Generally, however, just the opposite takes place because costs are never low except in a depression. And when everyone else's business is bad, so is our own. Far from needing more capacity, we are operating on short hours. Besides, when we expand, we usually pay for it out of profits, which are nonexistent in depressions. Most companies just don't build new plants in bad times.

When business is good, building costs are high, but then and only then do we need to expand. Failure to expand when business is good means poor customer service and lost sales. We would just be inviting competitors to take part of our market. So even though the cost of expansion is high, we expand; and since profits are good, we have plenty of money to pay for the expansion.

Another point: only in hindsight do we know that any period is a period of low prices. No one ever knows on a downswing whether prices will go still lower or if on an upswing whether prices will go still higher. Companies that expanded before or right after World War II probably thought that costs were high, but costs have skyrocketed since. Now we say that costs in the 1940's were low. Everything considered, it seems logical to expand plants in prosperous times, even though costs seem high.

MODERNIZATION

"To modernize (remodel extensively an old plant) or not to modernize" is a question that managements sometimes face. Companies with new plants have answered the question, so they have no problem. Companies with old factories but with not enough money to pay for extensive changes have to live with what they have.

Many companies with money, however, make their products in old plants and with much old equipment. Why? Don't they know about the many advantages to be gained from modernization?—clean, bright plant; favorable impression on employees, plant visitors, and customers; reduction in transportation and material handling costs; lower insurance rates, lower maintenance costs, and probably reduced direct labor costs.

Probably they know all about these gains. But they also know that they get them only if money, and usually much money, is spent. The money they spend for modernization is sure, the gains from it are not. Even though gains are probable, they are not in hand, and no manager can be sure how big they will be. It isn't surprising, therefore, that some administrations decide against modernization programs, particularly if the business horizon is cloudy.

Because the old plant and old equipment are fully, or almost fully, depreciated on the company books, production costs appear to be low (and maybe they really are low). Under these circumstances a company may make money for several years without modernizing. The time finally comes, however, when the equipment, in the process of wearing out, becomes less and less efficient. During the life of the old machines, new and improved ones have almost certainly come onto the market. Eventually the combined cost of labor and machine depreciation per unit of product may be less with new models than the cost of labor and repairs on the old equipment even with almost no depreciation. In the long run the failure to modernize or, at least, to install new machinery from time to time, may be fatal.

Modernization, so far as the appearance of the buildings, lighting, and cleanliness within the plant are concerned, is generally less important. Almost everyone in industry agrees that modernization is highly desirable, but *a great many companies carry on profitable operations in plants which are far from modern.* Their administrations appear to be uncertain that it will pay for itself. This is not so true of industries making consumer products. Nearly all of them find it worth while to modernize and to do a good job of plant housekeeping to impress visitors and customers. Some, such as food processors and pharmaceutical manufacturers, may be required by law to maintain certain sanitation standards.

PLANT LOCATION

In most companies plant location, while important, is a matter concerning which the administration seldom needs to make a decision. When it becomes necessary to expand or move, the location of the new plant should be decided on only after careful forecasts of markets and the company's future business have been made and after the merits of alternative locations have been weighed. Plant locations are taken up in Chapter 9.

STUDY QUESTIONS

1. How are your operations affected by a decision to be a leader or a follower?
2. Small companies are usually more flexible than large ones, but there are certain advantages to being big. What are they? On balance do they offset the disadvantages?
3. Discuss the interplant problems that arise in multiplant operation.
4. Under what circumstances would you recommend vertical integration?
5. Discuss the position of parts makers as distinguished from finished assembled products makers.
6. Under what conditions should a manufacturing company *not* own all of the assets it needs to do business? Which assets would you not own? Why?
7. Some companies (particularly defense industries) sell most of their output to the government. How does that affect their operations as compared to manufacturing for private business customers?
8. The text says to mechanize if your figures show it to be a tossup as far as saving money is concerned. What justification is given?
9. Is it ever wise to expand when building prices are high? Under what conditions?

CASE 5–1.   THE WATERMAN CHAIR COMPANY

The Waterman Chair Company employs 20 men. Its sales amount to $250,000 a year, but the profit margin is very narrow. The factory is a two-story frame building hemmed in by railroad tracks and warehouses. The product is a line of sturdy chairs (made of wood) such as are used in committee rooms and in school classrooms where movable seats are desired. For many years the volume of business has been steady and production has been at capacity. Unexpectedly the chairs have recently gained in popularity, and orders warranted a doubling of capacity.

Waterman has always bought good quality lumber in carload lots, then piled it out of doors with air spaces between the boards. The lumber is allowed to dry for almost a year. Then it is run through a dry kiln to remove every drop of moisture. After that it is cut and fashioned into chair parts. Chairs are assembled as orders are received.

Doubling the capacity of the factory would require a new site and new machinery. Modern woodworking machinery would have much greater capacity than the present out-of-date machines. Even though the output might be doubled, new machines probably would be idle three fifths of the time. Moreover, moving to a larger site, building a new factory, and installing modern equipment would require $150,000 of new capital. The owners do not have the capital and do not want to bring in outsiders.

An alternative to expanding facilities would be to farm out some of the operations. A lumber company in Tennessee (The Waterman Chair Company is located in Ohio) has the facilities and is willing to cut and mill the parts. Removal of lumber storage from the chair factory would make space for expanding assembly operations. Advantages of solving the problem in this manner seem to be: Volume could be doubled with a minimum of changes in the present facilities; half the work force could be dismissed; inventory of lumber could be reduced from a year's supply to 60 days' supply; the fire hazard would be reduced, resulting in a lowering of insurance rates; less electrical power would be purchased; capital turnover would be faster.

Point out any fallacies in the foregoing arguments. List as many arguments as you can against the proposed solution. If the arguments against overbalance the arguments for, suggest a more reasonable policy.

Chapter 6

MANUFACTURING ECONOMICS

INCOME TAX CONSIDERATIONS

Federal income taxes are high for companies that make much money. In 1956, General Motors made $1,740,000,000 but paid $890,000,000 of it to Uncle Sam. No one is required to carry on his business in such a way as to pay the most taxes, so when you have choices you ought to consider the tax angle.

Later in this chapter we discuss depreciation and how exaggerating it (the law allows you to exaggerate depreciation a little) saves taxes —at least today, even though they probably even out in the long run. Your machinery buying and new factory building decisions are influenced by how they will affect your taxes.

Maintenance is another area where taxes affect decisions. During lean years with no profits you don't fix up or repair anything that you don't have to. You would probably do that just to conserve cash, regardless of income taxes. But income taxes are another reason for undermaintaining in bad years. The reason is that all maintenance costs in bad years come out of your own pocket. In good years if you don't spend money, it is left over as profits and Uncle Sam takes half of it. So, do your maintenance work in good years because half of the expense is tax savings.

The Bureau of Internal Revenue knows this too of course and won't let you charge big expenses all to one year. A new roof on your factory building, for example, can't all be charged to one year. That is a "betterment" and must be shown as an asset and depreciated over several years. But in spite of BIR restrictions, you can in profitable years take care of lots of little things in the way of maintenance and do it with cheap dollars. Of course, if you make money every year, it doesn't matter much when you do things, although it does if you get into higher *tax rate* brackets some years than others.

Many research costs are like maintenance. In good years, go ahead with things that might not pay off, but don't go ahead with that kind of research in bad years. When income taxes were highest in the 1940's, some companies paid over 80 cents out of their top profit dollars in taxes. Naturally research flourished, costing, as it did, only 20 cents to the company for every dollar spent.

High taxes also encourage other programs. Job evaluation plans, morale surveys, and even pension plans are reduced in cost by tax savings.

High income taxes slow down the growth of small companies. Most of today's big companies got big back in the days when taxes were low and they could plow back earnings into expansion. Income taxes also help highly profitable companies stay ahead of less profitable ones. A highly profitable company finds that tax savings pay for half of its research or the depreciation on new machines. A less profitable company, paying 30 cents out of each dollar as taxes, finds the tax savings carry less of its expense.

There isn't time here to go into all of the angles of how income taxes help set management decisions. But don't overlook the years when you lose money. If you make money some years and not in others, the tax laws give you a break. You can, to a limited extent, average out the figures, offsetting good and bad years and so pay less taxes. There are quite strict rules about how and when you can do it, but if you qualify, you can save taxes.

BREAK-EVEN CHARTS

Break-even charts (see Figs. 6–1 and 6–2) are supposed to be useful management tools. They show, in chart form, how much business a company needs to do in order to break even (the no-profit, no-loss point). And they also show how much profit and how much loss the company would have at any other business volume.

Figure 6–1 is a hypothetical break-even chart for a company without much machinery. Its fixed costs are small. Fixed costs (depreciation,

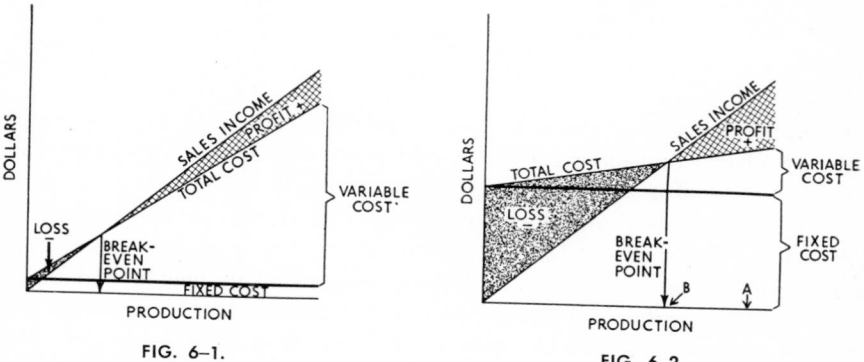

FIG. 6–1.   FIG. 6–2.

Figure 6–1 shows a company with low fixed expenses. Figure 6–2 shows a company with high fixed expenses.

insurance, property taxes, and so on) go on regardless of volume changes. Most of its total costs are "variable," meaning that they go up and down with changes in volume. Chiefly these costs are for labor and materials. Notice that this company will make some profit even at low volume levels. But notice, too, that profits are not enormous even at high production levels.

Now look at Figure 6–2. It could be the same company after buying a lot of laborsaving machines. Its fixed costs are high. It needs more business to break even. But its variable costs are low and profits high at *high production levels*.

Some people claim that break-even charts are very helpful in management's planning. Suppose that sales are now at point *A* on Figure 6–2. The chart shows that business can fall off to *B* before losses start.

It is claimed too that you can compare your company with competi-

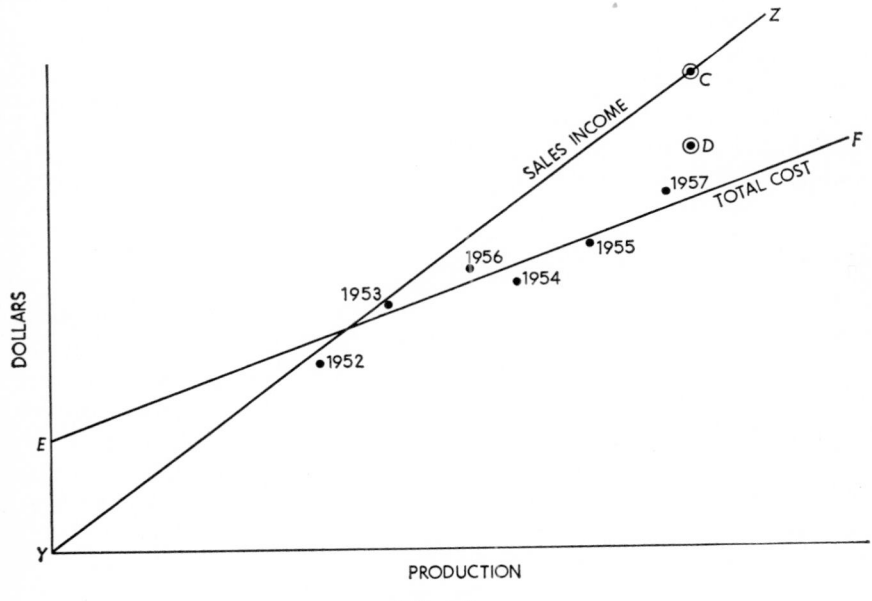

FIG. 6–3.

tors and see how you stand. You are supposed to be able to get enough information from published profit and loss statements to make charts of this sort for your competitors.

Actually industry does not use break-even charts very much. You can't make charts to compare yourself with your competitors because almost no one has a competitor whose business is directly comparable.

But worse—*you can't even construct a valid break-even chart for your own company.* If you make a chart using your own figures for recent years, you will get a series of dots as in Figure 6–3. You can then draw in a line representing sales income and another representing the costs you have incurred in these years. The two lines *EF* and *YZ* seem to tell you about how much your costs would be for all different sales volumes.

But they don't really tell you that. Actually, they tell very little about what your costs would be if sales went up or down. Look at Figure 6–3. You made up this break-even chart in January, using figures from past years. Now it is September. Your projection of this year's sales volume is *C*. Point *D* is your projected full year costs. Notice that *D* is not on line *EF*. Nor should it be, because line *EF* is based on *past* costs that were less inflated. Line *EF*, based on past experience, is actually of no value to you.

Suppose now that you forget past years and try to make a valid chart by starting fresh. First, find out what your present fixed costs come to and, on a new chart, Figure 6–4, plot point *G*. Then plot in point *D*

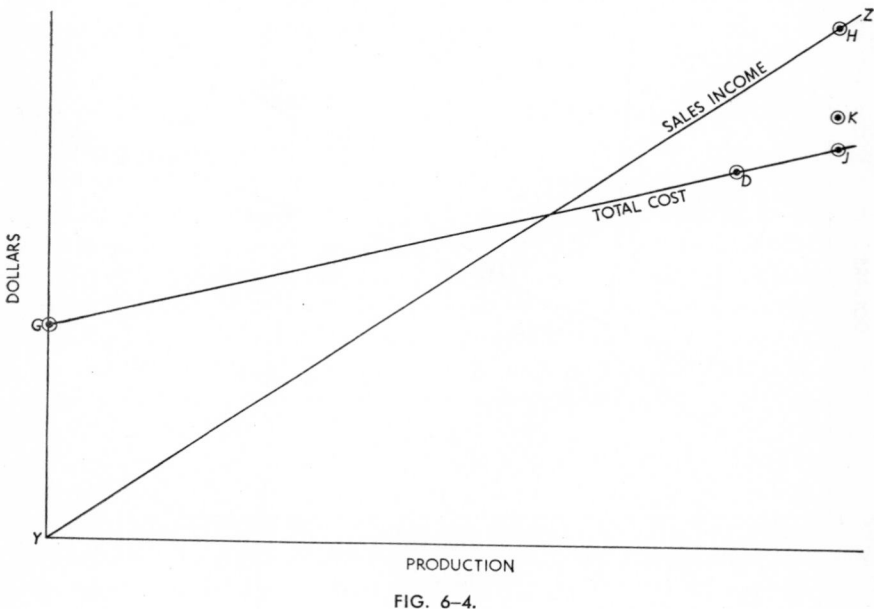

FIG. 6–4.

the same place it was on Figure 6–3. Now draw a line from *G* through *D*. Draw in also the income line *YZ*. Now you have a valid break-even chart—or do you? Let's project next year. Sales you expect to go up to *H*. The chart says that costs will go up to *J*. They will, but they won't stop there. They'll go higher because you will give your employees a pay raise and your suppliers who do the same will raise their prices for products you buy. So your next year's costs are likely to be at *K* instead of at *J*. Even your new chart is no good as a forecaster of costs and profits.

What if next year promises to be a poor year? You'd surely be wrong if you expected costs to slide down on line *GJ*. Just as in the case above, they would be higher than what you'd expect from line *GJ*. Not only will labor and materials rates be higher but many of your other supposedly variable costs will prove very hard to cut. It would take an all-out cost-cutting drive to get costs down to near line *GJ* even if labor and material prices stayed the same.

The cost part of break-even charts is only half the story. Income, the other half, is always in a state of flux. Break-even charts show how sales volume goes up and down *as if prices don't change*, but prices do change. That makes the income line unreliable. Also the product mix changes. If sales shifted from low profit margin items to high profit items, you'd have more profits even if total sales volume stood still.

So you find that the income line on your break-even chart is not much more reliable than the cost line. And because neither the income line nor the cost line is reliable, you can't learn a great deal from a break-even chart.

REGULARITY OF OPERATIONS

Long-term ups and downs in a company's business are partly reflections of general business conditions and cannot be wholly controlled by the company's administration. But seasonal ups and downs are more predictable. Because they are predictable, a company can sometimes produce fairly steadily in spite of them. If you expanded and contracted production with sales, your plant would have to be big enough to take care of peak sales, but you wouldn't work at 100 per cent much of the time. Operating that way would be very wasteful. Besides, you couldn't keep an efficient work force with such on and off employment.

Operating steadily is fine from the production point of view, but you can't forget money. Take autos for example. The late fall and winter months are low months, then sales pick up. Imagine Chevrolet making 50,000 extra cars in October, November, and December just to keep producing steadily! By the end of December it would have 150,000 cars on hand. Even at only $1,000 each, $150,000,000 would be needed to carry the inventory. By the first of April the inventory would be up to 300,000 cars and $300,000,000. Imagine too the size of the parking lot for all these cars and the condition of the last of them by the time they were sold in the summer.

Besides the staggering investments, look what happens if the market drops off. If car sales in the spring don't come up to what you expect, you have to cut back production, and even then it will take several months to clear the inventory. Such miscalculations can bankrupt companies. No company really knows for sure just what volumes it will sell. That, coupled with inventory carrying costs, limits stock piling, which means that you cannot have steady production and fluctuating sales at the same time.

But can't a company do anything to regularize production? Yes: (1) it can do a little stock piling; (2) it can try to stimulate sales in off seasons; (3) it can try to hold back some peak season business, promising later delivery and hoping that business will not be lost; (4) it can diversify—go into businesses whose peaks and valleys dovetail; (5) it can increase and decrease shop work hours; (6) it can hire or lay off some of its men as work goes up and down; and (7) it can farm out extra work during peaks and bring that business back in slack periods.

How effective are all these measures? No one of them can be carried far enough to be wholly effective by itself, but put all of them together and you get quite a leveling out in up and down production. But with big sales peaks and valleys you can't escape hiring and expansion, on the one hand, and layoffs and short hours, on the other hand.

Some people have a lot of faith in diversification with dovetailing peaks and valleys. That works pretty well as far as the company's finances are concerned. When one division is down, another is up, and the other way around. So things level out. But that isn't of much help to employees. GM's Chevrolet division might be down when GM's Frigidaire sales are booming. But you can't temporarily transfer men from Detroit to Dayton and from cars to refrigerators. You have to try to level out production in other ways.

INTENSIVE OR EXTENSIVE USE OF FACILITIES

A small plant operated day and night can turn out as much as a larger plant operating only one shift. Using a small plant all the time is using it *intensively*. Using a larger plant with a normal one-shift operation can be called *extensive* use.

Most manufacturing companies (excluding those whose processes require continuous operation for 24 hours a day) can operate 8, 16, or 24 hours a day. A plant operating 8 hours a day needs to be nearly three times as large as one in 24-hour operation in order to produce the same daily output. Similarly, operations can be carried on for 7, 6, or 5 days a week. The fewer hours you work, the bigger the plant you need for a given output.

Operating a small plant long hours looks like the best deal because the overhead costs per unit of product are reduced; but actually most of the time it costs less to operate a larger plant for fewer hours. Common practice is to have a plant big enough to take care of normal needs when operating 8 hours a day, 5 days a week.

Although single-shift production requires a bigger plant than 24-hours-a-day production, *equipment depreciation costs per unit of product may be about the same either way*. Three-shift operations permit one machine to produce almost as much as three machines would produce in one shift; but a machine used for 24 hours a day lasts only about one third as long as a machine used for 8 hours a day. Over the years about the same number of machines will have to be bought, so that the machine costs per unit may be almost the same either way.

Many overhead expenses, such as building depreciation, insurance, taxes, interest on investment, and obsolescence of machinery, are reduced when a small plant is used intensively. Also electric power can sometimes be bought at low rates during the third shift. But three-shift operation has costly disadvantages that often more than offset the gains. Second- and third-shift employees are paid higher hourly rates and generally are a little less productive than first-shift workers. Labor costs per unit of product are, therefore, higher. Six- and seven-day-week operations mean higher labor costs because overtime must be paid for Saturday and Sunday work and average hourly output is somewhat reduced because of the long work week.

Maintenance is easier with one-shift, 5-day operation than with three-shift, 7-day operation. Most repairs can be done in off hours with no interference to production. Less intensive use of the plant also permits you to expand production during peak periods with little increase in overhead costs because you don't have to expand the plant. When normal production calls for single-shift, 5-day operation, you are able to operate an additional shift or to work regular employees overtime for short periods, but there is no possibility of handling peak loads in plants already operating the maximum number of hours.

Many companies use parts of their plants intensively and other parts extensively at the same time; they buy the fewest possible of very expensive machines and operate them two or three shifts, while other machines work only the normal first shift.

Some companies use individual pieces of equipment intensively within the established work week by running machines as fast as they will go. The speed may be considerably faster than the machine manufacturer's recommendation—in fact, may be somewhat injurious to the machine. A company overspeeding its machines does not expect them to last their normal lives, but by pushing them to their limits, it increases output for the time being and lessens the number of machines needed. The investment in equipment, the space requirements in the plant, and the danger of obsolescence are all reduced. So the company is ahead if the gains more than offset the extra repairs and early wearing out caused by overworking the machine.

HOURS OF WORK AND OPERATING EFFICIENCY

As a rule, the fewer hours a man works in a week the more he turns out *per hour*. The difference is marked when you talk of long hours (50 hours a week and up). But as you cut from 50 to 40, the hourly increase in production is small, and it is doubtful if it goes up much when you cut below 40 hours.

We said earlier that most companies work a 40-hour week. Is that the best as far as labor costs are concerned? Yes. Roughly, here is how hours and productivity are related. Call a man's production in a 40-hour week 100 per cent. Put hours up to 48 (up 20 per cent) and you get only 17 or 18 per cent more *total* output because his *per hour* production will fall off a little. Now, go on up to 56 hours, and hourly output falls off considerably. Studies show that the long hours and fatigue of a 56-hour work week will cut hourly production down to 80 to 85 per cent of what you got working 40 hours. You'll do well if your 40 per cent increase in hours worked nets you 20 per cent more output.

What is the optimum? It depends on what you want, the most product possible regardless of labor cost or the lowest labor cost per unit. Almost always you want the lowest unit cost.

For men, somewhere around 56 hours a week (less on heavy jobs) gets the most total product. For women, somewhere around 52 hours is tops for quantity. Much depends on other things. How tiring is the job? Are the workers on piecework? Are they paced by machines? How long have the long hours been going on?

But if you want the *lowest unit cost*, stick to 40 hours, because long hours cut hourly output and because they have to be paid for at time-and-a-half pay rate (or even double time sometimes). Let's use an example. A man turns out 100 pieces an hour during a 40-hour week on a $2.00 an hour wage. So you get 4,000 pieces for $80; 2.0 cents each.

Now go up to 48 hours. Hourly production will drop a little, not just in the extra 8 hours but in the first 40 hours as well. Normally the hourly production will stay up around 98 per cent of the 40-hour figure. So we get 98 pieces per hour for 48 hours, or 4,704 pieces. Forty-eight hours of work (all over 40 is overtime) cost us 52 hours of pay, or $104. So we have 704 extra pieces for 24 extra dollars. The extra pieces cost us 3.4 cents each, *an increase of 70 per cent over 2.0 cents!*

Now go on up to 56 hours. By now hourly production is falling fast. Eighty-five per cent of the 40-hour level is a reasonable expectation. This gives us 85 × 56, or 4,760 pieces. For 56 hours we pay 64 hours pay, or $128. Now we have 760 extra pieces for which we paid $48 more wages. These extra pieces cost us 6.3 cents each— *over three times* as much as our regular 40-hour unit cost.

Small wonder most companies work a 40-hour work week. It seems anticlimactic to add that a 40-hour week also cuts accident rates and makes less absenteeism.

The future may change all this. Unions are talking shorter work weeks. If they get down to 35 hours or less, a new problem arises. A man's job is really only part time. Some men ("moonlighters," the unions call them) get ambitious and take on two jobs. And even those with one job do more work around home or move out onto a small farm near town and farm on the side. In many cases all these extras take more time and energy than the man's main job, so instead of producing more per hour worked, he produces less. It remains to be seen how shorter work weeks pan out.

First-shift (the day shift) production costs less than second-shift production. The night shift has more new men than the day shift, and both absenteeism and turnover (men quitting) are higher. Also night men do too much during the daytime and come to work tired. All of this cuts efficiency and boosts costs.

Night-shift work is likely to be only 85–90 per cent as efficient as day-shift work. Sometimes this does not show in the records, however, because troublesome jobs are all done on the first shift. Night men get chiefly easy jobs and long runs.

Night men are paid a "shift differential," an extra wage over day men. It comes to about 5 per cent. Add together lower output and higher wages and you will find that products made at night cost maybe 20 per cent more than products made on the day shift.

The effect of hours on efficiency has to be a secondary consideration in many situations. Whole work crews are often necessary. If you want 5 per cent more production, you can't get it by putting on 5 per cent more men. Instead you have to get it by having everyone put in enough more time to get out 5 per cent more work. Same thing when cutting. It takes full crews to operate. To cut, you have to cut everyone a little and not just lay off one or two men and let the rest work regular hours.

MAKE OR BUY?

Make or buy is vertical integration on a small scale. Make or buy is specific—this item, this order. Do you make it yourself or buy it? In general the pros and cons are the same as they are for vertical integration. They do not need repeating here.

But there are some differences. For example, you often make *and* buy at the same time. You make a part of what you need in your own plant and buy the rest outside. Sometimes you concentrate on making particular items while buying other items outside. Sometime which to make and which to buy is almost immaterial—you have the machines and the know-how to make the things you buy.

Why buy when you can make? (Remember, usually you make more money on what you make than on what you buy.) First, you are sometimes too busy and can't make everything you would like. Second, two sources of supply give you insurance. On difficult-to-make items this is important. A machine breakdown stopping one source won't close you down. Third, outside price competition helps keep you sharp on costs.

Making and buying at the same time has some disadvantages. It cuts the volume for both the inside department and for the outside maker. Cutting the volume may raise unit costs a little. Besides you need two sets of tooling, gages, and so on. And it may be hard to get both sources making the products *exactly* alike.

Sometimes you buy what you could make because the seller does it better and cheaper than you can. The A. O. Smith Company makes lots of automobile frames for big car manufacturers. The car makers could and do make most of their frames, but they still buy from A. O. Smith. Ford once tried making auto tires but went back to buying.

Make-buy decisions are influenced by the amount of money involved. Most metalworking companies could make the paper clips they use in their offices, but for $10 or $20 a year it isn't worth the bother. But add a few zeros and you get a different answer. One air rifle manufacturer, over the years, changed from wooden gun stocks (which he made) to plastic stocks (which he bought) for all his models of guns. One day he woke up to the fact that he was buying over $1,000,000 worth of plastic gun stocks a year. He soon decided to look into the plastics business himself.

Make-buy decisions on specific items often depend on work loads. When you are very busy, send lots of orders out. When orders are slack, bring them back. That lets you operate more evenly. As you go from boom to slack and back again the make-buy decisions become matters of priority. Which products go our first? Which last? Which come back first? Which last?

Usually you should send out the easy jobs first because vendors won't have trouble with them. But if you have had trouble making certain items and can find a really capable vendor, or if your costs are high, you might send the troublesome items out first.

Make or buy decisions for many individual items are often only today's decisions. They are not intended to be permanent; in fact, they may change tomorrow, and later change back again. Decisions about vertical integration on the large scale are more enduring. Some of them are never changed.

LOT OR CONTINUOUS MANUFACTURING

Products that have a continuing market can be made in lots or continuously. When made in lots, a large enough number to last for a while are processed together. They are put into stock and used to fill sales orders as they come in. Between lots no more are made. The machines on which they were made are used to make other products, also made in lots.

Continuous manufacture means making them all the time. Every day

100 or 500 or whatever is needed are made. The daily needs are forecast, and production is smoothed out at a given number daily. The machines used are used for that one kind of product only.

Assembled products are often put together continuously. Detroit's automobile assembly lines are classics in continuous assembling. Every 2 minutes a completed car rolls off the end of every assembly line. *Parts* for assembled products are, however, not often made continuously even in the automobile industry.

Processing and semiprocessing industries also use continuous manufacture. Continuous strip rolling mills are common in steel making (a semiprocessing industry). In less than one minute they make a steel billet a foot or more thick into a strip of steel $\frac{1}{20}$ of an inch thick, several feet wide (or whatever thickness and width you want) and hundreds of feet long.

Chemicals and oil refineries are examples of continuous manufacture in purely processing industries. Processing goes on inside tanks, vats, pressure vessels, and the like, and the materials go from one processing step to another in pipes and ducts.

Making products continuously calls for using equipment to make just one kind of product all the time. The machines are designed especially for the one job they are to do. This means a high first cost for machines. Setting up for continuous manufacture takes money and lots of it.

Continuous *assembly* does not cost so much, however. It is a matter of putting pieces together, fastening bolts, soldering wires, welding, and so on. Usually all it takes is hand tools, and they do not cost much. So continuous assembly is common.

But making *parts* continuously is another matter. Here is where the expensive machines come in to stamp, forge, shear, drill, bore, tap threads, plane, grind, hone, or otherwise give a piece of metal the shape, size, contour, and surface you want it to have. Of course if you make enough products to keep machines busy doing just certain operations on certain parts, you might as well have machines especially designed for just that work.

And if that happens for several successive operations, it is just a step farther to line up the machines next to each other and have a continuous production line. Of course there are problems. The rate of output of successive machines must be equal or some will be idle part of the time.

The next step, automatic transfer machines, is but a short step beyond lining up the machines. Put the product on a conveyor which moves it to the first machine, stops it there while the machine does its work, moves it on to the second machine for operation two, then on to operation three, and so on. All of this is of course automatic, but it is called automatic transfer machines, not automation.

Transfer machines are almost, but not quite, automation. Automation is the last stage. Design the machines so that they automatically inspect the product—check the dimensions—right along the line. If a machine turns out products barely passable, the inspecting part of the machine tells the operating part of the machine and it adjusts its tools so that the next products will be better. If the operating part of the machine doesn't get things fixed up, the inspecting part of the machine stops everything until a man fixes things right. This is automation.

What happens when you redesign your product? *You don't redesign your product* unless you are willing to spend a great deal of money. Many of your special machines and accessories go with the old design and are of no use for the new design.

Management has to decide whether it will go into automation, or stop with continuous production short of automation, or just make things in lots. Automation costs the most of all to start with but produces at the lowest unit costs *if* you have high volume and standardization. Continuous production short of automation costs less to start with but will never, at high volumes, get costs per unit down quite as low as automation. At the other extreme, making things in lots takes much less investment but at high volumes has much higher unit costs. But for flexibility and change with lower fixed costs, choose lot production.

Job-lot production versus continuous production is more than a matter of volume, standardization, and fixed costs. If management changes from lot to continuous production or automation, it must learn to do new things—not just to do old things better. It must forecast its business, and do it well. Of course, forecasting ought to be done in job-lot manufacture, but it isn't a must.

Also, if continuous production is to pay, you must consider production costs when you design your product. You can't have too many frills when you design a product with low-cost production in mind. You must give up some on variety and accept standard products.

Management must also go in for *preventive* not just *remedial* maintenance. It must try to foresee machine breakdowns and repair machines before they break down. *If management does not do all of these things, it may find its costs of continuous manufacture higher than they were with job lots.*

Sometimes management is almost forced into continuous production or even automation. It may hardly have a choice. If that is the way your competitors make their products you may have to make your products the same way or you will never meet their low costs.

ECONOMIC LOTS

If the decision is to make parts or products in lots and not continuously, the next question is: How many should be made at a time? Only a few at a time and frequent new lots? Or large lots less frequently? These are not idle questions because you get different unit costs, depending on how many units are made at a time. The number to make in one lot to get the lowest unit costs is called the "economic lot." It is discussed on pages 743–45.

DEPRECIATION

Machines and buildings wear out or "depreciate" day by day. Their value goes down. You know that this happens so you plan for their continual replacement.

Depreciation is not so simple as it at first sounds, and you need to understand it. When a man speaks of depreciation, he may mean the *loss in value* between a machine's cost and its present value. Or he may be talking about the physical *wear and tear* rather than the decline in value. Or he might mean something still different—*the proportion of its total benefits used up.* All of these uses are found. Or he may be referring to the *total depreciation* since the item was bought, or he may be talking about just *this year's decline* in value or *this year's physical wear.*

Besides all of these possible meanings of depreciation, you also have to understand "obsolescence"—meaning that new machines outdate old machines. Value declines are not always wholly depreciation. Obsolescence, as an idea, is easy enough to understand, but it is hard to know what to do about it in your accounts.

Suppose that there is a new and better machine than the one you bought last year—*but that you don't buy it.* If you don't sell your last year's car when this year's new model comes out, have you suffered any obsolescence? Suppose that you drive your old car 10 years. During that 10 years its value goes down, but is the loss in value obsolescence or depreciation? What about a factory machine? If the company uses it for years even though new and better machines are available, what do you call the machine's loss in value?—depreciation or obsolescence?

A purist would probably say that the moment a new and better machine comes out, it obsolesces all old ones—maybe not making them worthless but worth less. He, the purist, would say that this sudden loss in value is obsolescence and that it should be put into the company's records that way as a present loss. From now on the machine should be valued at a smaller amount (perhaps its market price if sold now), and future depreciation charges should be based on that amount.

In practice businessmen don't try to separate obsolescence and depreciation unless something drastic happens. If a company builds a factory to make propellers for airplanes and then jet planes become dominant, it loses a lot of money fast. It will probably never get to wear out the machines that make propellers. Its loss on these machines is nearly all obsolescence, with only a little of it being depreciation. But, except for such extreme cases, businessmen call all the decline in value depreciation even though they know full well that sometimes part of it is obsolescence.

Value. Mixing in obsolescence isn't the only thing that complicates a discussion of depreciation. "Value" is another complication. Remember, depreciation, bookkeeping-wise, is loss in value—but to find that out you have to know today's value of a machine. You know what the machine cost when it was new, but what is its value today? If you can't tell that, you can't tell how much depreciation has occurred.

How about using market value? At first that sounds like a good idea, but try it out. What is the value of the elevator that you put in 5 years

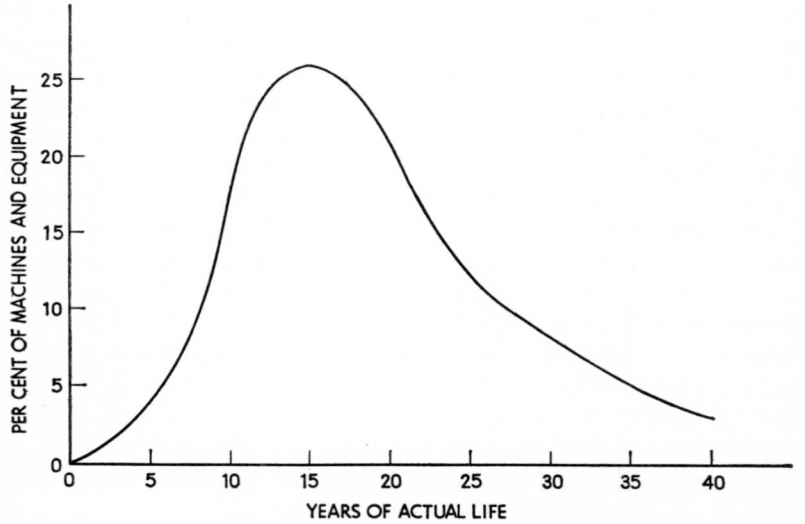

FIG. 6–5.   The Machinery and Allied Products Institute's estimate of actual life of machinery and equipment.

ago? It cost $100,000 and still runs well. How much are the fifty file cases in the offices worth? Some are old, and some not so old. They are of several kinds and were bought over the years at different prices. Also prices are higher today than when you bought most of them. Or how much is a blast furnace worth? Not so much to someone who would have to dismantle it and cart it away—not nearly so much as to you left where it is.

See the trouble? You just can't get a market-value figure that amounts to anything. For many items you could go out to used machinery dealers and get prices, but it would be a big job. And for other items you just couldn't get a good estimate of market price at all. Besides this would have to be done every year to see how much each year's added depreciation comes to. If prices in general went up, there might be no depreciation at all (possibly a profit). That would happen if the machines were worth more at the year's end in spite of their being a year older and more worn. Or if prices in general went down, there might be a year with three or four times the usual depreciation. Such irregularities would make annual profit figures meaningless.

Besides all of the reasons given above for not using market value, the federal government will not allow you to handle depreciation that way when you make out your profit and loss statement for income taxes.

DEPRECIATION METHODS

Pointing out that depreciation is complicated solves no business problems. Businessmen still have to show on their accounts a money-value figure for depreciation every year. And the way the businessmen keep their accounts must satisfy the United States Bureau of Internal Revenue, too. This is because of the tie-in between costs (including depreciation), profits, and income taxes.

The Bureau of Internal Revenue wants everyone to depreciate everything over its full life. Because no one really knows how long things will last, business practice is to write them off on a minimum—not a maximum—life expectancy. This means claiming that the machines won't last long and claiming full depreciation in just a few years.

Straight-Line Method.   Historically the straight-line method has been much the most common method for figuring depreciation. You take a machine's installed cost, minus its scrap value at the end of its useful life, and divide by the number of years it will be used. A $10,000 machine, expected to last 10 years and guessed to be worth $1,000 then as scrap, will have $900 depreciation every year. Straight-line depreciation is one of the methods that the BIR approves.

In practice probably no company depreciates every machine separately. Instead they are grouped into life groups. All machines with 10-year life expectancies are in one class in the accounts. Every time a new 10-year life machine is bought, its cost is added to the total for all 10-year life machines, and every year 10 per cent of the total value is written off ("charged" to that year) as depreciation.

There need to be several life classes: 5 years, 10 years, 15 years, and so on. But there are not thousands of separate depreciation accounts—not one for every machine.

Double-Declining Balance Method.   Using this method, you depreciate an item by a certain percentage of the balance every year. For simplicity in our example, let's leave out any scrap value when the machine wears out. As above, let's start with a $10,000 machine that you think will last 10 years. Use a 20 per cent depreciation rate. Take 20 per cent of $10,000 ($2,000) as the first year's depreciation. Beginning the second year the machine is carried on the books at $8,000; now, take 20 per cent of that ($1,600) as the second year's depreciation. The third year, take 20 per cent of $6,400.

You see what is happening? You get to take heavy depreciation in the early years of an asset's life, yet you take less and less as time goes along. This method never gets rid of all the value. That is why you might well neglect a machine's final value as scrap. When you finally scrap the machine, the remaining book value of the machine may be about the same as what you get for it.

Our examples above used 10 per cent of the first cost for straight-line depreciation and 20 per cent of the remaining value for the double-declining balance method. Could you have used 30 per cent? No. If you want to use the double-declining balance method, the highest percentage that the Bureau of Internal Revenue will allow is double the straight-line per cent. That is where the term "double-declining balance" comes from. So, in our example we couldn't go over 20 per cent, but we could have used 18, 15, or any other lower percentage if we had wanted to. You don't have to depreciate at the highest possible rate.

Sum-of-the-Digits.   Another method is the "sum-of-the-digits." Take a 5-year life item: Add $5 + 4 + 3 + 2 + 1$, get 15. In the first year, depreciate the item $5/15$ of its cost, next year $4/15$, and so on. For a 10-year life item the sum of the digits is 55, so the first year's depreciation is $10/55$ of its cost.

There are still other methods of depreciation, but no others are common in most manufacturing.

Both the double-declining balance method and the sum-of-the-digits make group depreciation more difficult. You can't mix up items bought in 1950 with those bought in 1955 as you can in straight-line depreciation. To use group depreciation with either, you'd have to have groups for every year. All new 5-year life machines bought in 1957 could be thrown together, so could 1957 purchases of 10-year life machines.

Both methods, too, get a little complicated if you follow the usual accounting simplification of asssuming that everything bought in a year was bought on July 1. You start off with one-half year's depreciation. That's all right. But next year you have to take one half of the first whole year's depreciation plus half of the second year's depreciation to get that year's depreciation. It can be done, but it is a little complicated.

DEPRECIATION CASH

Students sometimes miss the point that depreciation provides cash to the company. In 1956, depreciation brought in $350,000,000 cash to General Motors.

Here's how depreciation provides cash. Suppose you take a machine, bought and paid for several years ago. It has been and is still in use. At the end of last year it was worth less than it was at the beginning of the year—let's say $1,000 less. That is the depreciation.

Now suppose that during the year you sold $1,000,000 worth of products. Your costs come to $900,000, leaving a profit of $100,000. Then you paid $50,000 income taxes (we'll use a 50 per cent rate for simplicity—the actual rate may be more or less). That left you with $50,000 of cash from profits. One of the items in your list of costs that added up to $900,000 was $1,000 for the wear and tear on the machine we are talking about. Aside from this particular machine, your costs totaled $899,000, sales came to $1,000,000, and after taxes you had left $51,000 cash, or $1,000 more cash than the total of your retained profits. Remember: *you did not spend that $1,000 for the machine this year.* It is a decline in value of the machine which you recovered in cash.

That goes on all the time for all machines every year. *Depreciation*—thinking of it from the bookkeeping point of view—*is a conversion of an asset from one form to another*—in our example, from machine value to cash.

Now, of course, every year some machines come to the end of their lives and can't be used any longer. Some new machines have to be bought to replace them. Most depreciation cash doesn't lie around long. Most of it goes right back into new machines.

But—and this is important—*depreciation money is cash.* In your bank account depreciation dollars and profit dollars look alike. You can't tell one from the other (although you have to show them separately in your profit and loss statement to comply with the law). You can spend your cash (whatever its source) for machines, inventory, buildings, wages—anything (except dividends; the law limits dividends to profit dollars). When U.S. Steel says it is spending $200,000,000 for some new factories, most of it is probably just reinvestment of depreciation cash, although of course retained profits are also put to work.

Depreciation cash does differ from profits cash in that you don't pay income taxes on it. Since you really are just changing the form of your assets, the government agrees and doesn't tax it. This is important because no one really knows exactly the money value of this year's wear and tear on a machine. So if you exaggerate the depreciation, you build up cash faster than if you don't.

Let's go back to our problem. Suppose that instead of $1,000 depreciation for this year on your machine you said $2,000. Our sales are still $1,000,000, no matter what you say about depreciation. But your claimed costs are now $901,000. Profits now seem to be $99,000, and so you pay $49,500 income taxes. The only thing that has really changed is the tax. You still have $899,000 of costs other than your machine depreciation; you paid $49,500 taxes; total, $948,500; leftover amount, $51,500.

By exaggerating the depreciation you have $500 more cash on hand.

But aren't we making a mountain out of a molehill? No—that $899,-000 is not nearly all cash cost. It contains quite a chunk of depreciation on other machines and on buildings. Maybe you really paid out only $800,000 during the year and all the rest of the original $900,000 of costs was depreciation. Our little example is magnified many times over when all the depreciation is considered. Conceivably you could exaggerate the depreciation on everything and get your claimed costs up to $1,000,000. Then you would pay no taxes and get to keep all the $200,000 difference between $800,000 and $1,000,000.

The Bureau of Internal Revenue knows all about this too and won't let you exaggerate very much. It can and will veto fast depreciation schedules. Also, remember, fast write-offs of depreciation exaggerate today's costs and save income taxes today; but tomorrow there is less left to write off so costs are less and profits and taxes higher.

The Bureau of Internal Revenue will approve slightly accelerated depreciation write-offs because it doesn't want businessmen ending up with worn-out equipment not yet fully depreciated on the company's books. The possibility of obsolescence too makes faster write-offs desirable.

Fast write-offs help conserve cash in another way too. Remember that depreciation cash is not paid out in either income taxes *or dividends*. It is kept in the company and reinvested in productive ways. But if lower depreciation charges are made and extra profits are shown, some of the extra cash is paid out as taxes *and some more of it will go out as dividends*. At least in the early years after buying machines, a policy of heavy depreciation keeps money from flowing out of the business.

Inflation.   Inflation throws normal depreciation practices into a cocked hat. Take as an example a machine bought in 1950 for $10,000 (a machine with an expected 10-year life). And suppose you actually set aside the $1,000 depreciation cash every year. By 1960 the machine would be worn out and you have your $10,000 for a replacement machine. *But*, by 1960, the replacement machine costs $20,000. Maybe you thought that you were making money in those 10 years. If you happened to lay aside some extra money, it is a good thing, because you will have to have $20,000 to buy another machine. So did you make very much after all?

U.S. Steel in 1957 wanted to replace a 25-year-old open-hearth steel plant that had cost $10 million in 1932. It found that it would cost 64 million 1957 dollars to do it. Thompson Products, in 1956, wanted to replace a Warner and Swazey lathe bought in 1942 for $12,000. It found that a replacement would cost $35,000. To make matters worse, 1956 needs were more exacting. The 1956 model to do exacting work was priced at $67,000.

Companies want, during inflationary periods, to depreciate on the *replacement* cost of a machine, but the government has turned thumbs down. Actually, depreciating on a replacement cost basis still fails to recover enough cash. Suppose that, in our example above, the replacement machine's cost went up in price $1,000 every year and that the government did allow depreciation on a replacement cost basis. Depreciation cash would have brought in $1,000 for the first year, $1,100 for the second, and so on. But go on like that for 10 years and you have only $14,500, not $20,000. To some extent, but not wholly so, the normal tendency to overdepreciate takes care of the trouble. Improvements in machines also helps. The 1960 $20,000 machine will do more work than the 1950 $10,000 machine.

STUDY QUESTIONS

1. "A sound business decision is sound or not regardless of income taxes." Discuss this statement.
2. Are you really money ahead to expand such things as maintenance in profitable years and to cut them to the bone in bad years? Explain.
3. Break-even charts sound like a good management tool, yet they are not used very much. Why not?
4. How does inflation affect the possibility of using break-even charts?
5. Would you expect the cost line on a break-even chart to be wholly valid as a predictor of costs if your volume fell off, say one third? Justify your answer.
6. If you were president of a company making cameras, with a high seasonal sales peak before Christmas and another in early spring, what would you try to do to give steady employment to your men?
7. Why do most companies normally operate only 40 hours a week? Explain fully.
8. What do you do and under what conditions would you use a plant "intensively"?
9. If shorter work weeks boost hourly production and cut unit costs, why not work only 30 hours instead of 40? Explain.
10. How costly (in direct labor costs) are long work hours?
11. Would you ever buy anything you could make? When?
12. When should you definitely buy and not make an item?
13. Where is continuous production (as contrasted with lot production) more common, in assembly or in parts manufacture? Why?
14. What is the difference between automatic transfer machines and automation?
15. Some people say that it is possible to increase your cash account even in years when you lose money. Can you? How?
16. Compare obsolescence and depreciation.
17. What is "group" depreciation? When would you use it?
18. Which method recovers more depreciation in 5 years (on a 10-year life item), straight-line or double-declining balance? Explain.
19. Would depreciation on a replacement value basis take care of the problems made by inflation? Explain.

Case 6–1. The Trimble Tool Works

The Trimble Tool Works manufactures large planers and milling machines for the aircraft industry. Most of its sales are special, made-to-order machines, costing up to $100,000 or more. The company has a near-monopoly on such machines and usually has up to 2 years' backlog of orders. Because the customer companies usually object to the long waiting, the sales department accepts orders and gives a 1-year promise date for delivery. Those dates are put on the orders received and forwarded to the factory. Rarely does a customer get his machine on time.

The Trimble company has considered allowing the Riddel Printing Press Company to make machines for them on a subcontract basis. The Riddel company is large enough to do the work and has a reputation for efficient operations and for meeting its promise dates.

Analyze the Trimble company's problem. What bad practices are evident? What good practices are evident? Should Trimble allow Riddel to make machines to fill Trimble's orders?

Chapter 7

MACHINES

GENERAL PURPOSE MACHINES

Gᴇɴᴇʀᴀʟ purpose" machines (as distinguished from "special purpose" machines) are designed to do a kind of work rather than one particular job. They are, however, "general purpose" only to a limited extent. A drill press is made to drill holes, not to polish flat surfaces. But with a drill press you can drill one or many holes, large or small, deep or shallow, in hard or soft material, and in any location with little more adjustment than changing drill bits.

General purpose machines are standardized machines and are made in quantity by machinery manufacturers. If you want one, you can usually order it from a catalogue and maybe get it shipped at once from stock.

To operate general purpose machines, you need skilled men. Skill is necessary to arrange holding blocks and devices on the machine so that the product is held in exactly the right position while the operation is performed. Skill is necessary to attach tools and accessories properly to the machine. Skill is necessary to place the material properly in the machine and to guide the machine and control it as the operation is being performed. Skill on the operator's part is necessary to judge (by gaging it and inspecting it) whether work is being done satisfactorily.

General purpose machines run more slowly than special purpose machines, and the operator has to put each separate product in and take it out of the machine. So you get far less output than from special purpose machines. Also your labor cost per unit of product is much higher, sometimes many times higher. Products of general purpose machines require more inspection than those of special purpose machines. The operator can do much of this inspection as he works, but since the machine is not automatic, more inspection of individual pieces is required. On special purpose automatic machines, if the first and last pieces produced on a run are good, it is practically certain that all others are all right. With general purpose

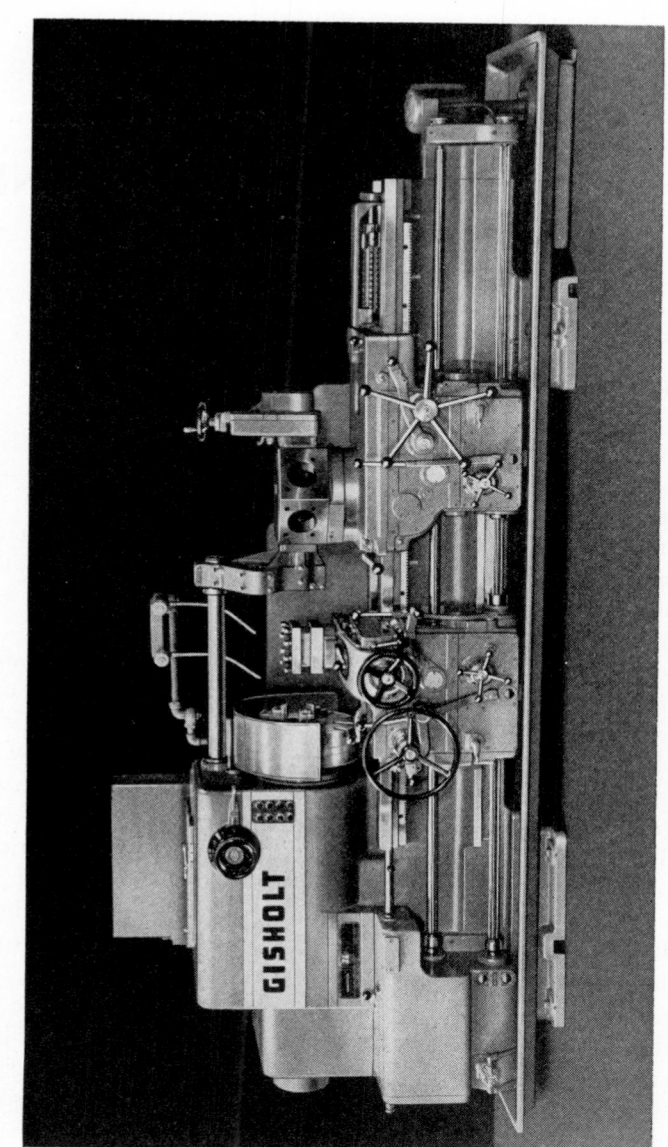

FIG. 7–1. A turret lathe, a standard general purpose machine.

machines the fact that one piece is satisfactory gives no certainty that the next one will be.

There is less risk of loss in the purchase of general purpose machines than in the purchase of special purpose ones because general purpose machines usually cost less per machine and because they can be used for varied jobs. Ordinary changes in product design do not make them obsolete. Furthermore, you can usually sell them as used machines.

As a rule, if the work is varied and if the volume on each lot of goods manufactured is small, you should always use general purpose machines. The cost per unit for product made on special purpose machines would be prohibitive on short runs because the machine cost (ordinarily high to start with) would be spread over so few units. With general purpose machines, which are used for years for hundreds of different orders, unit costs of products made in short runs are reasonable because only a small part of the machine's cost has to be carried by one order.

Maintenance costs are generally low on general purpose machines. The machines are usually fairly simple and can be overhauled easily. Repair parts are readily available. Special purpose machines are more complex, and since there are often only one or two of them in a production line, their breakdown is serious. Considerable preventive maintenance, therefore, is necessary to be sure that they do not break down during operations. Keeping the capacities of different types of equipment in balance is easier with general purpose than with special purpose equipment. Changes in product design in the sales of different products have less effect on the number of machines needed where general purpose machines are used.

SPECIAL PURPOSE MACHINES

Special purpose machines, designed to do specific operations, are better than general purpose machines in that they do the operations faster, better, and with less labor. Ordinarily, they run faster than general purpose machines because general purpose machines must run slow enough to let them handle heavy jobs sometimes. Also, most special purpose machines have exactly the right tool built in so that the product will be uniform and practically perfect. Automatic gaging devices and even automatic tool resetters are frequently built into the machine. It resets its tool if it gets out of adjustment. Nearly perfect quality is virtually assured, and inspection costs are low.

Special purpose machines invariably require but a fraction of the labor, per unit of output, needed for operating general purpose machines. The machine has its own work holders, so that the work is held in exactly the right position while the operation is performed. Machine setters set the machine up for the job, after which it will do nearly all the work. Products can be inserted and removed quickly by semiskilled workers. Indeed, the machines are often so automatic that they "feed" themselves and eject the product after the operation is performed. The worker needs only occasionally to fill a hopper, supply a roll of raw materials, or remove a tote pan of products on which the operation has been performed.

Individually, special purpose machines are generally larger than general purpose machines, but because of their productivity, you need fewer of them to turn out a given quantity of work. So you save floor space, even though the machine is bigger. Generally, too, special purpose machines cost more individually than general purpose machines, but, again, since

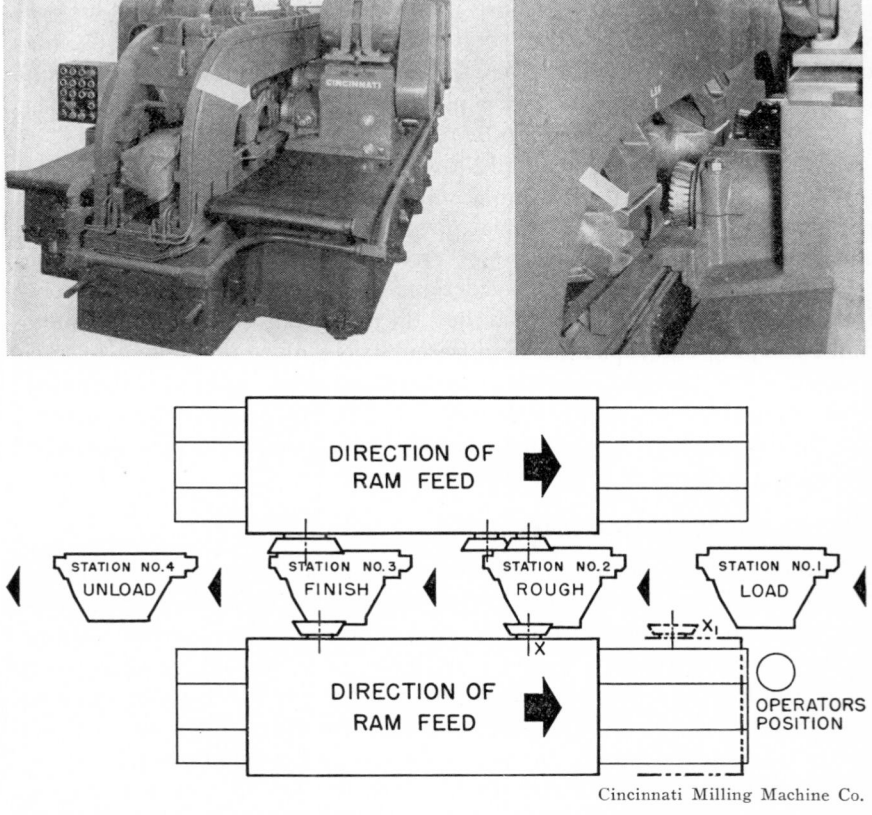

Cincinnati Milling Machine Co.

FIG. 7–2. A specialized milling machine set up to mill the front and back sides of steel castings at the same time. Arrows point to the castings held in place.

you need fewer, your investment in machines may be no higher than if you used general purpose machines. Don't count on this, however. It is nearly always much higher.

In spite of their productivity, be careful about buying special purpose machines. They are good for one thing and one thing only. Don't buy them unless you are pretty sure that you can use them enough to get your money back in the near—not the distant—future. This is very important in some industries. In automobile making, for example, tooling up (including buying hundreds of big special purpose machines) for a new model that will last for only one year may cost $50 million. Some of this tooling will be waste at the end of the year—whether it is worn out or not.

Naturally, you don't want to discard out-of-date expensive machines. Can you cut your loss any way? Often, yes. Make the machine with major sections that can be changed. Then you can convert it to do different (although similar) jobs. Automobile fenders, for example, are formed in huge presses holding removable dies. When models change, you take out the old model dies and put in the new. You still have a specialized machine but you don't have to buy the whole thing new every model change.

Automation is the 1950's' term for doing whole sequences of operations

SUCCEEDING OPERATIONS ON PRODUCTION LINE

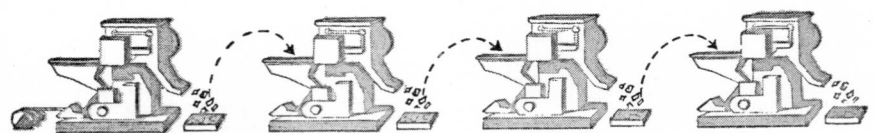

BEFORE   CONVEYORIZATION

UNIT AVAILABILITY = 90 % – LINE AVAILABILITY = 90 %

AFTER   CONVEYORIZATION

UNIT AVAILABILITY = 90 % – LINE AVAILABILITY = 55 %

E. I. Du Pont de Nemours & Co.

FIG. 7–3. Linking machines together in chain fashion may *lose* production for you, as Du Pont found out above.

automatically. Everybody thinks of it as new, but it is really new only in metalworking and assembly of machinery. Machines do whole sequences of operations—and have been doing them for years—in electric power production, oil refining, chemicals, paper making, and glass bottle making. The problems have, though, been so much more difficult in metalworking that up until the 1950's automatic operations have largely been confined to single machines.

Automatic "transfer" machines are the "almost automation" stage in metalworking (see Figs. 5–2 and 5–3, pages 102 to 104). An unfinished part, say a steel casting or a forging, is fastened to a conveyor which moves step by step from one machine to the next. The part stops long enough at each machine to have one or more operations performed on it. Separate machines performing successive operations are lined up on each side of the conveyor, and as the conveyor stops, each machine automatically reaches out and performs its operation on the part. As the operating parts on the various machines move back out of the way, the conveyor moves along another step, and the performance is repeated on the next units. The machines, though actually separate, are timed together to operate as if they were parts of one very complex single purpose machine. This machine grouping eliminates all product handling except the little that is needed before the first and after the last operation. Where the necessary volume is present, production at very low unit cost is possible.

Automation goes just a little further. Each of the machines that does its operation automatically has a "sensor" to check every operation all the time. The sensors continually *inspect* and *report* the dimension, weight,

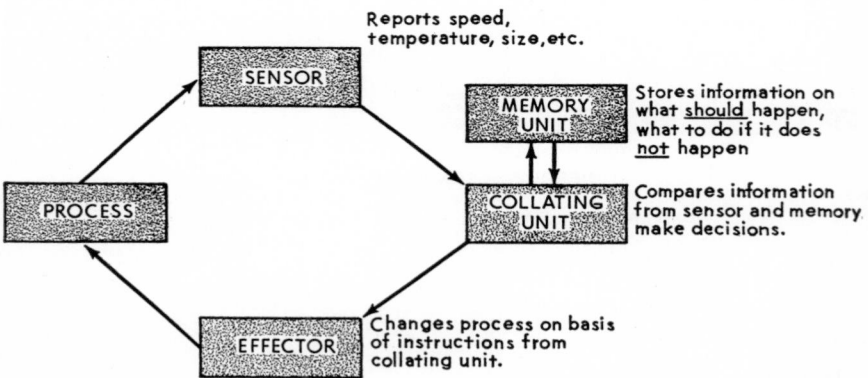

Factory Management and Maintenance

FIG. 7–4.   A schematic diagram of how a machine's operation can be controlled automatically.

thickness, hardness, or other characteristics of the products being turned out.

Besides sensors, today's automatic machines have "memory units" or master records of *what should be happening*, showing what the characteristics being measured should be. Next, the machine has to have a "collator" that *compares what is going on with what ought to be going on*. If the two are not the same, the machine has to figure out what to do and what changes to make to get back on the track. After all of this, the machine has to have "effectors" which *carry out the changes* and bring the operations into control again.

All this automatic activity requires a complex "nervous" system of electronic controls. Figure 7–4 is a schematic diagram of how this works. The machines electrical nervous system which does all this is called a "servo-system."

The more automatic the machines become, and the more costly, the greater is the temptation to keep a product's design frozen too long. The tremendous investment—some of which will be lost if anything is changed —makes a great temptation not to change. Not changing can be serious. You must have the courage and foresight, when product design changes are needed, to go ahead and change designs even if you have to junk some special machines. If you don't do this, your today's automated plant will still keep on running some day in the future long after it is just as out of date as some of our textile industry's plants.

COMBINATION GENERAL AND SPECIAL PURPOSE MACHINES

Production orders are sometimes for in-between quantities, not large, not small. They make long runs for general purpose machines, but they are not long enough runs to pay for special purpose machines. Is there an in-between area? Can you figure out some "half-special" machines? Generally, yes. General purpose and special purpose machines are not all black or white. There are shades of gray in-between—mostly you don't start with in-between machines, but you end up with them. The way to do it is to specialize general purpose machines or generalize special purpose machines. So much of this goes on that it is sometimes hard to tell

Mill and Factory

FIG. 7–5. A special machine tool attachment for a lathe so it can perform a grinding operation.

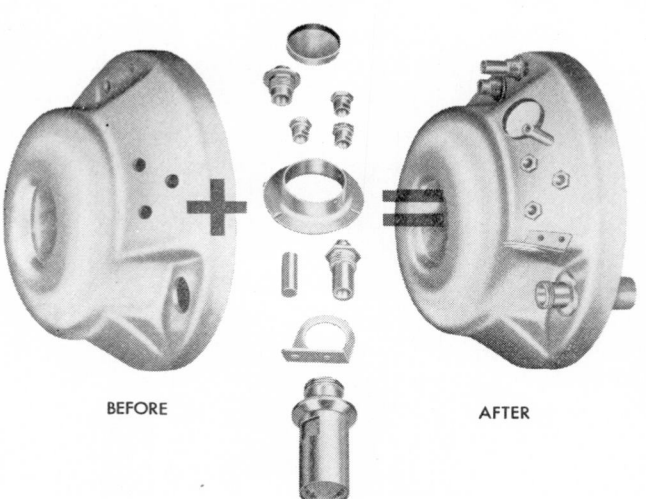

BEFORE   AFTER

National Electric Welding Machines Co.

FIG. 7–6. A merry-go-round automatic assembly machine. It assembles ten small parts into a refrigerator compressor housing and welds them in place at 360 housings per hour.

where a general purpose machine leaves off and a special purpose machine begins.

General purpose machines can be made into pretty good special purpose machines by adding attachments designed especially for the job. Special purpose machines can be made of combinations of standardized main parts. Take out some parts and put in others and you have a different special machine. Machines of wholly different types sometimes have interchangeable frames, beds, cylinders, pumps, electric and hydraulic controls, valves, coolant tanks, filters, etc. Combining these standard units in different ways lets you get partly specialized machines at low enough cost to use on medium quantity orders.

AUTOMATIC ASSEMBLY

The last frontier of handwork is assembly. Machines first took over the making of parts. Then advances were made in moving things mechanically from one operation to another. But putting finished pieces together is still handwork in most industries. Assembly lines for putting together airplanes, locomotives, automobiles, typewriters, adding machines, stoves, refrigerators, radios, television sets, and so on have been characterized by *people* putting things together.

Now assembly too is going mechanical. A supply of every part is loaded into its hopper (or magazine feed) located above an assembling machine along a conveyor. The first assembling machine along the line automatically picks out one of the frame parts of the product and fastens it on the conveyor. Then the conveyor "indexes" or moves it to the next work station (a foot or so away). There the next assembling machine picks out a part to be attached *and puts it into place in the frame.* Then the conveyor indexes again and moves the frame to the next station where part two is applied. Then more moves and more parts. Besides *placing* the parts, the machine *fastens* them there, so that finished assemblies come off at the end of the line. Whether you call all this one big machine or several little ones doesn't matter, you end up with the product put together *without* men doing it.

So far no one puts whole automobiles or any other whole big product together automatically, but small assemblies, yes. Probably you never will assemble very many whole products automatically, but the possibilities are great for small electrical products such as light bulbs, switches, telephone transmitters and receivers, radio tubes, radios, condensors, and the like. Also small mechanical products, such as scissors, wrenches, staplers, can openers, and a host of others.

TOOLING

The attachments, auxiliary equipment, and "gadgetry" needed to do operations on machines are called "tooling" or "jigs" or "fixtures." "Tooling" is a general term, including such items as cutting tools, grinding tools, hammering tools, heating tools, hand tools, gages, clamps, slides, chutes, automatic loading and unloading devices, powered chucks, transfer mechanisms, holders, jigs, fixtures, and templets. They may be standard or special and may be things that last or things that soon wear out.

Some attachments are designed to hold the product in exact position for an operation and to permit a worker to put the product in and get it out easily and quickly. Some attachments guide the tools. When a cover with a hole in it (technically a "jig") is put over a product to be drilled, all the operator has to do is to put the drill through the hole in the cover. The hole is sure to be drilled in the right place in the product. Other attachments allow two operations to be done in the time ordinarily taken by one. Still other attachments keep tools sharp or permit automatic gaging while the operation is in progress. If the run is long enough to justify the cost, automatic magazine feeds and automatic ejectors are useful.

The term "tooling up" is used in mass production to mean deciding on the equipment (machines, conveyors, hoisters, tanks, vats, ovens, etc.) itself as well as the accessories, getting and installing them, and making trial runs to eliminate the "bugs."

Special tooling often cuts the cost of an operation to a fraction of what it would otherwise be. But special tooling usually costs more than standard tooling and won't pay out on short runs. So you often have to use standard tooling even though it doesn't produce so fast. If you do decide on special tooling, making it yourself in your own toolroom will usually hold its cost down. Also, keep all old special tooling for a while. You may get a reorder of the product it was made for. Or you may get to reuse part of it on some future job, and so cut the cost of future tooling.

In choosing tooling it is important to reduce machine idle time caused by setting up machines. Design the tooling so that a worker can get it on and off the machine quickly. Idle machines—even when idle because of setup—make you no money. Also design the tooling so that it won't break down and lose operating time.

Standard tooling can often be bought from tooling manufacturers at reasonable prices. Specials come higher—so much higher that large companies make most of their own. Some companies make many of their standard tools as well. Large nut and bolt companies, for example, usually make their own taps for threading nuts and their dies for roll threading bolts.

Today's factory worker rarely owns any of the tools with which he works. Many factory jobs require the use of hand tools, gages, and so on as a regular part of the job, but they are generally company owned and are issued to the workers, who keep them in their possession. The company issues replacements when worn, or broken tools are returned to the toolroom.

Tool Control. Tools required for regular repetitive jobs are kept in the toolroom and are issued to the operator when he is ready to set up the job. Tools made up for single specific orders are sent to the job from the toolroom when the job dispatcher releases instructions for the job to proceed. While in use, the tools are charged to the operator. He may be required, as a receipt for them, to leave one of his tool tags or present a tool order which is filed by number so that the toolroom attendant knows at all times who has each tool. Usually such a checking system keeps tools from getting lost and keeps down both the inventory and consumption of expendable tools. After use, the returned tools are inspected and needed repairs made before they are put away.

Many companies have found that centralizing the sharpening of cutting tools is economical. The sharpening is usually done in the company toolroom by skilled workers. Carbide-tipped cutting tools, in particular, need more careful grinding than they usually get from machine operators.

Special as well as standard tools should have identification numbers, so that a record can be kept of the jobs for which each tool is used. If each tool has an identification number and if its storage place is entered on its tool record card, you can find it when you want to use it again for reorders. Identification numbers also make possible records of use, repairs, etc.

Tool costs are high in almost all companies, especially in those having varied products. But in spite of the high cost of tools you have to have enough of them (including extras of commonly used tools) so that men and machine won't be held up. Particularly, you don't want to hold up *machines* and get no output. When men are held up on a job, it isn't quite so bad. Often they can be put on other jobs.

Companies are becoming more conscious of tool costs than they used to be. Many companies keep detailed records of individual tools, their cost, repairs, and life. These help when you have to decide about new tools to buy or make.

Many companies, particularly small ones, are lax in caring for their tools. It is a costly luxury. Taking care of tools costs money but not taking care costs more. Expendable tools are too often wastefully used. Frequently cutting tools are carelessly ground and cutting edges of the wrong kind are put on them. Metal surfaces are sometimes bumped and scratched and allowed to rust in storage. Shops without a proper system of identification frequently lose tools. Then more time and money are lost locating them than would have been spent if they had been put away properly in the first place.

PORTABLE TOOLS

Portable tools are the rule rather than the exception in assembly work and in plant maintenance. Assembled products are often large and require welding, drilled holes, nut and bolt tightening, grinding, polishing, or spray painting, all of which can be done with portable tools. The assembler sometimes has to work in awkward positions and usually has to bring the tool to the place where the work is done. This differs from the usual manufacturing situation where the material is brought to the machine.

Most plant maintenance work must be done at the point of need, not in the maintenance department itself. Much maintenance work, therefore, requires the use of portable tools.

Portable power-driven tools are available for all the jobs listed above as well as for soldering, sawing, deburring, impact hammering, and many other jobs. Portable tools, to be effective, must be light in weight, so that the worker can handle them easily and can hold them in position while using them. Ordinarily, the weight of a power-driven portable tool plus the amount of hose or wire that must be lifted when the tool is used must be kept under 15 pounds if a man is to use it all day. Heavy portable tools tire the men out, and although you have to have them for some jobs, they are not practical for steady use.

Most portable power-driven tools have electric motors, usually within the tool itself, but they may be nearby on fixed mountings with flexible connecting shafts. Compressed air is also frequently used to power tools. Portable tools requiring no power are, for the most part, simple hand tools, of which there are hundreds of kinds. Generally it pays to replace them with power-driven tools if force must be exerted frequently or if considerable turning, twisting, or hammering is required. Power-driven tools are so much faster and so much less tiring to the worker that they should be used whenever they are practical.

CAPACITY BALANCE

Equally balanced productive capacity on all jobs is an ideal toward which to work, but you never get there. Ideally, every machine should be in use all the time the plant operates, yet none should need to be used overtime to keep up. The trouble is that as time passes and products and operations change, so does the capacity required for various operations. Some go up, and some down. If you had started from a balance, you would be out of balance almost right away.

On the other hand, as time goes along, you get to adjust capacity. Where bottlenecks develop, you buy more machines, and if other machines aren't used, you take them out to the boneyard. Or you may (and do) work on the demand side. If some department isn't busy, have the salesmen try harder for the kind of business that will use its machines. So while you never have a perfect balance between the machines you need and what you have, you should not too often be way off base either way.

There are several reasons why perfect balance is impossible, aside from changes. It is difficult to tell ahead just how productive any new machine will be. Also, part of the work cycle on a machine operation depends on how long it takes a worker to do his part. Sometimes he takes longer than he does other times. Also different men take different times.

Unavoidable delays, machine breakdowns, tool breakdowns, material shortages, and the like always occur. They are unpredictable, and they upset your balance. Sometimes, too, one machine is faster than another, and it would be foolish to slow down the fast one to the rate of the slow one. Better run it fast but only part time.

Perfectly balanced capacity is actually not as desirable as it sounds because there is no leeway for delays or breakdowns. Unless you carry big supplies of products between machines, all the machines stop quickly if any one of them stops for any reason. Most companies don't want big inventories around and prefer a little excess capacity as a reserve. So we are back to lack of balance—unless we just happen to have exactly the same excess for all machines.

In line production or "serialized" manufacture, balancing the productive capacity of successive operations as nearly as possible is very important. This time not so much because you want to keep the machines busy but because you want to keep the *men* busy. Be sure that the men's work assignments are equal in *time*. Otherwise there will be so many short waits that they add up to big costs. On short waits you can't give the men other jobs.

On the other hand, when you automate pretty heavily, you can forget about keeping the remaining *men* busy. In fact you will find that it pays to have some men standing around just watching and ready to fix anything that goes wrong right away. But when things go well, these men (there aren't many of them) have little to do.

SELECTION OF MACHINES

Machines are bought to do certain productive work. The first must, therefore, in selecting machines is that they be able to do the work and with the required degree of accuracy. The second must is that, considering the quantities and varieties of products for which they will be used, they do the work economically—at less cost than by other methods.

It is often hard to pick one machine over another because no one kind is better than all others in every respect. Think of yourself buying an automobile. Which is best for you? You just can't get a clear answer. Same with factory machines. Most of them will be used for many different jobs. Some have advantages on certain jobs but are not so good on others. Sometimes you need one kind of machine today, but you are pretty sure that tomorrow you'll need something a little different. So you end up getting a more expensive machine able to do both kinds of work.

As a rule, however, in deciding what machine to buy, pay most attention to today's needs. Extra spending to get frills which may be useful in the future is of doubtful wisdom. Maybe you never will need the extras, or by the time you do, completely new and better machines may be available.

The money end of when to buy and when not to buy machines is discussed on pages 154–64. Here we should note, though, that performance and repair cost records on old machines, if kept, help us calculate expected performance and operating costs of new machines. Most large, but very few small, companies keep records of this sort.

Foremen Preferences. Foremen often have strong likes and dislikes about the machines they want in their departments, and their preferences should be respected if it is reasonably possible. They like to think that their judgment is respected, and they will work harder to make the machines of their choice perform economically. Maybe their choices are just prejudice. But maybe they have pretty good reasons, though you can't put them into formulas and weigh their importance. In the first place, they are familiar with certain kinds of machines and will probably get greater production out of the kinds they know best. They know how to handle production difficulties on these machines; they know how to repair them; and they know how to train men to run them.

In the second place, the foreman probably wants machines somewhat similar to his old ones for standardization. Some of the repair parts may be interchangeable with those needed for other machines. Also his men can easily learn to run new machines that are something like the machines he already has. He can switch his men around from one machine to another in case of absences, breakdown, or other emergencies.

In the third place, some manufacturers give better emergency repair service than others. In the fourth place, some machines are designed for, and their manufacturers have available, better standard accessories and auxiliary equipment.

Used Machines. Used machines, particularly general purpose machines, are often available at bargain prices. They are not always bargains, however. A used machine is one that someone else no longer wants, possibly because it is worn out, obsolete, or broken. Secondhand machinery dealers often buy used machines, "recondition" them (repaint them), and offer them for sale. In buying used machines caution is necessary. It is a little like buying a used car. You need to exercise caution, but you won't be taking many chances if you buy from a reputable used machinery dealer. And you take still fewer chances when you buy traded-in old machines from machinery manufacturing companies.

STRETCHING MACHINE CAPACITY

Some companies have tried running their machines at very high speeds, higher than is recommended by the machinery manufacturers of engineering handbooks. Of course, overspeeding machines is hard on them and probably shortens their lives, so why do it? You get more output—*today*. This probably lowers your unit costs in spite of the greater depreciation costs. You also get by with fewer machines today. You cut your investment and your floor space used, and you lessen the danger of obsolescence. You wear the machines out before they have a chance to become obsolete. There are probably many places where this practice pays off; furthermore, it is not certain that all machines pushed to their limit wear out much sooner.

Overspeeding machines is not a common practice, however. Why not, if it is so good? Mainly because you may wear the machine out so quickly that you haven't gotten its cost back out of the extra production. Many times, too, your tool costs would skyrocket, and your quality might go down.

Machine capacity (and therefore the number of machines needed to do a given amount of work) is usually no hard and fast figure. Long runs decrease the down time required for setup and increase the average hourly output. Short runs cut hourly output. Complex tooling usually cuts the man-time part of the production cycle and increases the hourly output of the machine. If complex tooling is too expensive to be borne by the job, less expensive, simple tooling, but with lower hourly output, can be used.

Total output can be increased by working the machines more hours per day or more days per week. But *the increase in output will be less than proportional to the hours added* because of worker fatigue and, in the case of 24-hours-a-day and 7-day-a-week operations, because you have no spare time left for making repairs. Machine capacity can also be increased by providing relief workers who keep the machine in operation while the regular operator is away from the machine—even through lunch periods if you want the last ounce of production. Down time for repairs can be cut by keeping spare parts available in convenient locations, thus speeding up repair jobs.

When some machines are overloaded while other similar, but not identical, machines are idle, transferring some of the jobs to the idle machines is often possible, even though they are less well suited to the operation. Doing this helps compensate for temporary lack of balance between actual and needed production capacity. It helps keep all the machines busy and reduces the total number of machines required.

STUDY QUESTIONS

1. How do general and special purpose machines compare in purpose, design, cost, and conditions of use?
2. Under what conditions would you shift from using general purpose machines to special purpose machines?
3. What can you do with middle-sized production orders—too long for general purpose machines and too short for special purpose machines?
4. Is an automatic transfer machine "automation"? Explain your answer.
5. What things does "tooling" refer to? Can it help make a general purpose machine more special? What about a special purpose machine? Explain.
6. When and why should you use portable tools?
7. "If a company plans well it should be able to keep all its machines equally busy." Then you should have a perfect balance of capacity. What things interfere with reaching this goal?

8. If machines or men must be kept waiting, which would you prefer and why?

9. When buying new machines, how forward looking should you be? Do you buy a machine to do today's job? Or tomorrow's job? Discuss.

10. How would you figure machine capacity? What problems are involved?

11. Would you advise "stretching" machine capacity? Explain.

CASE 7–1.   THE LAPPERRE ELECTRIC COMPANY

The Lapperre Electric Company is primarily a producer of 110-volt AC fractional HP motors. They have a single factory, which is composed of a series of assembly lines surrounded by various subassembly departments. The company is at present scheduling an order for 10,000 ¼ hp 110-volt universal motors. One phase of this scheduling is concerned with the armature winding operation. This winding is done by machine and has had a time standard of 6 minutes per armature set by time study methods. The standards are loose enough for the average machine operator to exceed the standard by 20 per cent. The assembly line on which this lot of motors will be assembled has a capacity of two motors per minute. Actually, though, from previous experience, this line has an average downtime rate of 5 per cent. The production control department has four winding machines which are, or will be, available for this job.

Will it be possible for the armatures to be wound as an integral part of the assembly, or will it be necessary to wind and store some of them before the final assembly begins to insure uninterrupted assembly?

If it is necessary to wind and store some of the armatures, how many hours before assembly begins must the winding begin? (Assume winding will continue during assembly, so that in the ideal case the last armature will go directly from winding to assembly without storage.)

Chapter 8

CAPITAL INVESTMENT

WE HAVE seen that depreciation provides a company with some cash. Depreciation may bring in every year as much as 10 per cent of the investment in durable assets. If you have $10,000,000 worth of fixed assets, you may have $1,000,000 of depreciation cash coming in during the year. Retained earnings also provide cash. Most companies with $10,000,000 worth of fixed assets would get every year another million or two dollars from retained profits even after paying income taxes and dividends. It is not at all uncommon for companies, year after year, to have to put to work cash equal to one fifth or more of their fixed assets.

Perhaps you have not thought of having cash as a problem. But idle cash produces nothing. Officials have to put it to work. Capital investment is, therefore, a two-sided matter. On the one hand, you need machines and buildings; on the other hand, you need to put your cash to work.

The need for capital expenditures comes from two sources. First, fixed assets (other than land) are continually wearing out. Someone has said that machines are always marching down the road to the junk heap. Some machines reach the end of the road every year. The end of the road may be physical or economic. New machines on the market sometimes obsolesce old ones which may be economically worn out before they become junk. In either case, you have to buy machines just to keep on operating. You include here the machines that are bought to lower costs, to improve quality, or to let you make new models of products. Buying machines just to keep on operating is the first (and usually the most important) need for capital investment.

The second need for money is for expansion. Our country is growing. Most companies grow year after year. So they have to keep buying *more* plant and equipment year after year. Plant expansion creates a somewhat irregular demand for more capital because companies do not just add a little more to their factories every year. Some years they add very little; other years they build whole factories.

The money you have, and the money you need do not always match. Sometimes (not often) you don't have very many needs in sight. Much more often there are too many projects—projects whose total costs exceed the money available. But you really should not start with a notion of how much money is available before you know how profitable the machinery buying programs can be. You should study the projects on their own merits first—regardless of how much money they take and how much you have.

Only after you have looked over all the promising proposals should you decide what to do. Should you approve only as many projects as you can pay for and cut off the rest? Or do you go ahead and approve all of the real good ones even if, in total, they cost more than you have money for? And if you do, where do you get the money? Borrow it? Sell more stock?

Boards of directors have to decide such matters because new machines and new buildings are fixed assets. They set the course for the company's future. The board has lots of help on this, however. The treasurer and the board's financial committee study carefully all the proposals requiring cash and the means of raising it and make recommendations, supported by figures, to the full board. It then decides just how far it can go with approvals and how to get extra money if any is needed.

Years ago most companies bought machines without such careful study. They sometimes used mere rules of thumb in replacing machines. One rule of thumb was to replace every machine that got to be 25 years old. That policy would tell you when to get rid of an old machine but tells you nothing about what to buy.

Other old policies, still used sometimes, are: spend your depreciation cash on new replacement machines; or replace 10 per cent of your machines every year. These policies would tell you that you have to buy more machines and about how much you are willing to spend, but they don't tell you which machines to get rid of, nor do they help you choose the right new machines. Probably no one ever followed those policies slavishly, but they have been used as guides.

THE "FORWARD" LOOK

Capital expenditures are (or should be) wholly forward looking. The past is nothing except as it helps us foresee the future. The point is that *you are not just replacing machines*. Rarely do you *replace* a worn-out machine. And, it is immaterial to you (for the future) where the money you are going to spend comes from—whether from retained profits or from depreciation on a lathe or a planer that you already own. The only question is, which new investment will, in the future, produce the highest rate of return—it might be a lathe, it might be a planer, or neither one. Capital expenditure control is altogether a matter of *how best to invest this money* to bring the greatest future rate of return.

Since there are nearly always more profitable projects than you have money for, you have to choose from among them. Normally, the most profitable projects (those that promise the *highest rate of return* on the investment) are approved. But that can't be your only guide. Projects that aren't very certain to pay out may be approved if they might some day pay out very well. An electric power company may, for example, build a power plant to use atomic fuel. Perhaps that particular power plant isn't expected to pay very well but is expected to be the forerunner of later better paying projects.

"Must" capital items also go high on the priority list. "Must" machines are ones you can't get along without. A cigarette maker must have packaging equipment. Suppose that a competitor comes out with his cigarettes in little cardboard boxes—something you don't have but which catches the public fancy. You have to get new packaging equipment to wrap your cigarettes that way—and get it fast. It is a must. There is danger, however, in regarding any project as a must. It should be a must only if it is decidedly better than other ways *or* if the cost of *not* buying the equipment (in the cigarette example it would be the loss of sales) is much greater than the cost of buying it.

Capital expenditure decisions are not always clear and distinct from operating decisions. For example, you spend cash for research and for advertising. Should you? Or should you save on research and advertising and buy more machines? Sometimes you must choose between current operating costs and capital investments.

Approval of capital spending plans usually means that you will go ahead and complete the project. But not always. Suppose that you hardly get started when business turns down—unexpectedly. This calls for a reappraisal. Promising projects now look less promising, and urgent projects are less urgent. The ax is applied freely, and project after project is postponed or canceled even if you lose the costs of the groundwork you have already laid. You don't hesitate to stop half-finished projects if the crisis is bad enough. Of course this doesn't happen all the time, but it's far from rare.

"SAVINGS" AND ALTERNATIVES

It *costs* money to buy machines and buildings, and it *costs* money to use them. Yet we speak of their *saving* money. How can costs be savings? How is spending money, saving?

It isn't the spending that saves, it is spending wisely. It is nearly always possible to do things several ways—there are alternatives. All ways cost money, but some cost less than others. We say that one way *saves* money when it costs less than another way. *It is always a matter of cost comparisons among alternatives.* Nearly always one alternative is to keep on doing work with existing equipment. All other alternatives are "challengers."

Even expansion projects offer alternatives. We get to choose from among them. Do we expand or not? Do we do it now or later? Do we do it here or elsewhere? If elsewhere, where? How should we expand? Buy more? Or make more? What machines will serve best? Should we buy a few machines and run them day and night? Or more and run them days only? It is important to start thinking in terms of alternatives. Every machinery buying decision has alternatives. The best one is the one that costs the least; it "saves" the difference between its costs and the costs of other ways of getting work done.

A word of warning about how to figure savings. Be very conservative in your claims of the amount of overhead that you will save. Overhead charges are rarely less than 100 per cent of direct labor, and they may be 250 per cent or more of the labor cost. *Never take credit for saving that much overhead.*

But when you save direct labor shouldn't you take credit, in machine economy studies, for saving overhead? *Yes—but not at regular accounting rates, because savings in direct labor often do not actually cut overhead expenses much.* Credit the project with saving any overhead that really is saved; but don't use the overhead ratio that your cost accountants use in figuring costs. You will almost never save that much overhead cost.

MAKE-OR-BUY IN CAPITAL INVESTMENT

Make-or-buy has already been discussed but not as a capital investment problem. Actually, all vertical integration decisions are make-buy decisions with very important capital investment aspects.

Many expansion programs suggested by operating divisions are horizontal—just more of the same. A division wants to add to its plant or to build another plant to make the same things it already makes. Such proposals are not make-buy matters. But, a good many other proposals are proposals to make instead of buy.

You might think that make-buy decisions would be few, that once you decide to buy an item instead of making it, you would have settled the problem. But the picture always changes. Usually, as you grow, your purchases of outside items grow too. Then you find yourself buying maybe millions of dollars' worth of one or more items every year. Since the seller normally makes a profit on his sales, you ask yourself, "can't we make the item ourselves and make that profit ourselves?" The major division head often thinks, yes—so he puts in a proposal to spend money on machines to go into that business.

The Ford automobile company has recently put up its third glass factory so that it can cut down on its outside buying of plate glass for windshields. Make-buy decisions need not be permanent. But if you decide to make instead of buy you usually have to buy some machines. It becomes a capital investment matter.

REQUESTS FOR CAPITAL FUNDS

Today is a day of decentralization. Giant companies subdivide their operations on a "divisional" basis—with each division having wide decision-making authority. But *not so with capital funds*. This is one thing that presidents and boards of directors, even of giant companies, usually keep a fairly tight rein on.

The company's cash (including depreciation cash and retained profits) is the *company's* cash—not any one division's cash. It should be put to work (invested) wherever the highest probable long-range rate of return is in prospect. You might get cash from one division and invest it in another division. This just *must* be a top-level decision. Top levels must also decide such matters as *how much* money to spend on capital investment as against advertising, research, or similar things whose budgets can be flexible.

We have said that the president and the board of directors usually hold a fairly tight control over capital expenditures. In some billion-dollar companies, no division manager can buy a machine costing over $5,000 without board approval. That is a low figure, $10,000 being more common. But that doesn't mean that the board studies every machine purchase request, one by one. The board controls expenditures by reviewing either (1) whole expansion programs, or (2) over-all machinery replacement budgets.

Expansion programs and replacement budgets are made up and submitted to the board of directors by lower groups in the organization. Figure 8–1 shows how Sylvania Electric develops its capital expenditure program. Notice that details start in plants and the operating divisions. In all companies most proposals originate in the *operating divisions* of the company. Proposals must always be backed up with facts and figures. Operating departments do part of the analytical work needed to prepare a proposal, but they don't do the whole job.

In most giant companies, each major division has a planning and forecasting department. For example, the head of the Explosives Division of Du Pont has his own little group of forecasters trying to foresee the future market for explosives. But, besides the divisions' planners, every large company, in its central office, has long-range forecasters and planners who look ahead 5 to 10 years. They try to forecast the whole company's future business. These men work in a staff department reporting to the president. This gives us two levels of high brass to look over proposals that start down in individual plants.

All projects, big and little, go first from the plant to the staff of the *division*. After the division's staff checks them over, they go in to the *central office* staff, which also looks for bugs and flaws, helps work

The Need for New Facilities	Developing Action Plans			Over-all Company Review
Step 1	Step 2	Step 3	Step 4	Step 5
Replacement of: Worn-out facilities Obsolete facilities Reduce costs Improve quality For safety Expansion: Old products New products	Develop *Individual Project Plan* for Each Project (Must show cash required, when it is needed, savings and payout periods.)	Group Related Projects into *Programs*	Group Programs into *Division Program Summaries* Program summaries for next 2 years submitted to Step 5 by Nov. 1 each year.	Programs reviewed collectively for over-all financial requirements. Programs approved or disapproved Capital expenditure budgets approved for each division based on its approved programs. Sylvania has divisions: (1) Radio and TV, (2) Parts, (3) Radio Tubes, (4) TV Picture Tubes, (5) Lighting, (6) Electronics, (7) Atomic Energy, (8) Tungsten and Chemical, (9) Argus Camera
Done by: Managements of Individual Plants by: Industrial Engineers, Plant Accountants, Plant Managers	Done by: Managements of Each Major Division by: Cost Accountant, Controller, General Manufacturing Manager, General Manager			Done by: Top Officials, by: Operating Vice-Presidents, Financial Vice-President, President, Board of Directors

Adapted from diagram on p. 20, "Tested Approaches to Capital Equipment Replacement," American Management Association Special Report No. 1 (New York, 1954).

FIG. 8–1. Sylvania Electric's method for controlling capital expenditures.

out details, and sees that proposals are in line with the company's long-range plans.

Two kinds of proposals come out of all of this analysis: (1) normal machine replacement budgets, and (2) expansion programs. Individual machine proposals and individual projects become parts of one or the other of these two collective proposals. As the programs and budgets take form, they are studied and reviewed by the company's top officers. Finally, after every one agrees, the proposals go to the board of directors' finance committee and from there to the full board for final approval.

Notice that *staff departments do not approve or turn down* capital investment requests. All that they do is to make economic analyses of the projects. They figure out how well each project will pay out. After central office staff analysis some projects are dropped by the major division heads. But they are dropped because they won't be profitable and not because the central office staff turns thumbs down. It has no authority to do that. The remaining projects then go to the company's top officers for their review. They, the top officers, probably turn down a few of the projects that come before them. Projects approved by top officers then go to the board of directors for final approval.

A word of warning here about red tape. All of this preparing, analyzing, and getting approval can slow things up and can be costly. Down at the plant level where so many projects start, the engineer must not only *discuss* details with half-a-dozen other departments but must *get their approval* that it is all right from their point of view. So you go around to the general foreman, the superintendent, the safety engineer, the head of quality control, the purchasing department, the maintenance head, and probably some others. Explain your project to them and get them to sign. One company requires fifteen signatures! Its machinery analysis men find that some men are afraid to sign unless someone else has signed first, and so on.

But you have not finished. In fact, you have just started. Next, take it all up to the division head office. Here there are similar staff groups. Go through it all again and get everyone's approval. And of course each one tries to be at least a little critical. All of these men want to be sure that there are no bugs in your project as far as their specialty is concerned. After you get their approval, you are still far from finished. Now, you move up to the home office and get on the merry-go-round again.

If this is the way it works (and the above is one billion-dollar company's procedure), maybe the lower men should be given power to approve more of their own projects. You could easily spend $5,000 evaluating a $10,000 machine. There should not be as much red tape as all this.

The "Cash Flow." Not only does the board of directors have to pay attention to *how much money* an approved project will require but it has to pay attention to *when* the money will be needed. If (in November) it approves spending money that won't have to be spent until next August, maybe the company will, by that time, be able to get the money from profits and depreciation money not yet in hand but which will be in hand by then.

A "cash-flow" plan is needed. It shows, *by month,* for the months ahead, how much cash you will have, how much will come in, and how much will go out. Without a cash-flow plan you might find that all the outgo comes first and the income second. You could get into a financial jam.

Most of the board approvals are for things to be bought or built in the next calendar year or farther ahead on big projects such as new plants. Some time in, say November, the board will approve capital budgets for the next year and for farther ahead on the big projects. This includes budgets for both normal machinery replacement and for expansion or extensive repair.

Once the budgets are approved, the division heads can go ahead and buy the machines or place contracts for construction. But the home office checks continually to see that individual projects aren't costing more than planned. If this isn't done, it often happens that you spend your whole budgeted amount and still don't have the project completed.

EXTRA CAPITAL NEEDS

Emergencies. You can't see all of your needs way ahead. So you should never approve so many projects that there is no money left for emergencies. Probably it is safe, however, to commit up to 95 per cent of your money to regular planned projects. Holding back a little lets you have something left over for unforeseen but necessary emergencies.

Capital for "Extras." Machinery projects always cost more than their own bare cost. *All* of the extras must be included if the estimate is to be realistic. Two kinds of extras are not often overlooked—the installation costs and accessory costs. But three other kinds are often missed or underestimated—the cost of nonproductive facilities to go with productive facilities, the low and costly early production period, and extra working capital.

Installation costs include making a mounting for the machine; putting in all of the wiring connections and the steam, compressed air, or other connections; and actually putting the machine in and getting it to run. Accessory costs include tooling and machine attachments needed to use it. Often they add up to a good bit of money.

Production facilities can't be run without the help of many "non-productive" facilities. Putting in one new machine probably won't cause many extras, but put in many machines instead of one and it is different.

Putting in many machines means that you need more floor space, a bigger building, more of all kinds of services including more conveyors and more trucks. You will have more employees, and so will need more locker rooms. You will be running a bigger factory and need more foremen, personnel people, engineers, maintenance men, and so on. The costs of all of these must be added to the bare cost of the facilities.

And don't forget the costs of low production and extra scrap for days (or weeks) after a new machine is put in. That too adds to the cost of the projects.

And, finally, don't overlook the need for more working capital. A larger plant (the result of putting in more machines) will need a bigger inventory of raw materials, materials in process, and finished products. The company will also be doing more business and will have more accounts receivable. All of these are extras. *They take money too.* Of course the added accounts payable will supply a little of the added working capital but not very much of it.

But aren't these added capital needs small? No—sometimes they add up to as much as the cost of the machines and capital equipment! If you build a new $1,000,000 plant, you might need an extra million of working capital too. Whether the figure is that high or not, you can be sure that you will need several hundreds of thousands of dollars in extra working capital. All estimates of the capital requirements of projects need to include their working capital needs.

DISCOVERING MACHINE NEEDS

Replacement Machines.   When does a machine need replacing? When does your old automobile need replacing? Neither machines nor automobiles are like the "one hoss shay." They don't wear out all at once. Nor do they usually become obsolete all at once. Actually, old machines can be kept running for years and years if you keep on repairing them. But repair costs are usually high on old machines. Obsolescence too may be a slow process. Every new model of a machine makes it a little less economical for you to run the old one.

The point is that *you have to search out* uneconomical operations. You have to watch out for the point of uneconomical operation of old machines. You already have machines, and they get the work done, but should you keep on with the machines you have or consider new ones? You know what it costs to do work on the present machines, but could it be done at lower costs on new machines? Again, you have to hunt for places to improve.

This is one reason why machinery buying requests have to originate down in the operating divisions. They use the machines and only they can tell when old machines should be taken out of service and new ones purchased. Yet even in the operating divisions, there is nothing automatic about machine replacement. The opportunity to make an improvement has to be recognized. Then, calculations can be made to find out what is best to do. Remember, too, that repairing old machines and keeping them in use is always one of the alternatives. Machine replacement is rarely just a matter of which new machine to buy.

Also, remember that buying fancy new machines is really a *last* choice decision. Try first of all to improve the job all you can without a new machine. Use work simplification principles (see Chapter 29). Maybe you can cut out the job altogether. Buy a new machine only after you have tried your best to figure out how to operate at low cost without it.

Additional Machines.   Sometimes, as business picks up, you have to buy more machines. So you have to find out where you need them and how many. Bottleneck operations are good places to look first. If work piles up before any machines or if they have to be operated extra shifts, their normal capacity does not match that of other machines. All such tight spots should be looked into when you are considering getting more machines.

Labor Replacement.   Another place to look when thinking of machines is hand operations, particularly if very many men do handwork. Maybe there is no machine that can do the job, but maybe you could have one designed. Don't let the lack of a machine stop your thinking about mechanizing the job. Hand operations are places to look for opportunities to use machines.

METHODS OF ANALYZING PROPOSALS

We have said that capital investment is wholly a forward-looking matter. You have to try to calculate how productive new machines *will be* and how much it *will cost* to run them. All of these matters lie in the future, and forecasting the future is hazardous business. How can you know today what operations on what products you might use a lathe for in 1962? You can't, today, come very close on estimates of things that lie in the future.

Many capital expenditures are hardly good guesses, and many don't work out nearly so well as expected. Some people go so far as to say that you waste your time when you try to figure out—for years ahead— how a new machine will pay out. And, of course, they are right, but they are wrong too. You can't tell how things will work out. Yet, isn't it better to get the best figures you can to look at rather than to have no figures at all? Surely you can make a more intelligent decision if you base it on the best information you can get than you can if you do not have that information.

Nor are we saying that you can put everything into numbers—probably you can't. And, of course, nonnumerical or nonmeasurable factors should also be considered. For example, maybe you will have to buy one expensive machine instead of two less expensive ones if there is space for only one. Or maybe your foreman and his men are used to one manufacturer's machine and not other makes. But, assuming that you consider nonquantitative matters as best you can, surely when you have to choose between new machines, you will do better to have tried to forecast each one's performance.

Assuming that you ought to try to evaluate proposals, you are faced with how to do it. Have you ever tried to figure out whether you ought to trade in your old car this year or next? Or whether it is better to buy a year-old used car or a new one? There is no one good way to figure out which is the better thing to do.

Industry is in almost the same fix when it comes to figuring out the costs of buying one machine, or another, or getting along with old ones. There isn't any very good method. Besides, normal cost accounting records don't supply all the figures you need for your calculations. For example, does your company have repair cost records for individual machines? If not, you don't know too much about what it will cost to keep any particular new machine operating. You have to dig out some of the figures you need before you can make any calculations.

Actually, most companies use one or all of the following five methods:

1. First-year performance
2. Payback period
3. Full-life performance—regular dollars
4. Full-life performance—discounted dollars
5. MAPI method

None of these methods is perfect, but all have been used. Only number 4 is uncommon, and it is gaining favor—particularly for million-dollar projects.

FIRST-YEAR PERFORMANCE

In this method you calculate the costs of doing things by each of the alternative methods you are considering—*but for the first year only.* It is not a very accurate way to compare the merits of alternatives, and it isn't used often where much money is involved.

It is simple and easy to compute and so keeps down the costs of making analyses. It covers the period which you know the most about. And for short-lived items (tooling and accessories) one year covers quite a bit of their actual life. A longer-lived machine's use and value in more distant years ahead are not very predictable. Also, sometimes the one-year analysis shows that one alternative is very much better than others—so much so that it is obviously not worth going into more thorough calculations.

Here is a simple example of how to make an estimate of an item's first-year costs. Assume that a piece of tooling is being considered. It will cost $1,500 and will last 3 years. Using straight-line depreciation, its yearly depreciation charge will be $500. Charge also 20 per cent for interest on the investment, insurance, and repairs. Based on a first year's investment of $1,500, this will come to $300.

The job for which the tooling is used may run steadily, or there may be two or more shorter runs. Each time a new lot is made, the tooling must be put on the machine and "set up" for use. In our problem we will guess that this will be done five times during the year at a cost of $20 each time, or a total setup cost of $100. The total cost of the tooling applicable to the year is $900, made up of $500 depreciation, $300 carrying charges, and $100 setup costs.

Now turn to the alternative methods—figure them out too. If you did not buy this piece of tooling, how would you do the job? Calculate the costs of doing it the other ways. Then, all you have to do is to choose the method with the lowest cost for the year—whether it is the method we first computed or one of the alternatives.

Usually it isn't as simple as our example. We didn't include labor or material costs. Almost always there are differences in labor costs. Sometimes there are differences in material costs. Often there are differences in quality of products turned out. Perhaps one machine would be a greater obsolescence risk than another. Perhaps one is more safe to operate. Perhaps one is more likely to need repairs than another. Not all of these are "quantifiable." We can't express them all in numbers or money values. But everything that can be should be put into money values.

Suppose we found, in our example above, that the proposed item of tooling would save 15 cents a unit, as compared to the second best way of doing the work, but that the second best way used no tooling. With it we would not have to spend $1,500. Dividing $900 (the first year's cost of operation) by 15 cents gives us 6,000 units. That shows us that the proposed method will be better than the second best way in the first year if over 6,000 units are to be made. But if less than 6,000 units are in prospect, then the so-called second best way will be less costly. It will not pay to buy the tooling.

We can express these relationships in formula form. The volume at which it will pay to change from one method to another can be obtained by using the following formula: $N = (A - B) / S$, in which N = the number of units above which it will pay to put in more expensive (and more efficient) tooling or machine, A = total annual equipment depreciation cost plus carrying charges and repairs plus setup costs per year for the more elaborate equipment, B = total costs for one year for the less elaborate method, and S = savings in labor (and materials if there are any materials savings) and overhead per unit if the more elaborate equipment is bought.[1]

Using first-year costs is conservative—as compared to using costs for the full life of an asset. You judge the proposal on a *high-cost basis*. The second year's costs ought to be less than the first year's costs because

---

[1] This formula just gives you the "crossover" point of two straight lines, the lines you would get if you plotted the total cost of doing different volumes of work by each of two methods.

the 20 per cent carrying costs are applied to the depreciated value of the machine. On the other hand, repair costs are low in the first year and get larger as the asset gets older. First-year costs may be pretty good figures to use after all.

THE "PAYBACK" PERIOD

The "payback" or "payout" period is the time it takes to get your money back. Most executives want to know every new project's payback period before they approve it. They are particularly interested if there is much chance of a machine becoming obsolete very soon. Payback is used as a rough yardstick by which to judge projects. Obviously, too, payback should always be much shorter than the asset's expected life. You don't want machines to wear out before you get your money back.

Minor tooling and cost-saving devices usually have to pay out in a year or they won't be approved. Small machines are allowed 2 to 3 years. Large, expensive, heavy-duty, and durable machines may be allowed more time —occasionally 5 or more years. Businessmen don't, however, apply payback yardsticks blindly, and they change them up or down sometimes, depending on how much money they have and how good business promises to be.

Payback is not a very good yardstick because it tells you only how soon you get your money back. But no one ever buys a machine just to get his money back. You would want, over the years, to get back more than you put in—to earn money on the investment. Payback makes you regard all of the first money the machine produces as just getting your investment back. *After* that period *all* the income from the machine is return on the investment.

There is nothing wrong about looking at the machine's income that way except that a payback analysis ends with the machine having paid for itself. The part you are even more interested in—how much you will end up earning on the investment—is left out of the payback analyses.

Payback can mislead you about which machine to buy. Suppose, for example, that one machine will pay out in 3 years and another machine in 5 years. Using payback, you choose the first one. Nearly always that would be the right decision—but not if the first machine would wear out completely (or need heavy repairs) in 4 or 5 years while the second one would keep right on producing (and with few repairs) for 15 years. Payback gives good answers, however, where the alternative machines have more or less equal lives and repair expectations.

When using payback, don't mix up machine economy studies with regular cost accounting. Some people, in making machine economy studies, list and total up all of the costs of operating a machine— including its depreciation. They may do this for the first year, or for a typical year, or for the average year of the machine's life. Which of these they do is immaterial for this point. Then they compare that year's total cost to the total cost of doing the work the alternative way. Assuming that it is less, the difference in totals is the "saving" by using the proposed machine.

If you "save" $1,000 a year, then it would seem to take 10 years for a $10,000 machine to pay out. That isn't right, however, because at the end of 10 years you would have $10,000 of savings *and* you would have your $10,000 depreciation money. The machine really paid out in 5 years. At the end of 5 years you would have had $10,000 in hand. You would then have said that the machine had paid out.

But—and here is another weakness of payout—we have paid no attention to income taxes. Payout just assumes that all of the machine's income the first few years is the return of our investment. The Bureau of Internal Revenue won't let you call it all just getting your money back. It lets you call part *and only part* of the amount you get back depreciation. The rest is profits—part of which (probably 50 per cent or so) you pay to the government as income taxes.

Now our example has to change a little. Each year you will get $1,000 depreciation back plus $1,000 savings *minus $500 taxes*, leaving cash $1,500. $10,000 ÷ $1,500 = 6⅔ years, the true payback period. That it forgets taxes is not, of course, a very strong argument against payback because you can figure taxes in just as we did above. *But, as typically used, payback doesn't separate depreciation and savings so you wouldn't know how much to allow for taxes.* Income taxes are typically not included in the calculations, but they should be.

FULL-LIFE PERFORMANCE—REGULAR DOLLARS

This method is like the first-year life method except that you cover the machine's full life. Consider these two alternatives:

A.

Facts about the alternatives:

1 machine	
$20,000 installed cost	
8 years of life	
No scrap value	
$5,000 per year to operate, including labor, repairs, and all other items (but *not* depreciation)	

Figuring how they compare:

Depreciation in
  8 years $20,000
Operating costs
  for 8 years 40,000

Total cost $60,000
Average cost
  per year . . . . $ 7,500

B.

2 machines
$10,000 installed cost ($5,000 each)
10 years of life
No scrap value
$ 7,000 per year to operate

Depreciation in
  10 years $10,000
Operating costs
  for 10 years 70,000

Total cost $80,000
Average cost
  per year . . . . $ 8,000

On the basis of this analysis you purchase the machine in A rather than the machines in B. Don't make your final decision, though, until you see, in the next few pages, the answer you get using the discounted dollar method.

FULL-LIFE PERFORMANCE—DISCOUNTED DOLLARS

Another, and seemingly better, way to compare alternatives is to compare everything on the basis of today's values. This is particularly important when items have different lengths of life and different patterns of costs. *Discounting everything to today's values accomplishes that.*

The method of discounted dollars is called the "discounted cash-flow" method, or the "investor's" method, or the "present value" method. Although it is complicated to figure, big companies are now using this method more often than before and particularly for their big projects.

Discounted Dollars.   To understand the investor's method of judging projects you must first understand discounted dollars.

And to get at discounted dollars you start with compound interest. If you invest $1,000 today at 10 per cent interest, you will get $100 interest at the end of the year. Then you invest the $1,100 at 10 per cent. At the end of the second year you will get $110 interest. You get interest every year on the original $1,000 *and also on the interest from previous years.* Getting interest on the interest is called "compounding" the interest. In our example it is compounded annually. If you kept on this way for 10 years, you would have $2,594 at the end of the tenth year. If you got your interest every 6 months, instead of only once a year, and if you reinvested it immediately, you would have $2,654. And compounding it quarterly would give you still more.

Going back to the $2,594. $1,000 today equals $2,594 in 10 years from today, or *$2,594 ten years from today is worth $1,000 today. This is the nub of the discounting idea.* Today's value of any given amount of money at a future date is less than its future value. In our example, using 10 per cent interest compounded annually, we find that $1,000 is only 38.55 per cent of $2,594. In fact, *today's value of any amount of money 10 years from now (if we assume 10 per cent interest) is only 38.55 per cent of its 10-year value.*

That is the discounting idea that is used in the present value method of figuring machine economy studies. You can set up tables of how much today's dollars will grow to in future years and you can set up tables of today's worth of future dollars. Of course you get different answers for every different interest rate that you assume. Here is what $1,000 invested at various rates of return will grow to the amounts shown in the following table:

	INTEREST RATE (PER CENT)				
	5	10	15	20	25
At end of 1 year...........	$1,050	$1,100	$1,150	$1,200	$1,250
At end of 2 years..........	1,103	1,210	1,323	1,440	1,563
At end of 5 years..........	1,276	1,612	2,011	2,488	3,053
At end of 10 years.........	1,629	2,594	4,046	6,193	9,313

Here is the present worth of a future $1,000:

	INTEREST RATE (PER CENT)				
	5	10	15	20	25
$1,000 at end of 1 year......	$952	$909	$870	$833	$800
$1,000 at end of 2 years.....	907	826	756	694	640
$1,000 at end of 5 years.....	784	620	497	402	328
$1,000 at end of 10 years....	614	386	247	162	107

Perhaps you have wondered if these tables can be used for other problems—problems where sums other than $1,000 are involved. Yes, you can use these figures for other problems. Just move the decimal over one place and use the numbers as percentages. For example, $1,000 at 5 per cent compounded annually for 10 years will come to $1,629. Any other sum of money at 5 per cent for 10 years will grow to 162.9 per cent of the starting amount.

The same applies to the discounts. $614 put at 5 per cent interest and compounded annually for 10 years will grow into $1,000. Or stated as a discount, $1,000, 10 years from today is today worth $614, or 61.4 per cent of its 10-year value. If you assume a 20 per cent rate of return, then money 10 years from now is worth only 16.2 per cent of its 10-year value.

The "Present Value" Method in Machine Economy Studies. The "present value" method of analyzing machines to be bought puts everything on a current dollar basis. You propose to buy a machine today at say $10,000. Its cost is 100-cent dollars. During the first year you get back $1,000 depreciation, but you don't get some of that $1,000 back until the end of the year. To simplify our problem we will say that you get *no* depreciation money back until the end of the year, and then you get the whole $1,000.

Now look back at our discount table. Getting $1,000 a year from now is the same as having $952, or $909, or $897, or $833, or some other figure now—it depends on the rate of return. Actually, business companies usually use 20, 25, or 30 per cent in their calculations. That seems high, but remember things don't always work out well. There are risks. Also your machines may end up obsolete before you can wear them out. And if your new machines save money you will have more profits, and half of those profits go into income taxes.

Now let's apply the discounting idea to our problem on page 158.

You reduce everything to today's dollars—just as if you were paying all of the costs for each machine's whole life today, but in today's dollars. Then you compare.

Starting with alternative A: (See Table 8–1.) First you pay for it with 20,000 of today's dollars. There is no discount on today's dollars, thus today's value of that payment is $20,000.

TABLE 8–1

ALTERNATIVE A

		Discount Rate	Today's Value
Machine's cost paid today.............	$20,000	1.000	$20,000
Cost to operate: Year 1...........	5,000	0.833	4,167
2...........	5,000	0.694	3,470
3...........	5,000	0.578	2,890
4...........	5,000	0.482	2,410
5...........	5,000	0.402	2,010
6...........	5,000	0.335	1,675
7...........	5,000	0.279	1,395
8...........	5,000	0.233	1,165
Total for 8 years..			$39,182
Average cost per year....................................			$ 4,998

ALTERNATIVE B

		Discount Rate	Today's Value
Machines' cost paid today............	$10,000	1.000	$10,000
Cost to operate: Year 1...........	7,000	0.833	5,831
2...........	7,000	0.694	4,858
3...........	7,000	0.578	4,046
4...........	7,000	0.482	3,374
5...........	7,000	0.402	2,814
6...........	7,000	0.335	2,345
7...........	7,000	0.279	1,953
8...........	7,000	0.233	1,631
9...........	7,000	0.194	1,358
10...........	7,000	0.162	1,134
Total for 10 years.......................................			$39,344
Average cost per year....................................			$ 3,934

Next, it will cost you $5,000 to run the machine for one year. Rather than get mixed up with some costs coming soon and some late within the year, you will figure it as if you spent none of the $5,000 until the year-end and then paid it all at once.

What is today's value of $5,000 a year from now? Look back to the table on page 160 and look in the 20 per cent interest rate column. (We chose 20 but could have chosen any other percentage; you should choose the rate that you think that you could earn if you put the money to some other use.) Find the $833 figure. That tells you that $1,000 a year from now is worth $833 today. So $5,000 a year from now is worth 0.833 of $5,000, or $4,167.

Now go on to the second year. Again you will spend $5,000 to run the machine for the year. So again go to the table on page 160. Money 2 years from now is today worth 0.694 of its later value. So, $5,000 to be paid at the end of 2 years costs just the same as paying $3,470 today (gotten by multiplying $5,000 by 0.694). The table on page 160 doesn't show the multipliers for every year, but they can be gotten by mathematical formulas. That is how the other multipliers (0.578, 0.482, and so on) were obtained.

You end up with a today's value for everything that you will spend during the machine's life. Then you go on to alternative B and put all of its present and future costs on today's basis. Now add up all of A's costs and B's costs and divide by the number of years. This gives you the average annual cost of each in terms of today's dollars. Alternative A will cost $4,998; and alternative B, $3,934 a year.

This time you chose alternative B! And A isn't even a close second! On page 158 it looked like alternative A was better. But the analysis using regular dollars gave too little consideration to the fact that you had to pay out $10,000 extra right away. The discounted dollar analysis shows that you will be better off not to invest that extra money in alternative A.

MAPI

The Machinery and Allied Products Institute (MAPI), an organization of machinery manufacturers, has tried to come up with a "best" way to show how profitable a new machine will be. MAPI has published several books on the subject. In them you'll find some rather complex formulas. They don't look hard to a mathematician, but ordinary executives shied away from the formulas and wouldn't use the MAPI's method.

So MAPI simplified the method down to one easy-to-read chart, the one shown in Figure 8–2. Here's how it is used.[2]

You're thinking of buying a new equipment item. It's the challenger: costs, $20,000; estimated "primary service life" (its normal useful life without heavy repairs), 12 years; "terminal salvage value" (value if sold at end of 12 years), 30 per cent; and interest, 10 per cent.

Go across on the bottom of the chart (Fig. 8–2) to 12 years, read up to the intersection with the 30 per cent curve, read over to the vertical scale, and you find 7.2 per cent. To the 7.2 add the interest rate, 10 per cent in our example, and get 17.2 per cent. Take 17.2 per cent of

[2] This example is adapted from one given in Roger B. Orensteen, "Fastest Way to Figure Whether to Buy That New Machine," *Factory Management and Maintenance*, January, 1957.

$20,000 and get $3,440. MAPI calls this the challenger's "adverse minimum." Are you wondering how you add in the machine's operating costs? You don't add them in at all in this example because they are less than the old machine's operating costs.

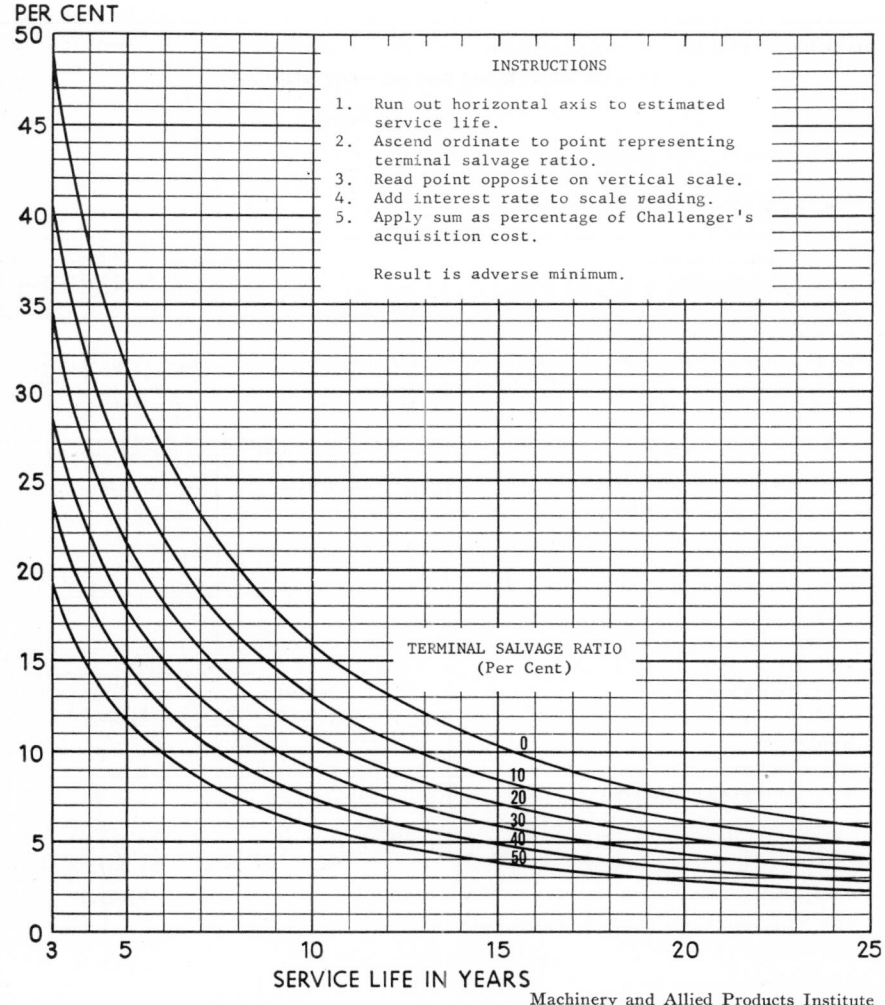

PER CENT

INSTRUCTIONS

1. Run out horizontal axis to estimated service life.
2. Ascend ordinate to point representing terminal salvage ratio.
3. Read point opposite on vertical scale.
4. Add interest rate to scale reading.
5. Apply sum as percentage of Challenger's acquisition cost.

Result is adverse minimum.

TERMINAL SALVAGE RATIO
(Per Cent)

SERVICE LIFE IN YEARS

Machinery and Allied Products Institute

FIG. 8–2. MAPI capital equipment analysis chart.

Now get the defender's figures. It is a 10-year-old machine with $3,000 salvage value today. Next year's estimated salvage value: $2,400. And next year it will cost $3,000 more to operate than the new machine. Now add: salvage value loss next year, $600; interest on present salvage value, $300; and operating cost excess, $3,000; and get $3,900. MAPI calls this the defender's "adverse minimum."

Comparison shows $3,440 for challenger, $3,900 for defender. Challenger wins. You get your new machine.

MAPI's method is certainly simplified compared to what it used to be. And while it is now widely used, it is still probably *not* used by most companies.

ALLIS-CHALMERS MFG. CO.   Date:_____

CAPITAL EQUIPMENT REPLACEMENT ANALYSIS

WORKS_____

1 Subject of Analysis   (3) Electric & (1) Gas Trucks

2

3 Anticipated Rate of Production   For moving material

	PROPOSED EQUIPMENT	EXISTING EQUIPMENT 11259-11289
4	Description: 2-Electric & 1 - Gas Fork	Purch. Date: 1935-36-37 Tool No. 11491-13226
5	Lift Trucks	Description: Lift Trucks
6	Est. Primary Service Life:_____10_____Years	
7	Est. Terminal Salvage Value = (X) = $ 1,500.00	Years of life to Date: 15-16-17 Installed Cost: 11,250.54
8	Est. Cost Installed = (Y) = $ 26,100.00	Location:_____ Dept. No.: 1378
9	Terminal Salvage Factor = $\frac{x}{y}$ = _____6_____%	Intended Disposal Scrap Resale, Salvage or Conversion Value $ 0

	FACTOR	PROPOSED EQUIPMENT	EXISTING EQUIPMENT
10	Direct Labor (For Anticipated Production):	$ 21,759.44	$ 29,012.58
11	Indirect Labor (For Anticipated Production):		
12	Defective Material Labor & Works Expense:		
13	Down Time:		
14	Power Consumption:		
15	Tooling:		
16	Supplies:		
17	Floor Space: (if usable)		
18	Property Taxes & Insurance:	528.26	378.49
19	Normal Maintenance:	1,500.00	1,500.00
20	Special Repairs:		
21	Sub Contract Costs:		
22	Other Items (explain on reverse side):		
23			
24	Totals: B $	23,787.70	A $ 30,891.07
25			B $ 23,787.70
26	Next Yrs. Variance in Operating Cost: (A Minus B):		C $ 7,103.37
27	(Next Years Capital Cost of Retaining Existing Equipment)		
28	Restorative Repairs $ 18,700.00 / Years Effective 5 + (Restorative Repairs $ $18,700.00 × 6%)		D $ 4,862.00
29	Resale, Salvage or Conversion Value of Existing Equipment $ × 6%		E $
30	Salvage Value Loss, Next Year		F $
31	Total Next Yrs. Cost for Existing Equipment (C + D + E + F)		G $ 11,965.37
32	Total Next Yrs. Cost for Proposed Equipment. Chart 14 % + Int. 6% Total 20 % × $ Est. Cost Installed 26,100.00		H $ 5,220.00
33	First Years Gain (+) or Loss (—) thru replacing existing equipment (G-H) (taking into account Depreciation, Loss of Efficiency and 6% return on Investment)	PLUS	6,745.37

Approved by:_____ Date:_____ Calculated by: G. Brushe _____ Date:_____

Allis-Chalmers Mfg. Co.

FIG. 8–3. Capital equipment replacement analysis.

NEW MACHINES—HOW MANY TO BUY

Often you find that one machine won't handle all of your work. You need two or more. How many machines will you need? That depends on (a) how much production you want, and (b) how productive a machine will be. How much production you want, you find out from future work schedules and long-range plans.

If the new machines you are thinking about are similar to some you already have, past experience will tell you fairly well how much they will turn out. If a machine is to be used for one operation, the operation cycle time can be figured by adding the machine time required per unit of product to the time it takes the operator to put the product into and take it out of the machine.[3]

This gives the *bare operation cycle time* per unit. To obtain an average *complete* cycle time, you have to add in enough more time to cover miscellaneous minor interruptions.

Machines can never operate all the time that the plant operates because they are idle while being set up, while the worker must be away from the machine, and so on. In many plants doing varied work the machines are expected to be in operation about 75 per cent of the time, or about 6 hours each 8-hour day. General Motors shoots for 80 per cent as a goal but often has to be satisfied with 70 per cent. You need to be realistic. Always figure a machine's probable output at what it can turn out in, say, 6 hours—not 8. And figure the number of machines you need on that basis too. And don't figure that two-shift operation will yield twice as much as one-shift. It will yield a little short of twice as much because second-shift production is a little less productive than first. Don't forget, too, in all cases where machines are used for operations on several products, to add together the time that each product will take.

Because so many things can't be predicted, it is impossible to figure out ahead exactly how many machines you will need. It is important to see, however, that *you have to do it anyway*. Saying that it is hard to do it accurately lets no one off the hook. Some time ago Ford built an automatic foundry to make its engine blocks. It was new, and no one knew just how it would work. It was set up to supply the expected needs running at 80 per cent utilization. When started it ran at 40 per cent! And, it took months to raise the percentage. To make matters worse the sales forecast turned out to be too low. More engines were wanted than had been expected. All in all the mistake was serious, but it is the kind of situation that anyone figuring on machines has to face.

Old machines being replaced will nearly always still operate. It is well

[3] For metal-cutting machines the machine time can be calculated by using the rate of travel of the material (usually in revolutions per minute or feet per minute of material moving past the cutting tool), the depth and thickness of cut, and the length of the cut. Recommended speeds and feeds for cutting metal are available in engineering handbooks.

to save them so that they can be used on occasional jobs. In fact, most companies have some machines bought 50 years ago as well as some bought yesterday. When other machines are all busy, old machines can be put to work on simple jobs with liberal tolerances. Keeping the old machines provides a little extra capacity. If several new machines need to be bought, keeping the old ones may save buying a new one. If $4\frac{1}{4}$ machines are needed, buy just 4 new machines and use the old ones for the extra work.

Returning to the question: how many machines? Calculate the bare cycle time to do the operation; add on some more time for odds and ends to get the actual expected full cycle time. Multiply by the quantity of product wanted in, say, one week. This gives you the load for the machine for that product.

Do the same for all other products that will use the machine. Add all their requirements together to get the total work load for the machine. If you have been working with minutes, divide by 60 to change to hours. Then divide by the number of hours that you will be able to keep the machine in production in a week. If you work the factory 40 hours a week and get 80 per cent utilization, use 32 as your divisor. This gives the number of machines you need.

BOOK VALUE OF OLD MACHINES

The book value of old machines is a problem to some people in machine economy studies. Suppose that you buy a 10-year-life machine for $20,000, use it for 6 years, depreciating it on your books at $2,000 a year, and then consider replacing it. Your accounts show it still to be worth $8,000. Suppose, too, that it has a value today of $3,000 if sold and that it will be worthless in 4 more years.

Now suppose that you are thinking of buying a new machine and want to compare the two—continuing to use the old machine as against buying the new one. Should the costs of using the old machine include $2,000 of depreciation for each of the next 4 years? You might say, of course, that this is consistent with what we have been doing. It is what the government requires for tax-computing purposes. It is what you would do if you had never thought of buying a new machine.

Why even think of not listing $2,000 depreciation every year? The reason is that *the machine is actually worth only $3,000, not $8,000.* From here on—in machine economy studies—the depreciation every year should be $750 (one fourth of $3,000) not $2,000 (one fourth of $8,000).

Don't mix up the past with the future and don't let accounting practices confuse the issue. Past depreciation charges have, in fact, been too low, but you get the wrong picture of the future if you carry past mistakes into machine economy studies.

This idea goes against the grain, and some people—even those making machine economy studies—don't see the point and don't agree with it.

Of course, it must be admitted that it is hard to get a today's price on every half-worn-out machine that we might think of replacing. But what really goes against the grain is the $5,000 loss on book value of the old machine. That isn't even considered in machine economy studies. It sounds as if the new machine is somehow responsible for that loss, but this isn't so.

Here is the hard point to see. If no new machine is bought, the regular depreciation schedule of $2,000 per year carries on, and in 4 years, $8,000 of depreciation is recovered. You seem not to have lost the $5,000. Yet if a new machine is bought and the old one sold, you get $3,000 cash but take a $5,000 loss on your books. What has really happened, though, is that you *have already suffered an unrecognized loss of $5,000*. If you don't buy the new machine and continue to recover $2,000 "depreciation" annually, you are actually recovering $750 of depreciation and $1,250 of unrecognized profits. In the next 4 years that unrecognized profit will total $5,000 and will offset the $5,000 unrecognized loss you have already suffered. Normal depreciation practices cover all of this up, and since it washes out in the end, it goes unseen.

Notice that writing down the old asset to its present used machine value makes it hard for a new machine to make a good showing. The old machine's future depreciation is now shown to be very low ($750 in our example instead of $2,000); that *holds down* the computed cost of keeping it in operation. The Machinery and Allied Products Institute recommends this practice, even though it works against the sale of new machines (MAPI's member companies are machinery manufacturers). It is the only right way to compare old and new machines.

POST-CONSTRUCTION AUDITS

New machines and buildings often cost more than expected and save less. Of course you check costs while construction is going on and you check the final costs, but you shouldn't quit there. You ought also to check up after 1 year, possibly after 2 years as well. Then you can see if the project is paying off as well as it was supposed to.

But, isn't it too late to do anything about it if it isn't paying out? Yes, but you can learn where your estimates were wrong—what you didn't allow for and what didn't work out. Such checking up helps you learn how to make better estimates on future projects.

Companies don't always check up. One reason is that it is hard to do. Often, it is almost impossible to isolate, all by themselves and in dollar values, the effects of an improvement. How worth while, for example, is a new air-conditioned cafeteria? Or, how can you figure the dollars and cents savings produced by a new conveyor in its first year? You have changed some operations because of the conveyor. You have changed the design of some products. You have changed operations along the conveyor, and you have added some new products and cut out some old ones, and both your product mix and total volume have changed. Trying, in 1959, to estimate what 1958's production would have cost had 1957's methods still been in use is often too big a job to be worth while. The difficulty (and cost) of checking up is often a good reason for not doing it.

Other less valid reasons for not checking up are not appreciating its value and just never getting around to it. But when they are reasonably possible, post-construction audits should be made.

STUDY QUESTIONS

1. Which is better, to limit capital expenditures to the money available or to approve all good projects, regardless of how much money they take, and then raise capital outside? Explain your answer.
2. Why do boards of directors want to watch capital expenditures closely?
3. What does the "forward" look in capital expenditures mean? When should we use it and when not?
4. It costs money to buy and to operate every machine. How can we say that a machine saves money?
5. "Make-or-buy is a purchasing matter not a capital investment matter." Do you agree? Justify your position.
6. Division heads know their new machine needs best. Why not let them have the final say on what they get?
7. How is the "cash flow" important in capital expenditure control?
8. What "extras" also need capital when a whole group of machines is to be bought?
9. "The future's not ours to see." What's the good of trying to forecast a machine's productivity and its operating costs?
10. How worth while is the "first-year performance" of evaluating projects? What are its drawbacks?
11. Would you ever use "payback" to compare alternative machines? When, if ever, would you not want to use it?
12. Does "payback" give you the true picture? Discuss.
13. What is the difference between the full-life performance—regular dollars method and the discounted dollars method? When would they give you different answers? Which is better to use?
14. Why do discounted dollars calculations use such extremely high interest rates? What does that do to your results?
15. Some people say that—in your calculations—you should pay no attention to the loss in book value of old machines to be discarded if new machines are to be bought. Do you agree? Why?
16. Assume the following data:

Cost of new tool	$800
Expected life of new tool	5 yrs.
Interest rate on invested funds	10%
Insurance and repairs per year	$80
Number of times used per year	10
Setup cost per time used	$10
Estimated savings from new tool:	
Labor cost, per unit	$0.05
Material, per unit	$0.015*

*Material cost increase.

Using the first-year performance method:

a) Compute the volume required to break even if you include a savings in overhead at 100 per cent of direct labor.

b) What would the break-even volume be if you omitted the overhead saving?

c) What do you think that the true break-even volume would be? Explain.

CASE 8–1.   THE METROPOLITAN COMPANY

The Metropolitan Company is considering replacing two old drill presses with a new one. The new one will do the same work as the two old presses. Each old machine requires an operator. The new machine will require but one operator, but one who will receive $2.40 per hour, whereas the old machine operators each get $2.20 per hour. The machines are expected to operate 2,000 hours a year. Electric power costs $1\frac{1}{2}$ cents per kilowatt-hour. The old machines each use $1\frac{1}{2}$ kilowatts of power hourly; the new machine uses 2 kilowatts every hour. Taxes and insurance come to 2 per cent of the value of the machines. Repairs are $200 each on the old machines and $100 per year on the new one.

The old machines cost $2,000 each to install, have been used 5 years, are expected to last for 5 more, and still have $200 salvage value each at that time. The new machine costs $7,000 installed, would be expected to last for 10 years, and at the end of that time have a salvage value of $700. Interest on the investment should be charged at 15 per cent.

Should the Metropolitan Company buy the new drill and discard the old ones? What will the company save, if anything, the first year if it buys the new machine and discards the old ones? If the company buys the new machine, how long will it take for the machine to pay for itself?

CASE 8–2.

Using the MAPI chart shown on page 163 and following the procedure shown in the Allis-Chalmers equipment analysis shown on page 164, decide, with the following figures, how much you will lose annually if you do not replace your present machine with the proposed machine.

At present you are using two old machines which have a current sale value of $1,750 each, but they are urgently in need of heavy repairs costing $6,000 each. Without repairs, the machines can't do the work. The heavy repairs, if made, will actually extend the machines' lives. If we make the repairs we think that the machines will have a sale value of $6,500 each after 1 year. After 5 years we think that they will still have a sale value of $1,600 each.

The two old machines each require an operator for 2,000 hours a year. Each man's rate is $2.50 per hour. Material handling costs to serve these two operators comes to a total of $1,000 a year.

The proposed new machine, which would cost $25,000, would replace the two old ones, would do the same work, and would operate 2,000 hours a year with one $2.50 an hour operator. The new machine's sale value after 1 year is estimated to be $20,000. After 15 years, you estimate that it will be worth $5,000. By that time you will probably have to junk it or make heavy repairs. Materials handlers to serve the machine's operator would cost $500 a year. Figure interest at 25 per cent.

Other comparisons are as follows. The new machine would save $150 a year on maintenance, lubrication, and supplies. It would save 50 feet of floor space having an annual charge of $1.50 per square foot. Tool costs would be lowered $500 a year. Besides there would be a product quality improvement valued at $200 a year. But insurance, taxes, and power costs would go up $200 a year.

Chapter 9

PLANT LOCATIONS

How important is a plant's location? Can it make or break a company? Or is it relatively unimportant? Most of the time it is probably not a make-or-break matter. Probably no location is so perfect as to guarantee success if products and prices are not right. But bad locations can be so bad as to bankrupt a company. Over the years many New England textile plants lost money while Southern textile plants made money.

It is commonly said that a company's location is of utmost importance, but that could be true only if certain locations are decidely better than others *and if the good locations are scarce.* Certainly some locations are decidedly better than *some* other locations, but there seem to be many rather than few good locations. How, otherwise, can you explain the spread-out nature of American industry? You find steel mills in Pennsylvania, Ohio, Indiana, Alabama, California, and elsewhere. Furniture-making centers are found in New York, Michigan, Illinois, California, and several southern states. Textile mills are found in the Northeast, Southeast, and West. Shoe factories are in Massachusetts, New York, Maryland, Ohio, Illinois, Wisconsin, Missouri, and California. Airplanes are made in New York, Maryland, Georgia, Ohio, Kansas, Texas, Washington, and California. Nor can you prove that Eastman Kodak's Rochester location is better than any number of others; or GE at Schenectady; or National Cash Register at Dayton; or Elgin Watch at Elgin, Illinois.

Industry's dispersion surely means that (1) location doesn't matter much, (2) it does matter but there are many good locations, or (3) most of our plants are poorly located. Most manufacturing has been so profitable for years that number 3 seems out or else number 1 applies and it really doesn't matter. Number 2—it does matter but there are lots of choices—seems to fit what we find.

Let's look at a few examples. A few years ago, General Electric put its Appliance Park (household appliance manufacture) at Louisville. Why Louisville? Would Cincinnati, St. Louis, or Indianapolis have done?

171

Probably—at least many other companies have built, in the last 10 years, new plants in those cities. General Motors put its Electro-Motive division (diesel-electric locomotives) at LaGrange, Ill. Why there? We could go farther: Why autos in Detroit? Tires in Akron? Airplanes in

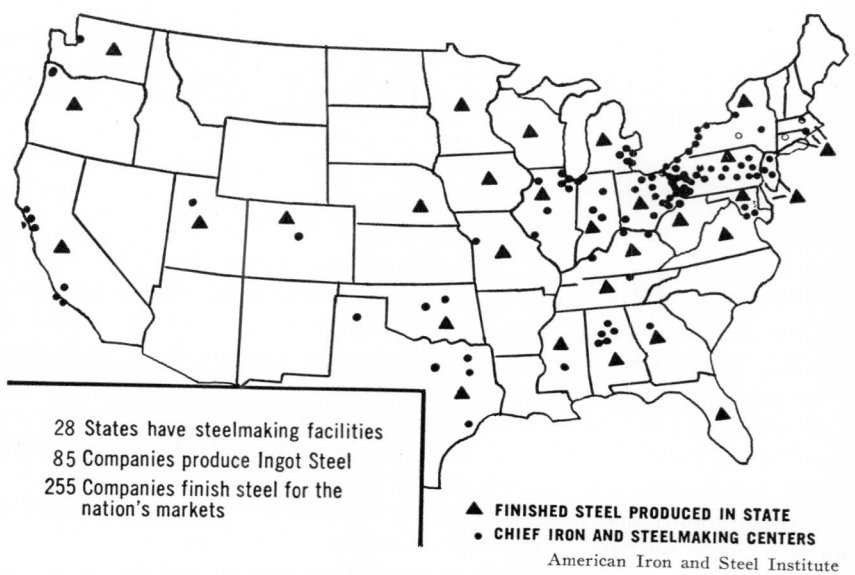

28 States have steelmaking facilities
85 Companies produce Ingot Steel
255 Companies finish steel for the
     nation's markets

▲ FINISHED STEEL PRODUCED IN STATE
● CHIEF IRON AND STEELMAKING CENTERS

American Iron and Steel Institute

FIG. 9–1.   Location of steelmaking companies in the United States.

Los Angeles? Even chambers of commerce can't prove to you that these locations are clearly better·than all others.

HOW LONG CAN A LOCATION STAY GOOD?

We live in a changing world. Many of today's old factories, now poorly located, were well located when they were built. Fifty years ago most factories were in cities where they had plenty of labor and streetcars to get to work. Now, many large city locations are bad because space is limited and workers do not want to drive into old congested parts of town and then have no place to park.

Fifty years ago you might have put your factory in New York City to be near your market. Maybe today you need a Los Angeles plant to handle a market nonexistent for your products 50 years ago. Even 20 years ago you would not have put a factory in Florida or Texas because of the summer heat. Now, with air conditioning and large local markets, you want plants there.

No company management should expect a location to stay good forever. If a new location is being considered, the company should first forecast its business as well as it can to see what its business will be like in 10 or more years. What products? What volume? Where will the customers be? Forecasting helps management choose locations that won't get out of date so fast. But even with the best forecasting you can't pick locations that will stay good forever.

RELOCATION

Whenever you *do* anything about location you *re*locate. *Location* is just a fact of life. Your plant is already located. You live with it, getting advantages if it is good, putting up with disadvantages if it is bad. Probably your officials spend little time thinking about the matter.

But if business gets worse or better, a new location may need to be considered. If it gets *worse*, maybe your poor location is an important cause. You can remedy it only by moving. Or if business gets *better*, you will burst at the seams if you don't expand—here or elsewhere.

Actually, plant relocation probably should be more common than it is. Many plants are in locations that get poorer every year—yet each year their officials put off moving. They really have a relocation problem but don't recognize it or haven't the courage to face the cost of getting a new plant. It's just like some people living in an old house. A new one would be nice, but building a new one is a headache and costs money, so nothing is done. In the case of factories you can go from bad to worse, finally losing money and then having a really hard time moving.

The need to relocate is clearer when business is booming. You just can't handle it all where you are. Several choices are available. (1) Don't expand, just take the business you can handle and let the rest go to competitors. (2) Don't expand, but take all the sales orders you can get and buy your excess needs from someone else. (3) Expand (if you can) your plant where you now are. (4) Keep the present plant and start another one somewhere else. (5) Move everything to a new larger plant and get rid of the old one. Of these choices most companies choose number 4 unless there is good reason to leave the old location.

Relocation problems do not arise often in small companies. Many presidents of small companies, never, while they are president, have to move or expand beyond their old plant. But large multiplant companies (several of our large companies have over 100 plants) are always expanding, building, or buying, or sometimes selling plants. Location problems, when they come, are important even to the big companies because, once installed, it is expensive to change or abandon plants.

IDEAL LOCATIONS

What would an ideal location be like?—forgetting for the moment that no location can be all good and no bad. At the *ideal* location every cost of operation would be minimum. It would be close to the market, yet you want to be close to raw materials too. The site should have good rail and truck connections. Ideally the community should have plenty of good workers—"good" workers being the kind who expect to do a fair day's work in exchange for a fair day's wage. Attendance should be regular and turnover low. There should be no labor-troubled companies nearby.

The people of the ideal community should want the company there. It should not be like turnpikes—everyone wants them but never right next door. The ideal community should want the company to locate there, and some of the people there should want to work at the company. City officials should be sympathetic and willing to allow you to cut a curbstone for a driveway, put in a traffic light to operate at shift change time, build a bridge across an alley, or put pipes and wires under streets where you have buildings on both sides.

The community should be pleasant for employee living. It needs to have good schools, churches, shops, medical facilities, ample housing at reasonable cost, and access to the plant by bus and employees' cars.

Other items are land prices, factory building costs, and local taxes. All should be low. There should be plenty of unoccupied adjacent land (available at a reasonable price). Electric power, good water, and gas should be available at low rates. Ample sewage disposal facilities are needed. Also service industries—so you won't have to keep such large staffs of maintenance electricians, plumbers, and so on. Also, no tight local laws about noise, smoke, refuse dumping, water pollution.

You may ask, why would any community want a company that asks so much? It sounds as if you propose to make noise and smoke, dump refuse, pollute the water, pay low wages, and not want to pay much tax. Your company should plan to be a good citizen. Otherwise it will not be welcomed into a nice community. You should build a trim, attractive building, set well back off the road and landscape around it to make it a credit not a blight in the area. Of course you don't want burdensome restrictions, but you should not do the things that make restrictions necessary.

FREIGHT COSTS

Hauling things around costs money so do as little of it as possible. Some companies spend as little as 1 per cent of all of their costs on freight. But for others it comes higher, in some cases up to 4 per cent of all costs. In rare cases (cement, plaster, gypsum) freight costs are much higher. Johns-Manville and U.S. Gypsum probably spend close to 20 per cent of their income for freight.

You can't eliminate freight costs no matter where you locate—all you can do is to keep them down. In one form or another the product must be hauled all the way from the raw material producer to the final user. You can locate anywhere between your raw material source and the market. Locate near raw materials and you cut raw materials freight, but you pay more freight to deliver your products. Or locate near your market and save finished product freight, but pay more on raw materials.

Now, all you have to do is to *locate where the sum total of freight costs is the least*. But that is easy to say and hard to do. You buy thousands of different raw materials from all over. And you sell nationwide. Where do you locate? It is hard to choose one spot and be sure it is the best. Besides, in 10 years your suppliers won't all be where they are today—neither will your customers. So, our rule (to locate where freight costs are the least) is not too helpful.

Furthermore, in most companies, freight costs don't count as heavily as other factors. If wages in one location are noticeably lower than in another, it will probably pay to go there even if freight costs are a little higher. Wage costs are usually five to eight times as much as freight costs. Wages usually make up one sixth of all costs so a small wage saving would offset any ordinary differences in freight costs.

In the last 50 years, the textile industry has shifted from New England to the South. More recently many furniture factories have followed. Their freight costs are surely higher, but lower wage rates more than offset them.

Freight costs don't amount to much when you make small high-value products like watches or cameras. As far as freight costs are concerned, it doesn't matter much where you locate. But for larger, heavier products it matters more.

Sometimes companies, industries, or communities manage to get freight rates set up so that the best locations don't get the best rates. Most coal used in Detroit comes through Toledo from West Virginia. But if it goes by water the 50 miles from Toledo to Detroit, it gets a special low rail rate across Ohio so that the total freight cost for coal delivered in Detroit is about the same as in Toledo. California oranges go to New York for the same freight charge as to Cleveland. Magazine publishers get low postage rates. This allows them to concentrate in New York and Chicago. If the rates were higher, they would have to decentralize more.

NEARNESS TO MARKET

Being near the market allows you to give better service to customers and saves freight costs. Of the two advantages, giving better service is usually the more important.

You can't always be near your market—your whole market, that is. It is too widespread. It may be nation-wide. Large companies with nation-wide markets set up plants in many parts of the country. That way they get close to most markets.

Smaller companies either have to give up being close to all their customers or to concentrate their selling in the area near their factory. That way they can be close to their market. Small plants in New England serve the northeastern states. Those on the West Coast serve that territory. Most small plants are started close to the owner's home. They grow and develop their market nearby. Probably the location of the plant determines their market area rather than the market determining their plant location.

NEARNESS TO RAW MATERIALS

Being near raw materials allows you to get better service and to save on freight. But, like being close to the market, it is sometimes hard to do. How can you be close to 5,000 suppliers who are located all over? Large companies have more than 5,000 suppliers. Chevrolet buys from 24,000 suppliers in 700 different locations. Also, if you have plants all over the country, they can't all be near the source of raw material, unless the material is available everywhere. Factories using farm products are not seriously limited in location because wheat, cotton, cattle—most agricultural products—are available in many sections of the country.

Companies using iron ore or other materials that make lots of waste often locate near their raw materials so that they don't have to haul the waste very far. Companies using heavy bulky raw materials also locate near their source to save freight. Where finished products are heavy, bulky, and of low value, freight costs limit the area they can serve. Cement plants, for example, mostly serve local areas and are found in many parts of the country.

NEARNESS TO SISTER PLANTS AND WAREHOUSES

Companies have always tried to place new plants where they would compliment sister plants and warehouses. That still is important: fill in the holes; put plants where you now have none and where markets are now served by long-distance hauls.

But now giant companies have added other restrictive policies. First, don't put a plant anywhere where it dominates the community. General Electric won't put a plant anywhere where it will hire more than one eighth of the people working in the area. GE's Schenectady plant would never be built by GE today. It is too big for the community; it dominates it. GE has over 100 factories now, so this policy rules out many locations where GE already is.

Second, don't put plants too close together. Ford Motor says 15 miles apart at least. Reasons are tied in with above but besides you avoid having two plants draw from (and compete for) the same labor pool. Third, another GE policy says don't locate a small plant in a great big metropolitan area where its corporate voice would be muffled, if not lost.

LABOR

Wherever you go you must have employees, so an ample supply of labor is a must. It helps if the labor available is already skilled, but for most companies, this is not necessary. Most companies expect to train new employees because the jobs are so varied and so highly specialized.

You never would find new employees already knowing how to do most of your jobs.

For regular factory or office jobs the work habits and attitudes of prospective workers in a community are much more important than the skills they already have. Most factory workers do semiskilled jobs. Almost any applicant can quickly learn to do the work. Today it is possible for companies to locate almost anywhere where there are enough workers, but it is still a good idea to locate in areas where workers have good work habits and where there are few labor troubles. If you move to a new location, you may have to move a few of your skilled workers and some foremen but you will recruit most of your new work force from around the new plant.

But *don't expect to recruit a good labor force fast*. When you move into a community, it will take time to get good workers. Good men aren't out looking for jobs in great numbers. At first you'll have to get along with more than your share of marginal people, drifters, and generally poor men.

Pay attention, also to quantity and distance. Don't plan to recruit beyond 20 miles from your new plant. If there aren't enough men to fill your needs within 20 miles, you will probably have trouble. Also stay out of vacation areas and avoid labor turnover from transients. But these days you can forget public transportation for employees. They'll come to work in their cars.

ELECTRIC POWER

Electric power, and lots of it, is another must for today's factories. But except for companies using enormous amounts of power, as in aluminum manufacture, it is rarely a deciding factor in choosing a location. Most locations can furnish all the electricity you want at low rates.

Power is usually so cheap (about one cent a kilowatt-hour) that it doesn't pay to make your own. You make your own power only if you have to locate, for other reasons, where you can't buy power. By and large you would rule out locations without plenty of power.

WATER

Some companies need a great deal of water—more than there is in some places. U.S. Steel's Fairless Works uses 250 million gallons of water a day. Only a big river (the Delaware) could supply so much.

For industries needing lots of water, locations without plenty of water are out. Such industries include paper, sugar refining, steel, rubber, leather, chemical, rayon, food processing, and others. Water is used directly in the processes or for cooling products or machines, or for condensing steam, or washing, cleaning, quenching, and air conditioning.

You get water from wells, rivers, lakes, or pipe it in from the mountains. Water from wells taps ground water. Tapped too freely, wells may deplete underground water faster than nature replaces it—then a shortage develops. Companies using lots of water need to be very sure that future supplies will be ample for their needs.

Most industrial uses for water require purified water. It needs to have scale-forming materials—such as calcium and magnesium salts—removed lest they cake up and clog pipes. If the community supply of purified water is not ample, the company must put in its own system. Even such cities as Chicago and Detroit, with the inexhaustible supply of Great Lakes water, have had water shortages occasionally as their growth outstripped their water purification facilities. During long hot dry spells in summer everyone sprinkles his lawn and that uses so much water that water-using companies sometimes have to reduce their operations.

Factory-used water is often contaminated after its use and needs to be decontaminated before it can be dumped back into rivers or lakes. Nearly all cities and states have laws against dumping waste of a harmful nature into waterways. Treating water before or after use is an expense to think of when comparing locations.

LAND COSTS

Land costs and local taxes are sometimes deciding factors in factory location, although on the whole they are relatively unimportant. Land cost may be as little as 3, and is usually less than 10, per cent of the total cost of a factory. As it is only a one-time cost, it usually figures little in the choice of a location. Furthermore, it is an investment rather than a cost, because it endures as an asset with value and can, if the plant is ever disposed of, be reconverted into cash.

LOCAL TAXES

Local real estate and property taxes usually are also relatively unimportant, and neither should, except where other considerations are nearly equal, be the deciding factor in the choice of a location. Most manufacturing companies have investments in plant and equipment and inventory of $7,500 or more per employee. Big cities usually have tax rates of from 2 to 6 per cent, so it would seem that the taxes might be anywhere from $150 to $450 per year per employee, but it isn't like that. Nowhere are assets appraised at their full value (although they are supposed, legally, to be appraised at full value). Appraisals in most cities are from $\frac{1}{4}$ to $\frac{2}{3}$ of real value. You end up paying about $1\frac{1}{2}$ to 2 per cent, or maybe a little more, of your assets' real value. That means anywhere from $100 to $200 per employee. A difference of anywhere up to $100 can be important, but usually the difference is nowhere near $100, so that it would, by itself, seldom be a decisive factor, particularly since *low tax rates often don't stay low.*

This generalization, that taxes should count but little in location choice, does not always apply, however. Many steel companies have investments in taxable property of over $12,000 per employee. Oil refineries and chemical companies have investments of $18,000 to $25,000 per employee. To them even small tax rate differences are very important.

Where communities furnish free sites or even rent- and tax-free buildings to new companies for a period of years, they usually get some new companies. Generally these handouts are for limited periods; after that, you pay rent and taxes. Companies shouldn't allow temporary inducements to overshadow the basic merits of alternative locations. If they do, they may find themselves located where, in the long run, over-all costs are high. Most big companies, however, aren't looking for free handouts; they expect to pay their way in a community.

Companies must pay many kinds of taxes besides property taxes. Several states and cities have income taxes on personal incomes. Many states and some cities have a sales tax. Thirty-three states have corporation income taxes. Unemployment and workmen's compensation insurance rates differ among states. Licensing and franchise fees may have to be paid. The effects of the various kinds of taxes should be weighed and their over-all effects appraised. Philadelphia and Toledo, for example, have city income taxes, but because of the income they produce, have very low property tax rates.

SECURITY FROM ATTACK

Since the early days of World War II, some factory locations have been determined by their relative security from possible enemy attack. During the war many plants making war goods were located in the mid-continent area far from the seaboard. Other plants, not making war goods, even today shy away from areas having ammunition, ordinance, and airplane factories, and even railroad marshaling yards, key bridges, and harbors, lest they be in the danger zone in case of attack.

Sometimes it isn't up to the company to decide where it puts a new plant. Companies building new plants to make defense products may find the government telling them to keep away from certain locations because of their vulnerability to attack. Government policy calls for important defense plants to locate at least 10 miles from any densely populated or heavily industrialized area. That may mean 15 to 20 miles from a city's center.

SPECIALIZED COMMUNITIES

Some communities develop into specialized centers of certain kinds of manufacturing. Akron, Detroit, and Grand Rapids are known as centers of the manufacture of rubber products, automobiles, and furniture. Specialized communities have several advantages. Suppliers of materials are located close by. So are companies making the equipment used by the prevailing industry. Local users get better service than those located elsewhere.

You can generally get workers with experience in your industry, so less training is necessary. If your products must be accurately made or if technical knowledge is important, this is a big advantage. Specialized communities sometimes take over part of industry's training job by offering vocational high-school training for jobs in the dominant industry.

Being in a specialized community is a mixed blessing, however. True, you can often hire skilled men. But since they can easily get jobs elsewhere, your own skilled employees quit more readily. You may end up with higher labor turnover. Same with labor matters. You may have to do the same things (pay, vacations, and so on) as everyone else or have labor troubles.

RELATED INDUSTRIES

Service industries are nearly always close to the industries using their services. So are industries using by-products from other industries. Synthetic rubber plants use by-products from special oil refineries. They are located right next door so the material can be piped in as it is made. Near Toledo, Republic Steel has a plant making powdered iron right next to a refinery so it can use the refinery's by-product hydrogen. Industries closely related to others usually locate near each other.

CLIMATE

Climate is important to some industries, although less so than years ago. Today you can control, generally at reasonable cost, the temperature, humidity, dust, ventilation, and fumes in a factory. This makes the natural climate less important than it used to be. You can put factories in the South now and in the semidesert parts of the West and Southwest. Before air conditioning you couldn't, because of the heat.

Climate still plays an important part, however, in another way. Factory officials must work where the factory is located and must live in that general area. Sometimes the choice of locations is influenced by the officials' (or their wives') preferences as to where they want to live. Many people like large cities, and some like small cities. Some like living in the North, and some the South. Sometimes the choice is based purely on climate; sometimes the climate is but one factor influencing the type of social, cultural, and educational life available.

Large multiplant companies rarely are influenced in the choice of locations by the personal preferences of the officials because they have many capable men, some of whom would prefer one location, others a totally different one. What's one man's Shangri-La is another man's Sahara. Small- and medium-sized companies, particularly those managed by the owner, are more influenced by the wishes of their officials in this respect.

PUERTO RICO

Puerto Rico is not a state but it is part of the United States commonwealth. By our standards its pay rates and standard of living are low. To attract industry, special inducements are held out. First, United States income taxes on corporations do not apply there. Puerto Rico has its own income taxes (about two thirds as high as in the U.S.), but new corporations pay none for 10 years. They are also free for 10 years from municipal license fees and from personal property taxes for from 5 to 10 years. And if you move to Puerto Rico yourself, there is no personal income tax on dividends for 7 years. Wages are only one third of mainland wages, but land costs $1,000 an acre and up. This is higher than most mainland site costs.

Some companies are putting up plants in Puerto Rico. Most, but not all, find it quite a paying proposition. Biggest disadvantages are that it takes longer than in the States to get efficient operations going and that transportation costs to the United States market are high.

URBAN, SUBURBAN, AND SMALL-TOWN LOCATION

That industry is moving into small towns is well known. Today, there is hardly a small town left without its one or two factories. But— and this may be overlooked sometimes—*most manufacturing is still done and most new buildings are still being built in and around cities.* Today's trend is to small factories, so small towns are suitable. But newer plants employing 10,000 to 15,000 are common on the outskirts of big cities. Plants that large can't be put in small towns because there aren't enough men.

The movement out from cities is forced by the lack of unoccupied sites, but there are other reasons too. Workers like to live out where they have more room and don't like to drive long distances downtown. Parking space is another problem that is solved better away from cities. Technical developments in the plant have spurred the movement, too. Progressive assembly lines, automatic groups of machines, power trucks, and conveyors, all have cut costs of moving materials around on a one-floor plant. This makes one-story buildings less costly to operate now than buildings with several floors. One-story buildings take lots of space, so moving out of the city is the answer.

Wage rates in small towns are almost always lower than in cities, although not so much lower as they used to be. Even at that they are sometimes one-quarter to one-third lower. Some small-town workers may, at first, be unaccustomed to factory work and turn out less work than city employees, but they soon learn. Before the advent of large unions, workers in small towns usually had no unions and didn't want them, so companies locating in small towns were relatively free from labor troubles. Some companies moving to small towns years ago probably were hoping to escape unionization of the employees. Today, however, small-town plants are almost as likely to be unionized as those in large cities.

When plants are located in small towns, many employees have small farms or gardens nearby from which they supplement their regular earnings. Seasonal layoffs during lulls in factory production are actually welcomed by some employees, who use the extra time to do their own work. This can be a disadvantage, however, if the peaks and lulls in an employee's two jobs do not dovetail and he absents himself from work at the factory to do his own.

Small towns have some disadvantages—mostly minor. It takes a good while—maybe a year or two—to train the unaccustomed new workers to factory ways. Your inventory tie-up is likely to be larger, particularly for spare parts for maintenance. And you will need to have a pretty complete maintenance department because you can't draw on outsiders. Also power failures are more common, and fire insurance rates are higher. Absenteeism during hunting season will be greater.

Many companies, wishing to leave congested city locations, go only as far as the suburbs, not to country locations. In surburban locations you get most of the advantages of both city and country. Often wage rates are a little below city wages, and labor is plentiful. Suburban factories are not far from the market provided by the city, which, in the case of small plants, is often its main market. Plenty of land for present and prospective needs is usually available at reasonable prices in suburbs. Taxes are generally lower than they are in cities. Building costs also may be a little less, but land costs and taxes, as well as building costs, are all, generally speaking, higher than they are in small towns.

Suburbs usually have better rail and truck connections than small towns, almost as good, in fact, as cities. Suburban plants are close to service industries. Located there, you wouldn't need to have so many of your own repair men—electricians, plumbers, and so on—as you would in small towns. Nor would you need to build your own power plant, as you would in a few small towns.

Suburban factories, like those in the city, don't carry the load of the community's prosperity on their shoulders alone. In small towns a medium-sized plant is everything to the town. If the plant prospers so does the community, but if the plant goes down, so does the community. Plant officials have to remember that; sometimes it keeps them from doing things they would like to do.

ORGANIZED INDUSTRIAL DISTRICTS

Factories, stores, and houses don't mix very well. They ought to be in separate areas. Factories need high-power electric lines, railroads, lots of truck traffic, and other things that are bad in residential areas. Whole industrial districts—factories *and only factories*—would be a happy solution to the problem of mixed areas.

Industrial districts are a good solution, but, in the past, we have very few of them, so few that they can all be listed here: the Clearing Industrial District, Chicago; the Central Manufacturing District, Chicago; the Trinity Industrial District, Dallas; the Industrial Additions, Wichita; Bergen County Industrial Terminal, Teterboro, N.J.; Los Angeles Airport Industrial Tract, Central Manufacturing District, Los Angeles; and the Fairfax Industrial District, Kansas City. Many new ones are now being developed, but those listed above are the only big and long-established ones.

An industrial district is hard to plan because you have to *own* all the land—several hundreds of acres—to make it work. But why do you have to *own* it? Why not use zoning laws to restrict an area to factories? The trouble is that zoning laws work only one way. You can't put a factory in a residential area but you can put a residence or a store in a factory area. The problem is to keep residences and small stores *out*. So the only way to work a factory district is to *buy all* of the land in an area and then sell only to factories. And that is the rub; it is next to impossible to buy up hundreds of acres along a railroad and fairly close to a big city.

In spite of all the money it takes and the troubles getting land, industrial districts are becoming more common. As long as they are not far from where workers live, they are preferred by most companies over other locations. Look at Figure 9–2. It shows airplane pictures of Dallas' Trinity District in 1947, 1951, and 1955. The industrial growth has been phenomenal. Notice, too, that from the air it looks neat, the buildings are well spaced, set well back from the street, and the area around is nicely landscaped. That is part of the plan. Factories can't be dirty, ramshackle, and poorly arranged. They must be a credit to the area rather than a blot on the landscape.

SITES

Choosing the area is the real job in selecting a location, but the site within the area must also be suitable. It must have, at least to some extent, all of the characteristics already discussed. Besides, it should be near a residential area where workers can live. It should have bus services and be near main streets or roads. Too often land zoned for industrial use is the poorest available; it is an old dump, or it is swampy or subject to floods or is inaccessible.

You would want a railroad siding, a truck dock, and, for some companies, a dock for ships. You need extra space too for trucks waiting to load or unload and extra siding space for railroad cars waiting. Being near a superhighway would also help.

1947

Industrial Properties Corp., Dallas

FIG. 9–2.   Growth of the Trinity District in Dallas.

1955

You need enough room for present buildings, for future expansion, and for parking employee automobiles (some cities require you to furnish your employees with parking spaces so they don't have to park along the street). You may need parking space at the rate of one per two employees, and your parking lot may approximate your plant in total area.

How much floor space will you need in your new plant? Of course it varies a great deal between industries. Your old operations will give you a clue, but here are some general guides: minimum—no extra space anywhere—200 square feet per worker; ordinary manufacture, with ample aisles and storage areas, 700; very spread-out manufacture, 1,500 square feet per worker.[1] These space requirements include all floor space, not just the space at the man's workplace. The 1,500 feet is quite high. Few companies would ever need that much space. Even 700 is high.

While you are moving you should prepare for the future and choose a site with more space than you need now. Westinghouse Electric uses a 5 to 1 rule: get a site five times as big as present floor space in the building. Even if you end up not wanting all of the land, you may want to control the land next to your new factory. If you don't, it will soon be built up with hot-dog stands, bars, loan companies, gas stations, and small stores. They look bad and add to traffic congestion.

Land for a site should be dry and able to carry the building's weight without much settling. If your operations make smoke or fumes, choose a site so that the prevailing winds will carry them toward the open country. The site must be zoned for industrial use and without anti-smoke ordinances. And it needs to have good police and fire protection. If your processes produce large quantities of waste which have to be carried away by water (common in chemical companies), the site must be next to a river or other large body of water.

If the factory is being moved from one location to another in the same area, the new site should, if possible, be close enough to the old one so that most of the workers can continue to work in the new plant without moving or driving a long distance to work.

The cost of alternative sites will be important only if there is a great difference in the prices and little difference in the merits. Besides the charge for the land, some sites will require more filling, grading, expensive foundations, or more costly connections to the utilities than other locations. The total expenditure, not just the bare cost of the land, should be considered in comparing site costs.

CHOOSING A LOCATION

Companies wishing to move or to put up a new factory (and even those which aren't thinking of moving) are besieged with literature

---

[1] See D. A. Muncy, "Land for Industry—A Neglected Problem," *Harvard Business Review*, March–April, 1954, pp. 51–53.

from all over the country—from big cities and small. Every community's spokesman praises his locations.

You might ask, why does a community want a factory? It is largely the businessmen who want it, and they want it because it boosts business. The United States Chamber of Commerce says that 100 new factory workers in a community make 175 more jobs in other lines and add 110 more households to the area. What with the extra jobs they make, when they spend their wages, 100 new factory workers in a community mean over half a million dollars more personal income and add a

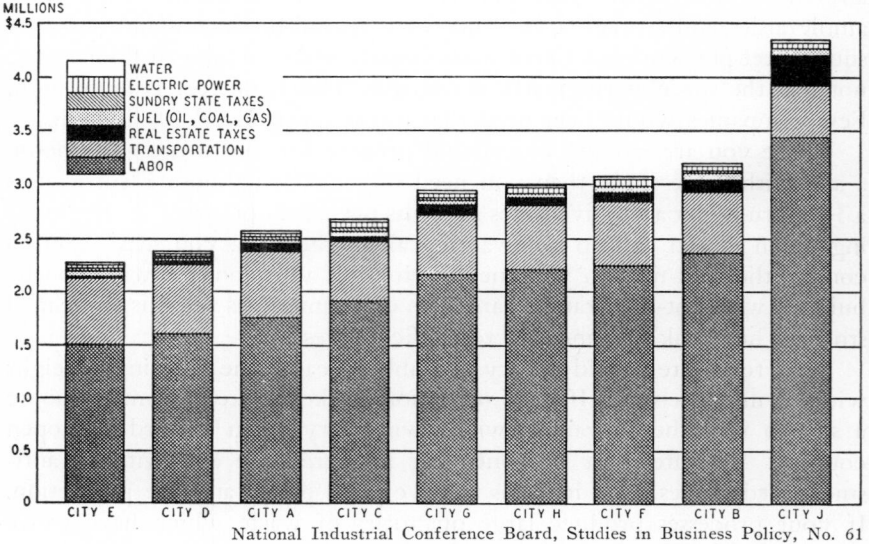

MILLIONS
$4.5

WATER
ELECTRIC POWER
SUNDRY STATE TAXES
FUEL (OIL, COAL, GAS)
REAL ESTATE TAXES
TRANSPORTATION
LABOR

CITY E   CITY D   CITY A   CITY C   CITY G   CITY H   CITY F   CITY B   CITY J

National Industrial Conference Board, Studies in Business Policy, No. 61

FIG. 9–3. Annual cost to operate a plant of 1,000 employees in various cities.

quarter of a million dollars to bank deposits in the community. Factories also pay taxes and help keep other people's taxes down. Small wonder that most communities want industry.

When you check into the various communities and their claims, you will find that many of the locations offered don't suit your needs. But after discarding the poor ones, you will probably have quite a few nearly equally good choices left over. You can choose any of them and probably do all right. You may end up choosing one location over another because of a relatively minor factor, such as a real estate tax exemption for several years. You let that influence you, though, only because more important things are about equal.

But before you make any final choice, compare different locations as well as you can. It would be easy if you could put everything into numbers and solve formulas. But you can't. Some things, however, can be stated in numbers and weighed. Figures 9–3 and 9–4 show how one company tackled the problem. Figure 9–3 is in numbers—in dollars—

showing the cost of running a new plant with 1,000 employees for a year. The company listed, for each community, the plant's operating cost for a year. Seven factors were figured separately, and their total summed up. Looking at Figure 9–3 you choose City E.

Now look at the nonnumerical factors in Figure 9–4. For each factor each city is rated: excellent, plentiful, very good, good, adequate, or fair; or, in the case of union activity, active, significant, moderate, and negative, but none of these ratings are numerical. Without numbers it is hard to judge which city is best. Cities A and C seem best. E is good but not as good as A and C.

Which city would you choose? E has it over both A and C when it comes to the costs of the seven measurable items—to the tune of $300,-000–$400,000 a year. But, being not quite so good in the seven non-

Factor	City E	City D	City A	City C	City G	City H	City F	City B	City J
(1) Labor supply	adeq.	adeq.	plent.	plent.	adeq.	adeq.	plent.	plent.	plent.
(2) Type of labor	good	good	excel.	excel.	excel.	excel.	excel.	excel.	excel.
(3) Union activity	sign.	sign.	neg.	neg.	mod.	sign.	sign.	mod.	act.
(4) Attitude	good	good	v.g.	v.g.	good	good	v.g.	v.g.	good
(5) Appearance	fair	fair	good	good	excel.	fair	good	good	good
(6) Transportation	good	good	v.g.	good	v.g.	good	v.g.	v.g.	v.g.
(7) Recreation	good	v.g.	v.g.	v.g.	v.g.	good	v.g.	v.g.	v.g.

National Industrial Conference Board

FIG. 9–4. Comparison of other factors influencing choice of plant site.

quantitative items, part (maybe all) of the gain would be lost. City E rates fairly good on every nonquantitative factor, but city A is better on every one. City A has a more plentiful supply of excellent labor. E has an adequate supply of good labor. Maybe E's advantage labor-costwise will disappear in the years ahead. E also has it over A on real estate taxes—something that also may not last.

Can you make a choice and convince yourself that you have chosen the best location for sure? Probably not, and probably it won't matter a great deal. Choose E or A (or another?). You ought to do well, as far as location is concerned—whichever you choose. The company that made this survey actually picked city A with C as second and E as third choice.

SOURCES OF INFORMATION CONCERNING LOCATION

Most communities have the welcome mat out for new factories. They want them because it means more jobs and more retail business. So a company thinking about relocating hardly has to hunt for information, once it becomes known that it is likely to move. It will be besieged with information from organizations urging it to "Locate in Metropolis," or "Come to Ruralville," telling the advantages of locating in a particular community. Naturally, such information is biased. It lists all the real and some claimed advantages and leaves out the disadvantages. Not all communities go after new industries so hard, but local chambers of commerce are generally active in seeking industry and are ready to furnish information.

Railroads usually are well prepared to furnish information about locating along their tracks. Electric power and gas companies also have departments whose job it is to interest factories in locating in their

FIG. 9–5.   Advertisements trying to woo new industry.

areas. Banks and real estate agents also can furnish helpful information. All these sources can supply information about particular sites as well as about general areas. The information from all these various sources is likely to be biased in favor of a particular community and must be discounted somewhat.

The United States Census of Manufacturers is taken every 2 years, and extensive reports of manufacturing by industry and area are published. Reference to these reports provides a wealth of information concerning the nature of the manufacturing already being carried on in all but the smallest communities in the nation. The federal Departments of Commerce, Labor, Interior, and Agriculture also publish considerable material which may be helpful for a comparative study of plant locations.

Most manufacturing companies so rarely have to pick a new location that they do not have location specialists on their staffs. Large management consulting companies and construction companies specializing in building factories can generally do a better job for their clients in making locational studies than an individual company can do. They can also get information about specific sites without letting anyone know the company's name. There are even plant location specialist consulting companies. The recommendations of both consultants and construction companies should be free from bias, since neither should have any reason for recommending one location over another.

You shouldn't look only into communities aggressively going out after new industry. Communities not actively seeking industries may have greater advantages than those which try to attract new plants. They may even, if you ask for them, make concessions equal to those offered by other places. Parke-Davis wanted to put a plant in Ann Arbor, Michigan, on a site that would require new sewer construction. When the company objected to bearing the nearly $100,000 charge, the city cut it to less than half.

When the search for a new location gets down to picking the exact site, it is well to have either consultants or real estate brokers do the final investigating of good and bad points of different sites. Better yet, get an option on the most likely site. The point is that you must keep your own identity secret. Any time a well-known company gets interested in a plot of ground (and people find out about it), its price skyrockets. Options protect you against price gouges.

MOVING TO A NEW LOCATION

Moving a factory to a new location is such a big job that it can be done quickly and economically only if all the details are carefully planned and scheduled in advance. A moving co-ordinator should be put in charge of the whole operation. Department representatives reporting to him should plan every detail of the transfer of departments.

Timetables and moving sequence schedules for each part of the change should be set up ahead. The exact location of every machine in the new plant should be determined and utility lines installed ready for use.

Unless orders can be filled by sister plants, stockpiles of finished products must be made up ahead, so that customers can be supplied while the move is under way. Incoming raw materials should be channeled into the new plant ahead of the move, and the old plant should use up its stocks so that little material will have to be transported. Finished goods stocks, too, should be kept low to reduce their moving costs, but they should not be allowed to fall so low that customers' orders go unfilled.

Before the relocation, everything should be inventoried and inspected, and scrap and junk eliminated. Machines should be crated or mounted on dollies or platforms ready to go. Heavy-duty hoists and industrial trucks should be made available to handle the machines. Employees should be told where to report and what to do in the new plant. Once the move is under way, it should be made quickly and should be directed by the co-ordinator, who should get reports of progress from both old and new plants. All of this may seem overly detailed, but it must be done if the move is to be made quickly and economically.

MOVING COSTS

The actual process of moving from one location to another results in production losses and numerous expenses, all of which should be considered before a decision to move is made. Many of the costs of moving are indirect and are easily overlooked when plans to move are made. Consequently, the actual cost of a move is likely to exceed the estimates. Materials and supplies may be lost or damaged during the transfer. A certain amount of damage to equipment is also inevitable in moving.

Some companies have found that more money and space are required in the new plant for employee and operating services than was planned because more racks, benches, chairs, lights, and handling facilities are provided than there were in the old plant. Even if no change is intended, these items may increase the space costs by 5 to 25 per cent. Sometimes partially worn-out equipment, not fully depreciated, is discarded and replaced with new when a move is made. The dismantling, transporting, and reinstallation of equipment may run as high as 25 per cent or more of the cost of the new space. Final preparation of the new space, office partitions, storerooms, painting, etc., can cost another 25 per cent.

If both old and new quarters are rented, double rent must be paid during the relocation. In addition, there are extra engineering, accounting, and supervision costs caused by the move, as well as disposal costs if the old property was owned. After the move is completed, a new plant almost always produces inefficiently for a time. Furthermore, even moves to nearby locations result in considerable labor turnover, making it necessary to break in many new employees who must be allowed time to get acquainted with the work.

STUDY QUESTIONS

1. Tell how you would go about picking a location that would stay good over the years. Explain thoroughly.
2. Is relocation as important as location? Explain and justify your answer.
3. Which would you rather be: near to your market or near your raw materials? Why? Explain.
4. A small toy manufacturer (who sells nationally) in the Detroit area is thinking of moving his plant to Fayetteville, Ark. Advise him and support your position.
5. Would you locate in an area where you could hire skilled workers? What are the good and bad points?
6. What has water to do with locations? Discuss fully.
7. If a small town gave you a free site and tax exemption for 10 years, would you go there? Discuss fully.
8. What has climate to do with locations? Anything? Justify your answer.
9. Why the movement by industry out of big cities? Are there any losses in moving away from big cities?
10. Tell what characteristics an ideal site should have. How big should the building be? How big should the site itself be?
11. Explain how to pick out a good new location.
12. What problems arise in connection with the actual move to a new location?

CASE 9–1. THE COSTELLO COMPANY

The Costello Company, located in Terre Haute, Indiana, made door hinges and latches for the construction industry, for automobiles, and other small hardware items sold to jobbers. It also operated a small foundry. The construction industry items, the automobile parts, and the miscellaneous hardware items were made in separate major departments. Employment was 1,500.

Because the company's business had grown, the factory was operating two shifts. Unit costs on the night shift were 15 per cent higher than those on the day shift. In spite of the overtime costs, Saturday work had been scheduled; but, even so, sales orders exceeded production and longer and longer delivery dates had to be quoted.

The Board of Directors met to decide whether to drop some lines, subcontract more work, or expand, locally or elsewhere (the existing plant could not be expanded, nor were there any satisfactory local premises available for rent).

The majority of the Board felt that the best solution to their difficulty would be to move the automotive hardware division nearer to Detroit, thus allowing the other departments to expand in the old quarters. Ralph Belden, the division superintendent in charge of automobile hardware manufacture, had lived in Detroit, but he objected to having his division moved there, mostly because his wife, a native of Terre Haute, did not want to leave.

The Board appointed Harold Menning, the company treasurer, to investigate possible locations. Menning came to the conclusion that, in the long run, the company's interest would best be served if it avoided a large city location and established its new plant in some small town within 100 miles of Detroit in Michigan, Indiana, or Ohio. In a number of these towns there were small plants that could be bought, although at a high price. Several of the plants under consideration could later be expanded, if need be.

Of the small plants available, the two best appeared to be one in Jackson, Michigan, and the other in Mount Clemens, Michigan. Labor costs in the Jackson, Michigan, area were about 10 per cent lower than in Mount Clemens, Michigan. On the other hand, freight charges were such as to absorb about 6 per cent of this differential for rail shipments and 8 per cent for truck shipments. The productivity of workers was about the same. Mount Clemens, nearer Detroit, suffered considerably from Detroit labor troubles. Jackson, on the other hand, being farther removed from the Detroit influence, had less labor trouble.

What problems should management consider and solve in this case before it takes action: (a) With respect to expansion? (b) With respect to location? What course of action should finally be taken?

Chapter 10

FACTORY BUILDINGS

FACTORY buildings have to be both big enough and the right shape to house manufacturing operations and services. If there is plenty of space, the building's shape usually doesn't matter too much. Operations can be fitted in. That is less true in purely processing plants such as oil refineries and blast furnaces. Foundries and power plants, too, usually need certain shapes.

The main job of factory buildings is to house the manufacturing operations. But that isn't all. They have to house any number of services. Some of the services need wires; others go in pipes or ducts. You need telephones, intercom systems, electricity of various voltages, hot and cold purified water, unpurified water for processes, compressed air, high-pressure steam, low-pressure steam, and natural gas. You need lights, heat, ventilation, and maybe air conditioning.

You need aisles, trucks, and elevators to move products and men. You need shipping and receiving docks for both rail and trucks. Besides, there are offices, a cafeteria, a dispensary, stock rooms, toolrooms, dispatching stations, timecard racks, locker rooms, washrooms, and toilets. Outdoors you need a parking lot for cars and storage space for coal and other materials not needing cover.

It is a long list. Factory services are much like services in a house. You don't think much about them as long as they work well. Let them be poorly arranged or get out of order and you find out how important they are. Factory buildings and their services are sometimes so poorly arranged that you can't operate efficiently. One authority says that two thirds of the reasons for high material handling costs have to do with buildings and services—high buildings with several floors, weak floors, low ceilings, columns too close, elevators off in corners, and so on.[1] Whether or not two thirds is the right figure, buildings and their arrangements and their services can help or hinder operations a lot.

In this and the next chapter in this book we deal with the plant and

---

[1] See "Building to Fit Your Handling Job," *Factory Management and Maintenance*, December, 1955, pages 84–90.

its services one after the other instead of together. We do it this way, even though it is unrealistic (everything is actually tied together), because this is the only way we can talk about them; we can't talk about everything at once. We don't design the building, then decide whether we will move materials by truck or conveyor. Nor the other way around either. We think of them together. The same thing is true of everything about the plant, its arrangement and its services. They need to be thought of as parts of a whole and not by themselves.

THE NEED FOR FLEXIBILITY

Factory buildings are rarely suited perfectly to their operations. How can they be when products keep changing all the time? They can't be. Management can't build a new perfect plant for every change, but management ought to try to keep the plant and its services as well suited to its needs as possible. Usually management can change only the easily changed things because changing the building costs so much. It is all a matter of relative cost. How much does it cost to change? How much do the inefficiencies cost? Sometimes it costs more to change than not to change.

Old plants, not well suited to today's needs, were once new and were probably well suited to yesterday's needs. Today's plants too, as they are first laid out, are well suited to today's needs. But changes come so fast that even new plants are almost always partly out of date before they are completely built. Actually new plants should be intended to be compromises between what suits best today and what will suit best tomorrow. Since we don't know tomorrow's needs for sure, we should build mostly for today's needs, yet spend a little extra to put in features that make changing easy.

Why all this need for change? Several reasons. Changes are needed because old products are dropped, new ones are added, or the sales of some items go up, others down. Besides, designs and operations change. Some old machines can be kept, some not, and new ones have to be added here and there.

How do you build for flexibility? There are many things you can do. Here are a few: (1) make ceilings high enough for overhead conveyors whether you need them or not; (2) put in extra electric outlets any place that is hard to get to and where you might some day need them; (3) allow space (or run wires) for high-voltage electricity to areas not needing it today; (4) put in heavy-duty floors; and (5) put machines in some areas on easily detachable mounts so that other permanent departments next door can easily expand. Doing these things costs a little extra in new buildings but cuts later remodeling costs.

TYPES OF BUILDINGS

Today it is the fashion to say that new plants are "built around a layout" or "built around the process." Actually, this is not the way new plants are built because most of them are large, rectangular, one-story buildings. Layouts and processes just don't all require rectangular one-story buildings.

Today's one-story factory building is 20 or more feet high. That is about double the height of ordinary offices, so the office part of the building is usually two stories high. In the plant proper, you find mezzanines and balconies alongside large, central open areas. Locker rooms, storage areas, and light manufacturing are all found on the mezzanines and balconies.

Turner Construction Co.

FIG. 10–1. A typical example of today's most popular type of new factory building. It is rectangular, one story high and encloses a large floor area.

Mill-Type Construction.   Yesterday's factories, like yesterday's houses, show by their style when they were built. Fifty years ago companies put up "mill-type"—sometimes called "slow-burning"—buildings. They were three to six stories high, had brick outside walls, many small windows, and thick wooden floors. Inside you found brick fire walls separating fairly large workrooms connected by heavy fire-resistant doors. Further protection from fire came from overhead sprinkler systems.

The outside brick walls carried their own weight and part of the floor weight too. The small windows cut down the daylight admitted. Inside were rows of heavy posts needed to carry the load of the upper floors. Mill-type construction was reasonably cheap and was durable. Maintenance costs were low. Fairly heavy loads could be put on upper floors—even if the machines made the floor vibrate. Mill-type buildings stood vibration well.

Why spend time on the buildings of 50 years ago? No one builds that kind of building today. No, but many of today's factories are housed in mill-type buildings. There are lots of them in older sections of cities in the eastern part of the United States. If they suit your operations, you can often buy them for one tenth the cost of new building space.

Steel Reinforced Concrete. Factory buildings built in the 1920's and after are likely to be of steel reinforced concrete. The frame is steel encased in concrete, and floors are concrete reinforced with steel bars.

Reprinted from *Life*

FIG. 10–2. This unusual building, located at Houston, Texas, and belonging to Corn Products Company, has no side walls, thus allowing dust and fumes to blow away.

Concrete and steel buildings are costly to build. They last a long time, and maintenance costs are low. But they are not very flexible; you can't change them around easily. Nor do they stand vibrations well, although they withstand fairly heavy operations without vibrating. Very heavy equipment can be put on separate concrete foundations on the ground floor. The building itself can't burn, although it can be damaged if its contents burn.

You get good natural daylight in concrete and steel buildings because the inside posts carry all the weight of the floors and the outside walls. That lets the outside wall be mostly glass.

One-Story Buildings.   Some kinds of buildings seem not to belong to any one period. Single-story buildings have always had their uses. Years ago most of them were made of wood or sheet metal and were of such light flimsy construction that they were really only semipermanent. Such buildings have low first cost and high upkeep cost. Fire hazards are high for flimsy wooden buildings. Heating costs are high. But you get a lot of space for very little first cost. You can put all of the equipment on separate foundations on the ground floor. You can get plenty of light from saw-tooth roofs or monitor roofs. Monitor roofs have higher center sections and windows on the sides of the step up. Both saw-tooth and monitor roofs increase building and maintenance costs, however.

One-story buildings of all kinds—whether they are flimsy or well-built—have many advantages. They can be as wide or long as needed and can easily be expanded. You do away with stairs, elevators and elevator wells, and ramps to connect floors. There aren't many posts to interfere with overhead cranes or to cut off light. If you have mezzanines you can see what is going on. It is easy and inexpensive to move materials from job to job because all the moving is horizontal —not up and down.

There are some bad features, though. You need lots of ground space. Also, if you have a flat roof and no glass skylights in it, you have to use artificial lights all the time in most of the plant. Besides, you will have to put in a forced ventilation system.

One-story buildings are so much better than high buildings that to-day no one builds anything else unless he just has to stay in cities where he can't get much land. Since most companies that build new plants do not have to stay in a crowded area, they put up new buildings on the city's fringes or leave the city altogether. Today's workers drive to work, so outlying areas are no longer hard for them to reach.

One-story factories put up in recent years are generally of the permanent type requiring much less maintenance than the flimsy buildings put up years ago. The framework of today's building is usually lightweight steel. The roof is supported by trusses of welded steel. Wood is seldom used. Exterior walls are often brick, though cinder block, glazed tile, precast concrete, gypsum blocks, asbestos cement, and insulated metal panels are also used. Brick is losing out because of high bricklaying costs. Outside walls composed almost entirely of windows are often found, as are the opposite extreme, no windows at all. Glass brick is also sometimes used. Partitions inside the building may be made of the same materials as the outside walls, or they may be made of wood, particularly plywood, or movable steel partitioning.

Multistory Buildings.   Multistory construction is generally more expensive than single-story construction because columns and walls have to be heavier to support the weight of the upper floors. Extra space is required for elevators, ramps, stairs, and posts. *Despite its shortcomings, multistory construction is the only possible way to get adequate space in cities* where land is either expensive or limited. Except in urban locations, multistory buildings have no advantage over single-story buildings from the viewpoint of construction alone.

Multistory buildings limit the use of natural daylight. Skylights, sawtooth roofs, and monitor roofs can be used on the top floor only. Even where steel-framed buildings permit many windows in the side walls, natural daylight is adequate only in the area close to the outside walls. Unless the building is narrow enough to permit natural daylight to reach the interior areas, considerable artificial lighting will be required. Many multistory buildings are therefore built in the shape of the letters U, E, L, T, or H rather than as a square or rectangle. The long, narrow areas permit natural daylight to reach everywhere. Narrow buildings also provide better ventilation. All these letter arrangements are expensive to build because they require more outside walls for the floor space obtained than do square, or nearly square, buildings.

The support posts in multistory buildings limit the size of spaces with overhead clearance. In many kinds of manufacturing, you need large floor spaces clear overhead for crane service. Recent developments in the use of truss framework and concrete floors permit multistory buildings to have from 40- to 60-foot spans with generous overhead clearance. Multistory buildings built in this way overcome one of the points of disadvantage as compared with single-story buildings.

BUILDING COSTS

Buildings are paid for when they are put up. But you do not charge the whole amount to that year's operations. You charge part of the cost (depreciation) to each year. Besides depreciation, you have yearly costs for insurance, taxes, and maintenance. All of these costs (including depreciation) must be added together to find out what the building costs you every year.

How much should the building cost per year? Its costs will always come to a sizable amount but will always be minor as compared to the costs of labor and materials. Depreciation and interest (if you used borrowed money) together should not come to 5 per cent of your payroll even in a new factory. Add insurance and taxes and you might be above 5, but you should still be well below 10 per cent of the payroll. Or, put in terms of your sales dollar—probably less than 2 per cent of your sales dollar.

A new factory's costs depends on what you want. In 1958, you could put up a simple building with a 10-foot ceiling for maybe $5 a square foot. But you'd have to go up to say $10 a foot for the usual new factory. Fancy ones might cost $20 a foot or more. Moving costs to a new plant are extra—over and above these figures. Costs vary, of course, in different parts of the country. Size also affects the *per square foot* cost. Big factories cost a little less per foot than small factories.

How does renting stack up against buying? It costs a little over one tenth as much (at least 50 cents a foot per year and up if you want nicer quarters) for rent alone. This includes *no* extras, so it isn't so great a bargain as it first seems. You pay extra for taxes, insurance, heating, maintenance—everything except depreciation.

Lowered Operating Costs. Companies building new plants always try to build improvements into the new plant. Almost always they end up with lower costs for: (1) handling (down 20 per cent or so), (2) supervision, (3) maintenance, (4) inventory, (5) shipping, and (6) insurance. Lighting usually is improved so much that it costs a little more. Employee morale and product quality both go up. Output per man-hour nearly always goes up, so labor costs, per unit of product, go down.

Suppose you spend one half to three quarters of a year's payroll on a new factory. That is about average. It won't take very many gains like those above to make it a very paying proposition. First, you get part of the money back by selling the old plant. This reduces the actual new cash you spend on the new one. Then your day-to-day costs are lower—so much so that many companies find that plants pay for themselves out of savings in 10 years.

Income Taxes. Don't forget income taxes. They affect building plans. Normally you can write off your building on a 40- to 50-year basis— meaning that you can list 2.5 or 2.0 per cent of its price as one of your costs every year. But if your building is needed to make defense products for the national safety, you may get permission to accelerate this depreciation. Usually it works like this: On a building with a 50-year life you normally write off 2 per cent a year. With accelerated depreciation you might write off half in the first 5 years, or 10 per cent a year, then the other half would be spread evenly over the next 45 years. In the first 5 years you gain by being permitted to exaggerate your costs, thus making your profits look lower. *This lowers your income taxes.* But notice that this is all a paper transaction up to the point of paying taxes. Your income is the same—accelerated depreciation or no—and (except for income taxes) your costs year by year are the same. Of course after 5 years it works the other way—calculated costs are less, profits higher, and taxes higher.

If you aren't elegible for accelerated depreciation, you still might be interested in the way the Bureau of Internal Revenue lets you depreciate a new plant. You can use the double-declining balance method. With it you (1) estimate the life of the building (say 50 years), (2) see how much depreciation you could take on a straight-line basis (2 per cent per year for 50 years), and (3) double it (4 per cent). Now depreciate your building *4 per cent of the balance* each year. Four per cent of its total cost the first year, 4 per cent of the remaining investment the second year, 4 per cent of the leftover investment the third year, and so on.

How does all this—accelerated depreciation and the double-declining balance method—affect building plans? You get a large chunk of your building costs back quickly, so (1) you don't have the money tied up so long, and (2) you don't take great risks of obsolescence. So you go ahead with buildings you would not otherwise gamble on. And this is just what the government wanted when it wrote the laws that way. But you can't yourself decide to build and use accelerated depreciation —you must first get government approval. You can, however, do your own deciding whether to depreciate on a straight-line or on the declining balance method. Don't forget though—no matter how you do it—that you end up with the same amount of depreciation after 50 years. All this manipulation merely lets you pay less taxes now and more later.

GETTING CONSTRUCTION STARTED

Your new plant will save you money only if you plan it well. It takes a year or more of careful planning to figure out the details. Everyone should get in on it—the company's engineers, maintenance foremen, product planners, and outside architects and contractors.

In spite of the need for careful planning, not all companies take the time. New factory buildings are often rush jobs. Once you decide to go ahead and once you get the money lined up, you figure that you lose money every day until the new plant opens. Every day of delay costs you money by failing to make the savings in prospect. So you don't mind too much about getting every detail planned. Instead you get going.

Sometimes the push has other pressure behind it. If you are going to put up a plant to use a newly patented process, you use up part of your 17-year patent protection every day after the patent is issued. If it takes 2 years to get into production, $\frac{2}{17}$ of your exclusive use of the idea is gone. Or suppose that you are in the automobile business and automatic transmissions become so popular that you need to build another factory to keep up. You move heaven and earth to get it into operation so that you won't lose any of your share of the market to competitors.

Hurry-up construction costs more than regular construction. You start your new building before it is fully designed. Details are worked out as you go along even though that sometimes means tearing out something just put in. Also, whenever work gets held up for some bottleneck, you have men work nights and Saturdays and put on extra men to move things fast. It costs money, but it is worth it.

Construction sometimes starts on hurry-up jobs before the contract is signed. Reputable contractors are fair about the price, which will finally be set later. (If they were not fair someone else would get the next hurry-up job.) The customer company often allows, in its construction budget, 10 per cent over its estimates to pay the costs of changes and hurry-up costs. Besides that, the contractor may get a bonus if he finishes before the promised date (or suffer a penalty if he finishes after it).

CONTRACT PRICES

Contracts for new buildings are let at fixed prices or on a "cost-plus" basis. On cost-plus, the customer pays all the contractor's costs plus a fee for him. This "plus" can be either (1) a fixed amount, or (2) a set per cent of the cost.

Fixed-price contracts are perhaps the most common kind. You know what your cost is—or think that you do. Fixed-price contracts are not perfect arrangements though. If the contractor's costs go up and he stands to lose, he may cut corners. Of course, the best contractors won't do that, but some will. More important, you always want to change a few things. If he is losing money on your building, the contractor will load on the charges for changing. Whether he loads the change costs or not, the building cost will vary (almost always upward) from the "fixed" price.

Cost-plus contracts are common on big contracts. They take so long that prices on labor and materials can change half-way through. The added costs are passed on automatically to the customer. (In fact, even fixed-price contracts nearly always say that if the price of labor and materials change, the price will change.) Cost-plus contracts give you more freedom to decide construction details as you go along. Of course the more freedom you have to change the less you can count on the building costing what you first planned. Your budget may be knocked into a cocked hat.

Cost-plus-a-fixed-fee contracts seem a little better than cost-plus-a-per-cent. Fixed fees don't tempt contractors to spend more. On cost-plus-a-per-cent, the more it costs the more the fee. There is little danger here, however, with reputable contractors.

Contractors are paid periodically as the building goes up. At each stage's completion (such as foundations in, or roof on) payments for work to date are made. The customer company's men, from its building department or its maintenance department, keep track of progress, inspect the work, and approve payments. But there is always a holdback. Even at the end of the construction you pay perhaps only 90 per cent of the money until every last minor detail is finished.

ROOM FOR EXPANSION

Successful companies grow, and their plants get too small. First you put machines in every corner, and then in aisles, as long as you don't block traffic completely. Finally you have to get more space.

When new buildings are built, bought, or rented, you know, of course, that you will grow still more in the future, so why not get enough building space at the start? It isn't done. Why don't young married couples start out in big houses? That isn't done either and for the same reasons. It costs too much when they do not yet need the space. It is much better to have too much business for the space than too much space for the business. But nearly always today plenty of *land* is bought for new factories—enough to give room for more buildings in the future.

Another reason for not building much extra space ahead of needs is that expansion needs may not materialize at all. Or expansion may require different machines and different departments from those you expected. Or when more space is needed, maybe you should really put up a new plant somewhere else instead of expanding the present one.

FLOORS

The right kind of floor depends on conditions of use. Processes sometimes spill water, oil, grease, acids, grit, or metal shavings onto the floor. Some kinds of floors withstand one but not the others.

Rubber-tired or steel-wheeled trucks carrying single loads up to three tons rumble across floors. Moving trucks impose a "dynamic" load of about one fourth more than the load's actual weight. Tote boxes or even skid loads of materials are sometimes dropped on floors. So, to withstand the impact of dropped loads, floors must be stronger than they need to be just to support a load. Factory floors should probably always be designed to carry at least 50 pounds per square foot; from there on up to 500 pounds in some cases. Both the wearing surface of the floors and the underflooring have to hold up. Today's increased mechanization is increasing the loads put on floors, so the matter of floor strength is getting to be more important.

When plain concrete is used as the wearing surface, the floors are not too satisfactory for most factory operations. It is excellent, however, as the subfloor on which to lay other types of surface material. Used as a base, it is usually from 5 to 7 inches thick. For a wearing surface, armored concrete (steel grating filled with concrete) makes a good durable surface and is said to last up to 15 years in aisles used by trucks and at elevator openings. Because concrete has no "give," it is tiring to workers who must stand on it all day. It also "dusts" and is hard to keep clean.

Two inches of asphalt applied over a concrete base lasts up to 20 years unless it is exposed to acid or very heavy loads. Special acid-resistant asphalt stands up for about 15 years in rooms where electroplating work is done. Brick, laid over concrete, is also used in plating and heat-treating departments. Wood blocks, laid over a concrete base, make a very good factory floor. The blocks are resilient to the worker's feet, are not unduly cold, are durable, and are easy to repair. They are, however, slippery when wet and collect moisture. They may swell and "pop up," and it is difficult to fasten machines to a wood block floor. Usually the blocks must be removed and the machine fastened directly to the concrete base.

Floors made of wooden planks have been used for many years and are still common. The base under the planks is often of wood, made by setting 2 × 6, or similar sized, boards on edge, thus providing a wood base 6 inches thick. This type of flooring is good where only light machines are used.

For particular places, such as offices, many other types of flooring —maple flooring, magnesite, terrazzo, asphalt tile, rubber tile, cork tile, linoleum, and marble—are used. Except for the maple flooring, none of them is common in the factory proper.

LOCKER ROOMS, WASHROOMS, AND TOILETS

Workers no longer wear their dirty work clothes to and from work and clean up at home. If they work on dirty jobs, they change into their work clothes when they arrive and, after the day's work, clean up and change back into their street clothes at the plant before going home, so it is necessary to provide good locker rooms and washrooms. Lockers must be provided to hold work clothes at night and street clothes during the day. You may need more than one locker per employee because the man's work clothes locker is too dirty for his street clothes. Work clothes, being dirty and laundered infrequently, may need airing out at night. In some companies they are aerated overnight on clothes hangers pulled up by rope and pulley to near ceiling level. Some companies arrange for regular laundering of the men's work clothes.

Locker rooms need to have good ventilation and need to be near washrooms and toilet facilities. They are often centralized, one area being made to serve large groups of workers. Over the years locker rooms have become larger. The trend has been away from the small locker room serving single departments and located in otherwise unused and poorly lighted corners. Stealing clothing, always something of a problem, can be better controlled in the large locker rooms because no one is allowed in the area except at shift change time.

Another recent trend is to do away with locker rooms altogether. Many factory jobs are now clean enough so that men do not have to change. All they need is a coat rack near their workplace. This saves space and expense, and the men like it when the whistle blows. It lets them get away sooner.

Complete washroom facilities, including shower baths, are sometimes unnecessary; but since most companies have at least a few jobs on which workers get very dirty, you have to have at least a few showers. You ought to have no less than one shower for every ten users. Circular type wash fountains for hand and face washing, one for every 30 to 40 users, or smaller basins, one for every 10 to 15 users, should be provided. Toilet facilities are needed in the ratio of one for every 10 to 30 employees, both at the locker room and in the various departments. A special retiring room should be provided for women employees. Some states require that it be equipped with a couch or cot if there are more than 100 women employees. Washrooms and toilets require plumbing connections and must, therefore, be planned for in the construction of the building, just as service facilities for factory operations are planned. Minimum washroom and toilet facilities are specified in most state codes. Usually the drawings for a new building are submitted to the state for approval before construction starts.

CAFETERIAS AND MEETING ROOMS

Today's new factories almost always are complete with cafeterias and conference rooms or even an auditorium—air conditioned, too, of course. Their operation and use is described in Chapter 20 along with other activities under the direction of the personnel department. Here, we are concerned only with the fact that they must be provided. In fact, you may have to provide for three places to eat: a factory worker cafeteria, an office worker cafeteria, and an executive restaurant with table service. In large plants, lunch hours are staggered so that only half or fewer of the employees eat at the same time. This allows good service without having an enormous restaurant.

Now and then, however, you find a plant—even a newly built one —that has no cafeteria at all. Workers just have big fold-up tables that they open down, seats and all, at noon. They can eat quickly, get in a game of shuffleboard in the aisle, and get back on the job all on a half-hour lunch period. They like the short lunch period because they get out earlier in the afternoon. And they like bringing their lunch because their meals cost less.

TOOLROOMS, STOREROOMS, DISPATCHING STATIONS, AND OFFICES

Production service centers, such as toolrooms, storerooms, dispatching stations, and factory offices for foremen, time clerks, production checkers, inspectors, and others require, in total, considerable space. Generally they should be as conveniently located to the operations and the workers as possible. In planning the plant layout, you need to provide plenty of space for such services and to provide it at properly located spots. In all too many plants, service centers aren't bit enough and aren't in the right places.

TIMECARD RACKS

In small factories timecard racks are usually put at the entrance to the plant. In large factories they are generally put at the entrance to individual departments inside the plant. They are located next to a time clock, so that they can easily be punched and put into the rack. Ordinarily they take up very little space, but their location should be planned. They need to be next to the timekeeper's office and along an aisle so the men can get in and out of the plant quickly at shift change time. Two or more racks and clocks should be provided where there are large numbers of workers or where there are two or more shifts of workers. When individual cost records are kept job by job, additional clocks and racks are necessary in every department for recording the labor time spent on each job done.

STUDY QUESTIONS

1. Suppose that a company's management figures show that it can save 10 per cent of its labor cost if it builds a new factory. Should it go ahead and build or not? Support your position.
2. How can a company building a new building build "flexibility" into it?
3. When would you build each of these kinds of buildings?
   a) One-story permanent type
   b) One-story corregated metal siding
   c) Steel reinforced concrete
   d) Mill type
4. Why do some companies today use mill-type buildings? What are its good and bad features?
5. Why all the rush to single-story buildings?
6. What would it cost to build a factory for 750 workers (including everyone) who need 450 square feet of space each for their work spaces—service areas take 40 per cent of the total space (in addition to the 450 feet per worker)? You need permanent construction for medium manufacturing.
7. Suppose in Problem 6 above that land costs were extra and were $2,000 an acre and you decide to get 4 to 1 (land space total = four times the new building space). What is your real estate tax bill on land and building (not machinery or inventory) if appraisals come to about 40 per cent of your cost and the rate is $2.80 per $100 of valuation?
8. Explain how income taxes can affect a company's building plans.
9. If you were going to build a new plant, would you prefer a fixed price contract? Cost plus a fixed fee? Cost plus a per cent? Why?
10. How would you ever know how much to pay the contractor at the end of each month during construction? Explain.
11. Compare types of floors. Which is best for general manufacturing when you use trucks and sometimes spill grease, oil, and metal chips on the floor?
12. Where is a good location for locker rooms? Why?

Chapter 11

PLANT SERVICES

COMMUNICATIONS SYSTEMS

THE factory is normally a beehive of activity that would stop the minute communications stopped. Men talk to each other giving and receiving directions, but they have to have means of communicating other than just talking. They send and receive written directions and reports. An inside telephone system is a must and usually that alone isn't enough.

Production control and sometimes other departments need their own "intercom" systems. Some companies also use Tel-Autograph systems. The sender of a message goes through the motions of writing his message on a metal plate with a stylus. The stylus is connected electrically to a receiving unit in one or more other departments. As fast as he writes it, his message is written on a paper in the other departments. His sending unit also writes his message on a paper in front of him so he can see it.

Teletypewriters are also used—often for messages *between* plants or distant offices—not so much *within* plants. You can type a message in Chicago and another typewriter in Cleveland types it out there (or in any number of places) at the same time. Or you can send from Cleveland to Chicago or other points just as easily.

Radio and television are sometimes used. Radio is very good for directing men, such as truck drivers and maintenance men, who usually are away from their home department. Television (not broadcast TV, just "closed-circuit" TV) is in a class by itself, as a way of seeing what goes on at impossible-to-watch spots, say inside a furnace, or to watch freight yards or plant fences. TV is also used more and more for sales meetings and stockholders' meetings. For sales meetings you don't have to bring your West Coast men to New York. Get them together in San Francisco and TV it to them. It is good at stockholders' meet-

206

ings too. You can show the stockholders views of the factories they own.

In the factory, some kind of "call" system is used. Officials away from their desks are paged by "auto-call" operated by the telephone operator. A code of short and long blasts on buzzers or horns, operating in all departments, pages the man, who then calls in from wherever he is. Some companies have public-address systems too for talking to all the employees at once or for music.

Pneumatic tubes may be used to transfer papers or very small quantities of materials, such as test samples. Their use is uncommon, but they are quicker and usually cheaper than messengers and intraplant mail service if very many papers have to be sent back and forth between two offices.

For the most part, the communications systems used in factories are electrical and require a network of wires to all departments. Wiring systems are usually relatively cheap and easily changed, so that it doesn't

FIG. 11–1. An operator using closed circuit TV to watch the steel rolling mills that he controls with this control panel.

Lukens Steel Co.

matter too much if you don't get them planned the best way at first. On the other hand, most city building codes require all such wires to be put into conduit pipes. Where that is required, changes are harder to make.

POWER

It takes lots of electric power to run today's factories—20,000 kilowatt-hours per employee per year. In 1920, factories used 3,000 kilowatt-hours per worker. Electric power costs 1 cent a kilowatt-hour; man power costs $10 a kilowatt-hour! Is it any wonder that we use more electric power every day?

Self-powered movable equipment (automobiles, industrial trucks, earth moving hoists, and so on) are usually powered directly by gasoline or fuel oil engines. Factory machines are often partly powered by compressed air or steam (mainly to open and close machines). Portable tools, spray guns, and air hammers sometimes also use compressed air. Steam and occasionally hydraulic power are used to run large forging hammers.

Nearly always electricity is the best and cheapest power. You can get just about any amount of it and at any time. It can be brought to the point of use with little loss in transmission. It may be generated in a company-owned power plant or by an electric power producing company.

Most newly built factories buy power unless the steam needed to run electric generators can be put to other use in processing or heating. A paper mill or a soap factory which can use both electricity and steam can justify making power. But even such factories ought to have a stand-by connection to supply outside power if their own power fails. This is, however, costly. One company found that to have a stand-by connection for 1,000 kilowatt-hours of electricity, it would have to pay $2.50 per kilowatt-hour, or $2,500 per month!

Cost isn't the only important factor in decisions concerning power. *Dependable* power is very important in industries where a shutdown of power even for short periods of time would result in heavy damage to the product and machinery. In many industries, if the power goes off, heated materials and liquids will cool and solidify inside the pipes, valves, and machines. Generally the rolls in rolling mills in the steel, rubber, paper, and linoleum industries would be ruined if the power went off while they were in use. Hundreds of tools on some of today's big automatic multiple-operation machines might break if an interruption occurred in the cutting cycle. To insure steady power, two power lines with automatic "throw-over" switches may be necessary. If one line goes dead, the other automatically takes over.

Electricity's cost is partly dependent on things that management can control. First, power used after midnight is priced lower because so little is used then. You can run some heavy equipment on the third shift and save on electricity costs. Second, a poor "load factor" costs extra. The load factor is your highest rate of electricity use divided by your average. Since the power company has always to be ready to supply you with your top demand, it makes a separate charge and makes you pay more than if you used power steadily (steady use would eliminate the peak). Third, a poor "power factor" costs extra. This is a condition that loses electricity in a way that doesn't show in the meter. Induction motors (principally those that start under load and run at different speeds) cause most of the trouble. Every now and then the power company makes a special check to see what your rate of power loss is. Then it raises the rate so that you end up paying both for what you use and for what you lose. Management can, by planning carefully, keep this loss down.

ELECTRIC POWER TRANSMISSION

Some electricity is lost in transmission, but not much if it is transmitted at high voltages. This is why it is usually generated at high voltages and transmitted that way to a point close to centers of use. High voltages are dangerous so, while electricity can be brought to the plant at 34,000 volts or more, most communities, by law, require it to be transformed (outside the building) down to, say, 4,160 or so to distribute to work centers inside.

At work centers it is stepped down again to the voltages the machines require. Many large machines take 2,300 volt power, while most small ones (using 1 to 75 horsepower motors) take 440 volts. But on nearly all machines the start and stop buttons work on 110 volts (to cut the danger to the men), so the machines themselves are built with their own transformers to cut part of their power down to 110 volts. Regular 110-volt current will take care of lighting all right but will carry only fractional horsepower motors.

All of these different voltages with connections with different machines mean that you have quite a network of wires and outlets in every department. You want to be sure that the lines are marked. Some companies paint switch boxes, fuse boxes, outlets, and electric plugs different colors to show their voltage. Most companies don't have to do that in very many places because there are only two or three voltages in any one area and the electricians and plant layout men know which is which. They'd better be *sure* that they know though.

Almost every plant layout change means changing electrical connections, motors, switch boxes, controls, and electric lights, so it is helpful if they are easily changed. If the law allows it, you can hang wires high along the walls or hang them from the ceiling (most communities don't allow much of this). Or they can be in "bus ducts" (enclosed channels) overhead, alongside, or in the floor below. The ducts have many access points. Putting wires inside of electrical pipes in the walls makes for a neat-looking plant. But such wires are hard to get at and that makes changes costly.

POWER AT THE MACHINES

Today nearly every machine has its own electric motors—one to operate its main moving parts, another to open and close it, another to move accessory parts, and so on.

Years ago all the machines in a department were driven by one big motor. It was mounted at one end of the department close to the ceiling where it was connected by a leather belt to a main drive shaft and by pulleys and belts to other drive shafts. The machines below

FIG. 11–2.   Lathes, drillers, and millers, Wheeler & Wilson Machine Co., Bridgeport, Connecticut (about 1900). Notice how the belts and clutch handles clutter up the overhead space.

were driven by pulleys with belts reaching down. Each machine also had its clutch handle reaching up to engage and disengage it from the always-turning drive shaft.

Separate motors for every machine get rid of several disadvantages of the old way. First, separate motors for every machine save electricity if very many machines are not used all the time. Second, there is no loss in power from belt slippage. Third, you get rid of the forest of belts and clutch handles reaching up to the ceiling. That helps both lighting and safety. Fourth, any motor can be taken out and repaired without affecting more than one machine.

Separate motors have some bad features. If all the machines run all the time, they take more power than would one big motor. Besides their first cost is higher. It costs more to buy and install hundreds of little motors than one big one. It doesn't matter that today's machine comes equipped with its own motor or several motors because they have to be paid for just the same as if they were bought separately. It probably was easier to oil and grease the old big motors and all of the many bearings along the drive shafts than to oil and grease so many separate motors and their connections to machines. On the other hand, many of today's motors have graphite bronze bearings or other kinds of permanently lubricated and sealed long-life bearings which require no oiling.

Many of today's machines are designed with the motor as an attachment rather than as an integral part of the machine. The motor drives the machine by flat belts, V belts, link or roller chains, or gears. Belts are generally of rubber rather than leather. V belts, link chains, roller chains, or gears eliminate the loss of power from slipping, yet allow the motor to be removed and replaced easily. This would not be possible if the motor shaft were also the drive shaft of the machine. The machine would have to be idle for all motor repairs. Flat-belt and V belt drives take up part of the shock if the machine is stopped quickly or if it is overloaded. Some machines with chain or gear connections are provided with a "breaking pin" which will break if the machine is overloaded, thus preventing the motor from burning out.

Power is sometimes transmitted to the machine by other than electrical means. Steam, as used in steam hammers in forging shops, can drive machines. Because of heat losses, however, it is impractical for most purposes unless it can be used near the point where the steam is made. Compressed air is used for spray painting, for trip hammers, and for opening and closing equipment. Machines and materials can be cleaned by compressed air and steam. Hydraulic power is sometimes used to transmit power. It is customarily used to transmit enormous pressures short distances at slow speed, as inside the gigantic presses which form steel.

Power may also be transmitted mechanically as, indeed, it almost always is *within* machines, where drive shafts, gears, universal joints, and ball and socket arrangements convey power from one part of the machine to the other. The mechanical transmission of power *to* machines from a power source is uncommon, although not unknown.[1] It is mechanically impractical to transmit power by a rotating shaft over any great distance. (The shaft would twist in two.) Reciprocating movement (back and forth) can be transmitted readily over a long distance on the pull, but not the push, part of the stroke. A continuous pull, such as is used for lengthy conveyors, can be used but is rarely found except to keep conveyors moving.

LIGHTING

Lighting is important in manufacturing, but no one knows how important it is. Many years ago the Western Electric Company studied the question for years but found no good answer.[2] The question was: What effect does lighting intensity have on production? The answer: Worker productivity depends on many things, lighting hasn't much to do with it. (In the study, workers sometimes produced more when told the lights were brighter when they really were dimmer.)

Today most people think that reasonably bright light helps production. But it must be well diffused—not glary. Some people still say, however, that the experts (who are usually in the lighting business) recommend all the light you can stand—not what is best. Be that as it may, today's factories are more brightly lighted than ever.

How much light do the experts say you should have? It depends on what you are doing. Figure 11–3 shows today's recommendations for various activities. Notice that the tables show how much light should *shine down* on a surface, not what should be *reflected back* to your eyes. Yet *you can see what comes back, not what goes down.* Perhaps it is logical, though, to set up the tables the way they do because the purpose is to help you decide how many and how big lights to put in. Naturally, you have to put lots of light on dark objects that don't reflect much light.

Lighting intensities are expressed as so many "foot-candles." A foot-candle is the brightness of light thrown by a standard candle on a panel one foot square at a distance of one foot. The amount of light the panel gets is one lumen. But what you see is reflected light. Re-

---

[1] The A. O. Smith Company, a large company making automobile frames, transmits power mechanically to its assembly lines in its Milwaukee, Wisconsin, plant. Such extensive use of mechanical power transmission is almost unique among large manufacturers.

[2] Results of the survey, made between 1924 and 1927, are written up in F. J. Roethlisberger, William J. Dickson, and H. A. Wright, *Management and the Worker* (Cambridge, Mass.: Harvard University Press, 1939).

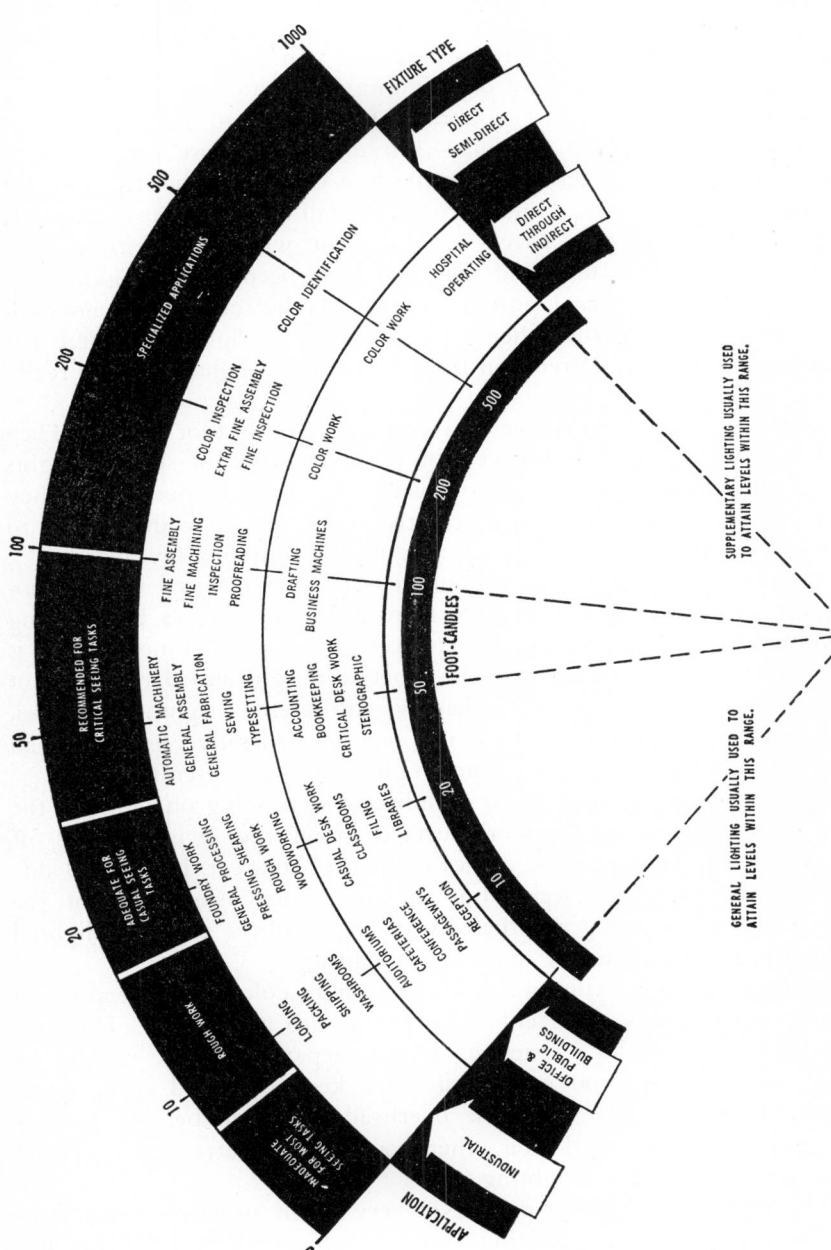

FIG. 11–3. Lighting intensities recommended for various types of work and methods recommended for producing the intensity needed.

flected light is measured in "foot-lamberts." A foot-lambert is the same brightness as a foot-candle. But if your surface absorbs half the light it gets, you have to give it 2 foot-candles so you can see 1 foot-lambert.

Figure 11–3 shows present-day lighting intensities recommended by the experts. They say that you need from 5 to 10 foot-candles for aisles, service areas, and the like—then more and more up to 100 as the work gets more exacting. Over 100 foot-candles are needed only for the most exacting work. Most factory jobs fall in the 20–50 foot-candle range. Actually, if you check your present workplace with a light meter, you will probably find that you have been getting along very well with less light than Figure 11–3 says. Maybe the recommendations are a little high. On the other hand, all types of light bulbs give less light as they get old. Better plan for a fourth more light than you really want.

Most companies light whole areas only to 25 or 30 foot-candles. Then if they need more light for certain jobs, they put in separate lights and mount them to shine right on places that need it. Sometimes they light certain limited areas more brightly. That way they don't have to pay for a lot of light all over when they need it only in a few places.

"Good" lighting is bright enough to serve yet diffused enough not to glare. You can cut down glare from reflected surfaces by painting machines and walls with flat rather than glossy paint. Good seeing is also dependent on moderate contrasts between light and dark areas but extreme contrasts between deep shadows and intense brightness are bad. Differences in brightness up to ten to one are generally regarded as all right for industry, but actually much higher ratios are often found.

Lighting is direct, indirect, or semidirect—depending on whether the light shines directly on the work surface, or whether it is reflected off the ceiling, or whether some comes each way. Indirect, being well diffused, is the nicest for seeing but the most costly since part of the light is wasted by being absorbed by ceilings. Offices are often lighted indirectly, but factories use more direct lighting.

Painting the walls, ceilings, and machines light colors helps keep down lighting costs because light colors do not absorb much light. They reflect most of it. Today's practice of using separate electric motors on every machine helps too because it helps keep overhead space clear. Figure 11–4 shows how clear the overhead space can be. But today's overhead conveyors work the other way. They clutter up overhead space and hamper good lighting.

How much does lighting cost? Not very much, usually a small fraction of 1 per cent of operating costs. In offices, about 25 cents per square foot per year; in factories, still less. But, even so, why not keep its costs as low as you can? One way is to use daylight. It is free. But it has some disadvantages. You get it through windows which have to be cleaned and which lose heat in the winter. You get natural daylight only in the daytime, and half the time it is too bright or not bright enough. It goes up to 8,000 foot-candles in direct noonday summer sunshine, and on a dark rainy day it goes down below 50 foot-candles. It varies in brightness from hour to hour, and on half-cloudy days

Woodward Governor Co.

FIG. 11–4. A well-lighted factory with fluorescent lights, light-colored ceilings and walls, and overhead space free of conveyors and other interferences to good lighting.

from minute to minute. It is bright near the windows and skylights but dims off in inside areas.

Sounds as if we should forget it—natural daylight has so much against it. But, no! It is still free. Nearly all companies use it. When and where it doesn't make enough light, artificial lights are turned on.

TYPES OF LAMPS

Artificial light comes from filament (or "incandescent") and fluorescent lamps (there are other kinds, but they don't count for much).

Filament lamps are older and more widely used than other kinds. Fluorescent lamps have been common for years.

Filament lamps and fixtures cost only two thirds as much to install as fluorescent lamps and fixtures. But they last only about 1,000 hours, while fluorescent lamps burn 3,000 to 7,000 hours. Frequent turning off and on has little effect on the life of incandescent lamps, but it makes fluorescents fail sooner. A 40-watt fluorescent lamp should last 7,500 hours if it burns an average of 3 hours per start, but its life drops to less than half of that when it is turned off and on frequently. Fluorescent lamps require starters which sometimes burn out and add to the expense caused by the burning out of the lamp itself. Maintenance and cleaning of reflectors is cheapest when incandescent lamps are used.

Fluorescent lamps operating on alternating current actually go off and on in phase with the current, usually sixty times a second. Although this is far too fast to see, it may create a stroboscopic effect, making fast-moving equipment appear to stand still. Fluorescent lamps are therefore generally used in pairs slightly out of phase with each other, thus eliminating the stroboscopic effect. Nearly burned-out fluorescent lamps flicker and are annoying to the worker, but incandescent lamps go out suddenly, leaving no light at all.

Fluorescent lamps give a more diffused and softer, cooler light than incandescent lamps, which usually require shielding. Fluorescent lamps give roughly three times more light than incandescent lamps for the same amount of electricity, so they save money there. Fluorescent lamps giving white light or light the color of daylight are available and are superior to all other types where color discrimination is important. Altogether, if lights are not turned off and on too often, fluorescent lighting will save one quarter the cost of lighting by incandescents.

Many factories follow a practice, particularly with fluorescent lamps, of group replacement. If they burn an average of 3 hours per start, their average life will be above 7,000 hours, although some will burn out sooner. Somewhere above the 4,000 mark but long before the 7,000 hours, it will pay to change them all and to throw away the old unburned-out lamps. Replacing them one by one as they burn out takes up to a half hour each of a maintenance man's time. If he changes them all at once, the job goes eight or ten times as fast. It is far cheaper to group replace lamps before 5,000 hours than to do it later one by one. Not only is it cheaper but you get better light. After 4,000 hours, because of old lamps and dirty reflectors, you probably lose one third of the light you should be getting.

HEATING THE PLANT

In most parts of the United States you have to heat factories in the winter. You can do it by bringing heat to each department from a central heating plant (by air, water, or steam) or by making heat where it is needed. Sometimes, today, when heat is made where it is needed, it is done electrically; although gas, oil, and coal are usually used, wood-burning stoves can even still be found.

Heating the plant is tied in with the manufacturing processes in some companies. Whenever you need high temperatures for processes, maybe you can use the heat afterwards to heat the plant. By-product heat rarely solves the whole heating problem because it is often too hot and too irregular. In other cases, as when water is used to cool heated products, there may be plenty of warm water, but it is not warm enough to heat the plant. Mostly, too, by-product heat is not available at night in factories operating only one shift. Furthermore, you don't want it all year round and so have to get rid of it during part of the year.

Steam and hot-water heating are the most common systems. In old buildings the steam or water circulates in several rows of pipes placed against the walls below the window level. In newer buildings radiators and even baseboard heating are more common.

General heating can be supplemented by "unit" space heaters. They are little individual heaters just for limited areas. Usually they hang from, and are close to, the ceiling. The heat is diffused by an electric fan blowing air over the heated elements. Gas unit heaters are popular in small plants in areas where gas is available at a low price. They require no boilers, steam piping, or floor space. Steam and hot-water unit heaters are also growing in popularity. Electricity is sometimes used.

A few of the new factories being built use radiant heating. Pipes are laid under the floor or are put into the ceiling with reflecting aluminum foil above them. Steam or hot water passing through the pipes heats the area evenly. Some people don't like radiant heating in the floor, however, because it makes their feet hot. Such piping systems are also occasionally installed on loading and unloading platforms and even in sidewalks to melt the snow. Radiant heating systems are usually installed permanently, meaning that the pipes are covered over by ceilings or floors and are sometimes even encased in concrete. Repairs, if needed, are expensive, but it is claimed that you never have any trouble with radiant heating systems. Radiant heating has a high first cost, but the expense of maintenance and operation is low. It might be damaged, however, if you rearrange things and have to make holes in the floor or ceiling.

Heating by electricity has increased in the past few years. As a system it is quite flexible, and almost any amount of heat can be produced anywhere in the plant. Electrical heat is clean and is safer than other types, but it costs more except where power is very cheap. That limits its use to small areas or to supplementing the regular heating system. It is, however, popular in certain factory processes, such as in drying paint.

Today's new factories are much better insulated than old factory buildings. Insulation can save a large part of heating costs. Well-insulated buildings cost more to build, but building is a one-time cost, and the savings pile up indefinitely. Well-insulated buildings keep out the summer heat as well as the winter cold, making for more comfortable working conditions the year round, and reduce the cost of air conditioning where it is used.

Fortunately for many factories, the work requires considerable physical activity on the part of the men, so that temperatures in the middle sixties are comfortable. For heavy work, as in foundries, temperatures below 60° are preferred. It costs roughly 15 per cent more to get up to 72° than it does to hold 65° when outside temperatures are at 20° above zero. The saving is even greater in large, high rooms using overhead crane service. Big high rooms are hard to keep warm at floor levels because warm air rises. Frequently, too, it is necessary to open large doors to the outside to admit industrial trucks from other buildings, or even freight cars on railroad tracks, thus losing considerable heat.

Hot air from a central source is not commonly used for factory heating but is by no means unknown. It is expensive to move it very far, and it needs large ducts and blower fans. There is sometimes trouble getting uniform temperature in all departments. A hot-air system has an advantage over other systems, however, in that it helps ventilation and the same system can be used to cool the plant in the summer.

VENTILATION

Ventilation—providing clean fresh air—is giving way to air conditioning. Many, perhaps most, of today's new plants are air conditioned. Most old and many new ones are, however, not air conditioned (or wholly air conditioned), so ventilation is still important.

Ventilation is usually less of a problem in factory departments than in offices. They, factory departments, are large open spaces with plenty of air for all. Windows can be opened, and even when they are closed, they fit loosely enough to admit lots of fresh air. Winter ventilation is another matter, however, because too much fresh air loses too much heat. Some factory processes or materials give off fumes or smoke or make the air hot, cold, dusty, or humid. Conditions can be so bad as to be unhealthy. Some vapor and dust can even explode. Such operations nowadays are air conditioned or at least are provided with exhaust fans to take away the old air.

How much new air do we need? Depending on conditions, experts recommend anywhere from 1,000 cubic feet and up of new air per hour per person. In offices, 2,000 cubic feet of new air would amount to one to three changes of air every hour. Factories ought to have more—say two to six changes. Assembly halls, particularly if smoking goes on, from six to twelve; laboratories, from ten to twenty.

You can have too much ventilation. Moving air—if it moves too fast—makes drafts, and employees complain. Air moving faster than 50 feet a minute is uncomfortable to most people. You can keep drafts down by introducing the new air from several openings up near the ceiling.

Forced-air ventilation is necessary in most of today's big spread-out low factories. Ducts are needed. They can be, as they are in so many houses, the same ducts used for winter heating. In fact, if you convert to air conditioning, you can use the same ducts for that too.

AIR CONDITIONING

Air conditioning controls heat, humidity, dust, and some odors. Mostly we think of it in connection with summertime—keeping the temperature and the humidity down.

Many factories are now air conditioned where the process needs it and often—particularly in light manufacturing—throughout the whole factory. In heavy manufacturing, or in large hard-to-air-condition areas, certain operations may be supplied with "man-coolers." Cooled air is blown across the openings of furnaces to keep cool the men putting things in and out of the furnace.

Some processes (such as making automobile windshield glass) need air conditioning because it keeps dust out of the air. Others (making cloth, paper, cigarettes) need it because it controls the dampness that the products absorb. Still others (making precision instruments and close inspection jobs in many industries) need temperature control because the metal being worked expands and contracts a little with temperature changes. Still other companies have air conditioning because they didn't put any windows in the building when they built it and have to have at least forced ventilation. Air conditioning doesn't cost a great deal more.

Air conditioning doesn't mean a constant temperature (say for all summer). That would be fine if people didn't go in or out. But the contrast is too great if it is 100° outside and 70° inside. On hot days the inside temperature needs to be a little higher than on not so hot days.

"It isn't the heat—it's the humidity." Look at Figure 11–5. Notice the "comfortable" area. High temperatures are fairly comfortable if the humidity is low. Damp hot air is more uncomfortable than dry hot air. Get the dampness out of the air and you will feel more comfortable. Hot air can hold more water vapor than cool air, and that fact is used in air conditioning to remove dampness from the air. Just cool off the air (inside the air-conditioning unit) down to near freezing. The water condenses out (just like dew on the grass) and goes down the drain. Then heat the air up to whatever temperature you want and you are rid of the humidity. You can also remove humidity from the air by blowing the air through dry filters, but the filters soon get soggy and have to be dried.

Dust also needs to be removed in complete air conditioning. The best way to do it is electrically (electrostatic precipitation). Pass the air over some wires with a high negative electrical charge (10,000 volts and up). That charges all the dust particles negatively. Then blow the air on past some metal plates that are positively charged. The negatively charged particles cling to the positively charged plates and the air moves on free

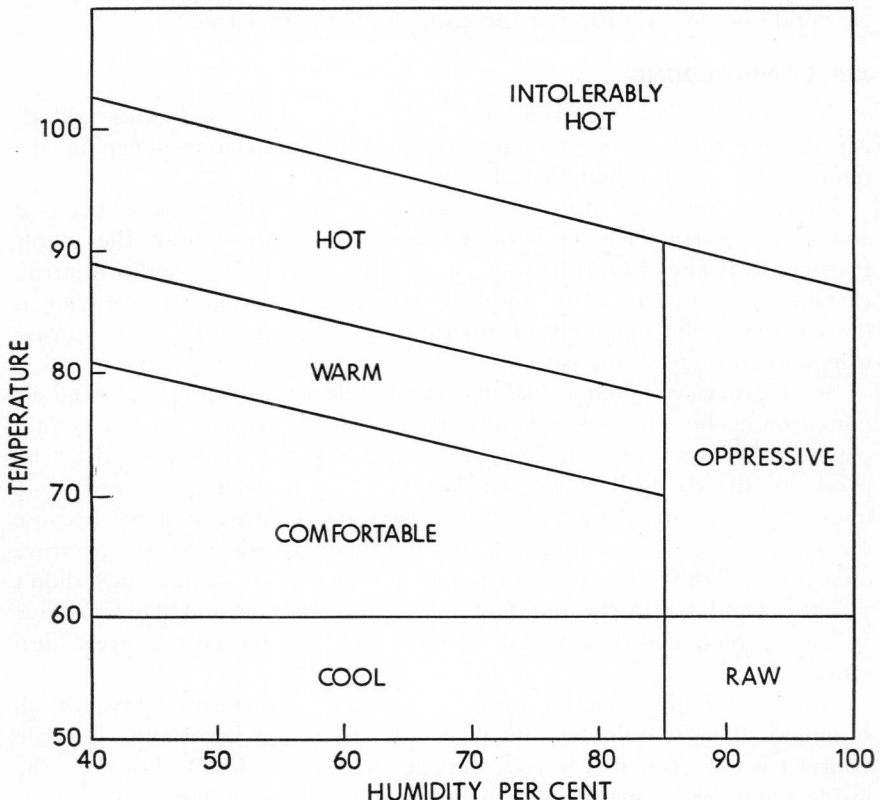

FIG. 11–5. Relationships between temperature, humidity, and comfort. Most Americans prefer temperatures in the low 70's with humidity 60 per cent or below. The English prefer it cooler and more humid.

of dust. Later you turn off the electricity and jiggle or wash the dirt off the plates.

The electrostatic method works even with sprayed paint and is now widely used for spray painting. As the paint is sprayed toward an object to be painted, it is given a negative charge. The product to be painted is given a positive charge, so, like the dust particles, the paint droplets are drawn by magnetism to the product to be painted. It gets a good even coat of paint, and there is not much paint mist left in the air to be cleared up. This saves nearly all the paint wasted by older methods and leaves the air clean all the time. Unfortunately the system isn't quite perfect, so you may still need a curtain of water behind the operation to catch the "overspray" and wash it down to a pan below.

You can get dust out of the air with filters as well as electrically, but filters are not so effective, and they have to be cleaned often. Of course, the simplest way to get rid of dust in the air is to blow it out of doors through a duct. If you don't have too much of it, and if you are not located in a built-up area, that might take care of the whole matter.

Odors, fumes, and smoke are another problem (although they too can be blown out of doors where you can do that). Not even the electrostatic method gets rid of all of them. Nor will filters do the whole job. Smoke, in particular, is a common unsolved problem. It seems impossible to get it all out of the air. Better not make it in the first place or locate where it doesn't matter.

Air conditioning is so good you might wonder why it isn't universal. Its cost is, of course, the catch. It costs more to put in the equipment (up to $2 per square foot of floor space) than it does to put in a heating system for winter and, in northern United States, costs as much to operate in the summer as heating does in the winter. And in the South and Southwest, summer cooling costs are several times winter heating costs. Its gains are, however, worth while. With it you get lower absenteeism, lower labor turnover, no hot weather shutdowns, high production, and high quality even in hot weather. And, if you are where there are very many 90° days in summer, you can hardly hire anyone unless you are air conditioned.

NOISE AND VIBRATION

Today's machinery moves faster than ever, and fast-moving machinery, whether it goes around or back-and-forth, vibrates and makes noise. Noise, or unwanted sound, and vibration are cousins if not brothers. When a machine shakes, the floor and building probably shake too. That is vibration. But vibration sets air waves in motion. And certain vibration frequencies our ears interpret as noise.

Vibration and noise are hard on products and men. The problems of controlling noise and vibration are about the same. Probably noise bothers men more and vibration bothers machines and products more. Vibration also has bad effects on machine mountings and on pipes and wires which must be flexible enough to hold fast in spite of the vibration.

High-pitched noises are annoying even when they aren't very loud, but low-pitched noises have to be louder to bother us much. Also irregular noises are more bothersome than continuous noises because we get so used to the regular noises that they don't annoy us at all.

Ordinary conversations are carried on at sound intensities of 50–60 decibels.[3] Many factories are extremely noisy; very few are quiet. A noisy factory makes almost as much sound as a subway train passing a station and makes more noise than a loud radio. In such a factory you have to shout to carry on a conversation. Table 11–1 shows the relative loudness of noise in various situations.

Loud noises aren't just annoying; they can cause partial deafness. How much noise and how long the exposure needed to be injurious varies with people. Doctors generally agree that long exposure to as few as 95 decibels will finally impair most people's hearing. Louder noises, of course, cause injury quicker.

It is curious that ear plugs, said to be commonly used in Europe, are seldom used in the United States except by persons living in noisy neighborhoods so they can sleep at night. They cut the noise reaching the ear by 25 decibels. Ear muffs can also be used.

TABLE 11–1

AMOUNT OF NOISE FOUND IN VARIOUS SITUATIONS

Noise	Decibels Above the Start of Hearing
Painful noise	130
Boiler factory	110
Subway trains passing station	105
Noisy factory	100
Very loud radio in home	80
Average factory	70
Typical office	60
Quiet office	50
Quiet home	40

Vibration and noise can't be eliminated altogether, but they can often be "damped," reduced, or confined to limited areas, thus reducing harmful effects. Noise from old and worn equipment can be reduced by putting in new and better-fitting bearings and parts. Noise from impacts such as is made by stamping dies is hard to stop, so you try to set those machines off by themselves. Vibration from heavy equipment can be minimized on the ground floor by mounting heavy machines on separate concrete foundations with small spaces between the foundation and the regular floor.

On upper floors other methods have to be used. All kinds of vibration

---

[3] A decibel is a unit of measure of sound intensity. Sound intensity differences are so extreme, however, that decibel measures represent powers of 10 and are not simple arithmetic differences. A sound of 60 decibels of intensity is ten times as loud as one of 50. Seventy is ten times as loud as sixty. One hundred is ten times 90, 100 times 80, 1,000 times 70, and so on.

isolators are used. Machine mountings are made of springs, rubber, felt, cork, and other elastic materials. Suspension arrangements are also sometimes used. These methods of vibration control are in addition to vibration reducers built into the equipment itself. In the machines, vibration and noise may be reduced by pads, snubbers, bumpers, flexible joints, shaft seals, and other means.

Machinery manufacturers know the disadvantages of vibration in their machines, since it cuts the quality of work their machines can do and shortens their life. Fast-operating machines have made necessary the solution of problems of centrifugal force in heavy rotating parts. Better-balanced, better-aligned machines have resulted. Parts which fit exactly, better bearings with longer life, and self-lubricating bearings make them operate smoothly at high speeds for a long time. Vibration cushioners have also been built into the machines, so that, in part, the problem of noise and vibration has been solved by the machine manufacturers.

Noise and vibration may be air-borne, structurally borne, or may be transmitted by diaphragm. If the source of the noise can't be eliminated, damping methods will have to be directed at the means by which the noise is conveyed. Baffles, curtains, and acoustically covered walls will reduce noise or vibration that is air-borne. Flexible mounts will reduce the amount conveyed by the machine structure. Heavy concrete masses with their high inertia reduce vibration. The separate foundations for machines, mentioned earlier, also help. If the walls and ceilings tend to act as diaphragms transmitting noise, soundproofing acoustical materials will help. Acoustical ceiling material is used extensively to reduce noise in offices and laboratories. Cloth draperies on the walls are also effective noise reducers but are used only in laboratories where occasionally you want to get rid of noise almost completely.

Most companies reduce over-all noise in the factory by separating the noisiest operations from the other work. Drophammers, sandblasting equipment, grinding machines, punch presses, forming dies, etc., are put in separate buildings. When a separate building is not feasible, they are put in a separate room away from other operations. High ceilings help dissipate the noise, and cinder block sidewalls, used in some plants, help to deaden the sound. Inside walls in factories are seldom insulated, nor is acoustical ceiling material used, but they could both be used further to deaden noise.

COLOR

Many companies use colors to brighten their factories. Light colors for walls and ceilings have been used in many companies for years, but light colors for machinery and floors are relatively new. Paint manufacturers point out that a dull green color is relaxing without being depressing and recommend it for machines. They recommend also a flat paint, of buff color, for the machine work surfaces. This makes for contrast, but not too much contrast, between the machine and the product. The use of light, but dull rather than shiny, pastel shades that reflect up to 60 per cent of the light reduces the cost of lighting and is said to improve plant efficiency and safety. Remember, however, that maintenance costs, particularly plant cleanup, are higher because light colors show more dirt.

In spite of the claimed gains from use of light colors by paint manufacturers, many factories are old and dirty, yet they seem to get along fine. Floors are usually covered with an accumulation of oil and dirt which is scraped off only infrequently by the janitor. Walls, ceilings, and machines are painted every 3 or 4 years or less often and are rarely cleaned. Sometimes you can't tell what color machines and walls used to be. Actually, machines are commonly painted black or battleship gray, although dull green is also common. Lighter colors may have real value, but the managements of some factories seem to doubt that they are worth the cost of the paint and maintenance. The newer the factory the more likely you are to find light colors used.

STUDY QUESTIONS

1. What preparations need to be made in the building itself for communications systems? Which systems and what kind of preparation?
2. Why do some companies make their own electric power when others don't? Explain.
3. Can management control its electricity costs at all? How?
4. When is it cheaper to have electric motors for every machine? When is it not cheaper?
5. What is the difference between a (1) lumen, (2) foot-candle, and (3) foot-lambert?
6. Discuss the following statement: "It is well to have sharp contrasts between light and dark so that details can readily be seen."
7. Why do some companies build windowless factories while others use large expanses of glass?
8. Compare incandescent and flourescent lamps.
9. If you had by-product heat from your processes, would you use it to heat your plant? What difficulties would there be?
10. Air conditioning a factory costs a good bit of money to put in and more to operate. Why would any management be willing to spend the money?
11. What is "electrostatic precipitation"? How does it work and how is it used?
12. What can you do to get rid of noise?

Chapter 12

LAYOUT

$\mathbf{A}$NY arrangement of machines and facilities is a layout—just as any house plan is a plan. But some are better than others. How can you tell a good layout from a bad one? What characteristics does a "good" layout have? A good layout is one that allows materials in process to move through the necessary operations rapidly and in the most direct way possible. It reduces transportation, handling, clerical, and other costs and increases inventory turnover. Space requirements are reduced, as are inventories in process and all the costs that a high inventory entails.

The never-ending struggle to keep the productive capacity of operations in balance means constantly adding machines in some places and taking them out in others. Mostly, because the business is growing, you have to add machines or you may have to replace old worn ones. In any case, machines must be rearranged. Relayout goes on all the time.

Companies making substantial alterations and improvements in their layout often report that the costs of making the changes are recovered out of savings in less than one year. Savings in labor costs and increases in plant capacity almost always result. Besides the direct gains from improved layouts, there are almost always by-product gains in improved manufacturing processes and methods that come from the careful study made in connection with layout work.

A large part of the savings from good layout comes from cutting out materials handling and transportation costs (discussed in Chapter 13). This subject is so closely bound up with plant layout, however, that you ought always consider the two together wherever changes are thought of. Materials handling costs can't be cut if the layout is wrong, and wrong handling methods, in turn, prevent good layouts.

Since the advantages of good layout are so great and so obvious, why does any company tolerate any other kind? There are several reasons. One is that management doesn't realize that its layout is poor. It isn't easy to tell when you make a variety of products, each following a different path through the plant. Or, second, management does realize that the layout is poor but, from lack of will or courage to spend the money, doesn't do anything about it. There is no denying that layout changes cost money, especially when one change makes necessary another and so on, in chain fashion. Usually, however, it is false economy not to change. You get your money back many times over.

A third reason (and a very important one) why companies do not all have good layouts is that a good layout doesn't just happen. Only by

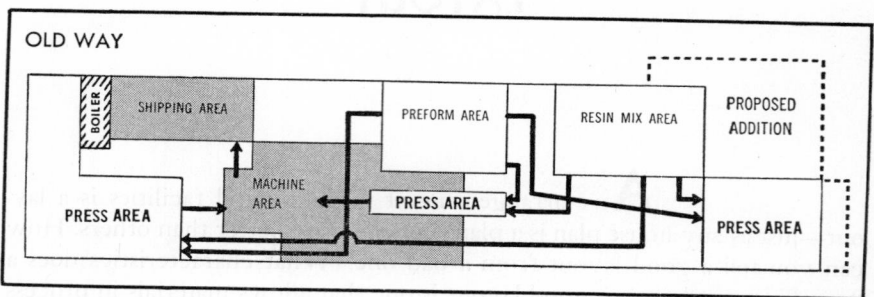

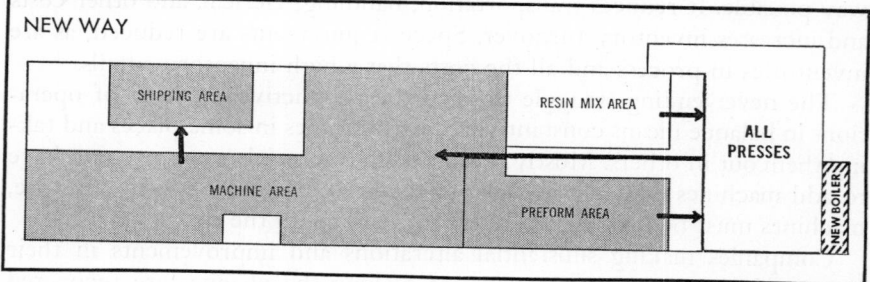

Factory Management and Maintenance

FIG. 12–1. Old and new layout. Departments rearranged to group similar equipment and cut product travel.

keeping constantly at it can you have and keep on having a good layout. Most companies make many products, each one following a different route through the plant. A good layout for one product is poor for another. Changes in the product mix sometimes change good layouts into poor layouts. The "best" layout (if unchanged) never stays best long.

Besides, there are design and process changes. They change the machines required, the space needed, and the arrangements. A "good" layout must therefore be a changing layout. It must be flexible enough to be changed quickly and with little expense and few holdups of operations.

EVIDENCES OF POOR LAYOUT

Though poor layout hampers efficient operations, neither its existence nor its effects are always recognized. Certain conditions are, however, either caused or made worse by poor layout. It is probably responsible for extra costs wherever the following conditions are found:

1. Materials move slowly through the plant.
2. Handling costs and inside material transportation costs are high.
3. Stock rooms and producing departments are crowded.
4. Aisles and individual workplaces are congested.
5. Service departments are given inadequate space and are inconveniently located.
6. Materials in process are frequently damaged or lost.
7. Failures to meet schedules and shipment promise dates are common.
8. Receiving docks are not cleared promptly, causing high demurrage costs and allowing materials to be exposed to the elements.

Most of the conditions listed above are found in one or more departments of nearly every factory, and they do not mean that the layout of a whole plant is poor. Their presence, however, is an indication of carelessness on the part of management. Or possibly business is so good that management is trying to put through more orders than it can handle. Well-managed growing companies often take on so much business that they are nearly bursting at the seams before they expand and add permanently to their physical facilities. Until they do expand, their layout may be just as poorly suited to their swollen operations as is that of poorly managed companies. But poor layout due to growing pains is not permanent and habitual, as it is in companies which are chronically careless.

OBJECTIVES OF LAYOUT

In general, here is what good layout tries to do:

1. Keep down materials handling and transportation.
2. Move materials rapidly through the plant. Eliminate points of congestion.
3. Provide enough, but not too much, space for operations, aisles, and storage areas. At the workplace, provide space for the worker to do his work and for storing materials before and after the operation.
4. Provide adequate and conveniently located service centers for products and employees.
5. Improve, confine, or eliminate operation with objectionable features— features that interfere with other operations. Some operations make the floor shake, others are noisy, some are dusty, or make fumes, odors, or heat. Avoid these conditions, if possible. If this can't be done, localize them by ventilation, soundproofing, etc.
6. Put together operations and equipment for ease of supervision and control of production. Don't, for example, put part of a department on one floor and the rest on another. Don't even split a department into separate rooms.

Flexibility of layout and *room for future expansion* are intentionally left out of the above list; but not because they are not important. They are. They are left out because they produce no *immediate* gain. In fact, they sometimes interfere a little with today's efficiency. Things are arranged for ease of change even if that means not having today's perfect layout.

The list also intentionally omits the "straight-line" idea. It is good to have materials flow through the plant as directly as possible (that is the essence of the "straight-line" idea), but the most economical layouts are frequently not literally straight-line layouts. "Odd-angles" layout (see page 237) may be better.

LAYOUT FLEXIBILITY

Although layout changes cost money, they are being made all the time. Being able to make them easily holds down relayout costs and interferes little with production during the changes. Considerable flexibility can be had in all original layouts if it is planned for; but if flexibility is not planned, changes are generally costly to make.

In one sense, all layouts are flexible. Almost any layout can be changed if you are willing to pay the price. But a genuinely "flexible" layout is one which can be changed at little cost. Changes in layout almost always mean moving some equipment. Factory machines require numerous services, and flexibility is limited if, in the change, many wires and pipes have to be changed too. Machines need power and light and sometimes compressed air, high and low pressure steam, gas, cutting oils, and water. Many companies put the piping and bus ducts for electricity in channels below the floor level, covered by removable sections of floor for easy access. The pipes and ducts are spaced to provide the services to all areas with a minimum of extra wiring or piping. Sometimes the channels below the ground floor level are regular tunnels large enough to accommodate men and trucks.

Layout alone can't give you all the flexibility you want. Machines and other conditions must also be flexible. Self-contained machines (those that have their own motor, lubrication system, cooling system, and supplementary lighting system if it is needed) give flexibility because they are independent of some plant services. Multipurpose machines, able to do a variety of jobs, and portable jigs and fixtures aid flexibility. It is aided also if the plant has large unobstructed floor areas, if the floor will take heavy weights, and if partitions are easily put up and taken down. Even very heavy equipment is, in a few companies, mounted on strong steel beams rather than on individual concrete foundations so that it can be shifted around more freely.

The basic arrangement of equipment and departments affects flexibility. Arrangements by "process," where similar equipment makes up departments, are more flexible than arrangements by "product," where production lines are devoted to the manufacture of specific products.

Good forecasts of future business reduce the importance of flexibility because if you know ahead what you are going to make, you can lay your plant out accordingly. You won't need to be so flexible be-

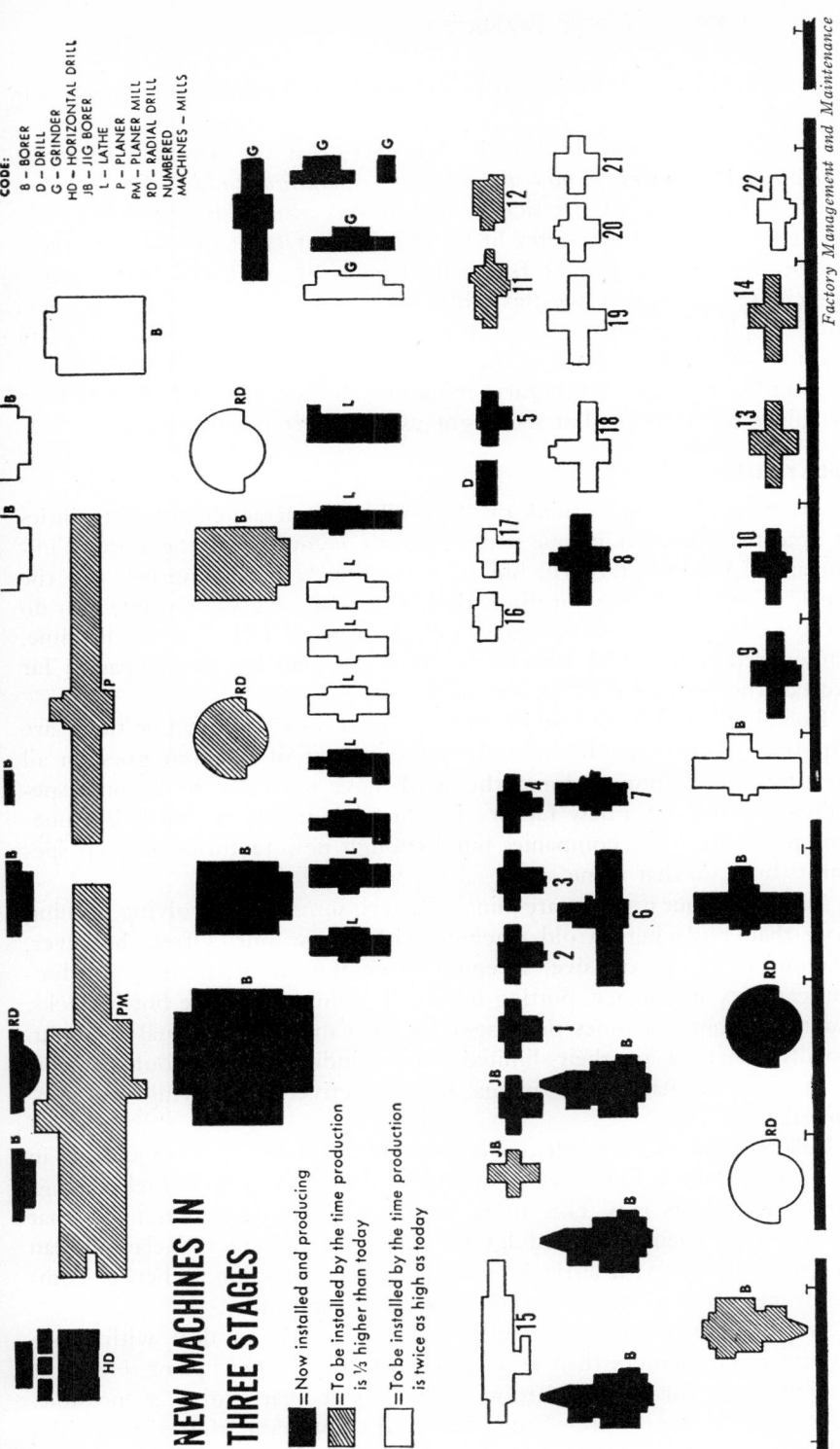

CODE:
B — BORER
D — DRILL
G — GRINDER
HD — HORIZONTAL DRILL
JB — JIG BORER
L — LATHE
P — PLANER
PM — PLANER MILL
RD — RADIAL DRILL
NUMBERED
MACHINES — MILLS

NEW MACHINES IN
THREE STAGES

■ = Now installed and producing

▨ = To be installed by the time production
is ⅓ higher than today

□ = To be installed by the time production
is twice as high as today

Factory Management and Maintenance

FIG. 12–2. Machine shop arranged with space for future machines.

cause you won't be making so many changes. Wrong guesses make for extra changes.

It should be emphasized again, however, that the *first and foremost objective of layout should be efficient operation today.* Tomorrow's needs cannot be known exactly, so flexibility should be provided only if it costs little and interferes little with current efficiency—*unless* there has been a long history of frequent changes. If we know that changes come often, then extreme flexibility may be worth while. It may pay, for example, to put machines on temporary mounts rather than fastening them to the floor or putting them on their own individual foundations. Generally speaking, temporary mounting is not as good as fastening machines to the floor, but we might use it to get flexibility.

RELAYOUT

Most people seem to think of "layout" as the arrangement of facilities in *new* factories. Of course a new plant's layout is of the utmost importance in a new factory, but new factories are the unusual, not the usual, thing. This does not mean that once you have your plant, you do no layout work; on the contrary, you do a great deal of it all the time. Undoubtedly, the total amount of relayout done by all companies far exceeds the total of new layout work done.

Relayout work is similar in many ways to new layout, but there are important differences. Because a certain amount of relayout goes on all the time, the engineers doing the work have a chance to become specialists. Laying out a new factory is a huge undertaking, but it is a one-time job; only giant companies build enough new factories to keep specialists busy on that alone.

Many relayout projects are minor matters, sometimes involving nothing more than replacing an old machine with a new one. Often, however, relayout is more extensive. Keeping machine and department production capacity in balance, putting in new machines to relieve bottle necks, and taking out machines no longer in use calls for continual relayout. Usually, because of their limited scope, individual relayout projects produce no dramatic cost savings, but collectively the savings are substantial.

Relayouts produce results faster than new layouts. Rearrangements in the factory take a few days or weeks to complete, after which savings start. New plants may take more than a year in construction, so that savings from their improved layout are delayed longer. Relayout can usually be done with little interference to production, whereas completely new layouts disrupt production for some time.

An engineer working on relayout projects has to deal with more limiting circumstances than an engineer planning a new plant. He must provide space for his installation with as little rearranging as possible. He is concerned with preserving, or trying to preserve, the existing aisles and with the location of existing machines, elevators, walls, doors, windows, posts, electric power lines, compressed air lines, etc. He must decide whether the floor can carry the load of an added machine. He must decide how the equipment is to be driven. If by electric motor, he must locate it and provide electric power for it. He must see that lights are properly placed so that the workers can see to run the machines. He may try to reduce the costs of materials transportation and handling or to mechanize it, but he can't do as much as he could if he were starting from scratch.

Relayout projects are sometimes big projects. One department may be expanded by taking away space from another. Whole groups of machines may be moved; walls may be torn down or new ones put up.

When several new machines are installed at one time, relayout work is more like new layout. Space limitations are eased considerably, with greater freedom in rearranging machines. General layout objectives can be considered and extensive improvements accomplished, most of which is impossible when relayout is confined to locating single machines.

Extensive relayout projects raise many problems because, generally, there is no extra space available. If one department expands another must contract. Often the department which can be contracted is not right next to the expanding department, so that moves have to be made in several departments. Costs can run high, depending on the number of departments and machines moved. Of course every one of these changes offers a chance to make improvements. The total savings may well take care of the high cost.

MACHINE SPACE

Whether you are installing new equipment or moving old equipment you have to know how much *space* you need. You already know how much space old machines take up, but for new machines it must be computed.

A machine needs floor space for its electric motor and electrical control panel, for its operator, for conveyors if they are used, and for the storage of material before and after the operation has been performed.

The *shape* of the machine must also be considered. Some machines are long and narrow, others are round, and some are nearly square. Some go up in the air 10 feet or more above floor level. Others extend downward several feet below floor level. Most machines are only 4 to 6 feet high and do not extend below the floor, so that only the shape of the floor space required needs to be considered.

In total, machines will always take up more space than the total of their separate space needs—because they never dovetail together exactly. You get a little flexibility, however, from storage spaces, which rarely need to be of any particular shape. The actual placing of machines is generally decided after experimentally placing machine templets in position on a floor plan.

FIG. 12–3. Progressive airplane final assembly line.

PRODUCT SPACE

In most companies the space allowed for storage, machines, conveyors, and aisles provides enough space for products in progress. Companies making large assembled products, such as locomotives, freight cars, and airplanes, must provide, in addition to the space for machines, aisles, etc., a large assembly or erection floor where the product is put together. Look at Figure 12–3! Just imagine the acres of floor space needed for assembling airplanes.

Usually big products are partially assembled in one part of the assembly area, then moved by overhead crane or by drag lines, or even by being towed by trucks, to another area, where more work is done. Each area is large enough to hold several products at a time; the total of the several areas requires enormous floor space, which usually must also be high and free from posts, so that the partially assembled products can be moved by overhead crane.

SERVICE AREA SPACE

All factories have to have service areas. Washrooms, locker rooms, restaurants, medical facilities, offices, toolrooms, stock rooms and temporary storage areas, weighing scales, elevators, stairs, and aisles may be secondary to the manufacturing operations, but they are necessary. They should be located close to work areas, where they can be most useful. Service areas may take up one third of the total space.

Some companies with unused overhead space put locker rooms and washrooms on balconies. But services should not just be shunted off into leftover corners without regard to their proper functional location. Convenience is a part of the service. Utility services, such as power, light, water, etc., also take up space, and the layout must put them where they are needed.

EFFECTS OF MATERIALS HANDLING EQUIPMENT

The kinds of materials handling equipment you use affect your layout. For example, hand or powered trucks require wider aisles than you need if you use conveyors. Forked trucks require wider aisles than other types of trucks. Sloped ramps from one floor to the next may be needed if you use trucks and if the elevator capacity is limited. Overhead cranes, if used, require open spaces free of supporting columns.

OVERHEAD SPACE

Overhead space, as well as floor space, should be considered in layouts. Using overhead space saves floor space and so saves money. Overhead conveyors and cranes can take materials directly to workplaces, which is something that trucks operating in the aisles cannot always do. Overhead conveyors are sometimes used for the temporary storage of

Link-Belt Co.

FIG. 12–4. An overhead conveyor serving factory operations.

materials between operations. This can result in substantial savings in handling costs, and it frees floor space at the machines.

Overhead space is also required for hot-air ducts if the building is heated by hot air from a distant source, and for ventilating and dust-removing ducts. The overhead space along the sides of wide departments sometimes has balconies where certain operations can be performed. You can also store supplies of parts on balconies and feed them to the assembly floor by conveyor or chute. Ordinarily, little floor or overhead space is needed for utilities. Electricity, water, steam, etc., are generally conveyed by wires and pipes in the walls, under the floor, or under the ceiling. Their location is important, but they do not take up much space.

If extensive use of overhead space is made for any purpose, building and machine models for layout planning are especially desirable. Flat drawings fail to show three-dimensional locations and are inadequate layout tools where overhead space is used extensively.

SAFETY AND THE EASE OF MAINTENANCE

Safety features should be included in layout. Avoid open pits and stair wells or protect them by guard rails. (In fact the law requires guard rails.) Avoid low, overhanging ceilings. If your men have to work in high-temperature areas or other dangerous places, provide safety equipment to protect them. Also remember ease of maintenance. Put electric power lines and other services where maintenance men can get at them.

LAYOUT PATTERNS

There are two basic patterns of layout. "Process" layout calls for the grouping of similar equipment, departments being based on the kind of *work done*. "Product" layout calls for the grouping of equipment required to make certain kinds of products, departments being based on the *products made*. Product-controlled layout is more economical if there is a large volume of standardized products. Lacking volume, a process-controlled layout is better. The layout of most companies, however, fits neither category perfectly because high volume and standardization characterize only certain products, not all.

Departments making parts for assembled products do not need to be laid out on the same basis as the assembly department. But where the standardization and volume of individual parts justifies it, a product-controlled layout is superior to a process layout here too. Often, though, the volume of many of the individual parts is too small to keep production lines busy making them alone. As a result, machines generally have to be used for several operations, in which case process layout is better.

PROCESS LAYOUT

Process layout groups together machines doing like work. Part of the gain from this type of layout results from combining fractional machine requirements. In product-controlled layout, if a machine is needed part time in each of several locations, each location has to have a machine. Process layout is also better suited to handling operations complicated by fumes, vibration, etc. It permits use of special fume ducts, back-to-back machine placement, and other variations of standard layout.

Process layout is flexible. Products requiring diverse operations can easily follow diverse paths through the plant. Both the general purpose machines requiring skilled men and supervisors and the job-lot method of production control add to the flexibility.

Process layout plants are less vulnerable to shutdowns than are product layout plants. If a machine breaks down, its work can be transferred to a nearby machine; the delay rarely interferes with the progress of other orders through the plant. Where products are varied and where limited quantities of each are made, manufacturing costs are lower with process layout than with product layout.

But process layout has its bad features too. Work routing, scheduling, and cost accounting are difficult. The same work must be done over and over again, each order being treated separately. Materials handling and transportation costs are high because they involve much manual labor. Materials move slowly through the plant, so that the inventories of materials in process are always high and considerable storage space is required. Automatic machinery is impractical for short runs. Inspection is a big cost item, and because general purpose machines have a low output, the machine and labor costs of operations are high.

PRODUCT LAYOUT

Product layout makes possible the use of automatic equipment, provides fixed routes for materials, and, wherever possible, moves materials by conveyor. Materials handling and travel distances are reduced, as is the inventory in process and therefore storage space. Product layout, however, is particularly vulnerable to interruptions because the banks of products between operations are small. Work stoppages at any point quickly end all operations. Because product layouts are so inflexible, design changes are costly. The rate of output is relatively fixed; additional output is generally possible only by working the whole unit more hours.

The comparatively simple machine-tending jobs in product layout make the training of new workers easy, but the highly repetitive nature of the work is monotonous to some workers. Many of the jobs are machine-paced, which some workers find objectionable. Production control is simpler in product layout than in process layout.

Group incentive plans, rather than individual incentives, apply to plants with product layout. The highly repetitive jobs make it worth while to do considerable motion study work for developing the best production methods. The investment is usually high in such plants, owing to the costly machines, particularly conveyors, and the need for duplication of equipment in different parts of the plant.

The cost of labor behind the scenes is high. Machine operators are but a part of the labor picture; they merely tend the machines. Machine designers, setup men, repair men, methods engineers, materials supply men, etc., are the other part of the picture. They are numerous because of the importance of perfectly designed machines and the necessity of keeping every producing machine in operation *all* of the time. The tremendously high productivity of automatic machines and the advantages of reduced inventory and handling costs, resulting in low unit cost, make it worth while, however, if you have the two essentials: volume and standardization.

STRAIGHT LINES

Straight-line layouts avoid backtracking and crosshauling. You can avoid this, however, only in product-controlled layouts, where most products follow the same paths through the plant. In general, too, you should try to reduce transportation distances. Here again product layout is better. But remember that the objective is to cut the *costs* of transportation, not the *distance* as such. Lengthy transportation distances, particularly if covered by conveyor, are not always costly.

Product-controlled plants and assembly departments of large manufacturers are often laid out in straight lines. (It is still straight-line lay-

Electro-Motive Division, General Motors Corp.

FIG. 12–5. An assembly line for making cabs for Diesel locomotives.

out, however, even if the product turns a corner now and then.) Products being made on today's assembly lines move down a conveyor to successive work stations where subassemblies and parts are attached. This is straight-line layout. It contrasts with process-controlled layouts, where assembled products are put together on a "unit" basis, subassemblies and parts being brought to one location for assembly. After a unit is complete, it is removed and another assembled at the same workplace.

ODD ANGLES

In an effort to group machines efficiently, you sometimes set them at odd angles to each other. Odd-angle layout includes semicircular, trian-

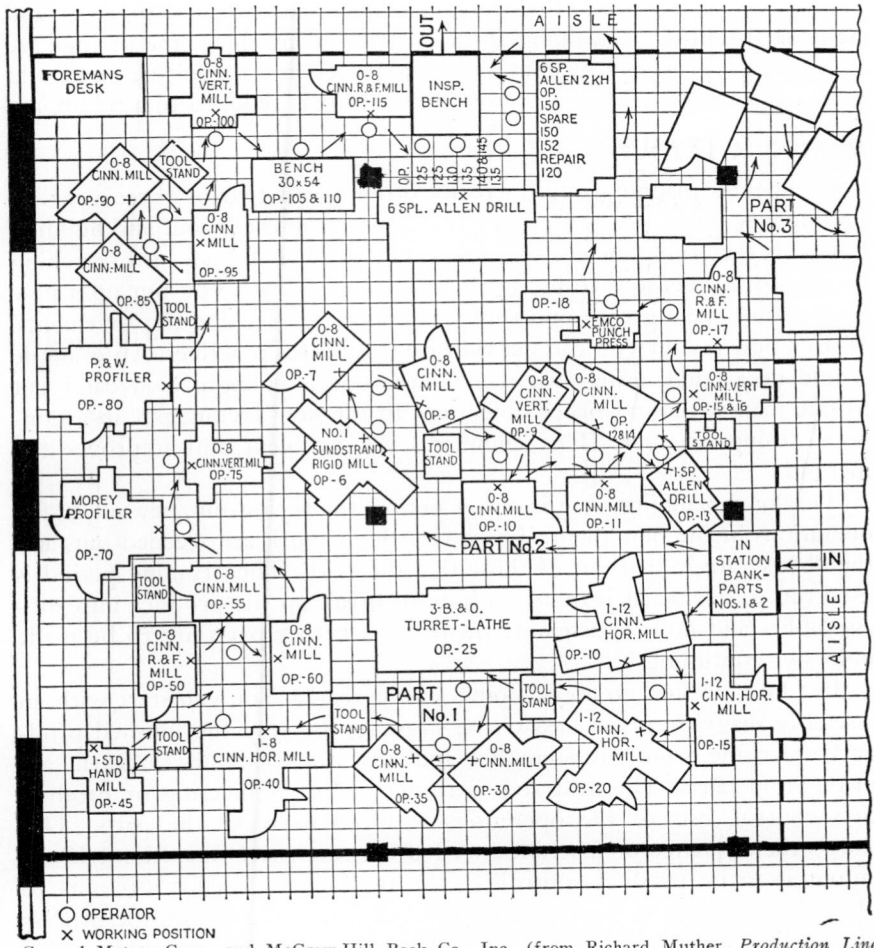

General Motors Corp., and McGraw-Hill Book Co., Inc. (from Richard Muther, *Production Line Technique*)

FIG. 12–6. An odd-angle arrangement of machine. Parts are placed in tote pans and handed from one operation to the next.

gular, horseshoe, and other patterns. Machines are often set at odd angles to each other in departments making large quantities of standard parts for assembled products. Odd-angle layouts make it easy to perform several successive operations on the same part. The machines are "set up" permanently and are used for one operation only. Sometimes assembly work stations are also put at odd angles to save worker time.

Most machines today, even general purpose machines, are semiautomatic. After the material has been put into the machine, it performs the operation with little or no care until the product is ready to be removed. The operator, free to do other work during the automatic part of the operation, often can operate several machines. His work is largely loading and unloading his machines. The cost of his labor can be divided among several machines. But if the machines are not close together and he must use his time walking from machine to machine, the savings are reduced. By grouping machines close together in a semicircle or at odd angles to each other, the operator's waste time is reduced to a minimum.

MAKING A LAYOUT

Companies planning new factories often spend two or three years in preliminary work. Designing the plant and setting the layout and building the plant take time but not that long. The extra time goes into searching for improved methods to use in the new plant. When you put up a new plant, you have a great opportunity to make far-reaching improvements. With a new layout you can get rid of old wasteful practices. An example would be a truck using two men where one is enough. You can't cut to one man without worker objection. In the new layout, put in a conveyor using no men. This eliminates the problem and improves the method.

The long planning time is also a period for trying out new ideas for operations in the new plant. Those that don't work are weeded out, and the "bugs" are ironed out of those that do work. The planning period is used too to decide such things as how to break up the product into subassemblies and how to assemble them and whether parts are to be made in lots or continuously.

Just how do you go about doing layout work? You can start with an assembly diagram, or process chart, showing the way the finished products are made from subassemblies and how subassemblies, in turn, are made from parts. The next step is to get, from engineering or production control, lists of the operations required to make the parts. This shows the sequence of machines needed for successive operations. If the layout is to be product-controlled, the preliminary layout attempts to place the machines according to the lines of flow indicated on the process chart. The first draft of the new layout is merely a starting point for the study of still better arrangements. From here on making a layout for a new factory is something like relayout in old factories. You juggle and rearrange machines until you get the best arrangement.

Assembly charts and process charts, illustrated in Chapter 29, are helpful in preliminary layout work. Charts are also frequently used in relayout for studying operation sequences. Charts are, in fact, so frequently used in relayout that standard forms, as in Figure 29–1 (pages 546–47), are used to represent instances of operations, transportations, inspections, etc. They are helpful to the analyst trying to improve the way a product is made.

The very first relayout drawings are sometimes made to show the permanently or semipermanently fixed items, everything that cannot be changed easily. All other elements are then indicated in their ideal positions. But the ideal arrangement nearly always runs into the permanently fixed items that get in the way. So you have to make adjustments—give up part of the ideal layout or move some of the hard-to-move items. Sometimes one gives; sometimes the other. Adjustments back and forth are made until the best compromise is reached. Keep as much of the ideal layout as possible without getting into costly changes of the existing layout.

Most layout diagrams are worked out on large sheets of co-ordinate paper with quarter-inch vertical and horizontal spaces. Co-ordinate paper makes it easy to show things to scale, and it is helpful in showing where things now are and how new things would fit in. Co-ordinate lines also make it easy to draw in departmental boundary lines and aisles and to draw them to scale. Blueprints or ozalid prints showing departmental arrangements can also be used, but they are more expensive to make up and to use than drawings on co-ordinate paper.

Little paper cutouts, or templets, cut to scale, are generally used to represent machines. To eliminate confusion, the templets should be identified by machine name. Many companies use a system of colored templets. Separate colors can be provided for machinery of different kinds and for conveyors. Visualizing the layout is easier with a color system. There is an added advantage in colors so chosen that they will produce contrasts in photostating. Templets can be placed at their appropriate places on the tentative floor plan and temporarily fastened with Scotch tape, so that they can be moved as alternative layouts are considered. It is a good idea to photostat the various layouts considered at one time or another. Then they can be reconsidered if later layouts appear to be less efficient.

Three-dimensional replicas or models of machines and equipment are often used today for new layouts. They give a much better picture to people who are not accustomed to reading drawings and blueprints. Officers of the company are not all good blueprint readers so they may want to see the layout in miniature before they approve spending the money. Drafting time is eliminated by the use of models; in fact, the total time required for planning a layout is said to be reduced if models are used. Models need only to be set on their proper places. They are faster and more effective, for example, than a drawing for showing piping arrangements. Many companies use models not only for machines but also for men, conveyors, pallets, and other space-filling items. Their use makes certain that adequate, yet not too much, space is provided for all essentials.

Today there are many companies making models of machines from wood or plastic. Models of individual machines cost from $1.00 to $5.00 each, so that they are more expensive than paper cutouts, although some companies can make their own models for less. If close fits are not involved, rough blocks of wood will serve as models. A layout model of a whole plant showing all machines and equipment will probably cost at least $2,000, and its cost may exceed $10,000.

The American Society of Mechanical Engineers has adopted a scale for models of one-fourth inch for each foot. Some machinery manufacturers supply their customers with models of standard machines for their layouts. Their models, as well as those available from model manufacturers, are usually made to this scale. It is important, where a tight fit is in prospect, that the over-all dimensions of the model be accurate, because an error in the model size is magnified forty-eight times in the machine itself.

Like the two-dimensional templets, models are sometimes painted various colors. In a layout revision, existing machines may be one color and new machines another color. Sometimes each type of machine is given a different color. Some companies paint each machine model in several colors, one color representing stationary parts, another color moving parts, still another the area of maximum overhang of traveling parts. Models are usually identified by name or number.

Some contractors of factory buildings do not favor the use of models. An oil refinery builder says that if you turn out all the drawings needed to make a model you might as well go ahead and build the plant. It is true, of course, that historically most plants were built without models, and serious errors were not often made. Models and replicas are seldom used in relayout work, first, because they were not used in the original layout and are not on hand, and, second, because if the changes are small, they can be easily understood from drawings and flat templets. After models have been used in original layouts, they can be kept and will facilitate future relayout.

One of the last steps in layout is making a new process chart so that the path which the materials follow through the plant can be given a final check. The big job of making up detailed drawings, showing exact locations of machines, motors, foundations, etc., follows; then the plans and schedules for making the changes; and lastly the actual changes themselves.

INSTALLATION

Relayout is generally supervised by the plant engineering staff, whether the work itself is done by the company's maintenance department or by outside contractors. Drawings or photostats of the final layout should be given to the people in charge of major phases of the work.

Putting in a relayout nearly always upsets production unless installation is planned very carefully. To keep down production delays, it is necessary, on large projects, to plan in great detail every step of the change from the old to the new. Detailed time schedules, showing the exact time when certain machines are to be moved and when new machines will be ready to run, permit moves to be made with almost no interruption to production. If possible, changes should be made over week ends.

On big projects it is well to take pictures which record the progress during various stages of installation and check the accuracy with which the layout plan is being followed. It is easy to miss errors when a new building is being built or considerable equipment is being installed. Besides, pictures of the progress can be used to support progress payments to the contractor during construction.

OFFICE LAYOUT

All manufacturing companies must provide numerous offices. Certain office arrangements are more economical than others. In general, the same methods of layout can be applied to the office as to the factory. The work to be done is first analyzed, equipment and work spaces determined, templets made up, and arrangements tried out on paper before the actual changes are made. This subject is discussed more fully in Chapter 42.

YARDS AND PREMISES

The inefficiencies of poor layout are just as real in outdoor materials storage yards as they are inside the factory walls. Pig iron, steel castings, bar stock, wire, coal, scrap products, scrapped machines, and many other materials can be, and are, stored out of doors without harm. Loading and unloading areas and docks for railroad cars and trucks, as well as storage yards, need to be arranged for efficient operation. Automobile parking lots for employees and visitors should be ample, paved, and accessible to factory entrances. No layout project is complete unless these external areas are included.

STUDY QUESTIONS

1. How can you tell a poor layout if you see one?
2. What do you try to do when you try to make a good layout?
3. The text omits flexibility and room for future expansion from its list of things you want in a good layout. Why? Discuss.
4. What would you do if you were trying to make a new layout flexible?
5. Compare relayout and new layout as to frequency, extent, and value to the company.

6. To get total space requirements for a department you must do more than just add together the square footage required for the machines. What more do you do?
7. Where is the best place to put service departments? Why?
8. When would you adopt "process" layout? When would you adopt "product" layout?
9. Compare odd-angle layout and straight-line layout.
10. How would you go about planning a new layout?
11. Some companies use three-dimensional replicas of machines in layout work, others don't. Why?

Case 12–1.   The Fairweather Toy Company

In the early stages of planning for a new factory building the Fairweather Toy Company has arrived at the approximate space and location requirements for the departments to be set up. A one-story building 300′ × 200′ facing east is to be built. The Machine Shop is to be on the north side of the building. The Receiving Department is to be located along the west side of the building, and the Packing and Shipping Department in the southwest corner of the building. A loading and unloading platform is to extend across the west side of the building, outside of the area given. There will be a railroad spur track there.

The Employment and Welfare Department and Reception Room for Employment and Purchasing Departments are on the south side of the building. The Production and Engineering Department and the Factory Manager's Office are toward the north end of the east side.

The general flow of work through the factory is as follows:

All raw materials and supplies first enter the Receiving Department. From the Receiving Department, materials pass into a Raw Materials Storeroom, and supplies pass into a Supplies Storeroom. Both storerooms adjoin the Receiving Department.

Raw materials enter only one department, the Machine Shop, where both machine and bench operations are performed. Work leaving the Machine Shop is known as "manufactured parts." They pass from the Machine Shop into a Manufactured Parts Storeroom. Manufactured parts are fed from the Parts Storeroom to two subassembly departments, Department No. 2 and Department No. 3. The Subassemblies Storeroom receives subassemblies from Department Nos. 2 and 3, and manufactured parts and subassemblies go to the Final Assembly Department.

The finished product next enters the Finished Stock Room. The finished product passes through the Packing and Shipping Department to be packed and shipped to the customer.

The following areas have been assigned to the various departments: Receiving Department—750 sq. ft.; Raw Materials Storeroom—1,500 sq. ft.; Manufactured Parts Storeroom—1,250 sq. ft.; Subassemblies Storeroom—3,000 sq. ft.; Finished Products Storeroom—3,750 sq. ft.; Supplies Storeroom—1,000 sq. ft.; Machine Shop—200′ × 30′, machine operation B 150′ × 45′, bench operation C 50′ × 45′; Department No. 2 (subassembly)—150′ × 45′; Department No. 3 (subassembly)—70′ × 50′; Final Assembly Department—245′ × 50′ less the area for the Subassemblies Storeroom, which is partitioned off in this department; Packing and Shipping Department—2,500 sq. ft.

The remaining area is assigned to offices and is to be divided approximately as follows: Production and Engineering Department—1,200 sq. ft.; Factory Manager's Office—400 sq. ft.; Cost Department (which includes Chief Cost Accountant's Office)—1,700 sq. ft.; General Accounting Department (which includes Controller's Office)—1,700 sq. ft.; General Office Department—2,400 sq. ft.; Secretary and Treasurer's Office—300 sq. ft.; Vice-President and General Manager's Office—400 sq. ft.; President's Office—600 sq. ft.; Sales Department—1,100 sq. ft.; Purchasing and Traffic Department—825 sq. ft.; Employment and Welfare Department—625 sq. ft.; Reception Room for Employment Department and Purchasing Department—750 sq. ft.

Lay out, on a scale 1″ = 40′, the floor areas for the Fairweather Toy Company which you think will give the most efficient flow of work. If the total space requirements do not equal the total space available, adjust the space allotted to the offices.

Chapter 13

TRANSPORTATION AND
MATERIALS HANDLING

THE WASTEFUL NATURE OF TRANSPORTING MATERIALS

Every company is in the materials transporting or "materials handling" business. Materials have to be moved from the incoming freight car to receiving inspection, then on to raw materials storage. From there they go to the first operation, then on to other operations, to and from temporary storage points between operations, to finished stores, to the shipping room, and, finally, to the outgoing freight car. During their trip through the plant, they are picked up and put down many times. *In and of itself, every kind of transportation or materials handling is waste in that it does not change the form of the product.* Getting rid of any part of it is clear gain.

How important is the problem? Are we talking about 2 per cent or 20 per cent of our costs? Probably few companies spend less than 15 per cent of their labor costs for handling materials.[1] Up to 30 per cent is more common, and over 50 is not unknown. How much money does it add up to? Something in the range of $1,000 per employee per year! A company with 10,000 employees spends $10,000,000, more or less, every year to carry things around! Giant companies may spend hundreds of millions annually to carry things around.

Actually it is hard to get exact figures on the cost of materials handling because companies vary and because accounting reports never show all of the cost as a single total. A total is hard to get because so much materials handling (picking up and putting down) is done by machine operators and assemblers incidental to their work. They are called "production workers," and none of their time shows on the records as materials handling cost. Worse yet, because the records do not show this cost, *it is*

---

[1] "How to Get More for Your Handling Dollar," *Factory Management and Maintenance,* July, 1955, pages 95–118.

often unrecognized as being wasteful. Besides, labor costs are not the whole story. To get it all, you need to add the costs of trucks and conveyors and possibly the cost of storage spaces and aisles.

Wasteful though transporting materials may be, it can never be eliminated completely, but it should be reduced wherever possible, both within and between operations. In the following pages we discuss how materials handling *should* be done to reduce handling costs. Actually, many companies, particularly small companies, do not give handling costs the attention they deserve. They hardly scratch the surface when it comes to analyzing and reducing materials handling costs. Improvements, if made, are piecemeal and are made only within single producing departments. Savings opportunities affecting several departments are overlooked.

AREAS OF GREATEST WASTE

The areas where the most money is spent are not always the places where the most can be saved. Most labor costs are incurred paying for productive operations. But such jobs are studied and improved continually, so that the materials handling costs within operations—even though often unrecognized as handling costs—are kept down fairly well. Moving materials between operations is also recognized as costly and so is usually well controlled. So are delays to production workers from materials not being on hand. They are known to be costly and are usually kept down.

General Motors Corp.

FIG. 13–1. Unloading a shipment of metal parts shipped loose. Even though the load will later be hauled away all at one time by a fork truck, the handling of the material is slow and inefficient.

Not so often recognized or controlled are the waste time and motion found in loading materials on and off trucks and conveyors. If loading is done by hand and if one or a few pieces at a time are loaded, the methods can probably be improved. Hauling part loads and "returning empty" are other wasteful, but common, practices. Putting materials into and removing them from temporary storages, supply banks, or storerooms make extra handling at every point. Toolrooms and jig and fixture storages also usually cost more than they should because of inefficient materials handling methods. Here, as in regular stock rooms, much of

General Motors Corp.

FIG. 13–2. Unloading another shipment of the same items shown in Figure 13–1. Loading and unloading labor costs are almost eliminated.

the work is handling materials or walking back and forth from storage bins to the issue window.

Waste from machine operations, such as chips, dust, metal scraps, and shearings, is often handled manually. In most companies waste is handled several times and too often inefficiently, particularly in the scrap and packing departments. Receiving and shipping departments and the receiving inspection department also do too much handling. Improper handling is also frequently responsible for failure to unload railroad cars promptly, thus causing demurrage costs.

The maintenance department is another place where handling costs are responsible for a considerable part of total costs. It is hard to be efficient when the work is so varied. The lack of direct supervision and the time used by the employees to get to and from individual jobs heighten the difficulties. But companies which have really tried to handle materials more efficiently in the maintenance department claim to have cut these costs considerably.

RULES FOR REDUCING MATERIALS HANDLING COSTS

The best way to handle materials is not to handle them; but if this can't be done, then "hands-off" handling is next best. Materials handling costs can be reduced by (1) eliminating handling whenever possible; (2) making the necessary handling more efficient; and (3) by mechanizing, largely by conveyors and power-driven trucks, whatever handling still remains. Money spent on handling materials is gone forever, but money spent on devices for handling will come back in the form of savings.

Wherever large quantities of materials follow the same, or nearly the same, path through the plant, a conveyor is generally the cheapest method of moving them. But where materials follow different paths, hand or power-driven trucks are better. In general, the cost per unit for handling materials goes down as the quantity goes up because you can afford to mechanize.

Materials handling costs will generally be kept low if the following rules are observed:

1. If possible, handle materials mechanically all the way from the inbound freight car to the outgoing freight car.
2. Avoid rehandling. While materials are being handled, do as many operations as possible on them. When materials are moved, take them directly to the point of use. Never move material twice while in the same condition.
3. Move materials in a straight line; avoid frequent changes in directions.
4. Move materials continuously, uniformly, and fast.
5. Pick up and put down materials as infrequently as possible, both within operations and in transit.
6. Do not mix materials which will require future sorting.
7. At every point where materials must be handled, experiment to find the best way and then never deviate from it except to improve it.
8. Reduce transportation distances. Although the costs of transportation generally are not proportional to the distance materials are moved, shorter moves cost less than long moves, and they reduce the inventory in process.
9. Lift all heavy materials mechanically. Men should not lift over 50 pounds from the floor to waist height. Still less should be lifted to higher levels. Lifting heavy weights is fatiguing to workers and is slow, expensive, and unsafe. Lifting is the most common cause of industrial accidents.
10. Mechanize even light lifting if it has to be done often.
11. Hire stock handlers if mechanization is impossible. Machine operators should do only the lightest lifting. Besides they should not spend their time lifting.
12. Bring materials to machine or assembly-line operators mechanically or use stock supply men.
13. Haul all heavy loads mechanically.
14. Transfer materials from container to container mechanically.
15. Use mechanical transportation for fragile commodities.
16. Handle finished parts and products as little as possible to avoid damage.
17. Handle and move all hot materials mechanically.

18. Use conveyors for large quantities of materials moving over the same path, particularly for powdered, granulated, or liquid materials which would otherwise have to be put into containers for transporting and later taken out.

Bell & Howell Co.

FIG. 13–3. A tiering truck stacking material in storage baskets at a high level. Insert shows how empty baskets can be collapsed to save space.

19. Save as much floor space as possible by using overhead space for conveyors and for stacking stored materials. Today's mechanical devices can stack materials high up for practically the same cost as on the floor. The floor space can be used more profitably for manufacturing operations.

20. Handle materials in groups rather than singly. Generally, the larger the size of the "unit load" handled, the more economical it is.
21. Put breakable or fragile materials on trays in layers, separated by wood or cardboard, the whole being held by steel strapping. Unit loads are less subject to damage.
22. Load products directly from the machines into holding baskets or pallet boxes (boxes on small movable storage platforms) which fork lift trucks can raise mechanically. Rehandling and manual loading and unloading of trucks are thus eliminated.

Boeing Airplane Co.

FIG. 13–4. Mobile racks on which parts for assembly are placed in the stockroom. After being filled, they are wheeled to the place on the assembly floor where they are needed.

23. Use pallets rather than skids.[2] They cost less, occupy less space, are more easily handled by fork lift trucks, and are more easily tiered.
24. Design pallets for effective handling. If they are made square in shape, forks can enter them from any side. If they get rough treatment, make them of steel and wood to hold down repair costs.
25. Use cheap, expendable, nonreturnable wooden, or even cardboard, pallets for shipping products. The savings in the cost of loading and unloading freight cars is far greater than the cost of the pallets. Freight-car

---

[2] Pallets and skids are two kinds of small movable platforms on which materials are put for storage or hauling. Skids stand higher off the floor and usually cannot be tiered. Pallets are lower and are generally covered on the bottom as well as the top, so that, when loaded with materials, they can be piled one on top of the other. Pallets may be any size. 40" × 48" with a 4" deck space is common. Figure 13–2 shows a pallet in use.

dunnage (wood bracing to hold loads in place) is usually cheaper, too, with pallet loads.

26. Use "work carriers," special racks to hold odd-shaped materials, with corner supports, so that they can be tiered.

27. Use fixed platform trucks only if materials must be accumulated from, or delivered to, many locations. Because fixed platform trucks cannot be "preloaded," materials must always be handled an extra time while the trucks stand idle.

28. Use pallets and fork lift tiering trucks to reduce truck dead-time required for loading and unloading.

29. Use small, maneuverable tractor-pulled trailers instead of trucks where substantial quantities of products must be moved long distances and where conveyors are impractical. Trailers are inexpensive, so that their idleness while being loaded or unloaded does not cost much. The power unit and the trucker need not be idle while the trailer is being loaded and unloaded.

30. Haul only full truckloads.

31. Work out two-way truck routes and so eliminate the "empty return."

32. Reduce the idle time of materials handling equipment by use of a schedule.

33. Use fast-moving equipment; then fewer trucks and men are needed.

34. Keep the dead weight (the truck) down and the live weight (the load) up, so that the energy is expended almost entirely to move material.

35. Keep floors reasonably smooth, so that loaded trucks will pull easily and not jar the load. Then materials will not have to be fastened down and yet will not be damaged or fall off.

36. Avoid steep inclines on truck routes, so that loads will not need to be fastened down. Steep inclines are dangerous to the load going down and take extra power going up. Even moderate slopes may require double the tractive power needed for level trucking.

37. Inspect, lubricate, and maintain the materials handling equipment regularly.

38. Use antifriction bearings and rubber tires on trucks. They save energy and the floors.

39. Use materials handling equipment to simplify maintenance work. Crane lift and elevating platform trucks are particularly useful in doing maintenance work in high places.

WHAT TO MOVE?

Men and *machines* combine to make *products* out of materials. The three have to be brought together. Which two do the moving and which stays put? Men and machines remain with you, but you sell the product—it ends up being taken away. So, in the end at least, the product has to be moved. But it doesn't always pay, during manufacturing, to move the product to the men and machines. Sometimes it costs less to move the men and machines instead.

When you make a ship, say the Queen Elizabeth, it is more convenient to make it in one spot and to bring men, machines, and parts to it. Factory products don't match the Queen Elizabeth in size (it weighs 84,000 tons), but many factory products are big and unwieldly enough to make it pay to move men and machines (usually portable tools) to the product. This is particularly true in assembly work where the product takes on its full size.

Airplanes, locomotives, and other large products are put together at "work areas." The areas are big enough to hold four or five products. As soon as a partially assembled locomotive arrives in position 1 in the area, a crew of men do certain work on it—usually attaching parts and assemblies. By the time they are finished, another locomotive has been put into position 2 in the area so they move over and do the same work on it. Then on to 3 and so on.

As soon as the first crew leaves position 1 another work crew carries on the assembly from where the first crew left off. When they finish, they move on to the locomotive in position 2 following the first crew. Meanwhile a third crew takes over at station 1 and does its work. Then it moves on to station 2 and so on. By the time the first crew is done at station 5, the locomotive in position 1 has been removed (by an overhead crane or—in the case of airplanes—by a tow truck) and another fresh one to work on has been placed there.

This method reduces product handling costs and is a great saving. But don't overlook the fact that this reduction was made possible only by moving the men and their tools instead of moving the product. Moving men and tools is also costly but, for large products, less costly than moving the product often. This method is almost as good as line assembly as far as men having access to the work is concerned. Each work area has permanent scaffolds and steps so that men can do their work high up on the product or low down, whichever is required.

ANALYZING MATERIALS HANDLING

Materials are handled so many places in the plant that no one person can find all of the places where improvements can be made. The actual handling is done by hourly paid workers, so why not ask them how to do it better? This is what some companies do. The foremen, too, are well acquainted with the picking up and putting down and hauling of materials that their men do. Ask them too for ideas. Searching out wasteful handling and getting rid of it should be a continuous objective of everyone concerned with materials handling.

Analyzing the movement of the main product in its entirety, from incoming to outgoing freight car, will show how many instances of transportation and handling there are. By viewing the over-all movements of products you can see rearrangements affecting several operations, rearrangements which you might miss if you confined your analysis of materials handling to one operation at a time.

Process charts, made on floor plans, are often the first step in a study of materials handling. It is actually easier to see on a diagram than it is in the plant itself. The path followed by materials can be traced, and operations and storage points spotted. Charts are useful, though, only where most products follow similar paths; you can't make effective charts for diverse products with diverse paths.

Any analysis of materials handling, whether by chart or by other methods, should show *how much* and *how often* materials are handled, *how they are transported*, and *how far*. The study should reveal any points of congestion that exist and their causes.

After taking the materials handling picture, try to reduce the handling by applying the rules we have given earlier. Most improvements can be made only if money is spent for rearrangements or for equipment. But look into all the possibilities for making improvements without spending money before you start recommending changes that cost something. Workers may, for example, be doing jobs inefficiently. Teach them the most effective methods for their work. Trucks may be traveling light or empty too much of the time. Schedule their work and map out regular routes. Maybe you can improve the situation without spending any more money at all.

It is not always easy to tell whether you should make a costly change, because the usual accounting records don't give you the figures you need for judging. Except for the scarcity of data, the problem is much like buying new machines to replace old ones. In both cases the important thing to remember is the long-run *cost per unit of product*, not the initial investment. Expensive equipment often produces low handling costs per unit over the years.[3]

A comparison analysis should include all items of cost and savings. If mechanization will reduce breakage, this saving should be added to the savings in direct labor. If a change to fork lift trucks require more aisle space than hand trucking, the cost of providing it should be included in any comparison of costs of the two methods. If the costs of performing preceding or succeeding operations are affected, these items should also be included.

Cost comparisons between the existing and the proposed methods of handling should consider the number of pieces of equipment needed and the number of years they will last. To get the number needed you have to know how fast the handling equipment will travel, how fast it can be loaded and unloaded, and how much time it will be idle. Knowing this lets you figure the amount of materials that one new piece of equipment will move, which in turn tells you how many pieces of equipment you need.

Cost is not the only element to be considered in selecting materials handling equipment. Other factors must be considered: the space required by the equipment in use, its flexibility, how it is powered, ease of operation, speed of operation, safety, durability, and its need for auxiliary equipment such as pallets and loading platforms. To the extent that these

---

[3] The procedure for making cost comparisons is the same as that described for machines in Chapter 8 on page 155.

are measurable they are considered in the cost analysis, but some are intangible and hard to evaluate. They should be considered, however, in the complete analysis.

"FIXED" VERSUS "VARIED" PATH EQUIPMENT

Equipment for moving materials may be divided into "fixed path" and "varied path" equipment. Either kind can be used to move materials between stock rooms and operations or between operations, or since they hold considerable quantities of materials, they may serve as temporary stock rooms. Varied path equipment handles materials in separate lots, whereas fixed path equipment usually handles material continuously. Varied path equipment is flexible, and fixed path equipment is relatively inflexible. Fixed path equipment is more economical if large quantities of materials follow the same path, but it is uneconomical if materials follow diverse paths. Varied path equipment must have portable power units for each piece of equipment or must be hauled by a man. Fixed path equipment usually can be driven electrically or, in the case of materials transported downward, by gravity.

Fixed path equipment fixes the path materials follow; parts going to assembly don't go astray. Mostly too you can get rid of identification tags, separate work orders, and records of individual operations. Conveyors can also be used to pace the worker. In assembly lines workers must keep up with the work.

The equipment selected should be as appropriate as possible for the job to be done. The less variety there is in the work, the more perfectly suited the equipment can be. Simple and standard handling equipment should be used where possible because it is cheaper and more easily maintained.

FIXED PATH EQUIPMENT

Big companies are usually heavily conveyorized. Chrysler's Plymouth plant in Detroit has over 27 miles of conveyors. They move parts to 1,600 machines for fabrication and to men using 1,900 hand power tools in assembly work. GE's Hotpoint electric stove factory in Chicago has nearly 2 miles of conveyors. A few are for storage to balance operations where some operations operate two shifts and others three.

Conveyors are not the only kind of fixed path equipment, but they are the main kind. Cranes traveling on overhead tracks are also frequently used. Elevators are common for vertical transportation, and chutes for combined vertical and sloping moves. Pipes, tubes, and ducts are often used in handling bulk materials (liquids, powders, and granulated materials).

Overhead Conveyors. Conveyors may be located overhead, at work level, or on the floor. Overhead conveyors generally operate by chain, cable, or connected links suspended from a monorail and have separate pans, hooks, or carrying cradles in or on which material is placed. The conveyor is generally driven by electric motors. Overhead conveyors are used primarily for horizontal transportation, but they frequently combine vertical and horizontal transportation. Generally they keep moving rather than stop and go.

Overhead conveyors save floor space and relieve aisle congestion, although usually they must come down to operating levels at certain points for loading and unloading. They are often used as "service" conveyors to move materials between stock rooms and to and from production operations. When used this way, the conveyor is loaded in the stock room and passes, at work level, beside the operators in the producing departments. As it passes by, workers help themselves from the pans of materials. Stock room employees keep the pans loaded at all times, so that production employees will not have to wait. The conveyor is an endless chain making the round trip continuously from stock room to producing department and back. Another conveyor may be used to move the products to their next stop, a temporary stock room or another operation.

Slowly moving overhead conveyors are sometimes used for temporary storage. They are out of the way and can hold substantial banks of materials. Both overhead and work-level conveyors are frequently an integral part of the producing process, an operation often being performed automatically or by a worker as the conveyor moves the material along. Painting, baking, cooling, cleaning, degreasing, electroplating, washing, and many other operations can be done in this way. Conveyors are also frequently used to move materials to and from automatic sack-filling and can-filling machines.

Work-Level Conveyors.   Conveyors at work level are more varied in form than are overhead conveyors. They may consist of pans or hooks hanging from and moving along a monorail. More often they are apron conveyors or rollers or moving belts. Usually they move continuously rather than stop and go.

The surface of apron conveyors is made up of a continuous succession of flat, square, or rectangular pieces of wood or metal. Apron conveyors are used for moving individual pieces of material or containers holding material. Roller conveyors may be "live" (power-driven and generally covered by a belt), or they may be "free" rollers, meaning that the material is moved along by pushing it from operator to operator. Free roller conveyors will move the material by gravity if the feed end is placed higher than the takeoff end. The materials must, of course, be in sizable pieces or in containers. Free roller conveyors are relatively inexpensive. Since sections of roller conveyors can be moved easily, they are among the most flexible kinds of mechanical handling equipment.

Belt conveyors, usually made of rubber, are particularly well adapted to moving bulk materials other than liquids without the need for con-

Woodward Governor Co.

FIG. 13–5. Use of a roller conveyor in connection with bench assembly work.

tainers. The rollers on which the belt rides are generally set so that the belt forms a trough to hold the materials. Belt conveyors are also commonly used in assembly work to move products from one work station to another. The belt goes down the middle of a long table, at each side of which assembly operations are performed. The worker takes the partially assembled product off the conveyor. Conveyors used this way generally keep moving, though stop-and-go operation is not unknown. Sometimes the lower level of the belt, as it completes its circuit, is used to convey assembled products, scrap materials, empty containers, etc., in the reverse direction.

Turntables, another type of conveyor, are used at work level by some companies. Turntables are mounted on central swivel pedestals and can be turned either by hand or by power. An operator sitting beside the table takes off the product he is to work on. After he finishes his operation, the product is put back on the table, which is turned a little, so that the operator performing the next operation can reach it. The second worker performs his operation and puts the product back on the table (or on another turntable on the other side of his workplace), and it goes on to the next operator. Generally the table carries a small inventory of products, so that it serves as a bank and helps to balance the operations. If one operator leaves his workplace for a few minutes, the work of neither the worker ahead nor the worker behind is delayed. Turntables are so simple, practical, and inexpensive that it is surprising they are not more often used.

The United States Rubber Company, in its Detroit automobile tire plant, uses another type of turntable. It is set close to floor level and is as large as a carnival "merry-go-round." Machines are mounted on it, and men work at them. It rotates slowly past parts supply points and products delivery points, thus reducing materials handling to a minimum.

Benches are sometimes used as conveying devices at work level. The product can be moved from one operation to another merely by sliding it along a smooth-surfaced bench, which is either the workbench where the operations are performed or a separate one installed for the purpose. Slides and chutes are variations of the bench idea.

Vibrating and oscillating conveyors are metal troughs which move a short distance toward the take-off end, jerk quickly back toward the feed end, and then repeat. They are sometimes used for short distance horizontal transportation—up to 100 feet, usually much less. The movement is rapid, hence the terms. Vibrating conveyors jiggle 1,000 times a minute or more; oscillating conveyors 250 to 300 times per minute. The effect is to move material steadily to the take-off end. This particular type of conveyor is useful for metal turnings, borings, chips, steel scrap, castings, sand, and material that is abrasive, wet, oily, hot, jagged, or irregular in shape.

Floor-Level Conveyors.   Fixed path conveyors at floor level are often used in assembling large products, as, for example, automobiles and farm tractors. According to which kind of conveyor is used, the products may be set on the conveyor or they may be towed or dragged by an arrangement having cables below the floor. When the tow line is below the floor, there may be an upright tow post to which dollies or trailer trucks may be fastened to provide power. Sometimes carrying cradles on wheels are attached to the tow line and materials are put in them. In still other cases the frame of the product is fastened to the conveyor; as it moves down the line, parts are added to the frame.

There are several other special kinds of conveyors. Belt conveyors with nonslipping slats or cleats are sometimes used to convey packages to upper floors. Bucket conveyors are frequently used for bulk materials, as are screw conveyors, which, when set at an incline, provide efficient transportation up or down. Enclosed screw-type conveyors can easily hoist 50 tons of material an hour, and bucket conveyors can handle even greater quantities. Twin screws, unenclosed and turning in opposite directions, are sometimes used for moving sacked materials.

Automatic Transfer Conveyors.   Automatic transfer machines like that pictured in Figure 5-3, page 104, use conveyors. Products are fastened down in exact position onto the conveyor at one end. It then moves a fixed distance (to the first machine) and stops while one or more machines do their work. Then it takes the product on to the next work station when it stops again. This is repeated until the product comes off at the other end all machined and ready to use. The conveyor is a most important part of this process, but it takes a back seat in our thinking to all of the automatic machines that do the operations.

Today we see automatic transfer conveyors used for automatic *assembly* work, particularly in electronics. The product's frame starts down the line fastened to the conveyor, then it stops and a part is automatically attached, then on to station two, where part two is attached, and then on again.

Automatic transfer conveyors must be very precise in operation. Their start-stop cycles must match that of the machines. So must their stop positions; they must stop at exactly the right spot. And, too, they need to hold the product rigidly. Products need to be held just so when operations are performed by the machines.

Other Fixed Path Equipment.   Cranes make up a second type of fixed path equipment for handling materials. Overhead cranes operating on tracks running the whole length of a work bay are common. They can service any point in an area at floor level or above it, whether it is accessible from aisles or not. They carry materials by means of hooks, buckets, or magnets. The operator travels with a large overhead crane, operating it from an attached cage. The operator runs smaller overhead cranes from the floor by means of suspended controls. A Gantry crane is a less common type of fixed path crane.

There are many other kinds of fixed path conveying equipment besides conveyors and cranes. Elevators, automatic and nonautomatic, are commonly used to move materials as well as men. They are a must in multistory buildings. Chutes can frequently be used to advantage where material is moved down hill, but if the materials are easily damaged, the slope must be moderate. Chutes may be smooth sheet metal or may be roller conveyors and may be straight, curved, or spiral.

Pipes, ducts and tubes are often used for bulk materials, particularly liquids. Air pressure and vacuum systems are also used for dry bulk materials. The B. F. Goodrich Company reports an interesting variation of the tube arrangement, a zippered rubber belt for moving powdered carbon black. A pipe feeds the carbon black onto the moving belt, which is immediately zipped into the form of a hose. The zipper edges of the belt hold it in the hose shape as it travels vertically and around corners to the unloading point, where it is unzipped and the carbon black released. Wear on the zipper catches may, however, limit the use of this type of conveyor.

Whiting Corporation

FIG. 13–6. An overhead crane in operation.

When materials must be moved out of doors, steam, electric, and diesel locomotives are used, also Gantry cranes and cranes on overhead tracks. Any of this equipment may move materials to and from storage yards.

Conveyors move enormous quantities of materials at low unit costs. Generally they move slowly, but some operate at high speeds. Trough belts can transport bulk materials at over 600 feet per minute, and the large ones used to transport ore move over 6,000 tons per hour. One such belt used to transport ore is over two miles long. Another, which is inclined, raises 1,200 tons of coal an hour to a height 860 feet above the level at which it is loaded. Such lengthy conveyor hauls are not usually made on one single conveyor but on several successive conveyors, each dumping its load onto the next one.

Belt conveyors handling other types of materials often travel 100 feet per minute and are sometimes run at twice that speed. When used for picking, sorting, or supplying materials to operators, conveyors usually run at a speed of 10 to 50 feet per minute. Conveyors used for an operation such as cleaning, painting, baking, drying, and cooling move very slowly, perhaps from 2 to 6 feet per minute.

VARIED PATH EQUIPMENT

Practically all moving equipment which can follow a varied path is some variety of truck. Manually operated trucks are generally four-wheeled platform trucks, which must be loaded and unloaded by hand. One variety of hand truck, the "lift" truck, hoists already loaded skids and so eliminates the need for the truck being idle at loading and un-

Towmotor Corp.

FIG. 13–7. A powered lift truck of the type that requires the operator to walk ahead to guide it.

loading points. Many varieties of "dolly" trucks (a "dolly" is almost any kind of four-wheeled carrying rack) and mobile racks are used. Some are especially designed for particular purposes and are generally used for short-distance moves. Even supermarket push carts are sometimes used. Today most lift trucks used for heavy loads are powered, although they require a trucker to operate the controls and guide them.

Hand trucking is generally confined to short-distance hauls, perhaps from a machine to a temporary storage. Trucks powered by gasoline motors or electric storage batteries and driven by truckers are faster and generally more economical for long hauls. Hand trucking is not only slow but, with heavy loads, a little unsafe. Truckers may try to pull too big loads or start and stop heavily loaded trucks quickly, and so may injure themselves. There is also more likelihood of damage to

Clark Equipment Co.

FIG. 13–8. Varieties of lifting arrangements that can be used in place of the ordinary forks on fork trucks.

materials being moved on hand trucks. Smooth and level floors are desirable for power trucking but are absolutely necessary for hand trucking. If hand trucks are used, there must be elevators large enough to hold the trucks to move them from floor to floor. If power trucks are used, ramps can connect the floors. Where the path of transportation varies, most plants use powered industrial trucks on which the driver rides.

Most industrial trucks in use today have power-driven pickup arrangements. The metal forks in front of fork lift trucks can be lowered almost to floor level, can run under skids or pallets, hoist them up, carry them to their destination, set them down on the floor, or stack one on top of another. This is all done mechanically and fast. Although fork trucks are very common, they do require 12- to 14-foot aisles, wider than are found in many companies. Walking fork lift trucks (where the trucker walks and guides the truck by a handle), being smaller and more maneuverable, require less room and can be used where aisles are narrower. One-way aisles can also be used.

Some trucks have, instead of two forks, a protruding platform which can be lowered and raised. Manufacturers of sheet metal and wire often substitute a ram for the forks. The ram is inserted into coils of wire or sheet metal, raised until the load clears the floor, and then the load is carried away. Companies making a practice of stacking materials use trucks with special hoisting equipment. Trucks with elevating scoops in front are sometimes used to move bulk material around.

"Straddle" trucks are used for moving long heavy stacks of sheet steel, pipes, lumber, etc. They drive directly over the load, which is on a platform with projecting edges. The truck's support rails are raised, lifting the load by the platform edges. Because they carry large and heavy loads, straddle trucks are larger than ordinary industrial trucks.

Industrial trucks with a fixed platform which cannot be raised or lowered and requires hand loading and unloading are used less frequently today than years ago. Fixed platform trucks are efficient only where materials must be loaded and unloaded at several stations. Some trucks are equipped with cranes for lifting and loading materials onto their fixed platforms. Crane trucks are especially useful where heavy materials must be lifted and where no other mechanical hoisting equipment is available.

Tractors and trailers are used by some companies for the transportation of materials. The trailers can be left around to be loaded and unloaded whenever it is convenient. When they are ready to be moved, a trucker hooks one or more, one behind the other, to a power-driven truck and hauls them to their destination. Any powered truck can pull trailers, but those without forks or platforms are best. The trucks, or "tractors," made especially for trailer pulling are small, maneuverable, and less costly than powered lift trucks. The trailers too are quite inexpensive compared to power-driven units, so the tractor-trailer method of transporting materials is a low-cost method. Whole trains of trailers can be pulled by one tractor; consequently, large quantities can be moved in a single haul. Tractor and trailer trains are particularly well adapted for long hauls (500 feet or more). Tractors can pull over 60 tons at $2\frac{1}{2}$ miles per hour on the level or 8 tons up a 10 per cent grade.

Self-propelled power shovels and cranes are often used for bulk materials (coal, ore, steel scrap, etc.) stored out of doors. Cranes can lift

Towmotor Corp.

FIG. 13–9.   A tractor-truck pulling a train of trailers.

up to 60 tons. Power shovels have capacities of $\frac{1}{2}$ up to $2\frac{1}{2}$ cubic yards per shovelful. Such equipment is large and expensive, but it is capable of moving great quantities of materials in storage yards. Shovels and cranes usually work by hoisting and swinging loads from one location to another. This is fine for loading trucks, railroad cars, or ships but not much good for long-distance moving.

Very large factories covering many acres find it necessary to install some kind of bus service to move their people from place to place. The distances inside the company's grounds, or even inside some of the large buildings, are so great that employees waste too much time if they have to walk from place to place. Of course, elevators are generally used for the vertical transportation of people as well as materials. Horizontal transportation for people is usually best handled when trucks or busses follow fixed paths at regular and frequent intervals. Fixed platform industrial trucks with seats are often used inside large plants. Regular motor coaches are used by many large companies for transportation. Some companies with operations spreading over a large area supply bicycles for mail delivery clerks and for others who must make frequent trips about the plant. Tricycles have occasionally been used both to move materials and to transport people. Fitted with a large box or basket, they can be used satisfactorily to collect materials from stock shelves for order filling. Motor scooters are also winning new converts every day.

MATERIALS HANDLING DEVICES

Fixed and varied path equipment is used largely when materials must be moved some distance. Often they also reduce the amount of picking up and putting down of materials. But most picking up and putting down must be reduced in other ways. Handling at production operations is often reduced by mechanical lifting devices, such as jib cranes, chain hoists, compressed air hoists, block and tackle, and winches. More specialized devices at the machines include materials holding fixtures, magazine feeds, automatic product ejectors, welding positioners, elevating sheet feed tables, and automatic scrap disposers.

Automatic transfer conveyors (discussed on page 257), which move products from one machine to the next and hold them in position during the operations, get rid of between-job handling altogether.

Another way to get rid of handling is to use slowly moving or stop-and-go moving conveyors that take the product past the operator, who performs his operation without removing the product from the conveyor. This is the method commonly used on assembly lines. It gets rid of handling the main product, but it does not eliminate handling parts, and it makes it necessary to handle portable tools. This method also requires that the men's jobs be carefully divided and equally balanced. Moving conveyors, in addition, are also used for certain processes, mentioned earlier, such as spray painting, dipping, paint drying, baking, electroplating, heat treating, degreasing and washing. Except for spray painting, the other operations listed can all be done merely by passing the material through a tank or oven. Sometimes the products are suspended from the moving conveyor, and sometimes they lie on a steel mesh conveyor. Though conveyors are an integral part of the manufacturing processes in many nonmetalworking companies, they are not credited with eliminating handling. Petroleum refining, chemicals, rayon, and paper are examples.

Many kinds of devices are used to reduce the handling required to get materials on and off trucks and conveyors or transferred from one conveyor to another. They include up-enders, down-enders, turner-overs, rotators, transfer equipment, elevators, and positioners for materials and platforms, portable elevators and conveyor unloaders. There are also many devices which permit handling loads rather than individual pieces. Tote boxes, skids and pallets are universally used. Carrying cradles, wire baskets, collapsable wire containers, wire-bound wood slat containers, sacks and movable racks are also found. Steel strapping is sometimes used to hold loads or packs rigid on pallets. A starch manufacturer is reported to have glued stacked paper bags of starch together so that a pallet load would be more rigid during shipping. Tote boxes, skids, pallets and other types of materials holders should be tierable, even if special corner posts for that purpose have to be provided.

Factory Management and Maintenance

FIG. 13–10. An "inverter" built into a conveyor. This one turns over an automobile engine block and starts it down the next conveyor.

Unnecessary walking and handling in stockrooms can be reduced by using rotary storage bins for small parts. They permit the operator to have more materials close by. Extra handling of received materials can be reduced if they come in unit loads and if they are on disposable pallets to permit mechanical handling. The purchasing department should specify that shipments be made in a manner which will permit economical handling when the goods are received.

CONTROLLING TRUCKING COSTS THROUGH SCHEDULES, INCENTIVES, AND BUDGETS

Trucking costs can be kept down to some extent by scheduling the use of trucks, by the use of incentives, and by budgeting transportation costs. Most companies try to schedule and direct the truckers to reduce waste time and backtracking of empty trucks. In all companies where materials follow substantially the same path through the plant, established routes are common. The trucker may even be expected to make his rounds at scheduled times.

Where products follow no fixed route in the plant, it is more difficult to keep truckers and trucks busy all the time. Today any number of companies use two-way radios to direct truckers. A central dispatcher keeps track of where the trucks are and directs truckers to their next haul by radio. The added efficiency nearly always cuts hauling costs 50 per cent or more.

Materials handling and transportation between jobs can sometimes be covered by incentive plans. It is not often done though. First of all it would, because of the varied work, take thousands of rates to cover all the jobs. It costs money to set up all these rates and to keep them up to date. Besides, it is difficult to check up at the end of a day on what a trucker says he has done during the day—unless quite complete (and otherwise unnecessary) records are kept of materials moved.

Some companies, nevertheless, use incentive plans for materials handlers and truckers. And they report that incentives cut handling costs. To keep down the costs of setting time standards, they use "standard data" (described on page 575). Standard data produce reasonably accurate standards at low cost.

Materials handling costs can be budgeted fairly accurately as far as the costs of conveyors, trucks, materials handlers, stock men, truckers, and elevator operators are concerned. These costs, for the most part, can be set apart and compared to the quantity of product made. They can be increased when production goes up and decreased when production goes down. In addition to these costs, the cost of picking up and putting down materials (which is a part of producing operators' jobs) is covered by direct labor budgets.

But the indirect costs of handling are harder to budget. Such things as aisle space costs, the poor service rendered by materials handlers to production operators, and unsafe handling methods do not lend themselves to budgets. They are important enough in the total cost picture to keep budgets from being very helpful to most companies. A few very large companies with materials handling departments may be able to use budgets to advantage, but most companies find that they can't really budget materials handling costs.

THE MATERIALS HANDLING ORGANIZATION

Because products are handled so many places in the plant, it is impossible to centralize completely the control of materials handling. Manual handling, within production operations, is almost always considered a part of the operations and is under the supervision of the foreman. In large companies both foremen and industrial engineers are always watching for ways to reduce handling within operations. Where transportation and operations or processes are combined, as along assembly lines or in electroplating tanks, the transportation equipment is designed to cut out handling.

Wherever materials are trucked rather than moved by conveyor, the truckers have to get directions from someone. They can belong to (and get their directions from) a central transportation department or to the separate producing departments, or the two methods can be combined. With decentralized materials handling the foreman in each department is responsible for moving materials between operations in his own department and to the receiving area of the next department. He has his own laborers and truckers. Stock room truckers generally are responsible for getting materials to the first production department.

Partially decentralized transportation is often used for long hauls and where the trucking needs vary from hour to hour. Foremen have their own men move materials in their own departments but not between departments. Centrally controlled truckers, who do not work for the foremen, move materials between departments. Often they follow regular routes. In still other companies, centrally controlled truckers do almost all the moving of materials both between and within production departments except perhaps spotting work loads next to machines.

Because it is so often done poorly when there is no one central department responsible for it, there is a trend in the direction of more centralization in the control of all kinds of materials handling. Specialists in a central department know the kinds of equipment being made, and they can look at moving materials in an over-all way. They can see cost-cutting opportunities that foremen don't see.

Besides, a central department can use power-driven trucks better. If materials transportation is decentralized, equipment has to be bought for each department needing it. It must be available, even though it will be used only part of the time. It is bad to buy trucks and then use them only part time. For this reason (with decentralized transportation) the company doesn't buy trucks for every department. This means that departments without power trucks must use hand lift trucks, and this is costly too.

Centralization helps here. Buy only as many trucks as you can keep busy, then shift them back and forth wherever they are needed regardless of departmental lines. Besides using fewer trucks, centralized control also usually improves co-ordination between departments. Some executives think that they lower costs too because, with centralized control, foremen complain if they don't get good service. This helps hold down costs. Perhaps you should not expect foremen complaints to solve the problem, but they help.

Ordinarily, when transportation is controlled centrally, it is directed by the production control department, which knows where materials are and where they are to go. As a department, however, production control is unlikely to be economy-minded as far as transportation costs are concerned, because its main job is to get products made and made on schedule, not to reduce costs. For this and other reasons, notably the technical knowledge required for mechanization and conveyorization, some large companies have a materials handling department closely associated with industrial engineering. Such a department can go into matters of the proper type of equipment, aisle and storage space requirements, and building design limitations, all of which are beyond the scope of the production control department.

STUDY QUESTIONS

1. Why is it so hard to figure materials handling costs?
2. If you were told to suggest places to look for waste in materials handling, where would you look?
3. Give the jist of five of the thirty-nine rules for better materials handling.
4. Which to move: men, materials, tools? Under what conditions would you move each of them?
5. Write out instructions telling a new man how to go about analyzing materials handling for improvement purposes.
6. Compare (give good and bad points) fixed and varied path materials moving equipment.
7. When would you use work-level conveyors? When not? Explain.
8. Compare overhead conveyors and floor-level conveyors. Be sure to bring out the good and bad points of each.
9. What are the pros and cons of using tractors and trailers to move materials? Where are they most suitable? Where are they poorly suited?
10. Why is materials handling not often paid for on an incentive plan? How is it that some companies do use incentives for materials handling jobs, while most others do not?
11. Suppose that you have been told to justify a recommendation for a central materials handling department. What do you say?

Chapter 14

MAINTENANCE

Machines and buildings are wearing out all the time, so, from time to time, they need repairs. On *machines,* wear on shafts, bearings, gears, belts, and other parts makes repair necessary. Electric motors must be serviced. *Transportation facilities,* too—elevators, conveyors, gasoline and electric powered trucks, hand trucks, hoists, and cranes—all need continual lubrication and repairs. *Plant services*—electric power, gas, water, compressed air and steam lines, washrooms, sewers, pumps, fire protection equipment, and heating systems—all need occasional upkeep. So do the *buildings* themselves—the roofs, windows, walls, floors, and foundations.

But just fixing things up is not good maintenance. *Good maintenance prevents breakdowns.* Breakdowns stop production, make men and machines idle, cause lost production, and put orders behind schedule. Breakdown repairs may have to be done on overtime, and getting orders back on schedule may take more overtime.

Breakdown repairs are also often bigger jobs than preventive repairs. It costs something to fix a loose front wheel on your car, but it will cost more to fix the car after the wheel comes loose on the road. Then you have to pay for a car wreck. Preventive maintenance may be the stitch in time that saves nine.

But preventive maintenance is like many other good things; it can be carried too far. If you let the garageman fix everything he says your car needs, you will have a big repair bill—and mostly for things the car doesn't really need. Preventive maintenance has its wasteful aspects.

Preventive maintenance really means *preventing breakdowns that cause work stoppages.* Curiously, this sometimes overrules engineering dictates. Suppose you find that a $500 motor will be ruined before long if you keep running it. *But if you don't keep running it, your production line will shut down with a $2,500 loss.* By all means keep it running, meanwhile moving heaven and earth to get another motor before that motor burns out.

Also preventive maintenance cuts, but cannot in the final analysis elimi-nate, repairs, because machines do wear out. Nor can it stop *all* break-downs. But if your maintenance men spend as little as 25 per cent of their time on emergencies, you are doing a good job of preventive mainte-nance. Normally, without preventive maintenance, they will have to spend 75 per cent or more of their time on fix-it work.

Preventing breakdowns in a factory depends on (*a*) not overloading equipment, (*b*) regular greasing and oiling of all moving parts, and (*c*) re-placing worn parts before they get bad. It helps, too, to keep on hand a small stock of hard-to-get repair parts. Better yet, on critical items, have stand-by (extra) machines ready to put in if the regular one goes bad.

In order to replace worn parts before they fail, you need, now and then, to inspect them for wear and to plan overhaul jobs. Often ma-chines in use a long time need overhauling, even when the exposed parts show little wear. The inside parts may need replacing.

On the other hand, don't go overboard on inspecting. It is cheaper not to inspect small motors in noncritical places than it is to inspect them. True, one will burn out now and then, but replacing it costs less than all the inspection.

Also give the inspector a check list of what to look for when he checks a machine for possible repair needs. Without a list he might inspect the machine and miss noticing the part that is likely to need repairs. Remem-ber, too, to look for some things often, others less often. Maybe you ought to look at a machine weekly for adjustment, monthly for ordinary wear, and annually for overhaul. Also old machines need more looking after than new ones.

Another quite different approach to preventive maintenance is to have trouble-free machines—those that are designed to be trouble-free. Of course, everyone wants the machines to be trouble-free, so the problem is how to design them or how to pick them out. One way is to keep repair records of the machines you have. Records will show which have been most trouble-free, and that helps in selecting new machines. Another way to work toward trouble-free machines is to ask maintenance men how the machines they repair could have been designed for less trouble. They often have good ideas. Most of the time, though, it is up to machinery-making companies, after hearing their customers' com-plaints, to design new machines to be more trouble-free.

Old factories require more maintenance than new ones. Old factory buildings, like old houses, need frequent repairs. Besides, their machines are older too, and they need more repairs than new machines. So much repair work has one advantage, though. There is always a backlog of needed-but-not-urgent "rainy-day" repair work. Maintenance men can be kept busy on the "rainy-day" jobs and then drop them at any time to take care of emergencies. Of course, there have to be enough men to do both regular and emergency work, otherwise routine repairs end up being emergencies themselves. Little things let go too long become big things.

In some plants, even old ones, emergencies are few. This might lead you to think that maintenance work is not very important. More likely, the lack of emergencies means that the maintenance department is doing a fine job of preventive maintenance.

THE "INHERENT INEFFICIENCY" OF MAINTENANCE WORK

Operating departments are happiest when nothing ever breaks down. They are next most happy when breakdowns are fixed quickly. They are least happy when breakdowns come often and are not fixed quickly. Executives feel the same way *except* that they are also interested in keeping the plant operating *without high maintenance costs*.

Bringing costs into the picture creates a problem. If you overmaintain (like allowing the garageman to fix everything on your car that he wants to), you get few breakdowns, but *you spend a lot of money for maintenance*—not high fix-it maintenance but high preventive maintenance. One way to solve the problem is to do less preventive maintenance but to fix breakdowns right away. At first this sounds good, but the only way that you can fix breakdowns right away is to have plenty of maintenance men ready and waiting, and *that is costly*. In between breakdowns the men are probably spending a lot of their time on busy work.

You can't escape it. If the factory is to get good maintenance service, maintenance costs can't be too low. Keeping the factory operating efficiently makes the maintenance department operate somewhat wastefully. The backlog of necessary-but-not-urgent jobs described earlier helps let both operating and maintenance departments work efficiently at the same time, but it is not a perfect answer, because so much of the fill-in work is not highly skilled. Using highly skilled men on it wastes part of their cost.

THE MAINTENANCE DEPARTMENT AND ITS DUTIES

Generally maintenance is assigned to the "plant engineer." He often has two main departments, a "machine shop" and a "plant maintenance" department.

The machine shop keeps *machines and equipment* in working order. Its employees include millwrights (general mechanics and men who move machines), machinists who can operate most machines, others who can run only one or two kinds of machines, sheet metal workers, welders, and others who repair machines and keep trucks and conveyors operating.

The plant maintenance group specializes in *building and building services*. Its employees are electricians, tinsmiths, welders, pipefitters, steamfitters, bricklayers, steeplejacks, painters, glaziers, carpenters, millwrights, oilers, window washers, janitors, charwomen, helpers, and laborers. The maintenance department also usually operates its own stockroom since it decides on and orders materials used on repair jobs.

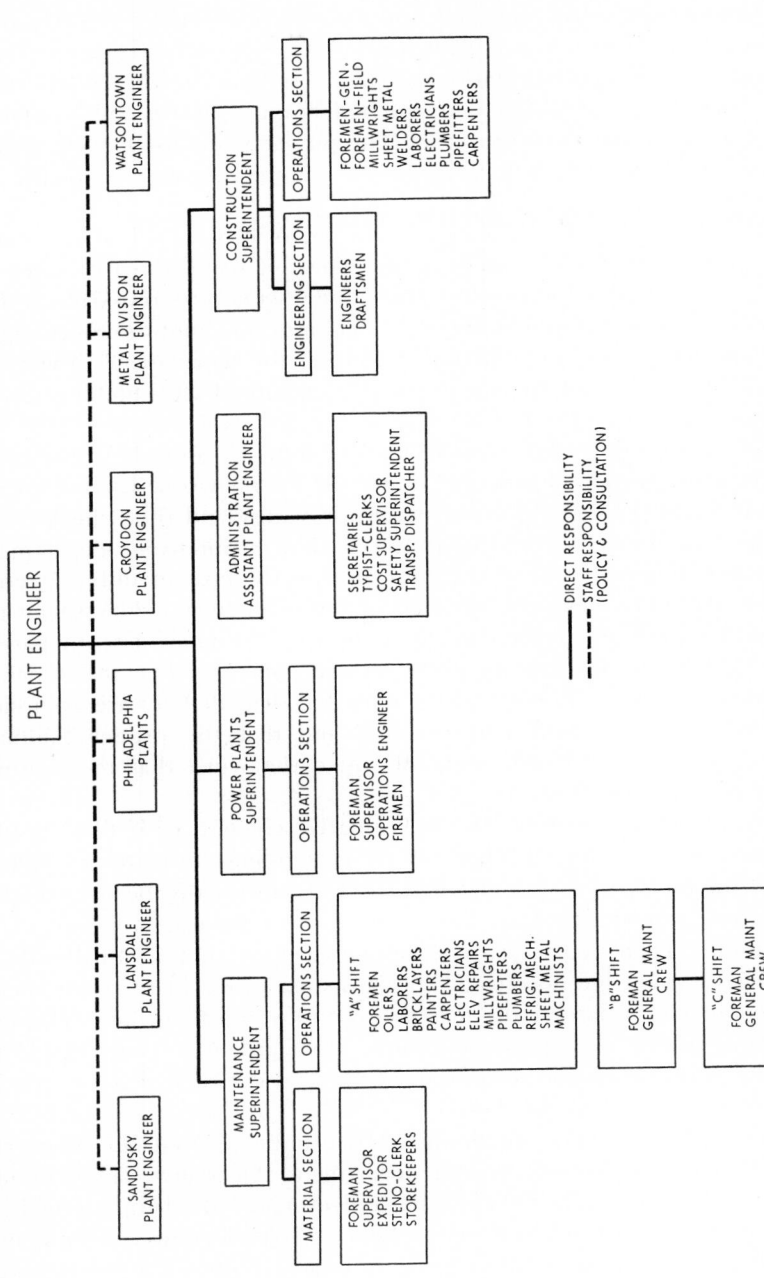

FIG. 14–1. The organization of the plant engineer at the Philco Corporation.

Power plants operated by the company are usually under the direction of the plant engineer. Power plant operation is generally subject to both city and state regulations. Stationary engineers who fire the boilers must pass examinations and be licensed; the boilers must meet specific requirements and be subject to inspection. The power plant itself needs maintenance work at times; boiler tubes, for example, must occasionally be replaced.

The maintenance department in most factories does all of the company's minor remodeling and relayout work. It tears down or puts up partitions between departments, builds new concrete foundations for equipment and makes mountings for machines and motors. Since some of the work requires construction drawings, the department should include one or more construction engineers acquainted with building codes and safety regulations.

Large construction jobs are ordinarily done by outside contractors with the maintenance department doing the liaison work. Its staff members may make some of the construction drawings, and they check those made by the contractor or the architect. The maintenance department advises the administration of the company on the cost of different construction methods. The staff members of the maintenance department inspect and approve contract work as it progresses. They pass on partial payments made from time to time, on the contract. The maintenance department's construction engineers must see that all laws are complied with, that project workers are insured and that the proper building permits are obtained. In the end, they give the word that the finished project passes inspection.

Certain kinds of repair work are regularly sent out, or if done inside, they are done by outside contractors. Rewinding burned-out electric motors, for example, is specialized work and can usually be done better and cheaper outside. Elevators and power plant boilers, however, can't be sent out. Their repair is sometimes hazardous, and it usually takes specialized knowledge, so outside specialists are called in to repair them. Some companies in large cities hire their window washing done by companies specializing in that work. Others hire gardeners from outside to take care of the lawns and shrubbery. Some send out their delivery trucks when garage work must be done.

General plant cleanup, including electric light maintenance, is nearly always assigned to the maintenance department. All electric lamps should be removed occasionally and both the reflector and the lamp cleaned. A surprising amount of dirt collects on lighting fixtures, and a considerable part of the money spent for lighting is wasted if they are not cleaned from time to time. Window washing is often one of the biggest cleanup jobs. Washrooms and toilets must be cleaned regularly. Floors must be cleaned, and waste baskets emptied.

Housekeeping in individual factory departments is sometimes assigned to department foremen instead of the maintenance department. This doesn't mean, though, that it will be well done this way, for foremen are notoriously poor housekeepers unless continual pressure is kept on them. Foremen are given the job because they have some control over making dirt, not because they are naturally good housekeepers.

Most floor litter comes from production machines. Nearly always a little more care by the operator (and not time-consuming care, either) could reduce the litter and the cleanup work. So most companies make each man responsible for cleaning up around his machine. But here too it takes pressure to make him keep his area clean. This is where the foreman comes in. He can demand tidiness from his men, but the maintenance department, having no authority over them, can not.

Departmental cleanup should keep aisles clear of material waiting either to be worked on or to be moved and keep the floor clean, free from oil, water, and such litter as shavings, chips, cuttings, grit, selvedge, and trimmings. Plenty of cans for scrap and waste should be provided. A departmental sweeper or janitor takes care of aisle and storage spaces, and a trucker from the scrap or salvage department empties the scrap containers.

The maintenance department must keep all fire prevention equipment in operating order at all times. To do this, the department must periodically inspect the sprinkler systems, valves, fire pumps, elevated tanks, portable extinguishers, fire doors, and sirens. Large plants with serious fire hazards may designate and train certain employees in each department as a fire brigade. In the training work the maintenance department probably has the help of the personnel department.

The maintenance department takes care of the premises outside the building. It maintains the parking lot and possibly provides traffic directors at shift change time. Fencing, landscaping, tending the lawn and keeping up the storage yards are all a part of the outside maintenance work.

AUTHORIZING MAINTENANCE WORK

All but the smallest maintenance projects need approval before the work is done. But why? Doesn't a leaky roof or a broken-down machine need fixing? Yes—and there already are men on the payroll who can do the work, so why insist on "authorizing" it? This is done to keep maintenance costs in hand and to furnish a record of the money spent.

Of course, leaky roofs and broken-down machines ordinarily are fixed right away (approval to spend the money will be quickly given if they cause emergencies). But should you have a leaky roof patched? Maybe it is getting so bad that you ought to put on a whole new roof rather than keep patching it. Or should you have a broken-down machine repaired? If it is old, maybe it would be better to scrap it and get another machine. Requiring authorizations lets someone higher up decide. He can see the over-all picture, and he knows how much money there is and what other things need fixing. He can better decide what to do. Many maintenance projects are not urgent so approval is not just automatic.

Actually, requiring approval, just by itself, helps keep costs down. Both the foreman and the maintenance head know that they are being checked, so both try to keep requests to a minimum.

Authorizations are not used for little things. Equipment inspection and lubrication (both part of preventive maintenance) should be done regularly according to a schedule and should require no individual job authorizations. Minor machine repairs, adjustments, or replacements of

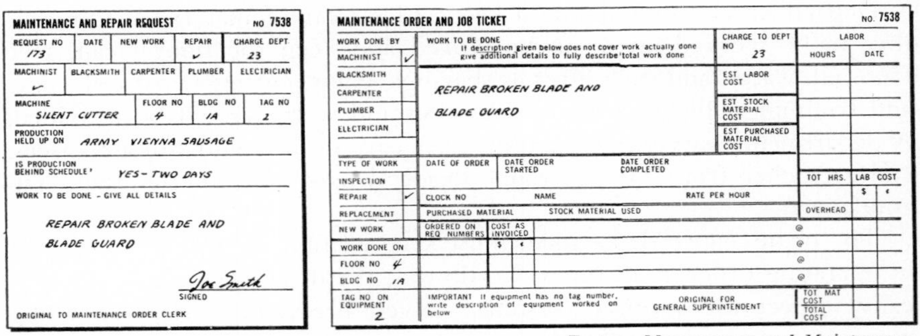

Factory Management and Maintenance

FIG. 14–2. A request for maintenance work and the maintenance order made up to cover the job.

worn parts are made by setup men or other workers in producing departments without specific authorization.

Substantial machine repairs, whether scheduled overhauling or repairs made necessary by machine failures, generally must be specifically approved and authorized. Maintenance work on buildings and service facilities, relayout jobs, and improvement projects are nearly all done as so many separate jobs, each requiring its own authorization. Wherever certain machines have to be overhauled at regular intervals, schedules can be set up providing for them to be overhauled after a certain amount of use. The approved schedule gives authority to work on individual machines.

Most requests for repairs to equipment come from foremen of producing departments. Maintenance jobs costing less than $50 can be done in most plants on the foreman's approval, but more costly projects have to be approved higher up. The first thing, then, is to estimate each job's cost to see if it has to be submitted for higher approval. If none is required, the foreman's request goes directly to the maintenance department, which then goes ahead with the repairs.

If approval is required, a request describing the proposed work and its expected cost goes to the superior whose approval is necessary. On large projects it may take considerable time to get approval because drawings showing how to do the work may be needed, materials and labor estimates made, and time and work schedules laid out so that the work can be done with as little interference to production as possible.

MAINTAINING BUILDINGS

Building maintenance deals with keeping the roof, inside and outside walls, windows, doors, floors, stair, and elevator wells, and foundations in good condition. Building maintenance is little in evidence and is always done by the maintenance department rather than the producing departments. The need for floor or window repairs is sometimes called to the attention of the maintenance department by people in the operating departments, but for the most part the maintenance department itself finds out, by regular inspections, what must be done, and then does it. Except for the smallest projects, the maintenance department must get approval, however, before going ahead.

Most repair work on buildings falls into the category of "repair work needed but not urgent," referred to on page 270. Such jobs as painting, tuck-pointing (replacing loose mortar around bricks), new floors, new roofs, etc., allow for a certain amount of desirable flexibility, but they should not be delayed so long as to become urgent.

MAINTAINING PLANT SERVICES

Plant services include electrical lines, switches, controls, motors, plumbing, valves, pressure vessels, heating, lighting and ventilating equipment, hot- and cold-water systems, steam and compressed air lines, and refrigeration equipment. Also weighing scales, chains, ladders, wire cables, wire rope, and transportation and materials handling equipment, such as conveyors, hoists, elevators, cranes, industrial trucks, and even automobiles and large automotive trucks.

Nearly always the maintenance department has the full responsibility for maintaining plant services. It must itself find out what needs repair, get approval to do it, then do the repairing. Maintaining services is different from maintaining factory machines. First, service equipment is often hidden away where no one sees it. Second, service items are numerous, but spread widely throughout the plant. And, third, and most important, many of the services are "musts"—they must work or the factory stops. And some more of the services are "musts" for safety reasons. Worn-out elevator cables, for example, could kill people.

Their being hidden away means that they must have scheduled inspection, which can be made when they get their scheduled lubrication, otherwise no one would ever know when they needed repair. Their being spread out means that it is easy to miss some of them, so the inspector must be sure to check all of them. Their being "musts" means that you must go in for preventive maintenance. Fix-it maintenance alone won't do.

Not all plant services are critical. Some can be maintained at the department's convenience. These include general plant cleanup, window washing, washroom care, janitorial and charwomen service, painting, maintaining outside premises (such as parking lots, storage yards, and rail sidings), and snow removal. The exact moment when these jobs are done often does not greatly matter. This doesn't provide very much flexibility, however, because window washers, charwomen, and the others can't switch jobs back and forth with electricians and other skilled men.

MAINTAINING PRODUCING MACHINES

Factory departments share with the maintenance department the responsibility for maintaining machines and other producing equipment. This is logical because careless or improper operation makes more re-

U.S. Pipe & Foundry Co.

FIG. 14–3. Chart comparing the time needed to oil cranes manually as compared with using forced lubrication systems.

pairs necessary. The first thing to do to cut maintenance costs is for the foreman to show the men how to run their machines properly. The next thing is to see that they run them that way—again it is a job for the foreman. Machine operators are expected to run their equipment at recommended speeds and not to overload them. Machine operators are also frequently responsible for oiling their machines and for watching for and reporting worn parts.

One company reports that it has cut its machinery maintenance costs materially by having the machine operator help the repair crew fix any machine broken through his own faulty operation. He sees the insides of the machine, learns better how to take care of it, and has no excuse for making the same mistake again.

FIG. 14–4. This loom, oiled by hand in the left picture, was redesigned and a forced lubrication system put in. Circles show the new connections. The redesign cost $1,200 and produced annual savings of $1,750.

Machines *should* almost never break down during operations (but they do, of course). Defective parts are rare in machines made by reputable machine builders. When breakdowns occur, therefore, the machine is being operated improperly, is overloaded, or is being operated with worn or improperly lubricated parts. If the employees in the producing departments do their part, there will be few breakdowns, because their careful operation and maintenance reduce the need for repairs. What repairs are necessary will be reported early and taken care of before trouble occurs.

Minor machine repairs are sometimes made by machine operators, setup men, or departmental repair men who work for the foreman. Minor though these repairs are, production would frequently be held up if you didn't take care of them right away. In fact, some companies are decentralizing maintenance and assigning some maintenance men permanently to certain production areas. Table 14–1 shows how Ford Motors does it in its engine plant in Cleveland. Notice that more than half of all maintenance men have permanent assignments in certain factory departments.

Machinists from the machine shop take care of machine overhauling and repair jobs of any real consequence. In some companies certain regularly used machines are torn down and rebuilt periodically, worn parts being replaced with new parts. Such a practice almost eliminates breakdowns during operations.

Lubricating and machine inspection for worn parts cannot always be done by the operator, nor can it always be done during operating hours when the machines are in use. In such cases an oiler (a maintenance department employee) makes his rounds at night, lubricating and inspecting machines for wear.

Production equipment can be designed to be trouble-free. Equipment which is difficult to lubricate or in which oil fails to get to inaccessible parts is poorly designed. Sometimes dirt gets into oil and grease cups and blocks the oil lines. You can prevent this by having enclosed forced lubrication systems built into the machines as in automobiles. Or you can have special graphite bronze bearings or other self-lubrication arrange-

TABLE 14–1

PLACEMENT OF MAINTENANCE MEN IN FORD'S CLEVELAND ENGINE PLANT*

	FACTORY DEPARTMENT				MAINTENANCE DEPARTMENT SHOPS
	1	2	3	4	
Machine repairmen	6	...	6	21	5
Hydraulic repairmen and pipefitters	6	6	6	13	9
Electricians	7	8	7	12	3
Oilers	4	2	3	9	2
Welders and tinsmiths	...	2	...	...	11
Millwrights	...	8	...	...	22
Fixture repairmen	6	...	10	20	...
Toolmakers, machinists, and machine operators	...	...	...	...	41
Carpenters and painters	...	...	...	...	4
Truck drivers and truck repairmen	...	...	...	...	18
Cleanup	6	3	...	3	45
	35	29	32	78	160

*See *Factory Management and Maintenance*, December, 1956, page 94.

ments for inaccessible parts. All such arrangements cut maintenance costs.

Machine attachments and tools, such as jigs, fixtures, and patterns, sometimes become worn or broken and consequently need to be repaired. Most companies have separate "toolroom" departments which make and repair jigs and fixtures, in addition to preparing the cutting tools and forming dies needed in production. Breakdowns of machine accessories hold up production just as surely as breakdowns of the machines themselves. Accessories too may need emergency repairs.

When machine attachments are returned to the tool storage room after use, they should be inspected and repaired (unless they were used for special one-time orders). Be sure to put a protective oil coating on all exposed metal parts that might rust or corrode during a lengthy storage.

MAINTENANCE IN LINE PRODUCTION

Line production in a factory operates almost like a single large machine. Everything operates or everything is idle; even a few minutes' delay in one spot quickly stops the whole line, and this is very expensive. Often it costs hundreds of dollars a minute! Sometimes a stoppage forces the whole line to stop unless it is cleared up in a matter of seconds. Actually, however, there is enough flexibility in most line operations to permit them to go on for a short time in spite of a minor delay at one point.

In line production, machinery and equipment *must* be maintained so as to avoid stoppages. This makes preventive maintenance, starting with the design of the machines and equipment, a must. Machines must be designed to operate dependably, accurately, and steadily for long periods without breaking down. Some of them are designed with removable sections which, in emergencies, can be replaced quickly with spare sections or parts. Even stand-by spare machines for some operations are desirable. In case of breakdown they can be substituted to reduce lost time, or when overhaul time comes they can be installed in the line during off hours so no production at all is lost. Also, in line production, you should keep a maintenance man close by all the time to take care of minor emergencies.

MAINTENANCE IN AUTOMATION

Automation, being a step beyond line production, makes preventive maintenance even more necessary. In automation whole sequences of operation go on automatically; stop one, and they all stop. Maintenance supervisors have to revise their thinking; instead of maintaining machines, they now have to maintain production. Maintenance men used to be on call to make repairs, now they are on patrol to anticipate them.

Automation makes even more demands on the maintenance department than does line production. The machines are more complex, particularly the electrical controls. Ordinary electricians and the jack-of-all-trades kind of machinists are hopelessly lost. They can learn to repair the automatic equipment only after special training programs, perhaps at the plant of the machine manufacturer. Or if not there, the machine maker's man comes in and shows the maintenance men how to repair the automatic machines.

EQUIPMENT NEEDED FOR MAINTENANCE

Most maintenance work, except machine rebuilding, has to be done at the location of the trouble by craftsmen who work only with hand tools or with portable power-driven tools. The portable equipment needed regularly by the department includes paint brushes, ladders, saws, hammers, blow torches, wrenches, welding equipment, mops, brooms, etc. Sometimes hoisting equipment and power-driven trucks are also needed to remove or place heavy motors and machines. The maintenance department should have one or more trucks assigned to it permanently. Also, you should supply your men with some way to haul their tools and supplies around. Maybe a $2 wheeled cart will do. Or maybe they need wheeled racks like those shown in Fig. 14–5, or possibly you should supply them with power trucks.

Any sizable manufacturing plant needs a complete machine shop capable of making, remachining, and repairing parts for production machines, conveyors, and trucks. Some companies design and make some of their own machines in their machine shops. Others make accessory parts, jigs, fixtures, simple conveyors, machine safety guards, or parts for obso-

Birtman Electric Co.

FIG. 14–5. An electrician's portable rack holding all of the materials that may be needed on most electrical repair jobs. The rack saves the electrician or his helper from having to go back to their shop for supplies.

lete machines. A wide variety of metalworking machinery is required in addition to general purpose lathes, millers, etc. According to what the plant is producing, the machine shop may also need one or more of the following: general purpose electric saw, sheet metal shears and brakes (machines for bending sheet metal), spot welders, paint spraying equipment, a flame cutter, keying cutters, paint cleaning tools, tungsten carbide drills, electric hammers, impact wrenches, angle notchers, benders, etc. A company cannot expect to get good maintenance unless it has good mechanics who are supplied with good tools and machines.

SUPERVISING MAINTENANCE WORKERS

Maintenance work is hard to supervise because the work is done all over the factory. Maintenance workers are scattered through the factory most of the time. Since their foremen can't be in several places at once, maintenance men work most of the time without direct supervision. On jobs requiring more than one man, they are often paired up into two-man teams, a highly skilled man working with a helper. Such a team needs little supervision, yet can handle jobs which one man could not do alone. Most maintenance men are not only highly skilled but dependable as well. Were they not, they would be very costly labor, because with the lax supervision they receive they could easily loaf or even sleep when they were supposed to be working.

Each craft group in the maintenance department, painters, carpenters, etc., has a group leader or foreman. He is a combination cost estimator, job assigner, and job inspector, and he may do a little training. Ordinarily his best men are his equals in skill and are capable of doing the work without his help. Young and less experienced men learn while working with the older men. In very large companies formal apprentice training programs for maintenance employees are sometimes used for teaching trades.

A great deal of time is lost by maintenance employees going to and from jobs, because they work wherever repairs are needed. Usually when a job is finished, they return to their own department for their next assignment; but much time can be saved if they telephone to the office to find out what to do next. Some companies use two-way radios to direct maintenance workers. Weatherhead Company found that with directions sent by radio 2 minutes are needed to get a maintenance man to a job; before using radio it took from 20 to 30 minutes. Besides, the maintenance service to production liner is better, so much so that Weatherhead has reduced the supplies of materials between operations. They are no longer needed for protection against lengthy interruptions to production.

Many small maintenance jobs are rush jobs and come to the department as telephone calls. They can't be scheduled ahead, yet they must be taken care of as quickly as possible. Sometimes neither the foreman nor any of his men is on hand when such a call comes in, so the department clerk takes the request. He knows where most of the men are working and can call one of them to care for small urgent jobs. For more important jobs the maintenance foreman can be located and told of the circumstances. He then investigates the trouble and calls men from less urgent work to take care of it.

Emergency calls often involve electrical breakdown in switches, motors, control panels, wiring, or lighting. They may come at any time. If any part of the plant is operating at night, at least one electrician should be on the job. He must be highly skilled, because he works without supervision and yet must be capable of handling all, even the most difficult, work himself. Many companies always have at least two men on duty if the plant is operating at night, so that no one ever works alone with high voltages or on other dangerous work.

Even if the plant operates only during the daytime, some maintenance work is done at night. Repairs that would interfere with production can best be done then. A good bit of the plant cleanup work, particularly sweeping and cleaning around offices and washrooms, is easier to do at night when no one is around. Maintenance men on night shifts are responsible to the night superintendent and to the day-shift maintenance foreman.

Maintenance machine shop employees, like other maintenance workers, often work in parts of the plant other than their own department. New machine installation work is done in the producing departments, and some machine repair work is done on the spot. Sometimes a machine needing repairs can be partially disassembled and the parts needing repair taken to the machine shop. But if the machine must be out of service for a long time, the whole thing is taken to the shop for overhauling.

Very large plants sometimes decentralize part of the work. They have one large central department which can do everything. But besides that they have several satellite groups serving certain areas. Satellite departments located in several places in the plant take care of all the repetitive maintenance in their areas. On big jobs and difficult work they call in the central department or turn the job over to it.

MAINTENANCE RECORDS

Small companies rarely keep machine maintenance records. Large companies, in contrast, keep fairly complete maintenance records for every machine and piece of major equipment. Where records are kept, each machine and piece of equipment has an identification number and each has a service record card in the office. The card shows the kind of equipment, when it was bought, where it is located, the kind of electric motor used, its serial number, accessories, etc. It also shows the maintenance requirements, particularly the frequency of lubrication. Some companies keep equipment record cards in Kardex files so that they can put colored cellophane tabs on the bottom of the cards. The colored tabs go on a date scale and show when the next machine maintenance is due. Foremen can readily tell from the tabs which machines are scheduled for attention. Naturally, the system does not show where breakdowns will occur, but it keeps maintenance foremen from overlooking regular preventive maintenance measures.

Spaces are provided on the card to record all maintenance and repair work done on the machine. The card should also show the machine down time and other costs of operation. Ultimately an analysis of this record can be made which will show how this individual machine compares with other similar units. Replacement machines can be selected more intelligently if such figures are available. A repair record can also be the basis for a schedule of periodic machine overhauling, if this seems

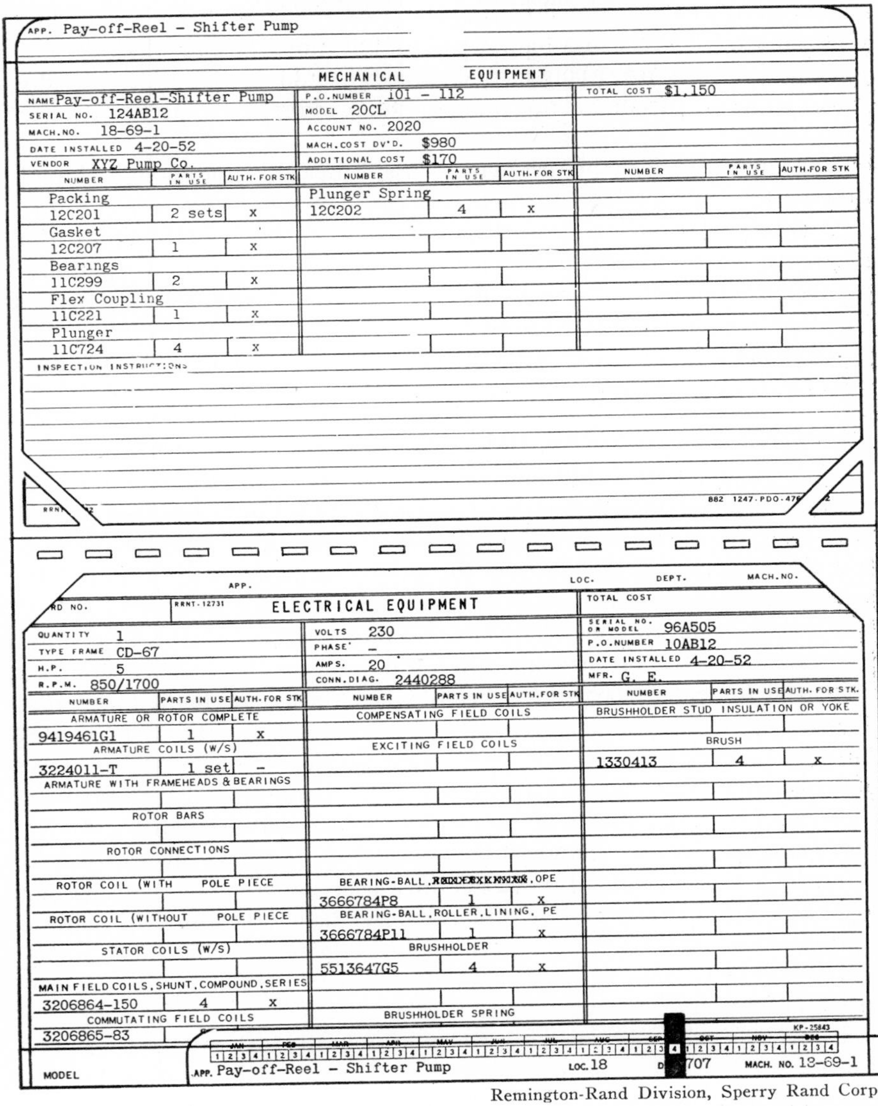

APP. Pay-off-Reel — Shifter Pump

MECHANICAL	EQUIPMENT							
NAME Pay-off-Reel-Shifter Pump	P.O. NUMBER 101 – 112			TOTAL COST $1,150				
SERIAL NO. 124AB12	MODEL 20CL							
MACH. NO. 18-69-1	ACCOUNT NO. 2020							
DATE INSTALLED 4-20-52	MACH. COST DV'D. $980							
VENDOR XYZ Pump Co.	ADDITIONAL COST $170							
NUMBER	PARTS IN USE	AUTH. FOR STK	NUMBER	PARTS IN USE	AUTH. FOR STK	NUMBER	PARTS IN USE	AUTH. FOR STK
Packing			Plunger Spring					
12C201	2 sets	x	12C202	4	x			
Gasket								
12C207	1	x						
Bearings								
11C299	2	x						
Flex Coupling								
11C221	1	x						
Plunger								
11C724	4	x						
INSPECTION INSTRUCTIONS								

882 1247-PDO-47

ELECTRICAL EQUIPMENT								
RD NO.	RRNT-12731					TOTAL COST		
QUANTITY 1	VOLTS 230					SERIAL NO. OR MODEL 96A505		
TYPE FRAME CD-67	PHASE —					P.O. NUMBER 10AB12		
H.P. 5	AMPS. 20					DATE INSTALLED 4-20-52		
R.P.M. 850/1700	CONN. DIAG. 2440288					MFR. G. E.		
NUMBER	PARTS IN USE	AUTH. FOR STK	NUMBER	PARTS IN USE	AUTH. FOR STK	NUMBER	PARTS IN USE	AUTH. FOR STK.
ARMATURE OR ROTOR COMPLETE			COMPENSATING FIELD COILS			BRUSHHOLDER STUD INSULATION OR YOKE		
9419461G1	1	x						
ARMATURE COILS (W/S)			EXCITING FIELD COILS			BRUSH		
3224011-T	1 set	—				1330413	4	x
ARMATURE WITH FRAMEHEADS & BEARINGS								
ROTOR BARS								
ROTOR CONNECTIONS								
ROTOR COIL (WITH POLE PIECE			BEARING-BALL, OPE					
			3666784P8	1	x			
ROTOR COIL (WITHOUT POLE PIECE			BEARING-BALL, ROLLER, LINING, PE					
			3666784P11	1	x			
STATOR COILS (W/S)			BRUSHHOLDER					
			5513647G5	4	x			
MAIN FIELD COILS, SHUNT, COMPOUND, SERIES								
3206864-150	4	x						
COMMUTATING FIELD COILS			BRUSHHOLDER SPRING					
3206865-83								KP-25643

	JAN	FEB	MAR	APR	MAY	JUN	JUL	AUG	SEP	OCT	NOV	DEC

MODEL	APP. Pay-off-Reel — Shifter Pump	LOC. 18	D 707	MACH. NO. 18-69-1

Remington-Rand Division, Sperry Rand Corp.

FIG. 14–6. An equipment record card. The tab at the bottom shows when the next regular inspection will be required.

necessary to avoid breakdowns. Upkeep records also help in cost accounting; they permit high machine charges to be assessed against products made on machines with high upkeep costs.

Maintenance cost records show points where high costs are incurred. From the records the maintenance foreman often can suggest changes that will reduce future upkeep costs. Frequent service to an electric motor, for example, may show that it is overloaded and that a larger one should be used. Frequent floor repairs at particular locations may show that the extra expense of a higher-priced, but more durable, floor at these locations will pay off. Maintenance records should, if examined carefully, show which types of valves, pumps, compressors, etc., perform better than others.

For large machines the maintenance record card is not enough. An additional file for each machine is necessary. In it should be kept all drawings (showing outlines, foundations, wiring, controls) and lubrication diagrams. Renewal parts bulletins, catalogues, and instruction pamphlets, if possible in duplicate, should also be kept in it. Unless they are signed for, they should not be removed from the file. An inventory list of the replacement parts, such as gears, motors, belting, which are on hand for each particular machine could be kept in the file.

CHARGING MAINTENANCE TIME AND MATERIALS TO JOBS

The variable nature and diverse locations of maintenance work make accurate cost record keeping hard and the control of costs even harder. However, most companies keeping maintenance cost records seem to feel that the costs of collecting the figures is more than paid for by lower maintenance costs.

It is important, in controlling maintenance costs, to charge all maintenance work to the department where the work is done. Then you can point the finger at department heads whose costs are high. Generally, day-to-day small maintenance jobs are charged to the departments through "standing accounts." An account number is given to each type of work done, and individual job costs are charged to the appropriate account. The replacement of an electric light bulb in an overhead fixture is charged to an account for electrical maintenance in the department. The replacement of a washer in a leaky water faucet is charged to plumbing maintenance, etc. On the other hand, the time of window washers, truck operators, oilers, and the like is generally charged to a general overhead account for the whole plant, not to the factory department in which the work has been done.

In many small companies job tickets for individual maintenance jobs are not used. At the end of the day the maintenance workers list the jobs they have worked on and the time they have spent on each, so that the accounting department can charge the cost to the appropriate account. But in large companies the maintenance foreman makes out a separate job card for each job not covered by standing accounts. Each job card is given a job number by the maintenance department clerk, so that workers can charge their time to it. In large companies maintenance workers may be required to ring time clocks showing the time they started and ended each job.

Large projects of the semi-improvement type, such as moving machines or small construction jobs, are generally handled as individual jobs for cost record keeping. They are planned ahead and their costs estimated before management's approval is given. After approval they are given an account number, and their labor and material costs are charged to that number.

Company practice varies widely with respect to charging materials costs to small individual maintenance jobs. Big projects are usually charged with the material they use. There are two good reasons, though, why the costs of the materials used should not be charged to little jobs. First, the cost of the paper work is considerable. You can easily spend 50 cents' worth of a clerk's time keeping track of 5 cents' worth of material (like the putty used when putting a new glass in a broken window). Second, the materials used in maintenance work (putty, window glass, electric wire, pipe, paint, etc.) are not used to make the company products and not much of any one thing is used. It just doesn't pay to keep records.

It is simpler to let the maintenance foreman order what he needs when he needs it. When the material arrives, charge it to a regular expense account on the company records, *as if it were already used.* Let your men use the materials on various maintenance jobs without making any more charges. Doing this doesn't need to interfere with big job costing, because the supplies kept on hand are too small to take care of big jobs. Materials bought for big jobs can be charged directly to them.

The maintenance department always keeps a supply of used materials and machine parts. Used pipe, plumbing fittings, lighting fixtures, electrical conduits, wiring, control boxes, wood flooring, bricks, sheet metal ducts, wire fencing, rope, cable, chain, conveyor parts, and many other items removed in the process of making repairs are kept, if they are usable, for future jobs. Having all these used items (which are free and would not be charged to jobs anyway) is another reason for letting the maintenance department keep its own stores and for not charging materials to jobs.

Used machine parts are generally stored in the machine repair shop and not with other items of maintenance stock. Worn bearings or other machine parts are often replaced before they are completely worn out, so they are saved for possible emergency use.

Today's factory machines nearly all have their own electric motors—or even several motors each. The total number of motors a company owns usually runs into the thousands. It is good to keep on hand a reserve supply of new and rebuilt motors of all popular sizes—or even unusual sizes where a motor's failure would be critical. Burned-out motors or those with worn bearings, or those needing cleaning can, then, if repair on the job is too slow, be replaced and repaired at leisure. After rebuilding, the motor is put into the motor stock and not back on the machine from which it came. Motors used from stock are charged to machines at an average price—not at each motor's own rebuilding cost.

MAINTENANCE LABOR COSTS

How much should maintenance cost? Materials will vary considerably with the jobs done, but maintenance labor costs are from 6 to 9 per cent of the total payroll—give or take a little for industry and company variations. Metal industries are toward the high side, and soft goods (textiles and others) are lower.

It isn't safe, however, to take the above figures too seriously because old plants take more maintenance than new plants—lots more. Also many maintenance projects are postponable for a while. In the same company the figures differ from year to year. Most companies "undermaintain" in bad years both to conserve cash and to make it look as if expenses were cut. Then they "overmaintain" in good years. Another trouble with typical cost figures is that they include only *maintenance department* costs and omit maintenance done by employees of producing departments.

BUDGETING MAINTENANCE COSTS

Most large, and some small, companies try to control their maintenance costs by budgets. The expected costs of repairing and keeping production equipment in operation are set up in separate budgets for each producing department. The foreman of each department is responsible for keeping his maintenance costs within the budgeted amount. Capital expenditures and big repair projects are covered by separate budgets.

If production goes up or down, maintenance costs ought not to change proportionally, yet they are affected by the volume of work done. They don't follow changes in man-hours, or number of employees, nor do they vary in proportion to departmental areas.

Most companies using budgets set fixed amounts for expenditures and then allow a small increase or decrease in the amount if the volume of business goes up or down. Budgets sometimes show what expenditures are allowed, month by month, for a whole year ahead. The figures are set after asking foremen of operating departments to forecast what their maintenance needs will be and in what month they will be needed. From the foremen's reports, the maintenance department estimates the labor time and materials required for the jobs listed by the foremen and converts them into dollars. The monthly estimates go up for review to higher executives. If the reviewing executive feels that the amount is too high, he cuts it, meaning that certain projects recommended by the foremen or the maintenance staff have to be put off.

During the budget period maintenance costs are collected by the accounting department, grouped according to the classifications set up in the budget, summed up by class, compared to the budgeted amount, and the amount of variance indicated. The report is studied, particularly those items or classes which have run over the budgeted amounts. Often an investigation of the budget reports reveals conditions that can be eliminated in the future, with the result that maintenance costs are reduced.

A word of warning about budgets and maintenance. Budgets don't keep machines from wearing out. *You can't budget maintenance costs out of existence.* Set budgets too low, and some things stay unfixed that ought to be fixed. This might go on until heavy and costly repairs are necessary.

Actually, many maintenance costs can be postponed again and again until it looks as if money is being saved. Sometimes money really is saved, particularly in the case of such things as painting (which can be overdone), but in most kinds of maintenance the apparent savings may be wiped out when a straw breaks the camel's back and a serious breakdown or accident occurs. Maintenance should be postponed only as a calculated risk.

MAINTENANCE WORKERS' WAGES

Maintenance men are usually paid by the hour—in spite of the fact that incentive wages usually reduce costs. Incentives work best when the work is repetitive, manual, measurable in countable units and capable of being checked easily, and when all, and not part, of a man's work can be covered. Most maintenance jobs lack one or more of the requirements, so incentives are not too suitable. Besides, it costs money to set maintenance job standards, and it costs more to keep all the records and to check up on the jobs the men say that they do.

In spite of the difficulties, though, many large companies (with fifty maintenance men or more) have put incentive systems in their maintenance departments and have reduced their costs. Maintenance workers are generally much less efficient than production workers—often only half as efficient. Incentives sometimes bring them up to three quarters as efficient.

Time standards used for maintenance jobs cannot be as accurate as those for regular factory operations. There is too much variety. No two jobs are exactly alike, so the standards set are averages that cover up considerable variation. Replacing light bulbs, for example, could be easy or it could mean using a ladder or even setting up scaffolding. Yet it would be impractical to have very many separate time standards for replacing light bulbs. Any standard set covering a maintenance job has to be an average time. For any particular job it may be too high or too low. This works out all right over a period of time—the jobs tend to balance out to the average. But don't average extremes together. If you were the worker, you wouldn't think much of the standards if they averaged together the time for screwing in a new light bulb with putting up scaffolding to change a light bulb. The one job might take ten or twenty times as much time as the other. Such extremes are too great to average together to get any reasonable average.

Is there any way to set reasonable standards for such jobs? Yes, there are two ways. They can be estimated or you can use standard data (discussed on page 575). In the estimating method, the electrician foreman makes estimates for electrical jobs, the carpenter foreman for carpenter jobs, and so on. The estimate is used as the standard.

The second and more satisfactory way is to use "standard data." Maintenance men have to get to their jobs, do the work, and get back. The walking time part of the job can be figured by formula. You know from past experience how many feet a minute a man walks, or if he uses a truck how fast it goes. And from a floor plan you can tell how far he has to go; that gives you the going and coming time. Past records tell you too how long it takes to put in light bulbs of various kinds and to place ladders or scaffolds. Just add up the times for each part of a job and you get a standard for it.

The file of times to do individual things is called "standard data." Standard data save time study because they work like building blocks. They can be put together to suit the job. An electrician fixing a broken wire would have the same going and coming time as if he were putting in a new light bulb, but the wire fixing part would be different.

Time standards, if they are used in maintenance, are nearly always tied in with wages. Men who do work in less than standard time are paid bonuses. But because maintenance time standards are not too accurate, bonus calculations ought to be based on weekly rather than daily performance. In that time the loose and tight standards will balance out.

Difficult though it is to set standards and to administer an incentive plan for maintenance employees, you want them to be able to earn bonuses if the factory men earn bonuses. Otherwise, semiskilled factory workers with low base rates plus big bonuses end up making more money than skilled maintenance men with high base rates but no bonus. When this happens, the maintenance men are naturally dissatisfied.

Many maintenance department employees are in the building trades. These men, the carpenters, painters, electricians, and others, could find jobs in outside building construction. The hourly rates of the construction industry are always much higher than the rates of maintenance department craftsmen. How then can a company keep its men? It can keep them because construction industry employees have to keep changing jobs and they work fewer days a year and must at times work under disagreeable outdoor conditions and go long distances to work. Factory maintenance men do not often leave to go into the construction industry. The possibility exists, however, and should not be forgotten in wage setting.

SAFETY

Maintenance and safety often go hand in hand. Accidents are sometimes caused by machine failure, particularly failure of machines which handle and transport materials and men. Good maintenance should prevent, or at least cut down, these accidents. The dangers that can result from broken elevator cables and faulty brakes on power trucks are well known and appreciated, enough so that regular inspection and good maintenance are the rule. But the dangers of worn overhead crane hoist cables, hooks, and chain and compressed air hoists are not so generally realized. Even worn ladder rungs and steps are responsible for occasional accidents. The maintenance department should include these things in its regular maintenance inspection routines, and it should also check safety stops (devices to stop the machine instantly if anyone gets caught) on machines.

Maintenance workers should themselves work safely and use safe equipment. Accident rates are generally higher among maintenance employees than among regular factory employees because much of their work is done at high levels and in awkward positions. They seldom have the advantage of special purpose tools for the tasks they perform. But because of the preventive nature of their work, they should be the most safety-conscious employees in a manufacturing plant, both for their own good and for that of other employees.

THE IMPORTANCE OF LAYOUT IN MAINTENANCE WORK

The ease of maintenance work is largely dependent on plant layout. Electric motors should be located for easy access because they need frequent inspection and oiling. Unless motors and equipment are accessible, repairs are difficult and expensive, and the temptation to neglect oiling them is ever present. Equipment not at floor level should have its own platform, stairs, and ladders. If machinery must be moved frequently, it should be installed so that it can easily be unfastened. Aisles should be wide enough for the millwrights to move whole machines, or else machines will have to be dismantled and reassembled in a new location at unnecessary expense.

STUDY QUESTIONS

1. Where should you put the emphasis? On "fix-it" repairs? Or on preventive maintenance? Give reasons for your answer.
2. Explain how preventive maintenance works. When would you use it? When not?
3. Is there really an "inherent inefficiency" in maintenance work? Justify your answer.
4. Write out a policy or a rule telling your maintenance department foreman what jobs to do using your own maintenance men and what jobs to hire outsiders for.
5. Should maintenance jobs be "authorized"? Why?
6. Should maintenance men work for factory foremen or for a maintenance department foreman? Tell when you would set up your organization each way.

7. How does supervising maintenance workers differ from supervising workers who work on the product? What problems arise? How do you solve them?
8. Should you keep maintenance records? Why?
9. How should you charge materials used by maintenance workers? What other ways are there? Justify your choice.
10. Some people think that they have a problem in setting pay rates for maintenance workers. What is this problem? What do you do about it?

CASE 14–1.   CARROLL MANUFACTURING COMPANY

Steve Toth, maintenance foreman of the Carroll Manufacturing Co., was very proud of his record. In this company of 2,000 employees, there had been no production holdups because of machinery breakdowns for 3 months. Ed Lindsay, the superintendent, praised Steve for his good record. Soon, however, the budget reports for the first half of the year, including the months of no breakdowns, were on Lindsay's desk. Upon analyzing them, he discovered that the maintenance costs were higher than they had been in the same period in the preceding year, although production was about the same.

What would cause such a situation? Is it desirable? Has Steve done a good job? Would you recommend any change in policies?

Chapter 15

RESEARCH AND PATENTS

RESEARCH and product development deal with the product, its design, how to improve it, how to make it, and even how to package it. Research has to do with learning nature's laws. Development (the subject of Chapter 17) has to do with putting that knowledge to work, but it is often hard to tell where research leaves off and development starts. In very large companies research and product development are separated. In smaller companies the engineering department does both.

Research has made possible television, jet airplanes, electronic computers, automatic gear shifts on cars, nylon stockings, sulpha drugs, and literally millions of other things. Nature never made such things. They are man-made. But man didn't just stumble onto them either. We have them because men were hired and put to work to try to find answers to problems and to unlock nature's secrets. New products result from consciously directed research.

PURE AND APPLIED RESEARCH

Research is "pure" or "applied" depending on its purpose. Pure research is research into nature's basic laws, regardless of how that knowledge can be used. Applied research tries to solve a problem, a definite problem, and usually one that now costs us money or will make money for us if solved.

Pure research almost always costs more than applied research and often doesn't make much money for its sponsors. In fact, it may fail altogether to unlock nature's secrets. For example, trees take sunlight and earth and water and make wood. Man would like to be able to do it too but, although probably millions of dollars have been spent on trying to find out how nature does it, man can't do it yet.

Actually, most pure research turns out to have practical applications, so the distinction between pure and applied research is not always too sharp. X rays, radio, and television have come out of what was at first pure research. On the other hand, artificial rubber, nylon, electronic computers, automatic gear shifts, and so on have come out of applied research. Specific problems were tackled and solutions sought. Applied research, aiming at limited specific goals—whether it is an improvement in product or process—is much less costly, project by project, than basic or pure research. Also it is usually successful. The question isn't, for example, "can we design an automatic gear shift?" but "how can we design it so that it works well yet costs little?" Most research being done today is applied rather than pure because applied research usually pays off well and is less costly than pure research.

All research, pure and applied, is a little risky because it doesn't always solve problems and you don't find this out until after you have spent your money. It is like drilling for oil in a promising area. You spend the money first, and maybe you get it back. Like oil drilling, too, a study of what other people have done in this area should be made before starting a project. Library research will show what has already been done and lets you start from where someone else has left off.

Individual research projects by no means always pay off. In fact, most don't. Du Pont reports that one third of its chemical research projects are "laboratory flops." And even after succeeding in the lab most of the rest prove impractical in production. Fewer than one in ten even gets into production, and some fail then.[1] RCA estimates that 90 per cent of its research ideas are useless.

How can we justify such waste? It isn't the waste that we justify; it is the golden 10 per cent of successes that makes it worth while. The successes pay for themselves many times over. Standard Oil of New Jersey says that every dollar spent on research brings back five dollars. The National Science Foundation reports that, in the last 25 years, research in American companies has brought in from 20 to 25 dollars for every research dollar spent. Monsanto Chemical estimates that one third of its 1956 sales came from new products developed through research in the preceding 10 years. One third of General Electric's sales come from products not made 20 years ago. RCA gets 80 per cent of its today's sales from products that came out of its research.

Besides the fact that research pays off, another important reason for doing it is that you can't afford not to. You must have new products all the time just to stay in business. Someone else's research keeps the "ghost of obsolescence hovering around every corner," as far as your products are concerned. Don't forget too that the government lets you call research a cost of operation. If you didn't do research, federal income taxes would take half of the extra dollars that you would have left over—so tax savings carry half of your research costs. The question isn't, "Is research worth its cost?" but, "Is research worth *half* its cost?"

---

[1] "The Age of Research," *Time*, July 9, 1956, p. 74.

WHO DOES RESEARCH?

Industrial companies do most, but by no means all, of the research carried on. Universities, technological research institutes, trade associations, governmental agencies, and consulting laboratories, all do research too. The Atomic Energy Commission, the Bureau of Mines, the armed services, and many other federal agencies do a great deal of basic research. Besides, particularly in aviation and electronics, the government pays private companies to do basic research. Over thirty trade associations operate research laboratories. But they are all small compared to many individual company research departments.

The North American Aviation Company has more than 4,500 researchers on its payroll of 62,000 employees and spends over $40 million a year on research. International Business Machines has 2,500 people on product development. General Motors has 25,000 men doing research, styling, and engineering, 4,000 of them in its technical center (320 acres, 25 buildings) near Detroit. The Merck pharmaceutical company has over 700 researchers, including nearly 200 Ph.D.'s. The Clevite Company (bronze bearings makers) has 3,300 employees with 350 in research. Several large companies have over 100 Ph.D. researchers on their payroll.

Besides what companies do themselves, there are many private, nonprofit research organizations such as Armour Research Foundation, Stanford Research Institute, and Rand Corporation, which each employ hundreds of researchers. The Mellon Institute and the Battelle Memorial Institute are other large long-established nonprofit private research organizations. The Arthur D. Little Company, a consulting firm, also does a great deal of research. Besides these private organizations every big university in the land carries on continuing research.

In total something around $5 billion goes into research every year in the United States. Two thirds of it is spent by private companies. One third of the total is concentrated in electronics and aviation. Four per cent of all aviation employees are researchers. (That is three times as high as in all industries combined.) Probably United States companies employ 500,000 research workers, including 100,000 scientists.

Most research organizations specialize in some way, but all spread out more as the number of projects handled goes up into the hundreds. Battelle specializes in fuels, metals, and alloys. Armour specializes in mechanical and electrical engineering. Stanford specializes in oil, aluminum, bromine, and other material. Rand works on aviation and electronic problems.

All companies actually get the benefit of lots more research than they do themselves. Besides the help they get from the public and semipublic agencies, they get the benefit of their suppliers' research. Thompson Products, Eaton Axle, Electric Autolite, and A. O. Smith are big auto industry suppliers. Their research improves the parts they sell auto companies, yet no one auto company foots the whole bill. The trend in the industry toward integration will mean that each of the big three will have to do its own research on springs, axles, wheels, wiring systems, and frames.

RESEARCH SUBJECTS

Large companies usually do most of their own research. In general they work on such matters as:

1. Discovery of basic chemical or physical relationships, particularly those having to do with the company's products or processes.
2. Improving the product.
3. Finding new uses for present products.
4. Developing new products.
5. Reducing the cost of the product by improving operations and processes.
6. Developing tests and specifications for operations and purchased materials.
7. Analyzing competitors' products.
8. Finding profitable uses for by-products.

In this list, notice particularly number 5, having to do with cost cutting, and number 2, improving the product. A great deal of small-scale research goes into these two. Foremen and time and motion study men should be making minor improvements all the time. Design and tool engineers, too, should be making little improvements daily. We don't think of this work as research, but it really is and in total is quite worth while.

Companies should resist the temptation to throw too many production problems into the lap of the research department, lest it have no time for exploratory research. If no basic research is done, the day may come when the company's technological improvements are held up for lack of further scientific knowledge.

In general, small companies do little real research, although some research is involved in the product designing done by the engineering department. In large companies, where much more is done, it is customary to set up a research division in the engineering department. If a company engages in extensive basic research, the department is made independent of and divorced from the engineering department. The director of research may be a vice-president; but whether he is or not, he reports to the company's top administration.

RESEARCH ORGANIZATION

Research work requires a reasonably stable organization which cannot be built up quickly. You can't hire researchers today, lay them off tomorrow, and get them back the next day. A company wishing to do research must commit itself, to some extent, to a continuing program.

Research projects of sizable proportions often require technicians with many kinds of technical knowledge. Chemists, physicists, biological chemists, and others may be needed. Within the research department

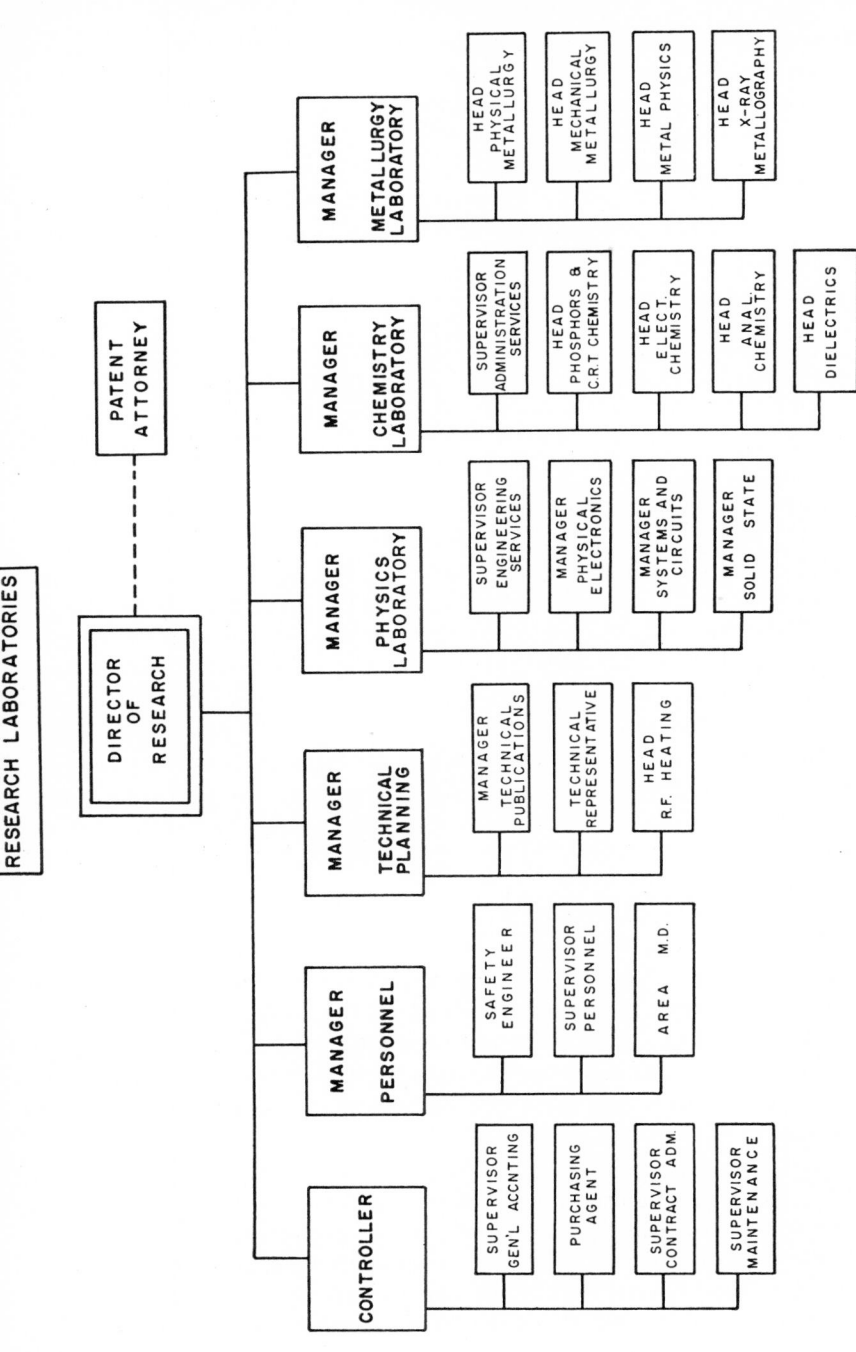

FIG. 15–1. Organization of Sylvania Electric Research Laboratories.

the technical specialists may be grouped (1) according to the fields of science, (2) according to the stage of manufacturing with which they deal, or (3) according to product. Figures 15–1 and 15–2 show two arrangements of research departments.

A project director responsible to the director of research should supervise and see through to completion each research project, reporting periodically on its progress and cost. He may assign parts of the work to individual specialists who work as members of a specialized group.

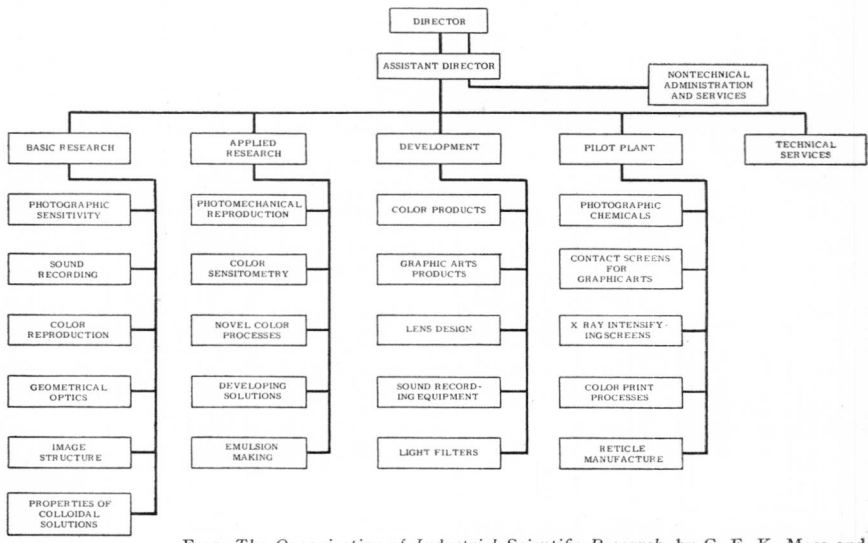

From *The Organization of Industrial Scientific Research*, by C. E. K. Mees and J. A. Leermakers. McGraw-Hill Book Co., Inc.

FIG. 15–2. An organization chart of a laboratory organized according to the stage of processing the company's product.

Some companies, instead of having the director divide and assign the work by specialty, take specialists out of their own groups and place them directly under him. With this method a project director can more easily co-ordinate the work on the various parts of his project. Specialists in the various fields can also more readily talk to each other about the project.

The knowledge gained from research, particularly of the "applied" variety, can often be used immediately in the factory, but certain transitional work must usually be done. Your researchers might find out, for example, that heat-treated surfaces wear better than nonheat-treated surfaces. Now you have to figure out how to heat treat the wearing surface of various parts. Another section of the engineering departments must devise new operations for doing this and write new specifications telling the factory how to do it. Design engineers must redesign products to include the improvements uncovered by the research department.

RESEARCH CENTRALIZATION

Giant companies usually do some research in one large central research agency, such as General Motors' Technical Center near Detroit. But they also do a good bit of research lower down in the divisions. You will recall that giant companies almost always are divided into major divisions, each handling, making, and selling a group of related products (a product "line").

Each division has full technical responsibility for its products and has its own research organization. The central research group (for the whole company) researches into the vast technical unknown to protect the company's future. And it works on new products not yet assigned to a division. It also oversees transferring new products to divisions, and it helps division researchers who ask for help.

International Business Machines has most of its 2,500 researchers in four different laboratories (each concentrating on one product line) in different parts of the country. Du Pont has ten manufacturing divisions, each with its own research department. General Electric has its 8,500 men in research and development spread out in 42 major buildings. Sylvania Electric, large, although not a giant, has three central laboratories (instead of one) and has, besides, researchers in each of its eleven operating divisions.

Decentralizing research and engineering makes some problems. At Sylvania, for example, one division is responsible for developing, making, and selling color TV sets. But another division is responsible for color tubes, and still another for all the other tubes a TV set needs. There must be lots of co-operative give-and-take as mutual problems are worked out.

RESEARCH FOR DEFENSE PRODUCTS

Defense products, particularly airplanes, missiles, and electronics are continually being improved, but only because large amounts of research are done. The first atomic bomb cost over two billion dollars to make. And many billions more have been spent since.

Defense products research has many quirks. Some of it is basic research and some of it is research incidental to production. And since the government buys defense products, it has a lot to say about research projects and their costs.

Sometimes it lets contracts for basic research. Then there are also contracts for making products which need some research incidental to production. Payment for such jobs is at a fixed price or is made on a cost-plus-fixed-fee basis. Fixed price contracts present few problems, but cost-plus contracts make problems. Two questions are involved: who pays for the research? and who holds the patents that come out of it, the company or the government?

Simple answers can't be given because there are "ifs" and "ands" and exceptions—and sometimes lawsuits. Even lawyers aren't sure until they win or lose the case. Contracts for research (not manufacture) would normally provide that the government pay for the work and own any patents. The government's payment—whether fixed price or cost plus —would be expected to cover the costs of the work done plus a reasonable profit.

Most government contracts—and the big ones—are to manufacture, not to research. Yet some research incidental to the contract is nearly always necessary. On fixed fee contracts, the government would just pay its bill. The company would own any patents coming out of the work and might or might not have made money on the research work.

But on cost-plus contracts it would probably be different. The government would be quite willing to pay the costs plus the agreed-upon profit for the products contracted for but would be very fussy about the research—was it necessary? did the contract really authorize it? The company would probably own the patent, and the government would probably pay the company for whatever it had spent on the research—but might well balk at paying a profit too on the research expense.

Why all this to do about patents? Does it matter? Isn't the government the only customer for their use? It does matter. First, some of the discoveries have applications to civilian products. Who owns the patent is then important. Second—and often more important—the government always wants two sources of supply for everything. It will divide its orders for your newly developed product, and your competitor will be using your new development. If you own the patent you may get royalties from him, but there will be no royalties if you don't own the patent.

Remember, too, that behind all this lies the American philosophy that the government should itself keep out of business and that private industry is more efficient than government-operated activities. This philosophy makes problems, however, in research since so much research depends on government money.

MARKETING RESEARCH

Marketing research (or "commercial" research) tries to find out what the customer wants—what products he will buy? how many? and at what price? Sometimes customers are asked by questionnaire what they would buy if the product were changed, or if prices were changed, or if they had more money.

Marketing research also looks at the problem from the broad general viewpoint. It studies the economic health of the nation, the position of the industry, and how the company stacks up with its competitors. It also studies sales trends of products and groups of products—both in the industry and in the company.

Out of all of this, the company finds out how it is doing and gets clues about its weak spots and where it should try harder. Marketing research may show that customers don't like the looks of the company's products. Or maybe they are inconvenient to use (as, for example, old stand-up kinds of vacuum cleaners). Or perhaps they get out of order too easily. Or maybe the company's line is too limited. We are losing sales because we don't even make certain popular items. Don't forget, though, that new products sometimes drive out the old. If we add a new low-priced item, will it undercut our market for higher-priced well-established items? Marketing research may also show that we need new package designs, or it may show that slightly lower prices would open large new markets.

Of course, whenever commercial research shows that new products should be developed or old ones discontinued, or redesigned, the engineering department should be told right away so that it can start the actual developmental work.

Large companies do a lot of commercial research, but small companies seldom do more than study the sales trends of their main products. No one, large or small, has to do without marketing research, however, even if he does not have such a department in his company. There are many capable outside marketing research organizations that do big or little jobs on a fee basis.

Marketing research is not always as helpful as you might expect. You do find out a lot, but often little of it is new. Any good sales department ought to know what the customers want. It ought also to know its own products' strong and weak points. Customer complaints about products and the repairs and services they need ought to tell most of the story. Any good sales department should also know the strong and weak points of its competitors' products.

If marketing research is of so little value, why do it? It doesn't cost a great deal, but it does cost something. Why spend even that? You spend the money because *sometimes* it turns up things you didn't know about, and sometimes you discover that things you thought were unimportant are really important, or the other way around.

Notice too that marketing research *creates* no markets. *It provides information*—it may tell you that here is a market that you don't know about. But, if it does, the market was actually already there—research or no research. Some administrators—particularly government administrators—lean so heavily on surveys that they will almost deny that a fact exists until a formal survey seems to prove it. Of course, it must be admitted that government officials have to be doubly sure of their facts because their every move is questioned by taxpayers and congressmen. On the other hand, surveys are not foolproof either. They can mislead you. Surveys of voter opinion "proved" that President Roosevelt and President Truman would lose in 1936 and 1948.

Actually, most business administrators make most of their decisions without benefit of formal surveys. In a sense, an informal kind of commercial research goes on all the time in most manufacturing companies. Administrators get reports all the time from their sales organizations on which to base their generally sound decisions. Formal commercial research is a valuable aid, but don't think that intelligent decisions can't be made without it.

RESEARCH COSTS AND PROJECT CONTROL

Research pays but first it costs. Only after the research on a project is done and money spent can it begin to save money or to produce income. RCA had $50 million invested in color TV before it reached the United States living room. Sometimes even successful research takes years to pay off. Big research jobs often take up to 5 years in the laboratory and then 3 or 4 more years to put the results to use.

Research scientists cost close to $10,000 a year each. You also need about as many technicians, stenographers, and other supporting workers as you have scientists. Also you need about $10,000 worth of equipment per researcher. A team of five researchers will cost you nearly $200,000 the first year and close to $150,000 a year from then on. Small wonder small companies do little research.

How much money *should* a company spend on research? There is no good way to tell. Actually, most large companies *do* spend about 1 per cent of their sales income and have almost 1 per cent of their employees doing research. Some go higher—even up to 5 per cent of sales. Du Pont spends 3.5; General Motors, 2.0; General Electric, 4.0 per cent. Aviation, electronics, pharmaceutical, and chemical companies spend the most. Large companies usually spend a larger proportion of their income on research then do small companies. Companies in heavily researched industries, such as chemicals and drugs, have to spend a lot because over a 10-year period half of their sales come from products not made when the period started.

Research budgets need to be a little flexible. Probably a good starting point would be to decide—as a policy—to spend a certain amount, say 1 per cent, on research. Then proposed research projects could, one by one, be reviewed to see which can be approved. You don't want to spend time, research talent, and money on too many "turkeys."

You never know ahead though what a project will cost, and you will have to spend some of this year's money for old projects still going on. A project's cost is so hard to figure (as is its worth, if it is successful) that sometimes a company will, at first, approve only an "exploratory" budget to look into its possibilities. More money will be put into it later if it looks good.

Ideas for reseach come from everywhere in the organization—sometimes from outside. Close to half of them come from the research de-

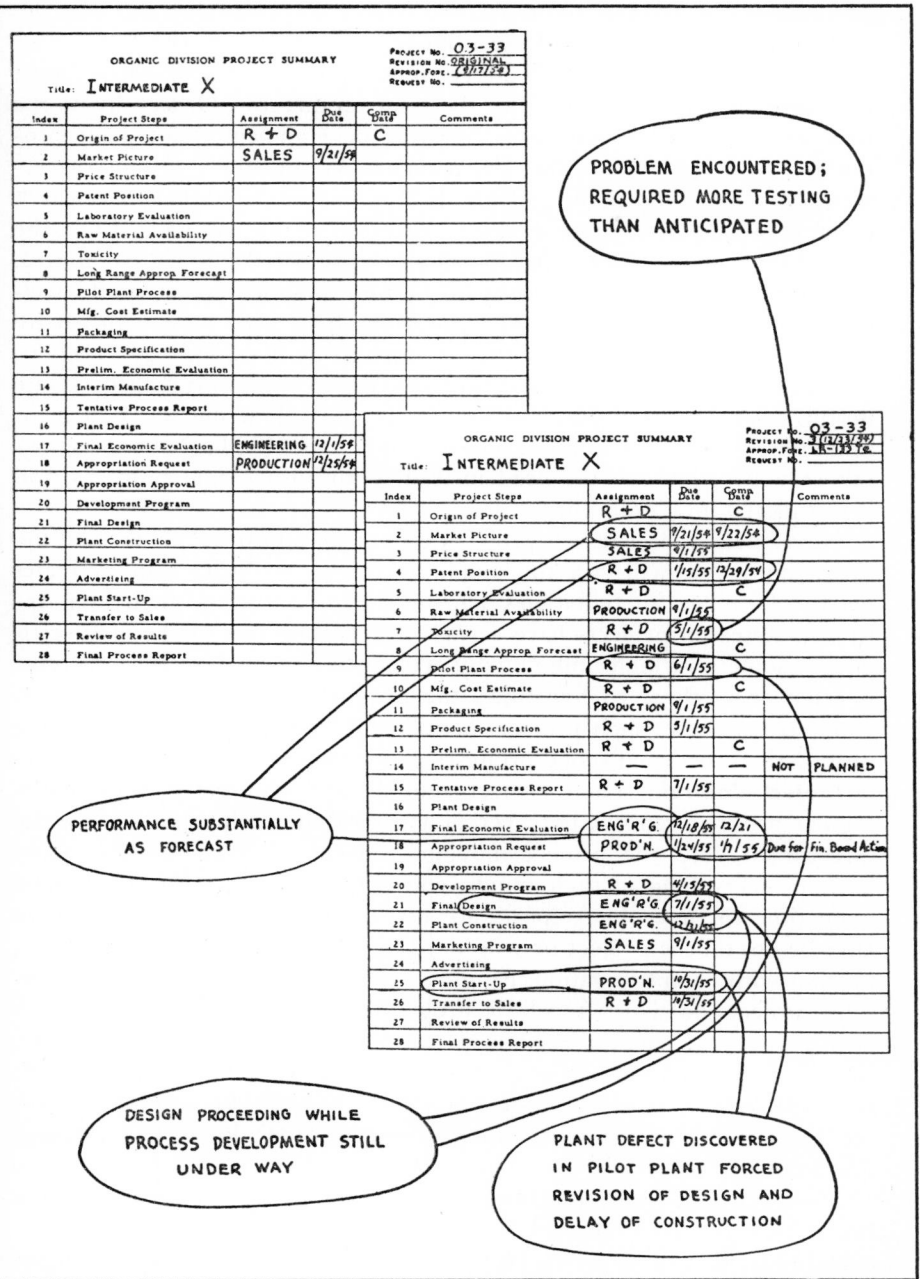

Monsanto Chemical Co.

FIG. 15–3. A research project progress report. Notice the circled items and explanations to help management understand what has been going on.

partment itself. Most of the rest come from the factory and the sales department. A few come from executives.

Dividing up the research budget among projects is a problem. Some companies leave dividing it up to the research director. Others divide the total appropriation among pure research, development, pilot plant production, and services to other departments. Within these groups the research director chooses the projects. Still other companies have a research committee—not the director alone—approve all big projects. Both the manufacturing and sales departments are represented on this committee.

The committee should not try to be too "practical" and should welcome imagination. Many useful innovations have been turned down by companies as impractical or valueless, only to be developed by competitors into profitable businesses. Years ago, for example, many people saw no future in the automobile and later in the radio. One nut and bolt manufacturer turned down the exclusive rights to "Phillips" head screws (those with a plus on the head instead of the usual slot), only to find it had passed up a gold mine.

Nevertheless, all research projects cannot be approved. There are too many, and some will cost too much and yield too little. Cost estimates need to be made for tentatively approved projects before their final approval. Research projects have a way of revealing new paths of investigation, some of which undoubtedly will justify pursuit, so the final cost is often from three to five times the original estimate. Of course, the committee reviews such projects periodically and approves more money only if the broadened scope promises greater benefits.

Project Control.   Each project should have a director who makes regular progress reports, both verbal and written. Such reports force the director to keep the project moving, prevent research workers from keeping everything in their minds, and permit the costs to be checked from time to time. The reports are useful to other workers who may later be put on the project or who need to refer to them, perhaps in connection with patent litigation. Progress reports make it possible to reconsider projects on which too little progress is being made. If there is too little promise of success, they can be stopped. There is a danger here, though. Some half-finished projects give you partial value even if cut off. But with others, it is all waste unless you finish. Also sometimes you are on the verge of answering the problem but don't know it. Canceling projects early may make you miss the boat.

Most research work is glamorous in name only unless some major breakthrough is accomplished. Not everyone gets to develop the Salk vaccine for polio and have his picture in all the papers. Research means hours, days, years of experimentation, observing apparatus and dials, recording, tabulating and interpreting data, then more experimentation, more recording—on and on. Most of this repetitive work is just clerical. It can be and is done by assistants and clerks. From one quarter to one half of research department employees should be helpers of various kinds. Trained scientists and research specialists should be freed of all possible routine so that they can spend their time on advanced work.

Researchers are a peculiar breed—or they like to think that they are. They don't like to be "controlled." They don't like to be held to budgets or schedules, or even to accomplishment. They just want to be left alone to do research. And of course you can't schedule research or control it like production. You can't just solve a problem by a given date or appropriate a sum of money and be sure that it is enough to pay for solving a problem.

Still, the attempt has to be made, or there is no control over the work at all. Budgets, project control, and reports, as discussed above, do the job reasonably well. Incentives are another part of the picture. How can one "incentivate" researchers? Certainly not by piecework. Usually they get good salaries. Beyond that the incentives are indirect. Professional and public recognition (Salk for the Salk Vaccine) are strong incentives to high-caliber researchers, but usually only a few at the top get such recognition.

PATENTS

In order to stimulate invention, our federal laws provide that inventors may patent their inventions and keep others from using them without permission. Patents are important to all manufacturing companies because, almost without exception, their products, their processes, or their machines are patented. Much of private industry's research would not be done if new products and processes could not be patented.

In the United States patents are issued by the Patent Office in Washington for new products or processes or for improvements on old products and processes. A patentable invention must be new, useful, and workable, but it does not need to be commercially profitable. If inventions have been in use for over one year without a patent's having been applied for, they pass into the public domain and cannot be patented.

Not all innovations are patentable. The thing that is patentable is *the way to do something—not the idea.* Flying to the moon by rocketship is not patentable, but the rocketship is. Laws of nature are not patentable, but the means of applying them to useful ends are. But drug companies can develop a new drug and patent its use for particular purposes.

Patented products must be marked "patented," if they can be marked, otherwise damages cannot be collected from infringers. Products on which the patents have run out may still be marked "patented" as far as patent laws are concerned, but the Federal Trade Commission considers doing this an unfair trade practice.

Patents run for 17 years and are not renewable. After 17 years they belong in the public domain. In effect though, they can often be extended beyond 17 years through the use of patented improvements. By the time the basic patent runs out, newly patented improvements have been made. Competitors can use the basic patent but cannot, without permission, use the improvement.

Patents are negative. They are not rights to make product but rights to keep others from making them. This distinction is important in the case of the patent for an improvement because it is usable only with the basic patented product and only with permission from its owner.

Patents can sometimes be used as competitive weapons. A company with a patent on a good product or process may try to develop all possible alternatives and substitutes for it and patent them, just to keep competitors from doing so. In this way the company protects its main patent. Or, a competitor may try to restrict the usefulness of someone else's patent by developing and patenting improvements on it. Such patents on improvements are of little use to him because he can't use them, but they keep the underlying patent holder from making those improvements himself and restrict the patent's usefulness and value to the holder.

Infringement lawsuits, primarily for purposes of harassment, have also been used. If a desirable and seemingly valid patent is held by a financially weak competitor, harassment suits would seem to be unethical. It is not unethical or illegal, however, to doubt a patent's validity. And if anyone alleges that another patent infringes on his patent, he has the right to have his case heard.

PATENTS AS LEGAL DOCUMENTS

Patents are legal documents, and since they are frequently valuable, the application for a patent should be carefully worded. Unless it is drawn up precisely, the application may be denied, perhaps on the ground that the device seems to be too similar to one previously granted a patent. Careless wording in the application may diminish a patent's value by restricting the patent's coverage. In such a case, competitors will be able to make products very similar to those patented without infringement. Roger Hoar, writing in a book on the subject, describes an instance where the use of the word "bolt" instead of "supporting member" made a patent practically valueless:

A claim covered a "two-part automobile spring, one part being rigidly held, and the other part being hinged thereto, etc." The [patent] Examiner rightly ruled that this claim was incomplete, as not stating what it was that held the rigid part. So the applicant amended by adding the words "by a bolt" and the patent was so issued. This unnecessary narrow limitation has prevented the patentee from asserting his patent against a Chinese copy of his spring supported by a link; whereas, if he had added the words "by a supporting member," instead of "by a bolt," the situation would be different.[2]

---

[2] Roger S. Hoar, *Patent Tactics and Law* (3rd ed.; New York: Ronald Press Co., 1950), p. 125.

Hoar also emphasizes the need for making a thorough search of earlier patents so that the application claim can be worded accordingly. His discussion follows:

Suppose you have invented a new hinge-joint for piping, which joint would be useful in many other fields. If your search indicates that the mechanical principle is broadly new, you will want to insert claims to a "mechanical movement." If the mechanical principle turns out to be old, but never used before on a *hinge*-joint you will want to claim a hinge-joint broadly, but go no further. If your type of hinge-joint turns out to be old in other fields, you will want to limit your claims to hinge-joints for *piping*, and then insert in your specification from the start some good arguments as to why piping presents such unique problems that a piping expert, even with these other patents before him, would not realize that the type of joint shown therein could be used for a pipe-joint.[3]

OWNERSHIP OF PATENTS

Large companies conducting continual research projects take out many patents. It is reasonable for the company to own the inventions and improvements developed with its money, materials, machinery, and other facilities and done on company time. Sometimes, however, employees invent things related to their work which they want to patent for themselves. Often there is a real question as to who owns the invention, the employee or the employer.

Employees who are not hired to invent but who do invent something would ordinarily be considered owners of their inventions and could claim ownership to patents. The employer, however, has a "shop right" (a nonexclusive right) to use inventions owned by employees if the developmental work has been done on company time and at company cost. Only the inventions of employees hired specifically to invent would ordinarily belong to the company.

Most large companies take care of patent ownership problems by having their technical men sign agreements to assign to the company, for one dollar, their inventions relating to company products or processes. Often the agreements cover inventions made by a worker even after he quits his employment if the inventions grow directly out of something he learned on the job. You don't want your men quitting and then patenting in their own names improvements worked out at company expense. Some companies, however, permit a worker to patent his inventions himself if the company does not elect to take out the patent.

THE COMPANY PATENT DEPARTMENT

Companies doing very much original work need to have a patent attorney and at least one draftsman skilled in making drawings for patent application. A company should have its own library of patents (copies

---

[3] *Ibid.*, pp. 80–81.

can be obtained from the Patent Office for 25 cents each) relating to its fields of work. New ideas can be checked against patents already issued to see whether they are really new or whether a patent application should be filed.

A patent library should contain copies of all regulations, periodicals, and court decisions relating to patents. It should receive the weekly *Official Gazette* published by the Patent Office in Washington, listing all new patents which have been issued. All new patents in its field should be studied by a company to see whether they can be used and to see that they do not infringe on company-owned patents.

PATENT PROTECTION

The Patent Office will deny your request for a patent if it thinks that your idea is not new, but the Patent Office is not the court of final recourse. If it says "no," you can appeal to a special patent court or to civil courts. But what if it says "yes"? You get a patent all right but *you* —*not the Patent Office*—have to defend your patent in court if someone claims that your patent infringes on his. Keep all records, applications, and correspondence on file against the day you may have to defend your patent in court.

A company's new products (even those not to be patented) should be cleared through its patent department before production is started. This helps protect the company against later infringement suits. It is particularly important for manufacturers of machinery, whose customers, the users of the machines, could also be sued for infringement.

Companies do not always want to patent *process* improvements because, once patented, the process becomes public knowledge. A patent would give a company the right to collect royalties from others, but infringement is so hard to detect that collection might be almost impossible. The company ought to keep a record of the process development, when it was first used, etc., to protect itself against a competitor's being granted a patent in the future. Prior use of the process prevents anyone else from patenting it. In fact, if a company uses a new process for over a year without patenting it, it would itself be barred from getting a patent.

If a company has a process it does not care to patent or to keep secret, it can prevent others from patenting the process simply by publishing an account of it in a technical journal. After publication it can still be patented within a year of the publishing date, but only by someone who can prove he had developed it before the journal came out.

Should two or more persons claim to have invented something, the one who first files an application for a patent has a decided advantage over the other one, who becomes the objector. If the second man can prove he developed the invention first, he will get the patent, but the burden of proof is on him. A person working on an invention can to some extent protect himself against its theft by writing a description of his idea, dating it, having two witnesses read, sign, and declare they understand it, and having the signatures notarized. The inventor should send this statement to himself by registered mail and keep the envelop unopened. Should the question of priority of the idea ever be raised, this letter can be introduced as evidence. It will strongly support his claim.

TRADE-MARKS

Trade-marks can be registered at the Patent Office. They get their validity from use, not from their registration. Their registration, however, gives the owner a right to resort to federal courts against infringers who use the trade-mark. The article itself, however, can be made, sold, or used by others. "Reg.-U.S. Patent Office" means that the trade-mark is registered, and not that the article is patented. Registration of trade-marks lasts for 20 years and can be renewed every 20-year period. A trade-mark tends to scare some competitors away and can be used for nonpatentable ideas.

The terms "Pat. Applied For" and "Patent Pending" have no legal status and give an inventor no protection, although they may prevent prospective competitors from entering the field. If a machine is made and sold by a competitor during the period when the originating company's patent is pending, its manufacture and use after that patent is granted constitute an infringement.

STUDY QUESTIONS

1. Distinguish between pure and applied research. Which is more common? Who does most of each?
2. What would your attitude be toward research if you found that half of the projects were flops? Actually, how many are flops? In the light of this record, would you recommend that a company with $1,000,000 sales a year do research?
3. What kinds of organizations do research in the United States?
4. How should you set up (how would you group the researchers) a research department? Why? Compare alternative ways.
5. Should a manufacturing company centralize its research? Discuss fully.
6. How much should you expect to learn from marketing research? What does it do for you?
7. How much should a company spend on research? Justify your answer.
8. If you can't approve all research projects, should you approve practical projects (those likely to pay off) or blue-sky projects? Support your position.
9. "Patents are negative." Explain.
10. If an employee comes up with a patentable idea about his job, can he patent it himself? Discuss.
11. How does a patent protect you? Discuss fully.

Chapter 16

DEVELOPMENT

DEVELOPMENT puts new scientific discoveries into practice. Some discoveries have to be incorporated into your *products*. Others will improve your manufacturing *processes*. Most development work falls to the engineers and not the researchers, but they often work together. Development and applied research overlap a great deal.

Development—as it relates to products and not processes—changes the product's design. But the transition is more than just designing a changed product. You have to try out the new ideas, see how they will work, and see how they can be put into products. Development—as it relates to processes and not products—has to do with machines, tooling, plant layout, and the design of many of the tools needed to make products. It often means that the engineering department has to run a laboratory and do some testing and research of its own.

Development also includes the many improvements in product and process that come out of the day-to-day back-and-forth exchange of information between engineering, sales, and production. The sales department tells engineering how the products are performing in the hands of customers and suggests where improvements can be made. It also finds out what competing products are selling well and what it is about them that customers like. That helps engineering design a better product. Engineering also helps the sales department by making cost estimates and by telling sales what the products can and cannot do, and helping sales in making up catalogues of the company's products.

Engineering helps the factory by supplying it with the end products of development and design—specifications and product drawings. It helps too by telling the factory how to make products and working with the factory if it has trouble making products that will meet the specifications. The engineering department should also run a technical library and watch for new developments that the company can use.

308

PROCESS DEVELOPMENT

New processes come out all the time. There are so many of them that it is a job just to find out about them. Yet you have to try to keep up because now and then a new process is revolutionary. And, besides, many of those not so spectacular will do some of your jobs better and cheaper. You need to use them in your own business wherever they apply.

Engineering and research should keep you up to date. Engineering journals and industry magazines generally contain descriptions of new processes and materials. Most companies subscribe to commercial "patent" services which list all patents granted in fields likely to concern them. Important new ideas from the outside should be adopted even if royalties have to be paid.

Besides the ideas from the outside, your own research department also comes up with new processes from time to time. They are always try-

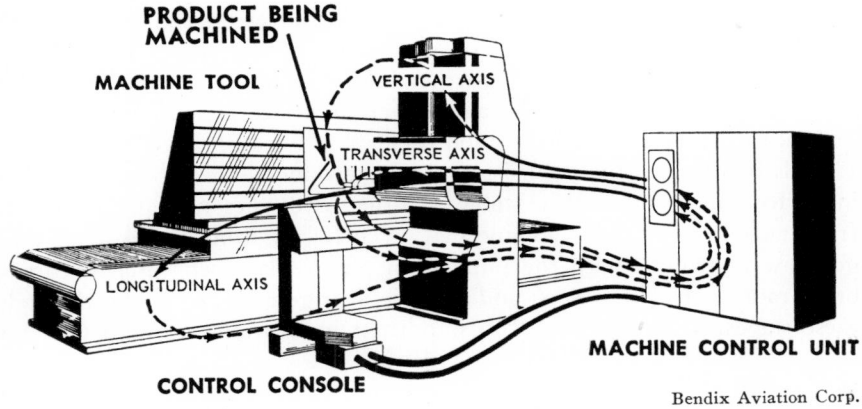

FIG. 16–1. Diagram of how Kearney & Treder's tape-controlled milling machine operates.

ing to improve processes where you have much trouble and all processes where you spend very much money.

There are so many new ways to do things that it is possible here to suggest only a few. Also good ideas catch on so fast that they soon are commonplace. In the first edition of this book, the then new shell molding process was described. Today millions of dollars worth of castings are made that way. Ford even has a whole factory in Cleveland making castings for automobiles by shell molding.

A milling machine operated automatically by a paper tape with holes in it was also described. At the time of the first edition, tape-controlled machine operation was experimental. Now Kearney & Trecker has such milling machines on the market. Bendix supplies all the electronic control apparatus, and K&T, the machine.

The whole area of automatic control over operations continues to grow. Not only do batteries of machines do whole sequences of operations but they check their own work. If products begin to be off-dimension, the machines reset themselves so that they make on-dimension products.

Today's trend toward "chipless production" may add even more to productivity in the future than automation. "Chipless production" means doing away with metal chips. Make the part the right size to start with. Don't make it oversize, and then have to cut it down. Use die casting shell molding, stamping and extrusion processes to shape metal. Cut out machining. You won't have much use even for an automatic milling machine if you don't have to shave off excess metal. Similarly, you gain by working cold metal into shape. You cut out the heating expense.

THE "INNOVATION" CYCLE

Most new products introduced to the public go through a cycle. First, the products are very new, don't always work very well, and are high priced. Only the venturesome consumer buys at this stage. Then comes a second stage. The product is further improved and is standardized, and it becomes dependable in use and lower in price. It sells in enormous quantities as it comes into common use.

This is followed by a third stage. The product is mature, dependable in performance, reasonably stable in price, and does not change much from year to year. Sales volume may even fall off some because all you get now is growth with the population plus replacement use. Automobiles, radios, television sets, and electric refrigerators all went through these stages. Industries based on important innovations seem to take up to 30 years to reach maturity.

Some products get out on the market too soon. It takes years (5 years or more) to perfect complicated things—to get out all the bugs in them. But venturesome customers don't want to wait. International Business Machines and Sperry-Rand had orders for electronic computers before they had any ready to deliver. Customers hear about your new things and want them right away—long before they are fully developed.

But is it too soon after all? Make a customer wait, and he goes to your competitor. Besides, the customer may be willing to put up with a half-engineered product rather than no product at all. The trouble is that in spite of all warnings he is likely to be dissatisfied if the product doesn't work well. And this is what you are trying to avoid. On the other hand, no product is ever fully engineered. You can't wait until the product is perfect before you start to sell it. Sewing machines have been used for over 100 years, but they keep changing for the better. The automobiles of 50 years ago or airplanes of 25 years ago were, by today's standards, not very fully engineered. You just can't wait for final permanent designs before you offer the product to the public.

What all this adds up to is that the sales department is continually pushing research and development to put all new findings into new products so it can start to sell them. The question is: when is the product well-enough developed to sell it? Somewhere along the line the design must be "frozen" long enough to get some products made. Yet new products can't remain wholly frozen very long. Engineers never get to do as much improving as they'd like before the product goes on the market.

"CRASH" PROGRAMS

The atomic bomb was developed in three years—normally it would have taken a lifetime. Research (and the design and development work that goes with it if you want to get a product out quickly) can often be speeded up, *if you are willing to spend the money*, but this is costly.

Crash programs mean putting hundreds of scientists and engineers on a project. Industry doesn't do this very often, but it does use a first cousin, the "task force." It is the same idea on a smaller scale. Chrysler had to do it in 1954 to put out a competitive car for 1955. Merck Company developed its penicillin process this way. In drugs and electronics, in particular, some break-through discovery (as the development of Salk vaccine for polio) forces all attention to solving related problems (such as how to manufacture it in bulk and to test it).

Crash programs save time in part just because more people are assigned to them. But there is a limit to how much speeding up you can do because some things come in sequence. You can't do step 2 until step 1 is done. Yet this is exactly where crash programs do save some more time. Teams are put to work trying to solve step 2 problems and even step 3 and step 4, as well as step 1, all at the same time.

How can this be done? You decide on what you want step 1 to accomplish, *then assume that it is done*, and start step 2 right away as if step 1 were done. Step 3 research is also started just as if step 2 problems were successfully solved. Suppose, for example, the problem is penicillin, which has been discovered to be very valuable but has to be made from plant mold—a slow and expensive process. Step 1 is to figure out how to synthesize it from chemicals. Step 2 is to figure out what processes and equipment are needed to make it synthetically. Step 3 is to install the equipment and make penicillin artificially. Of course step 3 would have to lag behind step 2 a little, but shortly after the program started, work on some parts of all 3 steps could be going on at the same time.

In the case of the atomic bomb the development of sources of uranium, methods to refine it to extreme purity, developing the bomb (theoretically), and developing a method of making it were all going on at the same time.

Crash programs are likely to be costly partly because some of the step 2, 3, and 4 work turns out to be wasted as earlier steps are actually worked out. And if step 1 doesn't work out at all, then all the rest of the work will probably be waste. But crash programs pay off if they solve a difficult problem years sooner. Chrysler stayed in business because it succeeded in its 1954 crash program for designing a better car.

PRODUCTS LIABILITY

People using products sometimes hurt themselves—or they buy medicine and get sicker instead of well. In either case some of them sue the company claiming that it is responsible. Or they abuse and misuse the product, then lie about how it got out of order, and blame the company.

Engineering and research must work together trying to develop the safest, most foolproof, products possible. They should be tested under all conditions of extreme use, misuse, and abuse. The company should know what its products can safely do and what they can't do. Advertising and package labels should carry proper instructions and warnings. Labels on packaged foods and pharmaceuticals should be carefully drawn up. Mechanical products especially should be designed for safe operation. Machine parts, such as flywheels and grinding wheels, should be strong enough to withstand the centrifugal force generated by their rotation at thousands of revolutions per minute.

In spite of all a company can do to make its products safe for users, claims will be made against the company on the basis of both alleged and real injuries and illnesses. The company's problem is twofold: products liability and public relations. Manufacturers of consumer products, in particular, are subjected to numerous claims, most of which are false or exaggerated. Many so-called "nuisance" claims, as long as they are for small amounts, are paid regardless of their merit, just to preserve good public relations.

Nearly all manufacturing companies carry products liability insurance. Probably their main motive is to preserve public good will rather than to save money, because they have to pay the cost of the claims anyway in the insurance premiums. The burden of fighting claims in court (and the ill will it generates) is transferred to the insurance company. Large claims and small claims disallowed by the company are turned over to the insurance company for settlement. Manufacturers usually assume the products liability hazard for the distributors of their goods. Indeed, in case of a lawsuit, they would probably be named as codefendants along with the distributor.

PILOT RUNS

Products made in large quantities are nearly always made by continuous-line production methods. Individual parts made in large quantities are also often produced by line methods. The engineering department determines the equipment needed, plans the layout, and supervises the installation of the equipment. To insure good line production, however, the engineering department also needs to supervise a "pilot run" on the line. Wherever things don't work right, engineering makes minor changes in the product design, tooling, or the workers' method of working. After one or two pilot runs production may be started. There will probably still be some trouble as the line is "run in," but after that things should go smoother.

Pilot runs find the "bugs" which always turn up and keep a production line from turning out as much or as good products as you want. Tools don't fit just right, or they don't work just right. A pilot run also may show that your engineers are asking for too much—closer tolerances or higher quality or more quantity than the machines can turn out. Maybe the standards can be relaxed, or maybe some more special tools or machines are needed. Of course there ought to be no serious problems by the time pilot runs start. If there are, some serious mistakes in planning must have occurred.

Pilot runs also provide cost information that may be needed in price setting. For whatever purpose pilot runs are made, the engineering department should analyze the troubles and recommend and put into effect the changes needed.

STANDARDIZATION AND SIMPLIFICATION

When you buy a new electric light bulb, you know it will screw into the socket all right. Why? Because light bulb bases are standardized. There are only a few kinds of bases made, and you'd have to ask specially to get even a Christmas tree bulb base.

Also you probably never even think about the light bulb's voltage. Again, because in the United States we use 110 volts everywhere in houses. That is standard too. Or suppose you need a new storage battery in your car. No problem there either. There are a few different sizes made but not many. Or you buy a new hose to sprinkle your grass. You never think of wondering if it will screw onto the water faucet. Of course it will. The size and screw threads are standard.

We have used the word "standard." By that we mean that there are only certain specific sizes made and sold. Some people prefer to call the process of cutting down on the number of sizes, "simplification." "Standardization," these people say, is something else. It is the process of writing down the size, shape, performance, and other characteristics of the items you decide to concentrate on. The two are so closely related that we will use them here as being nearly the same.

Standardization (including simplification) usually means that nonstandard items will not be made—except when the customer orders them specially and, unless it is a big order, pays extra for his nonstandard items. Sometimes safety or health standards have been enacted into law. Automobile windshields, for example, must be made of safety glass. Mostly, though, standardization is voluntary; manufacturers being free to standardize or not, as they see fit. Manufacturers of consumer style goods, such as women's clothes, find it difficult to standardize completely because of the consumer demand for "something different." But most industries, even those producing consumer goods, can and do standardize extensively, as for example in the setting of shoe sizes.

Industry-wide standardization requires industry-wide co-operation. It is generally sponsored by industry-wide associations, professional as-

Brown & Sharpe Mfg. Co.

FIG. 16–2. A few of the many kinds of cutting tools needed by industry. These can never be fully standardized, but unless you try to standardize as much as you can, you'll end up having a different tool for every operation on every machine.

sociations, or departments of the United States government. In the automobile industry the Society of Automotive Engineers has been instrumental in establishing many standards for materials and parts. Other societies have done similar work for other industries.

In addition to industry associations, there are two groups organized for the express purpose of setting standards, the American Standards Association and the American Society for Testing Materials. Another organization, the American Engineering Standards Committee, made up of representatives of many other organizations, helps co-ordinate the standardization activities of the organizations represented. Most professional engineering organizations, such as the American Society of Mechanical Engineers and the American Society of Chemical Engineers, take an active part in setting standards. Many governmental agencies also are active in standardization, especially the National Bureau of Standards. Altogether, these organizations have set thousands of standards.

The sales department can contribute to standardization (of the simplification kind) within a company by analyzing the sales volume of products and recommending the elimination of slowly moving items. It can also work with the engineering department in helping to develop products that are not standardized in appearance because they have different trims or finishes, but which can be made from basically the same parts, which can be standardized.

Standardization, within a single factory, nearly always concerns several departments. The engineering department should always discuss proposed changes with the departments concerned, particularly with the sales department, because in the event of a change, repair parts must continue to be made for products already in customers' hands.

Probably the best way to begin is to appoint a committee made up of representatives from the engineering, sales, purchasing, and production departments. In rare cases a standardization department (don't confuse this with the "standards department," a name sometimes given to the department setting production standards for incentive purposes) is set up. Some large companies make up manuals of standards covering the many areas in which standards are set. The manuals may cover types, sizes, and grades of products to manufacture, specifications of quality, specifications for processes and operations, testing instructions, standard machinery ratings, safety standards, and definitions of terms, abbreviations, and symbols for use on drawings.[1]

The agencies working on industry-wide standardization write and publish many specifications. Most companies use such specifications where they are available unless nonstandard materials are clearly better for the job. It is possible for standard materials to be too good for a particular use, in which case special, but lower quality, materials may save money. Ordinarily, though, standard materials are not costly because they are made in quantity. Also, because of the wide use of the standards throughout industry, purchasing can be done better because both parties understand exactly what is wanted.

Specifications of outside agencies are used for the most part in buying and selling between companies. *Within* every manufacturing company the engineering department must set up many standards, by far the greater part being the dimensions and characteristics of company-made products and parts and standards for individual plant operations. The engineering department sets standards for purchased materials where generally accepted standards do not exist, prescribes standard methods of

---

[1] The contents of a large number of standards manuals are summarized in *Industrial Standardization*, Studies in Business Policy, No. 22 (New York: National Industrial Conference Board).

testing products, and sets test scores which materials must pass. In equipment manufacturing companies the engineering department must also establish capacity ratings, the life expectancy of the equipment, and also the safe load limits for mechanical and electrical equipment.

Many standards concerned with the safety and health of workers and customers are incorporated into state and municipal laws and insurance company codes. The standards which boilers, elevators, and other dangerous equipment must meet are covered by laws. The building codes of municipalities often set standards for electrical wiring, plumbing, etc., as well as sanitation standards to protect employee and customer health.

ADVANTAGES OF STANDARDIZATION

Standardization reduces the kinds, types, and sizes of raw materials that have to be bought. That lets you buy bigger quantities of the sizes you do buy and so get lower prices per unit. Standardization also cuts your own manufacturing costs because you get longer runs on the fewer

From *Profiting From Industrial Standardization*, by Benjamin Melnitsky.
Chilton Book Co.

FIG. 16–3.

kinds of products that you still make. You can cut setup costs and use more specialized machines.

Suppose that your company made 2,000 items of plumbing fittings. If you had 100 of each one in stock, you'd have to carry a stock of 200,000 pieces. And if their average cost was as little as 25 cents each, you'd have $50,000 tied up in inventory. You'd need 2,000 bins and 2,000 stock records. Besides that, you'd have to keep similar stocks and records in warehouses and in the hands of dealers all over the nation. But if, through standardization, you could cut to 500, you'd surely cut over half of the costs of carrying your former inventory. Also, you would always be reordering larger quantities of fewer things and so holding down manufacturing costs.

DISADVANTAGES OF STANDARDIZATION

Some manufacturers, especially those making assembled products, do not accept industry-wide standardization because they find that using "the perfect part" is better than using a "standard" part not so well suited to their particular use. In fact the perfect part, originally nonstandard, may become the standard from usage.

Manufacturers using large volumes of nuts, bolts, wire, valves, bearings, electric motors, switches, and other parts also find frequently that the "perfect part" for a particular purpose is cheaper in *use*, even if it costs a little more to make than a standard part. Sometimes nonstandard parts are used in such quantities that they can be mass-produced and cost no more than standard items.

There are other reasons why industry-wide standardization programs often are only partially successful. Standardization tends to favor large, well-known companies. Small, or new, companies can rarely get much business by making the same things and selling them at the same prices as the big companies. They can't afford to go along with industry-wide standardization programs. They survive by offering something different at the same, or close to the same, price as standard products. These companies might be said to specialize in specialties, and by doing so, to some extent, they undercut a standardization program.

Furthermore, customers undercut standardization programs. Often they don't want the standard item unless it is priced lower. The sales department sides with the customer in this. One of its strongest selling points usually is that "our product is different." Take away that and sales has to talk lower prices and better service (better service because it is easier to keep all of the limited list of items in stock). But if you pass on to the customer all of the gain from standardization, has it helped you so much?

From the social point of view, there are two potential dangers in standardization. If new products are standardized too soon, before they have become reasonably stable in design, standardization may become an obstacle to progress. The development of color television in the United States was probably slowed down by the Federal Communications Commission's trying to force standardization on the industry when it was still in the developmental stage. In a product's developmental stage or in the early stages of an industry's growth, performance standards rather than form standards should be used.

Also, standards once set, resist change, thus retarding progress. Typewriter keyboards were, for example, frozen too soon, and that has stood in the way of improvement. They have poor arrangements of letters. We know how to arrange them better but can't make the change because millions of typists know how to use the present keyboards, to say nothing of our already having millions of typewriters with the bad key arrangements.

Improvements calling for different products, nonstandard in current and past products, must always be made if progress is to continue. A standard as of any given time is more the prevailing style than it is a permanent standard. Standards should not be permitted to freeze, being kept for their own sake; they are of value only as they improve the company's product and service and lower its cost.

PREFERRED NUMBERS

Many products can be made in a continuous series of sizes, from very small to extremely large, but to make them in such a series would be impractical. Electric light bulbs, motors, clothing, shoes, packaged food, tin cans, and many other items can be made in very small or very large sizes and in any number of in-between sizes. Manufacturers of such products must decide upon certain particular sizes. Only in this way can enough volume be concentrated in particular sizes to permit economical manufacture and sale. Today the makers of the products listed above, and many others, make most of their products only in standard sizes.

At some time in the past the leaders in these industries settled upon certain sizes to produce, thus reducing the number. Perhaps custom established a demand for certain sizes, and in time those sizes became standard. Interestingly, when custom does set sizes, they tend to follow a preferred number series.

Where a manufacturer can set his own sizes, he is likely to use a series of "preferred numbers" to help him decide what sizes to make. "Preferred numbers" are geometric progressions in sizes from small to large, each number in the series being *proportionally*, rather than absolutely, larger than the preceding number.

Generally a geometric progression of size differences (1, 2, 4, 8, 16, etc.) is more satisfactory to customers, and meets their needs better, than an arithmetic progression (5, 10, 15, 20, etc.). Geometric progressions provide several different small sizes in a series, yet hold down the total number of sizes more than would any arithmetic progression that provides several small sizes. When using preferred numbers, a manufacturer must decide the smallest size and the largest size to be made and the number of sizes in-between. These decisions having been made, he can compute mathematically the sizes he will have to make so that the proportional difference between them is the same.[2] Some series are even simpler. They use the square root of 2 (1.41) as a multiplier to get an approximation of the next larger size. Then you round the number off to get the exact size. You wouldn't, for example, make a 42-watt light bulb. You'd round it to 40 or 45.

But suppose that an electric light bulb manufacturer wanted to make 10-watt bulbs and 1,000-watt bulbs and only three sizes in-between. Using the preferred number formula, he would find that the sizes between the two extremes should be 30, 100, and 300 watts. Each size would be approximately three times as large as the next lower size. If he wanted to make eight sizes between 10 and 1,000, they would be 15, 25, 45, 75, 130, 225, 375, and 600 watts, each size being roughly two-thirds larger than the next lower size.

STUDY QUESTIONS

1. Research and development are usually mentioned together. Just what is the difference between them? Discuss.
2. What is the "innovation cycle"? In what way can knowing about it help management?
3. At what point in a new product's development should it first be put on the market? Discuss.
4. When, if ever, would you use a "crash program"? How does a crash program work? Discuss.
5. What do you expect a pilot run to accomplish? What would probably happen if you tried to cut out pilot runs?
6. If you were a manufacturer, would you standardize your product or not? Give reasons for your answer.
7. What arguments are there for and against standardization?
8. What are preferred numbers? How do you figure them? What good are they? Explain.

---

[2] The formula for computing this series is

$$n-1 \sqrt{\frac{\text{Largest size}}{\text{Smallest size}}}.$$

In the formula, n is the total number of sizes to be made. The answer obtained is the ratio between sizes, thus, 1.33 would mean that each size is 33 per cent larger than the next smaller size.

Chapter 17

DESIGN

Pʀᴏᴅᴜᴄᴛ design deals with form and function. Form design is the product's appearance. Functional design makes it work. The need for functional design is obvious—the product has to work or it won't sell. But why pay much attention to form design? It adds nothing to a product's performance. Chrysler found out in 1954 that form design was pretty important. Its Plymouth cars may have been superior in performance to Fords and Chevrolets, but people didn't like their looks and didn't buy them.

Looks, even packaging, is very important in selling anything to consumers. Often customers can't really tell if one product is better than another so they buy the one with the eye appeal. Possibly they think that the product with the best form design, which they can see, also has the best functional design, which they cannot see or judge. Often, too, competing products have different advantages and so are hard to compare. One vacuum cleaner, for example, may be the best for cleaning carpets, but another is best for draperies. Or one car may climb a mountain better than another that gives low gasoline mileage on the level. Which product does a consumer choose when he expects to use it under varied conditions? Probably eye appeal will win out. In fact, products which are altogether inferior in performances but with eye appeal often win out over superior products. Anyone who wants to stay in business must pay attention to form design.

Today, even machinery makers pay some attention to form design, although functional design is still the real essential. Companies buying machines want their factories to look streamlined and clean. Sometimes no one equipment maker's machines are way out in front of others, performance-wise, so the final choice is based on form, rather than functional, design. Machinery manufacturers, therefore, try to make their products look smoother and cleaner, covering up the moving parts of machines, except for the controls, which must be handled by the operator. Covers are put over all machine parts likely to splash oil or spread chips or dust around the machine. The machine covers, which should be easily removed for setup and repair purposes, have smooth surfaces and rounded corners to improve the machine's looks.

DIVERSITY OF DESIGN

People in the sales department want diversity because they want to satisfy every customer by selling him the exact product he wants. The factory, on the other hand, can supply products at the lowest unit costs only by making large quantities of a few kinds of products. The factory, therefore, wants a limited variety of products. In some companies the sales view rules; in others, manufacturing gets its way. A middle ground is better than either extreme, but if one view has to rule, it probably ought to be sales. You just can't push customers around, and you can often charge them more if they demand special products.

To a limited extent, both the sales department and the factory can be satisfied in companies able to give their products a varied appearance by using different trims or by combining standard parts in different ways. This gives the factory long runs for most of its production operations, yet gives the sales department the variety it wants by changing only the attachments, accessories, and decorations.

DESIGN BY IMITATION

Some companies, instead of trying to make different and better products, try to imitate the successful products of leaders in the industry. They make products as nearly like those of successful competitors as possible without getting sued for patent infringement. Style and design are practically impossible to patent, at least to the extent of preventing similar, but not identical, products from being made. Carbon-copy companies generally make a lower quality product than the original and sell it at a lower price. Companies doing the research and originating new products have the jump on the copying companies, but their advantage is often short-lived.

To some extent all companies imitate; whenever one manufacturer comes up with a product that catches on, whether from appearance or performance, the rest must try to follow or to do still better, otherwise the company with the product in current vogue will get nearly all of the business. On patentable inventions, the discovering company often lets others use the innovation on a royalty basis. This is good business. The first company gets some income from its invention; whereas it would make nothing on the invention if the competitors succeeded in imitating it or in developing a substitute. Eventually the copying companies are

From *Fortune*

FIG. 17–1. Design by imitation. Japanese imitation of Ronson cigarette lighters. Ronson lighters are on the left. Japan has now clamped down on such design piracy.

almost sure to come up with something similar, and what is worse from the originator's point of view, they might even come up with something better.

PRODUCT DESIGN RESPONSIBILITY

A single engineer should have over-all responsibility for a new product's design. Under him, other engineers should have charge of each major part—as for example the engine, body, and chassis of an automobile. The over-all engineer specifies over-all performance, size, contour, weight, and costs for each major component.

The component engineers have to work within the limitations set for them. Maybe they can't—then what? Then they go back to the over-all engineer with their story. If he has asked the impossible then, of course, he must compromise and respecify. This may affect other components too, so they too need respecifying. There has to be a lot of give-and-take until a final complete design is accomplished.

DESIGN SCHEDULES

Deadline dates are important to design engineers in industries bringing out annual models and in companies making "engineering-type" products, such as conveyors, mining equipment, or freight-car unloaders, to customers' orders. Deadline dates are set for designing each major part of the product. Certain parts of the product must be designed first; others, second. So an "order of design" has to be set up. Finally, of course, the factory has to have all the drawings or it cannot get on with production and meet its product delivery dates. If quick designing is necessary, several engineers can be assigned to a project, although this can't always be done because it would delay other projects or because only one or a few men can determine the first stages of design.

DESIGN AND PRODUCTION COSTS

In designing products, never forget production costs. If your first designs show that the product will cost more to make than the market will bear, you have to redesign it so that it costs less. Maybe you will have

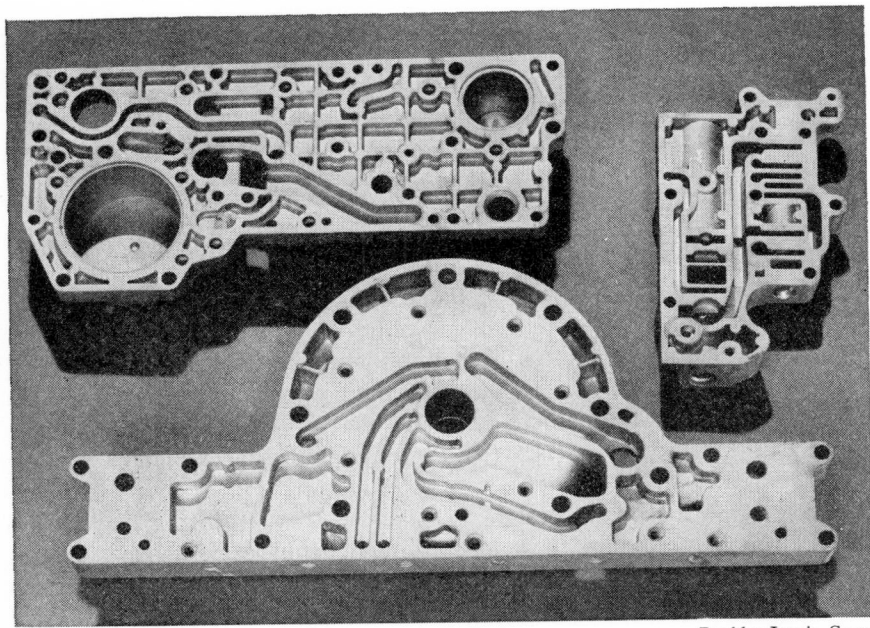

Doehler-Jarvis Corp.

FIG. 17–2. Die castings used in Buick's automatic transmission. Such castings are complicated, but they eliminate any number of machining operations you'd have to perform to make these parts any other way.

to cut quality in order to get costs down. This means a review of the sales possibilities of the low-priced but lower-quality product.

In Chapter 37 on purchasing we talk about something that purchasing agents call "value analysis." Design engineers too should be "value" conscious. Being value conscious means that you think first of what a part *does*. Then try to think of other ways of getting this work done. If two pieces have to be fastened together, don't think first of using a bolt and trying to design it so it can be made at low cost. How about riveting the pieces together? Or welding? Or making the parts interlock like pieces of a jig-saw puzzle? If you still end up thinking that a screw or a bolt will do the work best, *then* and only then, go ahead and figure out how to make it at low cost.

Most of the time the first design of a product is made by a design engineer who, of course, knows the company's machines and the operations they can do. He should also know about other ways to get operations done—ways that may mean buying other machines but which would cut production costs. It is so hard for him to see every possibility, though, when visualizing everything ahead that he usually misses a good many things. All new products have lots of manufacturing troubles at the start, many of which are because of impractical design.

A final design should be settled upon wherever possible only after a few products have been made (probably by hand processes) and tested. Doing this costs money and takes time, but it is usually worth it. The first design of a product is hardly more than the engineer's best guess as to how a product should be made. Making up a few and trying them out in use reveals weaknesses and shows you places where you will have trouble in manufacturing. You get a chance to make changes before quantity manufacture starts.

DESIGN FOR VOLUME PRODUCTION

Mass-produced items *must* be designed so that they can be made at low cost. Products with their subassemblies and their parts are first designed so that they will *perform*—but that is only preliminary design. Then they are gone over to see if changing them a little here and a little there will allow them to be made cheaper—to see if they can be made by less costly processes (as, for example, using a metal stamping in place of a casting) or out of less costly materials.

Parts should be finally designed so that, as they are being made, they can be quickly put into the parts-making machines and fastened down tightly for grinding, drilling, planing, or other operations needed to make them into finished parts. Sequences of operations should be studied to see if any can be gotten rid of or combined and performed together. And, as for the operations themselves, quality and speed should be built into the tools, even at considerable cost.

For assembled products it is particularly important to use subassemblies wherever possible. Lower unit costs almost always result for products manufactured in large volume if the final assembly can be little more than combining major subassemblies. The same holds true of major subassemblies themselves; make them up, as much as possible, from minor subassemblies. When you study a product's design, think of all the work done on assembly lines (and subassembly lines) as one large unit of work rather than as a collection of individual jobs. Looking at the over-all picture helps you decide where it is best to cut the large work unit into jobs that you give men to do.

Another must is that parts must be alike. Parts at the assembly line *must* fit. Assembly workers can't take time to hunt for parts that fit or to file or hammer stamped parts into place. Set your parts' tolerance close enough to make sure that the parts fit when they get to the assembly line.

In volume manufacture, product design must be decided in complete detail *before* production starts, and it must, practically speaking, stay frozen. Details cannot, as they often can in job-lot work, be determined after production starts. Actually changes can be made, but once production begins they are costly. It is, therefore, important that the design be definite and workable and that it undergo little change, so that the high investment in special equipment can be recovered.

MINIATURIZATION

An army expression says: "If your product is room-size make it desk-size; if it's desk-size, make it portable. When you can't shrink it anymore, pack twice as much power into it." For industry in general we can say: "Make it smaller and lighter in weight."

General Electric Co.

FIG. 17–3. A GE television set in the late 1940's and ten years later. The new model weighs less than half, costs less and gives a better picture.

Yet it isn't always so. Not everyone has to miniaturize. Miniature automobiles don't sell very well. A desk has to stay desk-size and a book book-size. Typewriter and adding machine keys can't be made any smaller or no one could use them. But even where you can't miniaturize the whole product, it usually pays to miniaturize the parts.

Miniaturization is very important in electronics. Here you try to cut the size of both parts and products. Early models of electronic computers, for example, had so many vacuum tubes that they needed to operate in air-conditioned rooms to get rid of the heat generated. Besides, they were big affairs. Now, most of the tubes are only pencil thick and only an inch or so long. Besides that, a great many tubes have been replaced by germanium transistors (or diodes). Mostly they are no big-

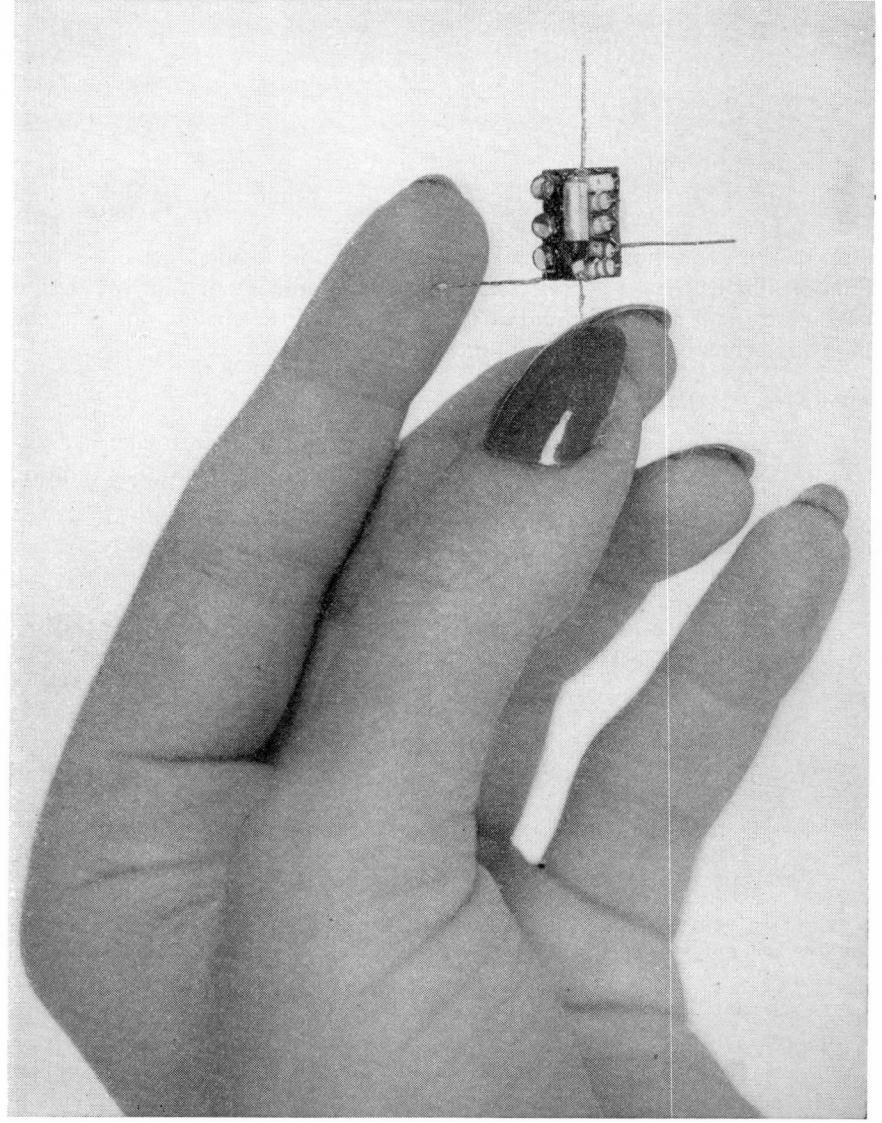

Philco Corp.

FIG. 17–4.   A tiny amplifier. Tiny though it is, it magnifies signals 10 million times. Its parts are so small that Philco calls them subminiature.

ger than a shoelace tip. Condensers and resistors, too, are of only finger-nail size. Even motors and gyroscopes come in bottle-stopper size.

Miniaturization is partly design and partly research. You couldn't make a fingernail-size hearing aid, for example, until germanium came out of research. Then miniature products using germanium had to be developed, and finally they had to be incorporated into hearing aids.

Miniaturization always results in using less material (but it may be more expensive material), so it is often worth while on that account alone. Often processing miniatures is, at first, expensive; then later it is less costly. Saving space and weight is, however, usually the main idea, particularly in airplanes and guided missiles. If costs are lower that is an extra. Repair costs, are, however, usually higher because there is no room for fingers, pliers, or wrenches. You need magnifying glasses, tweezers, and miniature tools.

REPAIRABILITY

Easy repair is important in product design. Sometimes, particularly in consumer products, easy repair has to give way to appearance. That is too bad, but it isn't serious if the product can be designed to be trouble-free. Present-day automobiles, for example, are less conveniently repaired than those of 30 years ago, and that makes repairs more costly. On the other hand, repairs are needed less often now, and few car owners make their own car repairs. The ordinary car owner doesn't know (or care) that the appearance he likes so much has made repairs difficult.

WARRANTIES

If your product doesn't perform well in use, you are in trouble. Maybe you have a legal responsibility to fix up whatever goes wrong and to do it free. But whether you are legally liable or not doesn't matter because you can't afford dissatisfied customers. You must turn out a good product so that operating troubles are few. And if the troubles are the kind that the customer blames the company for, you'd better fix his product up and at low cost to him.

Yet it is nearly impossible to turn out products that are always perfect. That is why you get a 90-day guarantee on a new car. Did you ever add up the costs of the free repairs? Comes to $35 an automobile. All of this is waste to the manufacturer. Most of it comes from poor assembly.

But it may be poor design. A few years ago Buick replaced free thousands of faulty rear axles that one model had. And a few years ago Ford on one model had quite a bit of trouble with back wheels not following the front wheels exactly. Where was the fault? Design? Manufacture? Turned out to be some fault both places. Fixing it up cost the company big money.

But whether from poor design or poor assembly, the company has to stand behind its product. Designers should never forget that their final judges are customers, not colleagues.

REDESIGN

As soon as a product is in production (if it is not a one-time item), plans for its improvement should be started. Actually, the biggest part of all product design work is "redesign." Minor manufacturing difficulties always cause some redesigning right away. After that, and as the product is used, performance weaknesses show up and call for improvements in design. And even if there have been no serious weaknesses, new models will have to be brought out before too long. Usually much of their new design is really just redesign of the old model.

Once a product is being made and sold successfully, too frequent redesign should be avoided. Changes should be made only for important reasons, because they require new drawings, new operations lists, and new tools or machines. Besides, changes make obsolete all the stocks of parts at the factory and in the hands of dealers. And they make customer's catalogues of spare parts obsolete too. It costs more to make little changes than they are worth. But if there are numerous small changes, they can be held up until several can be made at once.

DESIGN OF PARTS

The design engineer must decide the exact size and shape of each part of a product. He should see that the parts are strong enough, and if they are wearing parts, durable and hard enough to withstand use. He must decide the type of bearings and must design the lubrication system. He must decide how heavy a load the machine should take, how fast it should run, and the kind and size of motor and motor connections it should have. Wherever possible he should use standard parts unless volume is enough to keep down the cost of nonstandard parts.

WIRES AND TUBING

Wires.   Electricity makes our life easier. Day by day, consumer products and factory machines become more and more automatic. Behind it all is the use of more and more electricity. And *inside* the products are more and more wires.

Wires are not parts in quite the same way as other parts. Mostly their preparation for use is simple. Just cut off a length of wire, scrape the insulation off at the ends, and attach each end where it belongs. But of course it isn't that simple—not nearly that simple.

Even automobiles have half a dozen or so circuits—one for headlights, one to start the motor, one to keep the battery charged, one for left and right turn lights, one to roll up the windows, and so on. Each circuit needs its own wiring system. Every wire needs to be the right size and to have the right kind of insulation and terminal connection for its job. It has to thread its way over, around, and under other parts (but out of their way) between its terminals.

As long as wires are few they don't make too much trouble, but radios and TVs are as much wires as they are tubes and chassis. Most of the work of making them is the wiring, getting wires soldered to the right contact points. Quite a bit of the labor payroll goes to women handling soldering irons.

The problem becomes fantastic in electronics, electronic computers, and airplanes. Probably none of today's fighter or bomber airplanes has as few as 10,000 pieces of wire in it. Missiles too require complex wiring.

Designers have to plan all the wiring systems and must also figure out every wire's pathway. Other parts may need to be grooved and have holes drilled through them to allow the wires to pass. Clips to hold the wires in place must be planned. Often whole groups of wires follow the same path for some distance. They can be bundled together, but to reach their connections, some wires must be longer than others and each must have the right kind of terminal connection. Some wires will join the bundle part way along, and others will separate out sooner than the rest. Wire bundles (called "harnesses") are planned and are put together just as if they were subassemblies and then put into the product.

Wire Identification.   Wire identification is a serious problem when there are so many wires. First, in making the harness, many different kinds of wire are used, but there are more pieces of wire than there are kinds. A harness may contain several pieces of the same kind of wire. Yet each has to be connected up right. You don't want to get your horn connected up to the left turn light signal.

Airplane companies use both color codes and wire numbers, but their problems are so complex that neither is a perfect answer. With color codes the outside insulation is red, blue, green, or striped red and orange, blue and white, or checked, and so on. Colors give you many but not hundreds of combinations before they get so nearly the same as to confuse. With numbers, each piece of wire has a part number. The wire (insulated in white) is run through a little printing machine which prints the number on the outside insulation every few inches. Most airplane wires are numbered.

Printed Circuits.   Printed circuits also help when they can be used. The bottom of today's TV set is a printed circuit, not a maze of wires. Here's how it works. Draw up a diagram of the way wires ought to go on a panel—but *do not have any lines cross.* Then make a metal plate showing the circuit—a metal plate for use in a printing press (just like the metal plate from which this page is printed). Then buy a sheet of copper-coated plastic material (coated paper-thin on one side only) of cardboard thickness.

Now print, in ink, the circuit on the copper. Next, put the copper-coated plastic in an acid bath. The acid eats away all the copper except where the ink protects it (you recover the copper later from the acid so that it isn't wasted). Then wash off the ink. That leaves you the circuit neatly placed on the plastic just as if you had glued copper wires to it. Now drill holes through the plastic at the wire ends, and on the other side attach transistors, electronic tube sockets, condensers, or wires to the panel with their wire ends sticking through the holes and touching the copper lines underneath. Solder them to the copper lines just as if they were wires. In fact, you don't need to solder the joints separately, just dip the whole thing in molten solder and all the joints are soldered at once.

Printed circuits are more compact, less costly, and work better than regular wiring systems, and so are coming more and more into use.

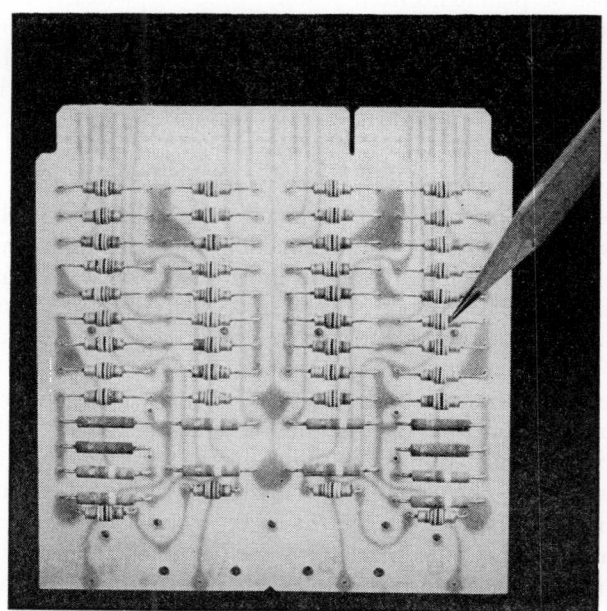

Ramo-Woolridge Corp.

FIG. 17–5.   Diodes mounted on a semitransparent plastic board with printed circuits that you can see on the back of the board.

Tubing.   Tubing is like wires except that there aren't so many pipes and tubes as there are wires. Yet even in an automobile there is a gasoline line from the tank to the fuel pump, another to the carburetor, hose connectors for the radiator, hydraulic brake lines to all the wheels, and, sometimes, rubber tubes to the windshield wipers.

Tubing is rarely bundled together, but it, like wires, must thread its devious way in, around, and over other parts. And, too, it is often best to fit tubing into the product as it is assembled rather than make and shape tubing before attaching it. Like wire its pathways must be planned. Failure to figure ahead the best pathways for both tubing and wires causes innumerable minor design changes when complicated products first go into production.

FIG. 17–6. Bending tubes to form in the tube shop.

SHOP INSTRUCTIONS

In some companies the engineering department designs the product and the shop decides how to make it. This is not only small-company practice but also the way some giant companies do it. It is the way Western Electric does it, and it is the way all the airplane companies do it. Design engineers do not tell the factory how to make a product. The manufacturing department's production engineers figure out how to make it. They can even redesign parts in minor ways to suit manufacturing needs. They can also change the way parts are put into subassemblies: does an automobile door go on the car and then the door on the body? The production engineers also can decide whether to make or buy some items.

But no matter who decides how to do the work, engineering makes up drawings and master bills of materials (parts lists). Master bills show subassembly arrangements, part names, identification numbers, how many of each part is needed to make one assembled product, and whether the item normally is made or bought.

A master bill of materials for an entire product lists subassemblies as if they were individual parts. Each subassembly, in turn, has its own master bill of materials. If the subassembly is composed, in part, of lesser subassemblies, each of them has its own master bill.

The production control department uses the master bills in making up production orders, as explained in Chapter 40. Items on the bill may be listed in order of part number, in order of assembly, or in order of the arrangement of the finished goods stockroom. Ordinarily, the master bills sent out by the engineering department are arranged in order of

General Motors Corp.

FIG. 17–7. A speedometer exploded into subassemblies and parts. One hundred fifteen parts, in all, are required to make a speedometer.

assembly. The production control department can rearrange them to suit its purpose.

In many companies, the engineering department not only designs products but also tells the factory how to make them. It even issues master route sheets for individual parts. Master route sheets (also known as process layouts or operation lists) list the operations necessary to make a part, the sequence of operations, the kind of machine required for each operation, the special tools called for, if any, and the amount of time each operation takes on one unit of product. They may even show the operation's piece rate and the worker's labor classification. They also show the kind of raw material needed and usually how much of it is required to make one part.

In some companies everything having to do with getting production started is turned over to a "product engineer." He will have the final say on how things are made. He may even have to decide the machines, order their purchase, decide the layout, supervise machine installation, and stay with the job until production is going smoothly. The product engineer will of course have had to decide all of the tools needed and order them. He also has the last word on materials to use, but production control probably places the orders for materials.

Manufacturing instructions are incomplete without test instructions. Engineering must write up instructions about how tests are to be carried out and how to tell good and bad parts apart. Often, special testing equipment has to be bought (or developed) for particular tests. Inspectors need to be trained in their use. Also procedures need to be set up to channel test results back to engineering so that it can keep informed about the quality of work done by manufacturing.

Engineering also has to provide sales with information about the product, how to use it, and how to service it so that sales can make up manuals and parts catalogues for customers. Engineering also furnishes information and sometimes pictures for advertising.

DRAWINGS AND SPECIFICATIONS

The last step in product design is to make drawings and specifications. Drawings show the exact size and shape of the product, its parts, and subassemblies. Features other than physical dimensions are described in writing in the form of specifications. During the process of designing, the product sketches and rough drawings were probably made, but before production can proceed, complete and exact drawings must be drafted.

Side, end, and top views are usually shown on the drawings. Perspective drawings are expensive to make and are rarely used. Only a little training is necessary to read regular drawings. One item only is put on a drawing unless it is convenient to show all the parts for minor subassemblies in one place. Most drawings show what finished parts or subassemblies look like when they are completed. Sometimes, however, drawings must be made showing what the item is like at one or more stages in its manufacture. Occasionally, drawings are needed to show how machines should be set up.

Before the drawings are released to the factory, they must be approved by the chief engineer, the plant superintendent, or possibly other officials high in the line organization, and given an effective date. Ef-

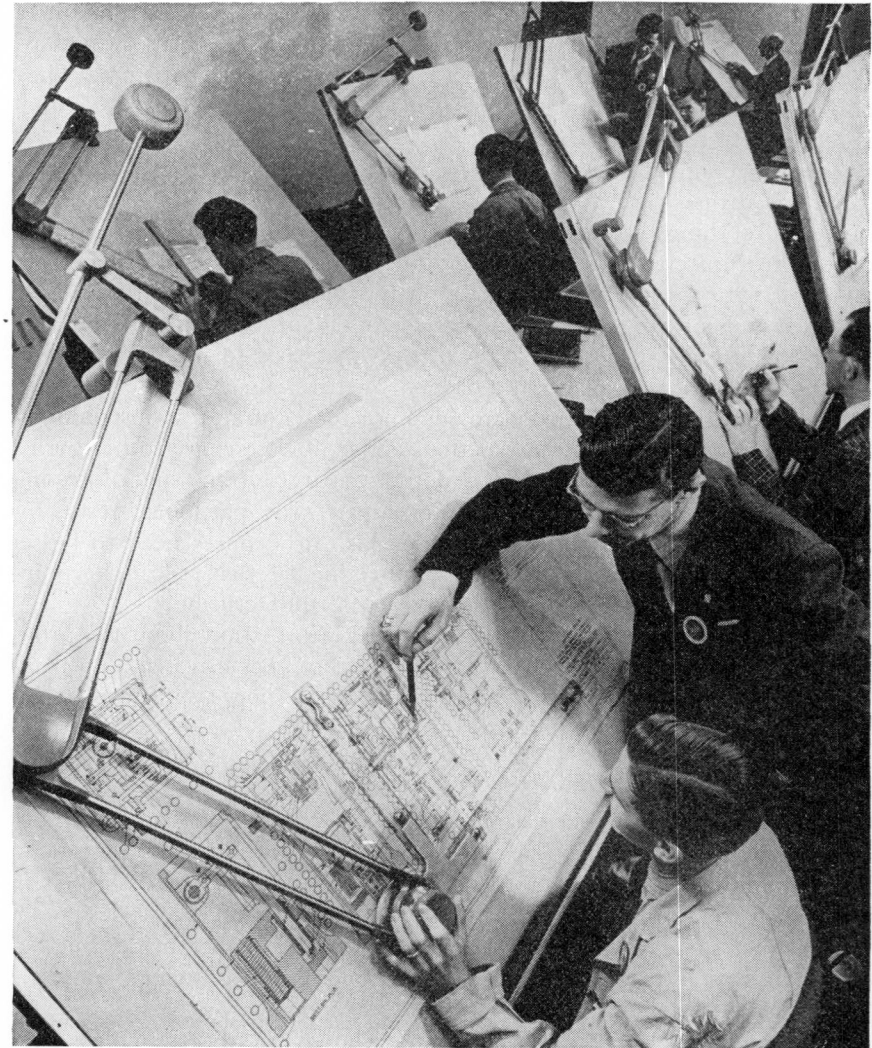

Woodward Governor Co.

FIG. 17–8. Making up a drawing for a complex product made from many metal parts.

fective dates are particularly important when old drawings are being re-placed or minor changes are being made on old drawings.

When similar items are frequently drawn, drafting time can be saved by using printed forms. The nut and bolt industry, for example, uses the same drawing for a long or short bolt, or for a thick or thin bolt, or for various threads per inch. You *read* the bolt's dimensions from *the dimensions shown*—you don't get them by measuring them off. The num-ber of threads per inch also is read from the instructions.

Standardized short cuts of other kinds are used. For example, screw threads are almost never actually shown on drawings. They are indicated by symbols. Standardized symbols are always used on electrical circuits, air conditioning, welding, and pattern drawings. Drawing time is cut still more by using printed adhesive transparencies of standard parts or standard electrical items such as switches or fuses.

TOLERANCES

Engineers have a tendency to set tolerances (permissible deviations from perfect measurements) closer than most foremen think necessary. Probably most foremen would complain about any but the loosest tolerances. Actually, however, there is no good way to tell how much deviation to allow. To be on the safe side and to be sure the product will work well, engineers tend to specify nearly perfect sizes. But tolerances set too close increase the manufacturing cost out of all proportion to their importance. Engineers setting such tolerances often err in demanding if not the impossible at least the impractical. Tolerances should be set as loosely as possible considering the work that a part has to do.

One company had this experience with tolerances (and its experience probably is typical). It asked its foremen to point out the specifications calling for tolerances with which they had the greatest trouble. Then the company took these up with the engineering department to see if they could be relaxed without hurting the product. Surprisingly, it was found that in most instances no one remembered who wrote the specifications and *no one cared whether the tolerances were relaxed or not.* What was just as serious, the company discovered that the few persons in the engineering department who did know and care about the specifications had no notion what those specifications cost in the way of extra work and rejections.

PACKAGING

Packaging is big business. It costs General Motors over $50,000,000 a year—yet GM does not have to package automobiles. Eastman-Kodak packages over 35,000 different items. Eli Lilley pharmaceutical company has over 5,000 package sizes for its 3,400 packaged items. Food manufacturers spend 10 per cent of all the money that they take in for packages. Industry as a whole spends over $10 billion annually on packaging.

Many products have to be packed individually after they are manufactured, and nearly everything has to go into some kind of containers for shipment. Some products go first into individual cartons, and then a dozen or more cartons are put into a carrying or shipping container. Packaging such items as soap flakes, crackers, and many canned foods costs nearly as much as the product inside.

Cutting Packaging Cost. Since packaging is costly, you should review all aspects of it from time to time to see if any part of it can be done more economically. On the other hand, however, never forget the effect of packaging on sales. If more expensive packaging will boost sales, by all means adopt it. In the food industry, packaging *costs* take a back seat to display value and customer attention.

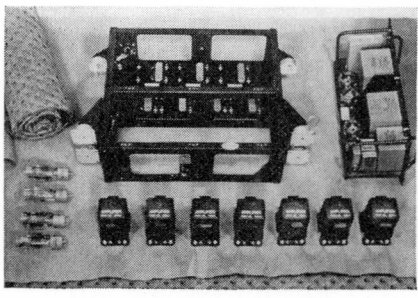

Assembly of parts of Amplifier Unit and all materials used in packaging.

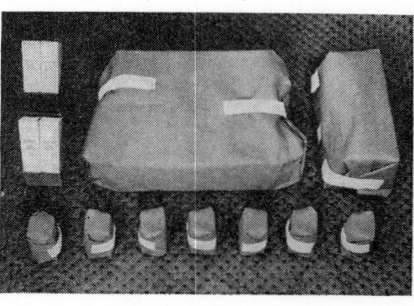

Each part (except 4 boxed tubes) is wrapped in paper and tape sealed.

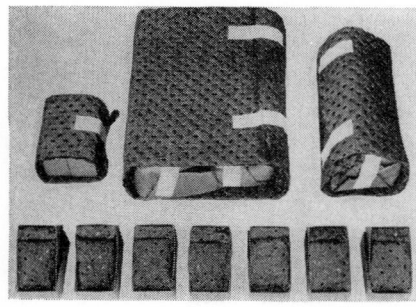

Each part including the 4 boxed tubes is overwrapped.

Kimberly-Clark Corp.

Completed assembly is inserted in wooden box for shipping.

FIG. 17–9. Packing small parts separately and then combining them into larger packages gives added protection against damage in transit.

Granted that sales appeal outweighs cost in many situations, it is still the factory's job to keep packaging costs down where it can. Here are some factors that bear on packaging cost that the factory needs to watch:

1. The cost of the individual cartons and the cost of the storing and shipping containers holding a quantity of the individual products.
2. The amount of labor required to get products into and out of cartons.
3. The amount of labor required to get individual cartons into and out of multiple product containers.
4. The amount of labor required to load and unload packaged material onto industrial trucks in the factory.
5. The amount of labor required to put packaged materials into and out of storage.
6. The amount of labor required to load and unload products in freight cars.
7. The freight rates for products variously packaged.
8. The losses from damage to products at all stages, particularly during shipment.

The possibilities of savings exist in so many places that your attempts to improve packaging should be continuous. You should consider packaging improvements in the light of their effects on *all* the cost factors, not just an individual factor. Sometimes it pays to spend *more* rather than less on packaging, particularly on consumer products, if it boosts sales or cuts handling costs. Preformed cartons and containers, for example, which come flat but can be shaped by the operators in a matter of seconds, are often economical in use. The labor saved far more than pays for the extra cost of such cartons. A change of package design that reduces manufacturing costs may also reduce sales, but it might work in the opposite direction and increase sales. A change may also reduce shipping losses but increase packing costs, or it could reduce both shipping losses and packing costs.

Intermediate packaging, sometimes needed between certain factory operations, is a phase of packaging often overlooked; yet it is a fruitful source of possible savings. In many cases subassemblies are made up and packed for storage until they are used in the completed products. Such packing is both costly and unproductive, except as it is necessary to identify and protect the intermediate product. Speedometers for automobiles are, for example, made up ahead, and they generally have to be kept in special trays or be packed separately for storage or for long-distance moves within or even between factories.

Packaging Ideals.   Like innovations in other kinds of research, those in packaging should be tested before they are adopted. In no other way can faults and weaknesses be detected and eliminated.

The shape and size of containers holding dozen and gross lots should permit quick, perhaps mechanical, handling into and out of storage and freight cars. Containers have to be sturdy enough to protect the product in storage and transit. For ease of handling, filled containers should weigh no more than 50 pounds. They should hold from 1 to 4 cubic feet of contents, depending on the weight. To facilitate interlocking when stacked, they should be rectangular instead of square. Filled containers must be strong enough to withstand the weight resulting from high stacking (up to 15 feet), rough handling in loading and unloading, and the bumps that occur in transportation.

Many companies have mechanized their package-filling work. Cigarettes, soft drinks and liquors, cosmetics, and many other industries use conveyors and automatic machines to fill packages. The package must be designed to permit the work to be done mechanically. Many kinds of equipment for mechanically filling packages are used: for example, automatic weighing scales; bottle, can, and sack fillers; also automatic capping machines and automatic bag sewing machines. Taping, gluing, and stapling can be done automatically if the volume warrants the cost of the mechanical equipment. Electronic equipment has even been devised to detect improperly packed materials.

Packaging Limitations. Companies are not altogether free to pack goods the way they want to. Restrictions are placed on the way in which many kinds of materials may be packed. Railroads have regulations, and the federal government has laid down rules governing the way in which such items as explosives and flammable liquids must be packed to be shipped in interstate commerce. Health and sanitation regulations govern packing methods in many food and pharmaceutical industries.

Products going into the export trade are frequently covered by the laws of the importing nation specifying the way the products are to be packed. Even without packing requirements on the part of foreign countries, export products require special packing. They may be subjected to 140° heat or banged about in the hold of a storm-tossed ship. They may be left on deck exposed to heavy rains, salt water, or freezing temperature. Export packages must withstand being handled with slings and hooks, being bumped and jarred as loading nets go through hatches, and repeatedly being rolled around and stacked. They may be unloaded onto bouncing lighters (small ships operating in shallow water) off the coast of cities without harbors. They may be conveyed by river boats, wagons, camels, or carried by men. Soft goods for foreign trade should be packed in lightweight protective material and compressed into bales secured by steel strapping. Because individual small boxes are handled more roughly than large loads, cased products should be made into large unit loads and securely strapped to cheap throwaway wooden or cardboard pallets.

Government contracts for items bought by the Armed Forces of the United States for overseas shipment specify how they must be packed and the package marked for identification. The instructions differ, depending on where they are to go, but the packing must be in strict accord with the specifications. Some must be packed to protect against heat with moisture, some against heat without moisture, some against extreme cold, etc. Since the Armed Forces do not always know where the material will finally be used, their packaging requirements must try to protect supplies against several damage hazards. Some of the government regulations require that the engineering department develop methods for plastic-coating materials or other packaging processes.

PACKAGE DESIGN FOR CONSUMER ACCEPTANCE

Manufacturers of products sold to other manufacturers do not have to pay much attention to making their packages look good. They can put all their emphasis on low costs and protection of the product. But the sales volume of many consumer products depends on the attractiveness of the package. This fact has been particularly true of goods sold in self-service markets, where the customer chooses freely from among numerous items on the shelf. It has been found that products sold in such markets should be packed in attractive but sturdy containers, which, to save shelf space, can be stood on end.

For consumers, packages first of all should be convenient to handle and should identify the product. A consumer wants—when it is feasible —a package that is easy to pick up and comfortable to carry. Besides, he wants it to be easy to open and close, to get out the product, and maybe to measure it.

In the case of some consumer products the "after-utility" or intrinsic value of the container boosts sales. Jams, jellies, olives, etc., are sometimes put in glass containers, which, when empty, can be used as drinking glasses. Sometimes products sold in foreign markets will scarcely sell unless they are packed in tin cans which can be used again as containers or, when flattened out, as sheet steel. Feed and fertilizer bought by farmers are quite generally bagged in gaily printed cloth sacks which, when laundered, can be used for dresses, aprons, curtains, and dish towels.

From an economic point of view, some types of consumer product packaging are wasteful. The satin-lined plastic boxes with hinged lids in which watches come certainly seem unnecessary. Surely one or more of the four wrappings (paper, lead foil, paper, and cellophane) on cigarette packages and on chewing gum are of so little value to the product as to be almost complete waste.

PACKAGING MATERIALS

The most common packaging materials are paper, paper board, wood, glass, and cloth. Translucent paper, cellophane, plastic materials, aluminum and lead foil, and tin-plated thin sheet steel are also used. Most of these materials are both plentiful and cheap. Such enormous quantities of them are used, however, that the reduction of waste is always a fruitful objective in this area of packaging. Over 15 billion glass containers, for example, are made annually in the United States. Companies should always try to use less, to waste less, and to make the cheapest possible material do the job.

Packages of bottled products and those which are fragile or easily injured are often provided with internal packing or "cushions" to prevent damage. Historically, "excelsior" (shredded wood) and corrugated paper have filled the need; shredded newspaper, however, is cheaper and is often used. Where their expense can be justified and where other materials are unsatisfactory, cellulose wadding and foam rubber are sometimes used.

Multiple product containers for shipping usually need to be sealed. If they are of cardboard, they can be sealed by using one of many types of adhesives, of which glue is but one. Packing boxes of wood are often held together with wire and steel strapping, as well as nails, and by adhesive tapes. Tapes, wire, and strapping are often used for binding several packages together.

STUDY QUESTIONS

1. What purpose does form design serve? What purpose does functional design serve? Which is more important? Why?
2. To what extent can you reconcile diversity of design with the factory's desire for highly standardized products?
3. If you were a manufacturer, would you ever use "design by imitation"? When? When not? Why?
4. How are design and production costs related? How should they be related? Explain.
5. How does design for high-volume production differ from any other kind? Explain.
6. Discuss miniaturization. When is it good? When not good?
7. How are warranties and design related? What does a design engineer have to do with warranties? Explain.
8. When should redesign start, and how often should it take place? Discuss.
9. Wires and tubes have, as the years go by, made design more difficult. How? Discuss fully.
10. What is a master bill of materials? What does it show? What is it used for?
11. Why is tolerance setting important? Explain fully.
12. If you set out to cut the cost of packaging, what factors would you have to deal with?

Case 17–1.   The McAuliffe Company

The McAuliffe Company is currently producing large, airtight explosion-proof electric power panels and their cases. Its engineers, however, have recently developed a watertight shockproof container for small delicate instruments. The United States Navy has shown a decided interest in this new product, which they believe will work well aboard ships and submarines. However, a competing firm has developed a similar product. It is only slightly inferior in shockproofing qualities to that of McAuliffe's. The competitor's product has been offered to the Navy at $4.70 per unit. The waterproof casing on the competing unit is made of steel. McAuliffe's engineers want to make the outside waterproof casing of brass, thus giving better rust resistance than the competitor's.

The Navy is interested in McAuliffe's product, but its representative stated that he could pay no more than $5.50 per unit and might not be able to pay that much.

McAuliffe's engineers calculated the costs of making the container in their company both from steel and from brass to be as shown in the accompanying table:

	Steel	Brass
Material cost per pound......................	$0.20	$0.40
Gross weight per container...................	5 lb.	6 lb.
Amount of material scrap per container.........	2.5 lb.	3 lb.
Value of scrap per pound.....................	$0.01	$0.08
Tooling cost.................................	$200	$100
Direct labor cost per machine-hour.............	$2.50	$2.50
Overhead cost per machine-hour...............	$1.25	$1.25
Output per machine-hour.....................	25 units	27 units

Can McAuliffe compete, making the container out of steel? If so, at what volume will its costs be below $4.70? At what volume can it manufacture the product from brass for less than $5.50 each? At what volume can it make the product from brass at a cost of $5.20? Should it take an order if it must bid as low as $5.00 to get the contract?

Chapter 18

PERSONNEL

Handling people gets so much attention that it is easy to forget that managers have to deal with other things—machines, materials, reports, records, products, taxes, and so on. Actually, most manufacturing companies spend much less than half of their income for payroll. Yet the emphasis on people is probably justified since so much depends on how well they do their work. All the nonhuman things in a business must be run by humans.

Today's management thinks of employees as individuals—as separate and unique individuals. Thinking of them this way means allowing as much as possible for individual differences.

The old idea was that there were certain jobs to be filled and that management had done its job if it filled the jobs with qualified men who were paid reasonable wages. What more could you expect? The company, of course, assumed no interest in any employee as an individual, nor did officials care about an employee's attitude toward his work or why he felt the way he did.

Today the pendulum has swung the other way. Human relations is the fashion today—it is almost a fad or a cult. A few people are beginning to say that you can overdo it—that so much emphasis on human relations weakens a department head's responsibility. He gets to thinking more about people and their relations than he does about getting work done.

HANDLING EMPLOYEES INDIVIDUALLY

If employees are to be treated as individuals, they must be treated differently, each according to his own individuality. It sounds fine in the abstract, but like many good things, you shouldn't push it too far. Just try to handle two similar cases in different ways without people feeling that you are playing favorites! Employees get to thinking that their boss is unfair all too easily without seeing clear-cut cases of one treatment for one man but another treatment for someone else. Parents with two or more children know how hard it is to avoid charges of unfairness.

The question is, which is more important, men's dissimilarities or their similarities? Certainly men differ, but they are also very much alike. Most of us want rules enforced on everyone, with *very* few exceptions, and then only for *very good* reasons. Another question is, how can you treat 10,000 people differently? The sheer weight of numbers forces you into policies, rules, and consistent practices.

Not only that, but unions and labor contracts run counter to treating men individually. Almost every time a new labor contract is drawn, management gives up another right to treat people differently. Merit rating is opposed as subjective. Unions prefer seniority. Piecework is opposed. Unions want no pay differences based on different production quantities. Men cannot be disciplined differently. Disciplining actions are covered by shop rules and labor contracts. If there are differences, the harshly disciplined man files a grievance charging discrimination. Layoffs, too, go first to the newest men on the payroll—not to the poorest workers. You can't have different practices in different plants when you have company-wide bargaining covering all plants.

Treating people as individuals certainly means that you should treat them differently if it means anything. Yet, in practice, you can do it only to a limited extent.

PERSONNEL DEPARTMENT WORK

Personnel work goes on everywhere in the organization. It is much more than just the work of the personnel department.[1] Personnel relations are personal relations—relations between supervisors and supervised, and relationships between workers. Personnel work permeates the whole organization. It affects all the people whose work must be directed and co-ordinated. Personal contacts occur continually through the whole organization. Every officer is truly a personnel officer.

What, then, is the personnel department responsible for?

1. It sees that the whole organization follows good personnel practices. Personnel is a staff department though and has no line authority over other departments. But it does have functional authority, and if it learns of any poor personnel practices, it can try to improve things. Of course help must be tactfully given or it will cause resentment except when it has been specifically asked for.

Private talks with department heads needing help makes the advice

---

[1] The terms "personnel" department and "industrial relations" department are here used as alternatives. In some companies personnel is the over-all term with industrial relations being the section that handles grievances. In other companies industrial relations is the over-all, with personnel doing the hiring.

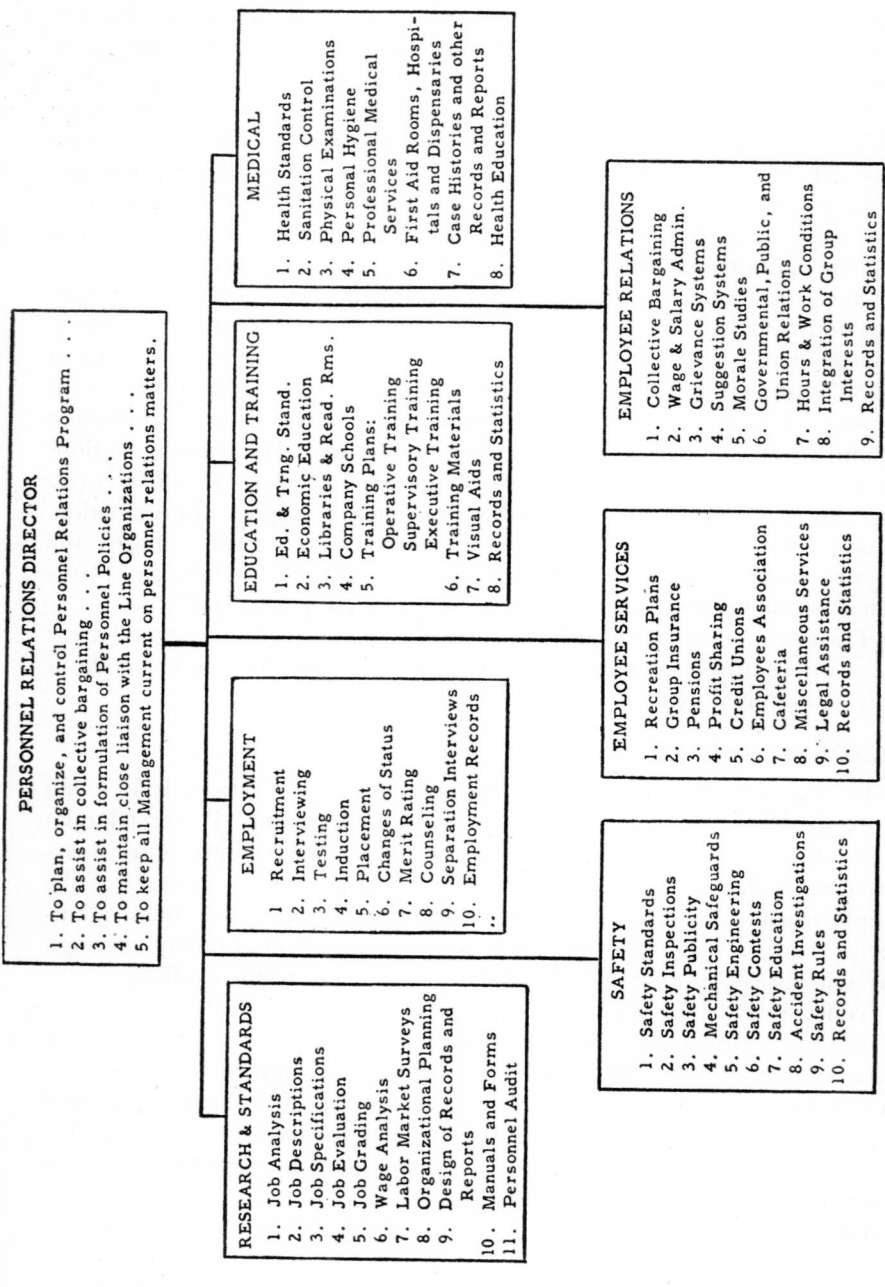

PERSONNEL RELATIONS DIRECTOR

1. To plan, organize, and control Personnel Relations Program . . .
2. To assist in collective bargaining . . .
3. To assist in formulation of Personnel Policies . . .
4. To maintain close liaison with the Line Organizations . . .
5. To keep all Management current on personnel relations matters.

RESEARCH & STANDARDS

1. Job Analysis
2. Job Descriptions
3. Job Specifications
4. Job Evaluation
5. Job Grading
6. Wage Analysis
7. Labor Market Surveys
8. Organizational Planning
9. Design of Records and Reports
10. Manuals and Forms
11. Personnel Audit

EMPLOYMENT

1. Recruitment
2. Interviewing
3. Testing
4. Induction
5. Placement
6. Changes of Status
7. Merit Rating
8. Counseling
9. Separation Interviews
10. Employment Records

EDUCATION AND TRAINING

1. Ed. & Trng. Stand.
2. Economic Education
3. Libraries & Read. Rms.
4. Company Schools
5. Training Plans:
   Operative Training
   Supervisory Training
   Executive Training
6. Training Materials
7. Visual Aids
8. Records and Statistics

MEDICAL

1. Health Standards
2. Sanitation Control
3. Physical Examinations
4. Personal Hygiene
5. Professional Medical Services
6. First Aid Rooms, Hospitals and Dispensaries
7. Case Histories and other Records and Reports
8. Health Education

SAFETY

1. Safety Standards
2. Safety Inspections
3. Safety Publicity
4. Mechanical Safeguards
5. Safety Engineering
6. Safety Contests
7. Safety Education
8. Accident Investigations
9. Safety Rules
10. Records and Statistics

EMPLOYEE SERVICES

1. Recreation Plans
2. Group Insurance
3. Pensions
4. Profit Sharing
5. Credit Unions
6. Employees Association
7. Cafeteria
8. Miscellaneous Services
9. Legal Assistance
10. Records and Statistics

EMPLOYEE RELATIONS

1. Collective Bargaining
2. Wage & Salary Admin.
3. Grievance Systems
4. Suggestion Systems
5. Morale Studies
6. Governmental, Public, and Union Relations
7. Hours & Work Conditions
8. Integration of Group Interests
9. Records and Statistics

E. G. Williams, Indiana University and Indiana State Chamber of Commerce

FIG. 18–1. Personnel department activities.

more acceptable. Or if several departments have common problems, group meetings give opportunities to put ideas across. Personnel must never forget that its job is to *help* supervisors handle *their* problems, not to "steal the show" or take over their jobs.

2. Personnel advises management and keeps it posted on what other companies are doing. It keeps up on wage rate changes in the industry and the area, on the cost of living, on supplementary unemployment benefit plans, on the state of guaranteed annual wage demands, on pay raises given by other companies, and so on. Personnel should figure out what information management needs, it should know where to get it, and it should get it and present it to management, showing management how the company will be affected.

3. Personnel keeps track of the company's health personnelwise. It studies turnover records, absentee records and grievances, and makes recommendations to management to improve bad spots.

4. Personnel staffs the organization. Working from schedules of future work, it figures out how many men will be needed on all jobs and lays plans to get more men wherever they are needed. It also helps plan for the company's future executive staff by offering training programs. Personnel does the company's recruiting and interviews and selects new employees.

5. Personnel handles grievance work—keeping all records of grievances, meetings, settlements, and it arranges all grievance meetings.

6. Personnel interprets the union contract to supervisors and helps them live up to it.

7. Personnel, in many companies, conducts the labor contract negotiations.

8. Personnel keeps all personnel records—records of personal data, jobs held, pay raises, and so on.

9. Personnel handles all records of hospitalization and insurance and other fringe wages.

10. Personnel often administers safety and the company hospital or dispensary.

11. Personnel publishes the company newspaper or magazine.

12. Personnel oversees the operation of the cafeteria.

13. Personnel administers merit rating and sometimes job evaluation and sometimes wage administration.

In connection with assignment number 3—keeping track of the company's health personnelwise—General Electric has developed an "Employee Relations Index" that lets management see how each department stacks up with every other department. Crucible Steel uses the same idea but does not put its figures together into one single index. Instead it uses a regular report, made up in standard form for every division and major department. The standard form allows different departments to be compared.

THE PLACE OF THE INDUSTRIAL RELATIONS DEPARTMENT IN THE ORGANIZATION

"Industrial relations" is the preferred title (as against "personnel") for this department in companies where it has wide scope and where its head reports to the president. Today the industrial relations head usually does report to the president, and he is often a vice-president.

This is a change from former practice. Industrial relations heads didn't used to be vice-presidents. Why the change? Labor contract negotiation is one very important reason. Industrial relations usually does the negotiating and must be able to speak for the company and to make decisions (after consulting the legal department and the company's top officers) which bind the company. This must be done by someone high in the organization because labor rates of pay involve a lot of money. Also the contracts often cover men in different chains of command (Chevrolet, Buick, Fisher Body, Frigidaire). No one division can negotiate for other divisions; it can be done only by a staff department reporting to the same man who heads up all of the different divisions.

In multiplant companies the industrial relations department reports to the president for still more reasons than negotiating. Besides negotiating, it has the responsibility for seeing that the company follows good personnel practices. This responsibility, too, requires it to report to the man who heads up all the chains of command that it serves.

But how is a home office staff department in New York any good to a misguided foreman in St. Louis who needs help? Here's how it works. The St. Louis foreman gets help from his own plant's industrial relations department. It operates in St. Louis, and there only. That department is responsible to the St. Louis works manager, a line officer. The St. Louis works manager is responsible to, say, the head of the Household Appliance Division, also a line officer. The division head has a sort of superior industrial relations staff. This super industrial relations staff helps the St. Louis plant's industrial relation department that helps the foreman. It is like the house that Jack built, though we haven't all the steps in yet. The division's industrial relations staff in its turn gets functional direction from the home office industrial relations staff in New York. The St. Louis foreman doesn't get any help directly from the New York staff, but he gets it three steps removed.

In single-plant companies, industrial relations does not always have such an exalted position. Its head is not a vice-president. In fact, there may be two or three different personnel heads, one in sales, one in manufacturing, and one for office personnel. Each one does his own hiring, and record keeping, and heads up whatever training programs there are (usually there are none). What with more and more records to keep, reports to make, and payroll taxes, deductions, etc., even small plants are coming to centralize industrial relations in one department.

How much does all of this cost? Fewer than 1 per cent of all employees are in personnel work. In fact, three quarters of 1 per cent is a reasonable figure, and big companies sometimes get it down to two thirds of 1 per cent. The salaries of personnel workers plus the costs of what they do (run a hospital, give tests, publish a magazine, and all the rest) come to from $70 to $80 per employee, per year. That is equal to about 4 cents per hour worked.

PERSONNEL WORK IN SMALL COMPANIES

Personnel functions in small companies are performed very informally. Most companies with 100 employees, for example, have no full-time employee doing personnel work. Only three or four men are hired every month. Hiring is generally done by the head of the department where the man will work. Physical examinations are rarely given; psychological tests never. Employee records are meager, complete enough only to meet the requirements of the wage-hour and the social security laws, and to provide the employee seniority dates as required in the union contract if there is a union. The chances are about 50–50 that companies with under 100 employees will have no union.

New men are trained on the job by the foreman or a fellow worker. Formal training is almost never given. Small companies rarely maintain a hospital or dispensary for first aid. About the only provision for injuries are bandages, adhesive tape, and iodine or mercurochrome.

Yet the main, basic personnel functions, such as interviewing, hiring, and training, have to be done occasionally by someone in small, as well as large, companies, so the appearance of no one's doing them is misleading. Someone, even in small companies, has to make out applications for workmen's compensation, hospitalization, and insurance. Someone has to prepare vacation schedules and to write and post bulletin board memos. Someone has to keep separation and furlough records. Then there are other things that may or may not be done—running a suggestion system, checking up on absentees, making sick calls, attending funerals or weddings. All of these can of course be neglected with no current harm being done.

BUILDING MORALE

In Chapter 4 we said that high morale is good and that management should try to create it. Personnel usually gets the job of seeing that you have high morale. Morale depends on the policies actually in force and *not on the policies to which lip service is given*. Personnel helps management by suggesting policies, and it helps see that the policies adopted are carried out. Unless disciplinary policies and policies respecting rewards for good performance and promotions are fair and are consistently carried out, morale can go down quickly.

Morale is not wholly within the company's control. Aggressive unions always try to convince the workers that their working conditions are bad, that their wages are less than elsewhere, that the company has provided no job security, etc. The union tries to build up this attitude so that the men will feel that they have to have a union to protect them. Unfortunately, from the company point of view, unions seem fairly successful in educating the workers to the union point of view. When they are successful, the morale of the group is lower than it would be without the outside influence. The personnel department should of course try to eliminate the genuine sources of dissatisfaction and try to build good morale in a positive way.

Many companies make occasional morale surveys to find out what workers think about the company and its practices. Morale surveys sometimes reveal unsuspected gripes, particularly where morale differs greatly from department to department. Answers to the survey questions, when tabulated by departments, pin point the weak spots, thus permitting the company to fix things up.

Some people are quite fearful about the effect of monotony on morale. They say that repetitive jobs lower the men's morale. Because some people dislike the monotony they find on repetitive jobs, some companies are trying "job enlargement." You "enlarge" a man's job by letting him keep on doing his regular repetitive work most of the time, but you also give him a few other things that need doing occasionally. That puts a little variety into the job and relieves the monotony. Large banks and insurance companies report that job enlargement increases output. Some factories, too, report it to be a good idea.

PERSONNEL POLICIES

Personnel policies are general rules and guides for dealing with employees. Examples of personnel policies are: promotions based on merit; equal pay for equal work (as between men and women); hiring a share of the handicapped persons in the community; and forbidding the solicitation of funds on company premises except for the community fund and Red Cross. Policies must also be set up for vacations, tardiness, absences, and matters covered by the shop rules.

In small companies and in some large companies personnel policies are not consciously arrived at and formulated. But, the larger the company, the more necessary it becomes that the policies be formulated and exact. In companies where no one has ever given any thought to policy formulation, every department head has to figure out for himself what he will do in any given situation, or he must ask his boss. If each department head decides his own policy, you'll get all kinds of policies. And if you ask the boss, he will be making, over and over again, decisions which could be covered by specific policies and carried out by subordinates.

In many companies the administration draws up idealistic lists of policies which are not carried out. It is not enough to make the list and forget it. Tell the members of the organization what the policies are. Besides, you must check from time to time to see that the policies decided upon are being followed. There is a strong tendency for them to get warped in their application. The farther down the line you get from the top of the organization, the greater the changes. Subordinates not knowing or understanding company policies carry out their own interpretations of policies or make their own policies.

The responsibility for adopting and carrying out good personnel policies rests with top line officials, but they often ask the personnel department to do it for them.

A multiplant company can rarely have consistent policies throughout its whole organization. The practices in each plant should conform, to some extent, to the practices in the areas where the plant is located, but that means diversity among the company's several plants. Union pressures, as well as area practice, affect policies. If one union represents the workers of several plants, it may press for the standardization of policies. Sometimes, where the employees of a single plant are represented by several unions rather than one, there must be diverse policies in one plant because the various unions make different demands. It is almost impossible to have, even if it were desirable, which is doubtful, consistent personnel policies on all matters throughout the organization of a multiplant company.

SHOP RULES AND THEIR ENFORCEMENT

"Shop rules" cover employee behavior in the shop. They restrict the things an employee can do. He must come to work on time and must not be absent very often. He must stay on the job and avoid "loafing" and too much visiting with fellow employees. He must do the work assigned and must do it reasonably well. He must not smoke where it is dangerous. He must not get drunk, gamble, or steal on company premises. These, and other regulations, make up the "shop rules." Be sure that your men understand the rules and the penalties for their violation. Put them up on bulletin boards, put them in the information manual you give to new men, and put them into "overalls" English.

No matter how reasonable the rules are, someone will violate them. You will have to impose penalties for violations. So you have to have a scale of penalties, to see that foremen know the penalties, and to impose them promptly in a consistent way when infractions occur. Penalties should match the seriousness of the infraction, but they should be progressive, too—progressively more severe for repetitive infractions of rules by an employee.

It would be nice if everyone obeyed all the rules. Then you would never have to take disiplinary action. Most companies try to develop what some people call "positive" discipline (as opposed to "negative" discipline). Positive discipline is self-imposed by an employee because he sees the need for a rule or because he wants the rewards that are given for heeding it. Compliance with the rule becomes voluntary. Some degree of positive discipline can be developed if the rules are reasonable, if their need is explained to workers, and if employees with

How Fairchild Tells Workers What's What on Company Rule Violations

RULES	PENALTIES				
	1st OFFENSE	2nd OFFENSE	3rd OFFENSE	4th OFFENSE	5th OFFENSE
► 1. Falsifying personnel records or company records.	Discharge				
► 2. Knowingly punching the time card of another employee, having one's time card punched by another employee, or unauthorized altering of a time card.	Discharge				
► 3. Permitting another to use your badge, using another person's badge, or altering badge.	3 days off	1 week off	Discharge		
► 4. Being tardy or absent habitually without reasonable cause. (Habitual —3 times in a 30-day period).	Warning	3 days off	1 week off	Discharge	
► 5. AWOL.	1 day off	3 days off	1 week off	Discharge	
► 6. Contributing to unsanitary conditions or poor housekeeping.	Warning	1 day off	3 days off	1 week off	Discharge
► 7. Unauthorized possession of firearms or explosives on premises.	Discharge				
► 8. Operating, using, or possessing machines, tools, or equipment to which the employee has not been assigned, or performing other than assigned work.	Warning	3 days off	Discharge		
► 9. Use or possession of another employee's tools without the employee's consent.	1 week off	Discharge			
►10. Causing material or parts to be scrapped due to carelessness.	3 days off	Discharge			
►11. Mistakes due to carelessness.	Warning	3 days off	1 week off	Discharge	
►12. Mistakes due to carelessness which affect the safety of the airplane and/or personnel.	1 week off or discharge	Discharge			
►13. Engaging in horseplay, running, scuffling, or throwing things.	Warning	3 days off	1 week off	Discharge	
►14. Wasting time, loitering, or leaving place of work during working hours without permission.	Warning	3 days off	1 week off	Discharge	
►15. Smoking, except in specified areas at specified times.	1 day off	3 days off	1 week off	Discharge	
►16. Threatening, intimidating, coercing, or interfering with fellow employees on the premises.	Warning	3 days off	Discharge		
►17. Vending, soliciting, or collecting contributions for any purpose whatsoever at any time on the premises, unless authorized by management.	3 days off	Discharge			
►18. Distributing written or printed matter of any description on company premises unless approved by Industrial Relations Department.	Discharge				

Fairchild Engine & Airplane Corp.

FIG. 18–2. Shop rules put into understandable form.

the best records are rewarded with praise or promotions or in other ways.

Helpful though positive methods are, negative disciplinary actions are, unfortunately, sometimes necessary. Violations of rules do occur, and something has to be done about them. Negative discipline is punitive. It punishes for noncompliance. The punishment may be verbal warnings, written reprimands, or laying the employee off (without pay) for one day or more. Serious infractions or repeated minor infractions are causes for demotion or discharge.

The Fairchild Engine & Airplane Corporation presents its list of rules and penalties for violations in the form of a chart (see Fig. 18–2).

The rules and penalties are publicized, so that all employees will know them thoroughly. Written notices of violations are given to guilty employees by the foremen, so there is no question about there having been a violation. The company reports that penalties are rare because everyone knows the rules, and grievances are few because the penalties are graded to the seriousness of the offense.

Negative discipline should generally be avoided. As a rule, its threat and its use tend to lower the morale of the penalized employee and of his fellow workers. Perhaps even worse as a morale destroyer, however, is the inconsistent use of negative discipline. Punishing violators in some instances and not in others is much worse than enforcing the rules in all cases. Negative discipline in industry must be carefully administered. If not, the morale is lowered, turnover is higher, and grievances multiply from employees who do not leave the company.

The personnel department has less to do with the formulation of rules today than formerly. There was a time when the company could make its rules and enforce them as it saw fit. Today, however, many of the rules are embodied in the union contract. Since they have to do with "working conditions," they fall within the sphere of collective bargaining.

ABSENTEEISM

Absenteeism is ordinarily not a serious problem. Normally it is a little over 2 per cent for men (5 or 6 days a year) and is around 3 per cent (about 8 days a year) for women. The rates are highest among single men, next among married women, then among single women. Married men have the lowest rate. Workers under age 20 have the highest absentee rate, and those over 30 have the lowest. It is higher among new workers than among established workers. Factory workers are absent a little more than office workers. Night-shift workers are absent more than day-shift workers. Mondays are worse than other days. So are the days after a holiday and the first day of the hunting season. Probably one third of your work force will miss as much as one day a month, but the more steady two thirds will hold your average absence rate down.

Long work weeks, particularly if continued for several months, increase absences because (1) the workers are making so much money that they can afford a day off, (2) they get tired of sticking so close to the job, and (3) the long hours take up all the odd-job work time at home. Finally comes the time when the odd jobs need doing. Married women, in particular, have to take time off occasionally to catch up on housework and errands.

Absenteeism because of sickness is responsible for most absences of short duration and for nearly all long absences. Most union contracts provide that an absentee not reporting the reason for his absence for three days is dropped from the payroll. Therefore, there are few cases of absenteeism for long periods except for sickness. Anyone having to be off work for a long time is given a leave of absence.

Absenteeism can be held down by investigations. Most companies check up on absentees. The department head or someone from the medical staff or personnel department calls the absentee by telephone after a day or two. Some companies follow this up with a home visit. Employees don't stay home from work for minor reasons when they know someone will check up on them. Of course, no company wants sick employees coming to work. Checking up doesn't cut sickness absenteeism much, but it does cut nonsickness absenteeism.

But really, what difference does it make whether an hourly paid man comes to work or not? If he stays home, you don't pay him. If you have to keep 103 men on the payroll to do 100 men's work, all that this amounts to is 103 men getting 100 men's pay. It isn't that simple, however. There are a number of little costs that add up to a lot. When a man unexpectedly fails to turn up, his machine is idle. You lose the production, and production schedules are upset. If you can put someone else on the absentee's job, he isn't so fast or good, so you lose some production and have more than the usual number of rejects. Also he may have to work some overtime. Or if the substitute is a member of a group, he holds them all up. Putting a substitute into the group isn't like having an experienced hand. All of this adds up. General Electric figures that for every dollar in wages that an absentee loses, the company loses two dollars. Probably most companies would come up with a lower loss figure than that, but whatever the right figure is, absences cause real loss to the company.

TURNOVER

Turnover is the going and coming of employees. Men leave and have to be replaced. You have to hire quite a few people just to keep an organization of the same size. For factories, 30 per cent a year is low, up to 50 per cent is common. Foundries often go up to 75 per cent! This doesn't mean that nearly everyone quits every year; it means that you have to fill some jobs (at the bottom) several times in a year. You have to hire 750 men in a year just to keep a work force of 1,000.

But, what is a turnover? You have a turnover when one man leaves and you hire another. What about men who are not replaced, or what about hiring additional men to increase the work force? Some companies call a separation a half turnover and a hire a half turnover. Normally this is all right, but it gives you a distorted picture if, say, you hire 100 extra men. In the turnover ratio it looks the same as if 50 men had left and 50 men were hired to replace them.

In order to give a clearer picture of what is really going on some companies do what the United States Bureau of Labor Statistics does. This Bureau (which collects and publishes monthly turnover figures for the whole country) computes a separation rate figure and an accession rate figure, but it does *not* combine them and does not publish combined *turnover* figures.

Turnover costs money. Whenever a man leaves, less work gets done, machines are unused, and products are not turned out. You have to have interviews, and personnel people spend time getting a new man. Then he has to be shown his job. At first he doesn't get much work out and he spoils products. Then, maybe, he quits, and you go through it all again. Probably most turnovers cost you at least $200.

You can never get rid of turnover but you can cut it down and save some of its costs. The personnel department gets the job of trying to hold it down—a difficult assignment since it is almost always someone else's employee who is quitting.

Personnel trys to cut turnover by finding out why men quit and getting rid of the reasons where it can. It studies the quits to see if some departments have more than others. It talks to foremen to find out why. It has termination interviews with men leaving to see what reasons they give. (The man gets his last pay check from personnel, and so has to come there after it.) Sometimes personnel is able to improve a situation and hold down future turnover.

PROMOTION, DEMOTION, TRANSFER, AND DISCHARGE

Personnel has no authority to promote, demote, transfer, or discharge a man (except in the personnel department itself). But personnel plays a part in all of these things.

First of all, it has all the records, the men's names, past and present jobs, past and present pay rates, and seniority dates, and it has to keep the records up to date if anything changes.

Promotions and pay raises are usually recommended by a man's boss to his (the boss's) superior. If the superior approves, personnel has nothing to do except to record the change. Usually he won't approve, though, without consulting personnel, not because personnel knows whether a man merits a raise but because personnel has to watch the over-all picture. Is this in accord with our labor contract? Is this department's wages getting out of line with those of other departments? Does this seem to be the best-qualified man for the job? By any chance does this seem to be favoritism? If it is a promotion, are there well-qualified men in other departments who ought to be considered?

Most companies follow a policy of filling vacancies from within, if possible. Promotion from within builds morale and is healthy, but only as long as it is not carried to extremes. If no outsiders are ever brought in except at the bottom, there is danger that the future company officials will lack breadth of background, in which case efficiency of operation may suffer. People who grow up in the company are likely to have fewer ideas for improvement and to resist change more than those who have been in other companies. A fixed policy of filling vacancies by promotion tends to become promotion by seniority alone, which is usually a poor basis for filling responsible jobs. Furthermore, such a practice admits newcomers only at the bottom, where it is possible to hire only poor prospects or unproved people.

Demotions are uncommon and rarely work out well, except when the work force is being reduced. Occasionally a man is promoted to a job, perhaps to the foreman level, only to find that he does not like the work. A demotion at his request may solve the problem. Much more com-

New Yorker

FIG. 18–3. "Harris, I've canceled your hospitalization and sick-benefit policy, closed out your old-age retirement account, cleared your case with the union, given proper legal notice to the Unemployment Insurance Bureau, and had a check drawn for your vacation credit, cost-of-living bonus, severance pay, and accumulated salary, including overtime. You're fired!"

monly, however, when a man fails on a job to which he has been promoted, he either does not realize he has failed or, if he does realize that he is not doing the job well, he still does not want to be demoted. You can offer him the choice of being demoted or discharged. This doesn't work so well, however, because he will probably take the demotion and remain a disgruntled employee for life. His morale and that of those around him suffer. Better get him a job in another company if this can be done. But if this can't be done, demote him into another department as far away from the old one as possible. Because of such complications many companies prefer to avoid demotions almost entirely by discharging a man rather than demoting him.

Transfers become important when business falls off. Most union contracts have provisions saying that employees with the least service must be laid off first. This may cause numerous shifts of employees between departments because some departments slacken off more than others. Unless the labor contract prohibits it (and most do), you can't lay off 2-year men in one department while keeping 1-year men in another department. These transfers have to be handled by the personnel department, which must be careful to carry out the terms of the contract exactly. No other department could arrange these transfers because it is necessary to use the employee seniority records, which the personnel department keeps, and since several departments may be involved in the shifting of men from department to department. The personnel department must work out the details and see that the men actually laid off are those with the least seniority.

The head of a department has the right to discharge an employee for cause. The shop rules and the union contract are fairly specific as to situations allowing the company to discharge a man. In most large companies, however, a foreman can discharge a man only from his own department, not from the company. If the personnel department is trying to fill vacancies in other departments and if another department head is willing to take him, the man may be given another chance. The personnel department is interested in discharges not only because they make vacancies which it must fill but also because it must not let discharges occur if they are not in accord with the labor contract.

REDUCED OPERATIONS—CUT MEN OR HOURS?

When operations must be curtailed because of lack of business, the hours of work can usually be reduced, or some workers can be laid off. Generally both procedures are followed at the same time. However, many companies find it difficult to operate regular hours with a reduced force because their operations require complete teams or work crews. So when cutting back is necessary, they reduce factory work hours instead of laying off workers. In some industries, the shoe industry for example, it is customary to cut the work schedules of everyone rather than lay off some of the workers.

Union contracts today often contain provisions covering the policy to be followed in case of substantially reduced operations. Generally they specify that hours of work will not be cut below 32 per week. Should further reductions be necessary, layoffs are to be made rather than cutting the workweek still more. For less severe reductions in work the company is free to lay off workers or reduce hours.

DISCRIMINATION

When you discriminate among people you pick some and turn down others. You ought to discriminate when you hire and when you promote men. Pick the best you can. That isn't what people are talking about, however, when they condemn discrimination and pass laws against it. They are talking about refusal to hire or promote men in certain groups without regard to their ability. Mostly they are talking about not hiring colored people; sometimes they are talking about not promoting women or colored people.

Many companies have discriminated against colored people and women in the past and some still do, but it is dying out. Social change is against such discrimination, and the change has been hurried along by laws forbidding it, by nondiscrimination clauses in government contracts, and by the long-continued labor shortage.

Discrimination cannot be justified on moral grounds, but the advocates of nondiscrimination usually look at only one side of the picture. Discrimination against women is required by law sometimes. It is illegal to hire women for most jobs in coal mining and certain other hazardous jobs.

Most states restrict the hours women can work. Some laws won't let you put women on stand-up jobs. Some states say that women can't work after 11 o'clock at night, or they can't work over 10 hours a day or over 6 days a week, or they can't lift more than 25 or 30 pounds. Men don't do these things often either, but once in a while they might have to. It is simpler to hire men to start with.

Women's absenteeism is at least a third more than men's, and their turnover is greater. The Bell Telephone Company has 60 per cent turnover among its women employees every year as against less than 10 per cent for men. Although this is extreme, women's turnover record does not recommend their employment. (The United States Bureau of Labor Statistics figures show that women's separation ratios in manufacturing industries are about 12 per cent over men's.)

In mixed groups of workers it is necessary to have two complete sets of locker rooms, washrooms, and toilets. It also takes better supervision for mixed groups than it does for either men or women alone. Women are more likely than men to take things personally and to think the boss is playing favorites. Consequently, better trained supervisors are needed.

Women don't have to worry about discrimination on jobs where manual dexterity is required or on monotonous jobs. They outproduce men on jobs where you need quick fingers, sharp eyes, eyes for color, or a memory for numbers. They also have more patience and are less annoyed than men by monotony. (Psychologists might object to this statement, but it is borne out in practice. Women stay on monotonous jobs and most men don't. Women often refuse transfer to any other job.) For many women (and some men) monotony is not a drawback but an advantage, particularly if the operation is quiet enough to allow talk. In industries where seasonal layoffs occur regularly, women workers are also often preferred. Stewart-Warner reports that many women workers (those earning their family's second income check) welcome seasonal layoffs as chances to catch up on work at home.

Industry is also accused of discriminating against old (or even middle-aged) workers—and certainly most companies do hire few men over 40 if they can get younger men. Of course, out-of-work middle-aged and old people include all of those who never could hold a job even when they were young, and being old doesn't make them any better. But some of the out-of-work old people are good, and it is too bad to discriminate against them.

Sentimentalists try to make out that old workers are better than young, and sometimes they are. But the race is to the swift—young workers out-produce old ones nearly always (and that cuts production costs)—so they get the jobs. In fact, why shouldn't they? If there are enough jobs for all, both groups will be employed; if not, one or the other will be unemployed. Which should it be? From society's point of view, shouldn't the best producers work?

Old employees sometimes have more skill than young (but most factory jobs take little skill). They are absent less often for reasons other than sickness. Turnover is lower, and they are better-satisfied employees than the younger group. But older employees have more disabilities than young men, so you have to be careful what jobs you put them on and you must keep them off jobs that will aggravate chronic, progressive disabilities, such as heart trouble. Also employers need to be wary of excessive workmen's compensation claims. Trivial injuries to older employees (who already had disabilities) have sometimes been blamed for death or permanent disability—with resulting high workmen's compensation awards.

Pension plans add to the reasons for not hiring old workers. Companies have to pay money into pension funds for all employees—how much depends on how much pension they will get *and* on *how long they will work for you before retiring.* A 20-year-old man's future pension might cost you $75 a year, but hire a man at 40 and buying his future pension will cost you $300 a year or more.

Today, old factory workers need fear layoff less than years ago. Labor contract seniority provisions protect them against being put out except for very good reasons.

Handicapped workers are often discriminated against, but most of our largest companies go out of their way to hire a fair share of them. Firestone Tire and Rubber Company has, for example, 150 deaf employees on its payroll. Often the nature of the handicap, perhaps blindness or an amputated hand, prevents the worker from holding most jobs. A "handicap" or "disability," however, is a relative thing. A man cannot do certain jobs, but he is not handicapped at all as far as other jobs are concerned.

Should a handicap prevent a man from producing enough to justify full wages, it is possible to pay him a rate in accord with his productivity. There is a provision in the Wage and Hour Law exempting handicapped workers from the minimum rates established. The majority of companies hiring handicapped workers put them on jobs where they can earn their way, however, or they pay them the going rate regardless. As employees, handicapped workers are very good. They are regular in attendance, except where their handicap interferes, and are appreciative of the opportunity to earn a living.

Some companies, particularly large ones, co-operate with the police authorities by helping former lawbreakers (who have served jail sentences) make a new start. In worthy cases, a man who has served his term and paid his debt to society is given a chance. His past is not made known to his fellow workers. Industrial companies perform a useful social function when they refuse to discriminate against such a man because he once took a misstep.

STUDY QUESTIONS

1. "Employees are individuals and should be treated differently according to their individual characteristics." Discuss this statement.
2. How can the personnel department, a staff department, get the whole organization to use good personnel practices?
3. To whom should the head of industrial relations (who heads the whole broad area of personnel) report and why?
4. Which personnel functions can small companies cut out? Discuss and justify your answer.
5. How can the personnel department help its company build good morale? What does it need to do?
6. Should a multiplant company follow the same personnel policies in all its plants? Why or why not?
7. What is the personnel department's responsibility in connection with shop rules?
8. Discuss negative discipline. Is there any place for it? If so, where?
9. How much does absenteeism usually amount to? Which groups cause most of it? Which the least?
10. What difference does it make whether people are absent or not?
11. How much is the normal turnover in American factories? How much might you save if you could cut it in half?
12. What can the personnel department do to cut turnover throughout the whole organization?
13. What part does the personnel department play in promotions?
14. Is demotion ever a good idea? Explain.
15. If sales fall off, what would you do in the factory, cut work hours for everyone? Or keep work hours unchanged and lay off some men? Why?
16. Can you ever justify discrimination? When? Explain.
17. Would you hire old men? Justify your position.

CASE 18–1.   DAY-VIEW TELEVISION CO.

The Day-View Television Co., employing 700 employees, made electronic devices for the Armed Forces, as well as TVs. About 400 of the employees were female and were, for the most part, married. Employment had been fairly steady for two years, and few new people had been hired. Nearly three fourths of the female workers had more than two years of service.

The government stepped up its orders for electronic items so the departments making those products had to go on a 48-hour week (six 8-hour days). Absenteeism, particularly among the female employees, went up. On Saturdays and Mondays it usually went above 7 per cent. The interference to production was considerable, and the personnel department was asked to try to reduce it.

Why is the absentee rate up? What should the personnel do? Is there anything management (in addition to what the personnel department does) can do?

Chapter 19

HIRING AND TRAINING

HIRING RATIOS AND THEIR EFFECT ON SELECTION

Mᴏꜱᴛ companies do not do as careful a job of picking new men as they would like. One reason is the scarcity of men. Most of the time since 1940 men have been so scarce that if you were very choosy you got no men.

The hiring ratio is another reason. Most hiring is to replace men who have left. A company with 1,000 employees has to hire from 300 to 600 men a year just to stay level. But this comes to only one or two a day. And the jobs are anywhere in the organization (although mostly at bottom levels because you fill upper jobs by promotion). Except for laboring jobs or office clerks, months pass between vacancies on particular jobs. This means that you can't go in very heavily for special tests to tell you which man will be the very best on each and every job. Nor can you have training classes—not for a laborer today, a typist tomorrow, a welder the next day, then an overhead crane operator, and so on. Big plants (5,000 men and up) can do much more to select good men and to train them because the costs of tests and training programs are spread over more cases.

There are dangers in picking men carelessly in order to hold down selection costs. First, when you fill upper jobs by promotion, the laborers you hire today are tomorrow's skilled men and day-after-to-morrow's foremen. What kind of foremen will they make? Hit-and-miss hiring today isn't likely to provide you with much good future foreman material.

Another danger in careless selection is that you will not screen out all the poor men and so end up with a poorer work force. It is only natural that, with careless screening, you will hire more poor men than if you tried to be very choosy. But, of course, you can fire a no-good worker and so pay only the price of some extra turnover for the mistake. This would be a calculated risk, and the savings from not having to select carefully might well be more than the cost of an occasional extra turnover.

The real danger, though, is that your foremen will not decide during a new man's trial period that he is so no-good as to fire him. After a month or two, the man's trial period is over, and he is a member of the union and is covered by the labor contract. Then you can't fire him without a very good cause; and if he is no worse today (when you want to fire him) than he was yesterday (when you could have but didn't fire him), you probably can't convince an arbitrator that he is so no-good as to be fired. If you fire him, he will file a grievance which will finally go before an arbitrator who is very likely to order you to reinstate the man. So you are stuck with him. When you hired him, maybe you hired $100,000 of future labor. It is a real question if you can afford not to be somewhat choosy when hiring new men.

AUTHORITY TO HIRE

When a man leaves, there is a vacancy. Normally he is replaced by promotion or a new hire. His replacement is not automatic, however; a request to hire a replacement has to be made out and approved by the department head's superior before personnel can act on it.

Why require approval? If the man leaving was doing useful work, don't you need a replacement? Not necessarily. Top management never knows exactly how many men are really needed in any department. So when a vacancy occurs, the top men sometimes look at it as an opportunity to cut the payroll. Staff departments, in particular, tend always to grow, and indirect workers (those who do not work on the product) tend always to expand in number. But they never shrink when production goes down. Top officials sometimes force some shrinking by refusing to approve hiring a replacement. This makes lesser department heads redistribute the work and cut out whatever half-necessary work they can.

Most hiring for the factory proper is done on the basis of a labor "budget." And most factory hiring is for men who work on the product or who are close to it. Their numbers change quite a bit with production but not wholly with it (you can, for example, lengthen or shorten work hours instead of hiring or laying off men). Planned increases in the work force are shown in the labor budget, and increased *hiring is authorized by it*.

The production control department knows ahead of time what products are to be made so it is told to figure out the number of men needed. This job (often called "manpower loading") is, in some companies, done by industrial engineering or by personnel. Before future work schedules are finally approved, their manpower needs are figured and submitted

EMPLOYMENT REQUISITION

N⁰ 5433

TO THE EMPLOYMENT DEPARTMENT: DATE_____19_____

PLEASE EMPLOY FOR THE_____DEPT. NO._____
                              (DEPARTMENT NAME)

ONE_____CLASSIFICATION NO._____
      (CLASSIFICATION NAME)
                                                                              A.M.
TO REPORT FOR WORK ON:_____19_____TIME_____   P.M.

EMPLOYEE WILL WORK ON	WORK WILL BE	NATURE OF JOB	EMPLOYEE WILL HAVE ACCESS TO
1ST SHIFT ☐	TEMPORARY ☐		FACTORY FACTORY AREA ☐ RESTRICTED
2ND SHIFT ☐	FOR_____DAYS		AREA NO. AREA
3RD SHIFT ☐	PERMANENT ☐		OFFICE AREA ☐ NAME
			ALL AREAS ☐

EMPLOYEE MUST BE EXPERIENCED   ☐   WILL BREAK IN APPLICANT   ☐
EMPLOYEE MUST FURNISH TOOLS   ☐   JOB REQUIRES TALL EMPLOYEE   ☐
REASON FOR REQUISITION: REPLACEMENT ☐   INCREASE IN SCHEDULE ☐

TO REPLACE_____BADGE NO._____
REASON FOR REPLACEMENT
AND REMARKS_____

I RECOMMEND MR._____WHY_____

SIGNED_____APPROVED_____
            FOREMAN OR DEPT. HEAD   AUTHORIZED SIGNATURE

(SPACE BELOW FOR EMPLOYMENT DEPARTMENT USE ONLY)

EMPLOYED MR._____DATE_____

BADGE NO._____CLASS NO._____RATE PER HR._____CTS.
ORIGINAL: EMPLOYMENT DEPT. COPY   TRIPLICATE: FOREMAN WILL RETAIN.
DUPLICATE: EMPLOYMENT DEPT. WILL RETURN TO FOREMAN VIA EMPLOYEE.

FIG. 19-1.   A requisition for a new man.

to top management. Sometimes the schedules are changed because they call for too many or too few men. But finally the schedule and its manpower needs get approved. Both personnel and the foremen are given the figures and plan accordingly. Individual requests to fill vacancies are not needed to keep employment at the level shown in the approved labor budget.

SOURCES OF APPLICANTS

Applicants for jobs come from many sources; some come to the plant and apply, some apply by mail, others come from newspaper advertising, some come on the recommendations of former employees, some are friends or relatives of present employees, some are recommended by high schools and colleges, others by public and private employment agencies, and some workers are obtained through labor recruitment in distant areas.

The best source of new employees seems to be former employees with good work records and the friends and relatives of present employees. Present employees are usually encouraged to recommend their friends who are looking for work. By and large, they don't recommend friends who are poor workers.

Companies differ in their policies about hiring relatives of present employees. A few companies refuse to hire a near relative of a present employee. Other companies, and they are more numerous, prefer relatives, but they put them in different departments and never in a department of which a relative is the head.

Casual applicants who come to the plant hunting for jobs include floaters so, as a group, they are not a good source of workers. Those who come in answer to advertising are usually better, although they are likely to include some who already have jobs. Most employers won't hire employees back and forth from each other because it drives up labor rates. Some employers consider "labor pirating" quite a sin.

Applicants coming from employment agencies often are fairly good, particularly if they come from private agencies. Private agencies won't send poor applicants because they want to be asked to recommend more men in the future. The main public employment agency is the United States Employment Service. Many companies feel that the USES sends poor applicants. Consequently, they do not ask the USES to send applicants when they have good openings. This just makes the situation worse. Good applicants don't go to USES because they don't expect it to have good openings.

Recent graduates of vocational high schools are a good source of new factory workers. They sometimes enter apprentice programs to become skilled workers.

College graduates are usually hired for staff or office jobs or for special long-time executive training programs. Representatives of the personnel department go to colleges and universities to interview graduates. The competition is so keen that you have to go after such men; they don't have to and won't come to you.

In a few industries the labor union is a source (or even the *only* source) of workers. Some craft unions, as for example in the printing trades, have had agreements for many years with employers to hire only union members. Under these agreements the employer has to take the men the union sends to him. Such contracts are now forbidden by the Taft-Hartley law, but the practice appears to be still in effect. Other craft unions are also sources of skilled labor supply. Industrial unions, whose members have varied skills, rarely go into the business of supplying workers.

During periods of extreme labor shortage, as during a war, you have to go after workers wherever you can find them. Some companies have tried door-to-door canvassing for women workers. Radio and television advertising has also been used. Advertisements can be put in out-of-town newspapers, particularly in small towns, or in large city papers if skilled help is needed. You may even find it worth while to open your own employment agency in other cities if you need a large number of men. Labor scouts can also make recruiting tours (with advance advertising) through areas where the shortage is less severe. Labor pirating from your nearby neighbor may be a sin, but it seems not to be a sin if you pirate from a far-off employer.

THE APPLICANT'S POINT OF VIEW

Many companies seem to have a blind spot when it comes to hiring men. It is all company and what the man can offer to the company. Then when he asks about money, advancement, or fringe benefits, the company representative acts as if the man had asked if he could sleep on the job.

Company men seem to think all that they need to say is "your advancement depends on your own efforts," just as if good were always rewarded. Many companies seem to expect an employee to marry the company and to put all else—family and everything—into the background. Small wonder some applicants prefer to work elsewhere. Interviewers would do well to remember that men shy away from such demanding employers. The company should be held up as a *good* place to work—as a place which offers the employee something. It can't be all take and no give for either the man or the company.

SELECTION AND HIRING

Getting the Right Man on Every Job.   Ideally every man should fit his job and the job should fit the man. Don't take that too seriously though. Most men can do most factory jobs so the problem is not one of finding the one and only perfect man for a job. Consider putting shoes, one by one, into a machine that nails rubber heels onto the shoes. Is that a job a man would just have to be born to do? Do you think any man is just perfectly suited to that job and that other men are not?

Or look at it from the man's point of view. When he applies for a job, he never applies for a heel-nailing-on job. He offers to work at (within limits) whatever job you have open. He isn't too much concerned with the job just fitting him.

We must admit, of course, that fitting men to jobs has more validity negatively. Everyone has his dislikes. If at all possible, you should keep men off jobs they dislike. On the other hand, it is too much to expect to find somewhere a man who just yearns to do each and every job—like the heel-nailing-on job.

Fitting men perfectly to jobs runs into another snag. Even if you tried hard to do it, you couldn't do it. Most labor contracts say that present employees are always to get a chance at vacancies on highly skilled jobs. If a long-service employee wants the higher-skilled job, it is pretty hard to keep him off it if he can do it passably well or if he can learn to do it passably well. As time goes along your men get promoted to jobs they want—or think that they want—no matter what you think about it. You might think that they are poorly fitted for the work, but your views don't count for much.

STANDARDIZED SELECTION INTERVIEW
(Short Form)

Date_____19____

Name _____ Sex: M___F___Date of Birth_____19____Soc. Sec. No. _____

SUMMARY

Rating: 1   2   3   4   Comments:_____

IN MAKING FINAL RATING, BE SURE TO CONSIDER APPLICANT'S STABILITY, INDUSTRY, PERSEVERANCE, LOYALTY, ABILITY TO GET ALONG WITH OTHERS, SELF-RELIANCE, MATURITY, MOTIVATION. ALSO, DOMESTIC SITUATION AND HEALTH.

Interviewer:_____ Considered for: Dept._____Job_____

Why applying here?_____
IS HE INTERESTED IN THIS COMPANY, OR IS HE LOOKING FOR ANY JOB? HAS HE THOUGHT OUT HIS PLANS?

Friends employed here? No_____Yes_____ Names:_____
WILL THIS HELP STABILITY?

How long to get here from home?_____ Mins.   What transportation?_____
IS THIS REASONABLE?   WILL IT MAKE FOR STABILITY?

WORK EXPERIENCE

Cover all positions. Account for every month. Treat Armed Forces experience in regular sequence as another job, rephrasing questions appropriately. Or cover it in more detail on the special form, Standardized Review of Armed Forces Experience.

	Job 1 Last or present position	Job 2 Next to last position	Job 3 Second to last position
Company Name			
Company location			
Employment dates	From 19 to 19	From 19 to 19	From 19 to 19
	DO DATES CHECK WITH APPLICATION? IS RECORD COMPLETE?		
Kind of work			
	WILL HIS PREVIOUS EXPERIENCE BE HELPFUL ON THIS JOB?		
Starting Rate	$ per	$ per	$ per
Rate at leaving	$ per	$ per	$ per
	HAS HE MADE GOOD WORK PROGRESS? HAS HE BEEN INDUSTRIOUS? AMBITIOUS?		
What was especially liked about job?			
	DOES THIS REFLECT MATURITY? AMBITION? HAS HE BEEN HAPPY IN HIS WORK? LOYAL?		
What was disliked?			
	WERE HIS DISLIKES JUSTIFIED? HAS HE RESENTED SUPERVISION?		
Reasons for leaving at this particular time			
	ARE HIS REASONS CONSISTENT AND REASONABLE? INDICATIONS OF DISCONTENT? DISLOYALTY?		

JOB 4 Company_____ City_____ From_____19___To_____19___
Rate_____ Kind of work_____
HAS HE STAYED IN ONE LINE OF WORK FOR THE MOST PART? Reasons for leaving at this particular time_____
ARE HIS ATTITUDES TOWARD HIS EMPLOYER LOYAL?

JOB 5 Company_____ City_____ From_____19___To_____19___
Rate_____ Kind of work_____
DOES HE GET ALONG WELL WITH PEOPLE? Reasons for leaving at this particular time_____
DOES HIS WORK RECORD SHOW ABILITY TO GET ALONG WITH OTHERS?

JOB 6 Company_____ City_____ From_____19___To_____19___
Rate_____ Kind of work_____
WAS HE INTERESTED IN CREATIVE WORK? IN WORK REQUIRING PHYSICAL ACTIVITY? Reasons for leaving at this particular time_____
IS HE INCLINED TO SEEK RESPONSIBILITY? HAS HE MADE PROGRESS?

Published by Science Research Associates, 57 West Grand Avenue, Chicago 10, Illinois
Copyright 1947 by Science Research Associates, Inc. All rights reserved. Printed in the U.S.A.
Developed by Robert N. McMurry & Company

SIF 1

Science Research Associates

FIG. 19–2. A part of a standardized interview form. Notice the questions in small type below the lines. They are intended to help the interviewer get full information.

Also any near-perfect placement of men would be upset if a layoff came. When new men (most of whom are near the bottom) get laid off, old men get demoted and transferred to their jobs. The jobs they end up with are often not those they can do best.

There is still another reason why you never even approach the ideal of the perfect man on the job. Since 1940 men have been hard to find. So you take the men you can get even though it means putting some of them on jobs that they can't measure up to as well as you'd like.

Perhaps we have overdrawn the picture of the difficulties of getting men on jobs where they fit. It is certainly an ideal to try for, but no one ever accomplishes it completely. Fortunately most people can easily learn to do most factory jobs, and most of the jobs are not particularly disagreeable to most workers—so we get along reasonably well. The thing to watch for is to catch the occasional outright misfit and try to put him on a job he can handle.

Selecting supervisors is, however, a different story. Here and at all levels above, it is important to choose well. Labor contracts and layoffs don't interfere with your doing a good job.

Regardless of the difficulties in placing men on jobs that they fit, you should try to do the best you can. How can you go about it? You have to deal with the *job* and the *man*, and you have to try to match them up.

The Job.   You start with the job; the interviewer needs to know something about it—something more than the job title which appears on the hiring authorization. Particularly, he needs to know the "man-characteristics" of the job. It isn't enough to know that a man has to run a machine that puts threads on the inside of bolts. The interviewer also needs to know that good eyesight is needed and that the man will have oily hands all day. Fair-skinned people are more likely to get skin rashes than are dark-skinned people. The interviewer should go out into the plant and see the workplace so he can tell applicants what to expect. He can do a good job only if he knows more about the jobs he is filling than a mere list of job duties tells.

The Man.   Second, there is the man. How can you tell if an applicant can and will do the job well? Application blanks, interviews, references, and tests all help some, but none alone nor all together are perfect.

Application Blanks.   Application blanks are somewhat helpful. The man's answers to the questions on the blank (if they are honest—and mostly they are) tell you something about him.

Application blank questions are of two kinds. The first type are those questions that identify the man—his name, address, and so on. These questions are of no help in selecting a man, but you have to have all of that information if he is hired. Then there are questions of the second kind. Those that help you find out what the man can do—his work experience, training, job likes, and so on.

Interviews.   If the application shows that the man might be able to fill an opening, he gets a regular interview. Here he is asked more questions and in turn gets to ask questions. If he still looks good, he may be given some tests or taken to the foreman to talk to before hiring him.

References. Most companies check up on a man's past employment, and some check his other references if it can easily be done (by phone, for example). References usually aren't worth much because applicants try to give names only of men who will speak well of them. Also most people try to give a man a boost when asked to write a reference letter. But, in spite of their limited value, references of applicants for more important jobs are almost always checked. They do help a little.

Even checking with former employers isn't very helpful, because the request for information rarely gets beyond the clerk who answers the phone in the former employer's personnel office. Ordinarily only the briefest notation of the cause for leaving is available on the man's record card, and that is what the clerk tells you when you call.

Tests. Of course, the best test of what a man can do is to try him out on the job. This would mean taking him out in the plant and stopping regular production while he tries to do the job. You can't do this so you have to choose men some other way.

Psychologists have done a great deal of work developing off-the-job tests to find out what a man can do and try to figure out how well he will do in the future. Some tests try to get at the man's characteristics: does he have mechanical aptitude? does he dislike monotonous work? and such things. Some tests try to get at his capacity to learn and to benefit from training. Some are so-called intelligence tests; others are problem-solving tests. Then there are also manual dexterity tests and trade tests.[1] Trade tests are prepared lists of questions that bluffers can't answer.

Tests are, as yet, far from perfect. They are better at predicting failure than success. If the test shows that the man seems not to have it in him to succeed, he probably won't. But if they show that he can succeed, you can't be very sure that he will succeed. Men fail for lots of reasons other than lack of ability.

The trouble with tests in hiring is that since jobs are different the tests have to be different too. If you have 1,000 men, you probably have 200 or 300 different jobs. But having 200 or 300 different tests is impossibly expensive. Besides, you could never "validate" them (check the questions to see if high test scores really predict job success).

---

[1] Here are a few sample questions from "A Fifteen Minute Oral Trade Test" by E. J. McCormick and N. B. Winstanley:
1. Q. What material is used in the manufacture of lapping plates?
   A. Cast iron.
2. Q. How many turns of a handle are required to make a half turn of the most common index head?
   A. 20.
3. Q. What is the meaning of the Brinnel Test?
   A. A method of determining the hardness of metal.
4. Q. For what purpose would you use transfer calipers?
   A. It is used to determine sizes of recesses and places where the legs of the calipers must be moved to get them out.

Actually you don't need a test for every job. Companies using tests usually have a number of them. Several are used when testing for any job, but different combinations are used for different jobs. This amounts to ending up with different tests for different jobs. But most companies using tests do not try to have even different *sets* of tests for every individual job, let alone different individual tests for every job. They use the same sets of tests for all similar jobs. None of this, however, solves the validation problem: will men with high scores on this battery of tests succeed on the job?

Most companies leave making up the tests to the experts. Most of the tests used have been developed by psychologists and are printed and are for sale commercially. In fact, in big cities, you can send men to commercial testing agencies which will administer tests and send you a report. This is done sometimes when you want an executive from the outside. If used, psychological test scores should be interpreted by a specialist. Untrained people often rely on them too much and read more meaning into them than they should. For that reason, test scores should be kept out of the usual personnel record files where nearly anyone can see them.

Students should be reminded that a great many companies, perhaps the majority, do not use tests. It is not uncommon for the applicant for a factory job to be hired on the same day, or the day after, he applies. He may be sent to talk to the foreman within an hour after he applies. The foreman may ask him further questions relating to his job knowledge and, if he is to be a machine operator, may even try him out on a machine.

If the foreman approves of the man, the applicant takes his medical examination, after which he is hired. Medical examinations are given in all but the smallest companies. The examination is usually the last step before hiring. Doing this last saves the expense of examining men who are not hired for other reasons. The purposes of the medical examination are: (1) to be sure the man is physically able to do the job for which he is to be hired, and (2) to record his physical condition at the time of hiring. After his physical examination, he is given a clock number and becomes an employee.

INDUCTION

A man's hiring is really not complete until he is on the job and working. "Induction" is the process of getting him there and started off on the right foot. It should help to give him that feeling of "belonging," to get him out of the feeling that he is still in the labor market looking for a job. It starts in the personnel office where he is told about the company and its policies. The company social benefit plans and shop rules are explained to him. He is shown where and how to ring in and out on his timecard. The incentive pay system, if any, is explained. He is assigned a locker and is shown the location of washrooms, first-aid facilities, and the cafeteria. A few companies take new employees on a tour of the plant or of that part of it which concerns them.

In large companies new employees are usually given booklets containing information about the company. The booklets tell all about the

FIG. 19–3. Booklets given to new employees at the Falk Corporation giving them information. The map, showing the locations of departments and offices, is an unusual feature.

company's products, history, and policies with respect to personnel, and describe the benefit plans and social activities that may interest a new man. Then there are also booklets or leaflets describing in detail hospital insurance, sickness and accident plans, life insurance, and pensions.

In his department the new man is introduced to his fellow workers, and the foreman explains his job to him. Some companies explain how his job fits into the whole picture. On the other hand, one radio manufacturer reports that his company tells women employees nothing beyond how to do their own jobs. More lengthy explanations confuse some of them, and most of them do not want any more explanation.

Induction is important for men but even more important for women workers (many of them are married and don't have to work, so they quit more readily than men if they don't like the job or their fellow workers). Mostly, men and women both adjust readily, but *without proper introduction to the job a few don't adjust and they quit.* You can cut that kind of turnover by good induction. It must be said, however, that most companies talk more about induction than they do about it. Everyone agrees it is a great idea, but not so many do anything about it.

ON-THE-JOB TRAINING

Almost all factory training is done on the job. One exception is when you have to expand rapidly: then you may set up training classes to speed up the training. Another exception is the classroom training for factory jobs that some city vocational high schools offer. A third exception is "vestibule school" training (common in textiles). A few machines, set apart from regular departments, are used to train new men who will later be put into a group of experienced workers where they must keep up with the others.

On-the-job training is the only kind of training possible in most cases, since not often can you set up factory machines in a separate training school. Also, on-the-job training is the only kind practical when hiring is for replacements with many jobs, because such hiring is spotty and irregular both as to number and kind of jobs to be filled. Weeks or months pass between vacancies on any given job.

Training on the job is usually quite satisfactory, not only for the simple tasks which make up the bulk of all factory jobs but also for the more skilled ones. You can't, in any case—even with training classes— make skilled workers overnight. Nor is there any need, ordinarily, to train them hurriedly. On-the-job training gives you about as many skilled workers as you need about as fast as you need them. Their training is, usually, a matter of gradually learning over months or years from older employees.

When a new man is hired as a machine helper or when an employee is upgraded from a laborer's or materials handler's job, he does what the machine operator tells him. At first he needs to be told exactly what to do, but he soon learns his duties. As he works, he watches the machine operator and learns something of the how and why of the machine's operation. The operator may occasionally let the helper perform one or more of his regular duties. At no time, except at the very start, is there any direct effort made to train the helper; yet before long and with little further training, he is ready to be a machine operator himself.

When the chance to become an operator arrives, he gets some more on-the-job training from setup men, assistant foremen, group leaders, or even the foreman. His first tasks are easy ones, hand-picked for him because they are easy to do. If he gets into trouble, his supervisor or his neighboring worker will tell him what to do. Pretty soon he does

U.S. Department of Labor

FIG. 19–4. On-the-job training in the use of "go-no-go" gages.

ordinary jobs well without further help, so he gets harder jobs. With these he gets some instructions, but for the most part he is on his own. In due time he becomes an experienced and fully qualified operator.

Most training for factory jobs is done in about the way outlined above. The best place to learn to run a machine is at the machine, and generally the best teacher is someone who knows how to do the job himself. Notice that the personnel department plays no part in this on-the-job training. Sometimes, however, methods study engineers do. It is their job to figure out better ways to do things, which they may have to show to the workers.

On-the-job training of the informal sort described here will not produce numerous highly skilled workers quickly: it falls down when speed is essential (as in wartime). Nor does it, since it is somewhat haphazard, produce uniformly good results. A good deal depends on the foreman. Workers cannot be counted on to absorb added skill merely from being around the department.

TRAINING SUPERVISORS

Before we get into *training* supervisors, remember that half the job is to pick good foreman material to start with. How can you do that? What do you look for? High skill on a machine job? No, that helps some, but a foreman's job will be *supervisory*. Machine operating skill is only one part (and usually not the most important part) of his job.

There is no foolproof way of picking men who will make good foremen. But try to get men who enjoy doing their work well, who are wholly honest, who will do what they know should be done, who have courage and won't let things slide or try to pass the buck. And try to get men who are genuinely interested in other people.

In small companies foremen usually receive no training other than what they get in the form of supervision by the general foreman or the plant superintendent. In large companies, on the other hand, formal training is often provided for new foremen. But whether they get formal training or not, most of the training they get is through supervision and not in classes. Training through supervision doesn't work out uniformly well, however. Sometimes the general foreman, like the foreman himself, is a top-notch machine man but weak on handling men. Both men's jobs are, however, managing men, and a new foreman usually needs training in this part of his new job.

Most big companies provide some kind of organized foreman training, but they stop short of running central, full-time schools with permanent teaching staffs. Two kinds of training, beyond on-the-job training, are commonly used.

One is a series of conferences usually called a "Foremanship-Management Conference Series," or a similar name. Many new, and most older, foremen won't admit they need any training, so calling it a conference series instead of a training program makes it go over better. Such a series of training meetings is held only occasionally, perhaps once every several years.

The training course, conducted on a conference basis, usually consists of about twenty one-hour weekly meetings. They are held during the day on company time and are led by members of the staff of the personnel department, although other company specialists are brought in for special subjects. Materials for some very good courses of this type (including reading material and a teacher's manual on each subject) can be bought already prepared. The conference leader ties in company experience in the meetings. Occasionally companies work out co-operative arrangements with nearby colleges and universities to offer training courses at night.

The second common kind of training is usually just for foremen and is incidental to something else. Many companies hold weekly one-hour foremen's meetings presided over by the superintendent. Problems of general interest are discussed; foremen are told about new products; company policies are explained; and inter- and intradepartmental difficulties are brought up. Everyone gets into the discussion, so these meetings end up being excellent training devices.

SKF "DO YOU KNOW" TEST

PART I   TRUE AND FALSE

1. A "slowdown" is not considered a violation of the "no-strike" clause.   T ? F

2. An employee working on an irregularly scheduled workweek is eligible for premium pay for the sixth day of work during his workweek.   T ? F

3. Learners' base rates are applied only on "set up and operate" jobs described in the Incentive Job Evaluation Manual.   T ? F

4. Except for part-time employees, all employees who are laid off from the company are eligible for severance pay.   T ? F

5. Eligible employees receive holiday pay for holidays listed in the agreement which fall on Saturday.   T ? F

6. Vacation pay for incentive workers is based on the employee's regular base rate current at the time of vacation.   T ? F

PART II   MATCHING

The following is a list of functions of stewards and of grievance committeemen. In the column to the right, opposite each function, write "S" if the function described is that of a steward, "C" if the function is that of a grievance committeeman, "B" if both the steward and the grievance committeeman perform the function.

FUNCTION   PERFORMED BY

1. Union recipient of rate sheet............ ____
2. Observes a check study................ ____
3. Signs the union standard grievance form.. ____
4. Attends Second Step meeting as a member of the committee.......... ____
5. Discusses for agreement the third week of overtime for a department...... ____
6. Receives notice of contemplated lay-off.. ____
7. Discusses grievances in the First Step.... ____
8. Represents several small related departments ____

PART III   COMPLETION

1. Employees working on the second and third shift receive a bonus of ____% based on their total earnings during the period such shift work is performed.
2. The foreman must answer written grievances presented in Step 1 within ____ work days from the time they are presented.
3. A maximum of ____ grievance committeemen may attend Step 2 meetings as members of the grievance committee.
4. The hearing for a discharged employee must be held within ____ hours after the action is taken by the foreman.

SKF Industries, Inc.

FIG. 19–5. An objective type examination to test foremen's knowledge of the company's union contract.

Many companies help the foreman too by giving him policy "manuals" to guide him. They tell him what he can do on his own, what he has to ask about before acting, what he can do but must report to his boss, and what is his relation to staff departments.

Still other activities which have educational value are, merit rating plans, orientation programs, mass meetings of all employees, rumor clinics, attitude surveys, company product exhibits, exployee counseling, and plant tours.

EXECUTIVE TRAINING

Most large companies have for years had special training programs for selected groups from which the company's future executives will some day come. Small companies too are going more and more into similar programs on a smaller scale. The programs are known as "Executive Trainee Programs" or some similar name. A definite program of job assignments and training meetings is laid out for each trainee for his first year or two.

At the end of the training programs trainees are put on some regular job, which is actually only a temporary assignment. From this—in time —they move up. Their upward progress is not dependent, however, on the opportunities ahead of them in their own department. Their records are kept by the personnel department and are reviewed whenever openings occur in any department, or, if the company has several plants, in other plants.

Early training alone will not make top-notch executives. Training has to be a continuing process. Job rotation to varied jobs along with progressive advancement gives men experience in several different departments. This broadens a man's understanding of the various parts of the business and prevents his becoming a narrow specialist (which would be a handicap in top jobs). During this period of advancement the man learns by the on-the-job method, by the supervision he receives, by attendance at meetings of minor executives, and by serving on various committees. In addition, most companies offer, from time to time, executive training "courses" or series of meetings for junior executives (those above the trainee level). Usually these courses are given as a series of semimonthly meetings, each devoted to a different subject and presented by a top company official or top man from college teaching ranks.

Where do trainees come from? Mostly straight from colleges and universities. But always a few should be moved up from the ranks into the executive trainee group. This adds to the pool of good men, helps morale, and throws the college men into competition with good men coming up the hard way. It also keeps the college men's head size down and helps control their "crown prince" complex. And, of course, having some men from the ranks get a chance at the good jobs reduces the resentment that workers in the organization sometimes develop if only those fortunate enough to go to college get such a chance.

In recent years management "institutes" away from the company have gained in popularity. Such institutes are now offered during the summer by most large universities. The student executives live in dormitories and attend discussion groups daily for from a week or two up to three months, depending on the school. Enrollment is limited to insure everyone having a chance to get in on discussions.

Although institutes are more popular than ever, the time they take is a handicap. To meet the need for short programs, the American Management Association has developed a series of "seminars" of two to six days. These seminars in the fields of production, marketing, and other subjects have proved very popular.

The company's specialists need to keep up to date in their specialities. The specialists are encouraged to belong to professional societies, to go to their meetings, and to read their publications. Consulting specialists are sometimes brought in to do certain work and to help the company's specialists. Universities and some of the consulting companies conduct short seminars or advanced courses in limited fields of specialization. H. B. Maynard & Company (a firm of consultants), for example, has offered its three-week course in "Methods-Time Measurement" many times and in several cities for years. By taking this course, industrial engineers are given an opportunity to go further into their specialty. In very large manufacturing companies, short advanced courses of study for specialists are also offered within the company.

CENTRAL SCHOOLS

Very large companies sometimes maintain central training schools. General Motors has operated the General Motors Institute at Flint, Michigan, for many years. The International Harvester Company maintains a permanent school in Chicago. General Electric has a large permanent school at Crotonville, N.Y.

Such schools serve many useful purposes. They carry on all kinds of formal training programs. Supervisors and other groups are brought in from the various plants and given classwork. The schools promote better appreciation of the work done in sister plants and broaden the outlook of trainees. Central schools are also very effective in sales and service work. Dealers, salesmen, and repair men who service the company's products can be brought in and given special courses.

Central schools do not replace local training. On-the-job training and educational supervision continue in each plant, as do all training courses calling for periodic meetings rather than full-time schoolwork.

There are disadvantages in the use of central schools. The expense of bringing men from distant plants and putting them up at hotels while they go to school is no small item. Then, there is a loss to the company in having a number of men away from their jobs for extended periods of time. Also, the school represents a steady continuing expense, although the educational needs of the company may be irregular. A certain amount of flexibility can be gained by drawing upon personnel men from individual plants to help when the load gets heavy, because they can be sent back when it lightens up. The men used in sales and service training can also be borrowed and returned. Central schools are ordinarily operated by the personnel department but may be under the sales department if the principal work done is in sales and service rather than factory training.

HOW TO TEACH MIDDLE-LEVEL MEN

"It's hard to teach an old dog new tricks," and so it is; yet all industrial teaching is to mature men, some even in their 40's and 50's. The problem isn't that older men can't learn; they can, but learning new ways isn't so easy as it is for 25-year-olds, and besides older men are more set in their ways—they don't want to change their ways. In general they are satisfied with how they do things and don't want to be taught anything. There are, of course, those who are eager to learn, but a teacher in industry has to sugar-coat the pill he offers.

How to do it? Have conferences, not classes. Have discussion leaders, not teachers. Let the group talk; let them develop their own answers. Although the leader may steer the discussion a bit by asking thought-provoking questions, he ought to keep himself in the background. He ought to try to get everyone to take part, and he should try to keep discussions from wandering too far afield. Every now and then he should sum up the thinking of the group—particularly after someone has talked unduly long, or after a conflict in opinion, or after some definite conclusions or opinions have been reached. This puts everyone on the track again and gives nondiscussors a chance to talk.

A discussion leader will inflate the egos of conference members to keep them taking part. Be free with "That's a good question," or "That's a good idea," or "Joe, what do you think of Bill's idea?"

It is best to get both problems and answers from the group. Members learn more this way than from a teacher handing them something. The leader may start things off with general questions or with a case or problem to be solved.

Visual aids should certainly not be neglected for parts of the training—particularly where things have to be explained. Moving pictures can be used effectively to add to group study programs because they dramatize situations and make them more concrete. Television offers great possibilities in training. An instructor can explain a factory operation, for example, by showing it to his audience on a TV screen while he explains what goes on. Charts, displays, and other visual presentations also help put ideas across. Demonstrations and trips to other companies, to see what they do, make training programs more effective.

"Buzz sessions" and "brainstorming" also have their advocates. With buzz sessions you break up your group into little groups during part of a meeting period. Members of the little groups get more chances to "kick around" their ideas. People who won't speak up in big meetings usually do talk in small groups. Afterwards the little groups are brought back together, and general discussion goes ahead. Brainstorming means having idea sessions. Let group members, one at a time and in turn, put any ideas that they have—however wild—before the group. The purpose is to capture ideas—not evaluate them. Don't allow criticisms of any ideas, at least not until a later time. Some companies report good success with buzz sessions and brainstorming.

Role playing is favored by some. Give the men a situation and let them act it out. Then let everyone discuss it. Problems are more real when you try to put yourself into someone else's position.

THE SUBJECT MATTER OF TRAINING

Just what is it that middle-level men need to learn? They need to know about the company's products, its policies (and reasons why), the records and reports they receive or make up and send out and, above all, how to supervise their people.

They need to know how to teach their men. Here is what you might tell a foreman about teaching. First, prepare your man: put him at ease, take it easy at first, ask him what he already knows about the job, try to get him interested in learning. Next, show him how: tell and show him; tell him clearly and completely, one step at a time; tell him where he must be most careful and why; make the job seem simple. Then let the man try out the job while you stand by. Get him to start slowly and carefully, build up his confidence. Then ask him why he does certain parts of the work, have him explain it to you. And, finally, tell him whom to ask if he has questions when you are not around. And after that, don't forget him, stop back occasionally to see how he is getting along.

Supervisors need also to be able to prevent grievances or to handle those that arise. Not many would figure out themselves how to do it without training. And how do you tell a foreman to prevent grievances or to handle those that come up? Tell him to make a practice of talking to each of his men now and then. He should tell each man how he is getting along, and he should show him how to improve his work. When a man does a good job, the foreman should tell him so—give him credit. And he should prepare his men ahead of time for any changes coming.

If a man has a complaint, the foreman should listen sympathetically, trying to understand the real reason behind it. He should think over the problem, make a decision, then tell it and explain it to the man. By all means, the foreman should not try to pass the buck. He should check later to see if the problem is solved. Foremen who do these things have fewer complaints than foremen who just let these things go.

A foreman has to give reprimands sometimes. Here he should learn not to act hastily but to keep cool and try to appreciate the man's position. He should be *sure* that a reprimand is deserved and consider how it will be received both by the man and his fellow workers. He should give the reprimand in private and make sure that it is clear and that what he expects of the man in the future is also clear. It will be received better if it is combined with suggestions about how to do better.

Supervisors need also to know how to delegate work to others so that grievances will be few. We won't repeat here how to do that. It is covered on pages 28–29. It too is a subject on which foremen usually need training.

REDUCING THE NEED FOR TRAINING

Today, American industry has carried mechanization and job specialization so far that the amount of training needed by the ordinary factory worker is small. Very few factory jobs require six months to learn. Most jobs can be learned in less than a week, while of some it can truly be said that ten minutes of instruction is enough.

Methods improvement and machine design improvement both try to simplify jobs. New jobs are often not as simple as they could be; they may require considerable skill, but as time goes on, machines are made more automatic and the manual part of the job is simplified. The end result is to cut the training needed by new workers. Specialization, even by itself, also reduces the skill and training needs as well as the cost of labor.

Activities which reduce the need for training (motion study, machine development, and subdivided operations) are carried on by departments other than personnel. The personnel department has an interest in them, however, since the results affect the worker's skill and the training he needs. During periods when many new workers must be trained, the amount of training work to be done by the personnel department may be reduced materially by the service rendered by the motion study and methods engineers.

STUDY QUESTIONS

1. About how many men a year, per 100 workers, must a company hire just to stay even? If the ratio were double what it is, would that help the company place men on the right job? Explain your answer.
2. How is hiring new employees authorized? Should every hire be authorized? Why?
3. The United States Employment Service is available to supply us with job applicants. Should we ever use other sources? Explain your answer.
4. "It is the personnel department's job to get the right man on the job." Discuss this statement.
5. Tell how to pick the best applicant for a job.
6. What does "validating" a test mean? Is it important? Justify your answer.
7. What happens when a man is inducted? When is it important? When is it not important?
8. "On-the-job training generally does not measure up to formal classroom training." Discuss fully.
9. How do you train a foreman?
10. How do you train an executive?
11. How would you tell a foreman to go about teaching a man a new job?
12. How can a foreman prevent grievances?

Chapter 20

OTHER PERSONNEL WORK

EMPLOYEE RECORDS

THE biggest "must" job of the personnel department is to keep the employee records. You need, for every employee, his name, address, hiring date, rate of pay, department, job title—what they are now and what they used to be. Also his badge and clock number, social security number, marital status, and number of dependents. Also dates and reasons for layoffs, discharges, resignations, leaves of absence, rehiring dates, rehiring rates, reprimands, disciplinary actions, and accidents. Some companies add records of a man's training, merit ratings, and suggestions made.

Personnel also gets all of the paper work having to do with fringe benefits (the benefits are discussed in Chapter 28). It has to keep all records, issue insurance policies, see that payments are made in sickness and accident cases, and make reports to insurance companies and to state and federal governments.

Most of these are records that even small companies must keep—some because the law requires it, some so that you will be sure to live up to the labor contract, and some to help you pick a person for promotion. You don't have to keep records of former employees very long, but they too have to be kept for a while.

Most companies use their records only as records—overlooking their value as information. Personnel ought to study the records to find which departments are having trouble, which workers are accident prone, and which jobs are dangerous, so that improvements will be made.

No one record card will take care of all the needs. Here is a list of eighteen forms used by Parker Appliance (and eighteen is few compared to most companies): application, destination card (temporary for new men), time card, tax card (shows dependents), insurance card, payroll rate card, job rate card, personnel record card (this is the most important record and is made out in duplicate, one for personnel and the other in the man's department), name card for alphabetical file, dispensary

379

NAME	Aadahl, Henry									OUT	OUT		NAME

TITLE Foreman, Automotive Screw Machinery
NAME Aadahl, Henry
SOC. SEC. NO. 153-10-9489

ADDRESS									TELEPHONE				
	89 State Street								Sunset				
	Buffalo, New York								1-5519				

NOTIFY	Irene T. Aadahl -- Wife

PREVIOUS EMPLOYMENT

NAME AND ADDRESS OF EMPLOYER	FROM MO.	DAY	YR.	TO MO.	DAY	YR.	KIND OF WORK	WAGES	REASON FOR LEAVE		REG. NO.
Todd Ship Yards, Brooklyn, N.Y.	6	10	44	2	17	49	Machinist	$2.50	Lack of work		
Sperry Gyroscope, Brooklyn, N.Y	8	3	40	5	29	44	Assembly	1.75	Lack of work		BIRTHDATE MO. DAY YR.
Arbuckle Sugar Refinery, Buffalo	9	18	30	7	15	40	Weigher	45 wk.	Out of Bus.		4 5 14
											MAR. STAT.
											S M W D S

EDUCATION

MED. CLASS.

	SCHOOL	YRS.	SPECIALIZATION	DATE CMP'L. MO. DAY YR.	DEGREE	1 2 3
GRADE	P. S. 229 - Buffalo, N. Y.	8		6 7 28	X	X
HIGH	Manual Training High School	2		6 9 30	X	MIL. SERVICE MO. DAY YR
BUSINESS OR TRADE						F
						T
COLLEGE						NON-CITIZEN

POST EMPLOYMENT — NIGHT OR EXTENSION COURSES

EMPLOY

SCHOOL	COURSE	DATE CMPL. MO. DAY YR.	GRADE	SCHOOL	COURSE	DATE CMPL. MO. DAY YR.	GRADE	P.T.	CO-OP	SUM
								INS. NO.		
								SPEC. SKILLS		

SUGGESTION RECORD

SUGG. NO.	AWARD	SUGG. NO.	AWARD	SUGG. NO.	AWARD	SUGG. NO.	AWARD	SUGG. NO.	AWARD

EASTMAN KODAK CO   APPARATUS AND OPTICAL DIVISION   EMPLOYEE RECORD   "VISIrecord"   8.25X8—.75
AO 295   PL 9502   NO. 336—V+6

VISIrecord, Inc.

FIG. 20–1. A copy of Eastman Kodak's employee record card. The cutoff corner allows the cards to be filed standing vertically in a drawer but with each card set over far enough so that the right edge and corner of every card can be seen.

record, attendance cards, notification of absence, reply card for absentees, warning notice, change of status notice, grievance form, termination form, and clearance form (showing that tools have been turned in).

NONFINANCIAL INCENTIVES

Personnel has to keep all the records and do all the leg work for non-financial incentives. One exception is praise for work well done. That is one nonfinancial reward given out by the man's foreman.

Basically most nonfinancial incentives give recognition that a man is outstanding in one way or another. It may be for long service, good attendance, safe work, or what not. Recognition may be a picture or an article in the company paper, a length-of-service pin, a suggestion award, or an honored spot at a testimonial dinner—all of which the personnel department arranges. These awards need to be consistent throughout the plant and to be administered by one department serving all departments.

Nonfinancial incentives tend to lose their incentive value unless they get support and publicity from management. They also need to be changed now and then. They are appeals to men's emotions, and some of them wear off. So don't keep on using the same ones too long. Particularly is this true of safety campaigns and production drives. And, of course, they should *never* be used instead of extra money if extra money is a proper reward. Praise instead of money wears thin. On the other hand, money doesn't seem a proper reward for not getting yourself hurt or for having been with the company for 40 years. An old-timer would probably rather get a gold watch than a check for its value. Just putting a man's name in the company paper helps swell a man's pride even if the occasion is not so great. Write it up when his wife has a new baby, or when he catches the biggest fish, or hits a golf ball the farthest, or if he has an unusual hobby—write that up. It makes him important for a day.

SUGGESTION SYSTEMS

Suggestion systems are common but not universal. Wherever they exist, personnel has to run them. The man on the job often has ideas about how to improve his job. Multiply one man's ideas by 1,000 men and you find that collectively their suggestions save big money. But unless a man cuts in on the money some way—gets cash for his suggestions—he won't keep on suggesting.

Payments ("awards") for suggestions accepted are either a percentage (often 10 to 15 per cent) of the first year's savings or fixed amounts on a scale, depending on the suggestion's importance. Besides money, suggesters usually get their pictures in the paper. Don't give little money payments, however, lest it make the suggester mad. He feels cheated. "Ten-dollaritus" kills off many suggestion systems. Big companies make a practice of paying big for good suggestions. Top awards are mostly in the $3,000 to $5,000 range. Eastman Kodak paid over $11,000 for a better way to assemble products; Clevite Company paid Charley Zamiska $28,000 for a less costly way to make bronze castings (Charley then bought a farm and quit). General Motors pays out between $2 million and $3 million a year for suggestions. Suggestions are not piddling business.

It takes a suggestion *system* to get suggestions. Otherwise there is no regular way to make a suggestion nor any way to settle upon an award. Without a system a man suggests a change to his foreman and like as not it is refused. The foreman resents the suggestion as a criticism of his work. Sometimes he turns it down and then later adopts it as if he had thought of it himself. Small wonder suggestions dry up.

With a suggestion system, you have regular printed forms and boxes, like mailboxes, to receive them. The idea goes before a committee—not just the foreman—and if it is accepted, the man gets the credit (and the award), not his foreman. Some companies even print up thought-starter ideas: lists of operations where suggestions are particularly sought.

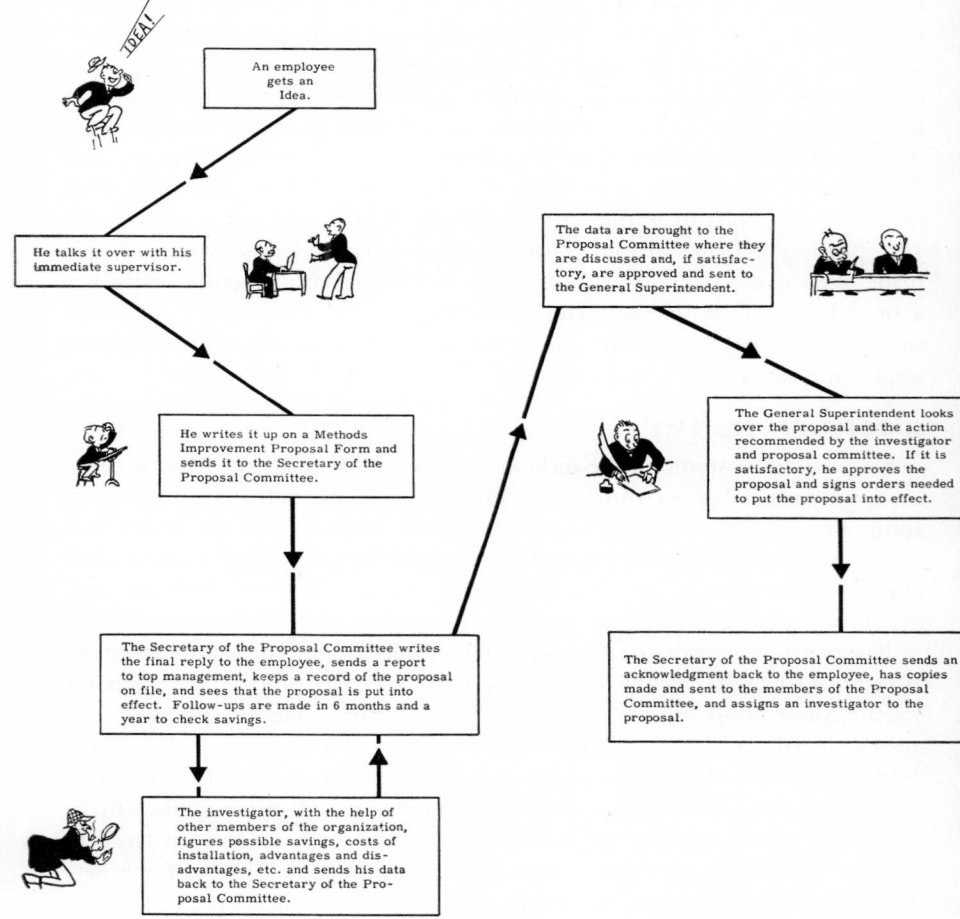

An employee gets an Idea.

He talks it over with his immediate supervisor.

The data are brought to the Proposal Committee where they are discussed and, if satisfactory, are approved and sent to the General Superintendent.

He writes it up on a Methods Improvement Proposal Form and sends it to the Secretary of the Proposal Committee.

The General Superintendent looks over the proposal and the action recommended by the investigator and proposal committee. If it is satisfactory, he approves the proposal and signs orders needed to put the proposal into effect.

The Secretary of the Proposal Committee writes the final reply to the employee, sends a report to top management, keeps a record of the proposal on file, and sees that the proposal is put into effect. Follow-ups are made in 6 months and a year to check savings.

The Secretary of the Proposal Committee sends an acknowledgment back to the employee, has copies made and sent to the members of the Proposal Committee, and assigns an investigator to the proposal.

The investigator, with the help of other members of the organization, figures possible savings, costs of installation, advantages and disadvantages, etc. and sends his data back to the Secretary of the Proposal Committee.

FIG. 20–2. A typical procedure for handling suggestions.

Only about one quarter of all suggestions are any good. The others are unworkable for one reason or another. And most of the acceptable ones are for minor—even trivial—improvements. But even these, collectively, are worth while.

Over the years, many suggestion plans have been started, but they haven't amounted to much and were dropped. Why? Stingy awards have been mentioned. But liberal awards alone won't make a system work; they may, in fact, make everyone but the few receivers mad. You see it is a touchy situation to ask for suggestions, then turn down three out of four and expect people to stay happy.

Here's what successful plans do:

1. *Acknowledge all suggestions* right away. Tell the man you have it and are considering it.
2. *Investigate all suggestions.* Don't turn a suggestion down without investigating. Is it good? Will it cost more than it is worth? If you can't use it, why not?
3. *Dispose of all suggestions.* Accept the good ones and give the men their awards. Reject the others and *explain why.* Don't leave the suggester hanging in the air.
4. *Make certain groups ineligible.* Foremen and methods engineers are paid to improve things. The same with other staff men. Design engineers should not get awards for improving the product. You might, however, let them get awards for suggestions not in line with their work.
5. *Pay well for good suggestions.*

JOB EVALUATION AND MERIT RATING

Job evaluation and merit rating are discussed in Chapters 25 and 26. Both ordinarily are "administered" by personnel, meaning that personnel writes descriptions and helps evaluate all new jobs. Once in a while industrial engineering keeps job evaluation up to date, but usually personnel does this. After all, personnel uses job descriptions in interviewing and has to handle all records about job titles when men change jobs. Also, an industry-wide or area-wide wage survey is commonly made in connection with job evaluation, and this is made by the personnel department.

Merit rating too comes under personnel (but not the actual rating of men, because only a man's superior knows him well enough to do that). Personnel oversees merit rating, tells people how to make ratings, and keeps the records.

LABOR LAWS

Employers have to obey all labor laws. It is personnel's job to know what these laws are and to see that they are obeyed in the company. For its knowledge, personnel depends on the legal department and on published interpretations of laws.

It is surprising how many laws (federal, state, and local) there are about employers that have to be obeyed. You aren't allowed to discriminate against Negroes, women, or others. Yet some laws restrict the work hours of women and children and sometimes forbid their employment. There are safety and sanitation laws and laws about pay. You have to stay above a set minimum; you have to pay time-and-a-half for overtime. Then you have to insure against injuries, and you have to pay unemployment insurance taxes and social security taxes. Also you have to keep hands off union things.

It isn't only that you have to know about the laws and obey them, but most of them make you keep a lot of records too—records that are otherwise unnecessary. You have to have records of who worked how many hours what day and what you paid him, and you have to keep these records for several years, in case this year someone says you disobeyed the law last year. You have to have all of these records to figure out how much tax and insurance premium to pay, because both taxes and premiums are based on your payroll. Then you have to keep some records, such as hours worked, just to be able to fill in required government reports. The job of keeping all of these records is split about 50–50 between personnel and accounting. But most of the job of keeping the plant obeying the laws falls to personnel.

LIVING WITH THE LABOR CONTRACT

Once labor contracts are signed, they have to be lived up to. They cover everything agreed to at the bargaining table, including methods of assigning jobs, giving pay raises and promotions, and what to do in case of layoffs. Personnel has to become the company's expert in interpretation—figuring out *exactly* what can be done and what cannot be done. It helps foremen carry out the contract by telling them what they can and cannot do.

SENIORITY

When a good job opens up, who gets it? The best-qualified man farther down? Or a reasonably well-qualified man who has been around longer? When business roller-coasters downhill and men have to be laid off, who goes home? The poorest workers? Or the newest workers?

At all but hourly paid levels the department head can do what he thinks best. He can choose the men to keep and the men to let go. But hourly paid men are almost always covered by a labor contract which lays down rules.

Seniority means preference for long-service men over short-service men —preference in job choices, preference in promotional opportunities (but only to better *hourly paid jobs*), and preference in layoffs (the last man on the payroll is the first off). Unions are strong for seniority because it is tangible and seems fair. Who is good and who isn't, and how good or how bad, are all rather subjective things. A man who loses out to a better man will never admit that he isn't as good as the other man. He sees it as favoritism. And everyone is a little afraid that he may come in on the short end of the boss's idea of merit. Also, no one likes to think that if he slows up a little after years of service he will be the first to go in case of a layoff, while younger men are kept. Seniority is an appealing idea, and it is in all labor contracts, although there are differences in how it operates.

Seniority in Promotion. Here's how seniority works in promotions. When a high paid hourly job opens up, men on lower paid jobs get a chance at it; if several want it, it goes to the man who has worked for the company the longest. Sounds simple.

But, suppose it is a machine setup man's job that is open and a janitor with 15 years of service wants it. It takes, say, three years of experience to learn to be a setup man—and not just experience as a janitor. So you qualify your seniority requirement and say that the applicants have to be able to do the job. This puts you into trouble again—a different kind of trouble. How can anyone ever get promoted? None of the applicants has done the job that is open, and none can do it well right off without help.

Then how do you fill the job? Here unions and companies part company. The company wants to promote the man who is most capable (presumably the man who could master the job the quickest and who would do it best in the long run)—seniority to be considered only if you have to choose between two more or less equally qualified men. The union wants to put in the man with the most seniority if he can learn to do the job reasonably well in a reasonable length of time. The senior man would be passed over only if he were obviously unqualified—as the janitor above.

You get into endless arguments about how well qualified is a man who hasn't done the job. Also, how much time should a man who wants the job be allowed for learning it? Also, must you let the janitor try to learn the job and fail before you let a machine operator with less experience try it?

Then there is the matter of area. Must you give a man in one department a chance at a job in another department as against a man (with less service) in that department? This needs to be bargained out and written into the labor contract. Usually men have, for promotional purposes, only departmental seniority; they can't use it for jobs in other departments.

Seniority in Job Assignments. Leaving out promotions, some jobs with equal pay are more desirable than others. There aren't too many of these situations. One would be the choice of working night or day shifts. Seniority usually rules here. If two men want one job, the longest-service man gets it.

Seniority in Layoffs. Here the idea is "the last on the payroll is the first off." This too sounds simpler than it turns out to be. How about skills? Do you lay off a skilled machine operator with three years of service and keep a janitor with four? Also you have the departmental problem, as in the case of promotions. Suppose your foundry's work slides off more than machine shop work. Do you lay off three-year-service men in the foundry while keeping one-year men in the machine shop? No, you don't. Layoffs are nearly always plant-wide—not departmental. The men actually laid off are the last on the payroll.

It works like this. All more or less common laboring jobs are called the "pool." When a department's work is cut down, you need fewer men. Men cut out of skilled jobs can "bump" men with less service or less skilled jobs, but only in their own department. They in turn can bump short-service men on less skilled jobs still in their own department. Finally, some bumped men get down to pool jobs. Here they can bump any still shorter-service man in the pool—*in any department*. There is no bumping across departmental lines except at the bottom. Bumping downhill skillwise is only within one's own department until pool jobs are reached.

Bumping downhill may be across job lines (if the labor contract is written that way), or it may be only down particular job lines. For example, can a man who sews shoes bump a man who cuts leather? No, the skills are too different. Or can a drill press setup man bump an automatic screw machine setup man? No, that would be bumping uphill skillwise. But the screw machine man could probably bump the drill press man even if he had never set up a drill press because it is bumping downhill skillwise, and since the work is somewhat similar, he could soon learn the drill press work.

There are pitfalls to watch for in seniority. If your automatic screw machines are short of work and you close them down for, say two days, must you let the setup man bump the drill press setup man? The question is, is two days a layoff? Better write your contract so that it is not—for layoff purposes.

International Harvester once did not have such a provision. It soon had hundreds of grievances claiming violation of its contract. Each man had a quantity of work to do daily, and all were on piecework. Those who finished early were given lower-paid work to fill out the day. The grievances said that whenever a long-service man ran out of piecework at, say, 1:30, the foreman should see if any man with less service still had unfinished piecework to do. He should then transfer that work to the first man and put the man with less service on the lower-paid jobs.

Imagine the foreman taking work from B to give A, then C to give B, and so on until quitting time. Next time the contract was written differently.

Foremen's Seniority.   If, because of a slump, a foreman has to go back to the ranks, how about his seniority? Suppose he has had 5 years in the department and has been foreman 2 years. Does he have 0 years? 5 years? 7 years? Normally, 5, but this too should be covered by the contract.

Superseniority.   Union officers have "superseniority," meaning that, for layoff purposes, they go off the payroll last. Superseniority is only going-down seniority, not coming-up seniority. Stewards and other officers get no preference in promotions.

Rehires.   Rehiring is supposed to be layoffs in reverse—last off the payroll are the first back on. Here too there are troublesome areas. Suppose one department picks up faster than another? Do you recall 1-year-service man A into a department where he never worked as against B, a 6-month service man who used to work in the recalling department?

Seniority Summary.   We have raised several questions about seniority in operation but given few answers. What are the answers? They ought to be in the labor contract. If answers are not in the contract, there will be arguments, grievances, and arbitrations—until, as new contracts are written, they do get spelled out there. Seniority practices are not standard, but here is more or less common practice:

1. The company has a free hand in selecting supervisors from the ranks. It does not have to consider the seniority of the man selected.
2. Promotions to high-skill hourly paid jobs follow merit, seniority being considered only if merit is about equal.
3. Seniority, for promotional purposes, is largely occupational or departmental, not plant-wide.
4. Union officials, including department stewards, have "superseniority" for layoff purposes.
5. Seniority does not allow workers with the greatest seniority to pick the piecework jobs they want, nor does it mean that if piecework runs low or runs out completely within a day, it has to be transferred to them.
6. In layoffs, seniority is, in the last analysis, generally plant-wide.

Now, what has the personnel department to do with seniority? It keeps all seniority records: how long has each man worked for the company? how long in the department? how long on each job? And it works with foremen on promotions, transfers, layoffs and rehires, interpreting and carrying out the contract.

VACATIONS

Office workers usually get 2 weeks of vacation after 1 year's service. Factory workers usually get 1 week after 1 year, 2 weeks after 5 years, and often 3 weeks after 10 or 15 years.

Vacations seriously hamper summer operations. Employees in most plants average a week and a half vacation, and practically all of it is taken during school vacations (June 15 to September 1). This means that everyone takes off 1½ weeks in a 10-week period. This is 15 per cent absenteeism. Add to this the normal 2 to 3 per cent absenteeism, and you are up to 17 to 18 per cent. It is hard to operate with every sixth man gone all the time. In fact, it is worse—long-service men (all your key people) get the longest vacations. Their absence hurts the most.

Most plants operate all summer and endure the absences. Some, though, close down for 2 weeks (probably the first half of July). Each plan has its good and bad points. Keep on operating and you keep on taking orders and delivering to customers. Employees like to pick their own times, and you don't overload recreational and travel facilities. But you can't operate efficiently, and you can't give everyone his vacation when he wants it. Closing down has the reverse good and bad points. Closing down seems to be a slowly growing practice. The personnel department, of course, has a big job of arranging vacation schedules if vacations go on all summer, but gets out of that job if you close down.

MISCELLANEOUS PERSONNEL DEPARTMENT DUTIES

In-Plant Feeding.   Most factories today have cafeterias for their employees. Concessionaires usually operate them under the general direction of the personnel department. Meals are generally served at slightly below cost, or at from 60 to 80 cents for meat, potatoes, vegetables, bread, butter, and a drink. Low prices encourage men to eat a good hot meal, usually a better meal than they would get carrying their lunch. Lunch wagons and vending machines are also permitted. They give workers a chance to get between-meals snacks.

On the other hand, not everyone has a cafeteria. Chrysler recently built a new highly automated motor factory to make Plymouth engines. It has no cafeteria. The men bring their lunches and eat at tables near their workplace.

Music.   A few companies play music through a public-address system occasionally during the day. Factory noise probably will keep this an uncommon practice. The music can be played from the company's own Hi-Fi system or can be, in big cities, piped in from a commercial source.

Plant Guards and the Parking Lot.   Plant protection is generally assigned to personnel. With this job goes supervision of the parking lot, issuing parking permits, assigning spaces, and handling traffic at shift changes.

Newspapers and Magazines.   Personnel usually has the job of putting out the company newspapers and magazines. It collects personal items, writes articles, and does all but print the magazine. Magazines provide an excellent means for explaining company products, policies, and plans to employees.

Large companies sometimes have both a company-wide magazine and separate ones for major divisions or separate plants. The public relations department may put out the company-wide magazine, but the personnel departments at separate plants put out local publications.

Athletics.   Most companies sponsor athletics, but a few do not. Bowling and softball are quite popular. Leagues are organized with teams from various departments. Personnel arranges schedules and gets places to play. Baseball, basketball, and golf also have their following. Company-sponsored teams in industrial leagues, competing against teams from other companies, are much less common than intramural sports, probably because so few can take part.

FIG. 20–3. A company-operated cafeteria.

Some men like to squeeze in a little relaxing exercise in their noon-times and even in the morning and afternoon rest period. Shuffleboard, ping pong, and rubber horseshoes all vie with the usual checker and rummy games for the men's attention. These make no work for personnel beyond getting the equipment.

Social Activities. Some companies have bridge clubs, dance clubs, hiking clubs, riding clubs, stamp clubs, and the like. Personnel tells newcomers about them and who to see to get in. Company picnics are, however, largely a thing of the past, and the office Christmas party is dying out.

"Open houses" are coming in. A skeleton work force keeps things going while other employees, their families, and the public are invited in and taken on conducted tours. Open houses build community good will and give a man a chance to show his family where he works. Open houses are probably good morale builders, except for the occasional employee who notices how much better working conditions are in other departments than his.

Company Libraries. Large companies maintain libraries for the use of their staff. Scientific publications and periodicals of interest to various departments are kept readily available. Although libraries cost money, they cost far less than maintaining adequate separate small collections of books in the various offices. When there is no library, there is a danger that books and magazines will accumulate in the offices of major department heads, where they will be little used. The personnel department usually has the responsibility for the library, although the engineering department may be responsible for technical books.

Reading Racks.   Have you noticed, on entering most big factories today, a rack of booklets alongside as you pass down a hallway? The booklets are of all kinds: How to Construct a Barbecue, The Transatlantic Telegraph Cable, booklets on home and family, inspirational literature—anything. You might wonder what it's all about. Employees seem to like the idea. Nearly all of them take a copy of every booklet. General Motors passes out over 10 million such booklets a year.

The booklets are free and are there for employees to take or not, as they see fit. Personnel selects the subjects and keeps the racks filled, putting in new subjects often. But why? Actually part of the idea is to furnish employees interesting reading material. But now and then you put in one about the company, its products, plants, processes, employees, or customers. These ought, of course, to be factual and undistorted.

Helping Workers Save.   Does a company owe it to an employee to help him save money? Do you want your boss telling you what to do with your money? The two questions are almost the same; yet maybe there is a difference. Surely the company should not tell workers what to do with their money; just as surely it can help.

Credit unions are the usual answer. A credit union is a small bank—restricted to employees of the company. It runs with a little help from personnel, and it is located next to the personnel office. It has its books checked occasionally by the government. It accepts deposits and makes loans. Employees can save by having the company make regular deductions from their pay checks and making deposits for them to their account in the credit union.

Loans to employees wanting to borrow are approved by a loan committee made up of employees. The borrower pays off by the payroll deduction plan, and so doesn't become delinquent. Interest is usually 1 per cent a month—only one half to one third of the outside small-loan rate. Profits go to depositors as interest, but if the profits are large, the interest rate to borrowers is cut.

The only other common saving plan is government bond buying by the payroll deduction method. Years ago many companies let employees buy stoves, refrigerators, and such items through the purchasing department, thus getting the company discount. Not much of that goes on today.

Helping Employees in Trouble.   Many companies try to offer a helping hand to employees in trouble. Counselors offer advice when asked, but employees' trouble often cannot be helped by advice alone. Often they need money to tide them over or legal help or both. Many companies will advance a week or so's wages as a loan to carry an employee over an emergency. Legal help includes looking over contracts and leases and telling employees what to watch out for. If an employee gets into a lawsuit, the company's lawyers will recommend a lawyer to him but *will not themselves serve as his lawyers*. Neither would they take an active part if an employee is arrested.

Sometimes factory employees buy too many things on credit, can't meet the payments, and then get their wages garnisheed. Years ago many employers discharged employees who had their wages garnisheed. Today most of them try to help the employee. One steel manufacturing company in the Chicago area receives 300 garnishments monthly against its 18,000 employees. Three thousand of its employees have had their wages garnisheed at least once. Almost all the garnishments are against the wages of colored and Spanish-speaking employees (of whom the company has 5,000).

A garnishee is a legal procedure. It is a court order requiring the company to report whether the individual is employed and how much it owes him and to withhold his pay. The company must report to the court what it owes the employee, after which it must send part of his pay (usually 10 per cent) to the creditor until the claim is satisfied. A garnishee causes a certain amount of trouble to the company, but few companies today would discharge a man because his wages were garnisheed, even repeatedly. Instead they would try to help him plan his affairs to prevent future garnishments.

Community Relations.   A company ought to be a good community citizen. This means helping with such things as the community chest drive, the Red Cross, and blood donors' drives. Money contributions can be taken out of men's pay, and blood donors can be given time off with pay to go to the blood bank center. All of these things cost the company a little money, but a good-citizen company will do them.

The personnel department sometimes co-operates with local civic leaders in a program of hiring a certain proportion of needy or handicapped people. Personnel needs to be alert to community good will and to seek to improve community-company relationships.

STUDY QUESTIONS

1. What are the records that the personnel department must keep? Why does it have to keep each?
2. What part does the personnel department play in administering nonfinancial incentives? Why should personnel have anything to do with nonfinancial incentives?
3. Why do suggestion systems fail? Write out instructions telling how to operate a suggestion system successfully.

4. Contrast the company and the union view of how seniority ought to work in promotions.
5. What are some of the problems you get into in trying to give some consideration to seniority in promotions?
6. How does seniority work in layoffs? What has personnel to do with this?
7. Vacations are a fine thing, but they make problems for the company. What problems do they make?
8. What should a company's policy be toward helping an employee to save money? What things should it do or should it not do?
9. What is a garnishee? What should a company do about garnishments?

CASE 20–1. THE MASTER BUSHING AND BEARING CO.

The Master Bushing and Bearing Company operated a small brass foundry for making its own castings. Andrew Stevens had been a molder for many years, having altogether 26 years of service. In recent years, he occasionally had too much to drink over a week end. His absences were more numerous than they were when he was younger. Finally, he was warned that he must be more regular in his attendance or be disciplined.

He failed to come to work on the three days before Thanksgiving; when he reported for work on Friday, he found that he had been discharged for failing to come to work for three days without reporting the reason. The discharge was clearly according to the shop rules and the labor contract.

Stevens said he had been sick in bed and had not gone out during the three days. He had not been able to call in because he lived at a boarding house where there was no telephone. He did not know his fellow boarders very well and had not asked any of them to call in for him—in fact, he had not thought about reporting the reason for his absence.

The union asked the company to reinstate Stevens, not as a molder but as a laborer, saying that his 26 years of service should entitle him to consideration even though the discharge was proper. The company's relations with the union were none too good; so the company took the position that the rule must be enforced in this case or the union would soon be pressing for further relaxation of contract provisions.

Comment on the disposition of the case. What do you think of the company's argument? What effect would this case have on labor-management relations? If you took Stevens back, what would you do with him?

Chapter 21

UNION RELATIONS

THE "PROBLEM" OF LABOR UNREST

W HY do men strike? What lies behind it? Are these problems which, when solved, would eliminate labor unrest? Is labor unrest new? No, it is not new. It is important to see that this is an age-old problem. Moses led the Israelites out of Egypt to get away from hard taskmasters. The peasants in England revolted against their masters in the fourteenth century. Strikes occurred in the early days of factories, 150 years ago. Strikes occur today in the United States, and employees in communist countries revolt now and then even at the risk of death.

Why do we have eternal labor unrest? Historically the lot of employees (or, centuries ago, slaves) was so bad that revolt held the only promise—slim though it was—of bettering their life. But we have strikes today in the United States—strikes by men making $100 a week who own automobiles, homes, TV sets, and all kinds of material goods. Why?

Striking to get more goods is an obvious and partly superficial answer. Employers would say, however, that the desire for more need make no trouble. All we have to do is to produce more, and we'll all have more—no need for strikes. People don't read history alike—but history seems to deflate that employer's argument. A bigger pie doesn't mean that everyone gets a bigger piece. Employees have to fight for a bigger piece whether the pie is bigger or not. Most employers, historically, have not willingly given more pie to employees. Employees have had to fight if they wanted more than crumbs.

How many times have you seen magazine articles about labor problems where writers talk about them as if there was a list of situations needing correction? They talk as if correcting the situations they list would bring eternal peace on the labor front. Articles of this sort are always turning up.

Let's look more closely at labor problems. *No situation of any kind in labor relations (or in any other field) is a problem unless someone thinks or feels it is a problem.* Any problem, including a labor problem, there-fore, has two aspects: the situation itself and the dissatisfaction with the situation. It takes a mental attitude of objection, desire for change, to make a problem out of a situation. Any situation can become a problem if someone thinks that it ought to be changed.

Labor problems are in a sense created by unions. They don't make the situations, but they are focal points of dissatisfaction; or, even more, they sometimes stir up the dissatisfaction. We are not here passing judg-ment on its rightness or wrongness. We are merely pointing out that nonproblem situations can turn into problem situations and that unions sometimes cause the change.

If there were no unions, such "problems" would rarely become im-portant issues, since individual employees dissatisfied with a situation would accept it, quit the job, or be discharged. Most employees, unin-fluenced by unions, accept the conditions that go with jobs when they accept the job—and do not think of them as problems. There are unions, however, and they press for changes in situations they regard as un-satisfactory. If management can't, or won't, change such situations, they become unsolved labor "problems."

"Progress" and Labor Problems.   Labor problems in the United States are strongly influenced by the concept of "progress," which is deeply rooted in our thinking. Everyone expects to be continually better off in a material way and to improve year by year, not century by century. Anyone who does only as well as his father did is dissatisfied. Our whole history has been one of more and more production so that most Americans do improve their standard of living continually. Union ob-jectives are cast along this line of "progress." *Each year brings new demands; each demand won is the steppingstone from which to start another year's demands.*

This idea of material progress perpetuates labor problems because, everything being relative, yesterday's satisfactory solution to a problem is not satisfactory tomorrow. Like the horizon, as we advance, the goal advances before us. In short, *the idea of "progress" prevents any per-manent solution to labor problems.*

Peace on the Labor Front.   Some companies, for limited periods of time, achieve industrial peace. Stability of industrial relations, however, is not a reliable measure of harmonious relations, nor can it be taken as evidence that there are no labor problems. Years ago there was more "peace" than there is today because unions were weak or nonexistent. Even conditions undesirable to the workers were not thought of as problems by most people. Workers who wanted changes were con-sidered "troublemakers" and were discharged by employers. Naturally, peace reigned on the industrial front.

Yesterday's "peace" was a company-dominated peace. Today's industrial peace is less company-dominated, but neither is it union dominated. In manufacturing it is uncommon for the company or the union to dominate labor relations completely. Sometimes today's peace is an armed truce, being maintained by each out of respect for the other's fighting strength. Usually both parties sincerely try to get along together and not to resort to open conflict. Such a peace can be and sometimes is preserved for many years, but it is inherently unstable, the "progress" idea contributing to the instability. Not only do union leaders need to make "progress" annually in the form of fresh gains from management but each leader must gain as much for his group as other leaders get for their members. The time nearly always comes, when the company thinks that it cannot grant all the new demands.

HISTORICAL BACKGROUND OF TODAY'S LABOR ORGANIZATION

Probably there are nearly 17 million union members in the United States today, with some 11 million of them in manufacturing. That comes to over three fourths of all factory hourly paid men. Most non-union men are in small plants. It was not always so. Until the 1930's big business kept the unions out.

Unions never got anywhere in the United States until after the Civil War. The first start of consequence was the Knights of Labor. It withered away in the 1880's, when the American Federation of Labor came along. You should know about the Knights of Labor, however, because its weaknesses showed the A.F. of L. makers how to make their organization stronger. But the A.F. of L.'s early strengths turned out to be weaknesses in the 1920's and 1930's and made some overhauling necessary.

The Knights of Labor was one big organization, such as, say, the Republican party. Everyone belonged to it (even owners if they wanted to). This didn't work because there was no common ground of interest. So the Federation of Labor set up separate unions for bricklayers, carpenters, machinists, and so on. Each union had local chapters to which men belonged. Here they got on common ground. Interests of all members were more or less the same. The Federation was a federation of *unions*, not of men.

So far so good. The Federation (learning from the experience in England of some of its founders) also objected to "dual" unionism. It would *not accept two unions in the same craft*. Each union joining the Federation got an *exclusive* charter to organize and represent its craft. Incidentally, unskilled crafts were, on the whole, neglected.

The exclusive charter idea gave strength to the A.F. of L. in its early days, but it made trouble later. The skilled craft unions set up membership and apprentice training rules that became too rigid. After World War I many factories grew to enormous size, and so could specialize plant jobs and operate more efficiently. Jobs calling for all-round skill were cut up into individual tasks requiring little skill. Machinists, for example, were rarely needed in such factories, but great numbers of individual machine operators were employed. An operator able to run only one kind of machine served no apprenticeship and was but a semi-skilled man compared to old line machinists. What happened to the jobs of machinists happened to jobs in other crafts as well. The lack of general all-round skill and the failure to serve an apprenticeship *disqualified the bulk of factory workers from membership in the existing craft unions.*

Within the Federation the craft unions wouldn't approve giving charters to new unions to which semiskilled workers could belong. Nor would they lower the bars and relax their membership requirements to let in semiskilled workers. The idea of all-inclusive industrial unions met with the opposition of several existing craft unions. They could visualize losing the few members they had in the large plants to such industrial unions. In the 1920's A.F. of L. unions made a few attempts to organize the employees of large companies into individual craft unions, but they got nowhere. None of the attempts was more than a piece-meal attack, nor could it be anything else with the craft unions operating individually.

The National Industrial Recovery Act of 1933 contained a section requiring employers engaged in interstate commerce to bargain collectively with their employees. The principal result of this provision was the creation of numerous company-wide unions, often under the complete domination of the company. After the NIRA was declared unconstitutional, the National Labor Relations Act (the Wagner Act) was passed in 1935, in which companies were forbidden to dominate unions and labor was given virtually a free hand to organize all employees working for companies in interstate commerce.

However, the organizational weakness of the A.F. of L. when dealing with large companies remained. As a result several large unions quit the A.F. of L., feeling that industrial unions were necessary. Under the leadership of John L. Lewis and his United Mine Workers, the CIO was formed.[1] The CIO unions contributed money to pay organizers who aggressively pushed organizing campaigns in the steel, auto, meat packing, rubber, oil, electrical, flat glass, farm equipment, maritime, and other industries. Their campaigns in the main were successful, and for the first time these large industries had labor unions. The A.F. of L. stirred from its lethargy by these activities; it set up several industrial-type unions and began increasing its membership through organization drives. Later Lewis withdrew his United Mine Workers' Union from the CIO and was readmitted to the A.F. of L., but still later the UMW

---

[1] Originally the Committee for Industrial Organization, later the Congress of Industrial Organizations.

withdrew again from the A.F. of L. Finally, in 1955, the A.F. of L. and the CIO merged into one large federation, the AFL-CIO.

Outside of the large federation there are several other groups of organized workers, the Railroad Brotherhoods and many unaffiliated independent unions.

UNIONS AS ORGANIZATIONS

Labor unions are big business. Top labor leaders' salaries do not equal those of company presidents, but they are upper-bracket salaries ($25,000 to $50,000), and there are often extras such as a house and car. The 18 million members pay in over one-half billion dollars a year in dues (monthly dues are almost always $3 a month or more). Sometimes the dues collection part of unions seems to outweigh everything else. Jurisdictional disputes over which union should represent workers can hardly be explained otherwise.

Labor unions have organizational objectives in addition to their general objective of serving their members. They are also political organizations in that their officers have to run for re-election every year. This creates internal political problems. Their leaders want to keep their jobs, so their first objective is to keep the union alive and their second objective is to get themselves re-elected. These objectives sometimes make trouble. How? To be a successful union leader you have to do something for your men—get pay raises for them, get security for them, see that they are treated fairly. But suppose that the company pays well and is fair, union or no. Then what? Then you must get *bigger* pay raises, *more* security, *more* fair treatment. It helps if you can find a few cases of unfairness to straighten out. Magnify them; tell your men that they merely show the kind of treatment that they can expect from the company. Then straighten them out, but be sure that the union gets credit for championing the put-upon workers. All this mountain-out-of-mole-hill-making makes extra trouble.

The big drives to organize factory workers into unions are in the past. Organizational drives often caused strikes. Today we are mostly done with organizational drives but we still have occasional strikes. There are various reasons, discussed on page 404, but one of them is their organizational value. A successful short strike strengthens the union. There is the feel and excitement of a contest. And, after the victory, the men are proud of the strong organization that fights for them. An occasional strike—a display of strength—reminds the members of the power and value of the union. Of course there is risk involved; a long or unsuccessful strike hurts the organization.

Local unions are units of national (usually called "international") unions. Part of the dues collected go in to the national union. What does a local get in exchange? It gets consultative help during negotiations, and if a strike occurs it may get money help.

International representatives sit at the bargaining table with the local union officers and usually do most of the union talking. They also tell local men what demands are being granted elsewhere and what to ask for and what to settle for. Sometimes they tell local people to be more belligerent or to ask for more, but sometimes they have to try to hold down the local men. If there is a strike, the international representatives are on the picket line and help plan strategy.

10 LARGEST UNIONS

1. AUTO WORKERS – 1,260,000
2. TEAMSTERS – 1,230,000
3. STEELWORKERS – 980,000
4. CARPENTERS – 750,000
5. MACHINISTS – 630,000
6. MINE WORKERS – 600,000
7. ELECTRICAL WORKERS – 460,000
8. LADIES GARMENT WORKERS – 380,000
9. LABORERS AND HOD CARRIERS – 370,000
10. HOTEL, RESTAURANT WORKERS – 300,000

FIG. 21–1. Membership of the ten largest unions in the United States. Together they make up nearly half the membership of all American unions.

Inside some unions there may be a lot of politics, but it is not always so. In most unions only about 5 per cent of the members take any part, and all political maneuvering that goes on is within these small groups. Here the locals differ from national unions. National unions have annual conventions where local union representatives elect national union officers. These conventions are often just as political as any Republican or Democratic presidential nominating convention. No lethargy there.

Unions have come of age, and this affects their organization. Probably no democratic organization can really be very democratic when so few of its members take part. But in unions, few taking part is part cause and part effect. There are plenty of stories about how the insiders in some unions keep the 95 per cent from being active.

Here are some of the things that have been done. Remember, though, these are by no means typical. Insiders sometimes call union business meetings at an early hour, then hold off on all important business until so late that everyone else has gone home. Or a meeting is called for one hour but started earlier. All votes on important issues are taken before the uninformed arrive. Sometimes meetings are held in small rooms. The insiders are told to get there early. By the time the outsiders get there, they can't get in. Or meetings are called on such short notice, or at such unusual hours, that only the chosen get there. Another device is to postpone action, or even to adjourn any meeting where too much opposition seems to be developing. The issue is taken up again at whatever later meeting the opponents happen to miss.

Really ambitious union leaders want to move up in their national unions and then on up into high office in the AFL-CIO. A great many national union officers seem to have such ambitions. These drive them to try to outdo each other. If Reuther gets certain benefits for the Auto Workers, can McDonald of the Steel Workers do less for his men? If he does do less, can he expect high office in the AFL-CIO? Also, he may find that he has some real competition from some young lieutenant in his own organization for his own job—someone who promises the members to outdo him.

All these internal rivalries have their effect on local labor relations because the demands each local makes on its employer are patterned at high levels. Local unions sometimes have to be sold on the demands they are asked to make, and they are by no means all behind them.

National union leaders sometimes lose touch with the rank and file. In recent years the union's drive for insurance, pensions, and guaranteed annual wages has not been universally popular. They all cost the company money—money that could be paid in wages. Young workers in particular would rather have a raise today than a pension in 1990.

The Guaranteed Annual Wage (or its cousin, the SUB, Supplemental Unemployment Benefits) is another issue about which it is doubtful if the rank and file is really concerned. Rarely does anyone other than the newest newcomer get laid off. Yet only laid-off workers benefit. Why would long-time employees want it? Because it isn't their money —the company says. But, you see, actually it is their money. To the company, it is tweedledum or tweedledee—pay it as SUB or as a wage increase, it doesn't matter greatly. Most long-service employees know this, of course, and aren't much for SUB.

THE EFFECT OF UNIONS ON LABOR PROBLEMS

The mere fact that a union exists creates some problems. These include union recognition, the union shop, the checkoff of union dues, the maintenance of membership, and paying shop stewards for grievance time. Without unions there would be no problems in these areas.

But besides these a union accentuates many other problems. We have already said that unions try to get management to take care of bad situations, and we have also said that if no real problems exist the union has to tackle the near-problems and magnify them into issues worth getting steamed up about. All of this is good in that conditions are continually being improved.

If you agree with the premise (given on page 393) that workers get higher wages because of unions, you pretty nearly have to admit that unions must have problems to solve and issues to fight for—which means that if none exist they have to make some.

Here is the reasoning. The union's only real weapon is to strike. So, to win anything more than the company would willingly give, the workers have to be willing to strike. Going out on strike and cutting off paychecks for a while is a serious matter. Workers don't do it unless they feel that something important is at stake. So it is necessary for the union to come up with such issues.

Be sure that you see this main point: *Union negotiators won't win much at the bargaining table unless they come there armed with the authority to call a strike!*[2] Union members must vote them this authority at a union meeting. And the members won't vote this way unless they think that the issues are important. So good issues have to be found or not such good issues have to be made to seem important.

COLLECTIVE BARGAINING

When you bargain collectively, just what goes on? Who talks to whom about what? The talkers are representatives of the employer and the employees. Usually each side has several representatives. They meet together and decide upon such matters as rates of pay, job tenure, seniority, rules violations and penalties, pensions, and any number of other matters. Look at Figure 21–2. It shows two pages from the index of subjects covered in the General Motors labor agreement.

How do the representatives get their jobs? The company's men are appointed by the president. Almost always the director of personnel or industrial relations is one. But picking the employees' representatives is more complicated. First, let's look at the law. Our laws *require* the company to bargain collectively with employee representatives, *if they have a union*. Notice, then, that if there is no union, collective bargaining is not a must, and there are no rules about how the company and its employees get together.

But what if there is a union?—and nearly always there is. First, the company doesn't have to talk to its representatives unless it is "certified" as the employees' bargaining agent. And how does it get certified?

---

[2] They don't have to be so armed for the early negotiating meetings. That can come if negotiations bog down.

By winning an election. Starting with a no-union situation, a union claims that most of a company's employees are members. An election is held under the supervision of the National Labor Relations Board. Employees don't have to vote. If a majority of those voting vote for the union, it is certified as the official representative of the men. The union's

INDEX

	Paragraph No.	Page No.
Additional Bargaining Units	2, 2a	1, 2
Alternate Committeeman	10	13
Appeal Committee	39	33
Appeal to Umpire, Withdrawal of	52	41
Appendix A—Employment Policies and Procedures		113
Appendix B—Journeyman Qualifying Periods		116
Appendix C—Skilled Trades Seniority as affected by Military Leaves and Formal Leaves		122
Apprentice Committee	120	84
Apprentices	120	84
Apprentice, Seniority of	125	87
Approval of Local Seniority Agreements	59	44
Approval of Shift Preference Agreements	75	54
"Authorization for Check-Off of Dues" Form	4h	5
Back Pay, Limit of Claims for	48-50	39-40
Bulletin Boards, Union	92-93	63
Calendar Week, Definition	82	57
Call-in Pay	80	57
Chairman of Shop Committee, Designation of	12	15
Change in Shift Hours	88	61
Change of Address, Notification of	74	54
Check-Off	4h-4r	5-11
Claims by Temporary Employes	56	43
Claims, for Failure to Give Work	49	40
Classifications, Establishment of Temporary	102	71
Coercion	6-7	12
Committee, Apprentice	120	84
Committee, Establishment of Sub-	14	15
Committee, Size of Shop	11	14
Committeeman, Call for—In Disciplinary Interviews	76a	55

INDEX—Continued

	Paragraph No.	Page No.
Temporary Employes—Claims by	56	43
Temporary Employes Defined	56	43
Temporary Employes, Recall of	70	52
Temporary Rates and Classifications, Establishment of	102-102a	71
Termination Clause	152	109
Time Allowed for Bargaining	19-19e	18-19
Time and One-half	85	58
Time Limits in Disciplinary Cases	77	55
Transfers	62, 63	46
Transfer of Major Operations Between Plants	96	64
Umpire, Appeal Procedure to	43	35
Umpire, Appointment and Term	44	37
Umpire, Interpretation of Agreements	55	43
Umpire, Powers and Functions	46	37
Umpire, Powers in Disciplinary Cases	47	39
Umpire Procedure—Certain Medical Cases	43b	36
Union Bulletin Boards	92, 93	63
Union Representatives, Visiting Plant	38, 43a	29, 36
Union Security	4-4g	3-5
Vacation Pay Allowances	137	96
Wage Agreements, Local	100	66
Wages, Cost-of-Living Allowance	101	66
Wages, General Increase	101	66
Wages, Hiring Rates	98	65
Wages, Negotiations	97, 102-102a	65, 71
Wage Payment Plans	90-91	62-63
Wages	97-102a	65-71
Wages—Improvement Factor	101a	66
Wages—New Jobs	102-102a	71
Waiver	154	111
Work, Equalization of Extra	71	53
Working Hours	81-89	57-61
Zones	13	15

FIG. 21–2. Part of the index to General Motors' labor contract.

bargainers are then chosen in union meetings and become the official bargainers for the employees.

Who can vote? Employees in a "bargaining unit." Bargaining units are discussed on page 406. Here we want to call attention to the fact that not all groups vote together. Office employees, for example, cannot vote in a shop election.

Collective bargaining takes place in meetings between company and union representatives—meetings that lead up to both parties signing a labor contract. The contract may be for one or more years. Then *no bargaining* goes on until shortly before the agreement runs out and bargaining for the new contract starts. So bargaining is a periodic, not a continuous, affair.

The law says that both parties must bargain collectively in good faith. Normally you might think that "bargaining" would be a sort of horse-trading business—I give in on this point, you give in on that, we each concede something, and so on until we finally agree on all points.

Collective bargaining isn't quite like that. Years ago employers had it all their way. An employee could take what the company offered or could quit. Collective bargaining is therefore always a matter of taking away some of the employer's former rights. The union always demands; the company always resists. The company gets nothing out of collective bargaining except to be free from demands and strikes for the duration of the contract.

Since collective bargaining is a matter of "labor demands, company gives," and since the law requires collective bargaining, some people think that the law requires you to give—that if you don't give you have violated the law. Not so. Neither party has to *yield* any points—each just has to talk in good faith.

Labor being in the demanding position has an advantage at the bargaining table that is not always fully appreciated. Asking for a Cadillac standard of living, a 30-hour work week, and cradle-to-the-grave security is easy. Who wouldn't like it? And we'd have it, too, if only you (the employer) would divide up your fabulous profits with us—after all we make all of that profit for you. You keep us from a high standard of living. Just sign here, and we'll have our Utopia.

It's as simple as that. But you see how all this puts the company on the defensive. It has to keep saying no and then try to justify its position. Saying yes only too often bankrupts the company. Kaiser-Frazer had higher wages and more fringe benefits than the big three auto companies in Detroit, but its high costs helped bankrupt it. Studebaker-Packard has the same problem.

What Does the Union Want?   In general, it wants (1) security for itself, (2) "more" for the workers, and (3) more control over jobs and working conditions. Sometimes it tries to get at number 3, more control, by trying to get the company to settle certain matters jointly. Often this works out to give the union a veto power over management decisions in the areas of "joint agreement."

What Does Management Want?   Management's objectives at the bargaining table are generally defensive—to maintain the status quo or yield from it as little as possible. Management wants (1) to keep its management functions, and (2) to be able to operate profitably.

Contract Negotiations.   When contracts are being negotiated, the international union representatives take the leading part. If raises are refused by management when the union demands are presented, the international representative of the union lightly brushes off the company's defense that it is unable to pay. He has heard such arguments many times before, but rarely has he seen a company get into financial difficulty because of granting a pay raise.

Collective bargaining meetings are frequently like poker games. The stakes are high (a wage increase of one cent per hour costs the company $20,000 a year for every thousand workers). Demands are made, positions taken, offers and counteroffers made. Some "horse trading" goes on, one demand is dropped if another is granted, etc. Better not take fixed positions or issue ultimatums early in the negotiations because you may have to retreat or yield points not originally intended to be given up.

Rarely are settlements made in one meeting. Meetings are recessed while the parties confer among themselves as to what to do or say next. The management representatives, who usually have but limited authority, confer with top management. The union bargainers discuss the progress of negotiations with the local executive committee or even at an open meeting of the whole union membership. Finally, after several meetings, an agreement is reached. It is then submitted to the union membership for ratification, after which the labor contract is signed by representatives of both sides. In the rare cases where no agreement is reached, a strike generally occurs.

Negotiating is a specialized procedure, and both parties are generally well advised to use specialists. On the union side, the international union representative is such a specialist. He becomes an experienced negotiator as he goes from one company to another guiding local union leaders in the presentation of their demands and counseling as to when they have gained the last possible concession. The union may also have one of its lawyers present at important negotiations.

When management's representatives from inside the company try to cope with these men, they are often outgeneraled. Law firms specializing in labor matters, including negotiation, have multiplied in recent years. They fill the need on the part of management for skilled negotiators on its side of the bargaining table. Some people deplore the entrance of lawyers into the field of labor relations, claiming that they introduce technicalities. But if you look at grievances that go to arbitrators for settlement, you will see that you had better get your attorney in on drawing up your labor contract. You wouldn't think of signing other contracts without having your lawyers look them over, so it is curious that some people think that you ought to sign such an important contract without legal help.

The nature of union demands has also made economists, statisticians, insurance specialists, accountants, and actuaries necessary in negotiations. Cost-of-living escalator provisions, "annual improvement" factors, hospitalization, sickness and accident insurance, pensions, supplementary unemployment benefits, guaranteed annual wages, and other similar demands force the company to investigate the cost of each demand so that it can bargain intelligently. If some of these demands are granted, specialists are also needed to set up and administer the new provisions.

Most multiplant companies deal with many different unions and must negotiate contracts with all of them. Sometimes the factory workers in different plants belong to different local unions of the same international union. Where such a situation existed in the past, each local usually negotiated its own contract. Now, however, the international unions are trying to consolidate these situations and, as far as membership in their union goes, to negotiate on a company-wide basis. Unions claim that company-wide negotiations eliminate the dissatisfaction generated by different contract provisions in different plants. Generally the companies oppose this practice, however, even though it produces consistent contracts for the different plants, because workers in different plants do not want the same things and because it is easier for the union to close down the whole company at one time.[3] If the union cannot close down the whole company at one time, a strike at one plant may not hurt the company much, because it can transfer orders from the closed plant to those still operating.

Recently, collective bargaining has developed in the direction of "patterns." The real bargaining is done by one or two of the largest companies in the industry, after which negotiations in the smaller companies are settled on the basis of the pattern set by the industry's leading company. Not all the companies in the industry can follow the pattern in every respect, but it sets a precedent and is generally followed.

Industry-wide bargaining is another growing practice. In industry-wide bargaining the representatives of the various companies meet with representatives of the union and negotiate for all companies in the industry that are organized by the negotiating international union. Such bargaining has long existed in coal mining but is new in most manufacturing industries.

STRIKES

We hear a lot about strikes and how they cause so much loss to society. Strikes are dramatic, and they make the headlines, but their cost to society has been exaggerated by some people. Does one third of 1 per cent seem a large part of the whole? That is all the lost time that strikes have caused in the United States in the last 25 years! And it has been down to around one fourth of 1 per cent since 1950. Less than one workday per worker per year—*normal day-to-day absenteeism is six to eight times as great.*

---

[3] One large company a short time ago was faced with insistent demands from unions in its eastern plants for more liberal pensions. Its West Coast plants were not interested in better pensions, preferring CIF or "Cash in Fist."

Besides, strike workdays lost are not often lost to society. If we can't buy one brand of shoes because of a strike, we buy another brand. The work lost by worker Smith in one factory is gained by worker Jones in another factory. Or if the coal miners go on strike, we buy from the stock pile of coal until the strike is settled. Then the miners build up the pile again. The days lost in June by miner Williams, he works instead in September. Also strikers usually don't just sit around while on strike. Often they get other jobs (although they aren't supposed to because then they aren't striking employees—they are technically ex-em-

TABLE 21–1

EXTENT OF WORK STOPPAGES, 1951–57*

YEAR	MAN-DAYS IDLE	
	MILLIONS OF DAYS	PERCENTAGE OF ESTIMATED WORKING TIME
1951..............	22.9	0.23
1952..............	59.1	0.57
1953..............	28.3	0.26
1954..............	22.6	0.21
1955..............	28.2	0.26
1956..............	33.1	0.29
1957..............	15.4	0.13

* Source: United States Bureau of Labor Statistics.

ployees). Westinghouse's employees, out on strike for most of a year in 1955, surely didn't just sit around all that time.

Any argument based on the figures of averages is, however, dangerous. Averages cover up extremes. It is small comfort to the employees or the management of a company to be told, after a lengthy strike, that no economic loss was suffered because the customers bought competing products, thereby giving greater employment elsewhere. Not all striking workers are able to find other work, and if they do, it isn't likely to be the kind of work they want. To individual workers and individual companies a strike is usually a serious matter. Generally, neither workers nor management let a strike occur over little things. Money is much the most common reason for strikes, although other issues are often involved.

Some people say that strikes settle nothing and that everyone loses by them. Strikes do settle issues, however, at least for the moment, because in the end the parties come to an agreement, sign a contract, and go back to work. After a strike both parties usually have a greater respect for each other, and both are more willing, in the future, to settle their differences by negotiation.

Strikes should be used sparingly by unions. A union member's ardor can be considerably dampened by an unsuccessful strike or even by successful strikes lasting too long or occurring too often. Companies are for that reason occasionally willing to let a strike occur. There is, of course, always the possibility that the company might win the dispute, but even if it loses, the workers are not so "strike-happy" the next time.

Furthermore, frequent strikes lose much of their sting. If strikes are frequent, management keeps its warehouses full and is little hurt by a temporary shutdown. Also, a struck company rarely loses permanently its regular customers, since the customers usually divide up their orders among several companies as a protection against a strike in any one of them. Then, too, as we said above, multiplant companies can often transfer orders from closed plants to those still operating, and do not lose much. Today's high taxes, too, lessen the harmful money effects of strikes. Lower profits mean lower profits taxes; the loss in net profits is likely to be less than half the over-all profits decline.

LOCKOUTS

When an employer closes his plant to impose his will on workers in a labor dispute, it is called a "lockout." It differs from a strike in that the employer not the union initiates the stoppage. Lockouts for the purpose of forcing employees to accept the employer's terms in bargaining are illegal.

If bargaining in good faith ends in a deadlock, the employer may continue to operate under the existing terms of employment, or he may put into effect the terms he offered the union, but he may not close down a plant because of the deadlock. He may, however, close down a plant for economic or for other reasons not connected with the union activities of employees; such a shutdown is not considered a lockout.

THE COLLECTIVE BARGAINING UNIT

Each collective bargaining "unit" bargains for itself. Usually there are natural dividing lines separating one group from another, as office and factory. The hourly paid jobs in a factory probably would all be considered as one unit; the workers on those jobs would all belong to the same local union, which would bargain for all of them. Sometimes, however, particularly in the maintenance department, employees belong to craft unions made up of employees doing only one kind of work. Where there are several bargaining units in the company, each unit bargains for its own members, the union representatives signing separate labor agreements with the company.

Large companies must deal with dozens of bargaining units. For the most part the locals belong to different unions, but a company having many plants may be forced to deal with many locals of the same union individually. In its bargaining with the various units it faces different demands, so that it is almost impossible to have consistent labor contracts in all plants.

LABOR CONTRACTS

The end product of negotiations is an "agreement," or labor contract, which is signed by the representatives of both management and labor. It covers in detail the items of agreement and holds good for a stated period, usually one or two years. It is printed, usually in a small pocket-sized booklet of some 75 pages, and copies are distributed to workers, union officials, and foremen. No two companies' contracts are alike, but the part of the subject index of General Motors labor agreements, shown in Figure 21–2, page 401, gives you an idea of the kind of things covered.

Labor contracts have tended to bind the company but not the union. Technically, both are bound to live up to the provisions for the contract's duration. But when workers in some companies get pay raises at a time when no raises are called for in the contracts of other companies, the workers left behind become restive. As individuals (often with the unofficial urging of union officers from behind the scenes) they object to living up to the contract. They try to put pressure on the company to scrap the contract before it runs out and to grant more concessions. They use such pressure devices as slowdowns in work, greater absenteeism due to "sickness," refusal to work overtime, lack of co-operation on the job, making poor products to raise the proportion of rejects, and wildcat strikes. Some or all of these activities may be specifically prohibited in the contract, but it is always difficult to prove that they are intentional, and some companies are slow to take disciplinary action when they occur.

GRIEVANCES AND ARBITRATION

In spite of everyone trying to get along, there will be times when someone will think that he has not been treated fairly and will file a grievance. Before we get into how it works, note that the company never files a grievance. It *acts*, it does something, such as discipline someone or fail to promote someone; then if the someone feels that the action is not in accord with the labor contract, he (through the union) files a grievance.

Grievance Handling Procedure. How to handle grievances is written out in the labor contract. There are all kinds of ways, but they nearly all include certain steps. As the first step, the man discusses it with his foreman. If he gets nowhere, he goes to his shop steward, and the two of them discuss it with the foreman. That is the second step.

If the grievance is still unsettled and if the employee wishes to pursue it further, it reaches the third step. A written statement of the grievance is filed in the personnel office, whose staff arranges a meeting between the union's grievance committeemen in the department, the fore-man, his superior, and a personnel department representative. If this group fails to dispose of it, it is carried, as a fourth step, to a similar committee, but a plant-wide one. Finally, after the fourth step, it can reach the fifth step, arbitration.

At any point in the procedure the company may agree to adjust the situation to suit the man and thus settle the matter. Or, at any time the

---

WARNING NOTICE

Company_____ Dept._____ Location_____ Date_____

Mr._____

Dear Sir:

I am giving you this formal notice in accordance with our conversation in which I told you that you are not measuring up to our standards in the following respects:

You have repeatedly taken time off without first making arrangements for your relief. This is in violation of Section 17 of the Uniform Labor Agreement.

Should there be any further violation of this section of the Uniform Labor Agreement, it will be necessary for us to take disciplinary action.

Supervisor

cc: Mill Manager
      Chairman, Union Standing Committee
      Supervisor
      File

Please understand that this written notice is intended for your benefit and that it is given primarily in order that you may have opportunity to correct your shortcomings. I hope that you will show an immediate improvement; otherwise we shall be forced to terminate your services.

Yours very truly,

ORIGINAL (THIS COPY FOR EMPLOYEE)   _____

DEPARTMENT HEAD OR SUPERINTENDENT

FIG. 21–3. A notice warning an employee of his violation of shop rules.

---

union may accept the company's position and drop the case. Sometimes grievances are traded off: the company grants one grievance, and the union agrees to drop another. Actually only a few grievances ever go to arbitration.

SUBJECTS OF GRIEVANCE

Grievances generally allege (1) that a disciplinary action (particularly in discharge cases) was unjustified or that a penalty imposed was too severe considering the circumstances; (2) that a worker meriting a raise in pay did not get it; (3) that piece rates have been set improperly (that they are too tight), or (4) that seniority rules were not properly interpreted and carried out in the case of a promotion or demotion when the work force is being reduced, or (5) that the company has not paid overtime wages when it should have.

It is important to be sure that foremen and workers understand the shop rules and penalties, so that violations will not occur and also so that the company will be protected against adverse arbitration rulings. If the company has made no real effort to acquaint workers with the rules and penalties, the workers usually feel that ignorance of the rule excuses a violation, and arbitrators sometimes agree and order restitution made to a worker who may have been properly disciplined. It is to the company's interest to see that all workers know and understand shop rules.

Some grievances are justified; perhaps a foreman has unintentionally violated the provisions of the labor agreement. You must train your foremen in the meaning of the contract in order to hold down grievances. The personnel department has to tell foremen what they can and cannot do under the contract. If you leave it up to the foremen to acquaint themselves with the contract without aid, most of them will have only a vague notion of what the contract says, and avoidable grievances will result.

Some companies have found it necessary to guard against grievances kept alive for their own sake because there are groups in the organization for whom a settled grievance is not an advantage. Such situations are uncommon. Some union grievance committeemen would rather talk over grievances with management than work at their regular jobs. It is said, too, that some workers in the personnel department drag out grievance work and so magnify the importance of their jobs. With such an attitude on their part and with a grievance committee that feels it must have grievances, it is safe to say that a company so handicapped will have too many grievances and too many cases going to arbitrators.

Some grievances are borderline matters not clearly covered in the contract or involving interpretation of the meaning of the contract. Has a company, for example, violated its contract if it discharges a shop steward (a union officer) for some good cause and makes him leave the premises immediately and before he has an opportunity to talk to other union officers, if the contract says that a discharged employee shall be given an opportunity to talk to a union officer before he leaves the premises? Has a company a right to discharge a man for engaging in a slowdown, which it later cannot prove, but in arbitration to claim that he also falsified his production records, which it discovered after the discharge while preparing its case for arbitration?

Does a company have to pay for vacations at hourly rates which include the premium for overtime when the agreement says in one place that vacations shall be paid for at the average hourly rate earned by the employee in the four weeks before Decoration Day and in another place that the term "average hourly earnings" shall exclude overtime premiums? Does a company have to pay four hours' "call-in" pay when its water tank developed a leak during the night and the wind blew the dripping water 50 feet onto a power line, where it froze, later breaking the line because of its weight and thus preventing work the following day? The contract provided for call-in pay if workers were not notified ahead not to report for work, unless the cause was an "act of God, such as power failure." These are relatively minor matters, but each of these disputes was carried to arbitration before it was settled.

Unions are in an unfortunate position with respect to grievances. In order to keep the support of its members, a union is almost forced to process through to arbitration most grievances that individual members insist on. It is hard to tell a member that his grievance has little merit and that the union cannot stand behind him. A union is almost forced to carry many discharge cases to arbitration because, above all, a union member thinks he buys security when he pays his dues. For its own prestige and preservation, a union must prove itself to the dues-paying members. If they have no job security, there is little the union can offer them. To maintain their position unions carry some grievances of little intrinsic merit clear through to arbitration as an indication that they are trying to win.

Because arbitration cases cost money, unions cannot allow too many weak cases to be carried through. Of those that go to arbitration the unions should probably lose more than half on the merits of the cases. An official of one large international union said that his union lost 70 per cent of the grievances it carried to arbitration. It is doubtful, however, that the high rate of losses weakens its member support because without the union none of the cases would have been carried to arbitration and none would have been won.

Arbitration.   Arbitration is widely used to settle labor disputes. In large companies a "permanent" (for the duration of the particular labor agreement) umpire is often chosen by the two parties to serve as arbitrator of all grievances carried that far. Such an arrangement gives consistency to decisions and, by laying down rules, helps eliminate future grievances. The permanent umpire arrangement is uncommon, however, except in very large companies. Most contracts provide that a new arbitrator be selected for each grievance case carried to arbitration. He is commonly chosen from a list of five prospective arbitrators provided by the American Arbitration Association. The union and management take turns marking off names of those they don't want until only one name remains; he becomes the arbitrator.

Arbitrators' decisions are nearly always carried out. If a company lost an arbitration case and decided not to follow the arbitrator's ruling, the union could go before the National Labor Relations Board and charge the company with being guilty of an unfair labor practice. The board would order the company to carry out the arbitrator's ruling, and if it did not then do so, the board would get a court order compelling compliance.

LAWS GOVERNING LABOR RELATIONS

Almost every manufacturing company is engaged in interstate commerce and is therefore covered by federal laws. Some states have passed laws that are similar to the federal laws, but, in practice, a summary of federal laws covers the legal requirements as far as labor relations are concerned by which all companies, inter- or intrastate, must abide.

In general, the laws, federal and state, provide:

1. Employers must bargain collectively with the representatives of their workers if the workers want to bargain collectively. If the employees want a union and in an election vote for a union, the company must bargain with its representatives.
2. Employers may not discriminate in favor of or against any employee or applicant for employment because of his activity or lack of activity in connection with unions.
3. Employers may not underwrite, coerce, or otherwise try to influence the union.
4. Employers are not guilty of an unfair labor practice if they fail to grant labor's demands.
5. Employers may tell their employees their views concerning labor matters, provided that they contain no threats or promises.
6. Employees are not allowed to coerce other employees to join or not to join unions, but *if* the employer and the union agree to a union shop, all employees must join the union.
7. Unions may not exclude employees from membership (and so disqualify them from keeping their jobs if there is a union shop) except for nonpayment of regular dues or regular initiation fees. Failure to pay union fines or assessments cannot be used as cause for exclusion from the union.
8. Jurisdictional disputes are unfair labor practices, and employers injured by such disputes may sue the participating unions.
9. Unions may be sued for damages when guilty of unfair labor practices.
10. Under certain conditions court injunctions can be obtained restraining union activities, including the right to strike.
11. Union officials must sign affidavits saying that they are not members of the Communist party, in order to have the protection of the law with respect to enforcement of unfair labor practice charges against employers.
12. Unions, annually, must file statements of their financial status and expenses with the United States Department of Labor.
13. Unions may not contribute to political campaign funds.
14. To cease operations in a plant where a strike is in process is not an unfair labor practice, nor is it an unfair practice to try to operate a plant after the union has called a strike.
15. It is legal (although practically never done) to replace striking employees with new employees who may keep their jobs (as far as the law is concerned) after a strike is over, *if the strike is for economic reasons* (a pay raise or other economic benefits); but *if the strike is for union reasons* (such as to get union recognition), the striking workers get their jobs back at the conclusion of the strike.
16. To hire strikebreakers in another state and to pay for their transportation across a state line is illegal. Advertisements for help in a struck plant must state that a strike is in progress.

Labor organizations are strongly opposed to the Taft-Hartley Act because it restricts their activities somewhat. Their position on this law has been mixed with emotion and politics, making an objective evaluation of its operation difficult. In the years since its passage union membership has increased and workers have gotten pay raises almost every year. But strikes have not diminished. Certainly the Taft-Hartley Act has not made the unions wither and die.

MORAL REARMAMENT

Moral Rearmament is Christianity in operation at the bargaining table. Sometimes deeply religious men on both sides of the table try to settle their differences by practicing religious tolerance and give and take during the week as well as on Sunday. In isolated cases it has worked very well and has resulted in peaceful settlements of explosive situations. Most employers and nearly all union people have little faith in Moral Rearmament at the bargaining table.

STUDY QUESTIONS

1. How, according to the text, can labor problems be solved? Explain the text viewpoint.
2. Do unions ever create labor problems? Explain your answer.
3. Tell how the idea of "progress" relates to union demands.
4. Why could the A.F. of L. never organize big business in the 1920's and 1930's?
5. How many members of unions are active in union affairs? Why?
6. Why is it necessary for successful negotiations for union negotiators to have the power to reject the company's offer and call a strike?
7. Who has to yield what at the bargaining table in order to have complied with the law? Explain.
8. Should you keep lawyers out of labor negotiations? Justify your answer.
9. "Strikes constitute a serious drain on the productivity of American industry." Discuss this statement.
10. What is a collective bargaining unit? Why is it important?
11. What steps do unsettled grievances go through if neither party agrees to a settlement?
12. When do unions file grievances? When do companies file grievances? Discuss.
13. How does arbitration work? Discuss fully.

CASE 21–1.   THE ACME METAL COMPANY

Hank Bishop, the union steward for the external grinding department of the Acme Metal Company, was suspected of falsifying his work reports and of ringing in the time cards of other employees in his department when they were late or when they wanted to leave early. The company could not prove this latter suspicion, but investigation of his production reports showed him claiming that on three specific dates his union duties took him away from his machine 5, 4, and 6 hours, respectively. The company pays for union duties of department stewards if the time is spent during work hours and on company premises. Bishop's machine is semiautomatic, and he does the same kind of work day after day.

The production reported by Bishop on the 3 days in question could not have been turned out in the time he reported. It would have taken at least 5, 5, and 3 hours, respectively, on the 3 days, to get out the work. Bishop actually did the work he claimed, but he had falsified his report of time spent on union work on those days.

The company has had good relations with the union and would not want to see the present officers unseated because a more belligerent opposition group is said to be trying to oust the present leaders. The company's shop rules and labor agreement both specify that falsification of production reports is cause for discharge. It is also suspected that others in the department are exaggerating their daywork claims.

What should the company do?

Chapter 22

THE FOREMAN

THE IMPORTANCE OF THE FOREMAN IN THE ORGANIZATION

THE foreman is the most important man in the producing organization. His department's efficiency is largely of his making. He supervises directly the manufacturing of the product. As far as the hourly paid workers are concerned, *he is management*. He approves their hiring. He has the power to fire them. He assigns jobs, recommends raises, and decides on promotions. He determines what disciplinary action is needed and metes it out. His power to make these decisions is not absolute, but nearly so.

He, not the personnel department, is the principal personnel officer of the company. The treatment that plant workers get comes from him. The personnel department can do little directly to change things in his department. It can help him and make suggestions to him, but to his men, the foreman is still management's representative. Most employees don't see or talk to an employee of the personnel department as often as once a year. In fact, most employees, except truckers, common laborers, and maintenance department employees, never see the inside of any department other than their own except on their way to or from work.

The foreman has to get new workers off to a good start, has to try to develop in them a sense of belonging to the organization, has to train them in the actual operations of the job and in work habits, has to give recognition for good work, has to be fair in work assignments and promotions. In other words, the foreman must do everything necessary to build a good work force in his department. If top management decrees that workers are to be treated as individuals, no amount of intention in the higher echelons will make that treatment a reality if the foreman does not treat the workers that way. If there are worker grievances, they generally concern something the foreman has (or has not) done. An appeal to him for correction is the first step in the grievance handling procedure. If the foreman does his work well there will be few grievances, and most of those that do arise will be settled satisfactorily within the department.

In recent years many companies have been concerned about channels of communication to and from their workers. The foreman is the main channel for these communications. He knows his men and can tell management what questions and problems they have and what they think of the way the company does things. And he can pass information down to the workers, explain company policies to them, and answer their questions. The information he passes up the line may, of course, be colored to make himself look good. There should be other channels too. Grievances getting to the personnel department are a second channel.

Sometimes information doesn't get passed down to the men the way it should. How can it, if the foreman himself isn't told? Management has to be sure to tell him about plans for the future so he can explain things to workers.

In Chapter 3, staff and line relationships were discussed. It was said that staff organizations often horn in on the line and usurp some of the line's authority. If they do, the foreman is the one whose line authority is usurped. He can't do his job well if his authority is impaired. If various staff groups begin to give orders instead of advice to line officers, the foreman usually ends up with several bosses instead of one. And it is not the specialized staffs but the foreman who, after all is said and done, has to get out production.

The foreman is more than just the chief personnel officer of the company. Much work which is generally regarded as staff department work ends up being done by the foreman. *Staff departments* often *plan* activities which *he has to carry out.* In some companies the foremen decide which job orders to work on first and which to work on second and which workers get which jobs. Sometimes production control makes these decisions. But whichever way the work is assigned, the foreman must see that the work is done and done economically.

The time study department sets piece rate standards, but it is the foreman who has to convince his men that the standards are fair and has to see that they operate satisfactorily. Engineering departments prescribe how work shall be done and set quality standards. Inspectors pass on the quality of the work. The foreman, however, has to see that the product meets the standards set and so passes inspection. If tolerances are too close and scrap too high, the foreman usually has to improve the quality himself, with little outside help.

In maintenance work the foreman probably is as important as the maintenance department. He has to see that machines are oiled, kept clean, and run properly. This reduces maintenance. And by watching his machines carefully, he can know when repairs are needed and request them before breakdowns occur. The foreman is also the chief safety officer in the organization, seeing that his men work under safe conditions, observe safety regulations, and use safe work methods. And, finally, in any well-managed company the job improvements made by the foreman and his better workers should far exceed the improvements made by the industrial engineering department.

All in all, the foreman is an important man—his place should not be underestimated in any study of factory operations.

THE FORGOTTEN FOREMAN

Foremen would be a happy lot if they thought they were considered to be as important as we have just said. Mostly they like their jobs even though there is hardly a foreman anywhere who thinks that the company thinks that he is very important. Some foremen would tell you that they are just glorified flunkies.

How can they get to feeling this way when their job really is important? Here's what they say on attitude surveys (not all of them say these things, but they are common answers): (1) you don't give us enough real authority, (2) you don't pay us enough, (3) you don't show any personal interest in us, (4) we don't get much chance for promotion, (5) you don't tell us what is going on and what is coming up next, and (6) you never ask us our ideas on anything.

It is a pretty damning list. Is management guilty? Probably yes in most companies on most counts. They *talk* about how important the foreman's job is but keep narrowing down the decisions they let him make, and they don't pay him much more than his men or ask him for his ideas or tell him about the company's plans for the future.

Foremen sometimes work on incentives and get production bonuses just like their men. A staff man (production control) sets work schedules, and in some cases assigns jobs to men. A staff man (personnel) hires new men, handles grievances, and keeps the men's personal records. A staff man (engineering) sets quality and quantity standards for the men to meet. A staff man (quality control) passes judgment on the quality of work done.

Besides these, any number of other things show the foreman that he is only a little man in management. He is not clothed with the "signs of office" of management. In one of Detroit's newest automobile factories most foremen do not have even a sit-down desk—to say nothing of an office, and certainly not an enclosed office. A foreman gets a stand-up desk without even a stool to sit on. And this plant is typical of many factories. What kind of a member of management can such a foreman think that he is? And suppose that a man has a grievance. When and where does the foreman ever get to talk to one of his men in private?

Many foremen don't even get a salary. They are paid by the hour just like their men. They work factory hours, not office hours; they come to work through the factory employee entrance; they eat in the hourly paid men's cafeteria, and at factory lunch hours. If the plant goes on short time and short pay checks, so do the foremen. Is it any wonder that a foreman thinks that he is only a glorified worker, or at best, low man on the management totem pole?

FOREMAN ATTITUDES

In spite of all the bad things about foremen jobs, most foremen like their jobs and want to keep them. And in spite of the fact that some workers turn down chances to become foremen, most men say "yes" when their chance comes. A foreman's work is varied and interesting to most men. It gives them responsibilities; it pays better and has greater promotional opportunities than regular plant jobs. Besides, the authority and prestige make it a desirable job. Most foremen, in spite of their gripes, like their jobs better than any nonsupervisory job they ever had.

Nearly all foremen come up from the ranks. Rightly or wrongly, they get their job because they have been good, dependable, skilled workers. That is one excellent qualification for this job, but there are others which they may not have and for which they need some training. A foreman doesn't run machines. He handles people, plans work, makes reports, and keeps records. He usually manages, with help, to master these parts of the job reasonably well.

But what the foreman wants out of his job and what his boss wants him to want are often miles apart. Most foremen have reached the height of their ambition and never hope to go higher. That is important because, feeling as they do, they want to satisfy the high brass only enough to keep their jobs, but beyond that all they want is for their department to run smoothly. Running a department smoothly and efficiently are often two different things. They can go on at the same time, but a foreman's headaches are fewer if he doesn't try to be so efficient. Give a foreman his choice, and he'll choose not to be so efficient.

Foremen do not want high quality standards because they are hard to meet and they increase scrap. And every foreman wants his men to be well paid (it is not his money) for doing a reasonable amount of work (an amount which they will do with little prodding). He wants his men to like him and to like working in his department. He favors high job base rates and loose piece rates so the men can make bonuses easily. His men can't make much money on jobs with tight piece rates, and they don't want to work on these jobs. He favors loose piece rates also because the efficiency of his department is, in part, judged by the apparent efficiency of his men. If an output of 100 pieces per hour on a job is judged normal, he won't be praised when his men turn out 100 pieces per hour. But if you say that 75 per hour is normal (on the same job), then an output of 100 pieces goes on the record as 133 per cent efficient. The foreman's record of performance looks very different. Furthermore, his men would make bonuses.

The foreman's sympathies are often on the side of his workers in labor disputes. Generally he, too, gets a pay increase if the union wins one for its members. On the other hand, the foreman opposes his employees on many grievances, since they allege he has been unfair in some way.

The foreman usually opposes merit rating in his department because it makes more work for him. It also keeps him from passing out raises

American Management Association

FIG. 22–1. *"Keltmeir, you're never late, you never sleep on the job, you do good work and lots of it. Keltmeir, are you bucking for my job?"*

to suit himself. Generally he is opposed to budgeting, both because it makes more work for him and because he must watch all operation costs more carefully. Motion study work, too, makes extra work and headaches for him. A motion study man from the industrial engineering department may figure out an improved method for doing a job, but it is the foreman who has to make it work and keep the operator happy. Often he looks at an improvement coming out of motion study work done in his department by an outsider as a reflection on his ability; after all, why didn't he think of it himself? Often he is quite opposed to understudy plans and special trainee programs because a good understudy is a competitor for his job. Special trainees are going places in the organization and are likely to get many of the good jobs. Their presence closes most of the promotional opportunities that might otherwise be open to him.

It is all very well to say that foremen should not have such attitudes. Certainly not all of them are so negative toward efficient operations. But it is still true that most foremen are pretty well satisfied with the way they run their departments and don't want to change. Top management sometimes deludes itself into thinking that foremen are in favor of certain moves when they aren't. Smart foremen keep their objections to themselves. Publicly they appear to go along with the programs, but privately their support often is halfhearted. When top management fails to understand this, it does not realize why foremen drag their feet.

Fortunately, from the company's point of view, some foremen set high goals for themselves and recognize that the efficient operation of their departments is the best way to keep their jobs and get raises and promotions. Two things can be done to develop more foremen with positive attitudes and habits of managerial thinking. First, insofar as those things can be predicted, foremen should be selected only from among those who seem likely to have the ability and desire to operate a department efficiently. Second, foreman training programs can be given in which the desirability of efficient operation is emphasized. Too many programs emphasize *how* the foreman can be efficient but fail to give him any evidence that his personal advantage lies in being so. Unless he is convinced of the need and desirability for efficiency, he thinks that all these training programs are only some more methods for getting more work out of him. Foreman training can be successful only if the foreman can see how it will do him some good.

WORKER RELATIONSHIPS

Normally, foremen and workers get along pretty well unless the foreman upsets things. Usually the foreman came up from the ranks and was "one of the boys"—a good high-skilled man. The workers can look up to him. As foreman he has to be a little more apart, but he and the men can still like and respect each other. The foreman is visible evidence that hourly paid men can get promoted. In fact, companies should publicize promotions of men to foreman's jobs to make sure that everyone knows that such things do happen.

The foreman spends most of his working hours in his department and is the only management representative well known to most workers. They are dependent on him for fair treatment and have to depend on him to represent them at other levels of management. Their union also represents them, it is true, but usually only when conditions are bad and need correction.

The workers generally want to like their foreman, so the stage is set for a good relationship if he measures up. Newly promoted foremen, understandably enough, often continue to see the men's viewpoint more than management's viewpoint, sometimes because they are not qualified by education and personality to feel at ease with other people in management's ranks. Foremen should not let this community of interest keep them from running their department efficiently, but a certain amount of it is good. The company and the workers both benefit if a foreman never completely loses the feeling of identity with his men. If a foreman thinks of himself only as a company man, he may not get so much co-operation from his men. Once in a while a foreman becomes such a strong company man that his old buddies hate him.

A foreman can easily kill the normal employee good will and respect that he should have on his job. Let him be "high hat," discourteous, impatient, practice favoritism, be unfair and inconsistent, make promises that he can't fulfill, and the men will turn against him. Or let him not discipline men who need it; that loses workers' respect, too. He can even lose the men's respect through no fault of his own but rather through the faults of higher management. Inconsistent policies, failure to consult him or to tell him of impending changes, failure to train him in how to be a good foreman, failure to back him up in his decisions, and failure to clothe him with outward evidences of membership in the management family will reduce the importance of his job.

A foreman's job is more responsible than the jobs he supervises, but it would be a mistake for him to give the workers the impression that he thinks their jobs are simple and unimportant. Foremen should never, by word or action, lower a man's dignity by suggesting that his work is unimportant. To belittle his job is to belittle him. Actually, most of these jobs are relatively simple and unimportant individually, but to the workers, they are the most important ones in the plant. Besides, almost all workers like to think that their jobs require skill in their performance. Don't ever, in front of a man comment on how simple his job is. If he admits it in his own mind, he hates you for reminding him of it. Mostly, though, he'll go on the defensive and tell you, "If you think it's so simple, let's see you do it."

Also listen to the man's gripes and his suggestions. Do they sound unimportant? They are important to him. Some workers even become annoyed if the foreman pays no attention to them. A little tactful attention on the part of the foremen to the things that are important to the workers goes a long way toward creating good will and smooth operations.

"PRODUCTION-CENTERED" VERSUS "EMPLOYEE-CENTERED" FOREMEN

Some people say that most foremen fall into one of two classes, "production-centered" or "employee-centered." They claim that of the two, employee-centered foremen get the better results—get more production from their men and with less supervision than production-centered foremen. The workers respond better to foremen who seem interested in *them*, not just in production. This view is all of a piece with today's philosophy of treating people as people.

DUTIES AND KNOWLEDGE REQUIRED

It is so popular to say that the foreman's job is a human relations job that many people forget that this is only part of it. A foreman's main job is to get out production on schedule, of good quality, and at expected costs. But, just what does he do? And what does he have to know in order to do the things he does?

Duties. A foreman's work doesn't fit into classifications of kinds of duties very well, but he does so many things that grouping them helps us talk about them.

First, a foreman has responsibilities dealing with *products*. Second, he deals with *machines* and equipment. Third, he deals with *men*.

One study[1] showed that foremen spend one third of their time on products, one eighth on machines, and the rest (just over half) with men (including *receiving* as well as giving directions). In other words, less than half of their time was spent dealing with their own men. Another study[2] found foremen in auto plants using one third to one half of their time chasing after materials and tools, running down details, or actually doing the work of their man. Merck and Co. found its foremen acting as messengers 20 per cent of their time. They were supervising only 30 per cent, did clerical work 15 per cent, and talked to fellow foremen 10 per cent of their time. Notice the common element in these studies: Foremen are only part-time supervisors.

Foremen ought never to do the work of their men. They have more important things to do. Besides, the labor contract usually forbids their doing the work of any hourly paid man. The hardest thing for a new foreman to learn is how *not* to work on the product. It is so much easier to do something yourself than to straighten out someone who is doing it wrong.

Responsibilities dealing with *products* include: planning for jobs and making sure that work can proceed, scheduling jobs and machines, and seeing that materials are moved to their next operations. A foreman must see that raw materials and supplies are used economically and that his men turn out products of good quality. He should try to improve methods, control his costs, and stay within his operating budget.

Responsibilities dealing with *machines* include: seeing that the men operate machines with care and that repairs are made when necessary. The foreman should provide safe working conditions and see that his men work safely.

A foreman's responsibilities dealing with his *men* are many. He must maintain a working force, win the co-operation of the employees, en-

---

[1] Reported in "Supervisory Selection Problems," *Personnel*, September, 1955, p. 111.

[2] C. R. Walker, R. H. Guest, and A. N. Turner, *The Foreman on the Assembly Line* (Cambridge, Mass.: Harvard University Press, 1956).

courage suggestions, and try to keep up worker morale and keep down absenteeism and turnover. He usually has the right to approve new employees before they are hired. After they are hired, he must get them oriented on their jobs and see that they are trained, and when new employees fail on the job, he must see that they are transferred to work they can do or are removed from the payroll. In some companies he assigns work to his men. He must merit-rate his men, either formally or informally, and recommend raises and promotions. He should handle his department so that few grievances arise and should settle, within the department, most of those that do arise. The foreman has to maintain discipline and handle disciplinary cases, including reprimands, disciplinary layoffs, and discharges.

He is the main channel of communication, up and down, between management and hourly paid men. He also needs to have good union relationships; particularly, he should get along with his department's union steward. And he should arrange the work so that the department can keep on producing whenever he has to be in other parts of the plant. Day-shift foremen must supervise the work of second- and third-shift foremen.

Knowledge Required.   The foreman needs to know certain things in order to do the things listed above. In all three groups of duties—those dealing with jobs, machines, and men—there are quite a few records to keep and reports to make. Foremen usually don't like this part of their work. They must approve production reports used for payroll purposes and must assign daywork jobs and check on all daywork or other allowances claimed by pieceworkers. Foremen in many companies determine the raw materials needed for production and write requisitions for them. They must have some knowledge of the company's accounting system in order to know the proper account to which materials or labor costs should be charged.

A foreman must know and understand company policies so he can explain them to his men. He should be thoroughly acquainted with the shop rules, the union contract, and the laws affecting labor-management relations. He must, if he is to do a good job, learn fairly well all the jobs he supervises, so that he can help the men on them; yet he must learn to delegate work to others. He needs to be a good teacher and be able to put his ideas across. He needs to know how to handle men and how to handle their grievances.

How many of the things that the foreman needs to know would a skilled hourly paid man on a factory job know? Almost none of the things listed so far. The jobs are different, and the knowledge required is different. This points up the weakness of the common method of promoting the most skilled worker to the job of foreman. The foreman's job is so different and so much bigger than the job of one of his skilled workmen that *ability to handle a machine skillfully should not be given too much weight* when choosing a new foreman. Machine operating skill is helpful because it gives a foreman's positional authority the additional weight of job knowledge. That increases his men's respect for him and helps him to help his workers, but he cannot succeed as a foreman solely as a skilled machine operator.

The list of a foreman's duties and what he needs to know also points up the need for training him. *He will never learn, on his own, all that he*

III. Union Security

(a) Any employee who is a member in good standing of the Union two (2) weeks after the execution of this agreement, and any employee who becomes a member thereafter shall, as a condition of employment, remain a member in good standing of the Union for the duration of this agreement. The Union shall, as promptly as possible, deliver to the Employer a notarized list of its members in good standing as of two (2) weeks following the execution of this agreement. The term "good standing" shall, for the purpose of this article, mean that the employee has not been delinquent in tendering the periodic dues uniformly required as a condition of retaining membership in the Union. Any dispute as to whether an employee is or has ceased to be a member in good standing shall be handled through the grievance procedure.

(b) Whenever an employee shall voluntarily so request in writing, the Employer will deduct from his pay the dues payable by him to the Union and shall pay them to the Union. Such requests shall be irrevocable for not more than one (1) year from the dates of their execution or until the date of termination of this agreement, whichever occurs sooner. All requests for dues deduction shall specify the amount to be deducted, and the times or dates upon which payments are to be made to the Union. The form of these requests shall be subject to the approval of the Employer.

III. Schematic

> *The Company maintains an open shop. However, employees who join the Union, must, as a condition of employment, remain members in good standing of the Union for the duration of this agreement.*

American Management Association

FIG. 22–2. Foremen, as well as their employees, need to know what the union contract means. Read paragraphs (a) and (b). Do you know what they mean? Now read the "schematic" explanation. Foremen can understand this.

---

needs to know. The general foreman, superintendent, staff departments, and fellow foremen may all help him, but he ought also to get some specific training on the things he isn't likely to work out for himself. It cannot be emphasized too strongly that if the foreman doesn't do the things he ought to do they will not be done by any other person. And he can't do things well that he knows little about. He needs training.

Unfortunately, but typically, most foremen in most companies never get to be good enough to be able to do all the things listed. Operations suffer accordingly. Most companies don't realize the price they pay for poor foremen because they have never had good ones. A good foreman is a man of real stature. His treatment and his pay should reflect it. When they do, the company is not much troubled by foreman indifference and the negative attitudes described on other pages.

MAKING THE FOREMAN MANAGEMENT'S REPRESENTATIVE

There is much talk nowadays about making the foreman truly a management representative, but not very many companies have given him any more authority to decide things.

Here's what they do in companies where they really try to make him a management man. They let him have the final say on new men; he passes on job applicants before they are hired. He passes out job assignments in his department. At International Business Machines, the inspectors work for the foremen; that, too, magnifies the foreman's job. Most companies have inspectors report to a chief inspector. They don't want foremen being responsible for doing work and then having one of their own men pass judgment on its quality.

In companies where a foreman is more truly a management team man, the higher ups tell him about future plans and policies, and ask him how he thinks they will work. And they finally decide what to do only after they have heard from him. His recommendations about promotions and pay raises are followed wherever possible.

Foremen, too, are human and need to be on the receiving, as well as the dispensing, end of a little praise now and then. Most foremen don't expect fast promotion to higher jobs, but general foremen's and superintendent's jobs should be filled by promotion from foremen's jobs. A policy of always bringing in outsiders is discouraging. A foreman also needs security in his job. You can't have high morale among foremen if they get demoted back to the ranks with every little business slide-off.

Staff assistance should be made available to the foreman, but staff men should not be allowed to dictate to him. The personnel department in particular should guard against taking the play away from him. Glenn Gardiner, Vice-President of Forstmann Woolen, does not even allow personnel counseling, because it plays down the foreman and lowers him in the estimation of his employees. Gardiner says personnel counseling is a damaging blow to the foreman's stature and that he loses prestige when counselors go around talking to the foreman's men.

Authority and prestige are of utmost importance. But there are any number of little things that round out the picture of the foreman as a management man. They include the "signs of office" mentioned earlier. Pay him a salary—not an hourly rate. Give him an office—not just a stand-up desk. Better yet, give him an enclosed office and an extra chair or two for visitors. Some companies don't agree with giving him an office; they'd rather make sure that he gets out and around instead of sitting in a chair in an office. Some foremen even prefer it this way. They say that it makes them feel more like "one of the boys."

Even such things as a nameplate on his desk help to identify him as management's representative in the department. Put his name in the company telephone directory. Give him clerical help, and don't expect him to do clerical work himself.

When possible, the foreman's hours of work should be the same hours, or nearly so, as those of the office workers rather than those of the factory. He should come into the plant through the front door and should not have to punch a time clock. He should have locker-room facilities with, or comparable with, other management personnel and apart from those of his men. He should have special parking lot consideration and should eat at the same time and in the same dining room with other management men. His identification badge should identify him with management, not just with his department alone. His vacation should be comparable to other management vacations and not be based on the factory vacation plan. Opportunities arranged for foremen to take observation trips through other factories pay substantial dividends in good will and a broadened view.

The importance of the foreman's job in the eyes of his men is enhanced by letting him pass out pay checks and letting him always be the first to tell his men of new plans and policies. When visitors are taken through a department, they should be introduced to the foreman. A meeting should be held with the foremen the day before the company's annual financial statement comes out, explaining it to them before it is released to the newspapers. During union contract negotiations, the foreman should be given a daily report on the progress, the demands, the position being taken by the union, and that being taken by management.

A foreman should never receive his first report of company decisions by the "grapevine" or from the shop steward (although news travels so fast by the grapevine that the company wishing to inform its foremen first can't always do so). A foreman should *know* these decisions because he has been consulted or told of them while in the formative stage. In front of his men, management must always back up the foreman in his decisions. If a foreman's decision ever has to be reversed, he should be told in private and he should tell his men of the change, not someone above him. Even in disciplinary cases where the foreman must consult with his superior, the foreman should mete out the discipline upon which they decide.

The foreman should also see that publicity and other information about his men and his department reach the company newspaper. He should pass out safety awards and suggestions awards. No one should be allowed to take the spotlight off the foreman, nor should the higher levels of management nor staff men be permitted to share that spotlight with him. Every indication and intimation should proclaim him as management's representative. It is unfortunate that, in practice, so few companies do put the spotlight on their foremen.

Does all this sound petty? They are such little things—all these "signs of office." One by one they are almost picayunish details, but put them together, and they amount to something. They are important in day-to-day relationships. A paint brush stroke isn't a picture, but put lots of them together, and you get a picture.

INFORMING AND TRAINING FOREMEN

Foremen training is discussed in Chapter 19 along with other types of training. We have only to note here that few men ever make good foremen without considerable training. Formal training courses are given in some large companies, but *most foremen get only informal training*. The supervision of general foremen and the superintendent, supplemented by staff help, is all the help most foremen get. It can be, although it rarely is, very effective.

Training, in part, means giving the foreman information, but he should also be given considerable information that is not just training. We said, for example, that the foreman should be told about the progress of labor negotiations, so that he will not have to hear about what goes on from the union steward. The same with telling the foreman about the company's financial statement, before it goes to the newspapers. These are matters of informing him rather than training him. Foremen like, too, to be given advance notice of changes that will affect them or their men, such as increases or decreases in future work hours or the number of employees. This too is informing but not training.

Foremen need to have all company policies explained fully to them, so that they understand them and can carry them out. Many large companies now have extensive "manuals" listing and explaining the company policies for the foremen. Management must see that foremen know the shop rules, measures of discipline, provisions of labor contracts, and labor laws, because they cannot dig all of these things out themselves.

Information more in the nature of training should be given foremen about how to supervise employees, how to teach them good work methods, and how to prepare all the reports they have to make out.

Foremen need to be told how to assign work. They need to be reminded to give exact instructions covering what is wanted and to explain how to do it if the men don't know how. They need to be reminded to pass the tough jobs around. They should learn to give praise and recognition for work well done, and always to tell men in advance the reason for any change in work assignments or hours.

Foremen also should be shown how to teach new workers. Teaching new men isn't just a matter of saying, "Here's your job, get going." A man will learn much better if the foreman uses the teaching method described on page 377.

Most foremen need help on how to handle grievances and reprimands. Of course, they should talk all important matters over with their next higher in command. A foreman should, on grievances, listen carefully to the complaint and try to see it as the man sees it. Perhaps the man does not understand the company's reasons for certain actions, or perhaps he does not understand the labor contract, or perhaps the man has a valid complaint. The foreman should be patient in trying to explain things and should certainly take care of valid complaints. And whatever the decision, the foreman should tell the employee and give him the reasons.

Reprimands are not quite like grievances. Here the company (the foreman) has decided that the man has done something wrong and

MEANING AND USE OF DISCIPLINE

Discipline is Educational— To Change Behavior

☆   ☆

WAYS TO ADMINISTER DISCIPLINE
Use In Sequence

CRITICISM—Friendly Discussion.

REPRIMAND—Severe Reproval. In Private. Usually Written.

PENALTY—Hardship or Inconvenience.

DISCHARGE—Last Resort.

WISCONSIN STEEL WORKS
INTERNATIONAL HARVESTER CO.
Management Training

BASE DISCIPLINE ON WRITTEN FACTS

Get and Write These Facts
—What Happened?
—Who Is Involved?
—When Did It Happen?
—Why Did It Happen?
—Where Did It Happen?
—Length of Service?
—Is This a Habit?
—What Is the Past Record?
—What Does the Contract Say?
—Mitigating Circumstances?
—What Action Is Indicated?
············

Reminders
—Discipline is Negative.
—Consider Effect of Action on Man.
—Consider Effect of Action on Group.
—Consult Others, if Necessary.
—Be Consistent.
—Once Administered, Forget It.
—Notify Those Concerned.
—Talk To Man Privately.
—Follow-up.

FIG. 22–3. An instruction card telling foremen how to handle discipline cases.

should be disciplined. The foreman should be *sure* of the facts and think over the situation before he does anything. If he is emotional about it, he should do nothing until he calms down. Then as he decides what to do he must remember: (1) the labor contract—the action must be in accord with its provisions; (2) the man—how he will receive it and how it will affect his future work; and (3) the other men—whether they will think that it is fair and reasonable.

When the man is told of the action, the foreman should talk with him and try to show him how to improve. He, the foreman, should make very clear to the man what is expected of him. If it is his work that got him into trouble, he should be told how to improve it.

Some companies give their foremen courses in elementary economics. They think that it helps make them better men and it helps directly wherever unions (as some unions do) pass out distorted information about wages, the cost of living, standards of living, and profits.

FOREMAN PAY

How much more than his men should a foreman be paid? Common practice sets this figure at 25 to 40 per cent more than the *average* of his men. That puts most foremen in the $6,000 a year and up bracket. A foreman's very best men on the top jobs may get only 15 to 25 per cent less than he. Is the difference enough? Probably yes if it always holds true.

But it isn't always so. During World War II, salaried foremen usually received no overtime pay (the wage freeze law did not allow companies to change their prewar practices) while their men worked, say, 10 hours a day and got 11 hours' pay. That put some of them above their bosses, who didn't like it at all. In fact, some foremen joined unions to see if they could raise their wages (during the war unions had managed to edge up factory pay scales a little here and there).

Some companies pay foremen overtime now so that foremen no longer get less than their men even on long hours. One plan classifies foremen into groups. The lowest-paid group gets paid the same overtime as their men—time-and-one-half for all overtime hours. The next higher-paid group gets time-and-a-third, and the next, time-and-a-quarter, and so on down. Top-paid foremen over large departments are treated like officials—they get no overtime at all. Another plan, used by some companies, pays all foremen extra for Saturday afternoons and Sundays.

Some companies have foreman bonus plans that give extra pay every month, based on departmental operating efficiency. Mostly this is gaged by comparing actual costs to budgeted costs. Labor efficiency is the main item, but other parts of the foreman's work are included, such as meeting schedules, labor turnover, scrap losses, maintenance costs, and the amount of supplies used. Bonus schedules are set so that foremen who do a good job get 10 to 20 per cent extra pay.

Yearly bonuses—some of the profit-sharing variety—are also found. Their size is most often based on the company's profits rather than on each foreman's work.

FOREMEN'S UNIONS

Top management got the scare of its life in World War II when foremen started to join unions. Its first reaction was one of horror at the foremen who could be so "disloyal" as to join a union. Then management went to work on why foremen wanted to join unions, out of which grew love-that-foreman programs and programs to make him a real member of management's team.

By law, foremen are not allowed (except in rare cases that don't apply to manufacturing[3]) to belong to the same union as their men. The law allows them to join unions of their own. *But, and this is important because it differs from the law about regular unions,* the law does *not* require management to recognize foremen's unions nor to bargain with them—refusal to bargain is not an unfair labor practice.

Then why have a foremen's union? Actually they are uncommon— rare, in fact. But the law allows management to recognize such a union if it wants to, and to bargain with it and to sign labor contracts. If management does this, the foremen's union has all the legal protections that regular unions have.

STUDY QUESTIONS

1. What part do staff departments play in making a foreman's department run smoothly? Just how does their work affect the foreman? Discuss.
2. What are foremen's common complaints? Are they justified? What would you do about their complaints?
3. Do foremen want to run their departments efficiently? Justify your answer.
4. Just what does a foreman spend his time on? What ought he be doing?
5. How different is a foreman's job from the job of his skilled men? What does he do that is different? What does he have to know that is different?
6. To what extent should a foreman be a management representative? How would you make him be truly a management representative?
7. What does it matter whether a foreman is truly a management representative or not? Explain.
8. What can management do to help a foreman handle his job? Explain thoroughly.
9. *a*) How should a foreman teach a job to a new man? Explain, step by step.
   b) How should a foreman handle a grievance? Explain.
10. If you were a foreman, would you join a union? Give your reasons. What arguments are there in favor of the position that you oppose?

---

[3] Foremen in the printing trades and a few others have, for many years, been members of the same union as the men they supervise. The law allows it where it has gone on for years.

Chapter 23

SAFETY AND HEALTH

ACCIDENT RATES IN FACTORIES

SAFETY people won't admit it—lest we backslide—but factories are pretty safe places to work. And this is in spite of the fact that factory work is inherently more dangerous than most other ways of making a living.

In 1956, manufacturing companies employed nearly 17 million men, of whom 13 million were hourly paid factory workers. There was a lost-time (one day or more) accident only once for every 40 men.[1] Or, put differently, if you work in a factory the chances are that you will have one lost-time accident every 40 years. Contrast that with the usual ratio of 1 to 20 for farming and 1 to 15 for transportation, construction, and mining. Only 1 man out of each 8,500 factory employees lost his life from an on-the-job accident. Contrast that with 1 of 4,000 in non-manufacturing industries.

It wasn't always so. Factories, as recently as 30 years ago, had three times the accidents they have today. It has taken constant effort to push the rate down. Safety engineers have found, too, that the effort can never be relaxed or the accident rate creeps up again.

There is considerable variation between industries. In 1956, several industries (electrical equipment, rubber, autos, and airplanes) had accident rates of only 1 accident per 125 men. That is very good. Most chemical industries were very good, too, with the explosives industry leading the safety parade in that group with one accident per 180 men. At the other extreme, the wood and clay products industries had 1 accident per 20 men.

Big companies generally try to do as good a job of safety as they can.

---

[1] Accident statistics are published in the *Monthly Labor Review,* Bureau of Labor Statistics, United States Department of Labor; and in *Accident Facts,* published annually by the National Safety Council, Chicago, Illinois.

They have the money to pay the costs of safety devices, the management is usually mindful of employee welfare, and, being large companies, they are more vulnerable to lawsuits and loss of public good will than are small companies. Enforcement of safety regulations by safety inspectors is also generally more strict in large companies than in small companies. Small companies typically do very little safety work.

Accident rates showing how *often* accidents occur tell only part of the story. How *serious* are they? Most accidents keep a man out of action only a few days, but some keep him out for a long time. The National Safety Council reports that, in most years, injuries lose 1.6 days per year per employee (not just those that get hurt, but everyone). Wood products, meat packing, leather, tobacco, and machinery have mostly minor accidents. But steel and cement making accidents are double the average severity. Injury-caused absences average out to as little as ½ day per man per year in the best industries and, even in the worst industries, almost never get up to 3 days per man-year.

First-aid accident cases, in which no work time is lost beyond the day of the accident, are not reported in accident statistics. Many companies do not keep good records of such cases. Unless failure to give proper aid causes serious disabilities, they do not constitute a really serious problem.

COSTS OF SAFETY

Safety precautions usually cost money; for this reason too few are taken in many small and medium-sized companies. But accidents cost money too.

The costs of accidents are hard to compute accurately. For the most part they are indirect or even intangible. The visible, direct costs, medical and compensation, may appear so low as not to justify a good safety program, but the total costs of an accident are at least double the direct costs.

The indirect costs include the value of production lost, the wages paid to the injured worker for trips to the doctor, wages paid to other workers for fixing equipment damaged by the accident, and the time that administrative officers and others use investigating cases. In the case of permanent disabilities, there is a loss of skill and earning power to the worker and possibly the cost of his support by society.

One estimate puts the cost of a broad safety plan including health, hygiene, accident prevention, good lighting, and ventilation at 1.5 to 3.0 per cent of the payroll. About half of the cost goes for salaries. Such a program, however, ought to save several times its cost. One company, through its safety program, reduced its industrial compensation costs from 1.2 per cent of the payroll to 0.5 per cent over a period of years. That adds up to about $35 per man per year, or $35,000 for a company with 1,000 employees; a sizable saving.

ACCIDENT HAZARDS

It usually takes a combination of unsafe conditions and carelessness on the part of men to make accidents. An oily floor does no harm in itself. Most people who walk on an oily floor do not fall; but when many people habitually walk on oily floors, falls are sure to occur. Cleaning off the oil would prevent most accidents, but so would a little extra care on the part of those who have to walk on oily floors.

Although you can't always get rid of unsafe conditions, you can sometimes. The first step in getting rid of them is recognizing them. Many situations are obviously dangerous—a piece of material sticking out into a dimly lighted aisleway, for example. Other situations, just as dangerous, are not obvious but would be revealed by an analysis of accident statistics.

A list of obvious accident hazards in factories could be lengthy and would include slippery floors and steps, ladders and scaffolds, unguarded balcony edges, stair wells, elevator shafts, low-hanging overhead objects, narrow aisles, blind corners, protruding materials, unguarded fast-moving machinery, particularly belts, gears, and cutting tools, flying particles from grinding wheels, chippers, etc., handling of heavy materials, and smoking by employees where there is danger of fire. In addition, in many companies, there are dangers from electricity, chemicals, irritating fluids, various kinds of dust, and explosions. *The problem of safety is not one problem but many;* the hazards are so different and so varied that many solutions, not one, must be found.

The National Safety Council collects figures on the nature and causes of accidents. They show that about one third of all disabling accidents involve fingers, hands, and arms. Legs, feet, or toes are injured in about one fourth of the accidents. Trunk injuries, including injuries to the back, stomach, abdomen, etc., caused for the most part by lifting, account for another quarter of the total. Head injuries, including eye injuries, constitute one tenth of all accidents.

MAKING WORKING CONDITIONS SAFE

Safe working conditions are management's responsibility. The degree of safety found in any plant is a matter of machine design, plant layout, lighting, good housekeeping, good maintenance, and the provision and use of safety guards and equipment.

Machine designers have for years been putting more and more of the moving parts under cover. This helps improve the looks of the machine by presenting smooth curved surfaces to the eye and also makes it safer to operate. Machinery purchasers now generally insist that safety features be built into the machine. Safety regulations have also played a part in safer machine design by requiring that gears and belting be covered or protected by guards to prevent injury to workers. The common practice today of providing every machine with its own motor has improved safety because no network of shafts, pulleys, and belts is needed to supply the machines with power.

Better and better equipment is being made for what used to be dangerous occupations. Boiler explosions, for example, are rare today because boilers are better made and because the conditions under which they are used are regulated and subject to inspection. Flywheels and abrasive grinding wheels practically never fly to pieces nowadays while in use; yet at one time such breakdowns were a serious problem. Acid burns and lung damage from fumes in electroplating have been materially reduced over the years. Dust explosions in flour mills and in food products and candy companies are almost unknown. In steel mills, burns from molten steel, let loose when ladles or other equipment break, have almost disappeared. The use of better equipment is largely responsible. Portable saws, drills, grinders, brushes, etc., and their extension cords are now much better protected than formerly.

Plant layout and good lighting are also important to safe working conditions. Narrow aisles with blind intersections cause accidents to industrial truck drivers. Poorly lighted aisles and workplaces sometimes cause accidents. The slope of ramps, if used by industrial trucks, should not exceed 10 per cent in grade. Pipes, conduits, drains, valves, heaters, fire apparatus, etc., should be located where they are convenient for access and repair but are out of the way of ordinary traffic.

Floors, stairs, and ramps must be kept free of water, oil, and grease. Spillage should be controlled and, when it occurs, cleaned up. Floors, if subjected to liquids, should be provided with proper drainage. Materials, containers, scrap, brooms, trash, and other obstructions should be put in places where workers will not stumble or slip on them and where trucks will not bump into them and knock them over. In the winter, loading docks, platforms, and aisles in outside storage yards should be cleared of ice and snow.

To remain safe, a plant must be well maintained. Worn machinery is not always dangerous, but worn materials handling equipment, crane cables, hoists, elevators, storage racks, or electrical wiring are very dangerous. Most of these situations are as dangerous to the maintenance men themselves as they are to others, if not more so. Poorly maintained industrial trucks and floors may also cause accidents.

In spite of all that can be done to create safe working conditions, there will still be a few situations which cause some people to have accidents. Aisles cannot always be straight, and it is impossible to remove all posts, overhanging projections, and step-downs. Such hazards should be painted a bright color to make them noticeable. Alternate diagonal orange and black stripes are sometimes used. Mirrors suspended from the ceiling at an angle permit truckers to see if anything is coming around blind intersections of aisles. Steps or sloping floors which might cause

falls can be coated with an abrasive, nonslip covering. All of these practices help reduce accidents.

SAFETY EQUIPMENT

Safety equipment can be of many kinds. Perhaps the best is equipment which is fastened onto the machines, thus making an accident
difficult. Machine guards are of many types, depending on the machine. Motors driving belts, gears, and electrical control panels are
often encased or are in wells surrounded by guard rails. Transparent

Torit Manufacturing Co.

FIG. 23–1.   Eyeshields above and dust collectors around and below these grinding wheels
make for safe operation.

shields cover grinding wheels. The whole wheel is sometimes almost
completely encased. Rotary saws, except for the cutting section, are
covered. Punch presses are usually equipped with a sweep arm or an
attached glove. With the downstroke of the punch, the sweep arm clears
the operator's arm free from the punching plate. The glove is fastened
to the machine in such a way as to draw the worker's hand back from
the machine as the punch descends.

Shears, brakes, and other sheet metal equipment are usually provided
with guards today. Forming presses for shaping metal are often equipped
with electrical control buttons; the operator must push the button
before the die will descend. There is a button for each hand; both must
be pushed before the machine will operate. They are located clear of
the die so as to make certain that the operator's hands are in the clear.
This device is especially helpful where two or more men work on a
machine, since, without it, one man might start the machine before the

others were clear. With the device, *all* workers must push the buttons and be in the clear before the machine will operate.

Safety devices on machines frequently pose difficult problems for the designers. First of all, safety guards must protect the worker; second, they must not interfere with the machine's working; and, third, they must slow down the machine's operation as little as possible. If a safety device slows down the work too much, the worker will try not to use it. Fourth, if serious accidents are possible, even though highly improbable, as in "calendering" in the rubber, paper, and linoleum industries, the safety device, if tripped, must be made to stop high-speed equipment instantly.[2] It must also be located so that it can be tripped almost instantaneously, should a worker get caught in the rolls.

Chemical and electroplating processes often give off noxious fumes and vapors. Other operations are extremely dusty. Most of the hazard to employee health can be eliminated by providing hoods, canopies, or ducts over the operation to convey the fumes and dust away by an exhaust fan.

A second type of safety equipment is the kind that is fastened to or worn by the worker. There are safety glasses, goggles, and hoods for welders. Rubber aprons, gloves, and boots are used by electroplaters. Leather gloves are needed for many operators where sharp, rough, hot, or cold materials are handled. Shoes with nonslip soles should be worn where floors are slippery. "Safety" shoes, having a steel toe cap, are a protection for heavy materials handlers. Respirators worn over the nose and mouth to purify the air are used for spray painters or workers in extremely dusty places.

With the possible exception of safety shoes, workers do not like to wear most protective devices. They find safety shoes no inconvenience, but safety glasses and respirators they consider nuisances. The injury hazard is often slight and the protective equipment uncomfortable to wear, so the company usually has to insist, on penalty of discharge, on its use. A Kalamazoo, Michigan, company had a strike when it insisted that women wear safety hats to keep their hair from getting caught in drill presses. And it is true also that the safety engineer sometimes is too fussy. Workers and even visitors in one of the big three auto companies must wear safety glasses all the time. The other two companies don't find them necessary, yet they have good safety records.

Except for safety shoes, most companies furnish safety equipment worn by workers. In order to encourage their use, many companies sell safety shoes, which look like regular dress shoes of medium quality, to workers at cost.

A third type of safety equipment is needed in case of a disaster,

---

[2] "Calendering" is a rolling operation in which materials are squeezed between closely set rollers.

particularly fire. In factories of wood construction, overhead sprinkler systems are required by law in many states. A water tank to supply water and to keep up water pressure in case of fire may also be required. Fire extinguishers and fire hoses should be provided at numerous locations in the plant. In most factories several types of fire are possible. Fire may be caused by defective electrical wiring, oil, explosive fumes and dusts, or other combustibles. Since fires of different kinds respond to different treatments, different types of fire extinguishers are needed. Burning oil or magnesium cannot be extinguished by water.

ACCIDENT PREVENTION: THE HUMAN ELEMENT

Most accidents involve both unsafe conditions *and* unsafe human practices. According to the National Safety Council unsafe acts occur in at least nine out of every ten accidents. Putting in safe machines, installing safety guards, and getting rid of hazards is not enough. Workers must work safely. We all know that unsafe acts cause accidents, but we expect accidents to happen to someone else, not to ourselves, so we keep on with our unsafe acts. And so accidents keep on happening.

Smoking during working hours by factory workers used to be forbidden in most factories. Now it is forbidden, as a rule, only where it creates a fire or explosion hazard. In spite of the hazard, however, workers sometimes do smoke in restricted areas. Many coal mine explosions have been traced to smoking. The company *must* try to enforce its no-smoking rules where safety is involved.

All company managements know that carelessness contributes to most accidents, so most of them try to educate workers in safety. Workers should be told of the hazards and shown how to work safely, but for the most part educating workers in safety is a matter of developing a safety-conscious frame of mind rather than teaching them specific things to do. Safety consciousness can be fostered by the way in which warnings of hazards are phrased. One company found that it was more effective to say "Even 240 volts can prove fatal—660 volts here!" instead of "Danger, high voltage."

Accidents are depressing, and no one likes to think about them. Quoting figures and showing pictures of accidents or injured workers only makes us look the other way. We don't get any "work safely" message from them because we won't look at them.

The fact is that relatively few workers do get hurt. Naturally, therefore, it is hard to sell safety to them. The author recently visited one factory in which every safety device seen in one department was out of operation. Safety push buttons on presses were permanently taped down. Sweep arms on punch presses had been removed. Gloves attached to punch presses, while still there, were not being used. The factory guide said the department had a very good safety record, had had no lost time due to accidents for months. In another factory making bolts on cold-heading machines, workers were seen to reach into the machine on the backstroke of the header, catch the bolt blank, and inspect it. The machine operated at approximately 75 strokes a minute and would crush the hand of any worker if it were caught. When the workers were asked why they did not use a wire basket, the answer was that no one had had such an accident within the memory of anyone there—at least 20 years.

Dun's Review & Modern Industry

FIG. 23–2. Humor in safety posters attracts attention and conveys a message.

In both of these cases the unsafe acts were almost sure to cause accidents; both the workers and the companies were indeed fortunate that they had not already happened.

Various schemes are used to get employees to work safely. Shop rules usually require that goggles and other safety devices be worn where conditions call for caution; sometimes the penalty for failure to do so is discharge. Some companies have tackled the problem through union management safety committees. One company makes any injured worker, upon his return to work, a safety committee of one in his department. He must look over the department for hazardous conditions and practices and report them. The company paper should give special recognition to accident-free departments. Sometimes a "dunce prize" is given to the department having the last accident. It is retained

Getting a second look for safety

Lively humor, a little sparkle, cartoons that are pointed, lift these industrial-truck safety cartoons above the usual level. From *Safety* *Saves!*, a 24-page booklet by Clark Equipment Co., Battle Creek, Mich., they are guaranteed to get more than one reading.

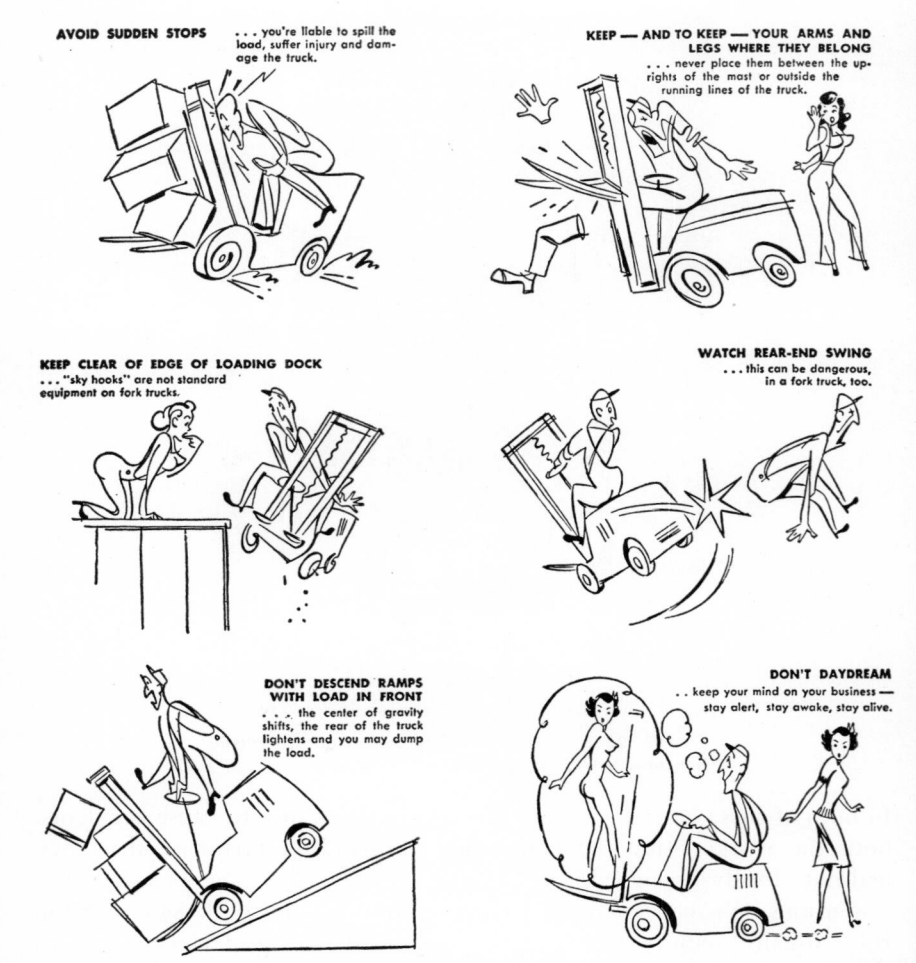

Clark Equipment Co.

FIG. 23–3. Cartoons emphasizing the damages from careless truck operation.

and must be displayed at the department entrance until another department has an accident; then that department must display it. Safety competition should never, however, be permitted to become so keen that minor injuries are unreported and untreated, just to save the record.

Posters and cartoons displayed on bulletin boards and in the company paper are effective in safety education. Sometimes they can be made humorous without being grisly. Workers look at "laugh-with-a-message" posters and laugh. They do look and, as a result, probably think a little more about working safely. "How-to-do-it" and "how-not-to-do-it" posters are less interesting than humorous posters and, of necessity, have to be quite elementary. "Misery" posters, aiming to make the reader aware of the grief that can come from unsafe acts, tend to stir up fear. Workers have more accidents when they are in low spirits than when they feel good, so such posters tend to defeat their purpose. Besides, they emphasize the *results* of unsafe acts rather than the acts themselves.

Accident records show that some workers are more accident-prone than others. Putting them on the safest jobs lowers the accident rate. But how can you tell an accident-prone worker ahead of time? You can't. And by the time a man has worked long enough to establish an accident record, a lot of damage has been done. Reassigning accident-prone workers to safer jobs is not, therefore, a quick way to reduce the accident rate. Unfortunately, too, the proper job for a worker is constantly changing. As one safety engineer points out, workers grow old and change even if the jobs don't. He recommends annual physical examinations for all employees, so that their jobs can always be suitable to them, not merely suitable for them at the time of hiring.

THE SAFETY ENGINEER

Safety is not self-generating; someone has to work at the job of safety forever. But who? There seems to be no perfect place in the organization for a man in charge of safety. Injury records are kept by the dispensary and are supervised by the personnel director, who also keeps records of workmen's compensation cases and their disposition. But safety is partly a matter of plant cleanliness and maintenance (the maintenance department's work), it is partly a matter of machine and equipment design (the engineering department's work), and it is partly a matter of safe working habits (the foreman's job).

Most large companies have a safety engineer, responsible for any and all safety work not directly the duty of another department. He watches for unsafe practices and hazardous conditions, recommends changes to remove hazards, analyzes injury records, works with departmental safety committees, makes safety reports, puts up safety posters, and handles correspondence with outside safety organizations. Probably he has no power to change unsatisfactory conditions, being allowed only to recommend changes; but he may have the authority to stop operations if they are being done in a needlessly dangerous way.

He should also see that equipment for fire protection and emergency first aid is available at strategic points and is in working order. In large companies, where fire is a definite hazard, he organizes and instructs emergency fire-fighting teams among the workers of each department.

A safety engineer can, by himself, do little to improve safety in the plant. Usually departmental safety committees of one or more employees in each department are appointed to help him. Foremen, too, are expected to help, particularly in detecting unsafe conditions. In the case of unsafe practices, the foreman is expected to train his men to work safely.

OFF-THE-JOB SAFETY

Employed persons suffer twice as many off-the-job fatal accidents as they do on the job.[3] And they have considerably more (although not double the number) nonfatal accidents off the job.

The safety-mindedness created by the company during work hours probably carries over into off-the-job activities. A safety-minded worker on the job is probably safety-minded at home, where figures indicate that safety is much needed. To the extent that the carryover takes place, the company's efforts at safety education bear more fruit than appear on company records.

THE HOSPITAL OR INFIRMARY

Most companies employing as many as 1,000 persons maintain a small hospital or infirmary (sometimes also called the "dispensary"). Many smaller companies also have good facilities of this sort; it depends on the hazards of the work and the attitude of management. Minimum facilities are specified by law in many states. The hospital or dispensary is usually administered by the personnel department and is generally located near it. Since the dispensary should be readily accessible to employees and to job applicants taking physical examinations, it should have doors inside to the plant and outside to the street.

Large companies often maintain almost complete hospitals with many facilities and several full-time employees. General Electric at Schenectady, for example, has a clinic that can handle 1,200 cases a day (employees there number 35,000). Many small companies need and have little more than an adequate supply of first-aid medicines and bandages. Others find that they need infirmaries staffed by a part- or full-time nurse and equipped with stretchers, cots, eye treatment facilities, two or three small rooms to handle cases privately, and a waiting room.

The infirmary's primary purpose is to furnish first aid in emergency cases and to take care of minor injuries to workers. Workers with cuts, abrasions, scratches, splinters, and the like are encouraged to come to the infirmary for treatment. Rarely do these minor injuries cause any difficulty if they are promptly and properly treated. When they are not, infection sometimes results. The nature of some factory operations may

---

[3] *Accident Facts* (1957 ed.; Chicago, Ill.: National Safety Council), p. 25.

cause skin irritations or bronchial difficulties. If the cause cannot be removed, the employees most susceptible to trouble can be put on other work.

When employees have a leave of absence on account of sickness or accident, they are not permitted to return to work until they have been cleared by the medical department. Physical examinations at this point prevent workers from returning to work too soon, perhaps aggravating their injury or exposing others to infection.

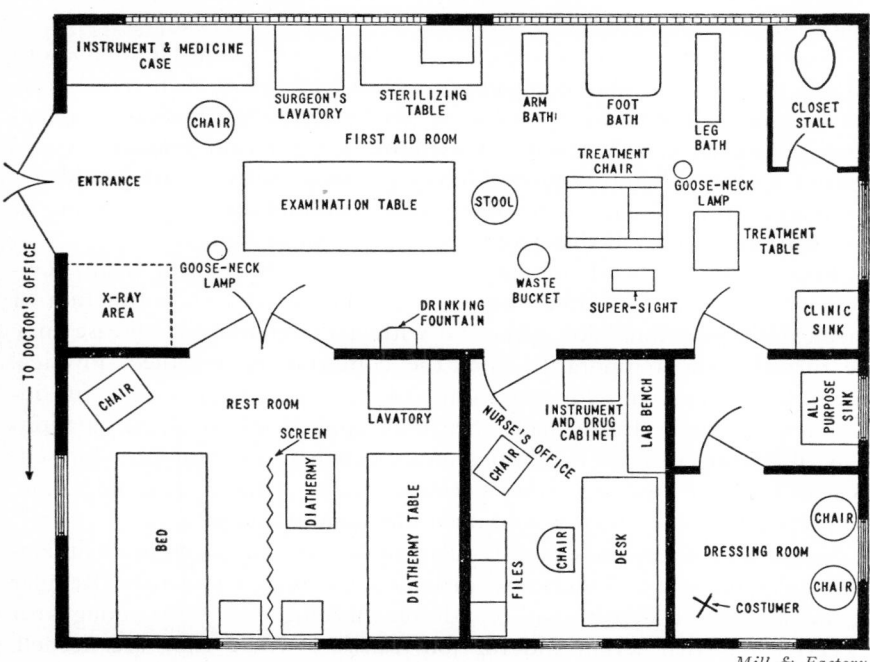

Mill & Factory

FIG. 23–4. Layout of the first-aid facilities of a modern plant.

The medical department keeps records of all cases and should analyze them periodically to see whether any general corrective measures are indicated. Records of injuries that cause lost time, and their treatments, are essential for industrial compensation purposes. Similarly, it is important to keep careful records of workers' disabilities which might later be claimed to have been caused by their work. In the case of all injuries, except minor ones, the worker is entitled to a workmen's compensation benefit; hence accurate records must be kept. The records should include a description of how the accident happened as well as the nature of the injury and the medical attention given. In companies where workers might contract industrial diseases, similar records need to be kept of the date and the nature of all illnesses and the treatment prescribed. Records of sickness and accidents causing lost time also are needed by companies having sickness and accident insurance because the workers who are not able to work are entitled to benefits.

EMPLOYEE HEALTH

Years ago labor unions opposed physical examinations saying that they would result in discrimination against persons with slight physical defects. Today everyone accepts them as a matter of course. Actually, it is impossible to hire only physically perfect men. According to the medical officer of one large company, 40 per cent of all employees have some physical handicap.

Nearly all companies, except the smallest, give medical examinations to new employees. Small companies with no facilities of their own sometimes send prospective employees to nearby doctors. Physical examinations help place employees in suitable jobs. A hernia, for example, would keep a worker off jobs requiring heavy physical effort, but it would not keep him from doing many other jobs. Without the examination, he might be put on a job that would be dangerous to him.

Preserving the health of employees by protecting them from newcomers with communicable diseases is another worth-while function of medical examinations. An applicant with a communicable disease may be turned away temporarily until the condition is remedied. Physical examinations prevent workers from making false injury claims for injuries which they already had when they applied. Physical examinations may also bring to light conditions unsuspected by the applicant himself. A man unaware that he has heart trouble might, without an examination, be placed on a job which would make the condition worse.

Some large companies give regular annual examinations to their employees. Free chest X-rays are provided in some companies. Regular examinations will detect many conditions needing care early enough for effective remedial action and for job transfers where they are needed. As a result of examination, glasses may be suggested in cases of persistent headaches due to eyestrain, etc.

The department may send an ailing worker home if his presence at work is endangering his own health or that of other workers. Health assistance is carried into the employees' homes by some companies. Nurses are sent to call at the homes of employees who have been sent home or have called in and reported that they were absent from work because of illness. The nurses suggest medical aid if it seems to be needed, report back the nature of the illness, keep in touch with the employee, and report his progress in cases of long illness. This practice tends to reduce absenteeism, since it discourages workers from taking a day or two off and then claiming they were sick.

INDUSTRIAL DISEASE

Industrial disease is a cause for concern in very few manufacturing companies because most industrial processing has no disease hazard.

It is responsible for only about 2 per cent of workmen's compensation claims.

If there is a disease hazard, however, every possible measure must be taken to protect workers. Some of the diseases, like silicosis, for example, often are very serious (so can exposure to rays from radioactive materials be). Efforts to protect the worker have already shown results. Years ago silicosis, lead poisoning, and other similar industrial diseases were more prevalent than they are today. Now equipment for collecting dust and fumes and the respirators in current use reduce the hazards which lead to industrial diseases. Furthermore, when possible, substitutions are made of different materials or procedures which do not cause disease. Also, diseases caused by the sensitivities of particular workers can be minimized by keeping allergic workers off jobs where there is any likelihood of irritation. Like accident hazards, industrial disease hazards can be reduced or kept low only by continued effort on the part of management.

SAFETY AND HEALTH REGULATIONS

All states and most cities have laws concerning safe working conditions in factories. They generally require that gears, pulleys, and belting at work levels be enclosed. Wells (holes in the floor) between floors must be protected by railings. Elevators must operate in enclosed shafts. Dust-collecting equipment must be provided for very dusty work. Similar equipment may be required for spray-painting operations and those giving off injurious fumes. Regulations usually require that metal stamping machines be fitted with safety guards or control buttons placed so that a worker cannot crush his fingers or hands.

Compliance with the law will result in much safer work methods than would otherwise exist in many companies. Unfortunately, safety laws are frequently violated. Safe methods are often a little slower than unsafe methods. Lower output means higher labor costs per unit of product and less economical use of machines. Safety devices cost money and do not increase output. Both the company and pieceworkers want more output, so there is strong temptation to use unsafe methods. They forget or do not appreciate the possibility of accidents and their costs.

In honesty it must be reported that safety laws can generally be violated with impunity. Almost never does a state appropriate enough money to hire enough inspectors to enforce the law. Saving money on safety enforcement budgets doesn't lose many votes for lawmakers, so they appropriate only very little money for such enforcement. If an inspector finds a violation, he reports it and orders the company to remedy the situation. The company is given time for remedial action. A year or more may pass before the inspector returns, at which time the warning is repeated if the unsafe situation has not been remedied. The enforcement provisions of the law should be strengthened.

Public safety regulations do, however, cause companies to use safer methods. Nearly all companies want their employees to work safely, and nearly all companies try to obey safety laws. The regulations probably cover some situations which might not have been recognized as hazardous or in which, through carelessness, the company would not otherwise have used safe methods. Most companies abide by the regulations regardless of the improbability of detection and penalty.

STUDY QUESTIONS

1. How much does safety cost? What do accidents cost? What items go into a figure covering all the costs of each?
2. Which cause accidents, hazards or people? Discuss.
3. How do you account for the long-run improved safety records in factories? Explain.
4. What kinds of safety equipment are available? Which is most effective? Why?
5. How do you get workers to work safely? What problems are there to solve?
6. How worth while are safety drives? Discuss their use and value.
7. What can a safety engineer do? How worth while is he? Discuss.
8. How much responsibility does an employer have for an employee's health? Discuss.
9. How effective are safety laws? Discuss them and suggest ways to improve.

Chapter 24

WAGE AND SALARY ADMINISTRATION

"REAL" WAGES AND MONEY WAGES

"R<small>EAL</small>" wages are the buying power of money wages. Your real wages depend on: (*a*) how much money you make, and (*b*) the cost of living. If you get a pay increase when prices go up too, you may not be ahead at all—it depends on which goes up the most. But your real wages (and your standard of living) go up any time your wage increase exceeds price increases.

As a nation we consume what we produce. If we produce more, we consume more; then we say that we have raised our standard of living. And if we produce less, there is less to consume and our standard of living goes down. It is important to get this over-all view because it is the reason why we can't all raise our standard of living just by raising everyone's pay. If everyone gets more money when production does not increase, then all that happens is that prices go up the same amount. We can't, as a group, increase our standard of living without producing more.

But can't one gain at the expense of another? Certainly. If some people get pay raises when others don't (and if production doesn't increase), prices probably will go up a little. The people getting raises come out ahead, and people not getting pay raises lose out a little. But, if production increases at the same time that pay raises are being made, then prices may not go up at all, and the gain in the standard of living goes to the people getting the pay raises. Other people aren't any worse off, but they don't share in the extra productivity.

Union leaders understand all of this, and that is one reason for trying for pay raises every year. If they can get a pay raise for their members, they are ahead as long as the cost of living doesn't go up just as much and just as quickly.

Almost all factory workers have received raises every year since

World War II, but the cost of living has soared too. How have the men fared? Very well indeed. In the ten years after 1946, hourly pay went from $0.97 to $2.07. Weekly pay went from $41.20 to $82.00. It would have gone up to about $100.00 if the costs of extras such as vacations, holidays, pensions, and so on were added—none of these were common in 1946.

But of course cost-of-living increases have eaten up part of the gain. Purchasing power is all that counts. But here too there is a big jump. An hour's work got a man 38 per cent more goods in 1956 than in 1946.

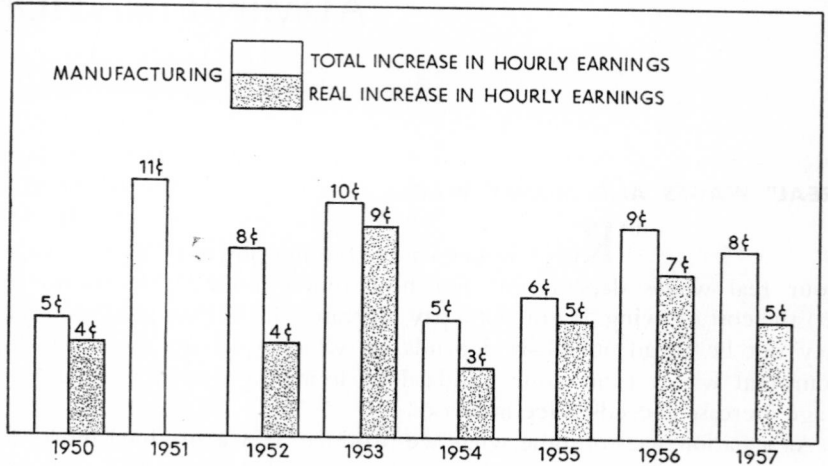

FIG. 24–1. Labor's "real" wage gains since 1950.

But, you might ask, how about take-home pay? Aren't there now more deductions than there used to be? Actually, there aren't. Social security tax deductions are higher, but income tax rates are lower.

WAGE POLICIES

What wage should a company pay? As much as it can afford? As little as it can get by with? As much as the union asks? As much as others pay?

Most companies say that they pay the going rate or a little more. Now, of course, not everyone can be above average so there must be some below. High wages give your people a good standard of living, and that alone is a good reason for trying to pay high. You also hope (1) to attract good workers, (2) to have low labor turnover, and (3) to have few strikes. If you get all three gains you can operate efficiently, and this in turn saves you enough money to pay high wages.

Maybe it works that way, but it is not certain. Job applicants can't tell whether one plant's wage scale is higher than another's. This is hard enough to do even if you have figures—which applicants don't have. Most men are hired for bottom jobs, so that all that applicants know about is the hiring rate for bottom jobs—and everyone has about the same rate for these. Your pay rates aren't likely to have much to do with the quality of applicant you get.

Even turnover is not necessarily affected much by pay rates. Not very many men quit any company, whatever its pay rates, when they get above the bottom jobs. If they did they would likely have to start near the bottom somewhere else. Often the skill they acquire at one company isn't needed anywhere else. And since other companies, too, fill good jobs by promotion from within, men part way up on your wage scale stay put pretty well. Besides, many employers won't hire anyone who already has a job. A man wanting to change would have to quit first, and that is too risky for most men.

What a company wants to pay and even what its union wants aren't the only things that count. Ability to pay *may* be a limiting factor. Generally it isn't though (Studebaker-Packard paid higher wages than General Motors for years—although it certainly was *less* able to do so). Ability to pay sets a top limit to wages if the company is losing money (Studebaker-Packard employees took a cut one year when GM employees got a raise). New England textile workers have taken wage cuts sometimes in recent years rather than see their company move south where low labor cost competitors operate.

By and large, a company can do very little about setting its own wage level where it wants it. Competition for sales keeps profits low enough to prevent management going overboard on the high side. At the same time unions and competition for workers keep a company from getting far behind the parade.

WAGE SURVEYS

"We will pay wages equal to or above the average." That is our policy. But how do we know if we are following it? We take a wage survey— ask the other companies what they are paying. This is easier said than done. Would you give a competitor a list of your men, their job titles, and their average hourly earnings if he asked for it? Probably not; most companies would not.

Then how do you do it? The most practical way is to have your trade association do it. It can probably get information from each company in the industry, and then send each of them a report of amounts being paid for a long list of jobs—and without revealing any company's identity. That would tell you what your *industry* is paying. It also saves separate companies in the industry having to make their own surveys.

But in your *community* you may be the only company in your industry. So you need a community survey more than you need an industry survey. Again, it is better for a central group (the Chamber of Commerce or the local Association of Manufacturers) to make it.

Surveys fall far short of telling you how you stack up. What good does it do you—a machine shop—to know what a nearby meat-packing house pays its pig sticker? Or what a nearby textile plant pays a loom tender? Or a foundry pays a mold maker? Or a furniture factory pays an upholsterer? Or a sheet metal shop pays a welder? Suppose that you have all of these figures and lots more—can you tell whether you are paying area average wages, or more, or less?

If community surveys are so worthless, how about the industry surveys? They too are of little real help. If you are in Pittsburgh and you find that you pay more than someone else does in New Orleans, are you ahead of the others? Well, maybe yes, but then your men live in Pittsburgh and have to pay living costs there. If they are higher than in New Orleans, then how do you really compare?

Besides, you almost never get direct comparisons. Suppose that you have several welders doing repair work on products and pay them $2.50 an hour on daywork. You find that someone else has some welders doing repetitive work on a $2.25 base rate job but earning $2.75 on piecework. Who pays better?

Then there is the matter of job titles. You pay punch press operators one rate, but you have separate higher paid setup men set up all jobs. You find that someone else pays punch press operators 20 cents an hour more. Are you behind? Then you find out that the other company punch press operators have to set up their own jobs. Who pays the most? But generally you don't find out about the setting up, since the job title didn't tell you. And if you didn't find out, you would have come to a wrong conclusion.

Why not just forget specific jobs and just compare company hourly averages? Now you get into the "job-mix." Suppose your average is $2.20 an hour and someone else's is $2.10. Are you ahead? It seems so; but you are not really paying more if you have lots of high-skilled jobs and few lower-skilled jobs, while the other company has just the reverse.

Another question is the "extras"—the fringe benefits. They are worth money to the employees, and they vary between companies. But, they don't usually show in wage surveys.

Where does all this leave us? It certainly sounds as if wage surveys are not much good. Here maybe we'd better backtrack a little because with all their imperfections there is no other way to tell how we stack up. This does explain, however, why most companies use surveys of trade associations, of local groups, or even of the United States Bureau of Labor Statistics only as general guides and not as being very conclusive.

LAWS AFFECTING WAGES

There are two federal laws, the Wage-Hour law and the Walsh-Healey Act, which regulate the wages paid by industry. All manufacturers engaged in interstate commerce are covered by the Wage-Hour law. The Walsh-Healey Act covers only companies having federal contracts in excess of $10,000. Both laws require the payment of wages at "time-and-a-half" rates for hours over 40 in one week; but the Walsh-Healey Act adds the same requirement for hours over 8 in one day. Agricultural workers, government employees, and various other groups are exempted from the Wage-Hour law. Seasonal industries are given limited exemptions from having to pay for overtime at a premium rate. Workers at supervisory levels and above are, for the most part, excepted from the overtime pay requirements.

The Wage-Hour law sets $1.00 an hour as the minimum wage. Wages nearly everywhere are much higher than that, so that part of the law doesn't mean much. Besides the minimum for all industries, the law lets individual industries set higher minimums, but none has been set so far. The Walsh-Healey Act allows the Secretary of Labor to set higher minimums for any industry as far as government contracts are concerned.

Several states have passed state laws like the federal Wage-Hour law. For the most part they do not require as high minimum pay rates so they affect manufacturing companies very little because, practically speaking, *all* manufacturing companies are covered by the federal laws. Few of even the smallest manufacturers are not engaged in interstate commerce.

WAGE "PATTERNS"

For several years now there has been a strong tendency for one or two major industries, or even one or two companies, to set patterns in wages that others follow. In particular, the contracts of the General Motors Company with the United Automobile Workers and of the United States Steel Company with the United Steel Workers have become patterns for smaller companies and for other industries.

Negotiations of companies that follow the leaders are often delayed until the "bellwether" companies' agreements are known. Neither the company nor the union wants to settle any sooner; the company for fear it may give too much, and the union for fear it may settle for too little. Once the pattern is set, companies in good financial condition and with good sales prospects generally follow the pattern closely, granting the same size raise and also agreeing to other provisions granted by pilot companies. Companies claiming that they can't give so much are often able to settle for less, but only after rather bitter negotiations and sometimes strikes.

"ESCALATOR" WAGE CHANGES

"Escalator" clauses in union contracts are agreements to adjust wages when the cost of living changes. If the cost of living (measured by the United States Bureau of Labor's Consumer Price Index) goes up, so do wages. It works on the downside too. If the cost of living goes down, so do wages; but the labor contract always limits downward adjustments to no more than a few cents, in *total*, from any high point. Adjustments are made only quarterly, not monthly, and wage changes are full cents, not fractions, per hour.

Escalator clauses are a post–World War II development because the cost of living has gone up so consistently since then. Naturally, unions would not be interested in them if the cost of living were not rising.

Escalator provisions do not change a worker's standard of living, but by raising wages along with prices, they preserve his standard of living by keeping his real wage intact.

"ANNUAL IMPROVEMENT" WAGE INCREASES

Productivity per work-hour has, in the United States, gone up between 2 and 3 per cent a year for over 50 years. That doesn't mean that today's man works harder than his grandfather (actually he works less hard and shorter hours), but today's man *and the machine the company provides* turn out more than his grandfather did with hand tools and simple machines.

If more is produced, who should get the extra? The person responsible? Or everyone? Most improvements are management-inspired, so you might say that the managers or the owners (stockholders) should get the gain. That would leave out employees and customers. Actually, over the years everyone shares.

After World War II General Motors granted a demand from the union for a wage increase every year (every year of a 5-year contract). It was called an "annual improvement" increase; the idea being that in this way the men were sure to share in the unending gains in productivity. The annual improvement increase was *in. addition to an escalator clause* to cover cost-of-living increases. At first, 3 cents an hour each year was agreed on; later it went up to 4 and then to 5 cents. Annual improvement pay raises caught on slowly but are now common.

When you get something at the bargaining table, you usually have to give something in return. When the United Automobile Workers at General Motors got their improvement factor into the contract, they had to agree not to oppose the introduction of more efficient methods and machines. How else could the improvement come about? Such an agreement by the union is logical and is the rule wherever there are guaranteed annual raises. And where that provision is in the contract, it has almost eliminated the trouble that so often came up years ago when new methods were put in.

WAGE DIFFERENCES

Some men are paid more than others. Because jobs are different and men are different, it is proper that some should be paid more than others. Your highest-skilled machine repairman should get more pay than the girl who opens mail and takes it around to the offices.

Differences in wage levels exist between one area and another, between one industry and another, and between one company and another. Within a company you find differences between office and factory, between high- and low-skilled jobs, between pieceworkers and dayworkers, or even between men and women. Company officials should always try to pay different wages when the jobs call for it, but they should not pay one man more than another when it isn't justified.

WAGE DIFFERENCES BETWEEN AREAS

In the long run supply and demand set wages in all communities. Places with lots of men and few jobs will have low wages. Places with lots of jobs and few men will have high wages.

Supply and demand keep pulling low areas up and high areas down. Men can and do move—not everyone, of course, but enough to help even things out. Men move out of low-wage areas into high-wage areas. That lowers the excess supply where they were and cuts down the shortage where they go. Companies move too. They put up factories in low-wage areas and expand less in high-wage areas. That raises the demand where it was low and cuts it where it was high. Both of these corrections—men moving and companies moving—are slow long-term corrections. It takes years to affect wage rates very much.

Multiplants companies have to face up to wage differences in different areas. They want to pay the going rate in the area or a little more, but that means that they pay different amounts for the same work in different plants. The company doesn't object to this, but unions do. They fight to get equal pay for equal work wherever it is done.

It sounds at first like a fair and equitable way. But it won't hold water. Remember real wages and money wages? If you pay San Francisco wages to your men in your plant in Alabama, they can live well indeed. Because the cost of living in Alabama is lower, they can buy many more things than can your San Francisco employees. Is it fair and equitable after all? Furthermore, no manufacturer will put a plant in Alabama if he has to pay high wages and high freight bills too. The Alabama man who gets equal wages will have no job.

Letting high and low area rates work themselves out—as men and companies migrate—seems to be reasonable. That means that multiplant companies should pay area rates or a little above—but should not pay the same wage all over the country.

WAGE DIFFERENCES WITHIN AREAS

Intra-area wage differences are the differences among companies in the same locality. Within an area the cost of living is the same for all workers, so that there is no economic justification for a differential in wages to equalize the standard of living of the workers in the various companies.

But even within an area there often are justifiable differences between companies. You compete for labor in the local area, but in selling your product you compete with your industry. If you have low-wage competitors located in other areas, you have to meet their low selling prices, and that will hold down your wages.

Another reason why some companies pay low is consumer resistance to high enough prices to sell the product. Laundries, for example, usually pay low. If they charge enough to pay high wages, housewives do more of their own laundry. But, not too often is there any good reason for big pay differences among companies in the same area.

OFFICE AND FACTORY WAGE DIFFERENCES

Today most companies pay factory men better than office people. Years ago it was the other way around.

How can we say that office jobs pay less when they aren't like factory jobs? One way to tell is with borderline jobs—those in the factory of a semiclerical nature. Use your office job evaluation plan and see what they should pay. Then use your factory plan for the same jobs and see. The factory plan will nearly always produce a higher rate. Another way is to trace the pay of office and factory jobs for the last 20 years. (The United States Bureau of Labor Statistics has many figures on this.) What with the shortage of factory workers for years and the yearly wage demands of powerful labor unions, factory wages have gone up and up and up. Office salaries are up too, but not so much.

Why doesn't job evaluation straighten this out? It is supposed to show up pay inequities so that they can be taken care of. Job evaluation doesn't straighten it out because almost all companies use two job evaluation plans, one for the factory and a different one for the office. Each plan straightens out inequities where it is used, but the two are never tied together.

But isn't it proper that factory men should get more than office people? Some people say yes, that office jobs are more steady, that office people have greater security, have greater promotional opportunities, and work in more pleasant surroundings. They used also to have an advantage over factory men by getting paid holidays and vacations. But now factory workers get as many extras as—or even more than—office workers.

People still want office jobs, though. Small wonder that employers let the law of supply and demand operate—particularly since office workers don't join unions to press their claims.

SHIFT DIFFERENCES

Night-shift men get 5 or 10 cents an hour more than day-shift men. It wasn't always so. Years ago if you worked the night shift it meant that you hadn't been around long enough to get on the day shift, or that you liked working nights. And you certainly got no higher rate of pay. But unions decided that such hours were undesirable and asked for more money for night men, so it is now the rule to give night men a little extra pay.

SKILLS DIFFERENCES

Skilled jobs pay more than unskilled jobs. We all agree that this is reasonable, and, today, we use job evaluation to tell us how much difference in pay there ought to be between jobs.

But don't supply and demand set rates for jobs? Mostly no—not for individual jobs. There is no supply of, say, internal grinder operators, or of materials handlers, or of assemblers, grade A, and so on. You just hire men for bottom jobs and train and promote them into various better jobs. You set your own pay rates for your jobs, most of which have no direct counterpart in any nearby companies. An exception might be such jobs as toolmakers where it takes years to train men. You may have to hire them occasionally from outside. If your rate for toolmakers happens to be lower than in other companies, you will have to come up to their rates.

But can you neglect supply and demand completely, even on bottom jobs? No. If men are scarce you may have to boost your hiring rate. But that means you'll have to boost rates on most of your lowest-paid jobs too, so that they will stay above the hiring rate. And that, in turn, means boosting middle rates a little. The effect is to push up all rates a little, but bottom rates the most.

Now, of course, you don't just raise men's pay as a management's decision any more. In fact, the law requires you to negotiate all pay raises with the union. So between contract negotiation dates, you do not raise hiring rates in spite of labor shortage. But at negotiating time, if there is a labor shortage, the union demand for high wages is granted willingly, not grudgingly. Supply and demand do affect your rates but in an overall way—not on specific jobs. It gets in, as it were, by the side door.

Skills pay differences have been cut in the last 20 years. Not that top skills don't still earn more than bottom, but *proportionally* less. Many of the annual pay raises have been "across-the-board" increases—everyone gets the same cents per hour raise. Unions like that because it seems so fair—everyone is treated alike. Also the men at and near the bottom (where most of the union members are) get a bigger proportional increase than men on high-skilled jobs.

Before a 25-cent raise, a $3.50 an hour job pays double a $1.75 job, but afterwards the $3.75 is not double the $2.00. The skilled man loses ground on such deals. Unions, today, are coming more to the idea of asking for equal *per cent* pay increases for everyone, so the differences are more often preserved. In the late 1950's, many unions recognized this problem and now allow skilled groups to bargain separately for pay raises.

PRODUCTION DIFFERENCES

Good producers should be paid more than poor producers. You can do that with day rates by paying two men on the same job two different rates. If Smith turns out more than Jones, pay him a little higher hourly rate. That works well if it is always so, but it makes Jones quite unhappy if Smith sometimes turns out less. Incentive rates are the best way to pay for production differences. Then every man's pay reflects directly his output. Incentives are discussed in Chapter 27.

OFFICE SALARIES

Office workers are nearly always paid a monthly salary. Years ago there was no regular job evaluation nor any regular merit rating. A man's salary combined his boss's idea of the importance of the job and also his appraisal of the man's work. The boss was really applying a kind of informal job evaluation and merit rating. Office men never knew whether they should be dissatisfied or not because no one ever knew what anyone else made. There probably were plenty of inequities, at least many office people thought so.

Today, most office people still don't know what their fellow workers make. But now most office jobs are covered by job evaluation which set bottom and top salary limits. Salary *ranges* (instead of fixed rates) are the rule for office jobs. There is less chance of anyone really being paid too little compared with his fellow workers. Also, in a great many companies, department heads have to "merit-rate" their people once a year or so. So there are no forgotten men.

Companies usually don't have to contend with unions very often as far as office people are concerned. That is only because office people don't join unions—not because it is prohibited. Partly because they don't want to drive office people into joining unions, companies usually try to be as fair as they can be with office people. But in spite of that office salaries seem to lag behind factory wages.

Piecework is sometimes used in offices for typists and file clerks, but it is uncommon. It is practically impossible to set really good piece rates on what office people do. On the other hand, production standards are becoming more common for budgeting purposes but not for pay purposes. Management is paying more attention nowadays to watching how *many* men there are in offices and to trying to hold down the number. For this purpose, you don't need highly accurate standards.

FOREMEN'S AND SUPERVISORS' SALARIES

Probably most factories use regular job evaluation (but a separate job evaluation plan from the factory plan) for the jobs of foremen and general foremen. This works quite well for comparing foremen's jobs, but it doesn't help set the proper difference between foremen's pay and the pay of their men. Actually, it is probably more important to see that foremen are paid noticeably more than their men than it is to pay them equitably among themselves. The 25 per cent figure quoted in Chapter 22 is a good general rule. Foremen ought to make about that much more than the *average* pay of their men. Usually this will put them a little above even their best paid men too.

EXECUTIVE SALARIES

Who decides the pay of top management? Not even the president gets to decide his and his top men's salaries. The board of directors has a salary committee, usually composed of board members who are *not* company officials. It decides what the top echelon gets.

Below the top, the president and vice-president decide—except that the board's salary committee must also approve. Of course, the salary committee doesn't know the junior executives and how much they should get, but it acts as a check and keeps the top men from giving out too many raises.

Both middle-level and top management jobs are too responsible to be properly evaluated by job evaluation. Someone has said that these jobs are "man-oriented" not "job-oriented." So salaries are largely fixed by custom, opinion, how well the present man fills the job, and how long he has been on it.

Highly paid men all like to keep their jobs, so there is some tendency for them not to "stick their necks out." They sometimes don't do things that really ought to be done for fear of criticism. Also some of them "go soft"—take it easy rather than do their best. They go in for "status-quoism," which we discussed in Chapter 4.

The point here is how to motivate them. You want them to keep on doing their best. Most big companies pay them salaries plus bonuses. The bonuses act as spurs and are almost as effective as is piecework for factory workers. Generally their bonuses amount to one quarter to one half of their salary in years when profits are high. Such arrangements are not, however, so liberal as they sound because the base salaries are below what the executive expects on the job and what the company expects to pay for it. Were there no bonuses, the base salaries would be higher.

How much do executives make? Presidents get from $25,000 to $100,-000 (base salary), depending largely on the company's size. Giant companies are far above this, however. The next two or three men each probably get about two thirds of the president's salary. From then on salaries are graded down to the level of superintendent (supposing him to be in charge of at least 500 employees) who gets maybe four times as much as a factory worker.

Income taxes being what they are, the matter of motivating top men is hard to solve. Long before an executive reaches a $50,000 salary,

Uncle Sam is taking more than half of any pay raise he may get, and he takes nearly all of any raise you give anyone with a $100,000 salary.

Our income tax laws give a little recognition to this problem. They allow you to give executives options to buy stock at or near today's prices. The options do not have to be counted as income because they are worth nothing or very little at the moment. Years later, if the stock is higher priced, the man can exercise his option and buy stock at his option price. Of course, this is a bargain. He is supposed to keep, not sell, the stock at least for a good while. If he keeps it for at least 6 months, he can call his gain a capital gain, not current income. Income taxes on capital gains are limited to 26 per cent, so he is way ahead.

Why does the government allow this? Also, why do stockholders go for it? The idea is that executives will work hard to make the company profitable so that its stock will go up.

Pensions also help give executives some money that they can keep. They don't get this until they retire. By then, with no salary, their income is low enough for them to keep most of what they get.

The administration of salaries of minor executives should be given considerable attention, because they constitute the group from which the future major executives will be drawn. Men in minor executive work need to be shifted from job to job occasionally to broaden their experience. They also need to receive periodic raises as they advance in stature. The salary a young man gets at any given time reflects the company's appraisal of him more than it does the worth of the job he happens to hold at the moment.

OVERTIME

Avoid overtime if possible. The most important reason is that it costs so much (see page 116). Important, too, is the shock to a man's pay when it stops. Cut from a 50-hour week to a 40-hour week and you cut off 28 per cent of a man's pay (from 55 hours' pay to 40).

Men don't like 28 per cent pay cuts so if they have any notion that you are going down to 40 hours they drag out their work. You'll have to keep on with the overtime just to get a normal 40 hours of work done. If you do keep on with the overtime, your costs are higher than ever because you aren't getting much production. But if you don't keep on with the overtime, you'll fall behind schedule because the men will work slowly hoping to force you back to long hours with high pay. It is best to return to the regular 40 hours and stay behind schedule until your foremen can get productivity up again—but it will be a struggle for them to do it.

Most companies follow a rather rigid rule. No overtime without permission. No foreman can authorize overtime without asking for approval. Not only does this policy prevent the men dragging out jobs just to get paid overtime but it also keeps pressure on department heads to get their work done in regular hours. On the other hand, overtime should be necessary once in a while. Department heads who can always get things done without overtime (considering that work loads vary) may have more men than they need.

But what should you do if work loads increase? If it is only a little, maybe overtime is better than hiring more men for just a short while. Besides, often you don't have extra machines and extra workplaces for extra men. Or maybe your operations require full work crews. You just can't put on a few extra men. All that you can do is to work the regular men longer hours. Remember too that you get poor production from new employees and that you increase your unemployment taxes if you hire new men for a few weeks and then lay them off, and they are unable to find other jobs.

Overtime decisions are not just management's decisions. The men usually have a voice in it too. Today's union contracts often give them a right to refuse to work overtime unless it is announced ahead and unless the whole department works long hours. This has a curious effect on assembly line work. If you work several lines and decide on short notice to work one of them overtime, you have to recruit some of the work crews for the overtime hours from other lines. You end up with a mixed crew, many of whom are on jobs strange to them. Yet production goes right along. You wonder if there is anything at all to the notion that men need training or that men need to be put on jobs that suit them.

The Wage-Hour Law and Overtime. Hourly paid and low salaried employees are covered by the Wage-Hour law requiring you to pay for hours over 40 a week at time-and-one-half rates. Office people didn't formerly have to punch a time clock, but now they have to so that there will be a record of their hours. The fact that they are on a salary doesn't prevent their getting time-and-one-half. If they work any overtime, you figure their salary on an hourly basis to see how much to pay them.

Some odd quirks have come out of the law. Because of it, don't let employees (factory or office) come in early or stay late. Why? Because their timecard record will show long hours. Once in a while a man will claim (months afterward) that he wasn't paid for his "overtime." His card shows that he put in extra time, but it doesn't show that the company didn't ask him to put in the extra time and that he wasn't working during that time. As far as government authorities can tell, you are guilty of not obeying the law. So, don't let people come early and make them leave when they finish their work.

Office people often work only 37½ hours a week, (8:30 to 12, and 1 to 5 for 5 days). Paying a week's pay for such a short week sounds liberal, but employers have sometimes regretted the practice whenever they had to go to overtime. Suppose that a man works 37½ hours a week for

$75.00. That is $2.00 an hour. Now go up to 45 hours. The man will have to be paid $95.00 ($80.00 for 40 hours at $2.00 each and $15.00 for 5 hours at $3.00 each).

But suppose that when you hire people you tell them that their pay is for a 40-hour week (although at the moment the work week is actually only 37½ hours). Your $75 for 40 hours = $1.875 hourly rate. A 37½-hour week costs $75.00, so does a 40-hour week. Now go up to 45. It will cost only $89.05; $75.00 for the first 40 hours and $14.05 for 5 hours at $2.81. It pays to be careful how you express hours of work and pay to office people.

Overtime by pieceworkers in the factory has to be paid for at time and one half of their average hourly earnings, *not their base rates*. Take a pieceworker whose base rate is $2.50 an hour but who averages $3.00 an hour on piecework. If he works 45 hours in a week, he gets paid $142.50 ($120.00 for 40 hours at $3.00 plus $22.50 for 5 hours at $4.50). His overtime hours are figured on the $3.00 figure, not on his $2.50 base rate.

Shift differentials also are figured in for overtime pay. A $2.00 an hour man on the second shift, with a 5 per cent shift differential, gets $2.10 for regular hours and $3.15 ($2.10 × 1.5) for overtime, not $3.00 ($2.00 × 1.5).

DAYWORK

All factories pay some men by the hour ("day rate"), and in factories using no incentives everyone is paid by the hour. There is no problem of "administering" "daywork" other than that foremen have to have the right number of men (and not too many) and see that they do a fair day's work.

But when you have pieceworkers, you get into problems about daywork. One is how can you keep nonincentive workers happy when they make less than incentive workers.

More problems come from the incentive workers themselves. What do you do when, occasionally, they have to do work for which you have no piece rate standards?

Years ago it was simple. You would have paid day rates for that work. The fact that a man is usually an incentive worker would have had nothing to do with it. All unmeasured work was paid for at day rate.

But, is it fair to take a man off his regular piece rate job and have him do an experimental job at day rate? (Remember, day rates mean less money for him—perhaps $2.00 an hour instead of his usual $2.50 or so average piece rate earnings.) Or suppose that a new job comes along, one on which there is yet no standard, should the man get only day rate for that job? Probably you would say no, and certainly the man on the job says no. He asks, why should I be penalized by being denied the chance to make my usual bonus?

Usually the company agrees and pays him his *average piece rate earn-*

ings for the hours on nonincentive work. The company agrees—if the man is put temporarily on a day rate job to help out the company and if there is still more piecework to be done. But, sometimes, there is only so much piece rate work to be done in a day. If the man finishes early and is given nonpiece rate work to do the rest of the day, the company would pay only day rate. There is an administration problem here, because, you see, you get into *"why* was the man put on nonincentive work?" His pay rate depends on your answer.

From the company's point of view it is bad to pay average incentive earnings for nonincentive work. First, it costs more because you pay high hourly rates for just ordinary production (the incentive worker almost always drops his pace when he gets on an unmeasured job). Second, it makes your problems with regular day rate employees worse. They are unhappy enough when incentive workers work hard and earn more than they do, but imagine their feelings when incentive men get high pay without working hard.

Third, it is bad to pay incentive workers their average earnings when they are not on incentive work because they soon get to thinking "once a pieceworker always a pieceworker." That means that they think you owe it to them to pay incentive earnings, no matter what work they are put on, and no matter how hard they work, and no matter whether you have incentive work for them all of the time or not.

Delays to Incentive Workers. Paying piecework earnings for anything other than piecework opens the door to abuses. Things never go perfectly all the time on any job. There are little interferences. They hold up the worker or make extra work for him. If they amount to very much, he says that the extra things are not covered by his piece rate and that he should get a little extra pay. This seems reasonable, and usually the foreman approves 15 minutes or so of pay to cover the interferences.

What it amounts to is that the man claims to have turned out his output in 7¾ hours. So you figure his piecework earnings, then divide by 7¾ to get an average hourly earning. Then you pay him for ¼ hour more at the same rate or at almost the same rate.

The abuses come in because no one knows how much time the interferences took—or even *if there were any*. The man says that there were some, but there is no clock record because they were just little things that turned up off and on during the day. It gets to be the custom to ask for allowances every day. And the foreman usually approves them. Now you are on the skids. The next step is for the man always to ask for enough to get his earnings up to usual. If he usually makes $20 in a day but today his piecework earnings amount to only $17.00, then isn't it obvious that interferences cost him $3.00? So you give him 1⅕ hours' allowance (at $2.50 per hour that will give him $3.00). Now he is back to $20.

But why should the man put forth incentive effort from here on? Why should he not just produce at a nice confortable rate all day and earn say $16 on piecework? Of course he then claims 1¾ hours' allowance to get him back up to $20. Suppose that you tell the foreman to disallow such claims? That is pretty arbitrary but is perhaps really more fair than approving big interference allowances because they are mostly false.

But when you clamp down you have a fight on your hands. The men won't give up their gravy train without a struggle. The safest policy seems to be never to approve any allowances except for delays reported to the foreman as they occur during the day. The foreman should not, at 5 P.M. or at 8 A.M. the next morning, approve claims for unreported interferences said to have occurred hours earlier.

Short Day Piecework.   Some companies have only so much piecework to do in a day. This happens in meat packing, foundries, assembly line production, sometimes in clothing and shoes. If a man hurries and gets done at 1:00 o'clock then what? Then (in some companies) he goes home or does whatever daywork that may be available. But for these jobs he gets the job rates for those jobs and not his average piecework earnings. If there isn't much of this daywork to do, it must be offered first to men with the greatest seniority.

LOST TIME

Lost time and some kinds of daywork are almost alike. "Lost time" is the time a man is idle through no fault of his own. If a man is idle for any length of time, he rings in on a lost-timecard and is paid either his base rate or a little under his average earnings for the time.

There isn't much lost time of that sort, however, that shows on the records as such. If the power fails or the machine breaks down, you put the man on other work or send him home. The work may be just clean up or some other half-necessary job so that although it shows on the record as daywork it is really almost lost time. You don't get much value for the money spent. Also the allowances for delays to pieceworkers that we talked about above (which are recorded as pay for daywork) are really pay for lost time as much as they are for extra work.

Still more lost time is paid for within jobs. Machine operating jobs often make the man wait a little now and then. The time study man puts these waits right in the rate the same as productive elements. So again we have waiting time that is reported as productive time.

But if the machine runs by itself for a long time after the man loads it, then that time is *not* put into the standard. Suppose that it takes 5 minutes for the machine to do its work, then 1 minute for the man to unload and load it. It is a 1-minute job—not a 6-minute job—as far as piece rates are concerned. The man does other work during the 5 minutes that the machine runs by itself.

The lost time that shows on the record ends up being only a part—

even a small part—of the lost time you are paying for. But does it matter? Yes. If your records only showed all the lost time for what it is— lost time—you'd bend every effort toward getting rid of it. But having so much of it shown as pay for productive effort covers it up, keeps you from knowing about it, and lets it go on forever.

There is still another kind of lost time to contend with. Sometime if you go through a factory a half hour or so before quitting time, you'll see some men just standing around killing time. You wonder what kind of poor management practice allows this. Actually, management would be only too happy to cut it out but can't.

It is usually the result of a strong union and loose time standards on some jobs. The men keep busy until they have turned out their self-set limit of work. Then they stop work, even though they have to sit around until the whistle blows. Even if they are working on piecework, they do only so much and then stop working.

They say: "This is our own incentive time. We worked hard to get ahead in order to have a little extra time. What do you care if we choose to sit around and loaf rather than turn out more work and make more money?" There is something to their point, of course, but it is too bad not to get the production that the idle machines could be turning out.

Actually, you won't find this situation in the best-managed plants. Work standards aren't so loose as to let a man do what you call 10 or 11 hours' work in 7 hours, thus giving the man an opportunity to make a good bonus and still loaf an hour. In most companies it will take a man his whole 8 hours to turn out what you call 10 or 11 hours of work. And if he is on piecework, he'll try to do that much before he stops. Otherwise he won't make as much as he wants to.

Now and then you'll see another kind of sit-down-and-rest factory job. Today's big, costly, and fast production machines do things automatically, *when they are running*. But sometimes something—usually something minor—goes wrong, and they stop. You need to get a man there right away to fix the trouble and start the machine going again. It pays to have men who mostly just watch, in order to cut the time the machines are idle.

PAYING SHOP STEWARD FOR UNION DUTIES ON COMPANY TIME

Companies are not allowed, by law, to pay in any way for the support of unions, lest they try to influence them. Of course they send "check-off" dues of union members directly to the union treasurer, but this is merely paying the men's money to the union for them.

Companies do, however, usually pay workers, shop stewards, and union grievance committeemen, at their average earned rate for the time they spend in meeting on grievance matters during work hours. Companies also pay union shop stewards for the time they spend away from their machines while discussing routine labor-management matters with workers in their departments. Often, too, the officers of the local union are paid for time spent on company property attending to union matters. If they check out and go to the union office, the company does not pay for that time.

Payment for time spent on grievance work is not, in the eyes of the law, a payment that supports the union in any way. Grievances are properly matters to be discussed in the course of labor-management relations, and the company is expected (though not required by law) to pay for it. Most companies do pay for it, however, although some of them place a limit on the amount they will pay in any one year for grievance time. Otherwise some men would rather discuss grievances too long. It is an easier way to earn their pay than to work on the job.

STUDY QUESTIONS

1. What is the difference between real wages and money wages? Of what significance is this distinction in bargaining over wages? Discuss.
2. Have factory workers really improved their standard of living since World War II? Discuss.
3. Do you believe that it is a reasonable policy to pay the going wage rate or a little more? Discuss how to do it.
4. How much can you learn from a wage survey? What limitations exist? Why? How can you overcome them?
5. Do wage laws affect wages much? Discuss.
6. What are "escalator" wage clauses in labor contracts? Are they good for the workers? For society?
7. Is there any way that agreeing to an "annual improvement" wage clause in a labor contract can benefit the employers? Explain.
8. What should a multiplant company's policy be toward wage differences in different areas? Why?
9. What has been the trend of office salaries compared with factory wages for 20 years? Why has it been like that?
10. How much effect does supply and demand have on wages? Explain fully.
11. How are executive salaries set? What other ways could it be done? Why aren't the other methods used?
12. Why do many companies have rather hard and fast rules against overtime? Should they have such rules? Discuss.
13. The text states that "daywork" paid to pieceworkers makes problems. How? How would you solve these problems?
14. Compare the nature of daywork and lost time. Discuss thoroughly.

CASE 24–1. THE HEAVY DUTY TRUCK COMPANY

Todd Evers' father, Jim, had worked for the Heavy Duty Truck Company for 25 years. His job as stock room clerk was not the highest paid job in the department, but he liked the work and the department head was glad to have so dependable a man and one who knew the stock so well.

After finishing high school, Todd and his parents thought it would be a good idea for him to work a year before he entered college. With his father's help he got a job at the Heavy Duty Truck Company, operating an external grinding machine. The work was piecework, and young Evers quickly became proficient. In less than 3 months, his pay check exceeded that of his father.

The father's feelings were a mixture of pride and chagrin. Todd's mother felt very differently, however. When Todd brought home a check larger than his father's for the second consecutive pay period and it appeared that he would continue to do so, she berated her husband severely. What kind of a husband was he anyway? Through all the years she had lived on his meager earnings. Now she finds that in only 3 months her 18-year-old boy can make more than his father. Before long, Jim had to move out of his own house in order to have any peace.

Jim brings his problem to you, his department head. What do you do? What is the basic problem? How about the "greater skill" of long-service workers? How do you propose to solve (a) Jim's problem? (b) The basic problem?

Chapter 25

JOB EVALUATION

JOB evaluation sets job base rates of pay. Base rates are the actual job pay rates if there is no piecework. But if there are incentives, almost everyone earns more than his base rate. Job evaluation does not set production bonuses, merit pay increases, extra night-shift pay, or overtime. *Nor does job evaluation set the over-all level of wages*—all it does is to tell which jobs should pay above our average wage and which should pay below and how much.

Job base rate differences ought to reflect differences in job difficulty. It is easy to say that it ought to be so but hard to put the idea into practice. For example, should a man who makes molds out of sand in our foundry be paid more or less than the man who sets up jobs on small milling machines in another department? The jobs are so unlike that it is difficult to say how their rates ought to compare. Yet that is just what job evaluation does. It measures job differences even for unlike jobs and tells us which should pay the most and how much.

There are limits, however, to the variety of jobs which can be covered by one single job evaluation plan. Usually all factory hourly paid jobs are evaluated under one plan, but another plan is used for office jobs. Factory and office jobs are so very unlike that trying to evaluate them all under one plan would take a plan so complicated that we use two plans instead of one.

Job evaluation has to do with differentials in job base rates rather than in plant-wide average wages. It is not a method for raising or lowering wages in general. Often, though, a community wage survey is made in connection with job evaluation, but it is not itself a part of job evaluation.

Job evaluation, almost unknown 30 years ago, is now almost universal for factory jobs and almost as common for office jobs. It cannot truly be called "scientific," since it relies on human judgment. It cannot hope to give answers which will be satisfactory to everyone. But even so, it has proved to be a useful tool which sharpens and refines the precision of the subjective judgments which must be made.

WHAT IS A JOB?

Job evaluation evaluates jobs, but how far should you go in separating almost like jobs? If every minor difference is called a different job, then you have almost as many jobs as you have people. Do you have one job or several, for example, when you have a man running a passenger elevator, another running a freight elevator with a hand-operated control, and another running a freight elevator with push-button control and automatic door opening and closing? Or, how many laboring jobs do you have, one or five, when you have men unloading freight cars, pulling lift trucks around the plant, loading materials on and off conveyors, sweeping floors, and helping machine operators? Or how about a machine helper? Is he a low-grade operator? Or is a learner on a machine different from a helper?

Before you decide you should ask: what difference does it make? It is a matter of doing a more refined job of job evaluation but at higher cost. The greater the refinement, the greater the accuracy of the evaluations since almost every man's work is evaluated separately—but you double or triple the cost by doing it that way. Besides, too many job titles multiply personnel's record-keeping work. Moving men around on similar jobs means changing job titles all the time even though the pay rates stay the same.

Few companies set minor differences apart so much as to have as many as one job title for each three men. A few go to the other extreme and have only one title per fifty men. How many job titles you should have will depend both on how different the work really is and on how much separation you want.

JOB DESCRIPTIONS

Regardless of the method used to evaluate jobs, written descriptions of the work are always needed. They serve the initial purpose of supplying information to the evaluators. Later they become permanent records, serving as references in hiring, promotion, grievance settlement, and other matters in the personnel department. For evaluation purposes, the specific things done by each person on each job must be recorded, although minute details are unnecessary. Details such as are needed for time study, for example, are not required for evaluation. Figure 25–1 shows the kind of information needed for evaluation.

SOURCES OF JOB INFORMATION

Most men don't express themselves well in writing, so you ought to have a trained analyst write all job descriptions. But he has to find out

THE NATIONAL SCREW & MFG. CO.
JOB EVALUATION OF HOURLY PAID EMPLOYEES
JOB DESCRIPTION

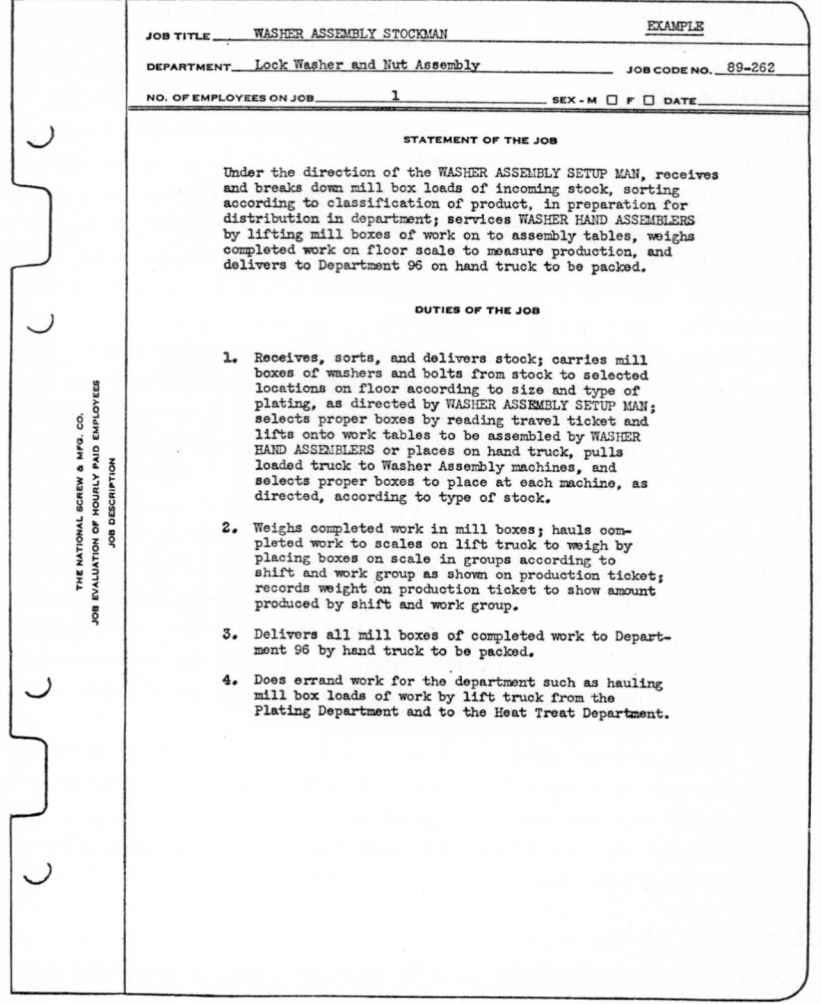

JOB TITLE WASHER ASSEMBLY STOCKMAN EXAMPLE

DEPARTMENT Lock Washer and Nut Assembly JOB CODE NO. 89-262

NO. OF EMPLOYEES ON JOB 1 SEX - M ☐ F ☐ DATE

STATEMENT OF THE JOB

Under the direction of the WASHER ASSEMBLY SETUP MAN, receives and breaks down mill box loads of incoming stock, sorting according to classification of product, in preparation for distribution in department; services WASHER HAND ASSEMBLERS by lifting mill boxes of work on to assembly tables, weighs completed work on floor scale to measure production, and delivers to Department 96 on hand truck to be packed.

DUTIES OF THE JOB

1. Receives, sorts, and delivers stock; carries mill boxes of washers and bolts from stock to selected locations on floor according to size and type of plating, as directed by WASHER ASSEMBLY SETUP MAN; selects proper boxes by reading travel ticket and lifts onto work tables to be assembled by WASHER HAND ASSEMBLERS or places on hand truck, pulls loaded truck to Washer Assembly machines, and selects proper boxes to place at each machine, as directed, according to type of stock.

2. Weighs completed work in mill boxes; hauls completed work to scales on lift truck to weigh by placing boxes on scale in groups according to shift and work group as shown on production ticket; records weight on production ticket to show amount produced by shift and work group.

3. Delivers all mill boxes of completed work to Department 96 by hand truck to be packed.

4. Does errand work for the department such as hauling mill box loads of work by lift truck from the Plating Department and to the Heat Treat Department.

National Screw and Manufacturing Co.

FIG. 25–1. A job description showing the details of the job.

about jobs from someone else. From whom? The best source of information about job duties might seem to be the operator himself. Generally, however, he is not the best one to ask. He doesn't understand job evaluation and may not think to tell you about parts of his work. Or he may exaggerate and give you a wrong picture.

A common source of information is the foreman. He knows what his men ought to be doing, although sometimes he doesn't really know or is too busy to supply accurate information. Sometimes he describes what the job content *should* be when, in fact, it is something different. He may fail to report extras that men have to do sometimes. On the whole, however, the foreman is a good source. The assistant foreman or group leader is also a good source.

After the job description has been written, some companies submit it to the employee on the job and to the shop steward. If they agree that the description is accurate and complete, they initial it.

Some companies, expecting to use the information for purposes other than evaluation, write down more information than you need just for evaluation. A few, for example, write down the normal chain of promotion, showing the jobs from which employees are promoted to the job being evaluated, as well as the positions to which employees are ordinarily promoted from this job. Some companies write down the kind of worker needed for the job by recording, for instance, the physical requirements a man must have to do the work. Neither the promotional chain nor the description of the kind of worker required is necessary for job evaluation.

METHODS

Although various methods for evaluating jobs have been tried over the years, only three are used enough today to justify separate description here. A fourth method, "over-all ranking," is also described in most textbooks. Today it is almost never used. Briefly, it starts with a list of job titles. These are arranged in order of job difficulty from easiest to most difficult by each of several raters. Their composite views became the ranking, and that in turn sets the job base rates.

The first of the three regularly used job evaluation methods is the "job classification" method. It is uncommon in industry but has been used for many years by the United States Civil Service. The second method, the "factor comparison" method, is used by a few industrial companies. By far the most common, though, is the third method, "point" plans. Today nearly all companies use some kind of point plan. Point plans vary in details, but they all use the same method and follow the same general pattern. Point plans end up by grouping jobs into "classes" or "labor grades," but don't confuse these with the "job classification" method of evaluating jobs.

JOB CLASSIFICATION

The job classification method used by the federal Civil Service for office and professional employees (but rarely used in industry) sets up ten classifications for jobs of different grades of difficulty. Each classification is defined by means of a description of a typical work situation and is phrased in general terms. The work situations described are for jobs of graduated difficulty. The evaluation procedure is to compare a job to the general work situation descriptions. The most appropriate one is selected, thus fixing the classification into which the job falls. Each job classification has a salary range which applies to all jobs within the class.

Using this method you first write the ten (or whatever number you use) classifications and set low and high salary limits for each class. Then you write up the job descriptions. Thirdly, you compare the jobs, one after the other, with the general description for each job classification and see which one seems best to fit the job. The job is then put into that class, and men on the job will be paid salaries within its limits. Whether they are paid the least or the most depends on their personal merit rating, which is not a part of job evaluation.

FACTOR COMPARISON

The factor comparison method considers the best rate paid for any job as being a summation of the amounts paid for five separate factors: mental requirements, skill requirements, physical requirements, responsibility, and working conditions. The evaluation procedure is one of deciding how much to pay for each factor by comparing the jobs being evaluated with the amounts paid on "key" jobs. The accuracy of job ratings depends a great deal on whether or not the key jobs themselves are correctly paid.

The first step in evaluation by the factor comparison method is to select a dozen or more key jobs to be used as bench marks with which other jobs will be compared. Key jobs must have certain characteristics. First, and most important, the base rate of every key job must be a fair rate and one which properly reflects the difficulty of the work. A check is provided in the procedure to eliminate prospective key jobs which prove to be out of line. Key jobs should, if possible, be well known to everyone, so that the evaluators and others can readily visualize their content when comparing other jobs with them. Complete written descriptions of key jobs are, of course, used; but better evaluations can be made if in addition to the descriptions the key jobs are well known to the evaluators. Usually they are jobs on which there are numerous employees.

When key jobs have been selected, they are used to make up a series of five rating scales, or yardsticks, with which the other jobs are compared. One rating scale is made up for each of the factors enumerated above: mental requirements, skill requirements, physical requirements, responsibility, and working conditions. Several evaluators who are well acquainted with all of the key jobs, using the descriptions for the key jobs, apportion the base rate for each key job among the five factors. Their several judgments are averaged and, after further review, are used to construct the scales.

Here's how it works. Each evaluator is asked to decide how much of the $2.00 per hour base rate paid for a machine operation job is paid for skill, how much for physical requirements, etc. He may decide that 75 cents is paid for skill, 29 cents for the physical requirements, and so on, until he has the $2.00 divided among the five factors. He repeats the process for each key job, apportioning the base rate among the five factors. For each job the apportionments of all the evaluators are averaged. In the example given above, their composite judgment might be that 80 cents of the $2.00 is paid for skill, 28 cents for the physical requirements, etc. The sum of the allocations for all factors must equal the total of the whole base rate, $2.00.

After the base rates for all key jobs have been apportioned to the five factors, you are ready to make up a rating scale for each factor. For each factor put a vertical scale on a sheet of paper and mark it off into cents per hour, as you see in Figure 25–2. Next, on each scale, to its monetary value for that factor, write in the name of each key job. Notice in Figure 25–2 that "patternmaker" is written in opposite $1.40 in the mental requirements column. In the skill column "patternmaker" appears opposite $1.48, and in the other three columns, opposite $0.48, $0.88, and $0.24. These add up to $4.48, the patternmaker's hourly rate. After spotting the first key job on the five scales, go on to the next key job, and so on, until all have been spotted on all five scales.

These five scales are used as yardsticks with which to compare all other jobs; but not until the scales are themselves checked. Look up and down each column and see if the pay differences for each job seems reasonable. If any seem to be out of line, take them out and cut those jobs off your list of key jobs.

Evaluation proper begins as soon as the scales are complete. The evaluation process for other jobs consists of making five comparisons. The job being evaluated is compared successively to each of the factor scales, and a decision is reached as to where the job being evaluated fits. The title of the job being evaluated is not written in along the scale with the key job titles, but the monetary value of the point where it belongs is noted. The five values obtained from the scale comparisons, one from each scale, are added. Their sum is the base rate for the job. With its determination the evaluation of that job is complete.

In some companies using the factor comparison method the base rates actually adopted and put into effect are not exactly the same as those determined by the evaluation procedure. Instead, jobs which should have almost identical rates, according to the evaluation, are grouped into "labor grades" similar to those described in connection with point plans on page 478. All jobs within a group or grade are paid the same base rate or the same range of pay, as is typical in point plans.

The factor comparison method is simpler and more readily understood than point rating methods. It keeps the evaluation in terms of money at all times, thus avoiding the extra step of translating points into money that is necessary in point plans. On the other hand, the money terms are regarded as a disadvantage by some people who feel that the evaluation procedure can be more objective if money is kept out of the picture until the end of the evaluation process. Furthermore,

JOB COMPARISON SCALE

DOLLARS	MENTAL REQ.	SKILL REQ.	PHYSICAL REQ.	RESPONSIBILITY	WORKING CONDITIONS
1.60					
1.56					
1.52					
1.48		PATTERN MAKER			
1.44		MACHINIST NO. 1			
1.40	PATTERN MAKER				
1.36				SUBSTATION OPERATOR	
1.32					
1.28	SUBSTATION OPERATOR				
1.24					
1.20	MACHINIST NO. 1				
1.16					
1.12					
1.08					
1.04					
1.00		SUBSTATION OPERATOR			
.96		PIPEFITTER NO. 2	RAMMER		
.92		PAINTER			
.88				PATTERN MAKER	
.84			POLEMAN		
.80			LABORER	MACHINIST NO. 1	
.76	PIPEFITTER NO. 2				
.72	PAINTER	DRILL PRESS OPERATOR		PIPEFITTER NO. 2	
.68	DRILL PRESS OPERATOR	CARPENTER'S HELPER		DRILL PRESS OPERATOR	
.64	CARPENTER'S HELPER		PIPEFITTER NO. 2	PAINTER	
.60				CARPENTER'S HELPER	
.56	POLEMAN		MACHINIST NO. 1		RAMMER
.52	LABORER		PAINTER	POLEMAN	POLEMAN
.48			PATTERN MAKER		LABORER
.44	RAMMER	POLEMAN	CARPENTER'S HELPER	RAMMER	PIPEFITTER NO. 2
.40			DRILL PRESS OPERATOR	LABORER	PAINTER
.36					
.32		RAMMER			MACHINIST NO. 1 DRILL PRESS OPERATOR
.28		LABORER			CARPENTER'S HELPER
.24			SUBSTATION OPERATOR		PATTERN MAKER
.20					
.16					SUBSTATION OPERATOR
.12					
.08					
.04					

Job Evaluation and Merit Rating, by Eugene Benge. National Foremen's Institute Manual

FIG. 25–2. Evaluating jobs by the factor comparison method. Jobs being evaluated are compared to five such scales.

the money terms do not always make things simpler, because when general wage rate increases are given, all of the rating scales and records of evaluation must be changed.

POINT PLANS

Almost all job evaluation plans in use today are point plans. They are of many varieties, but, for the most part, they follow the pattern of the National Metal Trades Association plan (it was first developed for the

National Electrical Manufacturers' Association) for evaluating factory jobs. Most companies that use job evaluation for office as well as factory work employ a different, but similar, procedure for the office.

The NMTA point plan evaluates jobs by measuring the amount of each of eleven factors in them. The method regards all factory jobs as being composed of varying amounts of the eleven factors. The amount of each factor in a job is determined and assigned a number of points. The total of the points assigned for all factors is the rating of the job. After all jobs have been rated in this way, a scale showing the monetary value of the points is set up. Reference to the scale shows how much should be paid on each job.

Point plans other than the NMTA plan use the same method for evaluating jobs, although they differ in the number of factors used and in the number of points assigned to the factors. These differences are discussed on the following pages.

Some people say that you don't need to use as many as eleven factors, that some of the eleven are so inconsequential that you could leave them out without changing the relative ratings of very many jobs. Their objection to using that many factors is the work involved. If you could cut the factors to five you would cut the costs of doing job evaluation.

It is true that if you cut out some factors the relative ratings would be changed only a little. But all that you have proved is that the most important factors are the most important. Certainly the credit given for the important factors largely determines every job's final rating. The question is, can you afford, just to save some job evaluation cost, to omit things that are usually but not always minor? Isn't it worth the extra cost to evaluate the minor factors if this is the only way that some 5 to 10 per cent of your jobs will get the full credit they deserve?

THE "MANUAL" OR "PLAN"

Jobs are evaluated, when point plans are used, by comparing them to several preset definitions of degrees of factors. If eleven factors are used, eleven such comparisons are made. For each factor a series of definitions of degrees, usually five, is set up. The definitions describe, in general terms, situations requiring the factor in slight amounts graduated up to considerable amounts. The definition which most nearly describes the requirements of the job being evaluated is selected and its value in points is given to the job.

The job factors considered, the degree definitions, and the point equivalents used in the procedure must all be decided ahead. They are agreed upon and put into a small booklet called a "manual" or "plan." Most companies do not develop their own manuals. They use one of the well-known plans or have a consulting engineer develop a plan to fit the individual company.

For a company to develop its own plan is, in a way, illogical. A company's justification for a unique plan is that "our jobs are different." Yet job evaluation is a technique for measuring differences in unlike jobs. If it can accomplish that objective, is there any need for companies to have unique plans? If it cannot measure unlike jobs in different plants,

4. PHYSICAL DEMAND

This factor appraises the amount and continuity of physical effort required. Consider the effort expended handling material (the weight and frequency of handling), operating a machine or handling tools, and the periods of unoccupied time.

1st Degree

Light work requiring little physical effort.

2nd Degree

Light physical effort working regularly with light weight material or occasionally with average weight material. Operate machine tools where machine time exceeds the handling time.

3rd Degree

Sustained physical effort, requiring continuity of effort working with light or average weight material. Usually short cycle work requiring continuous activity, the operation of several machines where the handling time is equivalent to the total machine time.

4th Degree

Considerable physical effort working with average or heavy weight material, or continuous strain of difficult work position.

5th Degree

Continuous physical exertion working with heavy weight material. Hard work with constant physical strain or intermittent severe strain.

National Metal Trades Association

FIG. 25–3. Description and degree definitions of the factor "Physical Demand" in the National Metal Trades Association job evaluation plan for factory employees.

the question might be raised as to whether it can measure unlike jobs in the same plant.

The NMTA plan regards all factory jobs as being made up of four groups of factors which should be paid for in job base rates: the *skill* that a satisfactory worker on the job must have, the *effort* required to do the job satisfactorily, the *responsibilities* inherent in the job, and the *conditions* under which the job is performed. The three individual skill factors are: *education*, *experience*, and *initiative and ingenuity*. The two effort factors are the *physical* and *mental demands* of the job. The four job responsibilities are: *responsibility for equipment and processes, responsibility for materials or product or both, responsibility for the safety of others,* and *responsibility for the work of others.* The two conditions under which jobs are done include *working conditions* and the *health hazards* of the job. In total, eleven individual factors are used in the evaluation procedure. Each of the eleven factors is described in the man-

POINTS ASSIGNED TO FACTORS AND KEY TO GRADES

FACTORS	1st Degree	2nd Degree	3rd Degree	4th Degree	5th Degree
SKILL					
1. Education	14	28	42	56	70
2. Experience	22	44	66	88	110
3. Initiative & Ingenuity	14	28	42	56	70
EFFORT					
4. Physical Demand	10	20	30	40	50
5. Mental or Visual	5	10	15	20	25
RESPONSIBILITY					
6. Equipment, Process	5	10	15	20	25
7. Material or Product	5	10	15	20	25
8. Safety of Others	5	10	15	20	25
9. Work of Others	5	10	15	20	25
JOB CONDITIONS					
10. Working Conditions	10	20	30	40	50
11. Unavoid. Hazards	5	10	15	20	25

National Metal Trades Association

FIG. 25–4. Table of point values for degrees of each factor used in the National Metal Trades Association job evaluation plan for factory employees.

ual, which also includes definitions for five degrees of each factor in terms of a general job situation. Figure 25–3 shows the definition of the factor "physical demands" and the definition of each of its five degrees.

Figure 25–4 shows the points which are given to jobs for each factor degree. It should be noted that some factors are weighted more heavily than others. Some point plans weight the factors differently from the NMTA plan. The weights used (as well as the factors chosen) are determined by judgment, so the procedure cannot be said to be a scientific one, nor can any system of factors and weights be proved superior to others. The NMTA plan has, however, been widely used, and it produces ratings in general agreement with many supervisors' ideas of relative job difficulty. Its factors and weights, therefore, appear to be satisfactory for general use.

Point plans, other than the NMTA plan, all use a manual such as the one described above. Some use more factors than the example shown, and a few less. Most of them set apart five or more different degrees of each factor. Some weight the factors differently. Some differ in the way points for degrees are allocated. The NMTA plan uses an arithmetic progression, as, for example, 10, 20, 30, 40, and 50. Some plans use a rough geometric progression, as, for example, 5, 10, 20, 35, and 50. The degree definitions should be written to parallel the progression used. Thus, in Figures 25–3 and 25–4, the degree which is worth 20 points should represent the same requirement of a factor whether it is degree 2 on an arithmetic scale or degree 3 on a geometric scale. The difference between arithmetic and geometric progressions has an effect on the computed relationship of points and their dollars and cents relationship, as discussed on page 477.

Most companies allocate only the number of points that go with factor degrees and never use intermediary numbers, such as 11, 12, 13, 14, etc. The use of intermediary numbers appears to add to the accuracy of the rating, but it presumes an ability on the part of the evaluator to detect single, minute points of difference. Such presumed accuracy is finer than human judgment can attain on such semiobjective matters.

SPECIFICATIONS AND ACTUAL EVALUATION

When a job is evaluated, it is compared successively to each factor in the manual. In making the comparison, the evaluators refer to the list of duties that make up the job. Such a list generally does not, however, furnish enough information for evaluation, since it omits, for instance, a description of the working conditions which are necessary to make the evaluation. A "specification" or secondary type of description, therefore, must be drawn up for each job.

The specification (see Fig. 25–5) is, in part, a rewrite of the job description, listing the requirements of each of the factors rather than listing the duties. The specification is divided into sections paralleling the factors listed in the manual. In each section is a statement of the job requirements of the job content of each factor. These are compared, by the evaluation committee, with the manual. The most appropriate degree of each factor is selected for the job, that is, the degree definition which most nearly covers the job content of the factor is determined.

Job evaluation committee members sometimes at first disagree about the appropriate degree. When they do, they review the rating and come to an agreement. Each degree of each factor carries a point value, so that the selection of the appropriate definition automatically gives the job its points. After the selection of the proper degree has been made for each of the eleven factors, the points are added up to get the total points the job is worth. The ratings obtained by comparing jobs with the manual are rarely used without being checked for reasonableness. Although none is perfect, there are three comparisons that help. First (for one factor at a time), look and see whether jobs you know are similar have been given similar ratings. Then, second (and also for each factor, one after the other), look at the list of jobs with the same ratings and see whether they are about equal as far as that factor is concerned.

JOB TITLE ___WASHER ASSEMBLY STOCKMAN___ CODE NO. _89-262_

DICTIONARY TITLE _____ CODE NO. _____

DEPARTMENT _Lock Washer & Nut Assembly_ TOTAL POINTS ___ CLASS __

EXPERIENCE   POINTS

Two to three months' experience required to learn which work goes to automatic assembly and which to hand assembly, and to become familiar with travel tickets to determine size and be able to recognize kinds of plating in order to properly sort material and service the WASHER HAND ASSEMBLERS.

SCHOOLING   POINTS

Must be able to read travel tickets and sort material accordingly. Equivalent of eighth grade education.

RESPONSIBILITY FOR PRODUCT OR MATERIALS   POINTS

Small losses might occur through misplacing product, mixing travel tickets, or incorrect pairing of washers and bolts in servicing WASHER HAND ASSEMBLERS

RESPONSIBILITY FOR MACHINERY AND EQUIPMENT   POINTS

Only equipment involved is lift truck and scales   Little responsibility for even small loss

RESPONSIBILITY FOR WORK OF OTHERS   POINTS

No supervision of others   Negligence in servicing WASHER HAND ASSEMBLERS or distributing and weighing up work would not seriously affect work of others

RESPONSIBILITY FOR SAFETY OF OTHERS   POINTS

Reasonable care in handling mill boxes and hand lift trucks around other workers in the department will prevent endangering safety of others

National Screw and Manufacturing Co.

FIG. 25-5. Part of a job "specification" from which the actual evaluation can be done. Some companies eliminate the specification and evaluate jobs directly from job descriptions.

Then, third, compare total ratings to see whether any jobs seem not to compare with others with the same ratings.

The use of both a description and a specification may seem to be unnecessary; yet few companies try to evaluate jobs directly from job descriptions, and few try to write up specification sheets unless they also have separate job descriptions, there are too many unanswered questions concerning how much of each factor is required. On the other hand, the specifications, if written without a supporting description, are merely a list of assertions relating to the job's factor content. The specification needs the support of the job description to justify the claims.

Together, the descriptions and specifications constitute a much better basis for job evaluation than either would alone.

It should be noted that job evaluation specifications are only indirectly "man" specifications. The specification may say that a trucker must pull heavily loaded trucks, but it does not say that the proper man for the job should be a big strong man. It may say that an inspector must inspect small items carefully and that considerable visual effort is required, but it does not say that the inspector should have good eyesight. It is but a short step, however, from a specification used for job evaluation to the making of a direct list of the characteristics that men on the job need. In the case of educational and experience requirements, the specification for job evaluation indicates the minimum education requirement and the number of years of experience needed. Some companies extend the job evaluation specification beyond the bare requirements so that it can also serve the personnel department in placement work.

THE MONEY VALUE OF POINTS

After all the jobs have been evaluated in terms of points, their monetary value must be established. The scale for translating points into money is usually determined mathematically by the "least-squares" method. This procedure requires that the computer know, for every job, its point rating and its existing job base rate. The point ratings come from the job evaluation, and the base rates come from the personnel department records. Where there are two or more employees with different base rates on a job, their rates may be averaged to get a figure to use as the present job base rate.

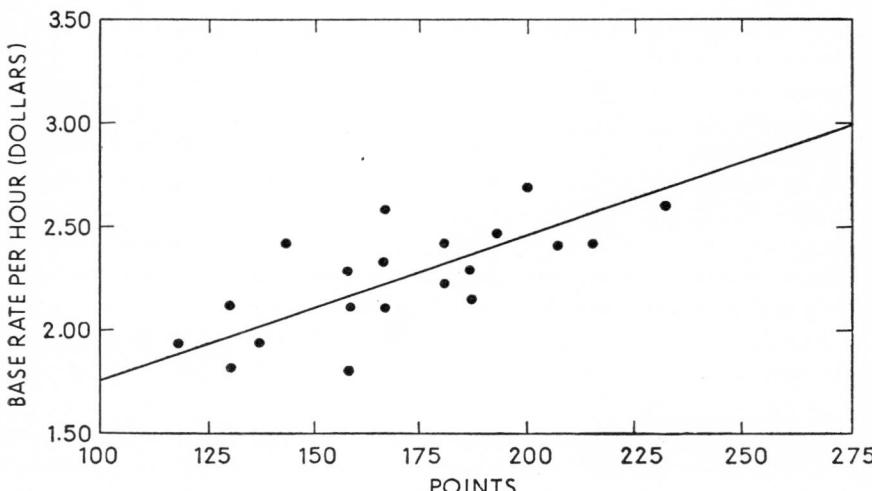

FIG. 25–6.   A "scatter-plot" of existing job wage rates and their job evaluation point total. The diagonal line (the regression line) shows the average relationships between points and hourly rates.

In general, highly rated jobs are found to be highly paid jobs, and, conversely, low rated jobs get low pay unless the informal job evaluation used in the past has been decidedly inconsistent. The least-squares mathematical procedure shows the exact money value of every job as if all inconsistencies were eliminated. The monetary value of points established can be shown as a table or they can be plotted on a chart, as in Figure 25–6. The monetary equivalents, when plotted in chart form, become a line, usually a straight line extending from the lower left to the upper right of the chart, and known technically as a "regression" line.

Most companies make up such a chart, showing the regression line. Ordinarily, too, they plot individual points for each job, as in Figure 25–6. The job points represent the relation of *existing* base rates to their evaluated point total. Points below the regression line show underpaid jobs, while those above show the jobs that are overpaid. If the old informal job evaluation produced base rates consistent with job content, the points will be close to the regression line. If not, many points will be farther from it. The regression line is almost never used directly as setting every job base rate. The actual base rates used are generally set for "labor grades," as explained below.

PROBLEMS IN REGRESSION LINE COMPUTATION

Slightly different regression lines are obtained if minimum or maximum job base rates instead of the average are used and if several workers on a job receive different rates. Slight differences may also be produced if many, rather than few, job titles are used. Differences may also result according to whether jobs are, or are not, weighted in importance according to the number of employees.

Some companies find that a curved regression line[1] (curving upward toward the right of the chart) reflects the relation between evaluation point totals and existing base rates better than does a straight regression line. The plotted dots are more likely to follow a curve if arithmetic progressions of points for degree factors are used, and its computation is relatively simple. The curvature is usually not pronounced and may not justify the use of a curved line, however. Rough geometric progressions of points for degree factors instead of arithmetic progressions seem to eliminate the tendency toward curvature.

Among companies using point job evaluation plans, common practice in connection with setting the regression line is as follows:

1. An arithmetic progression of points for factor degrees is used.
2. Few rather than many job titles are used.
3. Each job is treated as one job, irrespective of the number of employees.

---

[1] The ordinary least-squares formula gives you a straight line whether the dots tend to follow a curve or not. But a different least-squares formula will give you a curved regression line. It should be used if the dots do seem to follow a curve.

4. Average job wage rates are used.
5. The "least-squares" formula which produces a straight line is used to compute the regression line.

LABOR GRADES

The regression line showing the monetary value of all possible job ratings could be (but probably never is) used for determining the base rate for every job because there is a dollar and cents value for every possible point total. Were the line used to determine base rates, there

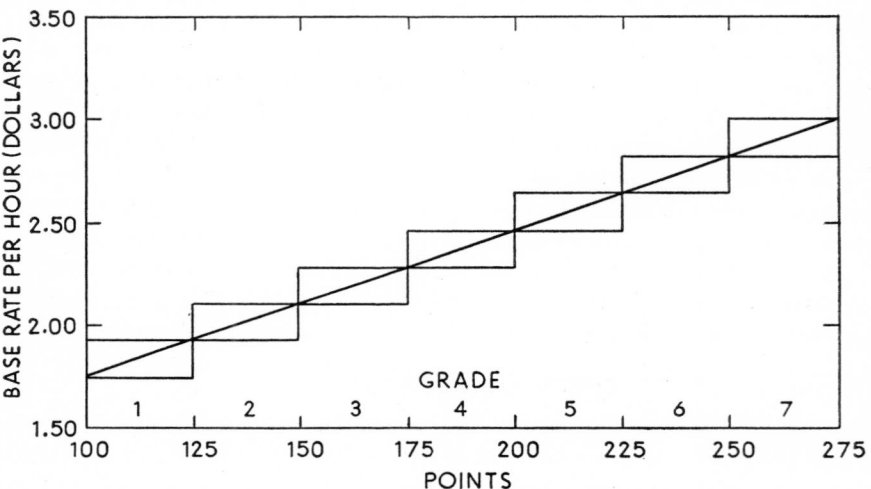

FIG. 25–7.   One arrangement of labor grades based on the regression line. Some companies use wider wage spreads for each grade so that the upper wage limit for one grade is above the lower limit of the next higher grade.

would be a great many different job rates because only jobs with identical point ratings would have identical rates. Every difference in rating totals among jobs, even a difference of one point, would produce different base rates. Such a base rate structure, though usable, would be unwieldy and awkward.

Furthermore, the fact that job evaluation is not a precise technique is a strong reason for grouping jobs in such a way that the same rate is paid to jobs with minor point differences. Every rating involves judgment to some extent and may, therefore, be challenged, even though it is reasonably equitable and fair. If the exact monetary equivalent of every job point total were used as the job base rate, every rating would be a potential grievance. Even minor upward adjustments in the point rating would be reflected in base rate increases. The unavoidable subjective nature of the evaluation process would make difficult the elimination of such grievances.

Considering jobs in groups is therefore customary. One group might comprise all jobs between 150 and 174 points; another, jobs between 175 and 199 points, etc. All jobs falling between the group limits are treated alike and are paid the same base rate. The groups are called "labor grades." The full range of point values for all jobs in the factory is usually divided into ten or more labor grades. Labor grades may be of identical point ranges or may have wider ranges for jobs of higher point value. To have the same range of points for all grades is more common, however.

The base rate for each grade is often treated as a range rather than a fixed rate. Instead of paying $2.00 per hour base rate, for example, on all jobs within a grade, some companies apply a range of pay, say $1.95 to $2.05 per hour. The limits of pay for the range usually follow closely what the regression line indicates. If, for example, the direct monetary value of a job rated at 150 points is $2.15, that will probably be chosen as the minimum wage paid for all jobs rating between 150 and 174 points. If the line shows that 174 points should be paid $2.30, that will probably be the maximum rate. It is important to note that the full range of pay for the labor grade is available to all jobs within the grade whether they are at the bottom or the top of the point range making up the grade.

The rate, within the range of pay, which is paid to individual employees is based on some kind of merit rating, either a formal plan or an informal one, such as the foreman's judgment. Employees on the jobs may receive the minimum amount for the grade, the maximum, or any figure between the two. New employees usually receive the minimum rate at first but soon get a raise to the middle of the range. This raise is often given automatically at the end of 3 months. Advancement to the maximum is not so automatic, often being based on merit.

It is common to have narrow ranges in pay (10 cents between minimum and maximum) for the unskilled job groups but to use a wider range for the labor grades made up of skilled jobs. If you don't do this you narrow the range, percentage wise, for skilled jobs.

While the use of rate ranges for labor grades is a common method of administering wages based on job evaluation, it is not the only method. Some companies, such as those in the steel industry, convert the regression line into a series of steps, paying one flat rate for all jobs within a grade. Others use the steps as job rate minimums and set no maximums. Nearly all, however, use the idea of labor grades and treat all jobs within a grade in the same way for base rate purposes. Usually, when labor grades are used, grievances challenging the correctness of ratings are confined to jobs just below the upper labor grade limits because no base rate change would occur if jobs near the bottom of the grade limit were boosted a few points.

EFFECTS OF JOB EVALUATION

Job evaluation is well established today in most companies and provides a satisfactory means for setting base rates on new jobs. When it was first introduced, it often caused changes in established practices not related to base rates. The range-of-pay idea was new to some companies which adopted it. Some companies using piecework incentives had to change to 100 per cent bonus plans. The range-of-pay idea is not, however, a necessary part of job evaluation. It is the rule, but you don't find it everywhere.

Another effect of the introduction of ranges of pay was to increase the use of formal merit rating plans as methods for setting personal base rates within the range. Most companies using job evaluation and rate ranges, however, have not adopted formal merit rating. Some are bound by union contract to grant in-grade increases automatically, according to length of service, while others prefer to rely on the recommendations of department heads.

Job evaluation helps the personnel department by furnishing it complete job descriptions, which help in hiring, promotions, transfers, and grievance work. If the union participates in the evaluation procedure, the good will, increased understanding, and respect between the union officials and management is also a worth-while gain. It helps lay the groundwork for better future industrial relations. Job evaluation of office and supervisory jobs produces a valuable by-product, in that it gives a clearer understanding of the lines of responsibility and authority. It detects careless and duplicate work assignments, and thus takes the initial step in getting such conditions corrected.

The introduction of formal job evaluation, however, where none existed before can have bad effects. Job titling becomes more precise than before, so that temporary transfers of men from job to job require changes in the records of the personnel department. Using a man from a low rated job on a high rated job for more than a few days may be a violation of the union contract unless the worker is officially transferred to the new job and paid its rate. Questions of seniority may also be involved if the labor contract requires consideration of seniority in promotions. Job evaluation may accentuate these difficulties if its introduction results in more job titles than formerly. Job evaluation, too, may possibly cause an undesirable freezing of job duties, as men often refuse to perform duties not in their job's regular list—particularly if the duty is in the list of a higher-paid job.

UNION ATTITUDE AND PARTICIPATION

Unions accept job evaluation, although not always enthusiastically. Since it is not 100 per cent objective, unions don't like it too well, because it cuts out lots of claims that jobs are wrongly paid. Once job evaluation is installed, a pay increase on a job can come only when the job content changes or when there is a general wage increase. Once a union accepts job evaluation in a company, it is permitted to challenge only the evaluation of new jobs and those only for a limited time, usually 30 days, after the job is rated. Unions can also protest that a job has been changed and needs re-rating when management hasn't done anything about it. In some companies new evaluations are made jointly by the management and the union.

HOW MUCH OF THE COMPANY SHOULD ONE PLAN COVER?

Job evaluation, by definition, claims to be a procedure for measuring differences in jobs. It would seem, then, that one plan could cover all jobs in the plant, or, for that matter, all jobs anywhere. Perhaps such a plan could be developed if enough factors were incorporated into the plan, but it would take double or more the usual number of factors. You'd have a hard time figuring out their relative importance. Also if a plan were drawn up with, say, 25 factors, then every job would have to be evaluated with all 25 factors in mind, even though many, perhaps most, of the 25 factors did not apply to the particular job. Using so many factors in a universal plan would needlessly complicate the procedure and still leave debatable the accuracy of the evaluations.

Job evaluation works best if the jobs covered are not extremely unlike, because then a reasonably brief list of factors is enough to cover all jobs. It is common, therefore, to have one plan for factory workers and a different plan for office workers. The jobs of outside salesmen are sometimes rated on still a different plan, while a fourth plan may be used for supervisors and executives.

To use only one plan would probably be unwise, even if all jobs could easily be covered by one plan. Now that the union wants to take an active part in the job evaluation program covering plant jobs, it would not be good practice and might even be construed to be an unfair labor practice to have the union representatives passing on the ratings for jobs outside of their bargaining unit.

Likewise—and this is an important point—the regression line showing the monetary value of point ratings should be based on data for jobs within the bargaining unit only. If jobs outside the unit were considered in computing the line, the evidence submitted to the job evaluation union committee probably would not substantiate the line as drawn. If a plant has to deal with several unions, each of which has jurisdiction over a certain group, separate regression lines may have to be computed for each unit. The jobs included should be only those in the unit. Lines so drawn might differ slightly from each other, possibly because one group may conceivably have been able to raise its whole rate level above the other groups through superior bargaining strength. A plant-wide job evaluation might show that ratings for some jobs are out of line, but, practically, they cannot be reduced. There seems, however, to be no tendency among companies to have a large number of job evaluation units, each with its own regression line.

OTHER BASIC CONSIDERATIONS

Job evaluation cannot solve all problems connected with the determination of job base rates. It gives no consideration to the supply and demand of the labor market, to labor's bargaining power, nor to the ability of the company to pay. These considerations all relate to the *general level of wages*. Job evaluation does *not* set the general level of wages. It is purely a device for establishing equitable differentials in pay among jobs within a plant. It does not even determine the total differential existing between the easiest and the most difficult jobs, but serves only to distribute jobs equitably between the limits set.

Job evaluation does not attempt to consider the relation of wages to anything outside the plant, such as the plant's proximity to worker residence areas, the transportation facilities available for workers, etc. It does not attempt to measure the contribution of a particular job to the finished product. Neither does it attempt to consider human factors, such as how well the worker is treated or how well he gets along with the foreman. It is concerned with the job to be done, not the man on the job.

The job cannot always be separated from the man on the job, however. In office work, in particular, the exact assignment of duties constituting a job is often the reflection of what the man can do. If he were to leave the company, that particular job would disappear. A new man would be assigned some of his duties and perhaps some new ones, but certain other duties would be transferred to other workers. Sometimes a man cannot and does not do certain parts of a job assigned to him. In that case, the job should be evaluated as he does it, not as it is assigned. Perhaps in such situations it is improper to say that the evaluation is completely independent of the man; yet for evaluation purposes the job can be regarded as the work done.

The evaluation process itself poses some difficult problems for the evaluators. One of the most difficult concerns working conditions. Most people probably agree that jobs which must be performed under poor working conditions should get more credit than jobs of equal difficulty which can be performed under good conditions.

Working conditions are, however, so different that it is hard to judge the allowance that should be made. In metalworking industries there are numerous jobs requiring the operator to work with his hands immersed in oil virtually all day. Workers with sensitive skins may get a skin rash from the immersion; yet other workers may not be affected by it in the least. Is such a job performed under bad working conditions? Some jobs are very noisy, and there may be a constant floor vibration. How bad are such conditions? Most workers are not conscious of these things after the first few days. Excessive humidity, high temperatures, dust, and other conditions may exist. How much credit should workers in these situations get? How much is it worth to work in a congested or dirty area? Is a job on which the worker must keep his hands in oil all day worse than a job which is very noisy?

So far, no job evaluation technique which solves these difficulties has been developed. A fair evaluation of working conditions is difficult to determine on many jobs. In practice, however, these problems do not cause too much trouble, since the element of "working conditions" is only one of several factors and there are generally only five degrees of disagreeableness to be distinguished from each other.

ADMINISTRATION OF JOB EVALUATION

Since the installation of a job evaluation plan is a big job, consulting help is often utilized. The plan is administered most often through the personnel or industrial relations department. Occasionally it is administered by the time study or industrial engineering department. No matter which department is in charge, staff members from all the departments mentioned usually participate in the original installation.

After the evaluation is in effect, maintenance is usually in the hands of the personnel department, because it makes more continual use of job evaluation than any other department. It uses job descriptions continually and handles all grievances over the evaluation of both old and new jobs. When the maintenance of job evaluation falls to the personnel department, it assumes the duty of writing up and evaluating all new jobs. In the long run, the maintenance of the plan is as important as, or more important than, the original installation.

The cost of the original installation of a job evaluation system is likely to come to about $50 per job evaluated or one half of 1 per cent of the annual payroll or more. Once installed, it costs about one tenth of 1 per cent of the payroll for maintenance. Percentage costs are higher in small companies.

STUDY QUESTIONS

1. What part does job evaluation play in determining a man's pay? Explain.
2. Does job evaluation raise men's pay? Discuss.
3. One company has as one job title for every five employees, another has one for every ten. Why the difference?
4. If you were a job evaluation engineer, how would you go about getting job description information?
5. How does a key job operate in the factor comparison plan? Explain fully.
6. How does the factor comparison plan avoid using points?
7. How is a job specification used in point job evaluation plans?
8. If a job evaluation plan measures differences in unlike jobs, why do we need more than one such plan?
9. Is a job specification also a man specification? Discuss the relations of these two things.
10. How is a regression line used in job evaluation?
11. Do men on jobs toward the upper limit of a wage grade get more money than those on jobs near the bottom of the same labor grade?
12. Do unions like job evaluation? What part, if any, do they play in it?

13. What effect, if any, does job evaluation have on the general level of wages in a company? Discuss the relations of these two things.

Case 25–1.   The Hi-Power Arms Company

The Hi-Power Arms Company has completed the evaluation of its factory jobs and is ready to set up labor grades and pay ranges for each. From the many job ratings, the following have been selected:

Job	Point Rating	Hourly Base Rates Used in the Past	Job	Point Rating	Hourly Base Rates Used in the Past
Automatic screw machine operator.............	275	$2.50	Machine operator (tool room)...............	311	$2.96
Bench lathe operator......	241	2.36	Punch press operator.....	271	2.48
Bench work—(filing and assembly)............	164	2.11	Soldering..............	216	2.23
			Stores clerk............	205	2.22
Casting grinder and polisher................	209	2.42	Tool crib attendant......	246	2.36
			Tool maker............	381	2.94
Drill press operator.......	224	2.31	Turret lathe operator.....	331	2.76
Milling machine operator..	311	2.59			

Plot the ratings and base rates on a chart on co-ordinate paper. Using the least-squares method, compute the line of relationship between points and money. (The formula for the line is $Y = a + bX$. It can be plotted by solving the following two equations simultaneously: $\Sigma Y = na + b\Sigma X$ and $\Sigma XY = a\Sigma X + b\Sigma X^2$. The point ratings are the X values, and the base rates are the Y values.)

Set up eight labor grades based on the line; and in an accompanying table show the point limits of each grade and, using a 5 cents per hour overlap, show the minimum and maximum wages to be paid for each grade.

Which jobs, if any, will have to have their base rates adjusted to bring them within the newly established limits?

Case 25–2.   Leslie Manufacturing Company

Bill Winters operates an overhead crane at the Leslie Manufacturing Company. He receives $2.39 per hour but has filed a grievance because he is not paid $2.45. The Leslie company's job evaluation plan places Bill's job in labor grade 7, which has wage limits of $2.33 to $2.45 per hour. According to the labor contract, the first 6 cents' increase of the range of pay available for a job is given to employees on all jobs after they have worked 6 months; the remaining 6 cents is given on a merit basis, although there is no formal merit rating plan.

Winters has been on the crane operating job for 9 months and has done satisfactory work, having been neither criticized nor praised for it. Winters bases his grievance on the claim that he is entitled to $2.45 on a merit basis and on the fact that his job is rated at 273 points, only 2 points under the maximum of 275 for labor grade 7 jobs.

How would you handle this situation? How can you avoid similar grievances in the future?

Chapter 26

MERIT RATING

NATURE AND PURPOSE

Good employer-employee relations cannot exist unless the employer tries to be fair and objective in granting raises and promotions to employees. Merit rating attempts to provide a basis for fairly administering such matters. Merit rating, or "employee rating," as it is sometimes called, is *man* rating as contrasted with job evaluation, which is *job* rating.

Merit is partly subjective and therefore incapable of measure by wholly objective methods. There have been many attempts to find objective measures of merit, but so far no one has found any which are altogether satisfactory. Consequently, employee rating plans are less common than job evaluation. Surveys show that about half of all manufacturing companies have formal merit rating plans. They are more common in large than in small companies and in offices than in factories.

The most important purpose of merit rating is to provide a basis for giving raises in base rates to individual employees. When used for this purpose, it helps eliminate inequities in pay among employees. In addition to its principal use, it helps in other ways. It insures, for example, that each worker periodically will be called to the mind of his supervisor. There is little likelihood that there will be "forgotten men" when an employee rating plan is used. Employee rating makes it possible to base promotions and transfers on a fairer basis than favoritism or happenstance, and thus improves morale.

When employees become acquainted with merit rating plans, there is often an improvement in morale, which seems to stem from their feeling that they are being recognized as individuals. They feel that the company is taking an interest in them. It is probably highly gratifying to a worker's personal pride to have a high merit rating. Merit rating should also help the employee in his personal development. If he is rated poorly on one or several items, these things can be called to his attention, and he should be given help in his attempts to improve.

Merit rating is said to better the quality of supervision by improving the supervision exercised and the process of selection of supervisors. Employee rating causes foremen to do a better job of supervision. They are compelled, as they rate their men, to think of each one, his short-

EMPLOYEE RATING	Name .... John Smith .... Clock No. P5 ...... Shift 1st
The Allen Manufacturing Co.	Job .... Stock Clerk "B" .... Date ....

This rating must be made with care and fairness for the interests of both Employee and Company. Consider employee objectively in terms of his *actual, typical, entire* performance for the period just ended (normally *six months*). Avoid snap judgments; concentrate on *one* factor at a time; shut out your *personal* feelings. Under "Data" give actual performance results where possible. In each section check square that best suits employee. If description fits adequately, check right square; if he doesn't measure up to description but is better than that for next lower rating, check left square.

QUALIFICATION	DATA	UNSATIS-FACTORY	SATIS-FACTORY	GOOD	EXCELLENT
WHAT HAS HE DONE? 1) Past performance in meeting quality standards	SCRAP AND SALVAGE Hours .... (or) Dollars	FREQUENT MIS-TAKES VERY CARELESS □ 10	SCRAP SOME-TIMES FAIRLY ACCU-RATE □ 12 □ 14	ERRORS RARE QUALITY-MINDED ☑ 16 □ 18	NO SCRAP UNUSUALLY ACCURATE □ 20
2) Past performance in amount of daily production, whether on machine or not *Total: 40*	PRODUCTION AVERAGE	CAN T EARN 15% BONUS BELOW STANDARDS SLOW WORKER □ 10	EARNS AT LEAST 15% BONUS FAIR PRODUCER □ 12 □ 14	OUTPUT 30-50 PTS ABOVE STANDARDS BETTER THAN AVERAGE □ 16 34 ☑ 18	OUTPUT MORE THAN 50 PTS. ABOVE STAND-ARDS UNUSUALLY FAST □ 20
WHAT CAN HE DO? 3) Knowledge of, and experience on, present job *Total: 20*	JOB STATUS Labor Grade ... 10A Job Rate	NOT UP TO REQUIREMENTS NEEDS CONSTANT HELP □ 10	FAIR KNOW-HOW SOMETIMES NEEDS HELP □ 12 □ 14	KNOWS MOST OF JOB RARELY NEEDS HELP ☑ 16 16 □ 18	MEETS ALL REQUIREMENTS MAKES MOST OF SKILL □ 20
HOW DOES HE GET ALONG? 4) Attitudes and actions regarding his job, the Company (including supervision) and fellow-workers *Total: 12*	DISCIPLINARY ACTION (Verbal or Written) None	SELDOM COOPER-ATES GETS ALONG POORLY REPRIMANDED MORE THAN ONCE LITTLE JOB INTEREST □ 2	SOMETIMES CONTRARY OR INDIFFERENT GETS ALONG FAIRLY WELL GIVEN REPRI-MAND LUKEWARM ABOUT JOB □ 4 □ 6	WANTS TO DO GOOD WORK MEETS OTHERS HALF-WAY SELDOM NEEDS DISCIPLINE LIKES JOB ☑ 8 □ 10	NATURAL TEAM-WORKER WELL LIKED NEVER NEEDS DISCIPLINE UNUSUAL JOB INTEREST □ 12
CAN YOU COUNT ON HIM? 5) Attendance over past six-month period	NO. ABSENCES Excused ... None ... Unexcused None	ABSENT MORE THAN FIVE DAYS □ 1	ABSENT FOUR TO FIVE DAYS □ 3 □ 4	LOST THREE DAYS OR LESS □ 6 □ 8	PERFECT RECORD ☑ 10
6) Neatness and care of equipment	RECORD OF DAMAGE None	SLOPPY ABUSES COMPANY PROPERTY □ 1	SOMEWHAT UNTIDY SOMETIMES MIS-HANDLES THINGS □ 3 ☑ 4	USUALLY NEAT CAREFUL WITH TOOLS, ETC. □ 5 □ 7	VERY ORDERLY HANDLES EQUIP-MENT AS IF HIS OWN □ 8
7) Safety	NO. ACCIDENTS Lost-Time ... None ... No Lost Time None	L T ACCIDENT VIOLATES RULES □ 0	N L T ACCI-DENT SOMETIMES CARELESS □ 2 □ 3	USUALLY CAREFUL OBEYS RULES □ 4 ☑ 5	VERY CAREFUL REPORTS HAZARDS □ 6
8) Promptness over past six-month period *Total: 28*	NO. LATENESSES One Min. .... Over 1 Min. .. 1	HABITUALLY LATE □ 0	OCCASIONALLY LATE □ 1 □ 2	SELDOM LATE □ 2 22 ☑ 3	NEVER LATE □ 4
Turn Over		RATING SCALE			
		UNSATISFACTORY 34-48	GOOD MINUS 69-75	GOOD PLUS 82-87	
		SATISFACTORY 49-66	GOOD 76-81	EXCELLENT 88-100	

Mill & Factory

FIG. 26–1. An employee rating form.

comings as well as his strong points. Once the shortcomings are noted, steps can and should be taken to eliminate them through training. Merit rating can be used to evaluate the worth of a foreman as well as of his men. When a new foreman is chosen, the ratings of all eligible candidates are compared. Consideration of each qualified person is insured, and better men are probably chosen in the long run.

Employee reaction to merit rating, on the other hand, can be negative if it is not properly introduced and administered. None of us likes the thoughts of being "rated." Employees often feel too that rating just gives management another excuse for holding them down and for not

---

GENERAL APPRAISAL

SINCE LAST REPORT THIS EMPLOYEE HAS: IMPROVED **X** ...STAYED SAME............. GONE BACK...........
(If he has not changed, do not fill out the rest of this side.)
REASONS FOR CHANGE, IF ANY ......Has further increased job knowledge & performance.
....

EXPLANATION, IF NECESSARY, OF QUALIFICATIONS (as checked on front side):
..Has gained more confidence in self through experience thereby increasing
..job knowledge and efficiency..

GENERAL QUALITIES (check phrases that best describe employee):
   ADAPTABILITY All-around .... Flexible ..X.. One-job man ....
   EFFORT   Always working ....X. Needs follow-up .... Must be prodded ....
   INGENUITY   Handy, original X. Routine worker, few ideas ....
   JUDGMENT   Uses common sense ....X. Unreliable ....
   SELF-CONTROL Calm on job ..X.. Sometimes excited .... Easily upset ....
UNDERSTANDING OF COMPANY POLICIES, PRACTICES AND RULES (check one):
   Unsatisfactory .... Satisfactory .... Good ...X. Excellent ....
IS EMPLOYEE FITTED FOR PRESENT JOB?   YES..X...NO...........
   IF NO, STATE REASON ....

DO YOU RECOMMEND TRANSFER NOW?   YES...........NO..X.
IS HE TRYING TO LEARN AND GET AHEAD?   YES..X...NO..........
SHOULD A VACANCY OCCUR, IS HE ABLE TO ASSUME GREATER RESPONSIBILITY? YES...........NO..X.
   IF SO, EXPLAIN HOW ...Not at this time but believe he will qualify in
.....due time..
LIST OUTSTANDING TRAITS AND QUALITIES ...... Good attendance, seldom tardy and
.....well liked by co-workers...

IN WHAT SPECIFIC WAYS CAN HE IMPROVE HIS PERFORMANCE? ....Can further increase job
....knowledge & develop a good memory...

FOREMAN'S SIGNATURE ....*Anthony Valley*...SUPERINTENDENT'S APPROVAL ....

THIS RATING WAS SHOWN TO AND DISCUSSED WITH ME ON ....
                                          (Date)
AND MY REACTION WAS ..I feel this report is fair and just
....EMPLOYEE'S SIGNATURE ..*John Smith*

Do Not Write Here

Personnel Department's Summary: *Good*

Date Recorded on Employment Record:
4-48-4-1M

Mill & Factory

FIG. 26–2.   The back side of the page shown in Figure 26–1.

giving them a pay raise. If an employee gets a poor rating and then no one helps him or shows him how to improve, it is small wonder that he doesn't like merit rating. Naturally, too, the rating has to be as fair as possible, so that no one can have a just cause for complaining about his rating.

Merit rating is known by many names. "Employee rating" is a commonly used term. Other terms in use include: merit rating, individual rating, personal rating, personal evaluation, employee evaluation, employee appraisal, employee progress reports, service rating, experience rating, and efficiency rating.

The differences in the names used for merit rating may be nothing more than name differences, but often the various terms reflect the purpose and use to which the plan will be put as well as the details of the plans themselves. Consequently, employee rating plans are characterized by more variety than is found in job evaluation plans. There is no single employee rating plan commonly and widely used. As between companies, variation rather than standardization is the rule.

MERIT RATING AND WAGE RATE CHANGES

Because you can't make merit rating altogether objective, it is imperfect as a basis for granting wage increases. But there are, nevertheless, differences in men. Some are better than others, and any good wage plan has to have some basis for paying good men more money than poor men. If you have no formal employee rating plan, then you have to do it informally. And when you do it informally, you usually do it in a rather haphazard way. The important point to remember is that you have to rate one way or another and that, on the whole, formal plans are better than informal methods.

When rating is used principally for setting employee pay rates, it is generally called "merit rating" and is confined as much as possible to factors for which objective measures are available. Subjective factors are minimized, although they cannot be fully eliminated. The reason for trying to be as objective as possible is obvious. Since employee ratings determine, in part, employee earnings, they are likely to be disputed from time to time. Workers who get no pay raise will claim that the rating is incorrect. The more objective the method of rating, the more satisfactorily such grievances can be handled. Plans which include some subjective factors may be as good or better for measuring true merit, but if their use makes it harder to convince an employee that his rating is fair, they are unsatisfactory plans.

In many companies the introduction of job evaluation changed wage policies somewhat. Remember that job evaluation commonly groups jobs into a series of labor "grades" or "classes." A definite wage range is generally attached to each labor grade. A man may be paid the bottom of the range for his job, or he may be paid any amount between that and the top. Using ranges makes a company establish a basis for deciding where, in the range, a man's pay is to be. Here is where merit rating enters. It is often used to decide where, in the range, each worker's rate is to be. Merit rate pay changes go only one way—up. No one's rate is reduced except in the case of a general wage cut in a depression.

Not all companies using job evaluation follow the "range" idea. Some (steel companies, for example) use fixed rates for each labor grade. All workers on any job in the grade get the same rate. Merit is, in these companies, important only when someone is to be promoted. In other companies no maximum is set for a labor grade. A minimum rate is assigned to each grade; unlimited raises can be given above that amount, depending on the merit rating of the employee.

Where minimum and maximum limits are set, raises in pay, within the wage range, are often partially governed by length of service. If, for example, a 15-cents-per-hour range is available, the first 5 cents may be given, after 6 months, as an automatic raise to all employees who started at the minimum of the grade. The remaining 10 cents is given on the basis of merit. Unions tend to press for the elimination of increases based on merit and to substitute length of service alone as the basis for raises within a wage range. Management is often agreeable to giving length of service some consideration but usually resists the complete elimination of merit.

METHODS

Many different methods or "plans" for formal employee rating are in use today. All of them have a common ultimate objective, rating men against men or against a theoretically perfect man. Actually, almost all the plans rate men to men indirectly by comparing them with preset scales. A man's place along the scale gives his rating, expressed in points. The procedures used are similar to those used in job evaluation except that they are designed to produce man ratings instead of job ratings.

As in job evaluation, merit ratings are usually summations of points credited for each of several factors, such as quantity or quality of work. The factors which are thought to be important in determining a man's merit are determined. Most plans use six or more factors for personal characteristics. For each characteristic, several degrees, ranging from bad to good, are set up, and each degree is assigned a certain number of points.

The rating is done by deciding which degree of each characteristic best describes the man being rated. The rater is usually given four or more choices of degrees and from these makes an appropriate choice. The choice automatically gives the employee being rated a certain number of points. The employee's rating is the combined total of points from all the characteristics in the plan.

The point total may itself be used as the rating, or it may be translated into a position on a percentage scale showing the proportion of workers above and below the employee who is being rated. The rating, expressed in this way, is called a "percentile" rating. When a man gets a 62 percentile rating, for example, it means that 61 per cent of the total group being rated had lower point totals. The rating procedure is complete at this point, whether expressed as a point total or as a percentile.

If employee rating is to be fully effective, you'll have to make ratings every now and then—not just once and then quit. Some companies rate all their employees once a year, a few do it twice a year. But that gets to be too often after the first few times.

FACTORS USED

Sometimes employee rating is merely "picture taking" of the employee, the end product being a series of answers to questions aimed at showing what manner of person he is, not how he measures up on the particular job he holds. Most merit plans, however, concern themselves only with factors relating to an employee's effectiveness on his present job or to his promotability.

It would seem that "merit" should be defined before factors can be selected to measure it. According to the dictionary, merit is "a mark or token of excellence," "worth, excellence," "a cause or reason of deserving well; a praiseworthy quality." These terms all define merit in an over-all way and give no hint as to how it can be measured. In practice, merit cannot be evaluated directly as a totality. Merit rating must, therefore, be a procedure for arriving at a quantitative measure of this over-all quality through several separate judgments concerning the factors which make it up.

If the purpose of merit rating is largely to improve the group rated by training, one set of factors is needed; if the purpose is to grant pay raises, another set of factors is needed. Differences also exist between rating plans for office workers and those used for factory workers.

Regardless of the purposes of employee rating, it is almost always desirable to include factors which relate to the worker's performance on the job and to his capability of further advancement. Such factors include the following: quantity of work done, quality of work done, knowledge of the job, ability to learn, length of service, attendance, and tardiness. On the whole they can all, except for knowledge of the job and ability to learn, be measured objectively.

Employee rating plans are rarely confined to these items alone. Usually several personality and behavior traits, such as dependability, co-operativeness, ability to get along with others, versatility, initiative, judgment, and loyalty, are also included. Personality, as such, is sometimes used as a separate factor. Even such factors as employee marital status and number of dependents are, in a few cases, included; also thrift, appearance, neatness, and personal cleanliness.

Among the factors listed above are several which bear no direct relationship to true merit on the job. When a company considers the number of an employee's dependents, his thriftiness, and such factors, it would seem that the rating system gets farther and farther afield. Even length of service is of questionable value as evidence of merit, although it is commonly used. Length of service is strongly favored by unions, yet it is doubtful whether length of service, when unaccompanied by increasing skill, is properly a matter of merit. Productivity is the basic economic justification for all wages, and length of service, in and of itself, does not increase productivity. If length of service is accompanied by increasing skill, the credit for that should be given in the form of a promotion or in the merit rating plan through some other factor, such as versatility or quality of work done.

Attendance is a reflection of merit only in a negative way. Poor attendance may warrant the discharge of the employee. Yet perfect attendance may be less desirable to a company than an occasional absence. Sick employees, for example, should stay at home. Reasonably good attendance, in that it shows reliability and dependability, is perhaps properly considered a part of real merit.

The quantity of output is a very common component of merit rating plans. It is perhaps the most important single element of true merit. Indeed, it is so important that many companies measure it separately and, by means of piecework or other incentive plans, pay directly for high levels of output. Yet, curiously, in many companies where this is done the average level of productivity is also considered in the employee rating plan. The employee may not only get a substantial bonus because of his extra productivity but may through merit rating (based partly on productivity) get an increase in his base rate as well. It would seem logical for such companies either to eliminate productivity as a part of their merit rating plan or to set up their plan so that productivity would have but little weight in the ratings of piece rate workers.

DEGREES OF FACTORS

Merit rating actually takes place in the process of selecting the degree of each factor which best describes the person being rated (see Fig. 26–3). The framers of the rating plan choose the factors and define several degrees for each factor. The defining of degrees is reasonably simple for factors capable of objective measurement, such as attendance or productivity. For all such objective factors a table of point values is set for various levels of accomplishment. The subjective factors are more difficult to measure in degrees, and yet usually they are, collectively, more important in the total rating than are the factors which can be measured objectively.

The framers of rating plans have phrased degree descriptions in many ways in their attempts to help the rater make his judgment. First, each factor itself must be adquately described so that the rater knows exactly what he is rating. Then the degrees themselves are defined. Probably the most common method of describing degrees and arranging the rating form is one that has come to be known as the "graphic scale," illustrated in Figure 26–3. In it each factor and its description is listed in a column at the left of the page. For each factor a horizontal line is extended across the page to the right. The line is used as if it were a scale going from bad to good (or vice versa). Beneath it are several definitions (usually four or more) of degrees of that factor. The rater reads the degree descriptions and puts a check mark on the line above the one applying to the person being rated. In most plans of this type it is

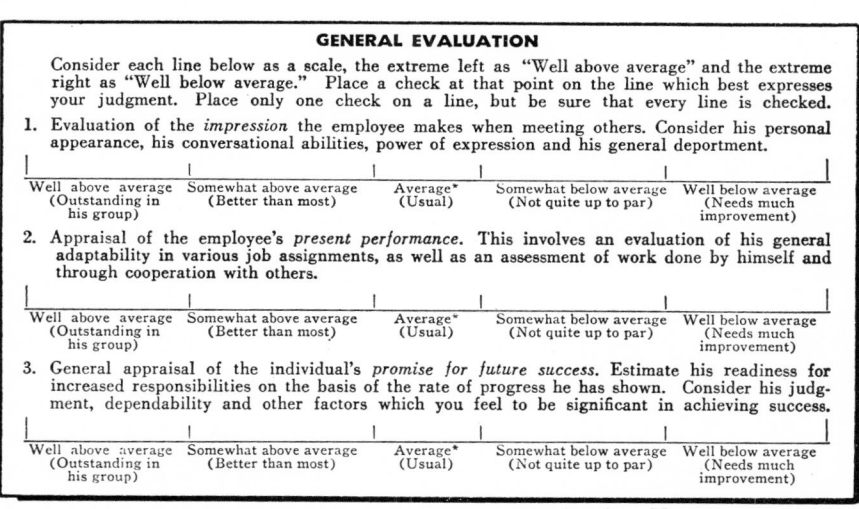

GENERAL EVALUATION

Consider each line below as a scale, the extreme left as "Well above average" and the extreme right as "Well below average." Place a check at that point on the line which best expresses your judgment. Place only one check on a line, but be sure that every line is checked.

1. Evaluation of the *impression* the employee makes when meeting others. Consider his personal appearance, his conversational abilities, power of expression and his general deportment.

| Well above average (Outstanding in his group) | Somewhat above average (Better than most) | Average* (Usual) | Somewhat below average (Not quite up to par) | Well below average (Needs much improvement) |

2. Appraisal of the employee's *present performance*. This involves an evaluation of his general adaptability in various job assignments, as well as an assessment of work done by himself and through cooperation with others.

| Well above average (Outstanding in his group) | Somewhat above average (Better than most) | Average* (Usual) | Somewhat below average (Not quite up to par) | Well below average (Needs much improvement) |

3. General appraisal of the individual's *promise for future success.* Estimate his readiness for increased responsibilities on the basis of the rate of progress he has shown. Consider his judgment, dependability and other factors which you feel to be significant in achieving success.

| Well above average (Outstanding in his group) | Somewhat above average (Better than most) | Average* (Usual) | Somewhat below average (Not quite up to par) | Well below average (Needs much improvement) |

American Management Association

FIG. 26–3. A "graphic" merit rating form. The rater may place his check mark anywhere along the line for each factor.

possible for the rater to check between degrees, although such a practice is not always followed. Later each check mark is translated into points in accordance with a predetermined scale. The point equivalents are not generally put on the rating sheets, but they may be. Usually certain factors are weighted more heavily and so get more points than others.

There are many variations of graphic rating scales. Look at Figure 26–3. Notice the horizontal line for each factor with degree definitions below the line. Some companies regard the line as a scale with point values from zero to ten. The rater can put a check mark anywhere along the line. Later, the place he puts it will be translated into a point value and added in with points from other factors to give him a point rating. Some companies treat each degree of a factor separately and allow no intermediate ratings to be made. Still another variation is to use descriptive words in place of phrases and to use the same words for all factors. When phrases are used, they are likely to be different phrases for different factors. When words are used, they are more likely to be the same, though they need not be. Words sometimes used include "poor," "fair," "good," "excellent," or "weak," "below average," "average," "above average," "outstanding." Some companies use only the letters A, B, C, D, E, and F instead of descriptive words or phrases (see Fig. 26–4).

In some plans the rater fills in descriptive words himself instead of checking off a choice. In a very few plans he writes in a descriptive phrase for each factor for the worker being rated. This latter practice

Read each block carefully. Decide which of the statements is **Most Descriptive** of the man as he carries on his job. Then, in the column headed **Most**, place an X over the letter which goes with the statement you choose. Next, decide which statement is **Least Descriptive** of the man and his job performance, and, in the column headed **Least**, place an X over the letter which goes with that statement. If you have any comments about your choices, write them on the line provided in each block. Answer every block. Only one **Most** and one **Least** should be marked in any block.

MOST LEAST

①
A A Familiar with all phases of the business.
B B Progressing slowly but surely.
C C Capable of doing more important work.
D D Needs close supervision.
E E Inclined to make hasty decisions.

②
A A Should be more business-like.
B B Has outstanding ability.
C C A natural leader.
D D Some question about his health.
E E Uses written reports skilfully to help in solving problems.

③
A A Has a mechanical sense.
B B Very serious-minded person.
C C Has capacity for better work.
D D Looks like a "comer".
E E His profanity creates a very unfavorable impression.

④
A A Doing everything possible to keep costs down.
B B Knows when to exercise his authority and when not to.
C C Unable to relax after a hard day's work.
D D People do not like to work for him.
E E Cannot handle several details of his job at the same time.

⑤
A A Not willing to make decisions unless he has very complete information.
B B Makes snap judgments about people.
C C Has not demonstrated up to now that he has the ability to progress further.
D D Very valuable in a new operation.
E E Good for routine supervisory job.

⑥
A A Would be very difficult to replace.
B B Lets difficulties get him down.
C C Alert to new opportunities for the Company.
D D Tries to run things his own way.
E E Tends to delegate things which will not reflect credit on him.

⑦
A A Insists on having more facts than needed in order to reach a sensible decision.
B B His personal life has begun to affect his work.
C C Can always be depended on to turn in a good job.
D D Calmly discusses problems with his people.
E E Can make a successful career for himself in U.P.S.

⑧
A A Avoids crises by anticipating the conditions which might produce them and planning for them well in advance.
B B Inclined to "pop off" on occasion.
C C An original thinker.
D D No one ever doubts his ability.
E E Lacks tolerance for weakness in other people.

⑨
A A Sometimes says the right thing at the wrong time.
B B Studies work closely for possible improvements.
C C Confidently relies on his memory which is not always accurate.
D D Gets good results from his people.
E E Quick to grasp information passed on to him.

⑩
A A Does not get the facts necessary for making decisions.
B B Receives constructive criticism well.
C C Can definitely be promoted whenever the opportunity affords itself.
D D Makes too many personnel changes.
E E He is ready to give credit to others for good work done.

⑪
A A Leans over backwards in accepting points of view of his men.
B B Quick to size up a situation.
C C Coordinates the activities of all the various parts of the work.
D D Has little knowledge of the work of other departments.
E E Will take some time for him to prove his worth.

American Management Association

FIG. 26–4. A "forced choice" rating form requiring the rater to make two ratings for each factor. The factor being rated is not itself described.

does not lend itself well to translation into points. In still other plans questions are used below the line instead of phrases or words. The questions may be phrased so that either a positive or a negative answer represents the high rating. Sometimes the possible degrees are listed vertically rather than horizontally beneath a factor description, but this arrangement is not often used on a continuous scale.

In some plans where the point equivalents are printed on the form along with the descriptive phrases or words, the middle rating is given zero points. Ratings above average have plus point equivalents, and those below average have minus point equivalents. Much more commonly, however, all points are plus, with more points being given for superior ratings.

A form of employee rating which is uncommon but should be mentioned asks a series of questions with "Yes" or "No" answers to each. This plan operates much as if the rater were taking a true-false examination, except that the questions are about a man's job proficiency or his characteristics. Usually when this method is used, the number of good answers determines the rating, but it is more often used as a section of a larger rating plan which includes some of the other procedures already discussed.

The United States Armed Forces use a rating form called an "efficiency report." It includes a section in which certain situations are described. The rater is asked to indicate how strongly he desires to have the person being rated serve in his command in those situations. Another section asks the rater to choose from among four definitions of each factor the one which best fits the person being rated. The definitions of degrees are complete in themselves, and the factor itself is not shown. An innovation in the Armed Forces rating form provides a place for the rater to check not only the degree definition which fits the worker best but also to indicate which one applies least. This serves as a check on the other ratings. Both job proficiency and personal qualifications are rated in this way on the Armed Forces form.

PROBLEMS IN EMPLOYEE RATING

Merit rating will encourage "merit" as your plan reflects it. *Be sure that your plan measures true merit.* Otherwise you'll encourage the wrong things. If you put attendance in, you may be getting sick people coming to work when they ought to stay home. If you put quantity of work in, you'll have to watch quality more than you did before or it will go down. And if you emphasize quality very much, the quantity will fall off. If you put in "co-operativeness," you're likely to develop a bunch of "yes-men." Choose your factors in a merit rating plan carefully and administer your plan with an eye to possible bad results.

Another problem is that almost all employee rating has to be done by amateur raters. You can't train every department head to be a professional rater, yet he has to do the rating. No one else knows his men so well. Rarely will you find more than two men who know a man's work well enough to rate him, and they are his boss and his assistant boss—neither of whom will ever be a professional rater. Personnel (which oversees ratings) tries to give all raters a little training but can't, of course, make them all good at it.

One thing that helps, and this personnel does, is to make the printed rating form as complete and self-explanatory as possible. Then it nearly always adds written instructions besides.

Experience shows that even after taking all these precautions the ratings are usually somewhat inconsistent. Some raters rate everybody high. Others rate everyone low. Still others rate men as being almost the same on all factors. You can pick out most of these rating habits by comparing the average ratings of different departments. If any department's ratings appear to be out of line, give those raters some more training in rating. Ultimately you ought to get most department heads trained well enough to do a reasonable job.

Department heads and raters in general are like you and me. We think of employees as complete people. We look at a whole man, not his separate parts. When someone asks us to rate a man factor by factor, we are likely to judge him "better than average" or "poor," etc., on all factors. This method puts the cart before the horse, and, as a rule, the results are not accurate. It would be possible, of course, for a man to be consistently good or poor on all factors, but it is quite likely that he will be better on some factors than on others.

The tendency to rate all factors alike is called the "halo" effect, since either an over-all rating or the rating on the first factor largely determines the ratings on all other individual factors. Another tendency found among raters is to rate all factors, hence all workers, as "average." This is sometimes called the "central tendency" effect. Some companies try to guard against these known weaknesses on the part of raters by reversing the scales on the printed rating form, that is to say, on one factor the degrees going from bad to good are from left to right, while on the next it is reversed: they go from right to left.

Other companies mix up the definitions so that they do not constitute a progression of degrees from bad to good in the order of presentation. The definitions for the highest degree might be in the middle of the line, etc. Obviously it is not possible to rate between degrees when this arrangement is used. Still a third method sometimes used to overcome the "halo" and the "central tendency" effects is to put each factor on a different sheet of paper. Several workers are rated on the same factor on one sheet. On the next sheet the same workers are rated on another factor, etc. The total ratings are obtained by combining the factor ratings from all sheets. This method breaks up the "halo" tendency but may substitute a tendency to rate all workers alike on each factor. All of these attempts to counteract weaknesses in the rating procedure are mechanical devices and probably only scratch the surface of the underlying problems involved in getting an objective employee rating.

Many companies find that supervisors' lack of interest in rating is a serious hurdle to overcome. Department heads frequently resent being asked to fill in rating forms for their employees every 6 months or even every year. If the interest and support of the supervisors is not obtained, their ratings will be carelessly done. The forms may be filled in quickly or, worse yet in factory departments, may be given to the department clerk to be filled in along with departmental forms. When foremen are

A	B	C	D	E
Outstanding, among best in the company	Superior, above average	Average	Below average	Falls among the poorest in company
Crose, Peter	Andrews, John Brown, Martin	Appleton, George Blake, James Carey, Robert Gilman, Sam Phillips, Alex	Doherty, John	Pratt, Jerome

FIG. 26–5. Avoiding the halo effect by having different sheets of paper for each factor.

opposed to various programs, they do not always voice their objections, which therefore may not be known. The personnel department must review ratings to see if they appear to have been given genuine thought. If not, they should not be used, and another attempt should be made to enlist the sympathetic support of department heads. Repeated failure perhaps indicates that the program ratings should be temporarily discontinued and then reintroduced at some later date.

The personnel department acting alone cannot wholly overcome this negative attitude. The administration of the company must also be behind a merit rating plan if it is to succeed. In particular, it must prove its intention to stand by the findings of merit ratings, giving raises and promotions where they have been shown by the ratings to be deserved.

DISCUSSING RATINGS WITH EMPLOYEES

Should you tell a man how you have rated him? Most companies say, yes. Some companies require the department head to go over each employee's rating with him; this is particularly true in a factory having unions. The form used by the United States Civil Service has a statement to the effect that it has been discussed with the man rated. Below this statement is a space for the department head to sign, indicating that he has done so.

The practice of discussing the rating with the employee is not, however, universal in industry. Some employers feel that the rating definitely should not be discussed with the person rated, since it may result in arguments. Also, we are all softies when it comes to hurting other people's feelings. Many department heads won't discuss their subordinates' ratings with them even if you tell them they must. If you insist, then they give very lenient ratings. Nearly all department heads want their employees to think well of them and want them to believe they are working in their interests. Lenient ratings may save arguments and make the foreman appear to be "a good fellow"; but if the ratings are not reliable, they are poor ratings and fail to serve the purpose intended.

A discussion of the ratings with the persons being rated is certainly the fairest thing to do. A man receiving a low rating finds out that he has been rated low and also the reasons for it. Without an explanation he might never have become aware of his weakness. The ratings offer an ideal opportunity to train and improve the worker. They also act as a stimulant to the department head to exert more effort in the direction of employee training. Without explanations to and discussions with the workers, you may lose much of the rating's possible value.

UNION ATTITUDE AND ITS EFFECT ON MERIT RATING PLANS

Many companies using merit rating confine it to supervisors and office employees. As a general rule, these groups have no union organization, so there is no "union attitude" to consider. In other companies the rating plan is largely confined to getting a picture of the employee and is not carried to the point where employees are rated and compared. Such ratings as are made are primarily additions to the personnel department's records and do not directly influence wages. With this setup the union is not greatly concerned.

In some companies, however, the rating plan relates directly to wages, layoffs, and promotions up to the supervisory level. Here the union attitude becomes important. Although unions usually oppose merit rating, they are not always opposed. The union's main objection to employee rating plans stems from the union's policy of placing seniority above all other considerations. No shop steward wants to tell a man he is not entitled to a raise because he is not good enough nor that he is not entitled to file a grievance if he fails to get a raise. The steward is the representative of the union members, the poor workers as well as the good. He must try to be "for" all the members. A union leader often agrees with the general principle that a company's future is endangered if too many poor workers get raises and promotions at the expense of the good workers, but rare is the leader who will follow through in individual cases of promotion or layoff. If wholly objective measures were available to measure merit, he might be held more strictly to account. But he is hardly to be blamed if he hesitates to try to convince a poor employee that he is so poor as to merit no pay raise or promotion when the steward has only subjective merit ratings to back him up.

Companies having strong unions have tended to emphasize factors in their merit rating plans which can be measured with relative objectivity and to minimize the use of subjective factors. Insofar as objectivity is encouraged, this is laudable, but there is a danger in that the rating arrived at may be a poor rating. There are instances, however, where merit rating plans which include subjective factors have been accepted by unions both as a means of determining raises and as one element to be considered in promotions and layoffs. One such plan which has been in operation at the Acme Steel Company for 20 years[1] operates as follows:

The form developed by this company contains ten factors on which each employee is rated: accuracy of work; quantity of work; use of working time; ability to work with others; ability to learn; safety; initiative and acceptance of responsibility; conduct on the job; care of equipment, tools, material, supplies, and power; and punctuality and attendance. Each employee is rated independently by at least two and usually by at least three or more supervisors. A correction for raters' tendencies (the tendency of any given rater to give consistently *high* or *low* ratings to all men rated) is made. . . .

The basic purpose served by these ratings is to supplement seniority in providing a basis for promotion or upgrading. Promotional sequences have been established so that a man going into a job in a certain unit must come from a certain stipulated lower unit. Men in this lower unit are ranked according to their corrected ratings, from high to low. To allow for some unreliability in the ratings, all men in approximately the highest 10 per cent on the basis of the ratings are considered equal in rated merit and the man with the longest seniority among this group is given the promotion if and when an opening at the next level occurs.[2]

STUDY QUESTIONS

1. Why would you want to "merit rate" your employees? What would you hope to accomplish?
2. How objective should you try to be in merit rating? Explain fully.
3. How do point merit rating plans operate? Describe fully.
4. Discuss the factors that should be put into a merit rating plan. Tell why you chose those and omitted others.
5. What problems are there in using merit rating? How do you solve them?

---

[1] The Acme Steel Company some years ago had a strike which went on for weeks after other steel companies had settled their strikes because of the union's unsuccessful attempt to have this plan thrown out.

[2] Joseph Tiffin, "Recent Developments in Merit Rating," *Operating Problems of Personnel Administration* Personnel Series, No. 144 (New York: American Management Association, 1952), pages 16–17.

6. *a*) What is the "halo" effect? What do you do about it?

   b) What is the "central tendency" effect in merit rating? What do you do about it?

7. How do you get foremen and other department heads to do a good job of merit rating? Tell what you would do.

8. Would you discuss merit ratings with employees? Give reasons for your answer. If you had answered differently, what reasons would you have given?

Chapter 27

WAGES AND INCENTIVES FOR FACTORY EMPLOYEES

How effective can pay incentives be? Will men really work harder if you tie their pay to their output? How important is money to a factory employee? Judging from some research studies you would think that money is not very important to most men. When employees are asked, "what are the most important things to you on a job?" they invariably put "being treated like a human being" first. Wages comes well down the line.

Yet most strikes are over wage increases. Certainly men don't go out on strike over unimportant things. Wages seem to be pretty important after all. Perhaps the questionnaires get the answers they do because the men think (and usually rightly) that wages are about the same in other companies where they might work. When that is so, other things become more important.

If money really isn't very important to men, then wage incentives won't be much good. Offering a man more money if he does more work will not make him turn out much more. Industry doesn't have to guess or rely on surveys, however. It has had many years of experience with incentive plans and has found that they raise production and reduce costs. True, incentives at times make problems where none existed before, and they cost some money to administer, but nearly always the men make more money and the product costs less.

But how can you get a less costly product by paying more wages? You get it because the men turn out lots more products for not quite so much more money. Partly they turn out more because they work harder than men on daywork and they gain too by not doing things the long way round and not wasting so much time. Being on piecework makes them want to do things the short way and not to waste time.

Some unions, as organizations, oppose incentives (as in autos and steel). But other unions (textiles and shoes) favor incentives. Workers usually would rather work a little harder and make more money. You don't find pieceworkers asking to be put on daywork jobs, but you often find dayworkers wanting to get a chance to do piecework jobs so that they can make some more money.

DAYWORK VERSUS INCENTIVES

Everyone is hired to do work so, one way or another, he is paid for his *productivity*. The methods of tying wages and productivity together vary, but most methods fall into one of two general types. Either you pay a man for his *time* (without directly measuring his output) or you pay him directly for his *output*.

Paying straight hourly rates is the most common method of paying wages to factory employees, and in many factories this is the only method used. Even in factories using incentive plans there are many jobs which are not suited to the setting of production standards, so that work is paid for by the hour.

A man's hourly rate, when incentives are not used, is often called his "day rate" or his "base rate." Of course calling it a "day rate" is, strictly speaking, a misnomer, but in industry this causes no trouble because everyone knows that a day rate means an hourly rate.

Day rates are simple to compute and easily understood. There is no concern, in computing wages, about how much work is done. A man's pay is his base rate times the number of hours he works. From the company point of view day rates are especially good any time that you can boost production because the added units cost nothing in wages. But, with incentives, the company saves less when output goes up because you pay the men more when they produce more.

Payroll work is simple with day rates, but cost accounting is more difficult than with incentive payments. With hourly rates, unit costs of production depend on how much a man turns out. If his output falls, unit costs go up because the hourly rate stays the same. But if he boosts his output, unit costs go down. Cost estimating is difficult, since labor costs per unit depend upon the rate at which the employee works.

Day rates have low incentive value. There is no direct relationship between output and pay. The reward for good work or for high productivity comes in the form of pay raises or in promotions, neither of which is certain or immediate. Pay raises, as rewards for good work, are usually small and are by no means proportional to the differences in productivity between employees. Even the small differences in pay which exist are given only where good work is recognized. And sometimes, because few and sketchy production records are kept for individual workers, a worker's good performance goes unnoticed. Formal merit rating, in companies which have it, makes it reasonably certain that a worker's high productivity will be known and that such pay increases as are available will be given to the better workers.

Incentive pay plans cause a man's pay to go up or down with his production. They are called incentive plans, or bonus plans, or piece-work. Piecework is actually one particular incentive plan (and probably much the most common), but some people call any or all kinds of incentive plans "piecework."

OUTPUT AND COSTS WITH DAYWORK AND INCENTIVES

Most workers respond to financial incentive systems; give them a chance to work harder and earn more money, and they go right to work. Often they turn out twice as much as ordinary dayworkers.

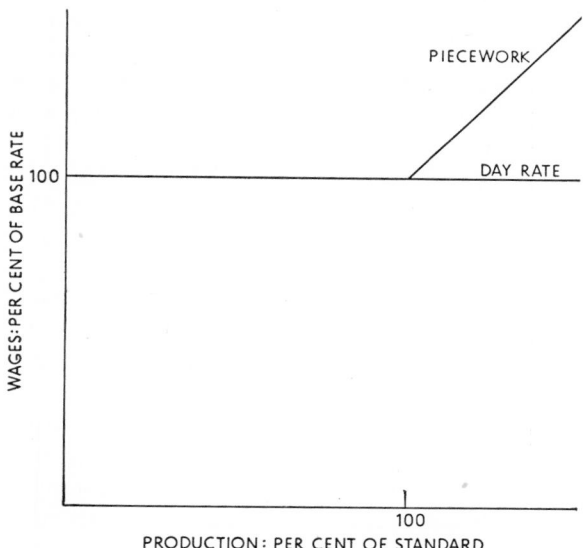

FIG. 27–1.   Earnings curves for day rates and piece rates. The day rate is assumed to be guaranteed (as it nearly always is) to pieceworkers if they fall below standard production.

There are many kinds of incentive plans. Most of those in use today pay workers proportionally for output above standard. This means that the man is paid his base rate for "standard" output (disregarding, for the moment, the fact that guarantees of amounts in excess of the base rate are common) and that he receives a bonus for greater output proportional to the extra production. Twenty per cent extra production per hour, for example, earns him a 20 per cent bonus.

In most companies using incentives, the "standard" output (usually determined by time study) is a greater quantity than day rate workers usually turn out. If a job is changed from hourly paid to incentive, a small increase in output is required before bonus earnings start.

Production above standard, however, does not reduce the direct labor cost per unit *because hourly earnings go up directly with production.* Thus a man on a $2.00 hourly base rate whose job standard calls for

100 units per hour gets paid $2.00 per hour for production of 100 per hour or less.[1] The piece rate is 2.0 cents each. If he produces 125 pieces per hour, the labor cost per unit remains 2.0 cents each, and he is paid $2.50.

But if a man turns out less than standard output, however, the direct labor cost increases because of the guaranteed base rate. If, in the above example, a man turned out 100, 75, or 50 pieces per hour, he would get his $2.00 regardless. But the labor cost per piece would go up from 2.0 to 2.7, and then to 4.0 cents.

Since nearly all workers "make out" (produce at least standard output per hour), how can a company benefit when the labor cost per unit stands

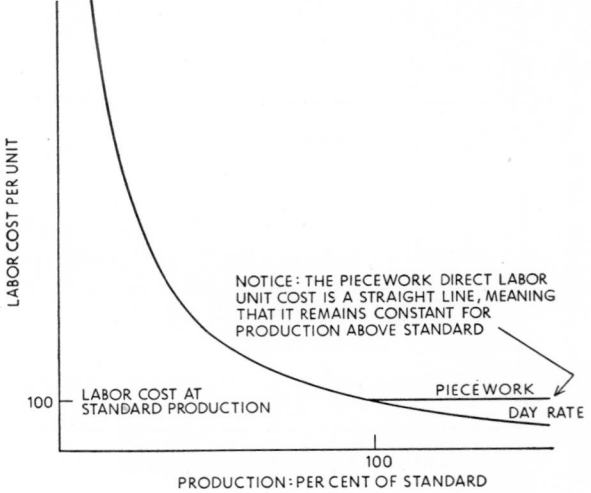

FIG. 27–2. *Unit cost curves for direct labor only.*

still at 2.0 cents each? Look at Figure 27–2. Notice that the per unit cost line (for *direct labor only*) stays flat for production above 100 per cent of standard. So why use incentive plans and encourage high levels of productivity?

The fact that the men make more money is one good reason even if there were no others. But probably the most important reason for wanting him to stay high is that you save in other ways, principally in overhead. Overhead costs are big items; nearly always they are at least equal to direct labor costs. Sometimes they are many times direct labor, the *total operating cost* in our example is $4.00 an hour ($2.00 for direct labor and $2.00 per hour for overhead). That comes to 4.0 cents a unit

---

[1] Guaranteeing a man his base rate as a minimum for less than standard production is almost universal now. According to old definitions you don't have a piecework plan if you guarantee the base rate. Today's companies with guarantees still call their plans piecework.

when producing 100 pieces per hour. Suppose now that the worker turns out 125 pieces in an hour. The cost of 125 pieces in an hour is $2.50 for labor and $2.00 for overhead, a total of $4.50, or 3.6 cents per unit. Here we have a 10 per cent reduction in unit costs, even though *direct labor costs per unit remain unchanged*. Look at Figure 27–3. Notice that *total costs per unit* keep on going down as long as production keeps going up. This is the main reason for the company wanting to have all the men exceed standard and earn bonuses.

Workers do not always produce as much as they easily could on incentive plans. When rates are very loose (overliberal), the men some-

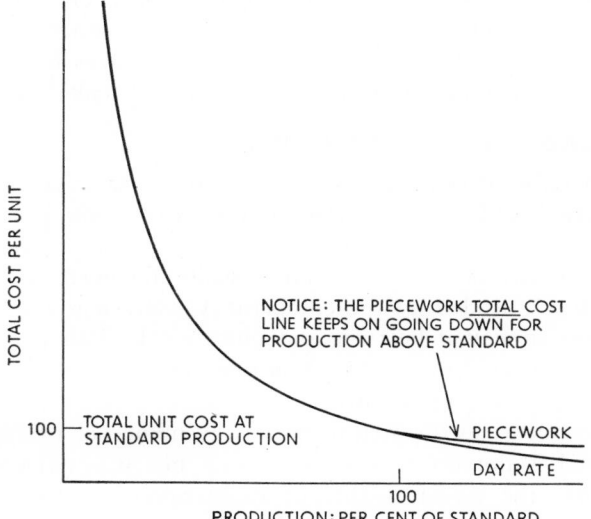

FIG. 27–3. *Total unit cost curve including direct labor plus overhead.*

times hold back because they are afraid that if they go all out and produce a lot and make a big bonus, the company will cut the piece rate. So they "peg" their production, holding it down so that their earnings will not tempt the company to cut rates. If any one man in the group doesn't see it this way, the others keep him in line.

One bad thing about incentive pay is that quality of work may suffer because all that the man cares about is *how many* he can turn out. Of course you pay the piece rate only for the good products (except when rejects are not his fault). This would seem to protect your quality. As long as his products pass inspection that is all the man cares. But you must put your quality standards in writing, and you must enforce them. The men (and usually the foreman, too) are likely to try to slip slightly off-standard things through. Inspection costs are a little higher than when you pay men day rates.

Actually it is not a bad thing to have a worker make products just good enough to pass and no better. You don't want him wasting time doing things too well. You can't afford to let a man put a high polish on a 10-cent-store electric light bulb socket. If your specification says that a dimension of a part is to be 4 inches and that it is acceptable if it is 2 thousandths of an inch oversize, then a man has done nothing bad if an item comes out 1½ thousandths oversize.

The point is that if the item is good enough to pass, it is satisfactory. Not that we object to greater accuracy, or more shine to a surface, but nearly always those things mean that the man has done too much work and made the item cost too much.

There is another side to the speed-quality matter. On many jobs there is no problem of your having to sacrifice quality in order to get quantity. Fast and good often go together. The fast man makes few mistakes. To take an example from the office, fast typists rarely make errors.

POSITIVE AND NEGATIVE INCENTIVES

It is generally agreed that incentives may be positive or negative in their operation and that, as between the two, positive incentives are better.

Positive incentives offer a reward, usually financial, to a man if he does some work needed by the company. Usually it is a matter of paying him more money if he turns out more work. This is a positive approach to the incentive problem. You offer extra money or added privilege in exchange for production.

Negative incentives threaten to take away money or privilege if something wanted is not done or if something not wanted is done. In its extreme form the threat is that of discharging a man if he fails to produce enough work or if he produces too much bad work or if he violates your rules too often.

Psychologically, positive incentives are surely better than negative. How much better it is to offer a man a reward than it is to threaten him with punishment! But aren't you kidding yourself about there being much difference? How can you offer a man a reward for doing something without saying (or leaving unsaid) that he won't get it if he doesn't do what you want? Or how can you say that a man who disobeys all your rules will get fired without implying that nonviolators will get to keep their jobs?

Every incentive is two-sided. You can talk all you want about one side—and probably you should always talk about the positive side—but the other side is there all the time. You ought never to forget this. Many companies in the past have introduced piecework, thinking of it only as a positive incentive. Later they discovered its negative aspects.

Picture a man who has been paid by the hour being given a chance to do the job on piecework. The more he turns out, the more he makes. He promptly applies himself, works hard, and earns a good bonus. Let this keep on for a while; soon he gets used to getting the bonus and expects it. From here on the incentive is all negative to him. All that he can do is to make less if he turns out less.

To most men incentive plans are positive at first but soon become negative—no matter how much management tries to talk up the positive side. Fortunately most pieceworkers keep their output up, so they don't feel the negative feature much. If outside influences make their production go down, the company usually gives them a little extra money to keep their pay up.

CHARACTERISTICS OF A "GOOD" WAGE INCENTIVE PLAN

A "good" wage incentive plan should be one that both employer and employee like. Here's what the *men* want: a plan that lets them make good money when they work hard, a plan that relates size of bonus to effort, a plan that has a high minimum wage guarantee, a plan that pays the bonus every payday (not at the end of the year), a plan that pays each man for his own effort (group plans are all right for small groups, but the larger the group the less effective the incentives to each man), a plan simple enough for the man to figure out his own bonus before he gets it.

Here's what the *company* wants: a plan that keeps the man producing at high levels so that machines are kept busy and costs kept down, a plan that pays good bonuses to the best producers, a plan requiring few records and simple to compute, a plan that allows quick verification of production reports on which bonuses are paid, a plan that causes few disputes.

The measure of a man's effort is his output of products, so a good plan must be based on accurate job standards. Piece rates should be set fairly, should be guaranteed against change, and should be consistent as between jobs. A given amount of extra effort on one job should earn a man the same rate of bonus that the same extra effort earns on any other job. Piece rates should always be set *before* the man does the work. No one likes to work against an unknown standard.

No wage incentive plan measures up to all of the requirements laid down. But the nearer you can come to it the better it will suit everyone.

DETERMINANTS OF INCENTIVE EARNINGS

Incentive workers' earnings are determined by (1) the ratio of their production to standard production, (2) the job base rate, and (3) the incentive plan in use. The ratio of actual output to standard output depends, in turn, on (*a*) how much is produced, and (*b*) how much the standard calls for. So there are really four determinants of a man's hourly earnings. Of these, only one—the *output*—is up to the man. His pay for this work will be fair if the other three are equitably set by the company.

Today the three determinants set by the company—*output standards, job base rates,* and *bonus plans*—are generally set as carefully and as equitably as the company knows how to set them. Output standards are discussed in Chapter 30, and job evaluation in Chapter 25. Here we are going to talk only about incentive plans and how they work.

MEASURED DAYWORK

"Measured daywork" is an attempt to combine the best features of incentive plans and daywork. The term may refer to either of two arrangements. One method uses time standards for jobs and requires records of the quantity of work turned out. In this plan workers are paid the hourly base rate for the job as a starting point. New workers on any job are classed as "C" grade workers. A record is kept of the number of standard hours of work done by each operator. Divide the total number of standard hours of work done by the number of hours the man took and get his efficiency ratio. Do that every pay period and for every worker. If a grade "C" man stays over a stated minimum for perhaps 3 months, he is promoted to a grade "B" worker and gets a raise, perhaps 10 cents per hour. If he beats a higher ratio for several months, he will be promoted again, this time to a grade "A" rating, and will get another raise. Raises are usually permanent even if a man's future production occasionally falls off to a lower level.

There is another and different plan also called "measured daywork." Using this plan you set daily quotas of output (use time study procedures to set the quotas) and pay a set hourly rate for meeting the quota. *Both the quota and the hourly rate are higher than they would be for regular hourly paid work.* If, for example, time study shows that normal production per hour should be 100 pieces, a typical pieceworker will generally turn out 130 or more and earn a corresponding bonus. If we assume a $2.00 per hour base rate, the man will earn a total of $2.60 per hour or more. With this kind of measured daywork, the hourly quota might be set at 130 pieces and the hourly rate at $2.60. No additional bonus is paid for production above 130 per hour, nor is there any pay deduction for production of less than 130 per hour.

Workers consistently falling below 130 would, however, be removed from the job and put on other work. Proponents of the second type of measured daywork claim that it reduces the disputes over rates common to most incentive plans, yet maintains high production levels. But some companies find that men argue just as loudly about the reasonableness of the daily quota as they do about individual job piece rates. Unless quotas are set correctly with this method, it is possible to end up paying high hourly rates without getting a corresponding increase in output.

General Motors' A-C Sparkplug division uses measured daywork but tries to cut out arguments by not emphasizing the quota, in fact, they don't even tell a man what his quota is. They try to get his mind off quantity and onto the idea that he should do a fair day's work. Then there are fewer arguments about what is expected when improvements go in. Improvements will, of course, increase the output. If your mind is on the quantity of output you may object, thinking that you are working harder. But if you are thinking of doing a fair day's work, you don't care particularly whether you do a lot of work on 100 items or less work on 150. A-C reports that its plan works very well.

STRAIGHT PIECEWORK

Straight piecework pays a set amount for every piece a man turns out. The more he turns out the more he earns, and the less he turns out the less he makes. It is the simplest and most common incentive plan. Today's piecework plans practically always pay the man at least his base rate in case his production falls down very much. Nearly always, though, a pieceworker makes a good bit more than the minimum guarantee.

Here's how a piece rate is figured. First find out how long it takes a man to do the operation at "normal" work pace. Normal work pace is not top pace but a pace that the man will beat when he really goes to work. How to get this time is explained in Chapter 30. Divide 60 minutes by the standard time (the time it takes when the man works at normal pace) for the job. This gives you the standard number of pieces per hour. Standard hourly output for a 4-minute job would, for example, be 15 pieces.

Now divide the job base rate by the standard output to get the piece rate. If the job base rate is $2.00 an hour, the piece rate in our example is 13.3 cents each ($2.00 ÷ 15 pieces = 13.3 cents). If a man turns out fewer than 15 pieces, he gets $2.00 an hour. If he turns out more, he gets 13.3 cents each for them. Twenty pieces per hour, for example, would bring him $2.66.

Standards used in piecework are usually set by time study and are more likely to be reasonably tight than loose. But they are not so tight as to prevent the men earning bonuses. Few pieceworkers earn less than a 10 per cent bonus, and most good workers will be in the 30 per cent zone. In unusual cases they may hit 40 per cent.

Piecework gets a little more complicated if you have pay rate ranges for jobs instead of single rates. In that case, you sometimes have men on the same job getting different personal pay rates. With wage ranges, it is usually better to change from piece rates to a 100 per cent bonus plan (described on page 510).

Here is the trouble that you get into if you try to use piecework when men doing the same job have different personal pay rates. On a certain job Smith has a personal base rate of $2.00. Jones gets $2.20. Standard output is 15 units per hour. Which base rate do you use to figure the piece rate? Do you divide $2.00 by 15? Or $2.20? Or do you use an average? Or do you figure two rates, one for Jones and one for Smith? Or do you use the job minimum rate, which in this example might be $1.90?

One acceptable (but not perfect) way is to figure the piece rate on the job minimum rate and then add an extra amount for the men's rates. Here's how that works: Divide $1.90 by 15 and get a piece rate of 12.7 cents each. Let Smith turn out 16 pieces and Jones 18. Smith makes $2.03 on piecework. Add to that 10 cents more because his personal rate is 10 cents over the job minimum. He ends up with $2.13. Jones earns $2.29 on piecework, then gets 30 cents more because his personal rate is 30 cents above the job minimum. His earnings total $2.59. This solution works well, but it has some disadvantages. First, it makes more work in the payroll department, and, second, the men don't get a bonus on their whole base rate.

Another complication to piece rates is "across-the-board" wage increases—the kind that often come out of contract negotiations in which everyone is to get the same cents per hour increase. They are discussed on page 519.

A discussion of piece rates would be incomplete if we didn't mention negotiated rates. In the clothing manufacturing industry and to some extent in the shoe industry, piece rates are and have been for many years negotiated. Generally no time studies are made. Management representatives and the union's piece rate negotiating committee sit down together and go over patterns and details of new product designs and determine rates for the various operations by bargaining. New designs are usually similar to old ones. Since both parties know the jobs very well, they know by comparison with existing rates about what the new rates should be.

Rates decided upon in this way are settled directly as cents per piece; *there is no fixing of hourly production standards* to be divided into job base rates. In fact, *there may be no base rate structure,* in the ordinary sense, at all. But the end product, the piece rates established by bargaining, embodies the negotiators' informal ideas of both base rates and time standards. As long as the two parties are satisfied with the rate, the intermediate steps normally taken to arrive at the end product—a piece rate—are unnecessary.

100 PER CENT BONUS PLANS

One hundred per cent bonus plans vary in names (some are called "standard hour" or "100 per cent premium" plans), but whatever they are called, they work the same.

As with piecework, you start with time standards for doing the job. And, as with piecework, the next step is to figure the standard hourly output. But, from here on, 100 per cent plans differ from piecework.

Standards are never expressed in money terms; they are just left as so many pieces per hour.

Now you go to the man's production. Divide his total production figure by the number of hours he worked to get an output per hour figure. In our problem Smith turned out 16 pieces and Jones 18 pieces per hour. Standard was 15. The next step is to divide each man's actual output by the standard and get a production (or "efficiency") ratio. Smith's ratio is 1.067; Jones' is 1.20. (We say that Smith was 107 per cent efficient and Jones was 120 per cent efficient.)

You are now ready to figure their earnings. Smith gets $2.00 (his base rate) times 1.067, or $2.13 per hour; Jones gets $2.20 × 1.20 = $2.64 per hour. Each gets his full per cent bonus on his whole base rate. If each had produced 33 per cent above standard, each would have gotten a 33 per cent bonus.

Notice that their having different personal rates makes no trouble at all. Nor do you have to pay any attention to the job base rate. Notice too that you can give Smith or Jones or everyone a pay raise without changing the standard for the job. Give Smith a 15 cents an hour raise and all you do is to multiply $2.15 × 1.067. This gives him $2.29. No need to change piece rates or time standards at all. When using piece rates, you have to recalculate them all (and you may have thousands of them) if there is a general wage increase. On the other hand, 100 per cent bonus plans require you to calculate an efficiency ratio every day for every man—something you don't have to do for piecework.

One hundred per cent bonus plans end up being very much like straight piecework as far as bonuses are concerned. They pay exactly the same as piecework except where different personal base rates are used. Some people consider them to be just a variation of piecework rather than a separate method.

OLD PLANS

Many different incentive plans have been developed since the turn of the century. Most of them, like obsolete automobiles, have had their day and are no longer used. Among them are the Halsey, Gantt, Taylor, Rowan, and Emerson plans.

The Halsey plan paid a man a bonus equal to full pay for half the time he saved. Ten hours' work in 8 hours got a man 9 hours' pay. The standards were loose. Gantt paid a low hourly rate for less than standard production, a fixed bonus for reaching standard, and piecework beyond. Taylor's plan used two piece rates, a low one per piece if a man didn't reach standard and a high one per piece (for all pieces) if he did reach standard.

Rowan's plan paid a bonus according to the proportion of the time saved. A man got paid his regular hourly rate for the time it took him to do a job. If he did it in less than standard time, he got a bonus. If he saved one quarter of the standard time, he got a 25 per cent bonus; if he saved half the time, he got a 50 per cent bonus. Emerson's plan required you to compute a man's efficiency ratio. Then you paid him a bonus, starting at a little below standard, on a fixed basis. Every added point of efficiency got a man eight tenths of a per cent bonus.

Perhaps the Bedaux plan should also be listed as an old one. It was introduced in the 1920's and is still used some. Right from the start the Bedaux plan ran into much employee opposition. Its wage payment features were like the Halsey plan except that its bonuses were three-fourths proportional to output above standard. A worker who turned out 125 per cent of standard work was paid 118.75 per cent of his base rate. Performance at 150 per cent of standard produced a 137.5 per cent bonus. Bedaux job standards were based on time studies, and job base rates were guaranteed.

The Bedaux plan troubles came mostly from the emphasis placed on the worker's performance ratio rather than from the wage payment feature. The Bedaux plan was the first to emphasize the ratio itself. Bedaux efficiency ratios were called "B-Hours," and started with 60 (not 100) as normal. The idea was that it was normal to do 60 minutes of work in an hour. More than normal or standard production (more than 60 minutes of standard work) per hour gave the man a 65 or a 70 B-Hour or more. Bedaux job standards were expressed as minutes of time to do jobs. A "5 B-Hour" job meant that you got credit for doing 5 minutes of work every time you did that job. At the end of a day the man's standard minutes of work done was divided by the number of minutes he worked to get his B-Hour.

Of course this is really just the same as the efficiency ratio used in the 100 per cent bonus plan except that you use a different set of numbers. Everyone's B-Hour was figured every day, and low producers were singled out for reprimands. Bedaux standards were usually tight standards, so it was hard to make a good showing. Besides that, some companies using Bedaux cut rates if the men made much bonus. Rate cutting was not part of the system, but it is small wonder Bedaux became a hated system.

THE SCANLON AND RUCKER PLANS

Since World War II two new varieties of profit-sharing plans have made headlines, the Scanlon plan and the Rucker Share-of-Production plan. Both are a kind of company-wide incentive plan. The plans work a little differently, and neither is quite like most other profit-sharing plans—in fact, proponents of both plans deny that they are profit-sharing plans.

The Scanlon plan gets management and the union to agree on a plant "normal" labor cost per unit. Then all cost reductions are shared 50–50 between workers and management. Results have been very good in the companies you hear about. A flood of suggestions for improvements always comes in from the workers. Loafers aren't tolerated by the other men. Production costs go down, and employee earnings go up.

The Rucker plan starts with the wage share of the sales dollar. In most companies wages take almost the same part of the sales income dollar—year in and year out. For companies that make most of their own parts for assembled products, wages will most likely take between 30 and 40 per cent of the sales dollar. In the Rucker plan you (company and workers) decide what the figure is, and then you put that share of all of your income into a wage pool.

So far the men have gotten nothing they didn't have before. Why would they ever agree to the Rucker plan? How can they come out ahead? They agree because they come out ahead every time a labor cost improvement is made. The same number of men get more work done, and payments into the pool stay at their agreed-on part of the income dollar. So every laborsaving improvement means more money for each man in the group. Payment of shares in the fund to workers is made quarterly—not every payday. As with the Scanlon plan, suggestions for improvement roll in and the team spirit among workers grows.

So far, however, we haven't seen much gain for the company. If all the labor savings from improvements go to the men, how does the company gain? It saves overhead because it gets more output from the same investment. Also many suggestions for improvement save not only labor but materials as well. Or they reduce scrap. The company gets all the gain here.

Both the Scanlon and the Rucker plans have had their greatest successes in medium or small companies. No one knows how either would fare in a depression, but they might hold up well. Both plans have most often been put into sick companies—most of which promptly got well. Both plans depend for their success on the wholehearted co-operation between management and the men—otherwise endless arguments could come up about how to handle price changes, wage raises, changing from making to buying, who stands the costs of making improvements, and such things.

HYBRID PLANS

Rarely is it wholly accurate to say that a company uses a certain wage plan. Most companies using incentive plans use different plans in different departments. A plan that fits semiautomatic machines doesn't suit hand operations at all; nor would it do for operations performed by groups or crews of men. Sometimes there are historic reasons for one department's plan. Or you might like to use piecework everywhere, but find some jobs that you can't time very well. So you have to leave them on daywork or figure out a makeshift plan for them.

Whether a company uses one or several plans, there are always changes in their wage plans over the years. The changes are rarely clean-cut changes from one method to another. They are usually expediency measures which alter the old plan by piecing and patching. You get strange and weird hybrid plans so often that they are almost the rule rather than the exception today. Sometimes the results are neither logical nor equitable. Here are two examples. Don't spend time studying these plans carefully. We just put them in to show you how mixed up some plans get.

Company A uses this plan in its thread cutting department in the manufacture of pipe fittings, such as tees, ells, couplings, reducers, and the like. The machines are semiautomatic, requiring only that the worker load and unload the individual pieces. The speed of each machine is constant, although different machines run at different speeds. Since the speed of the machines is constant, the best a worker can do is to remove the last piece and put the next one in place every time the threading tool advances and recedes. It takes the machine considerably more time to cut a thread (20 to 30 seconds) than it does for the worker to load and unload it (about 3 or 4 seconds), so the machines are made with several spindles (threading tools) and the operator actually keeps from eight to ten spindles going all the time.

The company allows 15 per cent of the worker's time as a personal and fatigue allowance and gives 15 minutes' wash-up time at the end of the day. These allowances come to approximately 11 minutes per hour when averaged out over an 8-hour workday, leaving 49 minutes per hour for operating the machine.

The theoretical output of the machine in 49 minutes is then calculated (the quantity produced if the worker never misses a stroke). Suppose that it comes to 1,000 in 49 minutes. Ninety per cent of that amount (900 in our example) is considered a good performance on the part of the machine operator. For 900 pieces the company is willing to pay a 30 per cent bonus. A man turning out 900 an hour is said to turn out 130 per cent of standard. If 900 is 130 per cent of standard, then standard is $100/130 \times 900$, or 692 pieces.

The job base rate is, we'll say, $2.00, but in this company 62 cents of it is an "override" (see page 519) and is not in the piece rate structure. So the piece rate part of the base rate is $1.38. Divide $1.38 by 692 and you get a piece rate of 19.8 cents per 100.

Suppose the man turns out 1,050 pieces an hour (remember this machine's capacity is 1,000 in 49 minutes, or 1,224 in 60 minutes, so he can easily turn out 1,050 pieces). Figure his earnings this way: 1,050 pieces at 19.8 cents a hundred = $2.08 piecework earnings. Now add the 62 cents override and get his earnings of $2.70.

Every machine job in the threading department pays the same base rate, and every man earns a 30 per cent bonus if he gets out 90 per cent of what the machine will do in 49 minutes. This is quite unfair to some men, however, because some machines don't have many spindles and the men running them are idle half the time. They earn their bonuses with much less effort than the other men. Long-service men use their seniority to get the soft jobs.

Company B sets time standards by the usual time study methods but increases the time allowed for operations by 30 per cent, to "sweeten up" the time for bonus purposes. A job which should take 2.00 minutes, for example, is allowed 2.60 minutes. Then when a man does the job in 2.00 minutes, he will earn a 30 per cent bonus. The 2.60 minutes is not, however, the whole cycle time allowed for the job, since it incorporates no time for fatigue, personal needs, or miscellaneous necessary parts of the job. If there are miscellaneous parts to the job, they are time studied and included in the standard. Personal time and fatigue, together, are allowed 15 per cent.

Continuing the example, if the combined allowance for personal time, fatigue, and miscellaneous parts of the job comes to 25 per cent, the 2.60 minutes is increased by that amount to get a total allowed job cycle time of 3.25 minutes per unit of production. Standard output would be 18.4 units an hour (60 minutes ÷ 3.25 minutes).

Here is how a man's pay is figured. Suppose that we assume that he turns out 25 units per hour. Twenty-five units per hour is 6.6 units, or 27.9 per cent above the standard output of 18.4 units per hour. The base rate for the job is $2.00 per hour, of which 60 per cent is considered "bonus factor" and 40 per cent the "nonbonus factor." The bonus factor is, accordingly, $1.20 per hour on this job, and the nonbonus factor is 80 cents. The employee gets a bonus of 27.9 per cent of $1.20 or 33.5 cents. His total pay is $2.00, the job base rate, plus 33.5 cents, his bonus, plus 54.4 cents override, bringing the total for the hour to $2.879. The override in this case is similar to Company A's override.

You can find more muddled up plans than these, but these show something of what goes on. Companies don't always get into such situations because they want to. Many of them come out of union demands to remedy an "inequity" on one job or in one department. Unions often claim that rates are not right on specific jobs and want them changed. Sometimes they carry their case to an arbitrator who may order the rate to be raised. Since most arbitrators are lawyers and unqualified to judge the fairness of a standard, they sometimes give wrong rulings. Whenever an arbitrator does rule wrongly, he compels a company to adopt or continue illogical practices.

Naturally most companies would like to get rid of such cumbersome practices. There is one good way to do it, and that is at the bargaining table. When negotiating a new labor contract, the company can usually trade off one of its concessions against one or more corrections of make-shift wage arrangements.

PRODUCTION CHECKING

Piecework brings out the dishonesty in men. Unless you check the number of pieces the men say that they turn out, many of them will exaggerate. You can have special count checkers or you can have inspectors check the count. They have to look over the products anyway.

False reporting is dishonest, but most of the men don't think of it that way. The company is fair game, and they justify it to themselves by saying that their wage ought to be higher anyway. Many men who are honest in most ways feel no qualms about trying to boost their pay by false reporting. And those who would not themselves turn in false reports would never think of telling on those who do.

The penalty for false reporting is usually, first, a reprimand, then a disciplinary layoff, and then discharge. The company would rather it would not happen, though, than to have it happen and to have to catch the man and punish him.

GUARANTEES

Incentive workers usually are protected by two kinds of guarantees, both of which are written into the labor agreement. The first guarantee obligates the company to set production standards so that "average" incentive workers working at "normal incentive pace" will earn a 15 per cent bonus (or some such figure). The second guarantee provides that incentive workers when *not* on incentive work will, in many situations, be paid an amount almost equal (often 85 to 90 per cent) to their average hourly earnings while on incentives.

Both types of guarantees cause trouble. With the first type of guarantee, newly set piece rates are frequently challenged. The man says that they are wrong and that he would have to work too hard to earn a bonus. Since there is no test which proves beyond question that a production standard is fair, the practical test is to see if the man can earn a 15 per cent bonus.

So the man tries out the rate and, sure enough, he earns no bonus. That, says the man, proves it, the standard calls for too much. But, actually, what would you do if you were in his place? How hard would you try to earn a 15 per cent bonus, thereby proving that you were wrong and closing out any chance you had for getting the rate loosened? Small wonder that trying out the rate proves so little and changes no one's mind about its fairness.

Assuming that the man sticks to his claim that the rate is too tight, he will file a grievance. The grievance claims that the company has not lived up to its contract requiring it to set rates on which the men can make a 15 per cent bonus. The question may finally go to an arbitrator who usually accepts the record at its face value (the record shows that the man "couldn't" make 15 per cent) and so orders the rate increased. When this happens the effect of the guarantee is to loosen up the rates.

The second type of guarantee also tends to undermine incentives. It concerns the times when a pieceworker is temporarily doing daywork. He, of course, wants to be paid his average piecework earnings when on daywork. If it is regular daywork, and if there is no piecework to do, then there seems to be no reason to pay him his regular piecework earnings.

But if you take him off piecework to do something special, should he lose? You say, no; it is reasonable to pay him his average earnings. That situation doesn't bother you too much. The difficulty comes when this happens: The man has trouble on the job; he has trouble with materials not being right, with his machine or with the tools; and he turns out less work—and suppose it is not his fault at all. Should he lose? Again maybe you say, no; you will guarantee him his regular earnings in such a case.

Now you are in trouble because neither the man nor you know how much these things delayed him. He says that they are responsible for all of his lost production for the day, and that may be true. But once you start paying him his average earnings no matter how much he turns out, he takes it easy from then on, claiming that he always has trouble and always needs to have his pay boosted up to his old earnings' figure. We talked more about this back on page 458 under administering daywork. Here we are concerned with the fact that guaranteeing average earnings always keeps edging us toward paying for more and more work at piecework rates when it is done at daywork pace.

COMPLEXITIES INTRODUCED BY INCONSISTENT STANDARDS

Inconsistent standards do not reflect comparable worker effort. With consistent standards, men on different jobs who produce just the standard quantity of work are working equally hard. And if men on different jobs put forth the same extra effort and produce more than standard output, they earn the same percentage extra as bonus. With inconsistent standards, men on some jobs can make bonuses more easily than men on other jobs because the standards don't call for the same amount of work. When the standards are set by time study, they are ordinarily reasonably consistent.

Inconsistent standards come from several sources. Even standards set by time study are not 100 per cent consistent, because time study men have to use judgment. The passage of time also brings about inconsistent standards because jobs change a little here and there. Often the standard is not also changed, so it no longer pays for the job as it is now done. Also, newly set rates are often challenged by the union, and some get changed. Generally, the rate set first by the time study man is consistent with other rates, so changing them makes inconsistent standards. Arbitrators (if the dispute goes that far) are of no help either. As we said earlier they are usually lawyers, totally unqualified to decide on rates, but they decide nonetheless. Probably they are wrong as often as they are right in their rulings, so they make some inconsistent rates.

Inconsistent standards seriously undermine the effectiveness of incentives. Since men can make big bonuses easily on jobs with loose standards, everyone wants such jobs. Men with lots of seniority end up getting them. At the same time men on other jobs have to work hard to make bonuses. It isn't fair. The incentive system ends up being a way of giving easy high paying jobs to old men. That could be what you want, but it isn't a production incentive plan. It is too bad not to be able to use your skilled men on the jobs that take the most skill.

Besides, men who could easily make high earnings on jobs with loose rates are careful not to make very much more than men on other jobs. Instead of pitching in and turning out all they can, they hold their production down and just loaf part of the time. It is too bad to lose the machine's production because that keeps your costs up.

Still another bad thing about inconsistent standards is that no factory worker ever admits that any rates are too loose. Instead, all the others are too tight. So everyone except the few men on loose rate jobs is dissatisfied. Complaints multiply. When everyone can see that some rates are looser than others, no one thinks much of the fairness of the incentive system. Men also get the idea that there is no such thing as a proper standard.

TENDENCY TOWARD LOOSE RATES

Once set, a piece rate stands unchanged until the job changes. But jobs are always changing in big ways or little. Little changes go unnoticed *unless* they make the job take longer. Not many changes taking longer are adopted, but sometimes for higher quality or greater safety, such changes are made. If the changes do take longer, they never go unnoticed because the man on the job knows that they take longer and asks for and gets a new rate.

But the small changes that shorten jobs a little here and there often go unnoticed by the time study man. Or no change by itself amounts to enough to justify restudying the job. Or the time study man is just too busy to get to it. Or the record of details of the job is so fuzzy that you can't tell for sure that a job is changed (and the worker says that it isn't) if you discover it 6 months after it happened. Or you knew all the time about the change and let it go for 6 months, and then try to change the standard. By then the worker (and the union too) says that since you let it go that long it is too late to change.

The upshot of all of this is that rates are always loosening up. If the time study men don't constantly try to keep all their rates up to date, the rates will be wrong. You will soon be paying for work that is no longer done. Men who used to make 15 per cent bonus get up to 25 and 30 per cent when they aren't doing any more work than before.

Now it is all right to give men raises year after year. But do it at the bargaining table; give men direct raises. Don't do it by letting the rates get inconsistent and loose. Remember, it is only the old rates that are loose; new ones are set correctly. It is the looseness of old rates that puts decided inconsistencies into your rate structure.

"ACROSS-THE-BOARD" INCREASES

We are getting used to seeing newspaper headlines saying that some union won a so-many-cents-per-hour raise for its members. This has gotten to be an annual occurrence. Reading farther, we find that part of the raise is a direct per hour raise and part will be the added cost of extras beyond wages. The extras we'll talk about in Chapter 28.

Most of a factory union's members are on medium- or low-skilled jobs, so the union is all for an equal raise for every one. (Skilled workers would like an equal *per cent* raise.) "Across-the-board" increases, as equal cents per hour for everyone are called, won't work into piece rates. So if you have piece rates you have to go in for "overrides" or "overlays." You use your old piece rates—the ones you had before giving the men an across-the-board raise—and then add the cents-per-hour increase.

Here is what happens when you try to put across-the-board increases into piece rates. Start with Smith and Jones, both on the same job, a $2.00 an hour base rate job. Smith just "makes out" (just barely earns his base rate) and earns $2.00 an hour. He is 100 per cent efficient. Jones, a better man, turns out 25 per cent more. He is 125 per cent efficient and earns $2.50 an hour. The two men average 112.5 per cent efficient, and their average wage is $2.25.

Your new labor agreement calls for a 25 cents an hour across-the-board increase. Twenty-five cents is 11.1 per cent of $2.25, so why not just boost the job base rate (and the piece rates too) that much? The new base rate will be $2.222. Men who average 112.5 per cent efficient will make $2.50.

Now you are in trouble. Smith, the 100 per cent efficient man, will get $2.22, a 22-cent raise, not the 25-cent raise the labor agreement calls for. Jones, the 125 per cent man, will get $2.78 (a 28-cent raise), so the two still average $2.50. The average comes out according to your agreement. Jones with his 28-cent raise doesn't object, but Smith does.

You can't solve this problem in any wholly satisfactory way. Not even the 100 per cent bonus plan solves it. It is better to negotiate the 25 cents' increase as an 11.1 per cent increase. Then you save all of the trouble *except* that your top producers will get a bigger cents-per-hour raise than your low producers. But isn't that good? The company thinks so, and so does the good half of the union's members.

The Smith-Jones troubles are multiplied many times in any actual case.

Besides, there are other problems when you begin to consider other jobs with other base rates. You have to go for the override if you give across-the-board increases.

Aside from wage equality and wage computing difficulties, across-the-board increases reduce incentives. Before the raise Jones outproduced Smith by 25 per cent and got 25 per cent more pay. After the raise (25 cents per hour across-the-board) Jones still gets 50 cents more than Smith, but his $2.75 is only 22 per cent above Smith's $2.25. Just keep on adding across-the-board increases and after a while he will get only 10 to 15 per cent more money for 25 per cent more output.

GROUP PLANS

Men sometimes work in groups or crews. For pay purposes you can't separate one man's work from that of others. No one man can, by himself, increase the group's output, although of course any man can, by himself, hold up the others. Group incentive plans are often used. Group incentives can be of the piecework type or of the 100 per cent bonus type.

If they are of the piecework type, you add together the men's base rates (they are likely not to be the same because some men's jobs take more skill). The group total might come to, say, $20.00 an hour. Suppose that their job is to assemble stoves. If 10 stoves an hour is expected, then the piece rate is $2.00 per stove.

Besides the piece rate, you need a distribution ratio for each man. If in a day the group put 95 stoves together, it would earn $190. But how much does each man get? It depends on his base rate's share of the $20. If Green is on a $1.80 an hour job, divide $1.80 by $20.00 and find that he gets 9 per cent. For the day Green gets 9 per cent of $190, or $17.10. But Brown, on a more difficult part of the assembly work, is on a $2.50 base rate job. His base rate is 12.5 per cent of the pool base rate, so he gets 12.5 per cent of $190, or $23.75.

The 100 per cent plan is simpler than piece rates for groups. If the group assembles 95 stoves when 80 is standard for a day, that is 119 per cent of standard. Every group member will get a 19 per cent bonus.

Group piece rates are not without their troubles. For example, is 10 per hour a fair standard? You can have arguments about standards just the same as with individual piece rates. Another problem is learners. A learner will hold up the other men so they will not be able to turn out as much work and will make less money. What do you do? Some kind of temporary allowance (extra pay) may have to be made to keep the old hands from losing.

Newcomers may, however, be extras—as when several men do the same kind of work. Then when a newcomer is added to the group, he doesn't hold anyone up. But he doesn't produce much and lowers the average output. Here too a temporary allowance is made. Maybe, at first, the new man's output is just added in with the rest while he is still paid outside the group as a learner. That raises the other men's pay. Then, after a while, the new man is taken off the learner's rate and he gets paid a share of the group total earnings.

Radio factories and automobile companies have occasionally had serious difficulties with groups working together as groups, even when not paid on an incentive plan. When extra output along an assembly line is wanted, it is often possible to put in more workers and to get more output. The Ford company a few years ago had a serious strike over this issue. It put more men along its automobile assembly line and speeded up the line proportionally. The employees called it a speed-up because more cars were wanted. The company pointed out that it was asking for no more cars per worker, but it had to give up the idea and return to the slower conveyor speed, using fewer workers.

Another problem when groups must keep all work stations manned all the time is relief men. It takes about 1 extra man for every 19 regular men just to keep all stations manned all the time. Of course the group pay is set up to provide 20 men's earnings for every 19 work stations so that relief men being in the group do not reduce the others' pay.

Group incentives work very well with small groups. A slowpoke is not tolerated. The others say that he "has his hand in their pockets." Also if one man gets held up, the nearest one to him will help him out because all lose if one gets held up. There is sometimes bickering, though, about the share each one gets out of the pool.

Group plans seem to work almost in reverse in large groups. Here a worker is afraid that if he works hard, all he does is make a bonus for someone else. There is a tendency for everyone to produce at a low level.

INCENTIVES FOR INDIRECT SHOP WORKERS

Most indirect workers in the factory (laborers, material handlers, truckers, crane operators, weighmen, setup men, inspectors, working subforemen, men in the toolrooms, stock rooms and shipping rooms maintenance department men, and factory clerical workers) are paid by the hour. You can't measure or count how much work these men do, so you can't put them on a regular factory bonus plan.

But why try to put them on incentives? For the same reason as for direct workers: so that they will turn out more work and make more money while you get lower costs. Most of them want to be on incentives because they see lower-skilled incentive men making more money (from low base rates plus bonus) than they make (with high base rates and no bonus).

This situation always creates dissatisfaction, and there is no good solution to the trouble. Indirect workers complain, saying that they should not be penalized and denied the opportunity to earn a bonus just because of the type of work they do. Why not just raise their base rates? If you raise the base rates of the indirect jobs, then the base rate structure no longer reflects the variation in the jobs. And if you raise the indirect men's base rates, then the pieceworkers will complain because they have to work hard to keep their pay up, while the nonincentive men get just as much or more money without working so hard.

Some companies give indirect workers who serve pieceworkers the same per cent bonus that the pieceworkers get. This is fair if you don't have too many service men—enough to give good service but few enough so that they have to work just as hard as the pieceworkers they serve.

Some companies just don't try to solve the problem. They let the pieceworkers have their high pay and let indirect men get along on their base rates. Still other companies give indirect workers either a flat 10 per cent bonus as a partial compensation or possibly half the bonus that direct workers earn. A few companies (and their number is growing) use incentives for the indirect jobs. You can do a reasonable job of setting standards for many indirect jobs (see pages 573–74). Some companies also put in special bonus plans for individual groups wherever it is possible. You can, for example, pay maintenance men bonuses for cutting machine down time.

QUALITY BONUSES

Quality bonus plans are used in some companies. Regular piecework plans pay for quantity, but there is a tendency for quality to fall off. So you have to watch quality more carefully. Usually setting quality standards and enforcing them takes care of this.

A few companies go farther, however, and pay quality bonuses in addition to the regular production bonuses. If used, quality bonuses are paid for keeping down rejects. Occasionally, when expensive materials are used, quality bonuses are paid for using materials economically.

Quality bonuses are uncommon, partly because some employers feel that it is illogical to pay a man a bonus for doing well what you hired him to do. There is a more practical reason, too, for not paying quality bonuses. Often scrap is low (less than 1 per cent), and losses don't amount to much. Also rejects aren't always scrap. All you lose is the cost of rework. Cut out all the rejects, and you haven't saved much—so you can't afford to pay much to cut out the rejects. Also, in regular piecework, you pay only for good work. This means that you have a built-in quality bonus in your regular bonus plan.

STUDY QUESTIONS

1. What is the difference between a base rate, a day rate, and a man's earnings?
2. Why does a company want a man on piecework to earn a bonus? Explain fully.

3. "Positive incentives are good. Negative incentives are bad." Do you agree? Give arguments in agreement and in disagreement.

4. *a*) From an employee's point of view, what characteristics should a good incentive plan have?

  b) From the employer's point of view, what characteristics should a good incentive plan have?

5. What determines a man's incentive earnings? Discuss.

6. Describe measured daywork. What are its good and bad points?

7. How can you handle different personal base rates for men of the same jobs if you use piecework?

8. Explain the differences between straight piecework and the 100 per cent bonus plan.

9. Compare the Scanlon and the Rucker plans.

10. How do guarantees complicate wage administration when you are using incentives?

11. Why do companies have some inconsistent standards?

12. "Standards always tend to loosen up." Discuss this statement.

13. Why not get rid of across-the-board wage increases? How can you incorporate them into existing piece rates?

14. Would you work harder or less hard if you were a member of a group being paid on a group incentive plan? Why?

15. Incentive plans for men who work on products are more common than for indirect workers. Why? What problems are there in putting indirect workers on incentives? What solutions are there to the problems?

Chapter 28

WAGE SUPPLEMENTS

"FRINGE" BENEFITS

Not only do factory workers usually get a direct money pay raise every year but they also get more and more company-paid extras or "fringe" benefits. The list is long but falls more or less into four groups. Benefits give: (1) money to men when they get sick or to their estate if they die, (2) money for time not worked, (3) extra wages for unusual work hours, or (4) pay for expenses in connection with workers' jobs.

In the first group—health payments—come hospitalization and surgical insurance, sickness and accident insurance, workmen's compensation, and life insurance.

The second group—payments for time not worked—might well be subdivided into two groups: (a) payments to employees who are still working, and (b) payments to former employees. Payments to present employees for time not worked include payment for rest periods, wash-up time, holidays, vacations, voting time, and jury duty. Payments to former employees include severance pay, unemployment compensation, supplemental unemployment benefits, guaranteed annual wages, social security retirement benefits, and company pensions.

The third group—extra payments for unusual work hours—includes payment for overtime, shift differential pay, Saturday and Sunday extra pay rates, and "call-in" pay.

The fourth group—payment for expenses in connection with workers' jobs—includes the purchase of tools and equipment needed to do the work, and of special work clothes, such as goggles, rubber aprons, gloves, and safety shoes.

There are in the lists above several items that workers years ago paid for themselves. Now, the employer pays for nearly all of them; he is, in fact, required by law to pay for many of them.

Unions have done an about face on fringe benefits since their early days. Many years ago unions wanted direct money raises—no fringes. They said, "Just give us [the men not the union] the money and we'll take care of ourselves." Today they want more money but they are just as insistent on the extras.

From the company's point of view it doesn't matter too much whether it gives its men a direct pay raise or agrees to pay for an extra frill. It is all labor cost to the company.

New Yorker

FIG. 28–1. "With me, Mable, you would always enjoy the comforts of security. I have an ample base salary with a cost-of-living escalator arrangement, group life insurance, and full Blue Cross coverage, and my ultimate future is assured by a substantial retirement annuity and, of course, Social Security."

Some employers get upset about the trend toward more and more extras. They point to their high costs. In 1957, they came to about $900 per employee per year. That amounts to 45 cents per hour worked, or 20 per cent of labor costs. And that is just the employer's share. Actually, fringes cost even more, but the employee pays a part of the costs himself. Employers who don't like this trend ask: Do the men really want all this? Wouldn't they rather do without benefits and get the extra money? Isn't all this just the union's doing?

Probably most workers, given the choice, would take the $900. Yet if they did they would get no vacations, no hospitalization, no pensions, and so on. Maybe they wouldn't give them all up after all.

The old idea, "give us the money and we'll take care of ourselves," doesn't work out very well in practice. We all manage to spend our wages regularly and have nothing left for a rainy day. So one good argument in favor of fringes is that they (the insurance kind of fringes) tide us over misfortunes and provide for our old age better then we would do for ourselves.

There is another strong argument in favor of fringes instead of direct pay raises. And that is that they are bargains. They are bargains two

Cents per payroll hour

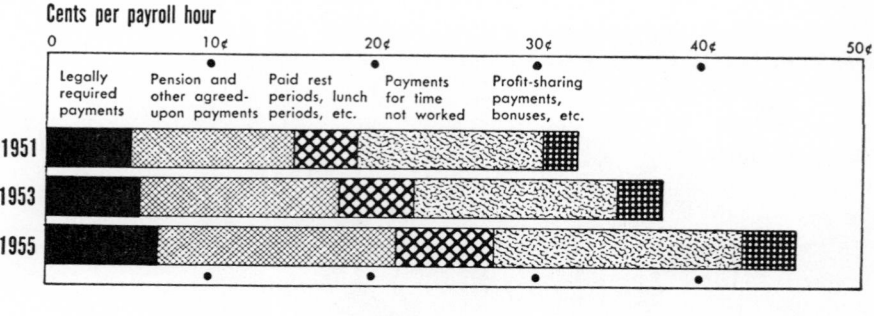

Dollars per year per employee

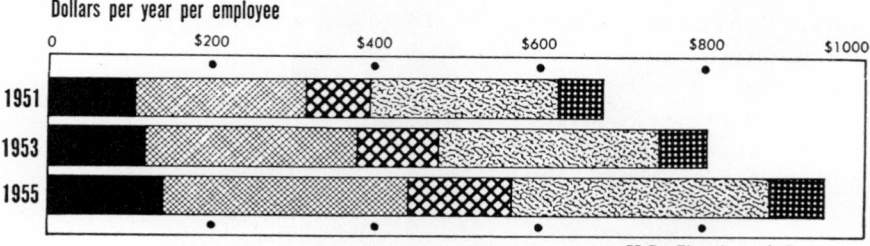

U.S. Chamber of Commerce

FIG. 28–2. Comparison of 1951, 1953, and 1955 fringe payments of 124 companies.

ways. First, if the men took the $900, Uncle Sam would take maybe $200 of it as income taxes. Given as a wage, or in fringe pay for vacations and holidays, it is taxable. But paid for insurance, or for most other fringes, *it isn't taxed, nor is the income taxed* if you get sick or laid off and collect benefits. Pensions are, however, in part taxable if you make enough to pay income taxes when you are old. Still, most benefits are income tax free.

Besides the income tax savings, which gives you more money to buy extras, there is a second gain. Company-bought extras, for all employees as a group, cost less than individually bought extras. So you get more for your money. It is a bargain all the way round: you have more money to spend for extras and you get a better buy.

HOSPITALIZATION AND SURGICAL EXPENSE INSURANCE

Hospitalization and surgical expense insurance pays part or all of such expenses. Blue Cross is the most common kind of hospitalization insurance.

It differs among communities, but, in general, it pays hospital board, room (semiprivate room), and other expenses (medicines, X rays, anesthetics, etc.) for the employee or members of his family who may have to go to the hospital. In case of long hospital stays, Blue Cross usually pays in full for 30 days, then half for up to 90 more days. Mental, tuberculosis, and certain other types of hospitalization cases are not covered by the insurance, or benefits are limited to 30 days.

Regular insurance companies also write hospitalization policies. They usually pay fewer of the expenses than Blue Cross and so cost less; but if you want more liberal benefits the insurance company will write whatever coverage you want, and will charge accordingly.

How much does hospitalization cost? For an employee only, about $50 a year, or 2½ cents per work hour. But to cover the whole family the costs run a little over double that. It used to be that Americans averaged spending in hospitals (and leaving out long illnesses) about one day per person per year. Now we use hospitals more, so the figure is higher.

Group surgical insurance (usually Blue Shield, a companion to Blue Cross) is becoming popular. It pays for operations but has a list of maximum doctor's charges that it will pay. Most doctors accept these amounts as their full fee for low income patients. But if you make very much money, the doctors will charge more and you will have to pay the balance. Most surgical insurance plans (they are less common than hospitalization) pay up to $200 (some go up to $300) for the most serious operations. That protection costs about $30 a year (for family coverage), or 1½ cents per work hour. Some people think that surgical insurance is just a waste of money because doctors up their charges when you have insurance. Maybe they do for some, but not for low income people. With them the doctor takes the insurance payment as full payment.

A few companies supplement regular hospitalization and surgical insurance with "major medical" insurance to take care of the big bills. General Electric and Lockheed Aircraft were the first big companies to put in major medical insurance. GE's cost is said to be under $60 a year. GE has two plans. Here's how one works. Employees pay the first $25, then insurance pays all from $26 to $250, then insurance pays 85 per cent and the man pays 15 per cent of all expenses over $250. The other plan pays 75 per cent of all bills up to $5,000, with the man paying the other 25 per cent.

In nearly all companies today the employer pays the whole cost of hospitalization. Formerly many insurance company plans were "contributory," meaning that the employees paid part or all of the costs. That was bad, though, because contributory plans were voluntary, and low-paid men often didn't join because of the cost. They are the very ones who always need financial help if they have to go to the hospital. Another bad feature about contributory hospitalization insurance is that all the sick people join the plan, and only some of the healthy people. That makes the rates go up pretty high.

SICKNESS AND ACCIDENT INSURANCE

Sickness and accident insurance, also called "health and accident insurance," pays money to a man who is losing wages when he is not working because of sickness or accident. Sickness and accident insurance benefits are in addition to any payments which employees might receive as workmen's compensation. Sickness and accident insurance is nearly always carried with insurance companies, although an employing company could pay the benefits directly itself.

From this insurance a sick man usually gets benefits that come to a little less than half of his regular earnings, although in some plans he would get more. Usually the size of the payment is related to the man's regular earnings, so a high-paid man gets more than a low-paid man. Insurance companies like to hold benefits down to amounts less than two thirds of regular earnings, to prevent malingering. A man sick and at home saves the cost of a noonday meal at work and does not have to pay income taxes on his benefits. Small wonder he gets well slowly when he nets as much for staying at home not working as he does when he goes to work.

Benefits paid to *injured* workers generally start the first day of the absence, but in most plans *sickness* benefits begin only after one week of absence. This saves the cost of handling all the records for short illnesses, cuts down malingering, and of course cuts the cost of the insurance. In case of long illnesses the benefits in the most common plans continue for 26 weeks (some stop at 13 weeks) before they run out. Most plans cost about 1 per cent of the payroll.

Several states have passed sickness and accident insurance laws. They are similar to insurance company plans except that they are compulsory. Both employers and employees pay into the fund, employee contributions being set at figures (depending on the state) of from $\frac{1}{2}$ to 1 per cent of his pay. Employers are taxed enough to cover the rest of the cost.

PAID SICK LEAVE

Federal government employees get paid for a set number of sick days a year. Unions have been asking for the same from industry. A few companies have agreed to 5 days' sick leave per year, but as yet paid sick leave is uncommon. Every day of sick leave you pay for boosts labor cost 0.4 per cent, so 5 days would cost 2 per cent of the payroll.

WORKMEN'S COMPENSATION

A hundred years ago it was almost impossible for a man injured at work to collect anything from his employer. If he sued the employer for damages, the courts held that he had accepted the hazards of the job when he took it. Later on the courts changed and would allow a worker to collect if he could prove that the employer was negligent.

Please make this report in **DUPLICATE** so that we can file copy with the Industrial Commission in your behalf.

FIRST REPORT OF INJURY

Industrial Commission of Minnesota
State Office Building, St. Paul

Case No._____   Insurance Carrier No._____

☞ ALL information asked for in this blank form MUST be furnished.   Read instructions on reverse side before filling this blank.

Employer	1. Employer_____Employer is { Individual_____ / Partnership_____ / Corporation_____ 2. Office address_____City or town_____ 3. Nature of business_____ 4. Business normally operated: Hours per day_____; days per week_____ 5. Name of insurance carrier (not agency) THE TRAVELERS INSURANCE COMPANY Policy No._____ 6. Location of place where accident occurred_____ 7. Date of accident _____ 19____, at_____o'clock_____M.
Injured Employe	8. Name of injured employe_____ 9. Address_____City or town_____County_____ 10. Occupation_____Sex_____Age_____Married or single_____ 11. Describe previous physical defects (eye, ear, hernia or other)_____ 12. Is injured an officer, a partner, or a manager?_____If so, state his position_____ 13. Are his wages carried on your regular payroll upon which your policy premium is based?_____Under which classification?_____If on payroll of another employer, give name_____ 14. Number hours employe worked: Per day_____; per week_____; days worked per week_____ 15. Wage rate: Per hour_____; per day, $_____; per week, $_____; per month, $_____ 16. Average earnings (including overtime): Per day, $_____; per week, $_____; per month, $_____ 17. If piece or commission worker, state: Total number days worked in past 60 days_____ Total earnings in this time, $_____; average per day, $_____; average per week, $_____ 18. Were wages paid weekly, semi-monthly, or monthly?_____ 19. If furnished, state weekly value of: Board, $_____; Lodging, $_____; Misc. $_____
Cause of Accident	20. Describe fully how accident occurred_____ 21. State work engaged in when injured_____ 22. Did injury occur in the course of his regular employment?_____ 23. Machine, tool, or appliance causing injury_____ 24. Suggest safety device for prevention of similar accidents_____
Nature and Extent of Injury	25. Nature of injury (describe fully)_____ 26. Did injury cause loss of time?_____Last day worked_____19____ 27. Has injured returned to work?_____On what date?_____19____ 28. If not returned, give estimate of probable disability_____ 29. Will any permanent disability probably result?_____ 30. Did injury result in death?_____Date of death_____19____ 31. Principal dependent or friend: Name_____ 32. Address_____City or town_____County_____
Medical and Hospital	33. Did employer provide or authorize medical attention?_____ 34. Physician_____Address_____ 35. Hospital_____Address_____
Important	DO NOT FAIL TO ANSWER FOLLOWING QUESTIONS 36. If non-fatal, state whether disability will continue beyond one week_____ 37. Does employer admit liability in accordance with the Minnesota Workmen's Compensation Law?_____

Dated_____19____   _____
                                                   (Firm or corporation name)

(Observe Instructions on Reverse Side.)   Signed by_____
                                                        (Name)   (Official title)

FIG. 28–3.   Injury report required to be made by employers in Minnesota to the Industrial Commission of Minnesota.

Employers were not held responsible if the injured worker's negligence or that of a fellow worker caused the accident.

Workmen's compensation laws now provide that employers carry insurance (in half of our states the law *requires* employers to take out insurance) which pays money to employees injured at work no matter how they get hurt, even if a man gets hurt while violating the company's safety rules. Also many states today make employers carry insurance to pay for occupational *diseases* as well as injuries.

Some state laws deprive men of the right of suing in civil courts. But in many states an injured man can elect to sue instead of taking the regular workmen's compensation award.

State laws keep changing every year, and no two states' laws are exactly alike. For example, most of them cover occupational diseases, but some do not. They also differ in what constitutes a compensable injury, but all agree that cuts, bruises, minor burns, etc., causing the employee to lose only 1 or 2 days' work, are not compensable. A broken finger is generally compensable only if it caused the worker to lose considerable time from work. The laws are in agreement though in covering employees of all but the very smallest companies (most laws cover all employees except those working in companies with less then three employees).

How much an injured man gets paid depends upon the nature of the injury and where he works. Every state has its own law and its own list of injuries and payments.

Workmen's compensation insurance in all states pays for medical expenses and also gives weekly benefits which partially replace wages. Mostly, however, they pay nothing for injuries lasting less than a week. This keeps down both the claims and the bookkeeping costs. Many states require that all medical expenses be paid. Most others set limits beyond which the employer is not responsible. Limits are usually set at figures ranging from $1,000 to $2,500.

The weekly benefits to be paid an injured worker are generally set at one half to two thirds of the employee's pay up to maximums ranging from $30 to $45 per week. Nearly all states also put a limit on how long the payments continue or how much they can amount to. For serious accidents payments continue a long time though, always at least 5 years, and in some states 10 years. Half of the states set monetary limits (ranging from $8,000 to $12,500). But if you are permanently disabled, some state laws provide you payments for life. Lump-sum death benefits are provided to heirs if a man is killed.

An accident that keeps a man from his job beyond the day it occurs is called a "temporary total disability." More serious accidents are called either "permanent partial disabilities," "permanent total disabilities," or those causing death. You get the same amount per week no matter what kind of an injury you have, but how long it keeps up depends on how seriously you were hurt.

States differ as to how the insurance is carried. A few have state plans and do not allow employers to insure with outside companies or to self-insure. A few have state plans but allow companies to choose whether to insure with the state, to self-insure, or to carry insurance with a private company. Most states, however, do not have state plans, and they allow an employer to carry insurance with an insurance company or just to pay claims themselves as long as they pay as much as the law requires.

Workmen's compensation costs are paid for by the companies. Usually they amount to considerably less than 1 per cent of the payroll, but they can go up to 2 or 3 per cent, or in rare cases higher, depending on a company's safety record.

GROUP LIFE INSURANCE

Group life insurance equal to nearly a year's pay is provided at company expense in many companies today. It costs about $12 per year (or six tenths of a cent per work hour) *for each $1,000 of insurance*. Insurance equal to a year's pay ($4,000) will come to about $50, or 2.5 cents an hour. Some companies give retired employees a small paid-up life insurance policy. That would raise the cost some more.

Most people don't realize it, but the social security law gives a small death benefit ($255 maximum) to heirs if a man dies. Much more important, though, is a widow's monthly pension, if the dead man had children under 18 years old. A widow's pension keeps on until the children grow up, then stops until the widow is old enough to get her old-age pension.

VACATIONS

Vacations are discussed in Chapter 20 in connection with the serious absenteeism problem they create. In most factories the average length of vacation is about $1\frac{1}{2}$ weeks. They cost approximately 3 per cent of the payroll, or 6 cents per man-hour.

PAID HOLIDAYS

Salaried office people have always been paid for holidays. Factory workers used to be paid only for the time they worked, so got nothing for holidays. Now all hourly paid factory workers get paid for holidays. Typically they include New Year's Day, Memorial Day, the Fourth of July, Labor Day, Thanksgiving Day, and Christmas. Sometimes election day and the man's birthday are added, making a total of eight.

Some labor contracts require the company to pay only for holidays which fall on regular workdays, since otherwise no loss to the worker is incurred. Holidays falling on Sunday but celebrated on Monday, however, usually must be paid for. Paying for holidays costs about $2\frac{1}{2}$–3 per cent of the payroll.

"WASH-UP" TIME

"Wash-up" time pay is common in industry only where the jobs are particularly dirty. The man is allowed to quit his job say ten minutes early to clean up. More time is allowed if he has to take a shower. Ten-minute wash-up allowances increase labor costs 2 per cent. But maybe they don't cost anything at all because men usually will wash up on company time anyway.

REST PERIODS

Rest periods are uncommon in factories (although they are the rule in the aircraft industry and are required by law for women in California) but, when used, are customarily of 10 minutes' duration, one in both morning and afternoon. This time amounts to nearly 5 per cent of the workday, so they seem to cost money. But, actually, they may not cost very much. Men take a little time out anyway. Besides, with rest periods, they might work enough harder when they work to make up for the time out. Most companies, though, seem to feel that rest periods are a real loss, that the men take the rest period and still take out the same amount of time on their own and don't work any harder because of the rest period.

In offices, unofficial "coffee breaks" became so common that they are now recognized and official. Probably regular rest periods in offices cost almost nothing because the unofficial ones took so long.

SEVERANCE PAY

Severance pay is sometimes given to men leaving the company. Most companies always did and still do give an extra week's or two weeks' pay to office employees who quit. It is uncommon, however, for hourly paid men, except that men leaving shortly before summertime are given part or all of their vacation pay. (Wisconsin law requires 2 weeks' notice to a discharged man or 2 weeks' pay in lieu of notice.)

Severance pay demands keep coming up at the bargaining table but are rarely granted. What the unions ask for is no mere 1 or 2 weeks' pay. They ask for, and in a few cases have won, agreements to pay big money to men leaving the company. American Newspaper Guild contracts call for 2 weeks of pay *for every year of service* of a laid-off (or fired) employee. The railroads, too, have stiff severance pay agreements. If railroads consolidate and cut out jobs, they may have to pay the men cut off as much as 60 per cent of their wages for 5 years after separation.

Most union demands don't ask for nearly that much (they always ask for a little until you agree to the idea, then year by year they up the demand), but the possibilities are so great that it is small wonder that companies resist. The U.S. Steel Company gives severance pay of up to 8 weeks' pay if 10-year-service men are laid off when a whole plant closes down.

When severance pay plans exist, they usually pay more to long-service men leaving than to men with short service. Men with less than a year's service get nothing. Most plans give nothing to men quitting or getting fired, but some plans pay regardless of why the man leaves. Laid-off men who will soon be called back to work don't get severance pay either.

Severance pay costs depend on the benefit formula, the length of service of laid-off employees, what kinds of terminations are covered, and how many people leave the company. The plans found in the plants that have them don't pay so much as to be a burden on the company. Nearly all such plants could reduce their work force by 25 per cent without spending over one quarter of 1 per cent of its payroll for severance pay. In fact, most of them could lay off half of their men, and severance pay still would cost only a little more than 1 per cent of the payroll. On the other hand, because of greater benefits for long-service employees, a complete shutdown would cost from 5 to 15 per cent of a year's payroll, a serious matter if a company were near bankruptcy.

Supplemental Unemployment Benefits (SUB), described on page 537, cut out any need for big severance payments. As SUB grows in popularity, as it seems sure to do, severance pay plans will be less important.

UNEMPLOYMENT INSURANCE

How does a man who is laid off fare? Not too badly if he can find another job, but if he can't, then what? Then he will be paid unemployment benefits. The money he gets comes out of an unemployment insurance fund, a fund built up by taxing employers (in a few states, employees pay part of the costs).

Unemployment insurance is part of the federal social security program, but it is administered by the states individually under the provisions of their own laws. There are, consequently, many variations in details of administration among the states. In general, all employers of three or more persons are covered and must pay unemployment taxes based on their payroll.

Not everyone out of a job gets benefits. First you have to have had a job in an industry (nearly everyone except government employees is covered) covered by the laws. You have to have worked long enough to be eligible. Usually that means 20 weeks out of the 52 weeks before you get laid off (but it doesn't have to be all with one employer).

After you are out of a job there are some more conditions. You have to be willing, ready, and able to work. This raises some questions. If you quit your former job, are you eligible? Your former employer wants you back, but you won't go. Are you really willing? Most states say no, so you get no unemployment compensation. Or, you got fired —are you really able? Some states say no. Or what if you are out on strike? Another no.

There is a trend, though, toward liberalizing the laws, particularly for quits or discharges. Also the men administering the law usually try to see it the man's way. As, for example, when you quit a job 30 miles from your home saying that it is too far, do you get unemployment compensation? Probably yes. Unemployment pay is so much less than regular pay (mostly it comes to between one third and one half of regular pay) that men who quit jobs have better reasons than just to collect jobless pay.

If you meet all the conditions and are still without a job, you get weekly unemployment benefit checks starting the second week (no check for the first week) and continuing for, usually, up to 26 weeks. Then you have used up your benefits and get no more until you again work 20 weeks.

During the 26 weeks, you must report regularly to the United States Unemployment Service to see whether they have found a job for you. If they get a job for you, you must take it or be cut off benefits. But a machinist doesn't have to take a job mixing concrete, nor does he have to take a job 30 miles away. You can turn down jobs not in your line or too far away. In most states men on strike receive no benefits, but you do get benefits if your plant closes down because of strikes elsewhere.

Jobless pay is sometimes abused. Men sometimes get a job and don't report it but keep on drawing unemployment pay too. That is, of course, fraud, and the man can be punished if he is caught. Housewives too, sometimes take jobs, get eligible for benefits and then quit, saying that the job is too far from home, or too heavy and too hard on them. Then they draw benefits when they really don't want a job at all.

Men too have been known to look for a job in Florida in the winter while drawing benefits. The law doesn't say that you have to stay at home and look for a job, but it sounds a little suspicious for, say, an unemployed Detroit automobile assembler to look for a job in his line of work in St. Petersburg, Florida.

Unemployment pay is such a real help to a man who loses his job that it is worth something to society to have him get it. But what does it cost? We have never had a real depression since the beginning of unemployment pay in the late 1930's, so we really don't know. In 1956 the reserve funds in the various states came to over $9 billion. Employer tax rates were averaging just barely over 1 per cent of the payroll.

Not all employers get off with so little. Records are kept by the states, and employers who lay off people (thereby costing unemployment pay) are charged higher rates than those that give steady employment. Steady employers get by with paying as little as ½ per cent of their payroll. Some states have a minimum clear down at 0.1 per cent.

SOCIAL SECURITY PENSIONS

Today's factory workers, if they have worked in a covered industry for 10 years, will get social security pensions when they retire at age sixty-five or over (sixty-two for women). How much they get depends on their wages during their work years. Top is $108.50 a month. To get that much a man would have had to average $4,200 a year when he was working.

If he made less than $4,200, his pension is figured this way. He gets a monthly pension equal to $60.50 for the first $110 a month of his average earnings plus one fifth of all earnings over $110 up to a total of $350. Earnings above $350 a month don't count. A man whose earnings had averaged $200 per month gets $78.50, while another man who averaged $350 would get a pension of $108.50. Should his wife be over sixty-two, his pension is increased by one half. A widow of a pensioner gets three fourths as much as her husband's pension would have been.

Social security is a rather costly program, and its top costs are still in the future. In 1957, employer and employee were each taxed for it at the rate of 2¼ per cent of the first $4,200 of every man's earnings in a year.

PRIVATE PENSIONS

Company pensions are not new in American industry, but they were uncommon until 1949. Then all of a sudden everyone put them in. The rush to pensions came out of a demand by the United Steel Workers Union that year. Refused at first by the steel companies, pensions were granted after President Truman's "Fact Finding Panel" recommended them.

The union's victory soon proved hollow. All the first pensions that came out of the 1949 dealings called for a certain amount of pension— and always it was more than social security pensions. *But companies had to pay only the extra.* Then when social security went up, the men's pensions stayed put while the companies just paid less. Most of today's plans have changed that and have made the company pensions an extra. The union's victory is no longer hollow.

Pensions have many angles that affect their costs. How old will people be when they retire? How long will they live afterwards? How much pension are they to get? How many employees will quit before they get that old and so get no pensions? How many will die before retirement? Will a man who quits own the money you have been setting aside for him? Should you pay pensions yourself? Or hire a bank? Or an insurance company? These and many more questions must be answered.

It takes actuaries to figure out what pensions will cost. They guess at how many of your men will quit before retiring, and they know about how many will die each year and about how long retired men will get pensions. They figure that a man retiring at 65 will live 13 years. It costs about $16,000 to buy an annuity of $100 a month for 13 years, so the actuary can tell you about how much money you have to pay in year by year during a man's work life in order to buy his pension.

Today's factory worker pensions mostly follow the pattern of the steel or auto industries. The steel formula works like this: a man gets 1 per cent of his last 10 years' average wage for every year of service. A man with 40 years' service gets a pension of 40 per cent of his earnings. But that includes a man's social security pension; the company pension only makes up the difference. Auto-type pensions are different. At Ford, pensioners get $2.25 a month per year of service. A 40-year service man gets $90 a month pension. But this time, *social security is extra.*

Notice that the steel formula gives bigger pensions to high-pay men than to low-pay men. In the case of autos everybody gets the same amount. Also notice that steel has a built-in inflation adjustment. If wages go up, so do pensions. In autos new higher pension rates would have to be negotiated.

Pensions usually cost between 5 and 10 cents per work hour, but some go above and others below those figures.

EXTRA PAY FOR UNUSUAL WORK HOURS

Today, you'd better stick to a normal 5-day, 40-hour work week because you have to pay extra if workers work longer hours. First off, every hour over 8 in a day or 40 in a week costs an hour and a half's pay. Sundays usually cost 2 hours' pay per hour of work. So do holidays, although many companies have to pay triple pay for holiday work.

"No-work" can also cost money. Labor contracts differ on this, but here are some common provisions. If you run out of work during the day and send men home, add 2 hours' pay for lack of notice. If they come to work in the morning and are sent home, give them 4 hours' pay ("call-in" pay) for lack of notice. Or if a plant suddenly closes down for several days, give the men 3 days' pay for lack of notice. *You don't have to pay though if the reason for no work is beyond company control.*

TOOLS AND WORK CLOTHES

Special work clothes and nearly all tools are furnished by the company. Only machinists and tool and diemakers usually own their own tools, and some companies furnish even their tools too. (In fact, most companies are convinced that they even furnish the tools their men have in their workshops at home.)

Years ago workers had to furnish all their own hand tools and all work clothing such as goggles, gloves, aprons, and coveralls. Except for coveralls and safety shoes the company furnishes everything today. Some companies furnish them too, and some even pay for laundering work clothes.

GUARANTEED ANNUAL WAGES

"We eat by the year, we need to get paid by the year." "We can't turn our expenses on and off, so we need a guaranteed regular wage." Unions, particularly in heavy industries, made this their big demand in the mid-1950's. Employers answered, "We pay wages out of income, if you can't guarantee our sales, we can't guarantee your wage." Employers made studies of GAW's costs and usually decided that it would bankrupt them.

But now some kind of guaranteed wage is common, and companies are not going bankrupt. How could they have been so wrong? They were wrong because they figured on extremes. They figured to guarantee too much to too many for too long. Of course the costs are high if you guarantee to pay full pay to everyone (or even one third or one half of your men) for a whole year of no work. And of course it would bankrupt you to do it starting today—before you get a reserve fund built up. Costs can be reasonable if you guarantee only a little to not many men for not long, and if you guarantee only to use up a fund already accumulated. That is how present plans work.

But GAW is not really working very well; it is largely a fizzle. By no means all unions want it, and many rank and file members oppose it. At the same time employers are not so opposed as they used to be.

GAW is not working well because it has turned out to be just another unemployment pay plan (paying, according to 1957 formulas, up to 26 weeks, a maximum of $25 a week, or—added to regular unemployment pay—up to 60 to 65 per cent of a man's wage). GAW has changed to SUB (supplemental unemployment benefits). Only laid-off men get benefits from it, and only relatively new men get laid off. No one objects particularly to this until he looks to see who pays the bill. All of the workers—old workers as well as new—are footing the bill.

But GAW was to be paid by the employer not by the employees—and so it is. What has happened is that employers pay money, say equivalent to 5 cents per man-hour, into a fund from which benefits are paid (once the fund is built up, the company pays only enough to keep it up, but not more than 5 cents an hour). But, without GAW (or SUB), all the men—old and new alike—would probably have gotten a raise of 5 cents an hour more than they did get. It amounts to everyone paying into a fund which will benefit only a few new men. Long-service men understandably are not in favor of SUB. But isn't the employer stuck if the fund runs out? No, if the fund runs out there are no more benefits.

There are also legal troubles. Ohio, Indiana, Oregon, and Virginia regard SUB payments as wage payments and won't make regular unemployment payments while SUB payments last.

SUB is, however, here and is probably here to stay. How to make it more workable? One plan in effect in several companies, is to have a fund for every man, not just a general fund for all. This cuts out long-service men's objections. But then you'd pretty nearly have to say that each man's fund belongs to him. This is just what the Libby-Owens-Ford (plate glass makers) plan does. In fact, after the man's fund gets up to $600, the company keeps on paying but the man takes out the extra in cash every vacation time. This amounts to a forced savings plan. Whatever the future of GAW, it has changed a great deal since the unions first asked for it right after World War II.

PROFIT SHARING

Profit sharing is over 100 years old and has proved very effective or of little value, depending upon whom you listen to. It is not common, and in the long run most plans started are discontinued, yet there are several that are over 20 years or more old (Lincoln Electric Company is the most outstanding). Quite a few of today's profit-sharing companies annually give all employees 25 per cent or more of a year's wage as a year-end bonus. The exact figure depends on how much the company earned. Part of the profits, commonly 10 per cent, goes into a fund and is paid out as a bonus.

Some companies don't pay out the bonus right away but put part or all of it into a pension fund. This would be a "deferred" plan. Several reasons for this. Usually employees who quit don't get all (maybe none) of their share in the fund, so it helps hold them. Also what is put into the fund for them isn't taxed. Of course their pension someday will be taxed, but at a low rate because their income will be low.

The Bureau of Internal Revenue passes judgment on all deferred plans because of the tax angle. It is afraid that companies will set up plans that will let top officials evade income taxes. Here are its rules: (1) the plan must *not* be limited to high paid officials nor give them disproportionate amounts, (2) neither the money paid into a fund nor the interest it earns can ever go back to the company, (3) there must be a set formula for figuring out what share of profits to pay into the fund, and (4) there must be a set formula for figuring out how much each man gets.

Aside from the tax angles, what are the good and bad points of profit sharing? First, it is supposed to have incentive value. Employees will work harder to earn their bonus. Although this is true, there are two weaknesses: bonuses are not tied to individual effort, and they are so long in coming as to be of little incentive value.

Second, bonuses can go up, *and down too.* They can be a way of raising your men's standard of living—or of *cutting it too.* Also, unions say that profit-sharing companies pay low regular pay rates. Then if your company has poor management, the workers in the factory are underwriting its costs.

STOCK PURCHASE PLANS

Some companies sell stock to employees, either for cash or on the installment plan, usually at a price a little below the market price. The idea is to help the men save and to make them a little more "owner conscious." Because stock prices can go up and down a good bit, manufacturing companies shy away from stock purchase plans for men at the bottom. You don't want the men losing their savings. Also there is too much good will to be lost if the price goes down.

Stock purchase *option* plans are popular today for high officials. Instead of giving them more and more money in salary or bonus, you give them an option to buy shares at a little below today's price—but the option is good for several years. Details of how this works are given on page 456.

STUDY QUESTIONS

1. Wouldn't it be better all the way around if all wage supplements were cut out and their cost paid to the workers as a wage increase? Give arguments for and against. Support the position you picked.
2. On sickness and accident insurance, benefits are never intended to be higher than about two thirds of a man's wage. Why? Discuss.
3. Does a man who gets hurt while disobeying company safety rules get workmen's compensation benefits? What is the logic behind this practice?
4. How are workmen's compensation benefits figured? Discuss.
5. How can laying off a worker affect a company's cost of doing business? Discuss fully.
6. How does the old-age pension (the kind the employer deducts part of your pay to help pay for) part of the social security program work? Discuss.
7. Is there any need for factories to have private pension plans? Are there many? Describe the most common kinds.
8. Why are companies now less opposed than they used to be to guaranteed annual wages? How do present-day GAW plans work?
9. Why is the government interested in profit-sharing plans? Explain fully.

Chapter 29

MOTION STUDY

How to make products at less cost? How to make them with less human effort? How to make them from less costly materials? *All* companies are *always* trying to solve these problems. They are always trying to figure out how to cut costs—and if they do cut costs today, they try to find more savings tomorrow.

You might think that, after a while, there would be few opportunities left to cut costs. It would get harder, as time goes on, if your products didn't change. But products do change. New ones constantly come along; old ones are redesigned; new models come out. To some extent you start improving jobs on new things from where you left off on old ones, but lots of new job improvement work has to be done on every new item.

Suppose, for example, you make regular lawn mowers. Then along come power lawn mowers; that means making motors, gears, mounts, and so on, and it means men doing new jobs—jobs you never had before. Next come powered rotary blade mowers. Again you have to make parts you never made before, and most of the jobs in making them are new. Then you find that some customers want power mowers they can ride around on, so you make that kind too. And again you get into new parts and new jobs. So, again you have to figure out how best to do the jobs. The job of improving jobs never ends. It doesn't ever get down to where it is impossible to make any more improvements.

Everything connected with cutting production costs can be lumped together as "methods study." Most of the work is engineering work of one kind or another, and most of it comes *before* motion study. Motion study is but one important part of methods study. It has to do with *how men do their work*—their methods and their movements—and with figuring out how to do the work with as little human effort as possible.

ATTITUDES TOWARD MOTION STUDY

Curiously, many people dislike the thought of motion study. "Efficiency" (the result of motion study) is a bad word. They seem to think that when you figure out how a man can do a job with less effort (maybe you bought him a machine), you somehow take advantage of him when he—using the new short method—turns out more products.

And the man on the job thinks so too. Buy a man a power lawn mower and he will mow maybe twice as much grass as he did before without working as hard, but he still talks about it as if *he* were doing twice as much work (spending twice as much effort) as he did before. The same thing happens in factories. Men are often against motion study because they are sure that they must have worked harder when more output results.

Motion study *reduces*, not increases, human effort. It means work smarter—not harder. There is certainly no good reason to do things the long way around. The very same man who thinks that motion study on the job makes him work harder will buy a power saw for his basement workshop at home. There, he can see that it saves his energy and lets him get more work done—*without his working any harder.*

JOB IMPROVEMENT LIMITATIONS

Jobs are not always improved as much as they could be partly because there is so much change. You are always having to start new jobs. Also some jobs aren't of much consequence, you spend so little money on them that it costs less to keep on doing them inefficiently than to study them carefully and figure out how to improve them.

Another important reason that jobs are not improved when they could be is that most people dislike the whole idea. Men trying to improve jobs must try to win almost everyone else over to accepting the idea of improving jobs. Suggestion systems help here—get everybody in on the act, ask everyone for his ideas.

You can go even farther. Make up lists of places where you think that better methods could be, but haven't been, figured out (a few companies do this). Spend a little time showing foremen and assistant foremen *how* to go about improving jobs. Some companies give "work simplification" training courses to them. Often they and their men are willing but don't know how to figure out how to improve jobs.

Another reason that jobs don't always get improved is that all department heads put getting the work done as their first objective; job improvement is way down on their list. Foremen must get out the scheduled work. Besides, they have men to direct and reports to make. They have to keep their machines in repair and to keep scrap down and do all of the other things a foreman has to do that we listed in Chapter 22.

There just isn't any time left to figure out job improvements. Besides, some improvements depend on other departments doing things differently too. No foreman has either the time or the authority to go around making changes in how other departments do things. And to top it off, most foremen are just about as negative toward motion study as their men are. It makes extra work for them, and they have to get their men to use any new procedures.

The upshot of all this is that you need an industrial engineering department (a staff department). Give industrial engineers the job of trying to improve jobs or of helping others improve jobs everywhere— even in the offices or in the maintenance department. It isn't enough to depend on machine designers, layout men (who arrange machines in the plant), and product designers. All of them must, of course, keep low costs in mind in all of their work, but there is much still to be done even after they have done their best. Jobs are just not improved much unless there is an industrial engineering department.

MOTION STUDY ON TRIAL

Motion study is one kind of research (although it isn't called research). You spend time and money trying to improve jobs. Usually you succeed but not always. Unfortunately you can't tell ahead of time how successful motion study (or any kind of research) will be, so sometimes part or all of your cost is wasted.

Because industrial engineers doing motion study are hired to save you money, it is not illogical to expect them to do it. In many companies they must, periodically, come up with figures showing how much they have saved. Also, on all projects that will cost much, they get the green light only after they estimate how much it will cost and how much they hope to save. This forces them to weigh savings against costs and keeps them from spending dollars where only dimes can be saved.

Having to prove their value in dollars and cents keeps them on their toes but is too bad in one way. They have to spend part of their time getting together figures that you don't need except to prove the savings. It is too bad to waste that money, particularly when, in total, industrial engineers save their salaries many times over every year.

MOTION STUDY FOR FUTURE JOBS

We have said that motion study aims to improve jobs. But how wasteful it is to start doing a job one way and then to have to change. Also—what with so many people opposed to changing—how much trouble it makes. Why not figure out the best way to do an operation *before* starting to do it at all?

Here is where motion study can really save money—and without getting anyone upset about it. Admittedly it is hard to see ahead of time just how every operation will be done and then to improve it. But this is just what mass producers of consumer products do, particularly those making annual models—automobiles, television sets, and so on. Industrial engineers try to visualize the operations at successive work stations.

They set about dividing work evenly among the men, arranging the work place, and developing tools—all ahead of time. When operations start, most of the changing has been done. Motion study used this way is very worth while.

WHAT MOTION STUDY TRIES TO DO

Ask a motion study man what he tries to do and he may give you the time-honored answer, "I try to find the one best way to do every job." That isn't really what he does though. He tries to find a *better* method. The difference is important. If he tries always to find the *best* way, he spends all his time trying for ultimates and spends all of his budget on too few jobs. In motion study you cannot afford to be a perfectionist. Usually you have to be satisfied with a better way figured out at reasonable expense.

In trying to improve jobs, a motion study analyst tries, on every job, to do three things: (1) to get completely rid of as many human movements as possible, (2) to shorten the movements that he can't get rid of, and (3) to make the necessary movements less tiring.

But the analyst should not stick solely to human movements, lest he overlook other improvements. Often he can't simplify a man's movements unless he rearranges the workplace or gives the man some special tools or changes the machine or even the product itself. In fact, the analyst should not do any motion study work at all until after he has improved the job all he can in other ways.

Suppose, for example, the job is for a man to paint a part. The reason for the operation is to cover a surface to protect it or to make it look attractive. You ought *not* to start with the way the man handles his paint brush. Start by asking, does the job have to be done at all? The engineers will have to answer that. Assuming that they say yes, then ask when, where, and how should the paint be put on. Maybe the paint ought to go on the part at no extra cost when the whole assembled product is painted. But, if the part must be painted by itself, then ask yourself how the man should get the paint on. He can get it on with a spray gun or a brush, or by dipping it or by smearing it on with a sponge. Pick the best method and now—not before—get down to the man's movements and how he should make them. Motion study should never be divorced from methods study.

Sometimes your first questions about a job must be answered by product design or tool or machine design engineers. Suppose the job you are analyzing is to drill a hole in a steel casting. Right away the question comes up: why not make the part out of a steel stamping and punch the hole instead of drilling it? Or suppose you see a man putting pieces of material, one after the other, into a machine. So you ask, could our tool engineers figure out an automatic feed? Again, motion study comes as the *last* step in methods improvement.

MOTION STUDY METHODS

The first tool a motion study man needs is an inquiring mind. He won't get far if he accepts such ideas as: "We've always done it that way." "The present method works, doesn't it? So it must be all right." "What is, is right." No, he'd much better assume that "the usual way of doing a job is the wrong way." Methods that just grow up are almost never as good as those you can figure out.

If waste motions carried red flags, it would be easy to improve jobs. But waste motions don't carry red flags. The analyst has to look at the job—and look at it part by part, not as a whole—to see what movements the worker makes. Then he, the analyst, must decide which are all or part waste. Then he has to try to get rid of them.

He has five working tools (beyond an inquiring mind) to help him in this. They are:

1. Process charts
2. Motion study principles
3. Suggestive questions
4. Micromotion study
5. Therblig analysis

These tools, described below, can be used separately or together. Of the five, numbers 1 and 2 are most often used.

PROCESS CHARTS

There are any number of kinds of charts that the analyst can make up to help him picture a job and to see ways to improve it. A chart is something like a picture. It holds things still while you study them, and it lets you see the over-all picture, not just one little thing at a time. You can see things better on a chart than out on the factory floor. Or, in the case of charts for new jobs, it lets you see, ahead of time, how they will work. If improvements seem possible, they can be made and a new chart drawn up—all before the new job is ever started.

Don't expect too much from charts. A chart does not improve a job —it takes a *man* to make improvements. All a chart can do is to help him see the possibilities. Also, don't use charts wastefully. They take time to make and are only tools after they are made. So, don't make them too neatly—never mind using India ink and don't spend time making fancy symbols. Make charts only good enough to serve the purpose.

On the other hand, don't dismiss the idea of charts as no good too quickly. Some people think that they go into too much detail. But that is where some of the chances to improve are. The big things, the obvious things needing fixing, are probably already fixed. You have to get down to details to improve jobs. Industrial engineers find charts helpful.

Process charts, of all kinds, show the details of something done. They describe, in words, what is done. Besides that nearly all charts show a symbol for each detail. How long an operation takes or how far something moves are also commonly shown. Summaries of how often each kind of detail occurs are also common.

Why symbols? What good are little squares, circles, triangles, and so on? They are classifications of details. Big circles are usually operations —they show that something is being done to the product. Little circles mean that the product is moved. Triangles mean storages. Squares mean inspections. Classifying the details helps the analyst by telling him how often this kind of activity and that kind of activity happen. And it helps him spot where. All of this helps him as he tries to rearrange details to combine some things and get rid of others.

When making charts be sure that you show what *is happening*— not what is supposed to happen. The only exception is in charting future jobs. Then be sure to chart how it *will be done*, not how it might (but probably won't) be done.

Names for kinds of charts are not standardized, but those we will use are fairly common. Here are the kinds of charts most commonly used.

1. Charts That Show the Complete Processing of a Product

a) Material Flow Chart. A material flow chart shows, on a floor plan, how the product moves through the plant. Symbols show where operations are done. This chart would have another sheet of paper describing the operations and other details shown on the chart by symbols.

b) Flow Process Chart. See Figure 29–1. This kind of chart tells the same story as the material flow chart but as a list without a floor plan. Notice the symbols printed to save the analyst's time. Also notice the spaces for showing how much time it takes to do things and spaces for showing the distance materials are hauled. Figure 29–1 is actually two charts, one showing a job before improvement and one showing how it is to be done after improvement. Notice that things done are cut, in the new method, from 12 to 9, moves are cut from 7 to 5, inspections from 3 to 1, delays from 5 to 2, and storages from 2 to 1.

c) Operation Process Chart. This is similar to the first two charts, but it emphasizes how and where parts come together and what happens before and after they are assembled.

2. Charts Showing Details of Single Operations

a) Man-and-Machine Charts. Lists the activities of a man (it could be more than one man) and the machine he operates. The vertical part of the page is a time scale. Activities are listed at exactly the time when they have to happen. Doing that makes sure that the man doesn't have to be two places at once. Symbols aren't often used on man-and-machine charts.

b) Operator Activity Chart. Figure 29–2 is a left- and right-hand chart without a time scale. List each hand's activities putting them on

107 '/min. CONSTANT SPEED	**IDENTIFICATION**	

SUBJECT CHARTED *ROUND AND HEX WIRE 9/16" IN DIAMETER*	CHART NO. __1__
DRAWING NO. _____ PART NO. _____	TYPE OF CHART *MATERIAL*
POINT AT WHICH CHART BEGINS *UNLOADING AT RAILROAD CAR*	SHEET NO. __1__ OF __1__ SHEETS
_____ LOCATION *STOCKYARD*	CHARTED BY _____
POINT AT WHICH CHART ENDS *BUNDLING DEPARTMENT*	DATE _____
_____ LOCATION *MILL OFFICE*	APPROVED BY _____
QUANTITY INFORMATION .	DATE _____
2,625 / HR	YEARLY PRODUCTION _____
43 / MIN.	COST UNIT _____
50 COILS / DAY	

PRESENT METHOD

QUANTITY UNIT CHARTED	SYMBOLS	DESCRIPTION OF EVENT	DIST. MOVED IN FEET	UNIT OPER. TIME IN	UNIT TRANSP. TIME IN	UNIT INSPECT TIME IN	DELAY TIME IN	STORAGE TIME IN
218 CWLS		UNLOAD FROM RAILROAD CAR	12'					
		MOVE TO STOCKYARD	150'					
		STORED IN STOCKYARD						
12 coils		MOVE TO PICKLE HOUSE STORAGE	200'					
		STORED UNTIL READY FOR PROCESSING						
		WAIT FOR FORKTRUCK						
12 COILS		MOVE TO PICKLING AREA	15'					
6 COILS		PICKLING 12 COILS IN TUBS, PLACE ON BUGGY	20'					
		VISUAL INSPECTION WHILE PICKLING						
6 COILS		MOVE TO WIRE BLOCKS	15'					
1 COIL		PICK UP AND PLACE ON SPOOL	5					
		STRAIGHTEN END AND POINT (3 MEN)						
		DRAW	10'					
		MINOR VISUAL INSPECTION						
		REMOVE FROM BLOCK	2'					
		WAIT UNTIL BLOCK IS RELOADED						
		PICK UP AND PLACE ON STRAIGHTENER	3'					
		STRAIGHTEN AND CUT 35 pcs. -12½ coil	15'					
		WHILE INSPECTING VISUALLY						
500 ps -12'		WAIT FOR MULE TO TOW AWAY						
500 ps -12'		MOVE TO WEIGHING STATION	225'					
500 ps -12'		WEIGH						
		WAIT FOR MULE						
		MOVE TO BUNDLING AREA	25'					
		WAIT FOR BUNDLERS						
		BUNDLE						
		PAINT ENDS						
		HOOK-UP ON CRANE AND PLACE IN	15'					
		LUB. AND DRAIN.						

H. B. Maynard & Co.

FIG. 29–1. Two flow process charts showing present and proposed methods.

the same line whenever they are done at the same time. Use small circle symbols for every activity, no matter what kind. They are for counting and high-lighting lack of balance of work between the two hands. Notice the workplace diagram and the drawing of the product.

In Figure 29–2 you may have noticed letters M-PP, P, UD, R, and so on alongside each little circle. They are classifications of movements using

SUMMARY									
TOTAL YEARLY SAVING—DIRECT LABOR				PRESENT METHOD		PROPOSED METHOD		DIFFERENCE	
		UNIT COST-DIRECT LABOR & INSP.							
		DISTANCE TRAVELED IN FEET							
INSTALLATION COST OF PROPOSED METHOD				NO.	TIME IN ___	NO.	TIME IN ___	NO.	TIME IN ___
		◯ OPERATIONS							
		⬜ TRANSPORTATIONS							
ESTIMATED NET SAVING —FIRST YEAR		⬜ INSPECTIONS							
		⬠ DELAYS							
		▽ STORAGES							

PROPOSED METHOD								
QUANTITY UNIT CHARTED	SYMBOLS	DESCRIPTION OF EVENT	DIST MOVED IN FEET	UNIT OPER. TIME IN	UNIT TRANSP TIME IN	UNIT INSPECT TIME IN	DELAY TIME IN	STORAGE TIME IN
218 COILS	① ⬜⬜▽	UNLOAD FROM RAIL ROAD CAR						
"	◯ [1]⬜▽	MOVE TO STOCK						
"	◯⬜⬜▽	STORE UNTIL READY FOR PROCESSING						
10 COILS	◯ [2]⬜▽	MOVE TO PICKLING AREA						
"	② ⬜⬜▽	PICKLE AND PLACE ON BUGGY						
"	◯ [3]⬜▽	MOVE TO WELDER						
"	③⬜⬜▽	PLACE ON WAYS						
	④⬜⬜▽	WELD LEAD TO END OF COIL AND WELD ENDS						
	⬠⬜⬜▽	OF ALL COILS						
	⑤⬜⬜▽	DRAW, STRAIGHTEN AND CUT OFF						
	◯ [1]⬜▽	+ INSPECT VISUALLY (Continuous process)						
	⑥⬜⬜▽	WEIGH						
	◯⬜⬜▽	WAIT FOR MULE						
	◯ [4]⬜▽	MOVE TO BUNDLING AREA						
	◯⬜⬜▽	WAIT FOR BUNDLER						
	⑦⬜⬜▽	BUNDLE						
	⑧⬜⬜▽	PAINT ENDS						
	◯⬜⬜▽	HOOK-UP ON CRANE, PLACE IN						
	⑨⬜⬜▽	LUB. + DRAIN						
	◯⬜⬜▽							
	◯⬜⬜▽							
	◯⬜⬜▽							
	◯⬜⬜▽							
	◯⬜⬜▽							
	◯⬜⬜▽							
	◯⬜⬜▽							
	◯⬜⬜▽							
	◯⬜⬜▽							
	◯⬜⬜▽							

FIG. 29–1. *Continued*

letters instead of circles, squares, and triangles. Usually they are left off operator activity charts. We'll explain their meaning on page 554 when talking about therbligs.

c) Simo-Chart. See Figure 29–3. The simo-chart (simultaneous motion chart) is an extremely detailed left- and right-hand chart. As with the other charts, there are varieties. Some show what every finger does.

Some try to classify each finger's activities into some twenty kinds of work, using colors to show which is which. Of course, doing all of that is too wastefully fancy even to think of unless you have a job that

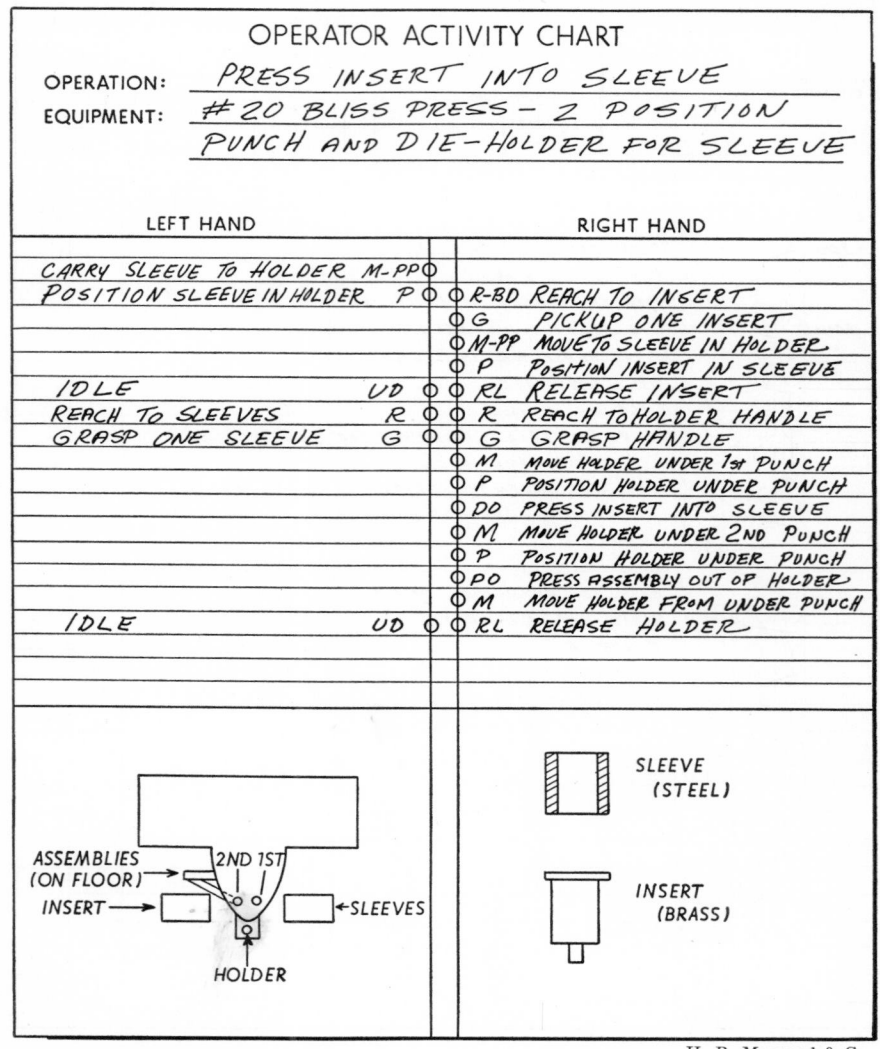

OPERATOR ACTIVITY CHART

OPERATION: *PRESS INSERT INTO SLEEVE*
EQUIPMENT: *#20 BLISS PRESS — 2 POSITION*
PUNCH AND DIE-HOLDER FOR SLEEVE

LEFT HAND				RIGHT HAND
CARRY SLEEVE TO HOLDER M-PP	○			
POSITION SLEEVE IN HOLDER P	○	○	R-BD	REACH TO INSERT
		○	G	PICKUP ONE INSERT
		○	M-PP	MOVE TO SLEEVE IN HOLDER
		○	P	POSITION INSERT IN SLEEVE
IDLE UD	○	○	RL	RELEASE INSERT
REACH TO SLEEVES R	○	○	R	REACH TO HOLDER HANDLE
GRASP ONE SLEEVE G	○	○	G	GRASP HANDLE
		○	M	MOVE HOLDER UNDER 1st PUNCH
		○	P	POSITION HOLDER UNDER PUNCH
		○	DO	PRESS INSERT INTO SLEEVE
		○	M	MOVE HOLDER UNDER 2ND PUNCH
		○	P	POSITION HOLDER UNDER PUNCH
		○	PO	PRESS ASSEMBLY OUT OF HOLDER
		○	M	MOVE HOLDER FROM UNDER PUNCH
IDLE UD	○	○	RL	RELEASE HOLDER

ASSEMBLIES (ON FLOOR)
2ND 1ST
INSERT
SLEEVES
HOLDER

SLEEVE (STEEL)

INSERT (BRASS)

FIG. 29–2. Operator activity chart.

takes only a fraction of a minute and has to be done millions of times a year.

Nearly all simo-charts use the vertical part of the page as a time scale, often with each line representing $\frac{1}{1000}$ of a minute. You'd have to use moving pictures to get such a fine time breakdown.

OPERATOR CHART---PRESENT METHOD

THE NATIONAL FOREMEN'S INSTITUTE, INC. --- WORK SIMPLIFICATION CHART

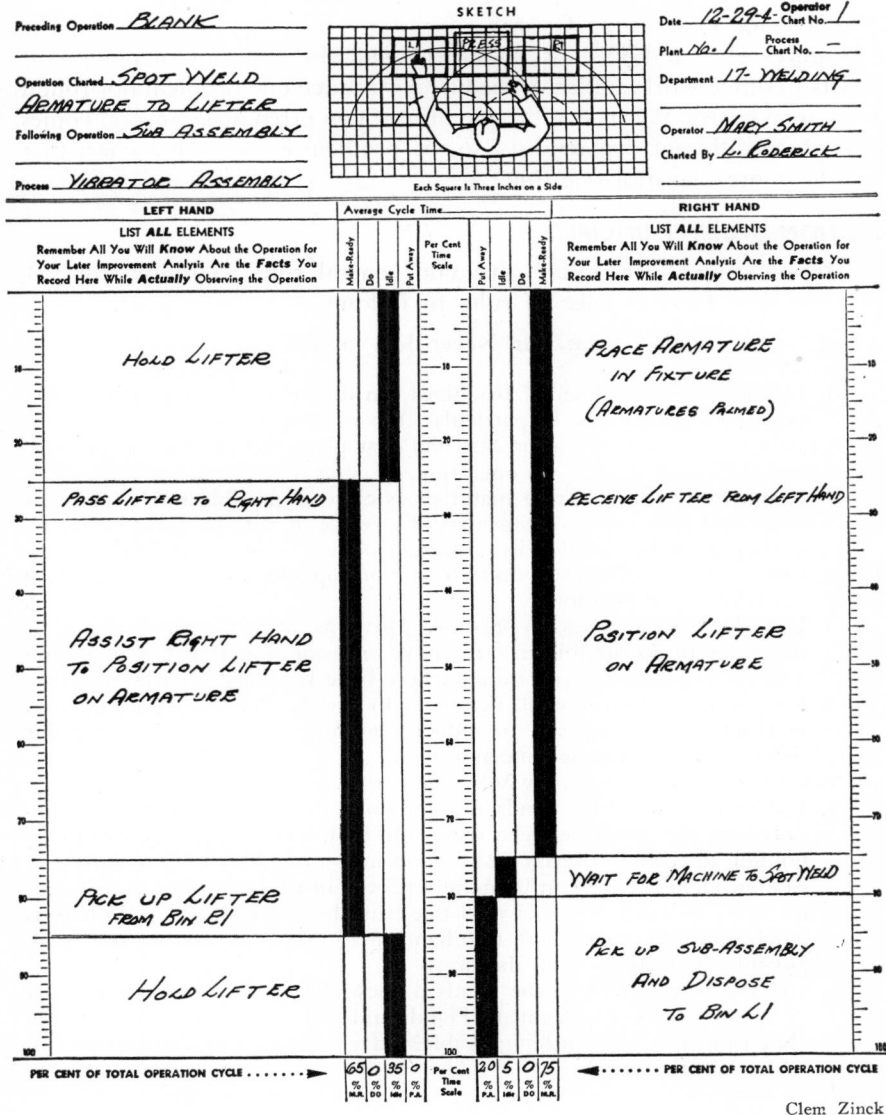

FIG. 29–3. Simplified simo-chart.

Clem Zinck

Figure 29–3 is a simplified simo-chart. It shows only what the hands do—not the fingers. And it classifies things into only four classes, make-ready, do, idle, and put away. The vertical scale is a percentage scale, not an absolute time scale. This lets you see what portion of his time a man spends on each. Look at the summary at the bottom of Figure 29–3. The left hand is actually doing the job *none* of the time! And the right hand is actually doing the job only 5 per cent of the time!

3. OFFICE PROCEDURES CHARTS

Figures 42–1 and 42–2 on pages 817 and 818 show an adaptation of charts to office work. Office procedures introduce one problem not found in factory charts. When you fill out a form, you often make several copies that go to different departments, so the problem is to make a chart that follows more than just one thing.

MOTION STUDY PRINCIPLES

Motion study "principles" give you general rules to follow for improving jobs. Here is a list of rules to follow:

I. *Rules for Intelligent Laziness.* Never do a job the hard way if there is an easier way.
  1. Don't do jobs by hand if machines can do them. Transfer everything possible to machines. In particular, try to design machines which not only will do the operation but will first place the product in position and then eject it after the operation.
  2. Eliminate handling. Bring materials as close as possible to the point of work and remove them by gravity if possible; if not, do it mechanically. If they must be handled by a man, handle as many as possible at one time. Design machines to do two or more operations, once the material has been put in position.
  3. Use the fewest motions possible. Move as little of the body as is necessary to do the job; in fact, move only the fingers if finger motion will do. Don't reach; put things where little reaching is necessary.
  4. Use fixed positions for all materials and tools. Put them close to and in front of the operator, to reduce searching as well as reaching for them. Motions then become automatic.
II. *Rules for Keeping Busy.* A whole man produces more than part of a man.
  5. Use two hands. Idle hands do no work. If both are not busy, redistribute the work between them. On light assembly jobs, mechanical holding devices can often make a job into a one-handed job, in which case an identical job can be done with the other hand. The man won't do twice as much work as with one hand but he is likely to do half as much more. Working with two hands may take practice, but it is quite possible. Typists do it all the time.
  6. Use the feet as well as the hands if they can be used to push a pedal or do some useful movement. Hands and feet can both be used at the same time. Does it sound impossible? Fifty million of us do it every day when we drive a car.
III. *Rules for Fatigue Reduction.* Tiring movements waste energy.
  7. Transfer all heavy lifting to mechanical lifting devices.
  8. Use momentum where possible rather than force. You can't, for example, easily push a nail into a board even with a hammer. But if you swing the hammer, its momentum does the job. Avoid momentum, however, if muscular effort has to be used to stop it.
  9. Continuous curved motions are easier and less tiring than motions involving sharp changes in direction.
  10. Assign all work to the body member best suited for it, as in typing; don't do it all with the little fingers.

FIG. 29–4. A well-arranged workplace. Parts for assembly are conveniently located in front of operator. Conveyors at operator's right bring and take away assembled units.

11. Use the body to the best advantage mechanically. If force must be exerted, exert it at heights and in positions where the body can employ the most force. If possible, arrange the work so that the operator can stand or sit as he wishes.

12. Eliminate working conditions that add to fatigue. Get rid of poor lighting, poor ventilation, fumes, dusty conditions, temperature extremes, and high humidity.

13. On fatiguing jobs, allow rest periods. The heavier the task, the more necessary are frequent short rest periods. Many short rest periods are better than a few long rest periods.

14. On monotonous jobs, provide an occasional break. Monotony and fatigue are related.

IV. *Rules for Placing Men.* Use manpower to its best advantage considering the jobs to be filled and the men available.

15. Where there are several workers doing the same job day after day, cut the job up into small tasks and let each worker specialize. Each will acquire greater facility and the group will produce more.

16. Put workers on jobs well suited to them and place only those suited on the job. Put women on jobs where they are better than men; usually light fast jobs requiring finger dexterity. Put men on men's jobs.

17. Never use high-priced labor on low-priced work even if the lower-priced work is but a small part of a high-priced man's job. Cut the job apart and assign work to the grade of worker required.

SUGGESTIVE QUESTIONS

Suggestive questions are next in the motion study man's tools. They are much like principles, but they are more numerous and detailed. Try thinking of some job you know about. Then ask yourself some of the questions below. See if the mere asking doesn't make you think of one or more ways to improve the job you thought of.

First there are general questions that apply to all jobs. They include: Who, where, when, why, and how is the job done? Is this movement necessary? Can it be eliminated? Can it be shortened? Can it be transferred to the machine? Can it better be done at another time? Can it be combined with another movement?

These questions should start you thinking, but they are not really what we mean by suggestive questions. Suggestive questions are more specific. Here are a few taken from a book that has 400 such questions. These particular questions apply mostly to metal products:[1]

If the operation is performed to improve appearance, is the added cost justified by added salability?

If the operation has been established to correct a subsequent difficulty, is it possible that the corrective operation is more costly than the difficulty itself might be?

Is this operation made necessary because of the poor design of tools that are used in a previous or a following operation?

Is the machining of a surface done merely to improve appearance, and, if so, can a suitable appearance be obtained in some other less costly way?

If design requires special tooling, can it be altered so that standard cutters, multiple drilling heads, jigs, etc., can be used?

Is the job inspected at the critical point instead of after the job is done?

Will patrol inspection eliminate scrap and expense?

Is the supplier furnishing material on which he has performed an operation not necessary for its use?

Could a part be made from scrap material?

Could molded or cast parts be substituted to eliminate machining or other operations?

MICROMOTION STUDY

This way of improving jobs means taking moving pictures of jobs, then running them slowly through a projector (even stopping the film to look at each picture separately). A clock with a large dial (with the hand making one revolution a minute) is often set up next to the job so that it shows in the picture. This allows you to tell how long movements take. You don't have to have a clock, however, because most cameras take 16 pictures a second. You can tell how long any movement takes just by counting pictures.

By studying the pictures a trained analyst can figure out how to

---

[1] Harold B. Maynard and G. J. Stegemerton, *Guide to Methods Improvement* (New York: McGraw-Hill Book Co., Inc.).

improve even short-cycle jobs. Nearly always, though, he will first make up some kind of left- and right-hand chart from the movie and then study it more than he will the movie itself.

Taking successful indoor movies is not an amateur's job. You usually have to put up floodlights and string wires around and generally disrupt a factory department in order to take the movies. It costs money to do all of this, and most of the people concerned—foremen and men on jobs—don't like the idea. Unions nearly always oppose it. Small wonder that micromotion study is rare in industry.

But aren't there any places where it works? Not very many. Not only do most factory people dislike it but there are not many places where it would pay anyway. It can pay off well, however, on little jobs (say, less than a minute) done millions of times. Industry has some jobs like that (making light bulbs, tin cans, nuts and bolts, bottles, and quite a few other items).

Suppose you had a 20-second job done 10,000,000 times a year. That comes to 3 a minute, 180 an hour, 1,440 a day, or 36,000 a year. It would take about 30 men at a labor cost of $60,000 to turn out 10,000,000 in a year. If you could cut the 20-second job to 15, you would save $15,000 a year. You might be able to do it without movies but you can forget the cost and nuisance of taking them if they help you make such savings.

Movies also have two by-product advantages. After improving the job, a moving picture of the new method is a perfect and a permanent record of how the work is done. Besides furnishing a record, movies help in the training of men—particularly new time and motion study men. They can run and rerun the films, and they can practice setting time standards without getting out into the factory until they have a little experience.

THERBLIG ANALYSIS

A therblig is a small part of a job—a very small part. It is much too short to time with a stop watch. A time study man analyzes jobs part by part, but his parts of a job (he calls them "elements") would stop at say "tighten bolt." Tighten bolt is, however, made up of the therbligs: move hand, get ready to pick up wrench, grasp wrench, move hand with wrench, position wrench, turn wrench, and so on.

The therblig idea goes back 50 years to Frank B. Gilbreth. No one paid much attention to it until it had a rebirth during World War II when the government set up training programs to show foremen how to improve jobs. Today, several consulting engineering companies use it as a bread-and-butter technique.

Here is Gilbreth's list of therbligs: search, select, grasp, move hands empty, move hands holding something, hold, release load, position something, pre-position something, inspect, assemble, take apart, use, unavoidable delay, avoidable delay, plan, rest.

Back on page 546 we passed by the letters *M-PP, P, UD,* and so on (shown in Fig. 29–2) without explaining them. They are merely letters standing for the different kinds of therbligs done on the job charted in Figure 29–2. *M-PP* means move the hand and pre-position the item in the hand (getting ready for the next therblig). P means position it. *UD* means unavoidable delay, and so on.

Just how, though, does all of this help us cut job time? It helps because it forces us to look at minor parts of the job. True, sometimes we can cut out whole jobs or big parts of jobs. But often still more time can be saved by looking at the therbligs, one by one.

Go back to our "tighten bolt" part of a job. The man reaches for the wrench and he reaches for the bolt, then later he reaches again putting the wrench out of the way. Put it and the bolt closer and he will save reaching time. Next, always put wrench and bolts the same place, and the man can pick them up faster. He doesn't have to grope for them or look each time to see where to find them. Again, you have saved time by studying the therbligs. Put the wrench in a slot or holder so that it sticks up and the man can get hold of it quicker. The same thing with every therblig. You need to look at each separately because different things are needed to improve each one.

After you do all of this, the element "tighten bolt" will take less time than it did before. But notice that the improvement came from looking at the details not the over-all.

Isn't it pretty expensive to go into such detail? How can it possibly pay off? First of all, this kind of analysis doesn't have to be expensive. You don't have to use movies or make up simo-charts to see that a man reaches too far for things. But you do have to use discretion about when to make detailed analyses. They do cost money. This kind of analysis is only for short jobs done thousands or millions of times. It wouldn't pay on long jobs done a few times. But even on them it isn't smart to reach long distances and to waste time in other ways if a few simple changes would save the time.

SELLING BETTER METHODS

Early in this chapter we said that most people (including foremen) are naturally against motion study. We also said that much the best way to get jobs improved is to have an industrial engineering department— not just to leave it up to foremen.

Men on the job and foremen and sometimes management all have to be sold on better methods—not just sold on the general idea but convinced that each and every improvement is workable. Men on the job oppose just because they don't like to change, and besides, back in their minds, there is always the fear that they might get laid off or be put on some other job that they won't like.

Foremen usually have to be sold too. Not too often are they the kind of foremen that management wants (the kind that just live to cut costs). Foremen are reluctant about some job improvements because they have to do all the work in getting their men to use the new methods. That makes more work for foremen. Foremen also have to keep quality up and, on some job improvements, are afraid methods improvements may make it hard for them to keep quality up.

But more important is a foreman's natural opposition to an outsider coming into his department and telling him how to run it. How would you feel if an outsider came in and suggested an improvement that you never thought of? Management would like you to say, fine, that's what we want—we welcome help in cutting costs.

But is that what you would say? Wouldn't you be like some foremen and resent it? They resent it partly because the suggestion was not theirs but more because, indirectly, it reflects on them. When the big boss hears about it, may he not say (or think) why didn't the foreman think of that improvement himself?

Whatever the reason, foremen often find fault with or drag their feet on a motion study man's suggestion. To contend with that, the motion study man is supposed to be quite a diplomat. He is supposed to plant a seed of an idea with the foreman and then let it germinate. Let the foreman go on and figure out the details on his own and then come forward with it as his own idea. He'll try very hard to make *his* idea work. But if the same idea were the motion study man's suggestion, he (the foreman) would have any number of reasons why it would not work. Planting the seed is the ideal way to sell an improvement. And often that is the way it is done. The analyst has to be an unsung hero.

Selling management on job improvements is almost wholly a matter of costs and savings. After all, management hires the analyst and certainly expects him to make savings. But so often savings come only after some money is spent rearranging the workplace, getting better tools, and so on. Approval is almost automatic if you can show management that it will pay off. Management only wants you to be sure.

MOTION STUDY'S VALUE TO SOCIETY

Motion study usually shortens jobs. Men end up making fewer movements to do a job, but they do the new job more often in a day—maybe hundreds of times, maybe over a thousand times, a day.

Some people get quite concerned about this. They say that this increases monotony and cuts out the satisfaction that men get out of doing whole jobs. They say that it has robbed the man of his personal liberty and dignity, stripped him of his pride in his work, weighted him with frustrations, and smothered his creative instincts. They say that all of this, from a social point of view, is a high price to pay for this kind of efficiency.

Let's look at monotony first. Repetition and monotony aren't quite the same thing. Repetition is on the job. Monotony is in the mind. Many people like repetition; to some it has a pleasant lulling effect. Many people object to being transferred away from repetitive jobs. There is a certain security in them. Such jobs present no upsetting problems. Once mastered, a worker's movements are automatic and he can daydream or, if it is not noisy, talk to his neighbors without it bothering anyone's work. Many women, in particular, like such jobs.

In the biggest survey ever made of factory worker attitudes, Roethlisberger, Dickson, and Wright, found no evidence that factory workers thought their jobs were monotonous. They concluded also that the loss of job satisfaction from doing specialized work was exaggerated. They also objected to the idea that today's jobs take no skill. They wrote as follows:

> The differences between the modern worker and the old-time shoemaker or carpenter, for example, are generally discussed in terms of differences in the amount of skill, intelligence, ingenuity, or interest entailed. None of these generalizations, however, has received much support from the Hawthorne studies. In modern industry there are jobs which call for as much skill and intelligence as those of previous days. Moreover, it is generally agreed that repetitive work was not unknown before the industrial revolution.[2]

People who talk about the "loss of worker satisfaction" surely can't have read history. As late as one hundred years ago a shoe cobbler made a whole shoe, but he worked from sun up to sun down and rarely lived to be 40 years of age. Seamstresses made complete dresses and men's suits, but many of them went blind young and died young.[3] There are innumerable cases on record of dissatisfied apprentices and journeymen in England long before the Industrial Revolution.[4] The average life expectancy was also very low. These men who performed whole jobs instead of parts of jobs may have been happy, but we have no record that they were. They produced very little, sometimes went on strikes, had miserable standards of living, and died young. History does not bear out the "happiness" theory of the good old days.

Suppose we say, however, that some people don't like repetitive work, and that most of us do get satisfaction from doing varied things and have a pride in workmanship that comes from seeing a whole job well done. Can we have motion study and efficiency and also get these satisfactions?

Some companies think, yes. Some play soft background music. Some use "job enlargement." That means giving people on highly repetitive

---

[2] F. J. Roethlisberger, William J. Dickson, and H. A. Wright, *Management and the Worker* (Cambridge, Mass.: Harvard University Press, 1947), p. 574.

[3] For accounts of working conditions in these industries see annual issues a century ago of the *Journal* of the Royal Arts Society, London.

[4] *English Economic History, Select Documents,* ed. A. E. Bland, P. A. Brown, and R. H. Tawney (London: G. Bell & Sons, 1930), contains an excellent collection of documents relating to the conditions of workers in England from the Middle Ages down to recent times.

jobs a few other duties that come up now and then. They interrupt the routine, give the man something else to do, and cut boredom. International Business Machines Company is given credit for starting this. It reports more production, fewer rejects, and less supervision. (Part of the extras IBM put into jobs is for men to check their own work instead of having inspectors do it.)

Job enlargement of another kind, job rotation, also is gaining in popularity. Let workers change jobs; let them switch around now and then. Everyone has more variety and ends up finding his work more interesting. Thought question: What does this do to the goal of putting men on jobs they fit best? Also won't the unions want such all-round skilled men to get higher pay? The plan works at nonunion IBM, but will it work elsewhere?

Still another kind of job enlargement, occasionally used and helpful particularly with groups, is to ask the men about how to divide up their work into work assignments. They get interested in how assignments are made and work better on the jobs they set for themselves than they do when industrial engineers divide up the work.

All of these methods help relieve boredom and raise interest and morale in jobs, while keeping most of the gains from methods improvement. But even if they don't end up making every job fascinating, society still has all the gain of much greater production, shorter hours for workers, more healthy workers, and better off workers and workers' families. No one wants to give up modern methods and go back to the ways of a century ago.

STUDY QUESTIONS

1. Why do people oppose job improvement? Discuss.
2. How can you do motion study work for future jobs? Why would you want to do that?
3. "I try to find the one best way to do every job," says a motion study man. Discuss this statement.
4. What tools or technique does a motion study man have at his disposal? Explain each briefly.
5. What good are symbols on charts? Give reasons for their use. Are there any reasons for not using them? Explain.
6. List and describe the kinds of charts that depict single operations.
7. The text gives seventeen motion study principles. Into what general groups are they put? Of what use are they?
8. Are charts or suggestive questions more helpful in improving jobs? Discuss.
9. Can you ever justify micromotion study? Justify your answer.
10. What is the difference between micromotion study and therblig analysis? When would you use each?
11. Motion study men often have to "sell" better methods. To whom? Why? How?
12. What can you do to relieve monotony? Discuss fully.

Case 29–1.   The Echo Company

George Sisson, time study man at the Echo Company, had a request from the small-parts manufacturing department to set a rate on operation 3, "mill seat" on back plate No. T–623. He went to the department, and the foreman took him out to see the operation being done by Stanley Kluka.

Sisson watched three work cycles, during which Kluka placed one back plate in his miller, performed the milling operation, removed the piece, inspected it, and laid it aside. The order was for a large number of pieces and was of the kind that could be, and ordinarily was, milled several at a time. Sisson believed that Kluka should put six instead of one in the mill and mill six at a time. Kluka refused to perform the operation that way; so Sisson called the foreman to ask if Kluka's method was really necessary.

The foreman smiled and said: "Come on, Stan, give us a real study. You know you should mill six at a time." Kluka replied rather heatedly: "Look here, who is being time studied? You or me?"

What should be done? Are there any poor practices apparent here? Should Kluka decide how he is to do his work?

Chapter 30

TIME STUDY AND
TIME STANDARDS

$\mathbf{T}$IME study is a procedure used to set production standards by timing operations, almost always with a stop watch. Nearly always, too, the end product, the time standard, is used in setting a piece rate.[1] But there are other reasons for wanting standards, so that you find some companies using time study which do not use incentives. Also sometimes production standards are set without using a stop watch. So, occasionally you find time study without time standards and occasionally you find time standards without time study.

By far the most common reason for setting production standards is for incentives. Other reasons are: to find out what operations cost, to find out how long they take so that you can schedule work, to find out how much a machine will turn out, to use when estimating the costs of new jobs never done before but something like old jobs, to set quotas for measured daywork, to find out how to divide up work along an assembly line so that the men have equal work assignments, and to compare the costs of doing things in different ways. You need standards, too, when figuring how many men and machines you will need to turn out future production.

ACTUAL AND "NORMAL" TIME

For some purposes you want to know *how long it takes* a man to do a job. For other purposes you want to know how long it *ought to take*. The two—actual and ought-to-be—aren't the same. Of the two, finding how long a job ought to take (time study men call this the "normal" time) is more complicated than just finding how long a job *does* take. But even finding how long a job does take is not too simple because men rarely do a job twice in exactly the same time. You have to get several figures and choose a time.

---

[1] "Time standards" and "production standards" are the same thing but stated differently. One says that a job is a 3-minute job, the other says that a man ought to do the job twenty times in an hour.

Time study for how long jobs take is largely fact finding. Time study for setting incentives is fact finding plus judgment. The end product is a "normal" time—the time that it takes an ordinary experienced worker to do the job while working at a normal work pace (but a pace when he is not really pressing himself). The *actual* time that a man takes while being studied may be more time or less time (usually less) than this abstract idea of normal.

Using his judgment, the time study man takes away from or adds to the actual time and arrives at his idea of normal. How does he decide how much time to take away or add? He just uses his own judgment (this is a fruitful source of argument later). How he judges is the subject of most of this chapter.

Here we have to hedge a bit on our definition of normal. Normal isn't really the time you expect a man to take. The time study man's idea of normal should be rather liberal. His standard should allow more minutes than most men take most of the time. Almost every worker will do the work in less than standard time, and so will turn out more than the standard amount of work and earn a bonus.

Having liberal standards helps men make bonuses but it makes unrealistic standards for scheduling. What do schedulers use as the truly expected time for work? Not the incentive standard, not directly, that is, because they would be planning for less output than they'd get. Schedulers do use the incentive standard, though. It takes only a simple adjustment to find out how much to count on the men turning out. If a man usually earns a 30 per cent bonus, he is turning out 130 per cent of standard work every hour. Schedulers just count on getting 130 per cent of standard output in an hour or a day. Knowing the man's usual bonus percentage lets them figure out what to expect.

TAKING THE TIME STUDY

It might seem that the way to time a job would be to look at the clock when the job starts and when it ends. The elapsed time is the time for the job. Sounds simple. But it is too simple to give accurate results.

Why Time Job Parts? You have to time the job part by part. But why? Don't the parts add up to the whole? Yes, but when you break the job down into parts (the time study man calls them "elements") and watch the man do the job several times, you find that the list of parts isn't always the same every time he does the operation.

If you timed the job only on an over-all basis, you'd never know about that. Or if you happened to notice it, you wouldn't know what to do about it. In order to figure out a proper rate, a time study man just has to write down what elements occur and how long each takes. Some of the irregular happenings are necessary for the job and some are not. To get a proper standard the analyst has to add time for the necessary miscellaneous elements into the standard on a prorata basis. Also he must take out the time for unneeded extra elements which men sometimes put in to mislead him into giving them a loose standard. Having timed the job part by part rather than in total lets him add in the proper time for odds and ends.

Still another reason for timing the job element by element is to get better times for the necessary regular elements. Often, in a work cycle, some elements are done quickly and others slowly, or maybe a whole cycle is fast or slow. You get a more accurate time for the whole cycle if you can pick out the *usual* time for each element and then sum up these selected element times.

Breaking the Job into Elements. The first thing a time study man does when taking a time study is to "break the job into elements." He watches the job done a few times, then decides the parts of the job which he will time separately and writes them down on his data sheet before he starts writing down any times. He has to decide exactly where one element stops and the next starts (the worker, of course, doesn't stop between elements) so that later, as he writes down the element times, he will have times for exactly the same movements. He can't time really short things accurately with a stop watch, so he won't try to isolate job parts that take less than, say, 4 seconds. His smallest elements will be no shorter than that. On the long end, he'll usually try to cut the job into parts that won't run over, say, 15 seconds.

Writing Down the Times. After writing down on his data sheet the descriptions of the regular elements, the time study man is ready to start recording times. Pull out Figure 30–1, page 568. We are talking about the element descriptions "swab core box, sand in, peen," and so on down to element 12. These are the elements this time study man first wrote in. As the study went along, some other things turned up. He had to write in some of these, elements 13–16. Besides these, some things turned up that took extra time. Notice the circled times and the notes at the bottom. We'll come back to them later.

In the study shown in Figure 30–1, page 568 the time study man, for some reason, started his watch running before the worker started to do the job. This does no harm but is unnecessary, so don't let it confuse you. Now, as the worker did the job, the time study man looked at his watch at the end of each element and wrote down the time. The watch kept running, so you can't tell as the study goes along exactly how long each element takes.

In our example the watch said 15 hundredths of a minute when the job started (most stop watches have dials that show hundredths of a minute not seconds). At the end of element 2 (element number 1 wasn't done at all in this first work cycle) the watch showed 28 hundredths, then after element 3 it read 60 hundredths (look down column 1 on Figure 30–1). After element 4 it read .74, then .92, then 1.06, and so on. Notice that element 7 and those following do not read 1.26 and 1.33 but instead say .26 and .33. That is merely to save writing in all the ones. The watch actually said 1.26, 1.33, 1.40, etc.

Follow on down column 1. Element 12 ended at 1.66, and the job is done—that is—it is done once. The man has turned out one product. The man, of course, goes right on and does his job again on the next product with no break in time at all. He goes on to element 2 (element 1 is omitted again). It finishes at 1.76, then element 3 ends at 2.06, and so on.

While taking the study, the time study man "rates" it—decides whether it is quickly or slowly done and how quickly or how slowly. Before he leaves the job he writes down his rating. He can use any one of several methods (described on pages 567–69). In our example the time study man put in quite a few ratings as he went along. He didn't wait till the end of the study and then make a single over-all rating.

Look in column 1, on line 2. See the 105? Stay on line 2 and go over to column 4 and 9. See the 100 and the 115? Those are three ratings on how quickly element 2 was performed on three of the ten times covered by the study. Or look on line 6, columns 1, 5, and 8. See the 120, 90, and 100? Those are three ratings on element 6. These ratings are written in as the study goes along. We'll see presently how to use them.

The figures in all of the right-hand 6 columns are written in later as the time study man "works up" his standard. So are all of the figures in the upper right of each square (the 13 in line 2 column 1 and the 10 in column 2, 06 in column 3, and so on).

Figure 30–1 is a typical time study data sheet, and the time study man's procedure is also typical. Most time study men use (as did ours) watches marked off in hundredths instead of seconds. Most time study men let the watch run all the time, but some don't. They use the "snapback" method. When an element ends and the watch is read, they press the stem at the top of the watch. Instantly the hand snaps back to zero and starts off again. Time study men like to do it this way because they don't have to subtract one watch reading from another to find out how long an element took. By letting the watch run in our study, our analyst left himself with about 120 subtractions to make.

He let the watch run, though, because the men on the job like it that way. They say that times are too short with the snapback method, that it takes time for the watch's hand to get back to zero and to start up. Also the hand doesn't start moving until the analyst takes his finger off the watch stem. If he doesn't let go right away, the watch won't show the full element time.

Our time study man handled extraneous happenings (he calls them "foreign" elements) in the usual way. Look again at Figure 30–1. See the circled times, the letter referring to explanatory footnotes, and, at the bottom, the explanations?

Our analyst, however, did not use the typical rating method. He rated the performance of each element about three times. Not many time study men rate individual element performances (it would be better if they did). Some are content to rate only the whole study in its entirety. Some others put down one rating for each element. Rating each one three times is better.

Besides the times for the job details, notice that the observer wrote down on his sheet the operator's name, the product, the operation name, the date, how long the study took, how many pieces the man turned out during the study, and when it started and stopped. It is well also to write down the tools and accessories and to make a sketch of the workplace and anything else that might be important later. They were on the back of the sheet used in Figure 30–1.

The method described above for setting a time standard is a common one and is considered good practice. It must be admitted, however, that many small companies set rates by less orthodox procedures. Some study the best worker they can find on a job, find out his rate of production, and arbitrarily decide the amount of bonus they are willing to pay him. Suppose that this superior worker turned out 22 pieces an hour and that you decided that at this production rate he should earn a 30 per cent bonus. Standard production would be $100/130$ of 22 pieces, or 16.9 pieces per hour, and the piece rate (if the job carried a $2.00 per hour base rate) would be 11.83 cents each. While this method of setting a standard leaves much to be desired, you don't always get bad rates. Department foremen, who in some companies set piece rates, quite commonly use this procedure.

Another method, described more fully on page 514, is often used with automatic equipment. Start with the machine's top output, then pick a figure, say 95 per cent at top output, as a goal. Set the piece rate so that a man who turns out that much production gets a 30 per cent bonus.

SETTING THE TIME STANDARD

Typical Element Times. On returning to his office, the time study man first makes his subtractions to see how long the job elements that he timed took. His watch read .15 minutes when he started the study and .28 at the end of element 2, so it took .13 minutes. That goes in the little box in the upper right of line 2 column 1. Element 3 finished at .60, so it took .32. By .74 the worker had completed element 4, so it took .14.

After the element times are written in, the analyst (the time study man) looks them over to see whether any are decidedly shorter or longer than other readings for the same element. Those that are, are circled and not used. As it happens, in this study, every unusual time was noticed while the study was being taken and a footnote was written in to explain it.

How can the time study man justify leaving out extreme times? He can't justify it if they just happen with no reason (and in that case he doesn't throw them out). But look at element 2, column 3. That element took .06 of a minute, way less than usual for element 2. It was so unusual that the observer wrote in a footnote to explain it—a footnote that tells us that the man didn't do the whole element. Look on down to element 5, column 3. This element took .37 minutes, far above usual for element 5. This too is explained in a footnote—the time covers all of element 5 and some extra work to correct for the half-done element 2 above. So you throw out both times, but, as we will see, this does not mean cheating the worker.

After making subtractions to get his element times, the time study man next picks one as the typical time for the element. Read across line 2; see 13, 10, 06, 13, 09, 13, 16, 13, 11 and 12? The 06 is circled (and not used) because it was not done in the usual way.

That leaves nine readings for doing element 2 nine times. The analyst added up the nine readings and got a total of 1.10 minutes (look in the total column, upper half of line 2). Then he divided by nine to get the average time .122 which he wrote in below the 1.10 total. Notice that leaving out circled time values does not mean that you cheat the man. You just add 9 time values and divide by 9 instead of adding 10 values and dividing by 10. In fact, putting *in* this particular circled time would cheat him. It would pull the element's average down from .122 to .116.

You have to select a typical (or average) time for every element, whether the element happens often or not so often. During this study element 1 happened only twice. Elements 13, 14, 15, and 16 happened only once so the time they took becomes their selected element time.

Computing the Standard.   You are ready now to use the time study man's performance ratings (performance ratings are explained on page 567). Look at element 2. He rated element 2 three times (see columns 1, 4, and 9). The first time the operator performed element 1 he took .13 minutes which was rated at 105. He was next rated on element 2 in work cycle 4. Again this element took .13 minutes, but this time it was rated at 100. Another rating was made in cycle 9. This time element 2 took .11 minutes and was rated at 115.

The time study man, looking at his three ratings, decided that for .122 minutes (the average time taken for performing element 2) a rating of 105 was appropriate. Now go down the column and note the performance rating for every element. For element 1, it is 100; 2 is 105; 3 is 105; 4 is 100; and so on.

Below the rating figures in the same column is the personal delay and fatigue allowance, the 11, 12, 12, 11, etc. These allowances are discussed on page 567. Notice that they differ a little and go as high as 17 for element 14; a heavy, fatiguing element.

The next column "crew" tells how many men are required to do the element; here it is one in every case.

The "allowed time" per element (the next column) is a calculated figure. Start with the selected element time, adjust for performance rating, and add personal and fatigue time. For element 1 start with .155, multiply by 1.00 (note that you move the decimal point over, the rating itself is actually a *percentage* figure), get .155, then multiply by 1.11 and get .172, the element allowed time. You could have multiplied by .11 and added the answer to .155, but it is simpler just to find 111 per cent of .155. Element 2 goes: $.122 \times 1.05 \times 1.12 = .143$.

The performance rating isn't always over 100 per cent. Look at element 14. Here you multiply: $.16 \times .95 \times 1.17 = .178$. The allowed time is above the selected time (.16), but only because the personal delay and fatigue allowance increased it more than the low rating (.95) reduced it.

Now we are ready to pay attention to how often things happen. The occurrence column tells this; element 1 has to be done only once for every 5 products. Everything else has to be done once for each product down to element 13. From there on it is once per 10. A word of warning: Don't take the study at face value here. Odds and ends of elements might just happen to be done in the right proportion during the study. But the analyst must get these ratios right. Ask the man how often he has to do each, and ask the foreman before putting in these ratios.

The last column is the allowed time per element, *per work cycle*, or per unit of product. It answers the question: How much time, *on the average*, is this element allowed? It is the allowed time per element times its occurrence ratio. For element 1 it is $.172 \times \frac{1}{5} = .034$. This is the column that you finally add up to get the time standard for the job, 1.827 minutes in this case.

Miscellaneous Elements. In our sample study several elements (number 1 and 13 to 16) turned up occasionally. Questions need to be asked and answered about odds and ends of elements before accurate standards can be set. (1) Are they all here? Are there others besides those that occurred during the study? (2) Is each one necessary? Should it be included or left out? (3) How often do the necessary odds and ends occur?

Are they all here? The analyst can't know about things that have to be done once in a while but that didn't turn up during the study. He should ask the man on the job if there are any other things and, if there are, should time them when they come up. That should insure everything being counted. But, to make doubly sure, the foreman and possibly the union shop steward look over the time study to see that everything that belongs in it is in.

Are the odds and ends necessary? The man stops his machine to see if the material is in right. Must he do this? After doing the work, he loads the product onto a truck and pulls it aside to a storage space. Should he do these things? Maybe they aren't needed at all or maybe they are someone else's work. Most men being time-studied are not above trying to put something over on the time study man if they can—anything to make the job take longer in hopes of getting a looser standard. The time study man must ask the foreman about questionable elements.

How often for necessary odds and ends? A man working on a machine may have to sharpen his tools now and then or gage the size of the product with a gage. No question about these things being necessary. But how often? Again, doubt what you see—ask the foreman. .

"Ratio Delay" in Standard Setting.   Odds and ends elements are today, in many cases, *not* handled as our example shows and as we have described. That (the way it is done in the example) is the best way if there aren't many odds and ends, but it is a costly way if there are very many. Also we said, "ask the foreman" how often things happen. But he sometimes doesn't know either. He can't tell you how often a man should gage his work.

"Ratio delay" can help us here. Ratio delay is a method for finding out how much time to give for odds and ends. It is not exactly time study, and it is sometimes used for other purposes than just to find out how much time to allow in a standard of odds and ends. To use it to cover odds and ends with time studies, first, take a regular time study. Do everything in the usual way except *do not set element times or frequencies for odds and ends*. Leave the standard unfinished for several days. During that time go past the job many times; noting each time *what* the man is doing; but don't stay at the job and take any times. Get a good many notations, 100 or more is good.

Now *count* how many times you saw the man doing main parts of the job and also how many times he was doing odds and ends. Put down the percentage of the cases when you find him doing main elements (those you time studied) of the job. Suppose that he was doing main elements in 75 per cent of the cases, odds and ends in 15 per cent, and was away from his machine in 10 per cent of the observations.

Now you make an assumption. You say that a man seen doing one kind of thing in 75 per cent *of the observations* must spend 75 per cent *of his time* on them. And the same for the 15 and the 10. That assumption is valid if you spread your observations around and take them at all hours of the day.

We are now ready to figure out how much time to allow for odds and ends. Seventy-five per cent of his time goes for main elements; 15 per cent for odds and ends. So odds and ends take $15/75$ as much time as main parts of the job. From our time study, we find that main parts (not including the fatigue and personal delay time) come to, say, 4 minutes. Then, $15/75$ of that, or $1\frac{1}{4}$ minutes, is the proper allowance to give for odds and ends, making the total time standard, 5.25 minutes. Then you add on an additional allowance for personal delay and fatigue (in our sample study that was done element by element, but it would have to be done all at once for the whole standard if you used ratio delay). We do not use ratio delay for personal and fatigue time allowances because these allowances are fairly standard from long use. Besides they are usually overliberal, so no one objects to their being fairly arbitrary.

Ratio delay is, today, well accepted and commonly used. It answers the worker's objection that a short time study is unfair because it misses too many odds and ends or that the time study man thinks that they don't happen as often as they do. And the time study man likes it because the worker never knows when he is coming past and so gets less chance to doctor up the job.

OTHER WAYS TO SET TIME STUDY STANDARDS

Our sample time study is typical in almost every way. But there are two places where it isn't typical. One is using performance ratings for several watch readings for every element and applying a performance rating to each element's selected time. The other unusual feature is adding in personal delay and fatigue time, element by element.

Most time study men would use only an over-all performance rating and would add the personal delay and fatigue also at the end. Using typical procedures you would get a selected element time, multiply each one by its occurrence ratio, and add the allowed time per element to get a total representing the *typical bare cycle time* observed. Then the performance rating would be applied to get *bare normal cycle time*. After that add personal and fatigue and get the time standard. This method is more common and takes less work to figure but is less accurate.

PERFORMANCE RATING

In our sample time study, the time study man put down several performance ratings (also called "pace" ratings or even "speed" ratings) such as 105, 110, 95, and so on. What, really, was he doing? What were those numbers? They were his judgment, as he watched the work, of how fast the man made his movements as compared to "normal." Normal is 100 per cent. Higher numbers mean that the man was going faster than normal. Numbers below 100 mean slower than normal.

How does the time study man tell "normal" when he sees it? This is the biggest sore point in time study. He just decides. But how? Doesn't he have any yardstick? Yes, but it is a little vague. It is in his mind.

An illustration may help us understand his yardstick. Suppose we talk about a man walking a mile. He can do it in 15 minutes if he hurries, or he can take 20, 25, or even 30 minutes, or any other time in between or longer. Most of us would agree that some particular rate, say 3 miles an hour (1 mile in 20 minutes), was reasonable to call normal. The next thing is for us (if we are in training to become time study men) to watch people walking and try to judge how fast they are going, keeping always in our minds a picture of how fast a man walks when he goes 3 miles an hour.

This may sound difficult, yet with practice a man can get pretty good at estimating how fast or how slowly a person walks. You can have new time study men practice on different people walking, say, 30 feet. At 20 minutes per mile it takes .114 minutes to walk 30 feet. So you, by timing the person walking, can calulate exactly what a perfect rating would be and so learn to rate accurately.[2]

But factory jobs are not walking. True. Suppose you get really good at judging walking. How can a time study man judge normality on jobs as unlike as wire drawing, cold heading, or packaging nuts and bolts? One answer is that he does it and does it pretty well. Proof that he can do it is that a good time study man will end up with two almost equal job standards if he sets one standard after watching a relatively poor worker and then, without checking that standard, sets a second one after studying a good man. Also, sometimes two or three time study men take separate studies of a job, and, without comparing notes, will arrive at standards within 5 per cent of each other. Sometimes they miss being quite that close, but generally they are. This proves that judging normality can be done reasonably well.

Of course this does not stop men from complaining. Often they don't say that you can't rate, they don't say that you aren't consistent; they say that your idea of normal itself is wrong, that you ask for too much. But they also object sometimes to the procedure of rating because it isn't 100 per cent perfect. They say that even if two time study men are only 5 per cent apart that is too much.

Rating Methods. Most time study men rate the worker's whole performance in total and write down only one rating for a whole study. Usually they use 100 per cent as normal. Some others, at the end of a study, rate each element (but not each time it was done) apart from the other elements. A few do it the way our sample does—rating each element several times.

A somewhat different method (called the Westinghouse method because it originated in that company) has the time study man rate the job in its entirety but on four counts, not just one. At the end of the study, he rates the operator's skill, his effort, his consistency, and the job conditions. Letters (A, B, C, down to F) are used for ratings. Later these ratings are compared to a fixed scale of percentages.

Suppose that you rated the job this way: Skill B-1, effort C-2, conditions E, and consistency B. In the table of per cent values (which is per-

---

[2] The Society for the Advancement of Management has prepared an extensive set of films covering many jobs for this purpose. Hundreds of sets of these films have been sold to industrial companies.

manent and unchanging) you find these numbers for the ratings you gave: Skill, +11; effort, +02; conditions, −03; and consistency, +03. Add them up and you get +13. This means that the man was rated as producing at 13 per cent over normal or the same as a rating of 113 in ordinary per cent ratings.

JUDGMENT IN TIME STUDY

People sometimes criticize time study for not being wholly scientific. Certainly it is not wholly scientific because it rests in part on judgment. But criticisms ought not be too harsh until something better comes along. Time study is a pretty satisfactory but not perfect tool.

Where does the judgment come in? Three places: (1) what elements do you include, (2) how often do odds and ends occur, and (3) performance rating. All have been discussed earlier. Of the three, performance rating is wholly a matter of judgment, the others partly so. And of the three, only rating has to do with the whole job; the others deal with only the minor parts of the job.

But, if rating isn't truly scientific is there any way that we can make it better—or even avoid it altogether? No, it can't be escaped. Many escape routes seem to be available, but not one of them stands up under scrutiny. Here are some of the ideas that sound so good at first:

Fallacy 1. Study all of the workers in a group. Use their average time as normal. Several objections to this. (1) You don't have several people doing most jobs. There is no group. (2) If the group members are good workers, as they should be and usually are, their average time is faster than normal. It would be unfair to set their pace as normal. Your standard would ask for too much production. It would be just as wrong to use the pace of a slow group as normal, although you don't find many slow groups. (3) Men can control their pace. Most workers slow down when being time-studied. There is no security in numbers. If you study only Smith, he is likely to slow down during the study. You don't get any closer to normal by also studying Jones, who also slows down, or others who do the same. All you do is to multiply your standards setting costs.

Fallacy 2. Pick out an average man and study him. Use his time as the normal time. Weaknesses: (1) On many jobs there is only one man, on others you have no average man (all of them ought to be better than normal). (2) If you do have both fast and slow men on a job, who is normal? The men would like for you to pick just about the slowest man. (3) Even an average man can slow down too when time-studied. He might give you an average performance, but more likely he won't. He knows that other men will work on the standard set by his performance. His pace must suit their wishes, or he'll have few friends.

Fallacy 3. Pick out a good worker and tell him to slow down to normal while the study is being taken. Weaknesses: (1) Has he slowed down enough? Too much? You must judge.

Fallacy 4.   Use standard times for every little human movement. Get the times out of a catalogue. Weaknesses: (1) Someone else's judgment of normality went into setting up the catalogue of basic times. You do escape making the judgment yourself, but all you do is to take the judgment of the standard data compiler instead. It takes judgment, too, to use the catalogue times.

It all comes back to judging. There is no escaping it. If you find fault with the common methods and reject them, you can only set still less accurate standards.

OTHER CONSIDERATIONS

Authority to Study.   Time study men don't just wander around the plant taking studies whenever and wherever they want. Studies have to be authorized. Most of them start as requests from foremen and are requests to set standards on new jobs. Some are requests to recheck old jobs that have been changed.

Foremen don't always want new standards because supervision is generally an easier job with daywork. But the top brass wants everything possible to be on standards, so the superintendent keeps after any foreman whose departments aren't largely on standards. Remember, management believes that incentives make more production and lower costs. Sometimes, too, the foreman's men keep after him to get standards set on their jobs so that they can make some extra money.

Picking the Man to Study.   Let the foreman do this. He knows his men and he knows who is doing what job. But get him to pick a good man, not a poor one. Several reasons for this. It gives you better standards, and it improves your post-mortem position.

How does it give you better standards? It cuts out part of the judging required. You don't have to decide that certain things done are unnecessary, because a good man just doesn't do unnecessary parts of a job very often. It also helps you judge how often odds and ends occur. With a good operator they occur only when necessary, so again you don't have to decide that certain things don't really have to be done as often as the man did them.

The point isn't that you won't ordinarily rule out unnecessary things or that you won't find out about how often odds and ends have to be done. The point is that with a poor man you have to make many such decisions. Occasionally you'll be wrong. With a good man there are fewer decisions and so practically no mistakes.

Don't forget the post-mortem position. You may expect your rate to be challenged. You are open to very little attack on your allowance for miscellaneous things if you didn't disallow anything. Also your performance rating is open to much less criticism if you allowed all the time the man took and more too. You are subject to more criticism if you cut off some time because you rated the man below 100. But if you picked a good man who would have made 25 per cent bonus on your new stand-ard while working at the pace observed, no one can say that the new rate is unreasonably low.

A word of warning, however. Be sure not to forget that you picked a good man. If you do pick a good man, and if he does a good job for you, he deserves a rating of over 100. Your standard should end up al-lowing *more* time than he took.

How about studying two or more men and at different times of the day? No need to do this. If you can rate performance well, you end up with the same standard in all cases. If you can't rate well, stop setting standards until you practice more. A fast performance gets a high rating no matter by whom or during what part of the day. A slow perform-ance gets a low rating. A 3-minute performance at 133 per cent gives a 4-minute standard. So does a 5-minute performance at 80.

How Long a Time Study?   How many work cycles should be timed? Probably 10 to 20 or more. It depends some on the job itself. If it takes only 1 or 2 minutes, take lots more readings. Also take more readings if the job varies, and not so many if it is consistent. Taking hundreds of read-ings is not usually worth while because all you do is find out more of the same.

MACHINE TIME IN THE WORK CYCLE

Many factory operators run semiautomatic machines. Once the ma-chine is set up, all that there is left for the operator to do is to take out the product just finished and put in the next one. The machine does the rest. While it works there is nothing for the man to do for a while. How should the time study man handle the element "wait for machine"?

It depends on how long the wait is, on whether or not the machine needs watching, and on whether there are other things that the man can do in his free time.

If the time is short, the wait is handled just like any other element —it goes into the standard. If you had a job taking 2 minutes to unload and load a machine and then a ½-minute wait, you would call it a 2½-minute job.

But if unload and load time is 2 minutes and then the machine runs by itself for 10 minutes, it is a 2-minute job—not a 12-minute job. You give the man other work to do during the 10 minutes—maybe running some other machines. If he runs other machines, you have to watch out that he doesn't have to be two places at once. Also don't expect the im-possible. Don't try to have him run six machines and expect perfect pro-duction from all of them. It figures that he could run six machines with 2-minute change times and 10-minute running times, but he'll get held up sometimes and will lose some production.

Sometimes the machine runs itself but needs watching. If it requires constant watching, the element "watch machine" goes into the standard. But often all that it needs is a casual glance now and then to see that all is still going well. Usually here you can give the man other work to fill in his idle time. You may have difficulty, though, in putting this idea across.

MACHINE CHANGE TIME

Machines nearly always have to be "set up" for each job. The tools, toolholders, material holders, and so on all must be put in place and adjusted. But before that starts, the old setup from the last job must be torn down and its tools and gadgetry put away.

The work of setting up on many semiautomatic machines is often done by a setup man who does nothing else. He is usually not an incentive worker, so you don't have to have standards for tearing down and setting up. But in companies where he too (as well as the men that run the machines) is on incentives, you need standards for his work.

Many men are on jobs where they set up their own machines and then run them themselves. You have three choices of how to pay for setting up: (1) pay for it by the hour, (2) set standards for setting up and pay for it on incentive, (3) put the setup time in with running time on a pro-rata basis and have one piece rate cover both setting up and running the machine.

Number 1, paying for setup at an hourly pay rate, is a poor choice particularly if a pieceworker is to be paid day rates for it. He feels that his pay is cut while he is setting up. But if you pay him his average earnings (instead of his base rate) while setting up jobs without standards, he will take a rest while doing it. In fact on his timecard he will exaggerate the time it takes and so boost his earnings. Paying anyone else —even a setup man—at hourly pay is also a little expensive because daywork pace is not very fast.

Number 2, having standards for the setup jobs, is a better choice, the best as far as incentives themselves are concerned. But it is bad in that you need to have hundreds of standards for hundreds of kinds of setups. They are slow and costly to make up because they are slow jobs. And you have to set standards after watching only two or three setups because the same ones don't come up often.

Number 3, allowing time for setup on a pro-rata basis within the regular rate, is chosen sometimes. This doesn't solve the difficulty of having to do lots of time study work or of having to set standards for setups on very few observations. It does avoid having hundreds of standards for setups on your records. But they have to be set anyway and put into the standard for operating a machine on an average basis.

This may not be bad when setup time is small compared to how long jobs usually run. Take running a mimeograph machine as an example. To run it, you have to put on a new stencil sometimes. But the main job is running sheets of paper through the machine. You know from past experience about how many sheets are run off each stencil (but remember that that is set by how many copies you want, not by how long the stencil can be used before it wears out).

Method 3 gets rid of a rate for changing stencils this way. Suppose that your average run is 200 sheets. If you run the machine by hand, maybe running 200 sheets takes you 4 minutes. Suppose that it takes 2 minutes to change stencils. Add the two together and get 6 minutes per 200 sheets of paper, or 3 minutes per 100.

That works fine if the runs do average 200. But suppose the operator gets lots of orders for 25 sheets. If he runs 8 such orders he has taken 4 minutes to run the machine and 16 minutes to change stencils, a total of 20 minutes. Yet the standard gives him only 6 minutes. Or suppose that he gets a run of 1,000. He takes 20 minutes to run them off plus 2 minutes stencil change time; total 22 minutes, but the standard allows 30 minutes.

Including anything—in this case setup time—on a pro-rata basis makes rates tight or loose if the frequency of occurrence changes. Sometimes you are lucky—long and short runs offset each other—but you can't count on it.

WORK SAMPLING

Work sampling is a way of setting standards that fills the bill sometimes when time study doesn't. It is not time study and uses no watches and collects no times. It belongs in a discussion of time study, however, because it has been developed by time study engineers and is used by them to set time standards.

Remember "ratio delay" from page 566? Work sampling is the same idea. You take many unrelated observations (maybe hundreds) of what is being done on whatever job you are studying. Then you count how often each kind of activity occurred and figure out what proportion each activity is of the total. *That also tells you how the worker spends his time.*

As ordinarily used, work sampling tells you what is—not what ought to be. In other words, it is a report of how the worker spends his time, but it doesn't tell you whether the work is being done at normal pace or at what pace. You could, however, pace rate every recording. An instance rated at 120 would later be counted into the total as 1.2 instances.

Work sampling can be used to find out how much machine down time occurs, how much tool down time, and how many machines a man can run. It can be used for factory production jobs, maintenance and other indirect work, and office work.

Not everyone favors work sampling—not even everyone who has tried it. It takes hundreds and hundreds of observations to give reliable ratios of how much time goes to doing little things. Men who favor work sampling claim that it is as accurate as time study and costs less than half.

Some companies have had the employees do their own work sampling —mostly for office jobs, but you could have factory men do it too. Douglas Aircraft, in its offices, had employees write on tabulation cards everything that they did—one card for each activity—but they didn't report times. Then, next, the company prepared cards for each activity and gave each man a supply of cards for each activity. After that, for several days, the man put a start and stop time on the appropriate activity card for everything he did. Analysis of the cards gave a good idea of everyone's work load and furnished valuable data for planning the number of men needed in the offices when production went up or down. Argus Camera, division of Sylvania Electric, had factory men fill out cards for all delays. They furnished information that helped cut down the delays and helped them set better standards.

Work sampling is said to work well on indirect jobs—maintenance, materials handling, stock room work, office jobs, and so on. Of course it costs some money to set the standards. One company with 400 maintenance workers added six standards setters and found that 300 men could do the work. The 100 men cut out of maintenance were transferred to production jobs. Another company added 12 standards setters and cut out 100 indirect men.

STANDARD DATA

Isn't time study wasteful? Aren't new jobs partly like old ones? And if they are, don't you already know how long the unchanged job elements take? Yes, new jobs are partly like old ones, and it is wasteful to time those elements all over again.

Setting time standards without having to take more studies has long been a dream of time study men. Two rather different methods are used. One uses job element times from past studies. Some people call this the "macroscopic" method. The other regards *all* jobs as being collections of very short minute movements (the "therbligs" described in Chapter 29); this is the "microscopic" method. Once you make up a catalogue of their times, you never have to do it again—*for any job*. All you have to do is to list every little movement the man makes, get times for each of them out of the catalogue, and add them up.

Macroscopic methods are like building a prefab house. You work with big parts (elements) of a job—just as a prefab house is made from walls, floors, cabinets, windows and roofs. Microscopic methods are like building an ordinary house. You make it out of bricks, nails, boards, and glass. Jobs, likewise, are made up of little movements, reach, pick up, carry, insert, and so on.

Macroscopic methods are limited to particular operations, such as operating a turret lathe; they cover any and all jobs done on that size and kind of lathe. Microscopic methods are universal and can be used for all operations and all jobs.

MACROSCOPIC METHODS

This method uses "standard data." Of course the therblig idea is also a use of standard data, but it usually goes by other names.

Standard data of the macroscopic type is often put into formula form, or it can be put on a printed sheet. Figures 30–2 and 30–3 show the front and back of a sheet for setting a time standard for a turret lathe job. Figure 30–2 shows three tables with element times printed in for numerous possibilities. In order to set a time standard for a new job, all the standard setter has to do is to decide (from information on the drawing) what the product weighs, what kind of clamping arrangements there will be, and what kind of gaging takes place. Then he picks the times that apply. In Figure 30–2 the times he picks are circled so that you know which they are.

Now look at the back of the sheet (Fig. 30–3). The handling times from the front of the sheet have been copied (.13, .27, .35, etc.). Two of these times are circled on the back of the sheet. This time the circle means "don't add in this element time because it is done while the machine is running and machine running time is counted in separately below."

Look on down the page to the .43, 1.16, etc., times. These are machine running times. They are calculated by starting with the .42-minutes-to-drill-an-inch figure. That figure is a standard figure for drilling when the machine goes at the rate of 340 revolutions per minute. But the hole to be drilled in this case is only ⅜ of an inch deep so the cutting time is .16, not .42. After that first cutting element, the machine's speed is changed (in .07) and the turret rotated (in .20). Now add .16 plus .07 plus .20 and get .43 for the first machine cutting element. After that you figure the machine time for machine element 2, 3, and 4 the same way. Then add the whole column and get 3.35 minutes.

Now go back to the front of the sheet (Fig. 30–2), to the "Calculation of Rate" section; find the 3.35 copied in there. On the next line down it shows .44 minutes for allowances. Where does that come from? Look at the "Down Time Allowance" section. Here we see that the company gives (for a whole day) 20 minutes for personal time, 15 minutes for unavoidable delays, and 20 minutes for tool care. These add up to 55 minutes, leaving 425 minutes for work (out of 480 in a day). Fifty-five minutes is 13.0 per cent of 425 minutes. That is where the 13.0 per cent comes from which is used in the calculation-of-rate section. For this job, which takes 3.35 minutes to do, the allowance comes to .44 minutes, giving a total of 3.79 minutes.

The operation for which we are setting a standard (Drill-Face, Bore, Air Starting Cams) is almost wholly a machinery operation. The worker can't speed up the machine parts of the job (they are set to run as fast

TURRET LATHE STANDARD DATA SHEET

Part Name __AIR STARTING CAM__
Operation __DRILL - FACE BORE__

Part No. __T-7772__
Oper. No. __10__
Dept. No. __40__
E. M. Q. __150__

Machine Name __J & L 8A__

Mach. Nos. __21611 - 21612__

TABLE 1 — MANUAL UNLOAD AND LOAD

WGT	MIN.	WGT.	MIN.	WGT.	MIN.
1	.12	11	.15	25	.20
2	.12	12	.15	30	.23
3	(.13)	13	.16	35	.25
4	.13	14	.16	40	.28
5	.13	15	.16	45	.31
6	.13	16	.17	50	.35
7	.14	17	.17	55	.40
8	.14	18	.17	60	.45
9	.14	19	.18	Hoist	1.60
10	.15	20	.18		

TABLE 2 — CLAMP IN FIXTURES

	1	2	3	4
Set Screws	.40	.70	1.00	1.30
Slotted Clamps	.25	.44	.63	.82
If Remove Nuts Add	.20	.35	.50	.65
Bar Clamp	.60	1.10	1.50	1.90
Bar Clamp For Piston Rods Over 1½"	1.50	2.90	4.30	5.70

Previous Rate __.15__ Previous Setup __.5__

TABLE 3 — GAUGING

	ALLOWED PER DIM.
Micr. O. D.	.21
Micr. I. D. ✓	(.27)
Depth Micr.	.35
Check Length ½00	(.15)
Thread Gauge	.30
Plug Gauge	.15
Profile Gauge	.15
Thrd. Micro.	.51
Valve Seat Gauge	.50
	.27

ADDITIONAL ELEMENTS

NO.	DESCRIPTION	MINUTES
	NONE	

TOTAL __X__

DOWN TIME ALLOWANCE

TYPE OF ALLOWANCE	MINUTES
Personal	20
Unavoidable Delay	15
Tool Care	
Rgh.	20
Fin.	
TOTAL DELAY	55
PER CENT	13.0 %

REMARKS

NONE

CALCULATION OF RATE

TOTAL ACTUAL TIME PER PIECE	3.35
Plus __13.0__ % Allowance	.44
Total Production Time	3.79
Plus __20__% Incentive Adj.	.76
STANDARD MIN. PER PIECE	4.55
STANDARD HRS. PER PIECE	.076
SETUP TIME HRS. __0.85__	

Computed by __WAC__
Date of Study

Checked by __E. A. C.__
Approved by __E. A. C.__

Tool Equip. Record by __WAC__
Date Posted

E. A. Cyrol & Co.

FIG. 30-2. The front side of a turret lathe standard data sheet. On this side of the sheet the part and operation are described; some of the manual elements are listed; allowance figures are shown; and the standard is calculated.

SETUP CHART   DATE

Part Name **CAM**   Part No. **T-7172**

Operation **DRILL - FACE & FINISH BORE**   Operation No. **10**

Dept. **40**

Mat. **C.I.**

Machine **J & L 8 A**   Code No. **A-8**

Allowed Setup Time **0.85 HRS.**   Run Time Per Pc. **.076**

FACE
CENTER DRILL
DRILL 1 ¹³/₃₂
BORE

HANDLING ELEMENTS   Wgt. 3 Lbs.

	Allowed Per				Pcs.	
	3 & 4	1A	J & L	4 A	Gisholt	
Unload and Load from Table No.						13
Tighten and Loosen in Fixture from Table No.						(27)
Gauging from Table No. 3						
Loosen and Tighten Chuck						35
Snug	.15	.15	.15	.45	.45	
Average	.25	.35	(.35)	.75	.75	
Heavy	.35	.70	.70	1.40	1.40	
Loosen and Retighten Chuck Jaws				.25 Min.		
Blow or Brush out Chips				.15 Min.		15
Change Tool in Slip Chuck			✓	.15 Min.		
Change Tool in Taper Holder				.34 Min.		
Oil - Tap - Plug - Bar or Reamer				.10 Min.		
File Burrs or Break Corners **DURING BORE** (/) No. x .12 Min.						(12)
True-up by Sight .50 Min. Indicator 1.00 Min.						

GAUGE DURING DRILL HOLE TIME

TOTAL ADDITIONAL ELEMENTS

	Change Speed or Feed	Pul Clear	Change Turret Station	Reset Same Station	Clear and Advance	Blind Hole Tap & ect.	Set Adj. Head	Total Handling Allowed Over Cutting Time
W&S 3&4	.06	.10	.19	.12	.16	.10	.06	.08
W&S 1A	.07	.10	.25	.22	.20	.16	.08	.08
J&L 8A ✱	.07	.10	.21	.20	.18	.18	.08	.10
W&S 4A	.18	.20	.34	.30	.25	.22	.12	.10
Gisholt	.10	.20	.40	.35	.30	.27	.12	.12
			SQ. HEX.	SQ. HEX.	SQ. HEX.			

	Minutes Per Inch	Length of Cut	Cutting Time	Change Speed or Feed	Change Turret Station	Clear and Advance	Blind Hole	Set Adj. Head	Over Cutting Time	
W&S 3&4	.42	3/8	.16	.07	.20		-	-	.27	43
W&S 1A	.37	2 3/8	.89	.07	.20		-	-	.27	116
J&L 8A	.27	3/4	.20	.07		.16	-	-	.23	43
W&S 4A	.19	2 1/4	.43	.07	.20		-	-	.27	70

TOTAL   3 35

TURRET	DESCRIPTION	R.P.M.	SUR FT	FEED PER REV
HEX 1	CENTER DRILL	340	-	H.F.
HEX 2	DRILL 1 ¹³/₃₂	243	90	.011
SQ 1	FACE EntD	340	235	.011
HEX 4	BORE 1.501/1.502	489	193	.011

E. A. Cyrol & Co.

FIG. 30-3. The back side of the turret lathe standard data sheet. On this side the setup is shown; the cutting elements are listed and detailed; machine handling times are calculated; machine handling times are listed; and cutting and machine times are summarized.

as the machine will do the work) so he could make very little bonus on this job. To take care of this the company has sweetened up the standard by adding 20 per cent more time, or .76 minutes, bringing the total to 4.55 minutes for the job. Now a man doing a good job will be able to make a bonus. Sweetening up the rate this way to let the man make a bonus on machine-paced jobs is a fairly common practice.

Constant and Variable Elements.   Some time study elements always take the same amount of time, no matter what the job, for example, turning the turret in our sample study. That is the same, no matter what product you are working on or what you are doing to it. Such elements are "constant" elements.

Other elements are "variables." They are different for different products and different operations. For example, in our sample study, drilling the hole is a variable element. Drill a bigger or deeper hole, and it will take more time. The drilling time varies.

There is another kind of variable element. Suppose that the job is making wooden packing boxes. Some take lots of nails, and others few. The time for nailing is the same *per nail*, but the number of nails needed varies with the box being made. The element itself, "drive nail," is a constant, but the total nail driving time per box varies—it depends on how many nails the box needs.

Most "constant" elements are obviously constant—but if there is any doubt about one of them, look over the times for that element as it turns up on different studies. If they are about all the same, use their average as the element's constant time.

But if the times for the same element taken from different time studies are different—very different—then you have a variable element. You must find out what makes it vary—something not always easy to do.

Look at Figure 30–4. The top chart is a time study man's first try at finding out why the times varied on an element "remove tubing and lay aside." He had taken 29 time studies of bending tubing, one each for 29 different jobs of bending tubing. Some were for short lengths of tubing, some for long lengths, some were bent a lot, some a little. But all were done on the same bending machine. Each time study was a complete study with a dozen or more watch readings for every element. Then each study was worked up and an allowed time developed for each element.

The element "remove tubing and lay aside" was one of the elements on every study so the time study man had 29 time values to work with. Notice that the element is not constant. The times run from .05 to .28 minutes.

The time study man's first thought was that the length of the tubing being bent caused the differences. So he got from each time study the length of tubing and the time for remove-tubing-and-lay-aside and plotted them, getting the top chart in Figure 30–4. As you see, the points are scattered all over—meaning that he didn't yet know why the times varied. The tubing length wasn't the answer. He also numbered the points with the time study number so that he could go back to the study and look some more to find out why the times varied.

The next thought was to see how far into the unbent tubing the mandrel was put. (The mandrel is a straight steel bar that goes inside the

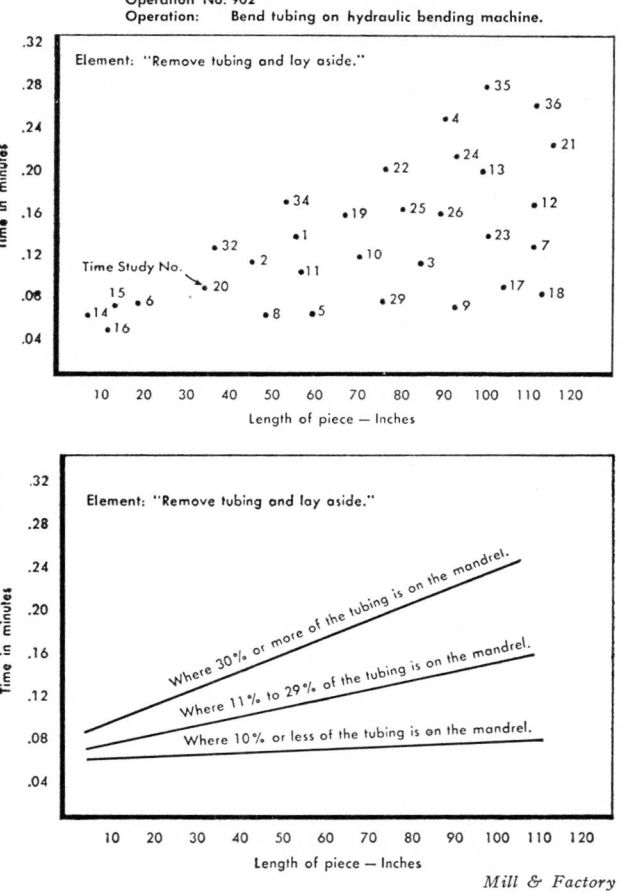

FIG. 30–4. Top: Work sheet for element "Remove tubing and lay aside." The dots are quite scattered, showing that the length of the piece does not alone determine the time. Bottom: Graph of the same element after considering the length of pipe that goes on the mandrel.

tubing from one end up to where you want the bend to start). It would seem that the farther into the tubing the mandrel went, the longer it would take to get it out in order to lay aside the bent tubing.

So the analyst went back to his chart and circled in red all dots from studies where over 30 per cent of the tubing was on the mandrel. Then he circled in blue all with from 11 to 29 per cent on the mandrel. Then

580   MANUFACTURING MANAGEMENT

in green all instances where less than 10 per cent went on the mandrel. Then a pattern—or rather three patterns—emerged. The red circles lined up pretty well, so did the blue, and the green. The lines you see on the lower chart in Figure 30–4 were drawn to fit the line up of the dots.

Using these three lines, you can tell ahead for new tube-bending jobs —without making new time studies—how long it will take a man to do this variable element. Just look at the specification for the new job. How long is the tubing and how much goes on the mandrel? Lets say 70 inches and 25 per cent. Read across the bottom on Figure 30–4 to 70 inches, go up to the 11 to 29 per cent line, and from the intersection go across to the time scale and find that it will take the operator .13 minutes to remove-tubing-and-lay-aside.

Add this time to the times for constant elements and for other variable elements (gotten this same way) and you have the new job's time. Does it sound like a lot of work? It isn't. You can set new rates in just a few minutes. Of course setting up the standard data is a big job. But once it is set up, setting individual job standards is easy. You get your stand-ard data cost back many times over by not having to take time studies in the future of jobs that are almost, but not quite, like old jobs. And you are sure of getting consistent standards. You eliminate the slight possibility—always present in regular time studies—of getting an occa-sional loose or tight standard. You also get rid of much bickering with unions about rates. Once the men have accepted the first few rates set by a formula, they usually accept, without argument, new rates set with the same formula.

MICROSCOPIC METHODS

In Chapter 29 we discussed therbligs—the basic, minute movements which make up all of a man's physical activities. Now we come to how long they take. After all, if we have fundamental movements, why can't we find out how long they take and then make up a catalogue of their times? That is just what microscopic methods do.

But how? The movements seem too short to time. It has been done by taking moving pictures of jobs and parts of jobs with fixed speed cameras or with big watches in the picture. That allows you to run the pictures slowly later and read elapsed times from the watch or to count the individual little pictures on the film.

But what do you do about performance rating? Moving pictures will tell you how long it took to make the movements observed, but how long *should* they take? The answer is that you must performance rate the movies just as you would a time study. The time study engineers who make up catalogues of therblig times run the movies over and over again (at regular speed—not slowed down). And they ask many experi-enced time study men to rate the performances. They finally set times for the fundamental movements.

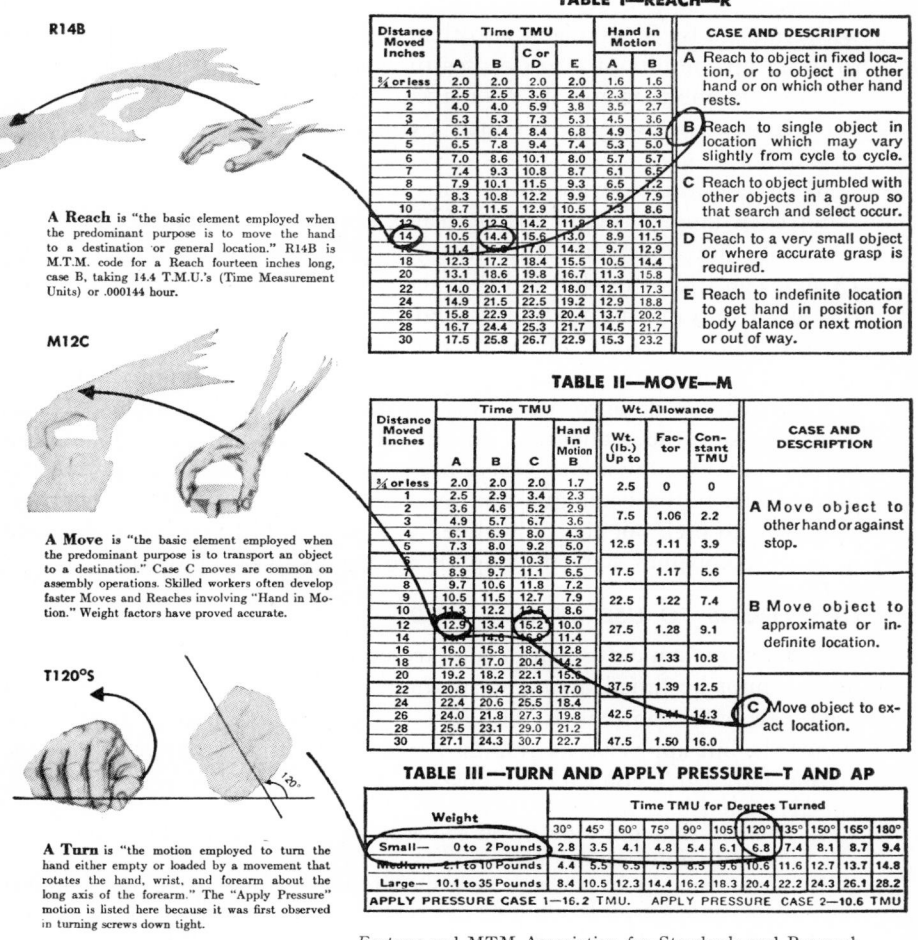

R14B

A **Reach** is "the basic element employed when the predominant purpose is to move the hand to a destination or general location." R14B is M.T.M. code for a Reach fourteen inches long, case B, taking 14.4 T.M.U.'s (Time Measurement Units) or .000144 hour.

M12C

A **Move** is "the basic element employed when the predominant purpose is to transport an object to a destination." Case C moves are common on assembly operations. Skilled workers often develop faster Moves and Reaches involving "Hand in Motion." Weight factors have proved accurate.

T120°S

A **Turn** is "the motion employed to turn the hand either empty or loaded by a movement that rotates the hand, wrist, and forearm about the long axis of the forearm." The "Apply Pressure" motion is listed here because it was first observed in turning screws down tight.

TABLE I—REACH—R

Distance Moved Inches	Time TMU A	B	C or D	E	Hand In Motion A	B	CASE AND DESCRIPTION
¾ or less	2.0	2.0	2.0	2.0	1.6	1.6	**A** Reach to object in fixed location, or to object in other hand or on which other hand rests.
1	2.5	2.5	3.6	2.4	2.3	2.3	
2	4.0	4.0	5.9	3.8	3.5	2.7	
3	5.3	5.3	7.3	5.3	4.5	3.6	
4	6.1	6.4	8.4	6.8	4.9	4.3	**B** Reach to single object in location which may vary slightly from cycle to cycle.
5	6.5	7.8	9.4	7.4	5.3	5.0	
6	7.0	8.6	10.1	8.0	5.7	5.7	
7	7.4	9.3	10.8	8.7	6.1	6.5	
8	7.9	10.1	11.5	9.3	6.5	7.2	**C** Reach to object jumbled with other objects in a group so that search and select occur.
9	8.3	10.8	12.2	9.9	6.9	7.9	
10	8.7	11.5	12.9	10.5	7.3	8.6	
12	9.6	12.9	14.2	11.8	8.1	10.1	
14	10.5	14.4	15.6	13.0	8.9	11.5	**D** Reach to a very small object or where accurate grasp is required.
16	11.4	16.0	17.0	14.2	9.7	12.9	
18	12.3	17.2	18.4	15.5	10.5	14.4	
20	13.1	18.6	19.8	16.7	11.3	15.8	
22	14.0	20.1	21.2	18.0	12.1	17.3	**E** Reach to indefinite location to get hand in position for body balance or next motion or out of way.
24	14.9	21.5	22.5	19.2	12.9	18.8	
26	15.8	22.9	23.9	20.4	13.7	20.2	
28	16.7	24.4	25.3	21.7	14.5	21.7	
30	17.5	25.8	26.7	22.9	15.3	23.2	

TABLE II—MOVE—M

Distance Moved Inches	Time TMU A	B	C	Hand in Motion B	Wt. Allowance Wt. (lb.) Up to	Factor	Constant TMU	CASE AND DESCRIPTION
¾ or less	2.0	2.0	2.0	1.7	2.5	0	0	
1	2.5	2.9	3.4	2.3				**A** Move object to other hand or against stop.
2	3.6	4.6	5.2	2.9	7.5	1.06	2.2	
3	4.9	5.7	6.7	3.6				
4	6.1	6.9	8.0	4.3				
5	7.3	8.0	9.2	5.0	12.5	1.11	3.9	
6	8.1	8.9	10.3	5.7				
7	8.9	9.7	11.1	6.5	17.5	1.17	5.6	
8	9.7	10.6	11.8	7.2				
9	10.5	11.5	12.7	7.9	22.5	1.22	7.4	**B** Move object to approximate or indefinite location.
10	11.3	12.2	13.5	8.6				
12	12.9	13.4	15.2	10.0	27.5	1.28	9.1	
14	14.4	14.6	16.9	11.4				
16	16.0	15.8	18.7	12.8	32.5	1.33	10.8	
18	17.6	17.0	20.4	14.2				
20	19.2	18.2	22.1	15.6				
22	20.8	19.4	23.8	17.0	37.5	1.39	12.5	
24	22.4	20.6	25.5	18.4				
26	24.0	21.8	27.3	19.8	42.5	1.44	14.3	**C** Move object to exact location.
28	25.5	23.1	29.0	21.2				
30	27.1	24.3	30.7	22.7	47.5	1.50	16.0	

TABLE III—TURN AND APPLY PRESSURE—T AND AP

Weight	Time TMU for Degrees Turned 30°	45°	60°	75°	90°	105°	120°	135°	150°	165°	180°
Small— 0 to 2 Pounds	2.8	3.5	4.1	4.8	5.4	6.1	6.8	7.4	8.1	8.7	9.4
Medium— 2.1 to 10 Pounds	4.4	5.5	6.5	7.5	8.5	9.6	10.6	11.6	12.7	13.7	14.8
Large— 10.1 to 35 Pounds	8.4	10.5	12.3	14.4	16.2	18.3	20.4	22.2	24.3	26.1	28.2

APPLY PRESSURE CASE 1—16.2 TMU.   APPLY PRESSURE CASE 2—10.6 TMU.

Fortune and MTM Association for Standards and Research

FIG. 30–5. Part of the catalogue of basic times used in the MTM system.

All of this is too specialized for most companies to do themselves. Several consulting companies make this a bread-and-butter item in their services to client companies. Number one developer and proponent of therblig times is the H. B. Maynard and Company of Pittsburgh.

Figure 30–5 is part of Maynard's four-page catalogue of therblig times. Maynard calls its times, "TMU's" (Time Measurement Units). A TMU is one-one hundred thousandth of an hour (this is about one thirtieth of a second). Notice that there are quite a few time values in this catalogue. You need special training before you can use the procedure and find correct time values.

MTM (Methods Time Measurement), as Maynard calls its method, is the best known of several therblig analysis methods. Men who like this approach say that you get practically perfect time standards quicker than with time study. They claim also that the thorough investigation needed to write up the bits of a job causes the analyst to see so many places to improve the job that you always make gains. Also that you control creeping changes, because you get such a complete record of how the job is now done.

MTM enthusiasts even claim that the rates are so perfect that no one —not even unions—ought to complain. Unions don't buy this, however —nor do they accept the idea that you get rid of performance rating. (You do get rid of it—but only by accepting the expert engineer's rating that went into making up the catalogue of times.) Unions and some others, too, object to some of the time values used. They question, for example, if there really are any basic movements. Turning your hand, for example, can be done so many ways that it is hard to catalogue them all and to be sure the catalogue furnishes the time for just the kind of turn that occurs. Or how about "exert pressure"? There are all kinds and degrees. Even if the catalogue does give the right time in its list, it takes judgment to pick out the right time. Although MTM is successfully used in many companies, it won't stop all arguments over standards.

LIMITATIONS TO USE OF TIME STUDY

Production standards can be and are used many places when the work itself cannot be timed. Being set without time study means that most of them are only approximations. Rarely are they as good as time study standards, but approximate standards are nearly always better than none.

But, why can't you time all jobs?

1. You can time only what you can see. That cuts out thinking and leaves you with only manual jobs.
2. If you time a job, it has to be a specific job—with starting and stopping points and separable into units so that you can count how many times it is done. You can't do that with, say, the work of a janitor or a plant guard (and many other jobs).
3. You don't time some jobs because they aren't repetitive enough. One-time jobs can't profitably be timed. You won't get back the time study cost out of future jobs being done better. This limits you to repetitive jobs.
4. Some jobs aren't timed because the man does too many things. A maintenance department carpenter, for example, does too many things to have standards for them all. His daily work report would sometimes be several pages long. Also it is too costly to verify what he says he did. And, when you don't check reports, most men on piecework will tell you that they have turned out more work than they have done.
5. It usually doesn't pay to have standards for only part of a man's work. If you can't put it all on standards, you won't get much efficiency out of him. He will exaggerate the time that he says that he spent on the daywork (for which he gets paid by the hour) and so keep his earnings up. He may have spent 4 hours on piecework and 4 on daywork (not in single stretches of time, but all mixed up during the day). But he'll tell

you that he did the piecework in 3 hours and put 5 hours in on the day-work and you can't prove that he didn't. It looks as if he did 9 hours of work in the day but he didn't. You are put in the spot of having to give him 9 hours of pay or of arbitrarily (although perhaps correctly) cutting down his claim of 5 hours of daywork.

6. There is little need to time study jobs where the man can't control the volume of work. If his machine paces him, he has to keep up or be taken off the job.
7. If quality is hard to define (as in a polished surface), standards may cause quality to fall off. The man will say that he has done the job well enough when he hasn't. Think twice before accepting this criticism though. A man on daywork can, and, if you let him, maybe will, shine a polished surface all day. You can't let him spend so much time on an operation that it makes your costs go way up. "Spit and polish" doesn't pay. Jobs where quality is hard to define are exactly the places where you do need production standards as well as quality standards.
8. Union opposition. Unions often oppose time study. Where a union has this attitude and where the union is very strong, it may be able to stop some time study work.

METHODS RECORDS

A job standard is a time allowance for doing a job the way it is *done today*. Next month's and next year's ways are likely to be different—and always more efficient. They will take less time, since we keep today's method if proposed changes aren't improvements. We will always know about big changes made in the future, but we often miss little changes. Pretty soon we are paying for one method when a shorter method is used.

Then we try to put in a standard covering today's method and promptly get into an argument. The worker says that there has been no change or that, yes, we used to do it another way but that was long before the standard was set, and that there has been no change since then. Here is where you need a fully detailed record to turn to. It costs more at first to get all the detail and to write it down clearly, but it so often saves arguments (and lets you go ahead and make changes in the standards that should be made) that you should always do it. Detailed left- and right-hand movement charts are fine records. Moving pictures are even better.

Trend toward Loosened Rates. Actually every company's rates tend to loosen up forever as creeping changes are missed. Besides, every newly set rate which happens to be loose—and there will be an occasional loose one—goes into effect and stays loose. But every tight rate is challenged and usually loosened after a restudy of the job. In total your rates are always loosening up.

The first effect is for bonuses to creep up. Maybe your men first make an average of 25 per cent bonus, then it works up to 35 per cent, and finally (this takes years) higher yet. Then it will probably stop at 50 per cent or so. Why will it stop? It stops because your best men are setting production ceilings for themselves for fear that rates will be cut. Actually, of course, your men are not averaging 150 per cent efficient. It is just that new methods take less time, but the men are still getting credit for the old standard times. The rates should be corrected.

New jobs, however, provide opportunities to work back toward proper rates. Old jobs keep dropping out, and new ones come in. Set the new standards properly, and the tendency toward loosening up stops. But the new proper standards for new jobs will look tight compared to the remaining old loosened rates. The point is *not* to set the new standards so loosely as to be consistent with the old wrong rates.

PROVING RATES

What if the man on the job thinks that a new piece rate or time standard is too tight? He objects, of course. Then what? Read your labor contract. Many contracts say that if he objects within 30 days, the company has to listen. If he lets 30 days go by without objection, the rate stands and may not be made the subject of a grievance.

Supposing that the man objects. What do you do? The first thing to do is for the time study man to look the job over again and to look over his worksheet again. Maybe he'll take another study. Possibly he'll change the rate but probably not, because his first standard should be right, at least as he sees it.

Suppose that he and the worker are as far apart as ever. By now the shop steward and the foreman are also in on the argument, but that doesn't often help settle anything. The question still is, how can this time study man prove the reasonableness of his standard? Sometimes the time study man has rather convincing proof. This happens if the worker he studied would have made a good bonus during the study had the new rate been in effect then. No one can say that the job can't be done so fast, because the man did it much faster during the study.

That doesn't get rid of many arguments, though, because those aren't the standards a worker objects to. He objects to the ones where he took longer than the time study man allowed. The obvious thing to do next —and it sounds quite fair—is to tell him to try out the rate for a while and see if he can't make a reasonable bonus. Once in a while, but not often, he does made a good bonus and drops his complaint. And once in a while, if he doesn't make a bonus during such a tryout, the time study man raises the rate.

Generally, though, the man on the job isn't going to prove himself wrong. He works on the job all right, but sees to it that he doesn't turn out so much work as to prove the rate acceptable. Tryouts like this usually crystallize everyone's opinion. The worker says, "See, I told you that the rate was too tight, and this proves it." The time study man says, "You held back; you didn't want to prove that the rate was right."

There is no good way to prove the rate. Once in a while the foreman—rusty though he is as an operator—does the job at bonus pace. But he is often too rusty to do this—and even if he does, the union turns thumbs down, saying that it will have no standards based on a "pace setter's" performance.

In most cases rate disputes are settled by the company standing its ground and putting the rate in. And if it does, union men usually drop the matter but store it up in their minds as one more minor grudge to dig up again at bargaining time. Companies can hardly give in and raise rates very often or workers will argue about all new rates, figuring that they will sometimes get them raised (whether they should be or not).

The union doesn't have to drop the matter, though, if the company stands its ground. It can file a grievance claiming that the company has violated the labor contract by setting an unfair standard. This can finally be carried before an arbitrator who will rule one way or the other. Arbitrators are almost never time study men and really can't tell if a rate is right or not, but they decide anyway, and their decision stands.

What policy should you follow with disputed rate when it is first disputed? Give in? If the rate is wrong you should give in, and if it happens often you should get rid of the time study man who sets wrong rates. But, assuming that the rate is actually right to start with, you cannot give in without ending up with inconsistent standards. Besides workers take giving in as an agreement that the time study man has made a mistake. And if you admit one mistake today, they will argue about future rates, saying that you have just made more mistakes. But if you refuse to change rates, you build up men's resentment. They'll remember it when negotiations come.

Some companies and some unions try to settle rate arguments on a factual basis. The union has its own time study man who checks disputed rates. You get rid of a few arguments that way, but not many. If the union time study man agrees with the company man very often, the workers say that he is only a company stooge and the union fires him.

A practical but drastic solution to a rate dispute is occasionally resorted to where the company feels very sure that the rate is perfectly fair. The man who claims that a rate is too low is told to try it out. He can't refuse because refusal to do work assigned is grounds for discharge. If he does the work fast enough to earn a bonus, the rate is proved right and the grievance is dropped. If he slows down enough so that he earns no bonus, the foreman reprimands him and tells him to produce or be fired. Sometimes he goes to work, earns a bonus, and the rate is proved to be satisfactory.

If he continues his slowdown, he is fired and a new employee is put on the job. Naturally, the discharged employee files a grievance, claiming that he has been wrongly discharged. The company denies him reinstatement, and the case goes to arbitration. *Meanwhile the new employee is making a substantial bonus on the job.* By the time the arbitrator hears the case the production record of the new man proves the reasonableness of the rate, and the arbitrator can hardly do other than uphold both the rate and the discharge.

This method of resolving rate disputes is uncommon, particularly after it has been used once or twice. After its use rate disputes are likely to be confined to the rare cases where adjustments really should be made. This method does not always work, because you have to find a courageous new employee who is willing to face the ill will of his fellow employees. This method tends to build up some employee ill will, but it also builds up worker and union respect for the company. It may also cause a strike if the labor contract permits strikes over disputed production standards.

TEMPORARY RATES

It often takes workers a little time to get into the swing of a new operation. Besides, the operation is probably not at first set up just right and it may take days or even weeks to get the bugs out. The men won't produce nearly as much as they will later. When should you set up the job standard? Right away or later? If a new operation is to be permanent, some people think that you should wait till after the bedding-down period because, at the start, the proper rate looks impossible to the workers. One alternative is to set a loose temporary rate.

Loose temporary rates raise problems, though, because a worker gets good pay for low output. As long as he does, he never turns out any more. Also he gets used to the pay and then thinks of the regular piece rate, when it comes along, as a rate cut. The regular rate may be so much stiffer than the loose temporary rate that he really may think that it is impossible and object strenuously.

Temporary rates are bad, too, because the time study man doesn't always get around to setting permanent standards when he should. Later, when he does get around, it is harder than ever to get workers to accept the new rate without argument. *Be sure* to label all temporary rates "Temporary"; also put them on pink or blue paper. Also, at the start, set an end date: "This rate does not apply after (a set date)."

But if temporary rates are so bad, how do you get over the early hump of low productivity on new jobs? It really does seem a little unfair to put a pieceworker on a job that will pay him less money for a while —particularly if part of the reason for low output is that the job isn't yet set up right. Probably it is best to guarantee him his past average earnings for a short time, *but not for long.* Men on long guarantees take exactly that long to learn the job well enough to make a bonus. Elgin Watch Company found that if you changed the guarantee period you changed the learning period! Men on short guarantees learned in a short time. Men on long guarantees couldn't earn bonuses nearly so soon!

RATE CUTTING

Rate cutting when time standards and wage incentives are used is the worst sin that management can commit in the eyes of labor. Fifty years ago, when time study was first introduced, rate cutting was common. A job would be timed and a standard set, perhaps carelessly, allowing, say, 5 minutes of time and 5 minutes' pay for doing a job. But if any worker, mistakenly trying to make all the money he could, began to turn out the products in 3 minutes each, he soon found the rate cut to 4 (or 3) minutes.

Rate cutting, common in the 1920's and not unknown today, naturally

George Lichty, used by permission of Chicago Sun–Times Syndicate

FIG. 30–6.   ". . . And with award for fine work in producing more than your quota, comrade, comes advancement! . . . We are raising your quota! . . ."

leaves a sour taste in the workers' mouth. Only once is enough to make the men mistrust management and oppose time study. After that the men put ceilings on their output and join unions.

Practically no one cuts rates. Most companies guarantee not to cut rates, and they don't cut them. Occasionally (or frequently, according to union charges) a company is found which cuts rates indirectly. The letter of the guarantee is kept, but not the spirit. What the company does is to change the procedure so that the old job is no longer done, then set new rates on the new methods. If the change is solely to get a lower rate, it would seem just to be an indirect rate cut. It would probably be hard to find any examples, however, where improvements weren't made at the same time. If they are, you'd have to have a new rate anyway.

UNIONS AND TIME STUDY

What do unions think of time study? And what difference does it make what they think? Answering the second question first. If a union is weak it doesn't matter what it thinks, but if it is strong its attitude may well spell success or failure—it may keep you from using time study at all.

What do unions think of time study? Mostly they oppose; mostly they oppose incentives as well. They say that incentives "pit one man against the other." Opposition to time study is more a union *organization* attitude than it is the attitude of members—particularly if the men make good bonuses. Here is a quotation from the union newspaper of one company's local union. It is the typical negative view.

Your union is receiving the full time study data on jobs in grievance and finds that the —— company has one of the biggest chiseling rackets in the time study of jobs, and the setting of piece work prices. The time study man who times you on new jobs, changes of method, etc. has the power to regulate piece work prices 40 per cent. This is done through the gimmick called "efficiency," which ranges from 80 per cent to 120 per cent on each time study.

The time study man is the sole judge of an employee's efficiency when a job is being timed. If when an employee is being timed, and the time study man decides the employee should have an efficiency rating of 80% he is immediately cutting an employee's wages 20% below OER [the job base rate] during the time study. At 100% efficiency an employee is being timed at OER. This is the key to [the company] speedup and wage cutting on piece work jobs.

The company is cheating employees out of their incentive or piece work earnings through their manipulation of an employee's efficiency while they are being time studied.

An example is Dept. 226 where most of the assembly jobs are being timed at 80% efficiency, meaning that after the price is set these employees must produce 20% more than they did during the time study just to make OER.

Through this manipulation of efficiency in time studies the company is lowering piece work prices, especially on new jobs in the plant, and cheating the workers out of their incentive earnings. The company is cheating workers out of the efficiency and experience that they have built up through many years on a job.

Each year the company is hiring less people and making more money than in previous years. They are making more millions in profit through their speedup and chiseling on piece work prices. This wage cutting policy of [the company] must be stopped and can be stopped with every worker in the plant giving their full support to the union in this fight. Support your union, and stop speedup and wage cutting by [the company].

But, though most unions oppose time study, some are all for it—or at least all for incentives—if they have something to say about rates. In the clothing industry the union has at times hired industrial engineers to take time studies and set standards. The International Ladies Garment Workers' Union has worked with employers in setting up standards for many operations in that industry in the New York City area.

WHO DOES TIME STUDY WORK?

Almost always you need a separate staff department to do time study work. Foremen sometimes set rates, but when they do it, it is often not well done. Almost always, too, methods study (including motion study) goes with time study to make up the work of the industrial engineering department. Should there be no special job improvement department or group assigned specifically to that work, time study may be associated with the production control department, one supervisor having charge of both types of work. Time study may be an independent department reporting to the factory superintendent. It is sometimes tied up with job evaluation. Occasionally, time study is administered by the personnel or industrial relations department, while in at least one company (a large one) it is under the controller because of its relationship to budget making.

There is considerable variation in size of the department, depending on how many new jobs keep coming along. A time study man may average three or four time standards per day on simple jobs. Ordinarily one time study man per 100 factory workers would be high. One per 1,000 workers would be low. Perhaps one per 300 would be more nearly typical. If the department also does considerable cost estimating for prospective jobs for the sales department or does methods improvement work, it will have to be larger. Industrial engineering departments often have somewhere near 15 employees for every 1,000 other employees.

STUDY QUESTIONS

1. Would a nonincentive factory ever use time study? When?
2. Do actual and normal times ever differ? Explain.
3. How can production control use standards set for incentives for scheduling production?
4. Why bother timing jobs element by element?
5. Explain briefly how a time study man makes up a time standard after he gets back to his office with his data.

6. What is the "allowed" time for an element? How is it figured?

7. What is "ratio delay"? Explain.

8. Explain briefly the following:
   a) Element
   b) Typical element time
   c) Foreign element
   d) Snapback method

9. Some people don't like leveling. Why?

10. Can you eliminate judgment in time study? Discuss.

11. Some people say to time study a good, not a poor, worker. Give their reasons.

12. What do you do with machine running time when you set a time standard? Discuss.

13. Should you have standards for setting up machines? What other ways could you handle setup time, yet have it on some kind of standard?

14. What is the difference between work sampling and ratio delay? When is each used?

15. Contrast microscopic and macroscopic methods for setting standards.

16. When and how does a time study man use constant and variable elements?

17. In practice, you can't use time study everywhere, even if you wanted to. Why not?

18. How can you prove the reasonableness of a newly set time standard?

19. What do unions think of time study? Why? What difference does it make what they think?

Case 30–1.   Washboard Assembly Problem

The following data cover the assembly and packing into a container of wooden washboards. The washboards are made up of two side pieces, one top crosspiece, one middle crosspiece, one bottom crosspiece, and a wooden back piece for the upper section of the board and a corrugated glass scrubbing board. The pieces are fitted together and held in place by six nails. Six washboards are packed in a container. The following is a copy of the observation sheet. The times recorded are continuous watch readings and are in hundredths of minutes. The number of full minutes is shown only when it changes.

Element	Operation Cycle						
	1	2	3	4	5	6	7
Assemble top to first side.............	.12	.58	.43	.36	.25	.15	6.01
Assemble back piece and middle crosspiece..........................	.29	.82	.60	.55	.41	.32	.19
Assemble scrubbing board and bottom piece............................	.44	.94	.76	.70	.55	.48	.32
Assemble second side piece............	.64	2.00	3.02	.89	.78	.63	.50
Nail six nails and lay aside............	.89	.33	.24	4.12	5.04	.91	.75
Get and form container................	1.08	......	......	......	......	......	.95
Place six boards in container and set aside............................	.51	......	......	......	......	......	7.31

Discard the extremely long and extremely short elemental readings and determine the selected elemental time for each element by averaging the remaining time values. Assume that the time study man rated the man's performance at 110 per cent of normal.

Determine the cycle time for the job before allowances are added. Assume that the allowances for miscellaneous necessary duties, for fatigue, and for personal time come to an additional 30 per cent. Determine the time standard for the job. Express the production standard in terms of washboards to be assembled per hour.

CASE 30–2.   THE TEMPLETON BRASS COMPANY

The principal product of the Templeton Brass Company, employer of 250 persons, is water faucets. It operates a small brass foundry and machining, plating, and polishing departments.

Piecework is used in the machining operations on water faucets. Nearly all of the rates were set two or more years ago when the company had a time study man. After he left, no one else knew how to set standards, and no one had the time to do it. The old rate which most nearly applied was used for operations on the few new designs since that time.

During the two years since the last standards were set by time study, however, certain lathe operations had been changed. By using carboloy-tipped cutting tools, it is possible to do certain turret lathe work with fewer tools and in much less time. The old time study records often do not show what kinds of cutting tools or how many cutting tools were used, although on some record cards the number of tools is shown.

In one case, on pattern 5534, operation 602, the record shows that four tools were used. The bare cycle time (for which the record provided elemental time data) came to .640 minutes per faucet. Additional allowances for fatigue, tool allowance, gaging, and handling were shown. They were .064 (10 per cent), .096 (15 per cent) and .01 and .02, respectively. The total time per unit came to .830 minutes, or 72 pieces per hour. On a job base rate of $2.40, the piece rate was $3.33 per 100.

The management checked and found that only three tools were now being used and that one element had been eliminated from the job. Actually, this was only one example of many, and the superintendent proposed that all jobs be retimed. The union objected, contending that in many cases any justifiable changes in the rates could be made by eliminating specific element times from the old list and computing new times. In the case of operation 602, that was done. The new time standard was .671, made up of a bare cycle time of .535 minutes plus fatigue .053, tool allowance .053 (reduced from 15 to 10 per cent because of the use of only three tools), gaging .01, and handling .02. The new standard production was 89.4 pieces per hour.

The operator complained and asked for a recheck of the job. The foreman used a stop watch and, on checking it, found that the operator was doing the job in a bare cycle time of .440 minutes. Adding this to the .109 minutes of allowance time given above, he could take out his fatigue time and still average one faucet each .549 minutes, or 109.3 pieces per hour, and thus earn a bonus of 22.3 per cent. The operator remained dissatisfied, claiming that he should get a greater bonus for that level of output.

Comment on the method of setting standards. What should the company do to dispose of the employee's complaint? What should it do in the future (remember that the union opposes time study and that the union is very strong in this plant)?

Chapter 31

OPERATIONS RESEARCH

"O<small>PERATIONS</small> research" is a broad term. It is, first, a viewpoint, second a way of handling problems and, third, it covers a whole series of techniques for solving problems. Originating in the military in World War II, it was by the mid-1950's well established in business.

Operations research, as a viewpoint, means looking at a whole problem—not just part of it. We look at problems from the whole company's point of view, not from one department's point of view. Suppose that you make electric stoves and the customers have trouble with burners burning out too soon. Look at the problem from all points of view. Do the customers have the proper voltage in their power supply? Are the burners made of the right material? Have you designed the stove to heat the burners too hot? How is your quality control? Are faulty burners going out in your stoves?

Maybe you'll find that the trouble is in the customers' source of electricity. Maybe it is your wrong choice of material from which to make burners. Maybe it is poor quality control. Maybe it is a metallurgical problem. Maybe it is two or three things. By looking at the whole picture you are more likely to find the cause of the trouble and to get it fixed.

Operations research as a way of handling problems means assigning a team of workers to problems. Include men with different backgrounds and from different departments. Having different backgrounds assures off-beat thinking that sometimes unearths unsuspected solutions to problems.

Some people would say that all that we have done so far is to give a new name to old ideas and practices. Good executives have always tried to see problems in their entirety. And good executives have always used committees which include men of various backgrounds to look into broad problems. O.R. critics have more objections. They say that O.R. often needs figures that are costly to get. And they say that O.R. often does needless rethinking about problems already solved. Also they say, O.R. is dangerous. If you overlook one or two important factors you get a wrong answer. Or if you overlook how an isolated situation fits into the whole picture, you may be led into wrong actions.

Probably there is much truth to what these critics say. Operations research enthusiasts agree that good management existed before anyone coined the term "operations research," but they claim that "operations research" has added an "extra." They say that before O.R. too many problems did not get the over-all treatment and that too rarely were committees appointed whose members had varied backgrounds. They say too that O.R. trains everyone to think and appreciate quantitative relationships.

O.R. doesn't make decisions. It informs you about costs of alternatives. It might tell you, for example, action A will cut absenteeism 20 per cent but will cost 6 per cent more in personnel administration costs. Action B will cut absenteeism 17 per cent and cost 2 per cent. This is the kind of information that lets management make intelligent decisions.

To most people, O.R. *means the third item in our list, the collection of mathematical techniques* used in solving many problems. Here, undeniably, is something both new and valuable. Among the mathematical techniques used are probability theory and linear programming. Linear programming, in particular, has proved most valuable.

Some of the mathematical parts of O.R. are today practical only because of electronic computers. Without computers the formulas and equations would be impossible to solve or would cost too much to work out. Computers have made possible the solution of many such problems.

OPERATIONS RESEARCH PROBLEM REQUIREMENTS

Mathematical formulas use numbers. You have, therefore, to quantify every factor involved in any O.R. problem. Sometimes you have to estimate using rather vague figures. Suppose, for example, the question is: Should we keep our work force intact over a seasonal slack period and let inventory build up? Or should we cut production and lay some workers off?

O.R. needs figures before it can get answers. You have to answer the following questions with answers that are numbers. How long will the layoff last? How many laid-off workers will we lose? How much will training and lost production cost until replacement workers are well trained? How big will the inventory get before we start to work it down? How long will it take to get back to a normal inventory?

The answer to every one of these questions is partly guesswork. To the extent that it is guesswork, the O.R. answer is also a guess. Don't throw O.R. aside too quickly, though. If you do throw it aside, have you answered the first question? Should we keep the work force up or not? You *must* finally answer it yes or no or choose a middle course and lay off a few workers. But without O.R. you are really doing little more than guessing. You don't know whether your choice is best, and you have no notion of the dollars you save if the action you choose is the best action or of the dollars you lose if it isn't.

Operations research can tell you, based on the best figures you have, that action A is best. Action B, having a cost disadvantage of x dollars, is next best. Action C, with a cost disadvantage of y dollars is third best, and so on.

Actually, is it so bad to put quantitative values on intangibles? Your first reaction is probably to say that it is very bad, that you can't possibly get good problem solutions doing that. But think again. If intangibles will bear on the result, *they do have a quantifiable effect* in the end. Are you better off throwing up your hands and saying you can't measure their effect? Or are you better off putting down your best estimate, rough though it is? You ought *not* throw out O.R. because it has to work with quantified intangibles some of the time. These "guesstimates" are the very same figures that you have to try to weigh in your mind if you discard O.R. On the other hand, having used crude figures in O.R., don't forget it. Answers should be used as approximations, not as exact answers.

A word of warning about linear programming. Operations research often uses linear programming. The relationships between factors *must* be linear or the answer won't be valid. Linear relationships mean that when one factor changes, so does another and at a given amount. An hourly paid employee's hours worked and his wages are linear. The more hours, the more money. Same with the example we use in discussing linear programming (pages 599–603), the more products, the more profits.

Linearity can be negative without affecting its validity. If you start with a $20 bill, the more you spend, the less you have left. We have negative linearity in our linear programming problem when we cut products A and B in order to get metal for product C. To get valid answers in linear programming there must be linear relationships among the factors.

TECHNIQUES OF OPERATIONS RESEARCH

Operations research uses many techniques. Most of them are variations of probability theory and linear programming. You hear of other procedures, but most are based on these two. Waiting line theory is an application of probability. "Stochastic" and "Random" processes are nearly always applications of probability or linear programming. "Game theory" has elements of both. So has "search" theory. "Mathematical models" are equations or formulas, usually of the linear programming kind. So are "multiple correlation" methods.

Probability theory we describe in Chapter 36. Linear programming is discussed later in this chapter. Multiple correlation is one particular kind of linear analysis. Waiting line theory (also called queuing theory) has to do with lack of balance between things coming and going. It can tell you what your peak loads in receiving and shipping (or other places) will be. It will tell you how long products (or men) will have to wait and how much idle time there will be in slack periods.

Stochastic processes, random processes, and mathematical models refer to setting up formulas and equations to represent relationships. These allow you to find out what results particular sets of circumstances will produce. You can even put figures in for all kinds of unusual situations and see what the results would be.

Game theory is probability with the addition of uncontrollable outside factors. Results are partly dependent on your decisions but partly on what your opponent (in business, your competitor) does. Game theory considers what he might do and tells you which action on your part is likely to work out best.

AREAS OF USE

Just what kinds of business "problems" can operations research solve. Here are three examples. Then we'll list others.

SKF Industries uses linear programming to schedule its automatic screw machine department. Its 125 machines include single-spindle, 4-spindle, and 6-spindle machines, which cost, individually, up to $50,000. It is important to use them effectively. SKF has 100 to 125 orders weekly for their machines. Individual orders call for anything from a few hundred up to several hundred thousand pieces. Parts made are for ball and roller bearings and consist of inner and outer races, cylindrical rollers, ball bearings, retainers, tapered sleeves, and lock nuts.

Some machines make parts complete, others do only part of the job, also the bigger faster machines have higher machine-hour costs than smaller slower machines. There are three or four different kinds of machines capable of making every part, but their setup times and costs to operate vary.

The question is, of course, how to allocate orders to machines to get the lowest unit cost. SKF lists for every product the ideal way to make it. Then if, because of machines being loaded, an order has to be produced in a less efficient way, the excess cost over ideal is regarded as a loss. Before linear programming, the excess over standard ran 21 per cent, this at a time when the department was operating below capacity. Linear programming cut the excess to 9 per cent and saved over $200,000 a year.

Eastman Kodak uses queuing theory to tell how many service men to have for direct workers. It calculates how much service work there is to do, how it peaks up at times, and how many service men to have for direct workers. Eastman balances out this idle time of service men against the delays to direct workers if they have to wait. Eastman ends up knowing the ideal number of service men to use.

Owens-Illinois, a multiplant company with many multiplant customers wanted to know where orders should be shipped from. It found that railroad freight costs in one year ran $800,000 over the ideal—what the cost would have been if every order had been shipped from the closest O-I plant. More careful placement of orders to plants the next year knocked this excess down $400,000.

We could go on. Here is a list of production problems O.R. has been used for:

What is the cost of leveling production?
What parts should we stock up on during stock periods?
Should we manufacture in lots or continuously?
Should we make or buy?
Inventory control: when to reorder? minimun stock determination, reorder quantities.
Plant location.
Proper balance between speed of operation and amount of scrap.
Scheduling, best use of machines.
What is the proper amount to spend on research?
Best use of scarce raw materials.
Proper number of men.
Balancing of operations along an assembly line.
Programming interplant shipments.
Evaluating methods improvements.

LINEAR PROGRAMMING

Linear programming means using mathematical formulas for solving problems—in our case, business problems. It is a method for arriving at the best choice from among alternative courses of action. Businessmen have always had to try to select the best alternative, but before linear programming (which came in in the mid-1950's) they had no good way for finding which course of action was really best.

Suppose that we use an example to show how linear programming works. We will use a hypothetical automobile factory. To make the problem simple enough to explain in a few pages, we will assume that our factory makes only two models, a 4-door, 6-cylinder sedan and an 8-cylinder station wagon. We will deal with three manufacturing departments: metal stamping, engine assembly and final assembly, in which there are two assembly lines, one for sedans and one for station wagons. Both can operate at the same time.

The stamping department can, in a week, turn out enough parts for 7,000 sedans or 12,000 station wagons. But it can't do both at the same time. We can have one or the other extreme, or we can have parts for some sedans and some station wagons. Same with engines. We can get 9,000 6-cylinder engines for sedans or 6,000 8's for station wagons or combinations between. The sedan assembly line can turn out 6,000 sedans as a maximum. The station wagon line's top is 4,000. Here, however, we can operate both lines at once. Boosting the output of one line does not mean cutting the other.

These facts give us several "parameters" (limits beyond which we cannot go). But no one limitation sets limits for all possible operating

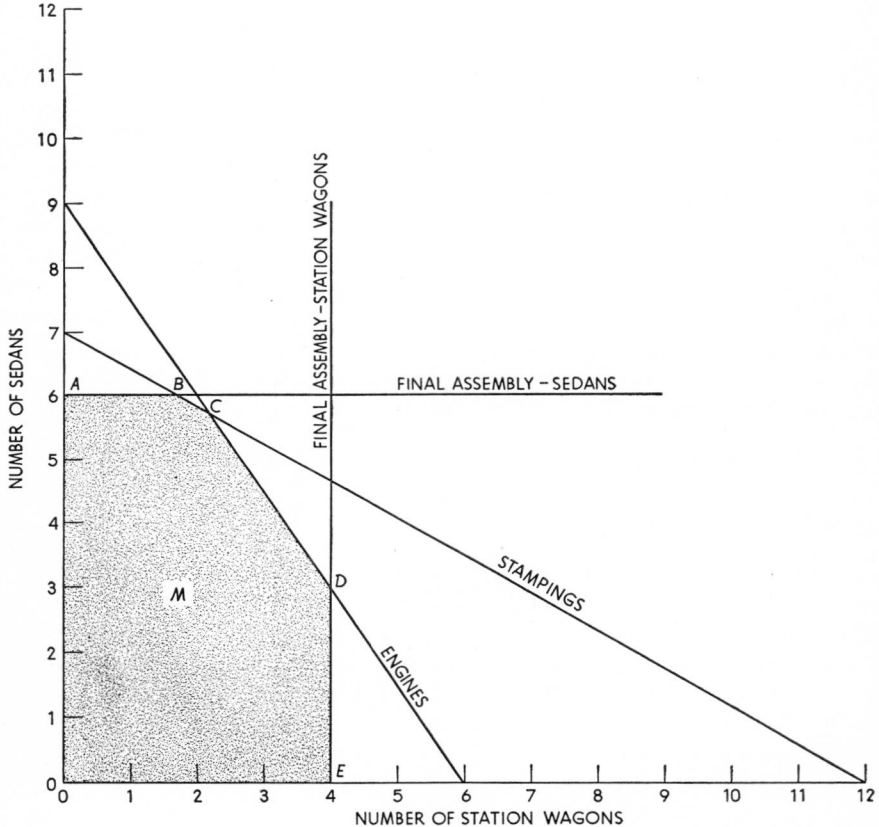

FIG. 31–1.   Chart showing possibilities of combinations for making sedans and station wagons.

combinations. We can make 9,000 6-cylinder engines, but we can assemble only 6,000 sedans. Here assembly limits us. Or we can, as far as assembly is concerned, assemble 6,000 sedans and 4,000 station wagons. But actually, we cannot do that because we can't make enough stamped parts and engines. Or our stamping capacity would let us make parts for 5,000 sedans and 3,430 station wagons. We cannot do that either. This time engines limit us. If we make 5,000 6-cylinder engines we can make only 2,670 engines.

Figure 31–1 shows in a chart all of the possible relationships. We can make sedans and station wagons in any combination in area M. We can make 6,000 sedans and no station wagons (see point A). Or we can make 6,000 sedans and anywhere up to 1,715 station wagons (see point B). But from there on, if we want any more station wagons, we must cut down on sedans because the stamping department is up to its limit. By the time we get down to 5,727 sedans and up to 2,183 station wagons (see point C), we run into engine limitations. From this point on as we cut sedans and increase station wagons, engines limit us until we get up to 4,000 station wagons (see point D). By this time we are down to 3,000 sedans. From here on we can increase station wagons no more because we are up to the capacity of the station wagon assembly line. We can cut sedans below 3,000, but that won't help station wagon production.

So far we have found out how the limiting factors set off the *quantity* of sedans and station wagons against each other. The plant is operating at its full capacity in at least one department at any point on the parameter line, the line connecting points A, B, C, D, and E. At points B, C, and D, it is operating at full capacity in two departments.

But we are in business to make money so our real goal is to find out at which point we earn the most. We want to "maximize" our earnings. Assume that we make $300 on every sedan and $400 on every station wagon. Here is how it works out profit-wise:

POINT	NUMBER OF		TOTAL PROFIT		
	Sedans	Station Wagons	Sedans $300 Each	Station Wagons $400 Each	Both
A.....	6,000	0	$1,800,000	0	$1,800,000
B.....	6,000	1,715	1,800,000	$ 686,000	2,486,000
C.....	5,727	2,183	1,718,100	873,200	2,591,300
D.....	3,000	4,000	900,000	1,600,000	2,500,000
E.....	0	4,000	0	1,600,000	1,600,000

Introducing the profit idea adds a factor that is a little hard to show on a two-dimensional diagram. We could draw in a third dimension and depict our answer as the maximum vertical point. For our purpose we have just calculated it by arithmetic above. We make the most money at C, producing 5,727 sedans and 2,183 station wagons. We could have used a formula instead to tell us which arrangement is best.

The Simplex Method. Many business problems have dozens of factors. When they do, we must turn to a different linear programming technique, the simplex algorithm, commonly called the "simplex" method. It allows us to solve algebraic equations having more unknowns than equations. We couldn't do that with ordinary algebra.

We'll use a simple example of apportioning two scarce metals to three products. Suppose that because of government regulations we are allowed to use only limited amounts of nickel and copper. We want to divide our supply among three products in such a way as to make the most profit.

We start with the materials requirements for our products:

METAL	AMOUNT NEEDED			DAILY ALLOTMENT
	Product A	Product B	Product C	
Nickel.........	2 lbs.	4 lbs.	6 lbs.	16 lbs.
Copper.........	3 lbs.	2 lbs.	4 lbs.	12 lbs.
Profit per unit....	$50	$60	$120	

At first glance you might say: product C yields the most profit, so let's make as many of it as we can first and then make up the remaining metal into the next most profitable item (product B). So we use 12 pounds of nickel and 8 pounds of copper to make 2 units of product C. Then we use the other 4 pounds of nickel and 2 pounds of copper to make 1 unit of product B. This leaves 2 pounds of copper left over. We would have $300 profit: $240 from the 2 units of product C and $60 from 1 unit of product B. We can't make any more products of any kind because we have used up all our nickel.

Don't be too hasty, though. In an actual business situation, we'd be dealing in much larger amounts: more nickel; more copper; more units of products A, B, and C; and more products. The point is that in our example we can't make fractions of products, but if we are talking about 16,000 pounds of nickel and 12,000 pounds of copper, we might find that the best answer of all was not to make 2,000 units of product C and 1,000 units of product B. Maybe (and it is actually so in our problem) we ought not to make twice as many of products C as products B and none at all of product A. Figuring out the exact combination to give us the most profit would be, by arithmetic or ordinary algebra, a long job.

The simplex method is much quicker and, as a method, can be used where there are many more factors than we use in our problem.

Here's how the simplex method works in our example. We start by saying: An unknown number of products A times 2 pounds of nickel plus an unknown number of products B times 4 pounds of nickel plus an unknown number of products C times 6 pounds of nickel will use up 16 pounds of nickel or less. We call the unknown numbers x, y, and z. We can make a similar statement for copper. We can't make up algebraic equations to help us get answers yet, though, because the best solution may mean having a little nickel or copper leftover. So we add two more letters: n for leftover nickel and c for leftover copper. Now we can set up equations:

Equation I for nickel: $2x + 4y + 6z + n = 16$
"   II for copper: $3x + 2y + 4z + c = 12$

Notice that our two equations, I and II, contain 5 unknown values: x, y, z, n, and c. From your algebra you will remember that if you have only two equations and five unknown numbers, there are several sets of five numbers that will fit the equations.

Using the simplex method, we never do find all of the possible numbers that might fit. We find one set and then look for other sets that will improve the result. The improved result that we are looking for is the greatest profit. For it we need to use a third equation, equation III. P in this equation means the profit. It is the "function" that we are trying to maximize.

Equation III: $50x + 60y + 120z = P$

We start our solution using equation I and assuming that we will make only product A and none of either B or C. In that case y and z are zero, and the three equations become:

$$\text{I:} \quad 2x + n = 16$$
$$\text{II:} \quad 3x + c = 12$$
$$\text{III:} \quad 50x = P$$

We make another assumption: that we will use up all of our nickel making products A. That makes $n = 0$, and we have $2x = 16$ and $x = 8$. Our nickel will allow us to make 8 units of product A. But when we try equation II with $x = 8$, it becomes $3(8) + c = 12$, or $24 + c = 12$ $c = -12$. We are 12 pounds short of enough copper to make 8 units of product A.

So we try equation II first. If we use up all the copper, c will equal zero and equation II becomes $3x = 12$ and $x = 4$. We have enough copper to make 4 units of product A. Using $x = 4$ in equation I tells us that there is enough nickel to make 4 units of product A and leave us with 8 pounds of nickel left over. Now we go to equation III to see how good a solution this is. It tells us that making 4 units of product A with a profit of $50 each will yield us a profit of $200.

As a second step in the simplex method, we try to see if a combination of products A and B would be more profitable than making only product A. We still omit product C; it will come in in the third step. Our equations now become:

$$\text{I:} \quad 2x + 4y + n = 16$$
$$\text{II:} \quad 3x + 2y + c = 12$$
$$\text{III:} \quad 50x + 60y = P$$

We hope to get a combination of products A and B that leaves no nickel or copper left over so we start by setting n and c at zero. This leaves equation I as $2x + 4y = 16$ and equation II as $3x + 2y = 12$. These are simple algebraic simultaneous equations. Solving, we get (using I first): $2x = 16 - 4y$, $x = \dfrac{16 - 4y}{2}$, $x = 8 - 2y$. Substituting in II: $3(8 - 2y) + 2y = 12$, $24 - 6y + 2y = 12$, $-4y = -12$, $y = 3$. Returning to equation I: $2x + 4(3) = 16$, $2x + 12 = 16$, $2x = 4$, $x = 2$. We can make 2 of product A and 3 of product B.

Our problem came out with whole numbers, meaning that when we make 2 products A and 3 products B, we will have used up all of both metals.

Now we must see how this affects profits. Using equation III: $50(2) + 60(3) = P$, $100 + 180 = P$, $P = \$280$. So this is a better solution than making 4 of products A and nothing else.

We still don't know about product C. We might be still better off making some products C and not so many of A and B. But the proposal above uses all of the nickel and copper. The only way to make any products C is to give up making some products A and B. How many products A and B will we have to give up to make one unit of product C?

Before answering let us note that the answer may be to give up a fraction of either or both A and B. But we can't do that. We can't give up making one fourth of a product A or a fraction of a product B. True, but remember that in an actual business situation, you'd be dealing in thousands. Giving up one fourth of a product A in our example might be the same as giving up 250 products A in practice. A fractional answer to our problem is a satisfactory answer.

We have to use algebra to get our answer. Let a stand for the amount that we would have to cut product A to get enough material to make a contribution of metal to 1 unit of product C. Let b stand for the cut in products B; a and b together will produce enough nickel and copper to make 1 unit of product C.

We now have two new equations. For nickel, the new equation is $2a + 4b = 6$. For copper, it is $3a + 2b = 4$. We solve these simultaneous equations as above, starting with the equation for nickel: $a = \dfrac{6 - 4b}{2}$, $a = 3 - 2b$. Substituting in the equation for copper: $3(3 - 2b) + 2b = 4$, $9 - 6b + 2b = 4$, $-4b = -5$, $b = \frac{5}{4}$. Returning to the equation for nickel: $2a + 4(\frac{5}{4}) = 6$, $2a + 5 = 6$, $2a = 1$, $a = \frac{1}{2}$. In order to produce 1 unit of product C, we must give up $\frac{1}{2}$ of 1 unit of product A *and* $\frac{5}{4}$ units of product B.

Will we be better off if we do this? We must turn again to the profit figures. Giving up $\frac{1}{2}$ of product A means that we will forego $25 of profits. Giving up $\frac{5}{4}$ of product B means giving up $75 in profits, making the total decrease in profits: $100. But 1 unit of product C brings in a profit of $120, so we should certainly make at least 1 unit of product C. We are $20 better off.

Would we be still better off to make more than 1 unit of product C? Yes, the relationship of profitability stays the same. It paid to drop some products A and B to make 1 unit of C, and it will pay just as well to keep on dropping A and B to make C. We should keep cutting A and B until we cut out one or the other completely. Which will go out first and how many products C will the metal saved allow to be made?

We started with the idea of making 2 products A. Every time we cut off ½ of one of them, we contribute to making 1 of C. 2 ÷ ½ = 4. Cutting out A completely would contribute metal toward 4 units of C. We started with the idea of making 3 of product B. Every time that we cut off ⅘ of B, we contribute metal to making 1 of C. 3 ÷ ⅘ = 2.4. Cutting product B out completely will contribute toward making 2.4 units of product C.

This, 2.4 units is, then, the number of products C to make. Product B is cut out completely. Product A has to be cut from our starting number, 2, at the rate of ½ for every product C. 2.4 × ½ = 1.2. 2 − 1.2 = 0.8. Eight tenths of a unit of product A can still be produced. Now, let's check the profits. We find that they total $328 (arrived at as follows: 2.4 units of product C at $120 each = $288, plus 0.8 units of product A at $50 each = $40. Total, $328).

This is the end of our example. We have maximized the profits by using all of both kinds of metal in the most profitable combination. The maximum profit product mix might, in some cases, leave some of one material over, but it didn't happen so in our example.

When you use the simplex method, you normally set up the figures, not in text form with explanations the way we did it but in table form with rows and columns of figures. You need such a set of figures for each step that we went through. The sets of figures are called "tableaus" or "matrixes." Detailed instructions about how to arrange tableaus and how to handle more complex problems are available in statistics textbooks.[1]

The simplex method not only tells you which is the best action among alternatives but it can also tell you how much it costs to follow other actions. In our problem, for example, maybe we ought to keep on making a few product B's to round out our product line with customers. Although our calculations did not go that far, the simplex method would show that for every product B that we make, we will lose $16. Of course we don't actually lose $16 when we sell a product at a $60 profit. But we do too if we look at the $76 we could have made by using the same materials making other products instead. Maybe, even knowing this, we will still choose to make some products B, but after looking at the simplex analysis, we will do it with our eyes open. We will know how much that decision costs.

STUDY QUESTIONS

1. Is the operations research "team" idea any different from regular committees? Explain your answer.

---

[1] A good brief explanation of the simplex method is found in Dakota U. Greenwald, *Linear Programming, An Explanation of the Simplex Algorithm* (New York, The Ronald Press Co., 1957). For a more thorough treatment, see A. Charnes, W. W. Cooper, and A. Henderson, *An Introduction to Linear Programming* (New York: John Wiley & Sons, Inc., 1953).

2. Operations research requires that you quantify everything. But can you do that? And if you do how good is your answer? Discuss.

3. What is meant by saying that linear programming depends on the factors having linear relationships?

4. What areas of manufacturing are suitable for operations research? Which are not well suited? Explain.

5. In the text automobile example using linear programming a series of "parameters" was set up. How does a parameter work? What has it to do with linear programming?

6. How does the simplex method differ from ordinary algebra?

7. Describe how we went about, in the text example, allocating scarce materials to products.

Chapter 32

COMPUTERS

ELECTRONIC computers, sometimes called "data processors," are industry's newest Buck Rogers creations. Best known and most complex of the computers are the "705" made by the International Business Machines Company and the "Univac" made by the Sperry-Rand Company.

Just what is an electronic computer? It is a collection of machines that will remember numbers and words, do arithmetic, compare, sort or merge different sets of figures, and print answers or lists—all at fantastic speeds. A computer will do whole sequences of steps, one after the other, without stopping between. It will remember hundreds of thousands of words or numbers. Electronic computers are not just bigger and fancier desk calculators whose wheels go around faster than ever. The work is done by electrical currents instead.

A computer isn't much to look at. As you see in Figure 32–1, a computer is a collection of steel cabinets arranged around a room. About all that you can see beside cabinets are a few control panels with little lights that flash on and off, a few switches, and maybe, behind glass fronts, rolls of tape that look like 16 millimeter moving-picture film.

You wouldn't see much more if you took off the cabinet covers and looked inside. You'd find, by the hundreds, wires fastened to panels, printed circuits on panels, electronic tubes, and transistors and diodes, all arranged compactly in neat rows. You would be more impressed with the electrical circuitry of the machine than with its mechanism. And properly so. Computers are electrical rather than mechanical.

Here's an example of what a computer will do in production control. Suppose that you, in the factory, get an order to make 100 automatic dishwashers in August. It is now April. You can tell the computer: "Here is a list of parts needed to make a dishwasher. Here is an order for 100. How many parts will I need?" The computer will figure out how many of each part you'll need and, if you want, it will print a list of the parts needed.

Then you tell the computer: "Here is a list of parts already on hand. Compare the supply of each part with the requirements for the August order for dishwashers. For each item, subtract the needed quantity from the total on hand and on order and get a new balance. Then print a list of all items that will be short and need ordering. Tell me how soon I must order each part to be sure that the new supply will be on hand on time. Give me, too, the remaining balances of all items I do not need to reorder."

You start with a list of parts that are on hand and on order, and a master bill of materials and an order for 100 dishwashers. You end up with a list of every part that needs to be ordered to take care of the August as-

Remington-Rand Division, Sperry Rand Corp.

FIG. 32–1. Remington-Rand's Univac.

sembly order. You also end up with a new up-to-date list of available parts. An electric computer can automatically carry through this whole procedure from beginning to end.

There are many kinds of computers, and their speeds differ greatly, but all are fantastically fast. Once you have worked out how to get a computer to do a job, it usually does the work hundreds of times as fast as men doing the same work.

Before being impressed, however, don't overlook the machine's first cost and the expense in working out its instructions. Most computers cost over $50,000, some (705's and Univacs) cost over $1,000,000. Or you can rent them from $1,000 to $35,000 a month. High-priced machines will do more things and do them many times faster than low-priced machines.

Depending on the kind, computers add or subtract numbers of any length at rates from 200 to 5,000 a second. They multiply 500 to 1,200 numbers a second. Dividing goes slower, 200 a second. Sorting records having 100 digits each may go as slowly as 100 records a second. Printing speeds are not quite so fantastic, but even so, they will print from 3 to 10 complete lines of print a second.

When a computer has to find a number it is remembering, it can some-times do it in less than one twenty-five thousandth of a second. Unless you are asking it to remember hundreds of thousands of numbers, it will rarely take a computer as long as a sixtieth of a second to find a number. If you want it to remember hundreds of thousands of numbers, you sup-ply the computer with a secondary memory through which it may have

Photograph, courtesy of International Business Machines Corp.

FIG. 32–2. Inside of IBM's 608 computer, the first to use all transistors and no vacuum tubes.

to search for half of a minute or more to find the number. In rare cases it might take 5 minutes.

We speak here of the computer remembering "numbers." It may as well be a word. It is just as easy for a computer to remember the name, John Jones, as to remember the number, 415,219. And it is just as easy for it to remember a part's name as its number.

Computers fall into two general classes: scientific computers and data processors. Some scientific computers are called analog computers. Scien-tific computers compute faster than data processors, but you can't put masses of data into them or get masses of answers out of them fast. They are best at solving complex mathematical formulas involving millions of calculations. Such problems are common in physics, chemistry, and the technical problems of aviation, missile, and electronic products.

Business problems (leaving out technical matters relating to product design) are of a different sort—less complex. They require making only a few calculations but doing them for masses of data. Here the data processor type of computer (sometimes called digital computer) is better.

The Bank of America uses a data processor for check clearing. It handles millions of checks every week. Prudential Life Insurance uses an EDPM (electric data processing machine) to make up premium notices and prepare them for mailing to its millions of policyholders. Consolidated Edison uses an EDPM for monthly bills for its 5,000,000 customers in the New York City area.

Manufacturing companies usually deal with tens and hundreds of thousands of items—not millions. Even so that is more than enough volume to justify using an EDPM. We have, in the United States, 200 manufacturing companies, each employing 10,000 or more employees. Making out their pay checks twice a month, or even once a month, is a big job. So is all the record keeping for hours worked, payroll deductions, and so on that goes along with making up the payroll. General Electric now has an EDPM doing all its payroll for over 20,000 employees at its Louisville and its Erie, Pennsylvania, plants. Sylvania Electric handles the payroll for all its 30,000 employees (working in all parts of the country) on an EDPM. U.S. Steel, Monsanto Chemical, and Westinghouse also have an EDPM handle payroll at one or more of their plants.

Inventory control is a popular EDPM application. Du Pont has a computer handle the records for its 50,000 maintenance stores items at its Penns Grove, N.J., plant. Chrysler uses an EDPM for controlling inventories of accessories. And the U.S. Armed Forces has over a dozen computers controlling our huge military inventories.

Ford Motor and Lockheed Aircraft both use an EDPM in production control. Ford uses it to make up assembly schedules for all its plants and for making out delivery schedules for suppliers. Lockheed uses an EDPM to make up 40,000 shop orders a week at its Burbank, California, plant. It takes that many new shop orders each week to get all the parts required in today's airplanes made.

HOW DATA PROCESSORS WORK

Data processors operate by electric pulses following one another many thousands of times a second. Sperry Rand's Univac computer operates at 2,250,000 pulses a second. These pulses magnetize minute areas in the machine. Magnetizing tiny areas lets the machine "remember" information. Electric pulses can also demagnetize and remagnetize areas in the memory section of a computer, thus changing the information it remembers.

Pulses also tell a computer what to do with information it is already remembering and what to do with new information it receives. They, the pulses, tell the computer to add, multiply, print, and so on.

Let's see how a data processor handles inventory control. You start with regular stock record cards—the kind everyone keeps. There is a card for every item. Each card shows the item description, its identification number, storage location, quantity on hand, quantity in order, and its unit price. You may also show each item's reorder point, reorder quantity, and how long it takes to get a new supply. If the item is a part, the card shows the assembly and finished product into which it goes.

Suppose that you want the computer to bring your stock record up to date after a day's operations. You first "read in" to the EDPM yesterday morning's stock figures. Think of the computer as being a set of pigeon holes or storage cells, each with a location number. Tell the machine to put into cell number 302 the quantity "500," that being the quantity you had on hand of item number 24,972. Tell the machine to put the quantities of other items into other cells. The machine will remember all of the quantities and will later be able to find them.

During yesterday's work you used some items, received some items, found out that you will need more of some items, ordered more of certain items, and so on. After you tell the machine what these transactions were, it will correct the record. If you issue 100 of item 24,972, you tell the machine: "Go to cell 302, there you will find a number; from that number subtract 100, erase the old quantity, put in the new balance."

Later, you tell the machine to "read out" (make a list of) the new balances of items on hand, or the items on order, or whatever you want. It will print such lists. If you put each item's ordering point into the machine, too, it will list separately, if you want, all items needing reordering. And if you usually reorder in standard quantities, you could also have your EDPM print up a list of items to be ordered and their ordering quantities.

What happens to your original stock record card? Does it disappear? Is it replaced by the computer? Ordinarily, no. You keep the card as before. But why? If you keep all the records you kept before you bought a computer, where's the gain? You keep the old card as a record of the item's use. It tells you how many you used each month, how many you have reordered each time in the past, how long it took to get new supplies, and the cost per unit on each order. You could keep all of this record on tapes instead of on stock cards, but most companies still prefer to keep one record outside the machine. Then how do you come out ahead? You are ahead because the computer does all the calculating. You can even get computers that will post the new record onto the stock record card automatically. But even if you don't, all you have to do manually is to copy to it. You cut out men doing the figuring.

You are also ahead in knowing where you stand all the time. Without an EDPM, you'd have to scan 50,000 stock record cards to know

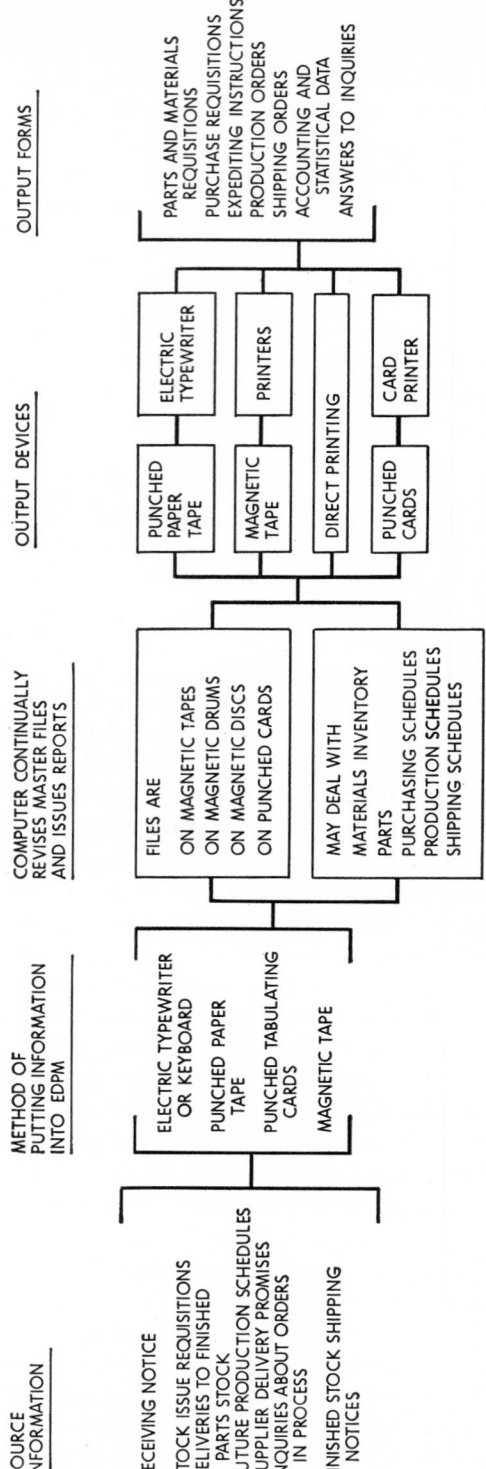

Adapted from "EDP Takes on Automatic Production Inventory Control," *Control Engineering*, September, 1955

FIG. 32-3. How an EDPM handles data.

which items need ordering. Since no supervisor has the time to do that, you never know exactly how your stock stands. You are actually dependent on each clerk who handles a group of 5,000 or 10,000 cards to tell you which items and how many of each he thinks he needs. Letting clerks control your inventory is a careless and costly method. Using an EDPM you lower costs by having better inventory control.

INPUTS

In spite of all the wondrous things that computers can do, they have to be given figures to work with and they have to be told, minute step by minute step, exactly what to do. You have to give them three kinds of information:

1. You give your EDPM basic figures. In our inventory control example these included item identification numbers, quantities on hand, reorder points, reorder quantities, and so on.
2. You give the EDPM figures representing things that are happening; quantities received, issued, future needs that you learn must be provided, quantities ordered, and such figures.
3. You tell the EDPM what to do with the figures. You give it a "program," a list of directions telling it what to do. In our example, you program the computer so that it subtracts issued quantities from old balances. Then have the EDPM compare the new balance with the reorder point. If the new balance is below the reorder point, tell the EDPM, by means of its program, to find out what the item's reorder quantity is. Lastly, your program can also tell the computer to print up a list of every part that needs to be reordered and the quantity to order.

This sequence of steps can be done inside the computer. It is not necessary to get answers to the intermediate steps in order to put them back in again. With ordinary tabulating machines you can do all of the above steps but only one step at a time. After each step, you have to have the machine make out punched cards with answers for that step. Then you put the cards back into the machine for the next step. EDPM machines cut out all this in-between work because they do the whole job at once. Besides, the EDPM will do it in a fraction of the time required by ordinary tabulating machines.

But after the EDPM finishes one job (such as getting a new balance on hand for one item), how does it know to go on? Don't you lose a lot of time getting the next set of directions into the machine? No, your program tells the computer to go right on. The program tells the machine how to perform a whole operation *and* what to go on to next, and what to do after that, and so on.

We have said that you "tell" the machine to do this and that. But how do you "tell" an EDPM to do something? How do you put figures into it? Before answering, let us note that you can get all the understanding that is necessary without knowing everything about how a computer works. We all know how to dial a telephone. We "tell" it the number we want, and it rings our number for us. We use it without knowing how a telephone works on the inside. We also drive cars without understanding exactly what goes on in the motor. Our job here is to learn a little but not everything about computers.

There is only one way to dial a telephone, but there are several ways to "tell" things to a computer. You can do it directly from a typewriter or bookkeeping machine keyboard, if it is wired up to the EDPM. You

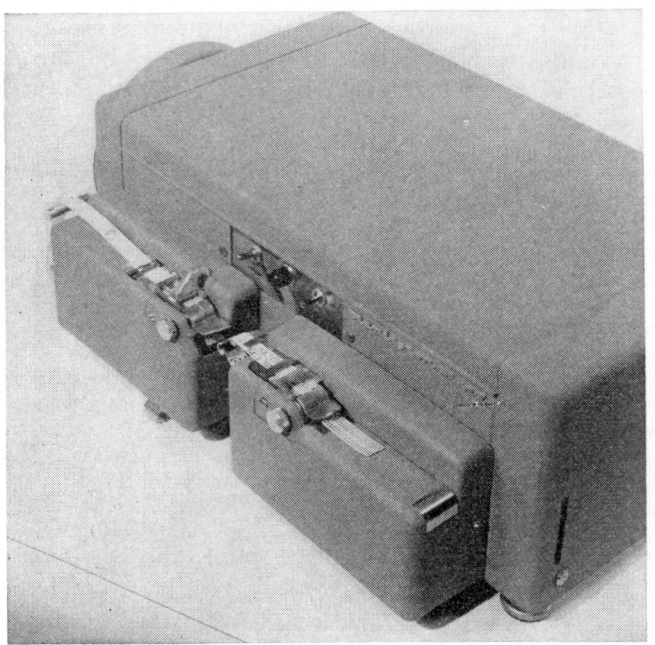

Remington-Rand Division, Sperry Rand Corp.

FIG. 32–4. Machine for punching coded information into paper tape.

can also use punched tape, or punched tabulating cards as shown in Figures 40–5 and 40–6, page 790, or you can use magnetic tape.

Most commonly, tabulating cards are used. Tab cards, size $3\frac{1}{4} \times 7\frac{3}{8}$ inches, show information by means of punched holes, as you see in Figures 40–5 and 40–6. Look along the top of the card. This printed line of information (printed mechanically by the tabulating machine) shows what the punched holes in the card mean to the machine.

Using tabulating cards is a good way to get the starting data into the computer's memory. But to do it this way, you have to have whole drawers full of cards into which you have already punched holes showing information in coded form. In our inventory control example, you would have to prepare a punched card for every item you carry in stock. When you put this stack of cards into a feed slot in the computer and push the button, it will read the information into its memory. EDPM machines will read cards at rates up to 4 a second. Since there are 80 spaces on a card for letters and numbers, this means that you can read about 20,000 characters (about 3,000 words) a minute into the calculator.

Another common way to get information into computers is by magnetic tapes. Tapes can be prepared on electrically wired typewriters or can be made automatically from tabulating cards. Magnetic tapes look like voice recorder tapes. They are about as wide and thick as typewriter ribbons but many times longer (up to 2,500 feet). To a computer, a tape is like a tabulating card, miniature in width but nearly half a mile long.

The tape is made with tiny cross lines of spots (much too small to see). The tiny spots can be individually magnetized. The combination of magnetized and unmagnetized spots in each line means, to a computer, a letter or a numerical digit. Figure 32–5 shows you how the

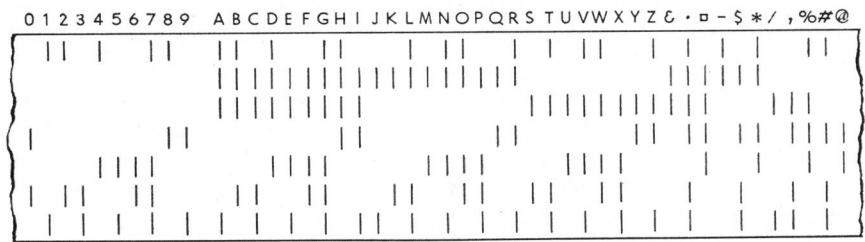

FIG. 32–5. Diagram of magnetic tape showing how letters and numbers are coded on a magnetic tape.

machine interprets the tape. The little cross lines on the tape are so small that 1 inch of tape (depending on the type) holds from 50 to 200 characters. A 2,500-foot tape holds from 1.5 to 6 million characters, or from 250,000 to 1,000,000 words. A tape supplants from 100,000 to 400,000 tabulating cards.

You can pass a tape over the computer's scanner which reads it at rates of 6 to 8 feet a second. At these speeds, the computer takes in information at rates of 12,000 to 15,000 characters (about 2,000 words) a second. Tapes put information into a computer about forty times faster than cards. Because tapes are so compact and so fast, they are replacing cards.

PROGRAMMING COMPUTERS

"Programming" means making up the list of instructions telling a computer what to do. Programming is a long process. For complex problems, it takes thousands of times as long to program a calculator as it does for the calculator to solve the problem.

It took GE in Louisville, 25 man-years of time to develop the program of over 200,000 instructions that its Univac needed to do the payroll for GE's 12,000 Louisville employees. Yet running off the payroll takes only 2 hours a day.

Programming work never has to be done again—unless you change the problem. You use a program indefinitely. In fact, you can get programs already made up if your procedures are standard. Computer manufacturers have libraries of programs on tapes and cards. A lot of programming work can often be cut out.

HOW COMPUTERS REMEMBER

Computers can remember tremendous amounts of information. Most computers have two memories, a small quick access (almost instantaneous) memory and a secondary, slower but infinitely larger, memory. The machine uses its quick access memory to retain numbers while it is calculating and to remember instructions. The information used only occasionally goes into the big, slower memory. The inventory record of 50,000 items would, for example, go into that memory.

Most computers are used for several kinds of work—payroll, cost distribution, budget make-up, incoming order records, inventory control records, accounts receivable records, and other uses. Big though the computer's memory is, there just isn't enough room in its memory to hold, at the same time, all the figures for all these jobs. This means that you have to clear out everything connected with one job before doing another. For this reason you would take out everything concerning inventories before you do payroll work on an EDPM.

A few companies avoid clearing the machine's memory by buying extra memory units which are never cleared of their information. When they change from one kind of work to another, the computer just switches memories. Extra memories are costly, however, so most companies don't buy them. This means that a memory *outside* the computer is needed to hold information between times.

You can store information outside computers in the form of printed lists, or on stock record cards, punched tabulating cards, punched tapes, or magnetic tapes. If information is stored as printed lists or on stock record cards, you have to convert it to one of the other forms before a computer can use it. If the outside information is on tabulating cards, they can be used directly to put information into the computer's memory. Same with punched tape and magnetic tape. They all store information *outside* the machine.

To use information, it has to be transferred *inside* the computer to its memory, either its quick memory or its slower memory. Quick memories are of several kinds: magnetic drums, magnetic cores, electronic tubes, columns of mercury, and other ways. Secondary memories are usually magnetic tapes or magnetic discs.

Magnetic drums are cylinders whose outside surface is covered with minute specs which can be separately magnetized. Some drums are as much as 1 foot in diameter and 2 feet long. Most are smaller. They rotate past scanners which read and interpret the way the drum's surface specs are magnetized. They pass the scanner at about 100 feet of

Magnetic Core Memory Made Up of Many Grids

Single Magnetic Core Grid

Magnetic Discs

Magnetic Drum

FIG. 32–6. Various types of EDPM memory units.

drum surface a second, so it doesn't take the computer very long to find information stored on them. Large magnetic drums hold about 60,000 characters, or 10,000 words, any of which the EDPM can find in about one one-thousandth of a second.

Magnetic cores are tiny metal doughnuts the size of beads that are put at every cross point of a woven wire grid. Each tiny core can be separately magnetized. You can get a tremendous number of cores into a small space by using stacks of grids. As memories, magnetic cores have small capacity, but they are extremely fast. The biggest magnetic cores made will store about 20,000 characters, or 3,000 words, any one of which can be found in about one one-hundred-thousandth of a second.

Electronic tubes can also remember. They do it by magnetized specs on the inside surface of the tube. They are similar to cores in capacity and speed. Mercury delay lines (also called acoustical delay lines) operate because electricity moves slightly slower through a column of mercury than it does along a wire. This operates as a memory. It can hold about 2,000 words which can be found in one ten-thousandth of a second.

Secondary memories are usually magnetic tapes or discs. Magnetic tapes we have already described as outside memories capable of holding 1.5 to 6 million characters. To make a tape into the computer's secondary memory you put it into the computer's reading unit just as you put a typewriter ribbon into a typewriter. Tapes thus become the computer's secondary memory. Searching time may be almost instantaneous if what you want is on the near end of the tape. But it can take as long as 5 minutes if what you want is half a mile away on the inside of the roll of tape.

Magnetic discs look like Victrola records. One of them will hold 100,-000 characters, any of which can be found in half a second. Discs are generally used in stacks, separated slightly, juke-box style, so that a reading arm can get to either surface of each disc. IBM's Ramac computer uses 50 discs as its memory. This gives it a capacity of 5,000,000 characters. Ramac can find any information on any of the discs in half a second, no need to run through half a mile of tape for anything.

Most computer memories, primary and secondary, can be added to by spending more money and having more units. You can use several drums, stacks of discs, or several magnetic tapes. If you do use several memory units, you increase the machine's memory capacity by as many more units as you add. Searching time goes up though if the machine has to search through one memory unit after another for information. The biggest EDPM machines, however, can search all the memory units at once, thus holding search time to a minimum.

OUTPUT

Having found answers, the computer must tell us what they are. How does it do this? For the most part it just reverses the input methods.

It will make up new magnetic tapes, tabulating cards, punched tapes, or whatever you want. It will also print lists.

Notice that, by using printed lists, you can get the output directly in final form if you want it that way. A printed list can be a bill of materials for an order, just have it printed on the proper form. Or it can be a shop order authorizing the manufacture of a parts lot. Or a list can be a review of scrap losses showing reasons why. Or it can be a tabulation of numbers and kinds of defects. In none of these cases do you need first to make up tabulating cards or tapes and then print a report from them. The computer can make your report without any intermediary steps.

Actually, although what we have just said is true, rarely do companies use their EDPM to print up lists. They don't do it directly because printing speeds are slower than calculating speeds. If you use an EDPM to print, the whole machine can operate no faster than the printer. So, for economy reasons, you have the EDPM put answers on cards or tapes and then run them through separate printing units.

EDPM ECONOMICS

Should you buy a computer? The answer is not an automatic yes. Johns-Manville concluded, after studying the matter, that the computer makers had done an excellent job of pricing their product so that most of the benefit went to them, not to the computer buyer. On the other hand, in 1958, you had to wait two years to get a computer if you decided to order one. Practically speaking, big companies have answered the question, yes. General Electric reports that it breaks even on its Univac at Louisville when it runs it two hours a day. Other companies report about the same findings. Many people think that you come out ahead with an EDPM if you can keep it busy more than one third of a shift.

Computers are practically error proof. Consolidated Edison found no errors by the machine in a whole year's operation. During that period its EDPM prepared over 50,000,000 customer bills. No magnetic tape wore out in that time.

Computers rarely break down. Users report them to be available from 95 to 98 per cent of the time. Down time of as much as 5 hours at a stretch is almost unknown. Such a performance record is possible, however, only if a computer is checked often in off hours and preventive maintenance carried on. Computers are, internally, delicate instruments. They need to be housed in a dust controlled room and, as they make considerable heat, one with temperature control. Air conditioning is, therefore, a must.

EFFECTS OF COMPUTERS

Most users of computers say they don't save money—directly, that is. They don't end up with fewer employees. But they all agree that they get up-to-the minute information, and they get more information than they ever had before. Gains, then, come from better control and the chance to make more intelligent and quicker decisions.

Computers force some reshuffling of departmental responsibilities. They have so much capacity that, in order to keep them busy, you have to bring in work formerly done in several departments. Paper work becomes more centralized. The systems and procedures used in different departments must be more closely co-ordinated than before. The computer can then easily make up, from the same basic data, the reports that different departments need.

As a result, management will probably learn to think of the company more as a whole instead of a series of separate departments. It will be easier for management to follow through the effects of its decisions and see the over-all results of its actions. Out of this should come a more intelligent direction for the whole company.

STUDY QUESTIONS

1. How is an electric computer different from a desk calculator? Explain.
2. How do electric "pulses" play a part in the operation of electronic computers?
3. What means are available for getting figures and instructions into electronic computers?
4. How can a computer "remember" words and numbers? How many words can a computer remember? How long does it take an EDPM to find words and numbers it is remembering?
5. Some people think that electronic computers will change certain management practices. Which practices would change? Discuss.

Chapter 33

COST REDUCTION AND COST CONTROL

Cost reduction and cost control ought to mean about the same thing. Cost control that doesn't try to keep whittling costs down is mere record keeping. Yet cost reduction that goes on forever gets to be old hat. Many companies have found that a special cost reduction drive pays big dividends even though what it amounts to is asking everyone to do better what he is (or ought to be) already trying to do well.

You might think that cost reduction would not be so important nowadays because costs and prices seem always to go up. You get used to it and so do your customers. Actually this trend should make you try twice as hard to keep costs down. You can't just sit back and say that if your costs go up so do those of your competitors. They all have to give raises too. True, they do, but what if some of them manage to keep their costs down? A competitor with lower costs can bankrupt you.

But even if everybody puts his prices up, you still have to contend with customers. They resist price increases and try to buy less or turn to substitutes. Or they may decide to make their own products and not buy them from you at all.

Every price increase probably loses some customers, so you must try to hold the line. You are rarely able to get all of a cost increase back out of sales prices. You always need to try to cut costs.

Good cost control also helps in pricing products. You can *predict* costs pretty accurately and can set prices intelligently. You also use cost predictions when planning new products and forecasting sales volume.

COST REDUCTION PROGRAMS

To keep costs down most companies find that they need an occasional shot in the arm—a special cost reduction program. Of course such a program will, itself, probably cost some money, but here you have to resign yourself to the need to spend a little money to save more money. Also, you may not get big results right away—it may take months to get into high gear.

Cost control is a state of mind as much as it is an activity. It is an educational process and attitudes change slowly. But the gains from having trained your men to be cost conscious ought to keep coming for a long time. It should end up being a new way of life that keeps on. We must admit though that many companies have never really put on a real cost-cutting drive and that some others that have, haven't accomplished much.

How do you go about doing better the things that you try all the time to do well? Some companies go at cost cutting using the "bull-of-the-woods" approach. The president tells his vice-presidents to cut 10 per cent out of their costs. The vice-presidents tell their work managers, the work managers tell the superintendents, the superintendents tell the general foremen who tell the foremen: cut 10 per cent. Cut, CUT, *CUT* comes the order to everybody at every level. No one cares much how you do it and no one shows you how to do it. Just cut costs *and* still get your work done as usual.

Bull-of-the-woods methods are ruthless, but they sometimes work. Often they are unwise. Pruning an apple tree is not a job for amateurs. Cutting limbs off right and left injures the tree and grows fewer apples. Ruthless cutting in an organization hurts too. Morale is hurt. Essential work is just about as likely to be cut as less necessary work.

Some companies go at cost cutting with a velvet-glove technique. They try to get the whole managerial team to pitch in and work together willingly and enthusiastically at cost cutting. They try to pinpoint weak spots so that they can be improved. Make no mistake, though, about velvet-glove cost-cutting programs. Beneath the surface they are hard hitting. You still expect to cut hard-to-cut items.

What should we do in order to have a successful cost-cutting program of the velvet-glove type? One that cuts costs, yet does it intelligently?

First, a cost reduction program needs top management interest—active interest. We all think that we have been doing a good job, that we have been working hard, and that we have done all that we can. But in spite of that we almost certainly can and will do better if the high brass works with us and if we know that they are looking over our shoulder. And we'll try especially hard if the high brass makes it clear that cost reduction performance is part of the basis for judging promotions and pay raises.

A cost reduction program ought to start with the top brass calling a meeting in the board of directors' meeting room to impress people. The general idea "we must cut costs" is put before everybody, and they are asked for ideas as to how to go about it. Probably the near high brass will decide to set up several committtees to handle different areas (product design, materials, manufacturing methods, office costs, and so on). One or more of the near top men will be on each committee, but some men lower down will also be put on these committees. Committee membership will cut across departmental lines. Be sure that some high brass sits in with underlings when committees meet. That adds greatly to the chance of success of a program. Also be sure not to leave out any area—include *every* department.

Why are these committees set up? What do we expect of them? First, we need their help in setting goals (*cost-cutting goals*—not production goals). We expect them to look over their area and set goals to shoot at—short-term goals and long-term goals. Have the committees look into all trouble spots and have them put a dollar value on the cost of each trouble spot. Have the committees set up recording and reporting procedures to tell the kinds and sources of trouble. The battle to reduce cost is half won when you have unearthed problems and found out what causes them.

Second, the committee members will, in the end, have to do the things that will cut costs for you. They won't do this as committee members but as heads of departments. As individual men some hesitate to do anything about costs, some defend the status quo, some want to go ahead but don't know how. Being on the committee lets them see the need for cutting costs. This makes everyone more willing to find cost-cutting opportunities and to try to make the cuts.

Third, no cost-cutting program goes by itself after it is started. After goals are set, and as time goes along, reports are made of what is done and comparisons are made against the goals. The committees make the comparisons. And they pay particular attention to all spots where we don't reach the goal. Where did we fail? Why? What else can we do to reach it? And so on. The committees go over all of these matters and so help make the cost-cutting program work.

Fourth, committee meetings help develop a climate in which people will *know* what costs are, and they will *want* to cut them, and they will *learn how* to cut them. The meetings are educational. Department heads who don't know how to go about cutting costs get ideas from their fellow committee members about how to do it. They also come to identify themselves more with the company and to think and work toward over-all company goals. Then they are more willing to work out solutions that are best for the company—not best just for their own department.

And, fifth, committees put on social pressure. You don't look good saying that you can't cut costs when everyone else has agreed to do his bit. Nor do you look good if you don't cut the costs you told your fellow committee members you thought you could cut. Every supervisor knows that his fellow committee members are watching his results.

How can a few near-top committees do all of this? They don't, or, at least, they don't do it alone. Each *committee* accepts the responsibility for overseeing a whole area. Each *man* on the committee gets a job of setting up one or more committees below him with the same kinds of assignments. Later on, he reports his own committees' cost-cutting successes back to the higher committee.

Members of these lower committees agree to set goals for cutting expenses under their jurisdiction and to get their men to do the same. The cost-cutting program ends up with *everyone*, including the foreman, getting in on the act. Everyone tries to cut costs. Some companies even discuss it with union officials before they go ahead, but don't expect union heads to give you any visible support. If they did, they'd probably not get re-elected.

You may ask, where does everybody get all of this extra time to go to committee meetings and try to improve things by cutting costs? Well, they just find the time. We all have time for the things that we think are important, and during a cost-cutting program that gets top priority. Nearly always we get the time to work at cost reduction by cutting down on things that we waste our own time on. We, ourselves, become more efficient.

"GOALS" VERSUS BUDGETS

But aren't cost-cutting "goals" just budgets? They ought not be—not quite. A budget is one kind of goal, but a cost-cutting goal ought to be different. A regular budget sets an amount that you can spend. You try to stay within it but you don't try very hard to beat it. Besides, with regular budgets we don't have meetings, daily or weekly, where we sit down—several of us—in committee and try to help each other reach the goal.

Cost-cutting goals ought to be real challenges. We help set them and we move heaven and earth to accomplish them. Also our special program gets more high-brass attention than do regular budgets. Progress reports are issued, and special attention and help are given to any of us who need it.

Do "goals" still look like budgets? They ought to in spite of what we have just said. Because this is just what the best managed companies do *all the time—with budgets.* This is what a cost-cutting program should end up doing—it should end up becoming a continuing cost-cutting program going on forever—and that is what cost control through budgets aims to do.

The difference ought to be in the shot-in-the-arm idea. We go all out to improve and almost always do improve. Then after we reach a new high plateau of efficiency, we'd like just to stay there—or, better yet, keep on getting still better forever. Our next set of goals ought to be always tightened up from the last set—a little more and more forever. After our first big effort we want the cost-cutting program to change into a permanent program for keeping costs down forever. That is when the difference between cost-cutting goals and regular budgets should melt away.

MAKING A PROGRAM WORK

Some experts say that you should start out by assuring everyone that no one will lose his job. They say that your program will not work well if men are afraid of losing their jobs. Fortunately, many of your reductions will save on materials and in other nonlabor places. But some of your cost cuts will have to be savings in labor costs. This means fewer men on some jobs. Normal turnover helps you here. You can avoid layoffs nearly always just by not hiring new men to replace those who quit. Put displaced men on the jobs left open when others quit. Perhaps you should not make outright promises that no one will lose his job because you might have to lay off a few men at the bottom.

Setting goals is itself the first step in the actual program to cut costs. But it is only the first step. Department heads, big and little, have to be told what their goals are—and in detail, not just in total. Of course they helped set the goals, so it won't come as news to them. But each one should get a detailed program of goals to reach in cutting costs in his own department.

Second, each department head in order to carry out the program will have to get up-to-the-minute reports of how he is doing—reports that high light places where he isn't doing so well. Probably this means changing your accounting system. It means that you must keep your accounts apart for departments as much as it is reasonably possible. Very likely it will mean *more* reports and *more detailed* reports. This is where you spend some money to save more money—on better reports. You must also make the reports alive—put in charts that show up bottleneck areas or places where you missed out.

But above all, you want to make each *department head* responsible. Give *him* up-to-the-minute reports of how *his* department is doing so that *he* can fix things up right away. Don't worry here about perfect accuracy. Not only does this let you get after bad things sooner, but when things go well, it makes the feeling of accomplishment come sooner. Also, don't depend on department heads to figure out how the reports should be made out—figure this out for them, design the reports to give them what they need.

Show every department head how to use the reports. Try to keep the reports simple, yet be sure that the reports *measure, compare, review,* and *evaluate* and give *him* a chance to plan to do something. Let him appraise the work of his department hourly, daily, weekly, and over longer times.

Making a single man responsible for each cost center may force you to make some changes. Maybe you didn't have sharply drawn lines separating areas of responsibility. Better set them up if you want cost reduction to work. *Men* make costs and *men* can cut costs—and they do much better if *one* man has the responsibility for a cost center. Then there is no doubt about who has to take action to cut cost.

Third, you need to stand ready to *help* and to *show* department heads how to go about cutting costs. Most of them have no idea how to cut costs. Explain overhead to foremen, show them how using machines effectively cuts costs. Develop a spirit of cost consciousness in them.

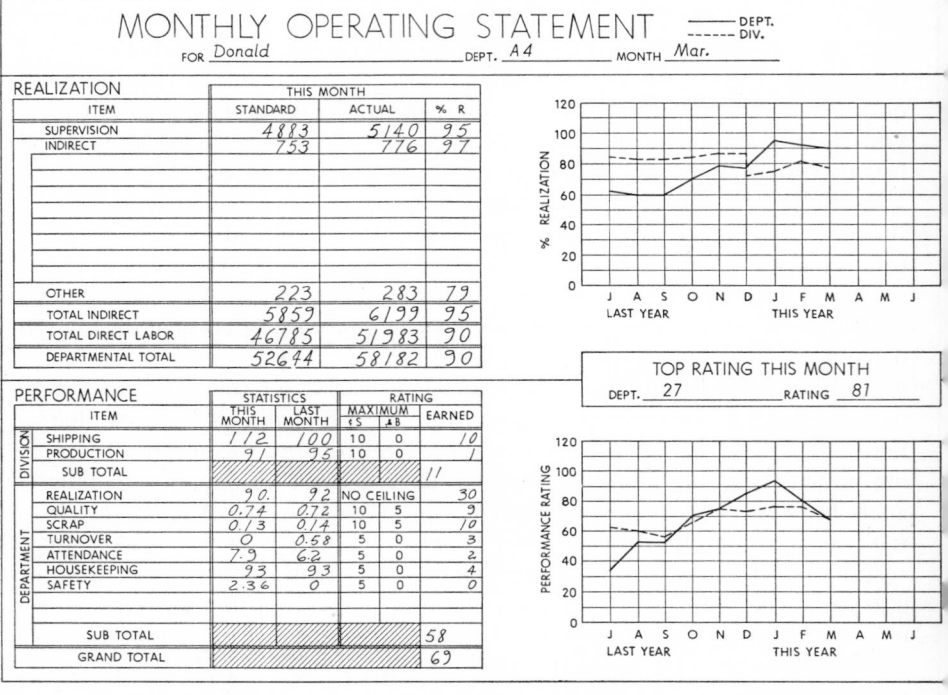

FIG. 33–1. A labor control report showing a department's operating performance.

Let committee members give each other ideas. Give staff or other help to department heads.

Fourth, you need frequent *review* (daily would be good) *by every department head's boss.* And you need occasional (weekly) review by the committee responsible for the area. Let each member be chairman while his department is being reviewed. But don't strip departments of their supervision during a meeting. Operations must go on.

Put some brass on the committee—the superintendent of production, the vice-president of production, the manager of manufacturing, and maybe a budget officer and one or two staff men. These members keep the pressure on everyone to do his best. But pressure is the wrong emphasis. Try to avoid finger pointing and don't make review meetings into punitive sessions. No one is on trial. You want to be corrective not

FOREMAN'S COST REPORT
(WEEKLY LABOR)

Department   **A**_____

ACCT. NO.	ACCOUNT	LINE NO.	DOLLARS THIS WEEK			DOLLARS MO. TO DATE		
			Allowed	Actual	Variance	Allowed	Actual	Variance
	DIRECT LABOR	1						
	Standard	2	3578	3853	(275)	10734	11258	(524)
	Substandard	3	465	493	(28)	1396	1546	(151)
	Total Direct Labor	4	4043	4346	(303)	12129	12804	(675)
	BURDEN LABOR	5						
	Waiting Time	6						
315	Waiting for Stores	7						
320	Waiting for Setup or Tools	8						
330	Waiting for Machine Repairs	9	15	14	1	45	59	(14)
340	Power and Plant Breakdowns	10						
342	Waiting for Inspection	11						
344	Waiting for Work Assignment	12						
345	Parts and Materials not Delivered	13		1	(1)		1	(1)
	Total Waiting Time	14	15	15		45	60	(15)
	Employee Activities	15						
158	Voting Time Pay	16						
164	Jury Duty Pay	17						
165	Reporting and Call-in Pay	18						
166	Accident Reporting Time Pay	19						
167	Employee Welfare and Services	20	5	5		15	4	11
168	Union Activities	21	12	15	(3)	36	29	7
169	Minnreg Veteran's Activities	22		4	(4)		12	(12)
	Total Employee Activities	23	17	19	(2)	51	45	6
	Training	24						
174	Instructing New Help	25	20	12	8	60	37	23
175	Training School and Orientation	26						
	Total Training	27	20	12	8	60	37	23
	Overtime	28						
190	Premium Pay Direct Departments	29					2	(2)
	Setup and Adjustment	30		9	(9)		71	(71)
157	Setup for Direct Labor—Reg. Production	31	225	190	35	675	720	(45)
159	Setup Adjustment—Regular Production	32	20	15	5	60	56	4
160	Setup for Direct Labor—Gov. Production	33	150	176	(26)	450	415	35
161	Setup Adjustment—Government Production	34	40	22	18	120	52	68
162	Tool Trouble	35	150	109	41	450	340	110
	Total Setup and Adjustment	36	585	521	64	1755	1654	101
	Salvage Created By:	37						
080	Operating	38	15		15	45	43	2
081	Inspection	39						
082	Methods	40						
083	Production Planning	41						
084	Engineering	42						
085	Procurement	43					17	(17)
086	Prior Operating Departments	44	50	150	(100)	150	284	(134)
	Total Salvage	45	65	150	(85)	195	344	(149)
	Department Administration	46						
115	Group Leaders and Setup Supervisors	47	140	97	43	420	318	102
120	General Clerical	48	16	16		48	46	2
118	Scheduling of Manufacturing Operations	49						
119	Scheduling of Assembly Operations	50						
	Total Department Administration	51	156	113	43	468	364	104
	Premiums	52						
192	Bonus for Night Shift Work	53	185	179	6	555	530	25
193	Wage Adjustments	54						
163	Lunch and Wash-up Time	55	65	66	(1)	195	198	(3)
196	Suggestion Awards	56						
	Total Premiums	57	250	245	5	750	728	22
127	Labor Not in Standard—Misc. Production Labor	58						
	Repairs and Maintenance Labor	59						
187	Oil and Clean Machines	60	135	132	3	405	396	9
258,303	Tools and Machine Repairs and Maintenance	61						
	Total Repairs & Maintenance Labor	62	135	132	3	405	396	9
	Repair and Rebuilding	63						
358	Ordnance Returned Goods	64						
360	Regular Customer Repairs	65						
363,364	Rebuilding on Production Dept. R and T No.	66						
	Total Repair and Rebuilding	67						
	Miscellaneous Labor	68						
173	Experimental Work	69		62	(62)		169	(169)
199	General	70						
116,170	Stockmen, Inventory Control	71	191	177	14	573	517	56
	All Other	72	76	21	55	228	54	174
	Total Miscellaneous Labor	73	267	260	7	801	740	61
	Total All Labor	74	5553	5813	(260)	16659	17174	(515)
	All Inclusive Ratio (Total all Labor/Stand. Labor)	75	155	151		155	153	

American Management Association, Special Report No. 4

FIG. 33–2. Minneapolis-Honeywell's weekly department performance report.

punitive, although you really do want to keep some pressure on everyone. Reviewing performance makes opportunities to help, also to praise a good performance. But if a man misses his goal—then ask why? What happened? What is the problem? Job held up because of no man on the machine? Absenteeism is the problem. Machine breakdown? Prevention maintenance is needed. Extra operations needed? Why? Unusual scrap? Why? Let's get rid of the cause.

Fifth, you need to *help* men make savings. The power to remedy trouble may be beyond a department head's authority—that is where the committee comes in. Or if it is beyond the committee's authority, it can go higher. Or if you have a particularly tough problem, let several committee members pitch into it and see if they can't improve things. Also put in special temporary *reports* of bottleneck areas and stay close to them until you get them fixed up.

Sixth, *don't slip back.* Keep charts of performance. Compute departmental efficiency ratings. If anything slips back, look into it right away. Talk it over with the man responsible. The sooner you spot a decline and work on it the sooner you get it fixed. Doing this helps keep your men sharp too; they usually know when something goes wrong, and they'll be after it fast if they know that you will soon be looking into it.

Seventh, keep working toward long-range goals as well as short-range goals. As a day, week, or month comes to an end, you start on a new period which has its goals just like (or just a little tighter than) those of the last period. If you cut scrap from 5 per cent to 4, next you shoot for $3\frac{1}{2}$, and so on. Be careful though that the tightening up of goals doesn't move so fast as to be discouraging.

WHERE TO LOOK FOR COST SAVING

Cost savings opportunities are everywhere—in every department and in every expense. Mostly they are in little things, not big ones. But lots of little things are done so often that they total up to big amounts. You normally do a good job on the big costs—particularly the big expense items in the factory—so your program has to be set up to find and stop little cost leaks. On the other hand, never overlook the big items. Go after them harder than ever. You don't want to end up saving pencil stubs and turning out lights when big inefficiencies are costing you big money.

Here are some ideas that you can follow up just in the production end alone:

Item

Low Production:

Show men how to do their work the best way. Too many new men? Hold down turnover, keep the men you have. Too many shifts of men from job to job? Go after absenteeism, keep men on the job. This cuts shifting men around to keep jobs moving. Men not suited for jobs? Put them on jobs that they can do well.

Watch the *individual men* who are low producers. What are they doing wrong? Also watch the good men. What do they do that the poor ones can copy? Keep bad work down, then good work will go up. Cut out "Fittin' and Filin'." Train new men well before putting them into a group. On assembly lines don't just have relief men, have *trained* relief men so that they won't hold up the others. Make job improvements *before* you go into production. Saves money and cuts grievances.

Waste Time by Men:

Don't interrupt the men. Don't keep men waiting for instructions, tools, or orders. Cut waste time by men at starting and quitting times. Start promptly and don't quit until closing time. Don't let men lengthen the rest periods or coffee breaks. Don't let them waste time around the sandwich carts. Hold down clean-up time—both of the work area and personal clean-up time.

Indirect Labor Costs:

Factory department heads rarely watch this as carefully as direct labor costs. Don't allow foremen to let indirect labor take a back seat in their thinking about costs. Pay particular attention to indirect labor because it tends to go *up* with mechanization. Since you spend more here, watch it more carefully.

Budget indirect labor costs. Who are indirect workers? Inspectors, material handlers, truckers, cranemen, janitors, maintenance men, salvage workers, methods men, foremen, clerks, superintendents—everyone who doesn't work on the product, *plus* direct workers when they work on indirect jobs.

Don't pay indirect men unearned bonuses or give them base rate boosts just to get their earnings up to pieceworker level. Use *no* temporary rates. Get standards set quickly for new jobs. Pay daywork *only* for jobs in the experimental stage. Don't call setup costs direct labor costs. You don't get any products out during setup.

Put every bit of indirect labor that you can on standards. Where you can't time study it, use work sampling to set standards. Put indirect labor on incentives and get your money's worth. Here you'll boost your standards setting cost, but the savings you get usually pay off more than ten times the cost of setting the standards. Shoot for 90 per cent of payroll on standards. Cut the time of direct men on indirect work.

Don't duplicate work. If one department inspects everything that it sends to the next department, don't have the next department do it over again. Don't inspect incoming products from reliable vendors.

Labor Losses and Allowances:

Pieceworkers earning less than their guarantee get paid the guarantee: cut these losses by getting them up to earning at least the guarantee as soon as possible. Pay allowances for special conditions: get rid of the special conditions that hold the man back and so cut this loss. Payment for meetings (grievance meetings in particular): cut out all the meetings you can and shorten those that you have to have. Cost of rework: paying to fix rejected products is waste; do better work to start with. Machine down time: keep machines running and cut this cost.

Maintenance:

Can you cut the machine down time for repairs? If you can, it keeps production up and costs, per unit, down. Is some *one* person responsible for low maintenance costs? You get better results when one and one only is responsible (the foreman probably). Cut the amount of machine repair by training men how to use machines properly. Plan maintenance jobs; use standards, even if they are only estimated standards; evaluate performance. Show maintenance men how to fix machines faster.

Inventories:

How much (expressed in both dollars and in so many months' supply) of each class of material do you have on hand? How much is reasonable? Are any items stocked above reasonable amounts? Hold back on replacement orders while the extra is used. Maybe you should carry less inventory and take the chance of running out occasionally.

Can you use linear programming to tell you which items to stock up on to keep men working during a short seasonal slump? What is the proper lot size to use? Should you make big quantities now and then? Or little quantities more often? Cut dead time between operations; move materials through the plant fast. Cut paper work; let men help themselves to little things; don't use requisitions for them.

Materials Shortage:

Why do they happen? What can you do to cut them out? Don't let little things hold up big things (as a parts shortage of a small part).

Schedules:

Schedule up to capacity. Cut machine down time. Don't accept it as a fact of life. Try to do something about it. Only machines running earn anything for you. Schedule jobs to be done at certain times. *Make* foremen meet schedules—or give reasons why not. Reschedule quickly when work isn't done. Adhere to shipping schedules. Plan better and cut out stock chasing.

Schedule changes. Who causes them? Does sales know what they cost? Don't allow them, after production has started, except when it is urgent. Is production control at fault? Does tooling arrive on time?

Engineering Specifications:

Make tolerances as liberal as possible. Cut out fine finishes. Don't ask for parts to be made so good that they'll last forever. Standardize your drawing symbols so that factory men won't have to puzzle them out. Use simplified drawings; cut out unnecessary views, details, lines, dimensions, arrowheads. Dimension things from one point. Make draftsmen be careful how they use "block" tolerances—the kind that say "all unspecified tolerances are $\pm.005$ inches."

Engineering Changes:

When should they be made effective? Don't let them apply to products in process unless they are urgent. Hold up single changes and make changes in a group whenever possible. Avoid changes that make you rework or throw away present supplies.

Supplies and Perishable Tools:

Budget these on the basis of cents per standard hour of work done. Make men turn in worn-out tools before giving them new ones.

Accident Costs:

Do your foremen know what accidents cost? Have some meetings and tell them. Have accident prevention meetings. Compare this month with last month and last year. Look into all places where the record is bad; find out why, fix up the cause.

Remember, all of the above suggestions have to do *just with making the product*. Also, notice that you aren't trying to get all of your savings out of labor—labor is only one of the places where you spend money and only one of the places to save it.

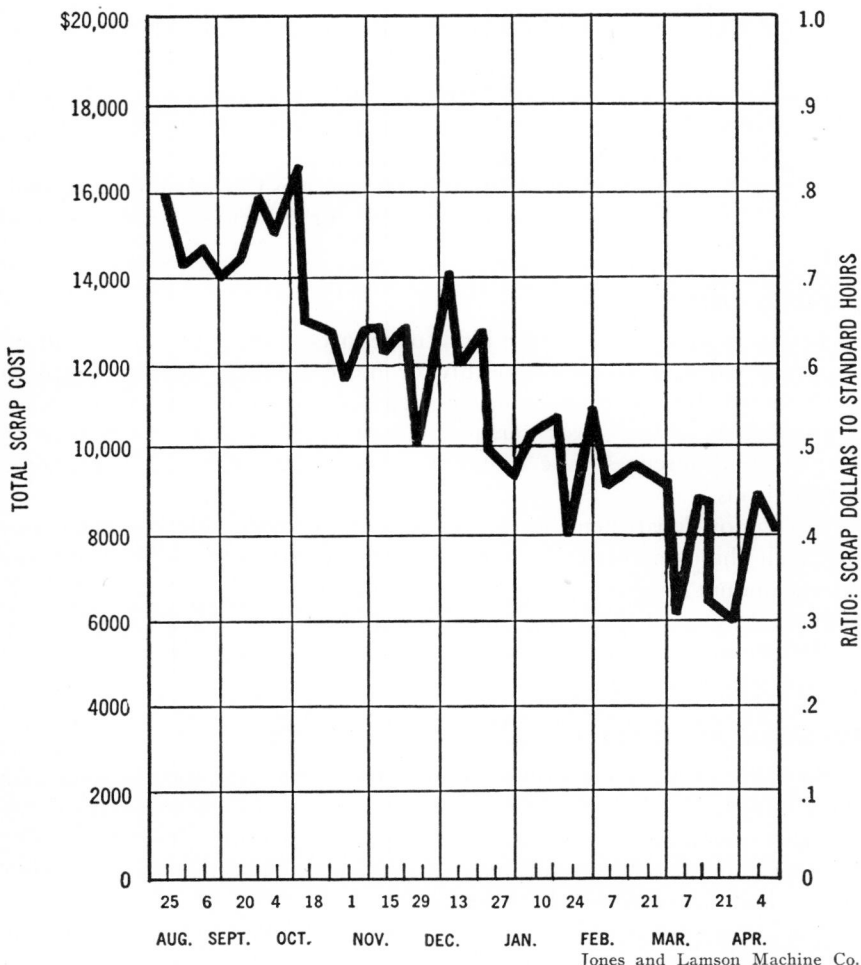

Jones and Lamson Machine Co.

FIG. 33–3. Jones and Lamson cut its ratio of scrap dollars to standard hours in half in 10 months through its cost reduction program.

There are just as many places to save money in offices, paper work control, traffic, selling—in every part of the company. For example, you could look into the leaks that the sales department causes in manufacturing, such as special products, nonstandard items being sold at regular prices (but they cost more to make), gold-plated or fur-lined free trimmings, free repairs, too many returned goods, orders for one each of many things, rush deliveries, and estimates for special items.

Don't overlook office departments in cost reduction programs. Their costs often seem to be variable as business goes up (they go up too), but when business goes down, they become fixed—can't be cut. Their department heads need to be pushed to un-fix (cut) some of their fixed costs.

We could fill a book with examples of where to look and what to try to do to cut costs. Truly the possibilities are everywhere. In fact, they reach into major management decisions, such as should you move to another town. But department heads, big and little, when left to themselves, don't think of all of these things. Or, if they do, they think that they aren't very important, or they think that it isn't their job to do anything about it—particularly if the problem or its remedy affects several departments.

REPORTS NEEDED

Probably you will need two kinds of reports to make your cost-cutting program work. You need monthly or more frequent reports for each department that go to top management. They show the department's performance—actual costs versus standard costs—and are drawn up to emphasize differences. Use tables of figures and charts to drive home comparisons.

But minor department heads need weekly or even daily reports showing such things as material usage, amount spent on direct and indirect labor, amount of good work done, amount of scrap, and machine efficiency. Be sure to make out budgets and charts for indirect labor.

Remember, too, that reports cost money. If any reports are no longer needed, cut them out.

FOREMAN ATTITUDES TOWARD COST REDUCTION

So many of your costs actually are incurred at the bottom level that the foreman is a key man in every cost reduction program. We have said that cost reduction is a frame of mind—an attitude—more than anything else. If you can get foremen (as well as other supervisors) to *think* cost reduction, costs will be kept low.

But doesn't he already have that mental attitude? Every department head should have, but few do, foremen in particular. Phil Carroll does a fine job showing us the foreman's attitude in his book *How Foremen Can Control Costs*.[1] Here are his chapter headings:

Why should I worry about costs? Our company makes lots of money.
Costs are not my problem. That's the cost man's job.
What's the big hurry? We got plenty of time.
All my men are working. What're they hollerin' about?
Stock chasers drive me crazy. Every day they want something else.

---

[1] Phil Carroll, *How Foremen Can Control Costs* (New York: McGraw-Hill Book Co., Inc., 1955).

See the timestudy men. They're running the plant.
I get all the headaches. Nobody helps me get things right.
All I do is change setups. Why don't they get some long runs?
Can't they find any good men? All they have are punks.
How come my scrap is up? Cost men don't know how to figure.
Tools don't cost much. And they last a long time.
Material cost is my problem. But I can't do anything about it.
Maintenance won't fix 'em. How can I keep my machines running?
Why can't they let us alone? They're always makin' changes.
We always do 'em that way. Then we know they'll come out all right.
They think they're inventors. But their suggestions won't work.
Why do they gripe so much? Isn't anything right around here?
It's only a little change. Why stir up trouble?
Engineers can't understand. They never come in the shop.
You can't timestudy indirect. No two jobs are alike.
Why bother with budgets? They're just a lot of numbers.
Overhead is a mystery to me. We just listen and grin.
Why so many reports? I sure hate paper work.
Who cares about competition? We've been successful for years.

Do you get a picture of the foreman? This picture is typical—not rare—and not always just of foremen either; some higher-ups are the same way. Can you imagine such a foreman cutting costs? Carroll's foreman is your raw material. He is the man you have to instill with a *desire* to cut costs and with some *know-how* so that he can do it. Small wonder, too, that you probably will have to keep prodding him.

You must expect, at the start, for him to be opposed to changing his ways. If you get him up to where he co-operates reluctantly, that is a gain. Finally you hope to get him to be favorable. You'll win him over more readily if you keep him in on the act. Don't just use directives. Don't take his department leadership away from him.

PITFALLS IN COST REDUCTION

Cost reports comparing performance with goals are the heart of cost control. You need to be very sure that they show what they seem to show and that *reported improved conditions mean improved conditions*.

For example, maintenance costs go down (for a while) if you let everything go to rack and ruin. Or scrap is cut to zero if you pass everything. Production is grand (for a while) if you run your machines as fast as they will go. (But better not look at tool costs.) Also rework costs on rejects are low if you just scrap the rejects (but don't look at scrap costs). Absences will be low if you insist that everyone come to work every day (but do you want sick men at work?). You need to look at *all* the figures, not just one or two, to see if things are better.

Also, be careful about judging a foreman's efficiency right after some methods improvements have been put in. Often there are some bugs in the new methods. His efficiency will go down for a while, yet you certainly want the improvements made. Remember this in judging his performance, or he'll hold back on future improvements.

Even cutting out idle time can be wrong (but not often is it wrong). Big expensive machines or series of machines ought to be kept operating. Their idleness can cost hundreds of dollars a minute (it does in a steel rolling mill)! If one or two half-idle men have to be close by all the time to keep big machines going, by all means have some idle men and not idle machines.

Be careful too about interpreting other figures on reports. Is a department's indirect labor ratio up? That shows that you are spending more labor dollars for indirect labor *per direct labor* dollar than you used to. Normally that is bad. But be careful with your interpretations. It isn't always good to have a low overhead ratio. The overhead ratio will go up every time you cut direct labor costs unless you cut indirect proportionally, too. It is good for you to have cut direct labor even if that leaves you with a higher ratio of indirect to direct.

Same with overhead. When you mechanize, overhead goes up and direct labor comes down, so the ratio between them goes way up. One General Motors' plant in its New Departure division has an overhead ratio of over 1,500 per cent! Overhead is over $15 for every $1.00 of direct labor payroll! Is that bad? No, because it resulted from automation which, it is true, boosted overhead costs but at the same time saved far more direct labor costs than the overhead increase.

You can keep your overhead ratio down too by buying parts instead of making them. You substitute material costs for machine and labor costs. You may cut your overhead ratio but end up spending more money, and you surely don't want that.

You can even reduce your overhead ratio just *by letting direct labor costs go up!* Using your direct workers inefficiently will make direct labor costs go up and the ratio of overhead to direct go down! No one would want that, yet if you look just at the overhead ratio your worst foremen would look the best.

Don't cover up overhead in your direct costs. For example, if you put an allowance in a man's piece rate to pay for delays, his pay is partly pay for delay, but it all shows as direct labor cost. By paying for it *within* the rate rather than as an extra outside you show too much for direct labor and too little for wasteful overhead. Your overhead ratio gives you a false picture.

Don't rely on totals and averages if you can also get details. Suppose that you meet the budget total by spending too much on one item and staying under the budget on another. The total is O.K., but the details show you that you have a bad spot to fix up.

Also, how do you figure costs? On an average basis? Perhaps on a per pound basis? So you look at a department's reduced cost per pound and praise the foreman for reducing costs. But a heat treating department will have low costs per pound when it handles big chunky items. So will a foundry. Next week, with smaller items, the costs go back up. For a while the record looked good, but it didn't reflect more efficient operations.

Look searchingly, also, at savings claimed for improvements—particularly savings in overhead. Often they are only illusions or else they won't stay nailed down. Suppose, for example, that you speed up a machine so that it now does its work in 7 hours instead of 8. Its overhead charge is $10 an hour. Have you saved $10? Are your taxes less? Is building depreciation less? Are research costs less? They are all overhead items. No, you probably still have $80 worth of overhead a day. Better raise your hourly charge to $11 or more. You surely have not saved $10 in overhead costs.

Floor space is another example. Accountants say that floor space costs so much a square foot—for office space say from $3.00 to $5.00 a foot per year. You cut down the space used for some job by 30 square feet. Have you saved any money? Again maybe not. Unless you use the saved space profitably for something else, you haven't saved anything at all.

Also improvements in work methods—particularly for indirect people of all kinds, including office people—are often not worth making because they won't stay nailed down. Suppose you cut a one-hour task to one half-hour. Do you gain anything? Often you don't. The employee just soaks up the time and does no more work. Or, as soon as the improvement man leaves, the man goes back to his old hour-long method.

Pointing out pitfalls (and there are many more than we have listed) in interpreting figures warns us of dangers but doesn't tell us how to avoid them. Truth is that there isn't any good way out. You just can't devise figures that tell you the whole truth and nothing but the truth. But you must always try not to let the emphasis on a good figure cause your men to make the figures look good at the expense of the true situation.

BUDGETS

Day by day and week by week you need to control your organization's activities. You plan for things to happen, then check up and find out what did happen and, when necessary, make new plans. Most of your plans involve money so you use budgets.

Budgets can be plans for money income or money outgo or both. In the factory budgets are always spending plans. But what good is a spending plan? It helps to cut spending. Viewed just as a plan it won't do that, but it is more than a plan.

It is also a goal—you try to keep costs *down* to the planned amount. A budget ought to motivate you. It is also a yardstick. Actual costs will be compared to it to see where and how much you went over. That will lead you on to "why?" and what can you do to keep it from happening the next time? Then you do things to keep from spending too much the next time. So you arrive at your real goal—controlled, and often lowered, costs.

Budgets don't solve all problems however. A budget to increase sales or to cut costs does not, by itself, do either. With or without budgets you ought already to be doing your best to boost sales and cut costs. You can't budget yourself into a profit. No? No, but budgets help you get there. True, they don't, by themselves, keep you in the black, but with budgets most of you do a better job than when you don't have them. In a sense you *can* budget yourself into a profit.

Budgets need to be used with discretion. Remember the "pitfalls" a few pages back? Suppose that you set a low amount for a foreman to spend for repairs. If he spends less, that is good, or is it? True, you have today saved money, but was it wise? How about the undone needed repairs? Or suppose that you set a low ratio of rejects as the goal for the foundry foreman. He meets it, but partly by sending to the machine shop some castings that should have been rejected in the foundry—castings that make trouble and extra costs in the machine shop. Budgets can make supervisors too "department-minded" and not enough company-minded.

Also, budget makers tend to tighten up budgets a little every time a new one is made out. Usually this is good, because you should always try to do a little better forever. But once in a while it is bad, because supervisors might pace their cost reduction efforts to the budget. If they get a really good cost-saving idea, they might put it into effect slowly or bit by bit so that they can beat every new budget without much work. Why should they make one grand showing and then have to contend with new tight budgets?

That (holding back on improvements) isn't what you want and isn't what you get from your good men. But the temptation is there, and you must try not to let them fall for it.

When you use budgets, the review of the past is an important part of this procedure. But don't get off the track. Budgets are wholly forward-looking. The past is frozen, only the future is fluid. You can do nothing about the past; you look to it only to help you do things better in the days ahead. Budgets are plans for things that are to happen.

But *people* have to make these things happen. So budgets are plans for things that are to happen in terms of the *people* who will make them happen. What does this mean to you? It means that you need budgets covering responsibilities of people. You need a budget for the works manager—it includes all items over which he has charge. Also you need one for the plant superintendent, and other budgets for each foreman and every other supervisor. Each one's budget covers *his area and only his area* of responsibility. Then the results of *his* work will show when you review his performance at the end of the budget period.

But aren't we emphasizing the wrong thing? You make *products*, and running departments is wholly for that purpose. Why not set up budgets for product costs, not department costs? You can and do set up product budgets. They help you control the costs of our products. Yet they are *not* the real control. The real control is department budgets, not product budgets.

If a *product's* cost goes over its budget, it will stay there unless some *person* cuts it in the future. Only people can act. If a product's cost goes over its budget, you have to find out why and trace the cause back to a department. Then you go over the matter with the *man* in charge. It is his job to get the costs back in line.

BUDGETS AS SPENDING LIMITS

Budgets are usually only *plans* for spending, but they can also be used as *authorizations*. As authorizations they let a department head spend the budgeted amount for each item without asking. Actually, because work has to be done, a supervisor can spend more, although he'll have to explain it later. But if he is spending very much more, he'd better report it right away so that the man at the top knows what is going on.

Budgets *limiting expenditures* are commonly used on construction or repair jobs, research projects, or for special nonrecurring expenses, such as a foreman training course. Budgets even for special projects do not, however, provide perfect control over the amount of expenditure because the costs of work, once started, cannot always be held down to the amounts originally planned. When a project uses up its budget before it is completed, it is usually better to go ahead and finish it rather than drop it and lose the money already spent. But at least you get to decide whether to keep on or not.

Sometimes, particularly on large complex products, companies must choose between meeting their schedule and meeting their budget. Usually when a plant is very busy, any job that gets behind schedule can be gotten back on schedule only by working overtime. If the delivery date is important to the customer, it is usually better to deliver on time even if the overtime makes your costs go over the estimate.

"CONTROLLABLE" AND "NONCONTROLLABLE" COSTS

Some of the costs of running a department are in no way controllable by its supervisor. For example, a foreman has no control over his department's assessment of general factory overhead costs, nor is he expected in his budget to hold that cost down.

A foreman's "controllable" costs are those over which he can exercise *some control*. They include direct and indirect labor in the department, materials and supplies used, repair costs, losses from poor workmanship, accident costs, etc. Calling these things controllable does not mean that you expect the foreman to be able to get rid of them altogether, but just that he can, by trying, keep them down.

The savings which you expect from budgets come altogether from keeping controllable costs down. Budgets usually set the amounts for controllable cost elements at low enough figures to make the department head do a good job if he keeps within the budgeted figure.

Controllable costs are set apart in considerable detail—*item by item* —in each department's budget. During the budget period the records of each department's costs of operating are also kept item by item, so that comparisons can be made between budgeted and actual expenditures individually for direct labor, indirect labor, and each of the other items. Reports are made showing these comparisons, and the department heads are asked to explain all cases where actual costs exceeded budgeted amounts.

Most noncontrollable costs are noncontrollable *only for minor departments*. The share of the general factory overhead assessed against one foreman's department is noncontrollable as far as he is concerned. But in the factory manager's budget some general factory overhead items *are* controllable as far as *he* is concerned. The cost of the factory time keeping department, for example, is a controllable item in the factory manager's budget. On the other hand, the charge for depreciation on the factory building is noncontrollable, even in his budget. The distinction between a controllable and a noncontrollable cost hinges on whether the head of the department covered by the budget can, in any way, hold it down.

MAKING UP BUDGETS

You have to start your spending plans by looking at the past. Most of the things that you will spend money for tomorrow, you spent money for yesterday. So you need to know, for yesterday, how much you spent for each item, where (in what departments) did you spend it, what for, and how many products did you turn out.

But what if you don't have all of those records? Maybe you didn't keep all of these figures for every department. If not, then you are not in a very good position to make up a budget. Also, if you have not been keeping records that way, you'd better start right now if you expect to use budgets, because budgets will require that kind of record keeping.

Next you go to the future. What are you going to make, as far as you can tell ahead, in the coming year—what products, how many of each, when, in what months? From this forecast you go on into more detail. How many man-hours of work will be done in each department? How much will you spend for each expense in every department, month by month?

The job sounds easy—just decide how much it will cost to do this and that. But anyone who has tried to budget for a vacation knows that it is one thing to say "make a budget," another thing to make it, and still another thing to live up to it.

The accounting department gets the job of making up budgets, although it alone does not decide all the figures that are set as goals. The company's over-all forecast of sales is gone over by the top men of the company. After they approve it, it becomes the basis for all of the manufacturing budgets. First you have one over-all manufacturing budget showing how many of each product to turn out each period and how much to spend.

The over-all budget is itself, however, a total of all the budgets for every subsidiary department's operation. Details of exactly how much to allow each department for its every expense are usually decided only after talking to its head. Tell him how much production he is supposed to get out and ask him, item by item, how much he will need to spend to get the work out.

Don't mistake though. You are *not* going to let him set his own budget. What kind of a figure would he set for himself? He knows that the budget is a yardstick by which his work will be judged. If he keeps costs below the budget, you will say that he has done a fine job. Naturally he will set a comfortable goal—one he can easily beat.

Then why ask him if you aren't going to pay any attention to what he says? You do pay some attention. He gets a chance to tell you how volume changes will change certain costs. Supervision, for example, might stay the same for minor changes, then jump if volume goes up to where you need another supervisor. Asking a foreman about these things lets him get in his say and makes him more agreeable to the budget he gets, even if it isn't just the way he would set it.

Budgets are usually set up for a year or more ahead and are kept that far ahead by being extended every quarter. There are quarterly, monthly, and weekly budgets for near-future periods. It is these near-future period budgets that are of the most use in controlling costs. Longer-range budgets are for longer-range planning, particularly financial planning.

KEEPING THE BUDGET CURRENT

Monthly and weekly budgets are really part of the year's budget. But as the year goes along sales turn out to be more or less than you expected and the product mix changes. As each new month comes along the question comes up: should the budget be revised so that it is reasonable for the operations actually expected?

Some companies do not revise budgets often—not oftener than once every three months. At first that does not sound very smart. But there is some reason for it. If you make new budgets every month, then your original year's budget might almost as well not have been made. You are just going on from month to month letting events take their course. You lose part of the idea of a budget furnishing goals to achieve.

If you do not revise often, then you can expect more variation between actual and budgeted performance than if you revised. Part of the variation will be due to changed production schedules, and only the other part will be due to good or bad performance. You'll need to remember that when analyzing the variances.

"FLEXIBLE" BUDGETS

We have already said that changes in production volume and in product mix upset budgets because you end up asking for (and getting) different quantities of products from those you first planned on. Naturally the old budget is not a fair statement of cost expectations.

TABLE 31–1

BUDGET

FINISHING DEPARTMENT, WATSON MANUFACTURING COMPANY

Month ―――――, 19――

	STANDARD HOURS OF DIRECT LABOR		
	70,000	80,000	90,000
Labor cost at $2.50 per hour...	$175,000	$200,000	$225,000
Other variable costs...........	35,000	40,000	45,000
Semivariable costs............	18,500	20,000	21,500
Fixed costs..................	100,000	100,000	100,000
Total....................	$328,500	$360,000	$391,500

Accountants have tried to take care of this by setting up "flexible" budgets—budgets that vary with volume and product mix changes so that they are always fair statements of cost expectations. But, actually the possible combinations of changes are too great for any kind of flexible budget to cover everything.

What the accountants do (they call it using "flexible" budgets) is to set up budgets for several different levels of production (see Table 31–1). Table 31–1 shows three budgets, one each for 70,000, 80,000 and 90,000 standard hours of work. In a real situation, of course, you would have fifty or more cost items in the budget, not just four.

After a period is over, accountants use, when comparing actual costs with those budgeted, the budget for the level that is nearest to the actual level of production. (Look at Table 31–2.) Notice that at the close of the period it was found that 90,000 standard hours of work was done. This means that the third column of figures from Table 31–1 sets the budget figures. In our example direct labor ran $7,500 over the budget. Variable and semivariable costs ran $2,500 under, so the total was $5,000 over the budget.

But what if the department turned out 91,000 standard hours of work, not 90,000? You have no budget for that. Then what? You could make up a new budget just for that level of production, but you don't. Instead you use the budget for 90,000 hours. You would expect that the extra 1,000 standard hours of work done would run up your direct labor and the variable and semivariable costs a little.

That would show on the analysis as variances (the "over" and "under" columns in Table 31–2). But as you look over the variances, item by item, you can, in your mind, allow a little. You know that a little extra expense is justified. It is better to handle minor production differences this

TABLE 31–2

REVIEW OF OPERATIONS
FINISHING DEPARTMENT, WATSON MANUFACTURING COMPANY
Month _____, 19____

	Budget	Actual	Over	Under
Direct labor, 90,000 standard hours at $2.50............	$225,000	$232,000	$7,500	.....
Other variable costs..	45,000	44,000	.....	$1,000
Semivariable costs...	21,500	20,000	.....	1,500
Fixed costs.........	100,000	100,000	.....	.....
Total..........	$391,500	$396,000	Over $5,000	

way than it is to go to the expense of making up whole new budgets to cover the exact quantities made.

Here are some things that flexible budgets are *not*. They are not hazy or vague budgets. They are not free-wheeling budgets. They don't allow supervisors to spend money the way they want to. Nor do you have a flexible budget when you just throw away an old budget and make a new one. Also flexible budgets do not mean making new budgets every week or month. Nor do flexible budgets automatically adjust upward if a machine breaks down. That is exactly the kind of variation that all budgets, flexible budgets included, are intended to show up.

BUDGET VARIANCES

Budget variance should *never* go unnoticed—particularly the bad ones. Someone spent too much—why? Department heads have to explain. But what good does explaining do? Isn't it like locking the barn door after the horse is stolen? Yes, but you want to get your men into the habit of locking the door all the time, so that no more horses will be stolen.

A foremen who knows that he will have to explain variances tries not to let them happen. Those that are justifiable he knows will be accepted, but he can't squirm out of labor inefficiency so easily. He has to try to keep within the budget and so keep your costs down—which is just what budgets try to get him to do.

STUDY QUESTIONS

1. Distinguish between cost reduction and cost control.
2. How can a "velvet-glove" approach to cutting costs ever accomplish anything? What other ways are there?
3. How can committees help reduce costs? Explain.
4. Contrast cost-cutting goals with budgets.
5. List and explain the seven steps needed to make a cost-cutting program work.
6. Suggest a few places in production to look for cost-savings opportunities. In each case, what action should you take?
7. How do you go about getting foremen to cut costs? Why do they need special attention?
8. "Beating the budget is a good idea." Do you agree? Justify your position.
9. How bad is it to have a ratio of indirect costs to direct labor costs of 5 to 1? Discuss fully.
10. Would you ask a department head to help set his own budget? Give reasons for your answer.
11. Why are budgets for people (as distinguished from budgets for products) so important?
12. Which costs are "controllable"? What good does it do to classify some costs as controllable?
13. How do flexible budgets operate? Why use them?

Chapter 34

THE CALCULATION OF COSTS

WHEN do you make money on a product? When you sell it for more than it costs to make. Sounds simple but it isn't easy because many costs are not incurred just for one kind of product. You have to assess products with their shares of the general costs of doing business. Such assessments have to be fairly arbitrary, so the cost figure you get is only an approximation.

What, for example, does a meal at home cost? Do you count part of the house rent? Do you count part of the cost of your car for going to the store for groceries? How about the cost of the silverware you use? How about your wife's time? It would take quite a lot of figuring to get a cost figure. And even then the figure you come up with would depend on how you assessed overhead.

A factory's problem is no easier. It is just as hard there to figure out what it costs to make a product. And it is just as crude a figure when you get it. There is really no need ever to figure labor and material costs to the fourth decimal place of accuracy when you know that you have to spread overhead on with a shovel. The implied accuracy of detailed product cost figures is specious.

But you make money and stay in business only if you sell things for more than they cost. So you still have to do the best you can—even if your cost measures of what it costs to make each kind of item are crude. You need cost figures so that you can set selling prices. And inside the factory you need cost figures for budgets and controls. Besides that the government makes you keep certain cost records, even insisting that you keep them in the way it says. Why? Your calculated profits and the income taxes you pay on them depend to some extent on how you figure costs.

In a book on manufacturing management we are not interested too much in the details of how accountants figure costs. But we are interested a little. Budgets and controls use cost data so we ought to know something about how they are figured.

641

PAST AND FUTURE COSTS

Cost accounting is nearly always two-sided—it tells you how much things *have been costing*. That is historical. And nearly always, too, cost accounting tells you how much future products *are likely to cost*. Most of the cost accounting that you see is the record keeping that tells you about past costs, but the more valuable part of the work tells you about future costs. That helps you set budgets and plan for the future.

It isn't fair though to dismiss the record keeping part of cost accounting as just record keeping. Records of what happened yesterday furnish you with the figures you need to *control* your organization. You compare yesterday's actual cost with the plan, see where they are different, find out why, and correct bad spots. Improvements in the future are built on records of past performance.

JOB-LOT COSTS

Job-lot costs are used in companies doing varied work. You give every job a number to identify it and set up an account for it in the cost accounting department. (Production control uses the same job number when scheduling the lot's production.)

As a job moves through manufacturing, you list, in its account, all of its costs. From materials requisitions you get the value of the materials used. From factory workers' job tickets you get the cost of labor put on the job. Then calculate overhead (discussed on page 646). Add these up, plus any other costs incurred for the job, and get the cost of making the lot. Divide by the number of units and get the unit cost.

What do you do though when you have to quote a price on a future job that sales wants to bid on? You do the same thing. List all of the materials that you *expect* to use, the labor that you *think* it will take, and again assess overhead at your usual rate. Add and get your probable cost.

PROCESS COSTS

Continuous production must use "process" costs. Process costs are always average costs. You can't very well separate the cost of making one gallon of gasoline from another, or one television set from another of the same model, or of one bolt of cloth from another of the same cloth. Nearly all products follow the same path through production. To find the process average cost, just keep a record of how much it costs for a day or a week to carry on an operation. Divide by the number of units produced and get the operation's average cost. Where there are several operations in a process, add the cost of each one and get the total cost per unit for the whole process.

"DIRECT" AND "INDIRECT" COSTS

Direct costs are those you can trace directly to a product—the cost of materials you use and the cost of labor put on it. All other costs are

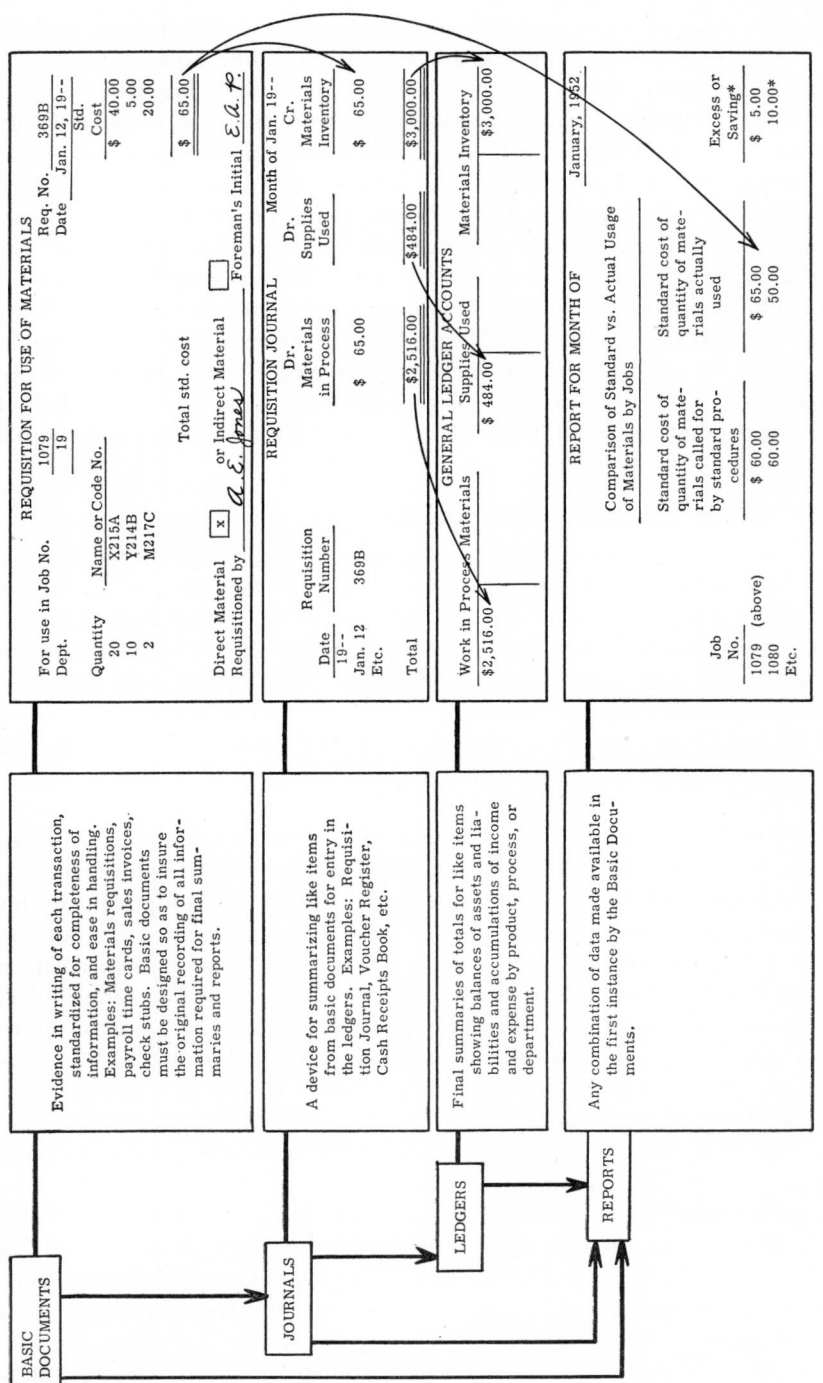

FIG. 34–1. Sources of accounting information and the way in which it is used when standard costs are used for job lots.

indirect—costs not incurred for any one product. Indirect costs include the wages of men who don't work on the product, supplies, all office expense, insurance, depreciation, and taxes. In total, indirect costs often amount to double the direct costs. Unless you use direct costing (described on page 649 and not to be confused with direct costs here) you always charge every product with a share of the overhead costs. Every item's "cost" includes its own direct costs plus its share of indirect costs.

Some people call direct costs "variable" costs. They mean that the *total amount* you spend for them goes up or down along with production. The more you produce the more you spend, in total, for these items. Indirect costs are called "fixed" costs, meaning that their total is not affected much by volume changes. Don't take either of these terms as hard and fast, however. Not all variable costs would be cut in half if you cut production in half. Nor would every fixed cost stay unchanged if you halved production.

COST "ELEMENTS" AND COST "UNITS"

In getting a product's cost, accountants have to deal with (a) the items you spend your money for: materials, labor, services, depreciation, insurance, taxes; and (b) the things for which you want cost information: products, operations, and areas of responsibility. What you spend money for, accountants call cost "elements." What you want information about, they call cost "units."

Cost accounting *collects* information about what you spend money for. With that information it then *computes* the costs of products, operations, and areas of responsibility.

In general, the larger your cost unit, the more cost elements you can charge directly to it. If the cost unit is one manufacturing department, the foreman's salary, as well as depreciation on all equipment in his department, becomes a direct cost of that department. But if the cost unit is a large department occupying a whole building, even depreciation on that building becomes a direct charge to that area of responsibility.

Notice that your *cost collecting procedures* must pay attention to *cost units*. If you want to find out the costs of small areas—a single department, for example—you must set up your cost records so that they show that single department's costs apart from others wherever you can. You will need to set up separate departmental accounts paralleling most of your plant-wide accounts.

You probably have a plant-wide account for floor repairs. Subdivide it by departments, so that later you can charge each department with its own floor repair costs. Do the same with supplies, tools, and as many other things as you can. If you don't do that you'll later have to apportion the plant-wide costs of floor repairs, supplies, and tools to departments without knowing just where you actually spent the money. It is better to keep each department's expenses apart.

Same thing with *product* costs. Charge everything directly to the product that you can. It leaves you with less apportioning to do later and gives you better costs.

"Load" Centers. A "load" center (or "production" or "machine" center) is just a part of the department. Often it is one very big expensive machine or group of similar machines. As far as cost accounting is concerned, a load center is one kind of costing unit—it is a distinct part of the plant. Its costs are collected separately just as if it were a department. Collecting costs for load centers helps you pin point costs and so helps control them. And it lets you figure the hourly cost of operating the load center so that you can charge the right amounts for its use to products using it.

ALLOCATING COST ELEMENTS TO COST UNITS

The end product of cost accounting is the cost of the cost unit. But we have said that departments are cost units and products are cost units. How do they tie in with each other? Department costs are often end results in themselves, but they are also steps on the way to getting product costs. You can't get good product costs without also having gotten department costs on the way.

Back on page 634 we said that *only people* could do anything about costs. You want *department* operating costs so that you can trace responsibility to *men*. The *man* in charge of every department is supposed to keep his department's costs down. Department operating cost figures are, therefore, useful in themselves.

How do you get department costs? To start with, you keep *in each department's account* all of its own department costs. To its own costs you add a share of overhead costs incurred outside the department. Allocating the outside costs requires several steps. First you assess *plant-wide* overhead costs to *all* departments. Then, second, you assess the costs of all *indirect* departments to the *operating* departments (those that work on the product). You have to do this because you can't allocate costs to *products* except by charging them with the costs of departments that worked on them. So you have to charge operating departments with the costs of all nonoperating departments. After having done this, you sum up the department's own overhead, its assessments, and its direct labor and material costs, and you have the cost of running the department. If department costs were all that you wanted, your cost accounting job would be done.

But since you want product costs too, you will have to allocate each operating department's costs to the products it turned out. How is this done? Start by comparing the direct labor cost to the rest of the department's costs (its own overhead plus its overhead assessments). Suppose that last year your direct workers in a department put in 1,000,000 hours of work and that they were paid $2,500,000 in wages. This comes to an average of $2.50 per hour. And suppose that the department's overhead costs came to $3,750,000. The overhead is equal to 150 per cent of direct labor costs. (We are leaving materials costs out of our example because they are usually charged directly to the product and do not have to be allocated.)

Now, turn to your record of direct work done in the year. How many labor hours or dollars were spent on product A, product B, and so on. Suppose that your record shows that your men put in 20,000 hours working on product A. And suppose that they turned out 50,000 units of product A. Direct labor costs came to $50,000. The overhead assessment, at the rate of 150 per cent of direct labor, came to $75,000. Total costs (omitting materials) came to $125,000, or $2.50 each for product A.

Now you have the cost of making product A in this department. But product A also required work in other departments too. Figure each one the same way and add them all together to get product A's total cost. And, of course, add in materials costs too. Notice that product A's cost in each department is figured separately. This way you can make heavy charges for overhead to products that are made on big expensive machines. Departments with expensive machines will have overhead charge rates of 400 or 500 per cent instead of 150 per cent as used in our example.

ALLOCATING OVERHEAD

We said above that you have to allocate overhead costs to departments. Actually, you can't allocate most overhead expenses the way we did in our product A example. There, we used direct labor hours records to tell us how to apportion overhead. Picture, for example, trying to allocate real estate and property taxes that way! Or depreciation! Departments without many machines but with lots of men would get big assessments. Heavily mechanized departments with fewer men would get off lightly. That just reverses the cause of the expense. Your heavily mechanized departments boost your taxes and depreciation. You ought to assess mechanized departments with heavy tax and depreciation charges.

Accountants solve this problem by looking at each overhead item by itself and allocating it in the most logical way they can think of. Real estate and property taxes and depreciation on buildings might be allocated to departments according to the amount of their floor space. Depreciation on machines ought to go to departments according to the machines they have, based on each machine's depreciation schedule. Electric power ought to go to departments according to the power that they use.

"ABSORPTION" OF OVERHEAD

In our product A example, we found that overhead amounted to 150 per cent of direct labor costs. That was last year's experience figure.

Barring changes this is what you expect for the year ahead. But if volume goes up or down (and you don't know whether it will change or not), this ratio will end up being different for the coming year.

If your forecast is for no change in volume, you will start out the year saying that the cost of this year's products will all include overhead charges figured at 150 per cent of direct labor. And if your volume doesn't change, this will be about right. But suppose that you have a good year, that you sell one fifth more products than you forecasted. Direct labor will cost you $3,000,000 instead of the expected $2,500,000.

During the whole year you keep charging overhead at 150 per cent of labor, so you assess products with $4,500,000 of overhead costs. Your overhead might actually stay at last year's $3,750,000 since most of it is fixed cost. If it does stay the same, you end up overcharging your products to the tune of $750,000. Probably, though, overhead costs will go up some, so the overcharge is a little less than $750,000. Say that overhead actually comes to $4,000,000. You end up the year assessing $500,-000 too much. You "overabsorb" your overhead, overstate your costs, and understate your profits.

If business goes down, the reverse happens. You end up passing on too little overhead (underabsorbing it), understating costs, and overstating profits.

What can you do about this? It doesn't seem very smart to quote wrong costs all year and then all at once wake up at the end of the year and find that you have made more or less money than you had thought. That isn't the point. You know full well all year long exactly what is going on. You don't wake up and discover it at the year's end.

Then why quote wrong costs all year? That isn't exactly the way you look at it either. You want to know what your costs are, including a normal overhead assessment, if you can get your usual sales volume. You try to set selling prices to yield some profit at that volume level. You know that greater volume will *reduce* the proper overhead assessment on every item. You know full well that you will end up making *more* per unit than your first calculation (for expected normal volume) showed. And you are just as well aware of what happens on the downside.

The real point is that you don't go out and cut prices when business is good in order to hold profits down, *nor can you raise* prices when business is bad. You let prices pretty well alone, so you may as well let your calculated unit costs alone too and then just recognize that, because of overhead, high volume results in extra profits while low volume makes losses.

GETTING BASIC FIGURES

A cost accountant starts with figures that other people send him. He gets figures from materials requisitions, worker job tickets, inspector scrap reports, repair work orders, and many other sources. Everything he needs comes to him on reports that someone else makes out. Mostly, too, the others design their reports to take care of their own needs, not his. He often plays second fiddle and has to take information the way they give it to him. Sometimes he doesn't get all the information he needs. Besides, he is at the end of the line. Any time that information passes through two or three hands before it gets to a person, he doesn't get it very quickly.

You can never make *cost control* work well unless you get the figures it needs to *cost accounting* and get them there quickly. Remember, in Chapter 33, how we harped on the need for up-to-the-minute reports? Too often a little false economy in getting figures *to* cost accounting keeps it from getting cost figures *out* soon enough to be of much value.

COST ACCOUNTING PROBLEMS

We noted earlier that what you say an item costs depends in part on how you assess overhead costs. How you should do it is cost accounting's biggest problem. But there are other problems besides that. Here are several questions that also must be answered by management. And, as with overhead, you get different cost figures depending on how you answer them.

The first question is: Should you use "standard" costs or "job-lot" costs? Here is the problem: Successive lots of materials usually end up costing different actual amounts of money per unit of product. That is because some lots are bigger than others, thereby making the setup-cost-per-unit different. Also men work at different paces, the amount of scrap varies, the price of purchased material changes, and so on.

What do you do about it? Are you to say that the items made in the lot finished on January 15 cost you a different amount from those in a lot finished on February 15? The items look alike and are alike, and you'll probably sell them for the same price. Or, if they are parts, you will put them into finished products whose costs will be figured as if the part had the same cost each time. Most companies use some kind of standard cost. Usually this standard cost is the average unit cost that you get when you figure several lots together.

Some companies, however, use quite a different kind of standard cost. They figure out every product's *ideal* cost—what it ought to cost if everything goes perfectly.

But how does this do them any good? Actual costs never get so low. And you certainly couldn't use this kind of cost as the basis for setting selling prices. Companies using standard costs of the ideal kind use them in factory budgets. They aren't just trying to delude themselves. What they are after is to keep forever before them the cost of inefficiencies. They regard all of the excess over ideal as the cost of inefficiency. They feel that knowing its cost will help them improve.

Your method of *collecting* cost figures depends on whether you choose job-lot costs or standard costs. If you use job-lot costs, you collect each lot's costs and figure the cost of each unit. You charge the items into finished parts or finished products inventory at that unit price.

But, if you use standard costs, you don't keep the costs of successive lots apart. Instead you find out the combined cost to make several lots as a total. Then divide by the number of units and get the average unit cost. This average will be used as the standard cost for the next accounting period ahead.

Standard costs are a must in continuous manufacturing because you don't have separate lots. These standard costs can be either the "average" kind or the "ideal" kind.

A second question is: Are you being realistic when you follow the time-honored practice of assessing *products* with *all* the costs of doing business? Suppose you are making electric light bulbs. Should you say that an electric light bulb costs should include the cost of labor plus material plus *overhead?* How realistic is it to say that a light bulb's share of the real estate property taxes is $0.0002 per light bulb? Some people say that you should not add to a product's cost the costs of any expense not directly connected with it.

This method is called "direct costing." In direct costing you say that an item costs *only* its direct costs (largely labor and material). All overhead costs, such as building depreciation and taxes, you regard as costs of doing business and not as part of the cost of making a light bulb.

But if our *products* don't bear *all* of your costs, then who or what does? The products do end up carrying your costs, but they do it as a group—not individually. If you use direct costing you show very low costs to manufacture. When you start to calculate your profits you first subtract, from income, all direct costs, leaving a large gross margin. Then subtract all overheads and find the profits.

You end up with the same profit that you'd get if you did it the conventional way, so why make any change? One reason is simplicity. Direct costing is simpler than conventional costing. A second reason is that an item's computed cost does not go up and down as your total volume changes. That seems to be a very worth-while advantage because it remedies a weakness of ordinary methods. With ordinary costing, the units produced when you are operating at half time have to stand their own direct costs plus *all* of the overhead. Low volume makes them seem to cost a great deal—but it isn't their fault that you don't have more volume over which to spread the overhead. The reverse happens in high periods. High volume cuts the overhead assessments to each product, so they seem to cost less. But do they? Direct costing is still new and not common, but you may hear more of it in the years ahead.

A third problem is "joint" costs. You spend money buying one raw material but you get two or more kinds of materials. When a meat packer buys a cow he gets meat, leather, and other things. How does he allocate the cost of the cow to products? How much did he pay for a sirloin? For hamburger? For leather? A workable answer is "look to the income." If sirloin brings in 5 per cent of your sales income, charge sirloin with 5 per cent of the cow's cost.

Most companies working on nature's products in early stages of manufacture find that when they buy one material they get two or more. Usually only one is valuable, and the other has to be thrown away. But not always. Copper ore sometimes contains silver too. Both are valuable, so you would divide the ore's cost between copper and silver.

Sometimes waste materials can be made into something worth money. If so, they are called *"by-products."* But unless they are worth a lot, they are never charged any material costs. Just consider the materials as free and charge as costs only the work done on them to make them salable. Meat packers do this with medicines gotten from animal waste. These medicines are claimed to be very profitable, but that is partly because the companies figure that their raw material is free.

A fourth problem is machine "setups." You have to get machines ready for jobs. Usually this means taking off the special tooling for the last job and fastening on tooling for the new job. Some setups are simple, taking only a few minutes. Some take hours. Some take several men.

You can charge setups to specific orders. Or you can charge setup costs to an overhead account for setups. You must do one or the other, and neither suits perfectly. If you charge the order, then the cost per unit of products made in different lots will vary inversely with the size of the lot. The bigger the lot the less the cost, and the smaller the lot the more the cost. The bad part is the way costs per unit jump around.

But if you charge setups to overhead that is bad too. Then the high cost of frequent small orders is never noticed because the wasteful part —the cost of extra setups—doesn't get charged directly to the orders. If it were, it would be seen. It gets into the costs, of course, when you allocate overhead to products. But getting into costs that way doesn't point the finger at the cause. An injudicious management can mislead itself about how much it saves by keeping inventories very low and re-ordering little dribbles often.

A fifth question is: How closely should you try to tie costs to the products which get the benefit of the expense? Should today's research costs be assessed as a cost of making today's products? Should today's foreman training program cost be charged to today's products? Logic says to charge the products that will get the benefits. Practically, it gets too involved, so you end up charging most such costs to today's products.

STUDY QUESTIONS

1. How accurately can you compute a product's cost to make? What makes it hard to do? Explain.

2. Why bother with past costs? Aren't we just wasting our money on something we can't do anything about? Discuss.

3. Contrast job-lot costs and process costs. Tell how you get product costs each of these two ways.

4. What is the difference between direct costs (not "direct costing") and indirect costs? What difference does it make? Explain.

5. What are cost "elements" and cost "units"? How are they related? Explain.

6. How can you allocate overhead to a product? Show the steps that you go through.

7. What base for allocating overhead do you think would be appropriate for allocating:
   a) Workmen's compensation taxes
   b) Building depreciation
   c) Electricity
   d) The works manager's salary
   e) Real estate taxes
   Give reasons for your choices.

8. Can you "overabsorb" overhead? How? Is that good? Discuss.

9. Contrast standard costs and job-lot costs. When would you use each? Why?

10. What is "direct costing"? Explain fully and give its good and bad points.

11. How can set up costs be charged? Which is better? Why?

CASE 34–1.   ECLIPSE IRON FOUNDRY

"We can't make any money on that job, it has too much labor in it," said Joe Guzik, foundry foreman, to Harry Taylor, cost estimator for the Eclipse Iron Foundry. The Eclipse foundry, *like its competitors*, always estimated costs (on which prices for jobs were based when quoting prices on prospective orders) on a per pound basis. Complex castings were quoted at a higher price per pound than simple castings, but the difference in price did not seem to be great enough to cover the extra labor costs. Guzik was right about the company making no money on jobs that took considerable labor.

Should Eclipse start quoting higher prices for castings requiring extra labor? What will happen if it does quote prices that fully cover costs? Should the estimates be based on the cost of the man-hours required plus materials cost?

Chapter 35

QUALITY STANDARDS AND INSPECTION

"Quality," to most people, means "high quality." And it is a little like mother, God, and country—everyone is for it—the more the better. But do we really want the highest possible quality of everything? Ten-cent stores sell millions of pounds of candy, millions of water glasses and dishes, and millions of other things—practically *all* of which are admittedly of low quality. We don't all buy very many things from 10-cent stores, but neither do all of us buy Cadillacs. Isn't what we really want the best quality that we can get *for the money we are willing to spend?*

That is what quality means to a manufacturer. He tries to make the best product he can *for the price that he can get.* Not that he objects to high quality, as such; but, as a rule, the higher the quality, the higher the cost. Worse, even, costs go up faster than quality. A little more quality costs a good bit more money. A manufacturer also wants to make a product of consistent quality. Customers stay better satisfied if products all perform about equally well.

It is true, though, that year by year the quality of most products improves. It improves because we are always learning new ways to make things better and less costly. So does our competitor. So both of us, in order to stay in business, must always improve quality or cut the price for the old quality.

A manufacturer must usually aim at a *particular* quality, *not the best.* He must try to build like the one-hoss shay—so that every part of his product wears out at once. It would be foolish for an automobile maker to make such durable engines that they still work fine long after the rest of the car is ready for the junk heap.

Large companies generally compete on a high quality and service basis rather than on a price basis. They emphasize quality in their advertising and have educated the public to expect good products. They believe that "Price is soon forgotten, but quality is long remembered." Probably that is true, but most of us have to watch expenses. Often we won't pay much more for extra quality. Cadillacs cost only twice as much as Chevrolets, but Chevrolets outsell Cadillacs 10 to 1. Besides, as consumers, often we can't tell high quality from reasonably good quality, and we also know that sometimes we pay for high quality but don't get it.

A product's quality is determined by the characteristics it possesses. It is necessary for the manufacturer to decide what the characteristics of his product should be, and then have the engineers design a product which embodies these characteristics. They must describe the product's design (its quality characteristics) to the factory in language that it can understand. And the engineers must set the limits of acceptability for deviations from perfection (the "tolerances") and set up inspection methods. These steps are all necessary to insure the manufacture of a product of the desired quality and of a consistent quality.

PURPOSES OF INSPECTION

Why do you inspect products? To weed out inferior products, of course. But if you stop with that answer you overlook most of what you *should* be doing. You should inspect things while they are being made, not only to catch the bad items but also to save wasting further work on them.

But the big reason for inspection is preventive—not remedial. You want to *stop making* bad items. This makes the inspection job a little different. You have to find out where and why bad products are made that way. The inspector decides whether an item passes or not, and he must give his reason why. From his reports you can find trouble spots, and you can find out why bad products are made. Then you can concentrate on fixing up the situation so that there won't be so many rejects in the future.

It pays to inspect soon after an operation is performed—the sooner the better—not because it will do the already produced bad item any good but because if the first products on a run are bad, you find it out before very many others have been made the same way. In fact, on semiautomatic machines, the operator must usually stop his machine after he makes a few pieces and get them approved before he can go ahead. Once the machine is set right, only occasional rechecking is needed.

Bad work reports often focus management's attention on problems beyond the foreman's ability to solve. Maybe the quality standards are too tight, tighter than they need to be. If so, management, can relax them. Maybe you can cut rejects by using better materials. If so, you will have to decide if it is worth it. Maybe your machines are too old and worn to do as close work as is demanded. You will have to solve that one, too. You have to choose between high scrap, or buying new machines, or relaxing the standards. Or maybe the problem is worker training. If so, the foreman can do something about that.

Inspection also makes sure that the product works and that it works without hurting anyone. Since the safety of a product's operation is generally in its design, safety is more an engineering responsibility than it is an inspection department job. So also is testing and inspection done to see that the product will do the job it is intended to do.

EXPRESSING QUALITY STANDARDS

Before the factory can make products of specified quality it must have directions that it can follow. Its quality instructions usually come to it as drawings and written specifications. Drawings show shapes and dimensions. Written specifications describe such characteristics as color, tensile strength, hardness, and chemical composition. Drawings and specifications describe *what the product should be like* after it is made rather than *how to make it*. Only occasionally do they tell the factory how certain operations are to be done, although sometimes drawings are made showing what the product should be like after certain specific operations in its processing.

Except where curving contours are involved, as, for example, in automobile fenders, dimensions are among the easiest characteristics to describe. Drawings show the exact dimensions wanted and the tolerances (permissible deviations) permitted. On most metal parts made today the tolerances are limited to two or three thousandths of an inch or less. Rarely is more deviation acceptable, and even closer tolerances are common. Tolerances are usually expressed as the desired dimension plus and minus the permissible deviation, as $\pm.002$ inches.

Other specifications given the factory usually are either descriptions of the kind of raw material to be used or test scores which must be made when certain standard tests are applied to the product.

RESPONSIBILITY FOR QUALITY

Top managers set quality policies and decide their products' general characteristics only, although if you make only one or two products they will want to see final designs and to approve them. Mostly, though (and always if you make many kinds of little things), top management leaves it up to engineering, sales, and the manufacturing heads to agree on details of product design. Engineering decides on materials to use and sets tolerances and quality standards, but does it keeping in mind the product's need to perform, on the one hand, and its cost to produce, on the other. The engineers also develop inspection and testing procedures and equipment and specify the tests that the product must pass to be acceptable.

Inspection enforces the quality standards that the engineers set up.

Inspectors nearly always report to a chief inspector who reports to the works manager. But it is wrong to say that inspection is responsible for quality. It just passes judgment and helps spot causes of defects.

Some companies have both an inspection and a quality control department. When they do, there may be some confusion about their duties. The inspection department has most to do with passing judgment as

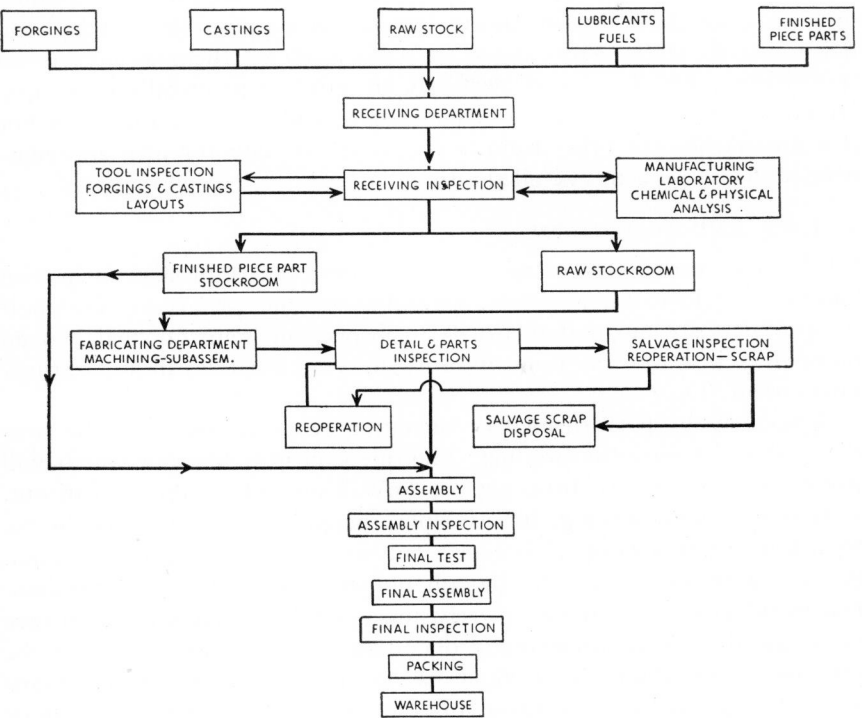

FIG. 35–1. Relationship of inspection to production.

products are made. Quality control deals with incoming materials and purchased items and with the finished components and finished whole products. Quality control also sets up control charts to help check quality during production—charts of the kind described in Chapter 36.

Probably the heaviest responsibility for quality lies with manufacturing. *It makes the product.* Whatever quality characteristics—size, finish, contour, color, or whatnot—the product has, the manufacturing department puts into it. If it does not do its job well, no amount of police effort by inspection will catch all the defects, and the end product will probably suffer. And, even if inspection does catch all the bad work, the factory's poor work makes it costly (because of both the scrap and the inspection costs) to get the proper quality into the finished product.

The factory is often accused of being quantity—not quality—minded.

Foremen don't see why the engineers ask for such exact measurements. Partly their objection is just lack of understanding as to the real need for exactly fitting parts. But partly also it is knowledge (knowledge that engineers share, too) that every specification is a little arbitrary.

Everyone knows that products slightly beyond the pale are acceptable for most purposes. Suppose, for example, that a new car, supposed to go 100 miles per hour, will actually go only 85. Or suppose that a china dish has a speck of dirt on the underside. Or suppose that a telephone has a scratch on it. You'd have to reject each of them as not up to specification. But they are all perfectly all right for practically every use. Of course you have to cut off somewhere and say that this goes but that doesn't. On the other hand, it is easy to see why foremen and engineers don't see eye to eye all the time.

TESTING AND INSPECTION

"Testing" is one kind of inspection. "Inspection," a broader term than "testing," includes all activities, including testing, performed to see if the products are up to standard. If to inspect an item, you have to do more than just look at it or measure it, you usually call it "testing" rather than "inspecting."

Tests may be performance or operating tests, or they may be tests that end up ruining the product. The question may be, how much will products stand before breaking, or how long before they wear out. In tensile strength testing, for example, the products are broken in the test. A test may also be a chemical analysis of a sample of the product. It, too, destroys the sample, though not all tests destroy the product. Hardness tests, for example, merely make a slight dent on the surface of the product. Performance and operating tests are usually part of the final inspection after the product has been made. Tests are necessary wherever you can't tell if the item is all right just by looking at it or measuring it.

But even looking and measuring often get to be too fine for the naked eye. Angles of teeth on gears, angles of threads on bolts, curvatures on small parts, the sharpness of cutting edges, the smoothness of surfaces, etc., often can be checked only with special magnifying equipment. Very close tolerances on dimensions, angles, and curves can be checked only with comparators and other special measuring devices. Even though complicated equipment is often used, this type of checking is called "inspecting" rather than "testing" because the product being checked is only looked at and is not destroyed, marred, or tried out in use.

HOW OFTEN TO INSPECT

You can inspect *during* operations, or *after* operations. How can you tell when to do it? The ideal to aim for is never. Always inspect as little as you can get by with while still insuring your product's quality. Passing judgment on or reporting on a product's quality is largely waste. True, you must do it, and doing it improves your end product, but you can cut down on it only if you make things *right* when you *make* them.

Since you can never reach the ideal (no inspection), you still have the question of when to inspect. It comes down to the matter of costs. What does it cost to inspect versus what does it cost not to inspect? In actual practice, companies usually do spend 5 per cent or a little more of their labor cost for inspection. The ratio goes up with mechanization because other labor costs are cut more than inspection. Here are several rules about *when* to inspect:

1. Inspect *after* operations that are likely to produce faulty items so that you will not do more work on bad items.
2. Inspect *before* costly operations so that you won't do those operations on already spoiled items.
3. Inspect *before* operations where faulty products might break or jam the machines.
4. Inspect *before* operations that cover up defects (such as electroplating, painting, or assembly).
5. Inspect *before* assembly operations that can't be undone (such as welding parts or mixing paint).
6. On automatic and semiautomatic machines, inspect *first* and *last* pieces and some in between.
7. Inspect *finished parts.*
8. Inspect and test *finished products.* Be sure that nothing gets shipped out without inspection. *From here on, the customer is the next inspector.*
9. Inspect *before* storage (includes purchased items).

HOW MANY TO INSPECT

Should we inspect some, most, or all of our products? Our rules for how often still apply. Ideally we'd like to inspect none. Practically we must inspect some. One large company inspects 5 per cent of production during runs of machined parts but goes up to 10 per cent for hand-produced items. For extrusions and stampings, it cuts inspection clear down to 2 per cent.

How many to inspect is again a matter of weighing the cost of doing it versus the costs of not doing it. But here the element of probability is more important than it is in deciding *when* to inspect.

Probability is important because you *must* rely only on samples in so many cases. Must? Why not use 100 per cent inspection (look at every item) if it is important? In lots of cases, you can't use 100 per cent inspection. Samples—and small ones too—are a must in all cases where you use a *destructive test.* You test a few and then say that the rest of the lot is like the sample. Probably so but not certainly so. That is where probability comes in. It is discussed in Chapter 36.

Samples are also a must with all bulk materials. You can't test a whole coal pile to find out its heat content, nor can you look at every grain of wheat in a freight car to see if it is moldy. Material that comes in chunks, grains, powder, or liquid form must be sample tested, not 100 per cent inspected. Because of inspection costs, samples are also nearly always used for many other items that could be 100 per cent inspected. More about that in Chapter 36.

One hundred per cent inspection should be carried out only if the inspection is inexpensive or if it is highly important that every item be acceptable. In most cases an inspection of samples is sufficient; this is particularly true after automatic machine operations. Where casual looking at the item will suffice, try to combine doing this with the next manufacturing operation. The man doing the next operation often must handle and look at the item anyway. He can throw out obviously defective items and save the company the expense of inspecting.

INSPECTING PURCHASED GOODS

Always inspect all bought items: First, to see that you get the right kind and quantity so that your manufacturing won't be held up. Second, so that you can send back damaged or unsatisfactory items and get new ones right away. And, third, for the record, so that you know what has come in and been put into stock and so that you can go ahead and pay the bill.

Normally you can still return defective items even after you first accept them. Vendors will take them back whether they are legally obligated to accept them or not—because vendors want to keep you as a customer.

Most materials and even parts are easy to handle in receiving inspection and create no problems. But bought components often make trouble. The specially designed instrument, the hydraulic pump, the electrical control—these are hard to inspect or test. Most receiving inspectors have no notion as to whether they are good or not. They will need to get from engineering special checking instructions. But if the bought product is extremely technical, the engineers themselves may have to approve the incoming products.

It is very important to check technical items right away because if anything is wrong with them you must move fast to get them reworked or replaced or your product's assembly will be held up.

The receiving department, with the occasional help of the laboratory, also inspects all purchased raw materials. The receiving department is usually under the direction of the stores department, although it may be administered by the purchasing department. Historically, the receiving inspection department has usually had no direct connection with the factory inspection department, but today it is often tied in closely with the factory's quality control division. Even if it is not, if it applies sampling inspection techniques to incoming materials, it will probably have the help of the quality control division in setting up the proper methods. If purchased materials have a high rejection rate, the company's quality control staff frequently contacts the vendor and helps him work out better control of quality. This was rarely done years ago.

INSPECTING MATERIALS IN PROCESS

Inspectors actually do very little of all the inspecting that goes on. Every worker inspects his own work enough to tell if he is doing the job right. And if things go wrong he and maybe the setup man, assistant foreman, or foreman try to straighten things out so that he turns out good products again. Also, on jobs that are running along all right, the man keeps checking now and then to see that the products are still all right. Workers catch a good bit of the bad work that comes their way from earlier jobs and throw it aside for the inspector to look over. Easily seen defects are usually caught this way.

All of this inspecting by noninspectors comes under the foreman. But regular inspection by inspectors may or may not be under the foreman. Mostly it is not. The inspectors in a foreman's department nearly always work for a chief inspector who reports to the works manager.

Why have this separate chain of command? Why not have inspectors report to foremen? Remember, back in Chapter 2, our principle of organization: "Separate checking up from doing." That is why. Nearly everyone agrees that you ought not let anyone pass final judgment on the quality of his own work. Why? Because they are afraid that you'd get quantity and not quality. Probably they are right, although the works manager is responsible for both. Why is it so illogical for the foreman to be responsible for both too? Yesterday, when the works manager was a foreman, we were afraid to trust him with both. Today that he is works manager, we say that it is different.

Probably there is a real difference. Today he has a bigger job and can see and appreciate the need for both quantity and quality. It is a little different with a foreman. He is always under pressure to operate his department economically; he has to keep production up and rejected work down. He can do this by turning out large quantities of good products. Or he can have his inspectors (if they work for him) pass everything so that there will be no rejected products. Maybe the bad work that is passed will never be caught. The foreman will have a good record, but the company has an inferior product.

A few companies (International Business Machines is one) believe that you *can* make a foreman responsible for both quantity and quality, so they put the inspectors under the foremen. Also, in many companies, the inspectors located along assembly lines work for the foremen. Letting the foreman have charge certainly helps make his job more important and is worth while on that score.

Regardless of the method used to inspect work in process, the *final inspection* of the product ought to be done by an independent inspecting department *not* reporting to factory foremen. Final inspection, unlike most in-process inspection, often includes a performance test. Performance testing can rarely be used to test partly fabricated products.

Statistical quality control procedures have been introduced in recent years in many companies. "Control charts" are frequently used in these companies. They are kept at the machines, and the quality of products being produced is recorded every half hour or so either by the machine operators or by patrolling quality checkers. The checkers are specialized floor inspectors who check only the output of machines where control charts are used. They may report to the foreman or to a quality control chief.

The engineering department sometimes cuts out large amounts of inspection of products during their manufacture by building automatic inspection devices into the machines. The machine or its tool may even be automatically reset to correct any deviation from standard. The engineering department also helps in the work of inspecting work in process by developing special inspection devices, so that the workers on the job and the inspectors can inspect well and quickly.

FLOOR VERSUS CENTRAL INSPECTION

In most cases the operator himself can and does inspect the products he makes as he does his work. He knows pretty well whether the operation is producing a product which will pass inspection. Sometimes, however, he can't tell, positively, by looking at his product whether it will pass. And in other cases, particularly if he is on piecework, he is all interested in quantity, not quality (although ordinarily bad work is not counted when figuring a pieceworker's earnings, so he can't forget quality). Usually, however, he catches most of the defects, whether caused by his own or earlier operations. Not many obvious defects reach the inspectors (except in the case of products made in large quantities on automatic machines where the workers operate several machines and inspect the products from each only occasionally).

Inspection by an inspector can take place either at the job or in a central inspection crib. If it is done at the job, it is called "floor" inspection. Both floor inspection and central inspection have advantages as well as disadvantages. Floor inspectors, sometimes called "patrolling" or "roving" or "first piece" inspectors, go from machine to machine, where they are able to catch bad work before any large quantity has been produced. The machine operator must get the inspector's approval of his setup after running a few pieces of product before he goes ahead with the rest. Patrolling inspectors also go around the department on a regular cycle, check the products of semiautomatic machines from time to time, and record the measurements on control charts at machines where charts are used. Defective operations are caught and remedied before serious loss has occurred.

As a rule, floor inspectors should have the authority to stop the opera-

Woodward Governor Co.

FIG. 35–2. Inspecting small piece parts. The inspector in the foreground is checking the length. The next inspector is checking the bevel on the end of the pieces.

tion if it is out of adjustment. On the other hand, if the item is badly needed by assembly or by the customer and if the defect can be remedied by rework later, engineering may approve the operation continuing temporarily even though unusual numbers of off-standard items are coming through.

Floor inspection saves extra handling of materials, and with it materials move faster through the plant. They don't have to be hauled to and from central inspection, nor do they lie around there waiting their turn to be inspected. And, of course, floor inspection is a must with big unwieldly items.

You need good inspectors for floor inspection because they have to decide on their own without the help of a nearby chief inspector. Also,

Eastman Kodak Co.

FIG. 35–3.   A contour projector in use. A magnified shadow of the part is projected onto a screen on which the proper contour is drawn, making it easy to check contours and dimensions that you couldn't measure any other way.

to be a floor inspector, you have to be a man of conviction because the man on the job objects to almost every rejection you make and wants you to change your mind and pass his work. You have to be able to stand on your own two feet. Besides, floor inspectors should tell the man what is the matter with the rejected items so that he can fix it up. Some companies would even want a floor inspector to tell the man how to change his machine adjustment so that it won't make any more bad products.

One bad thing about floor inspection is that men and machines sometimes have to wait for the inspector. He is busy off somewhere else when a man gets his machine all ready to go, but the operator can't go ahead with the job until the inspector approves his setup.

Another bad thing about floor inspection is that the inspector has to carry around his inspection tools. He can't carry around delicate testing or measuring equipment, so inspection requiring them has to be central —if not in a central department, at least at the inspector's work bench. Most roving inspectors have a home inspection work bench somewhere in the area where they check over things that take special gages that are too tricky to check right at the job.

Central inspection is almost the reverse of floor inspection. Materials to be inspected are trucked to a central inspection crib, where they are left to be inspected. Central inspection has several advantages. First, it saves inspectors' time because there is always work piled up awaiting inspection. Second, you can hire cheaper inspectors because they work under close supervision and are away from the pressure of the men whose work they inspect. Third, special equipment can be used to good advantage at a central inspection location.

But there are some bad features to central inspection. First, materials handling and transportation costs are higher because of all the trips that materials make to and from central inspection cribs. Second, there are more delays, so materials move more slowly through the plant. And, third, scrap losses and rework losses are higher because of the time lag between production and inspection. By the time you find anything bad, probably lots of bad work has been turned out.

Central inspectors sometimes check the quantity of the operator's output when he is on piecework, but floor inspectors ordinarily do not check workers' reported output.

Assembly line inspection of mass-produced products is really another type of floor inspection in which inspection becomes just another operation along the line. The inspector, instead of going from job to job, inspects each unit as it comes along. Occasionally inspection on a sample basis is done. This method is a form of central inspection and is used, for example, for inspecting automobile body tops made of single sheets of steel stamped into the proper form. The contour of the stamped sheet of steel can be checked only by taking a body top from the line occasionally and inspecting it at a center, where it can be carefully checked against a master.

The final inspection of a product is usually done centrally. If the product is an operating mechanism, it is put through a performance test.

INSPECTION SHORTCOMINGS

In one sense the costs of inspection are largely waste. Looking at a product and saying that it is good does not change it. Pulling a bolt apart to see how strong it was gives the answer but breaks the bolt, thus

FIG. 35–4. Automatic inspection of holes for pistons in automobile engine block. This machine inspects four holes at once.

wasting all the work which went into making it as well as the time of the testing machine operator. Wasteful though the inspection process is in many ways, it is necessary. And in some cases it is directly productive, as when the first products from newly setup automatic machines are inspected and the setup changed if the first products do not pass inspection, or when you reset it later after a spot check shows that it is out of adjustment.

Inspection is not only to some extent wasteful but it is also partially subjective. Often the inspector has to judge whether a product passes or not. For example, an inspector discovering a slight blemish on a surface must decide whether it is bad enough to justify rejection.

Judgment is involved in almost all inspection, even when mechanical devices such as micrometers, gages, or comparators are used, because they are always borderline cases. In the case of micrometers a tight fit of the micrometer as against a loose fit probably changes the measurement indicated by at least 0.0005 of an inch. Plug gages and thread gages can fit snugly or loosely. The inspector must decide whether the item passes or not, and his decision is important because he enforces quality standards. If he passes products which should be rejected, he is really making a new unofficial set of standards for the company. If he rejects products which, in the opinion of others competent to judge, should pass, he is changing the standard and probably costing the company money by throwing out good products. Care must be taken to be sure that inspectors don't substitute their own standards for those set by engineering.

Inspectors are human beings. All of them make errors once in a while, so you can't count on their doing a perfect job—in fact, you can count on their doing an imperfect job. Particularly in central inspection the work is often repetitious and monotonous, making mistakes more likely than on production jobs. Inspector fatigue doesn't often cause an inspector to reject good products by mistake. Nearly always it works the other way; a tired inspector misses some of the bad products and doesn't get them laid out. But even if he isn't tired he'll miss some of the bad ones.

In one study of how much bad work inspectors actually miss, 100 defective items were mixed in with a large lot of good ones. The inspectors were not told about the experiment at all. Then the whole lot was 100 per cent inspected by regular inspectors. They found only 68 of the defectives. Still without telling the inspectors, the lot (with the remaining 32 bad ones still mixed in) was sent through inspection again as if it were another lot. They found most but not all of the defective items. The process was repeated a third and a fourth time, after which 98 bad ones had been found, but 2 of them were still in with the good products.

This little experiment may surprise you. What kind of inspectors do we have who do such poor work? Well, they are just human; they do miss things now and then. Also they do have to pass judgment. Maybe they saw the 2 defectives all right but decided that they weren't bad enough to reject. Suppose you had to look at 100 pieces of toast in a restaurant and decide which were too burned to serve to customers? Factory inspectors don't pass judgment on burned toast, but some of their deciding is just about that hard to do. We just have to recognize that inspection is partly subjective.

We also have to be very careful about letting inspectors think that they are using their own judgment. We ought to try to cut out all of the judging that we can. Inspectors like to judge and to think that they have superior judgment. Some think that just passing things that are like the drawing says is only a girl's job—anyone can do that. They prefer the kind of judging that allows them to pass things *not* in accord with the drawings. Be careful that they don't set and follow their own standards.

INSPECTION BONUSES

Inspectors, like machine operators, want to have a chance to work hard and earn bonuses. Management wants its inspectors to work efficiently. But it is hard to put inspectors on incentives because you can't tell whether an inspector has inspected a product. With incentives, all an inspector would have to do to make a big bonus is just to tell you that he inspected a big number of products. Maybe he did, maybe he didn't, or maybe he gave each item a lick and a promise.

Must you, then, give up on incentives for inspectors? You ought not to give up easily, because so much of what an inspector does is quite suitable for incentives. He picks up items and puts them down, or measures or tests them first, or puts them into a testing machine first. All of this is manual and can be time studied just as easily as factory jobs. Then, if you allow a reasonable amount of time for the inspector looking at the item or gage or testing machine score, you can set up a time standard for inspecting.

Actually it is possible to set up inspection time standards for most repetitive inspection jobs (the kind done centrally—not by floor inspectors). Bad items are sometimes troublesome however. Suppose that an inspector is checking telephone receivers to see if they work. Those that work take a minimum of time. But on those that don't work he may have to check half a dozen wires before finding the one that doesn't work.

You may need to set up two rates, one for good items and one for bad ones. Be careful though that your inspector doesn't get so much extra for finding bad ones that he yanks a wire loose on a good phone receiver now and then just to find it and make more money.

Then there is still the matter of whether the inspector really inspected everything that he claims to have inspected. The best way to check on this is to have a superinspector (not on incentives) go carefully over (reinspect) some of the products supposed to have been inspected. If he finds bad items still there, the first inspector is penalized. The superinspector also looks over a few rejected items. If he finds good items in with them, again the first inspector is penalized.

REDUCING INSPECTION WORK

Most inspection requires handling of the product being inspected. The piece is picked up, turned over, and put down. That is repeated half a dozen times during the product's manufacture. It all adds up to quite a few inspectors doing largely manual work. Repetitive manual jobs, including inspection, can often be mechanized. Of course you can't exactly mechanize the visual part of inspection, but the manual part, yes. Even the visual part of inspection can sometimes be transferred to the machine. In the automobile industry, for example, mechanical selectors sort oversize valves from undersize valves and put each in with other valves of the same size. In the bearing industry, ball bearings are sorted mechanically by size. Such mechanical devices eliminate or transfer to the machine even the visual part of the inspection job.

A different approach to the problem of mechanizing inspection is to build machines that check their own work. Some of today's machines do that; some will stop the machine if it is out of adjustment. Others will even correct their settings so that they are put back into adjustment. Thickness gages on calenders in the paper, rubber, and linoleum industries are examples. They give continuous readings of the thickness of the material being produced, although usually they do not automatically reset the machine if it gets out of adjustment.

Still another approach to the problem of cutting inspection costs is to improve the machine itself so that it doesn't get out of adjustment. Such machines (as for example the presses and dies that make automobile fenders) can turn out only good pieces when they are set properly. All you have to do is to inspect the first few pieces, then another piece occasionally just to be sure that the machine is still in adjustment and that there has not been too much wear.

Sometimes you don't need to know a part's exact size, but only that it is between two limits and not beyond. This lets you cut inspection time by using special gages (go-no-go gages, see Fig. 19–4, page 371) that incorporate the two dimensions but show no measurements. They have two slots, one for the product's smallest and one for the largest acceptable dimension. A part that cannot slide into the first slot is too big. A part which slides into the little slot is too little. But if it passes the first set and not the second set, it is just right. Go-no-go gages are so simple that you can use unskilled men to inspect.

Left to themselves, inspectors don't figure out the best way of doing their work any more than do other employees. Motion study men are often able to eliminate waste movements and find ways to do inspection with less work and so get it done at less cost.

Another way to cut inspecting costs is to inspect samples rather than all of the products. To do this right you have to know something about the chances you are taking that the uninspected products are like the sample. Sampling inspection is discussed in Chapter 36.

"SELECTIVE" INSPECTION

"Selective" inspection is sorting inspected parts by size so that over- and undersized parts can be matched together. It is important, of course, only where parts have to fit together and work as mating parts. Selective inspection cuts the losses that you would otherwise have where close fits are necessary. Instead of rejecting or reworking parts just over tolerance limits, they are put into piles by size and used with matching parts having offsetting discrepancies in size.

Automobile motor blocks are an example. They have holes for the pistons. If inspection shows that one or more of the holes is either too large or too small, you don't have to either rework or throw away the block. Instead, match each hole with a piston that fits. That isn't hard to do because some of the pistons come out a little too large and some a little too small.

Naturally, you don't want to carry this too far. Products which vary too much from the standard have to be reworked or scrapped. Also, assembly work is a little more complicated with selective inspection, because the parts are not completely interchangeable. But, properly operated, selective inspection is not only economical but actually *makes a good product*, since, in spite of the fact that the parts are imperfect individually, they are matched to compensate so that the assembled product operates with well-fitting parts. You won't even be making trouble for future repairs because, after the product has been used long enough to need repairs, the repair parts aren't going to fit too perfectly no matter whether the original block and pistons were perfect or not.

JIG, FIXTURE, AND TOOLING CHECKING

On long runs, special attachments and special tooling for machines almost always do the work faster, better, and at less cost. All these attachments need to be inspected periodically. As long as they stay in adjustment, every product turned out is sure to be nearly perfect, but if they get out of adjustment, just as surely, nearly every item made will be unacceptable. Rather than wait for unacceptable products to appear, better check the tooling for wear every now and then.

INSPECTION AND TESTING EQUIPMENT

Quality standards today are so high that in many cases the inspector can't tell by looking at a product whether or not it is acceptable. He has to have special gages and testing and measuring devices.

The inspector has to check many characteristics, including dimensions, smoothness of surface, contours, hardness, strength, ductility, resistance to abrasion, ability to withstand flexing, resistance to rust or wear, amount of internal strain, shrinkage, chemical analysis, plasticity, viscosity, color, fastness of color, solubility, life of the product in use, efficiency and speed of operation, electrical connections, and other things.

Sometimes the test simulates the product's use (or even abuse) to see how long it lasts before giving out. In other cases you use the item in its normal way until it wears out. Light bulbs are burned until they burn out. Auto tires are put on cars and driven day and night till they wear out. Paints are put on trial pieces and put out on the roof to see if they fade and to see how they weather. Most tests give answers about a product's acceptability right away, but with "wear-out" tests you have to wait for answers.

If you don't have to be too accurate, measurements, surface finish, and contours can be inspected visually with only hand tools such as micrometers, go-no-go gages, or ring and snap gages. But for close measuring (to detect variations less than one one-thousandth of an inch) you need to go to some kind of magnifier or electronic inspection gage. There are many kinds of magnifiers which throw an enlarged shadow of the product's outline on a screen where its contour or size can be compared with the specified contour already marked on the screen. You can now get surface smoothness gages that are accurate to a millionth of an inch. You can even get a device to gage the thickness of a coat of paint. Automatic electronic sorters to sort items by size have already been mentioned in connection with selective inspection.

Hardness tests generally are made on Rockwell or Brinell machines, both of which press a ball or wedge-shaped diamond point against the material being tested. The measure of hardness is read on a scale of

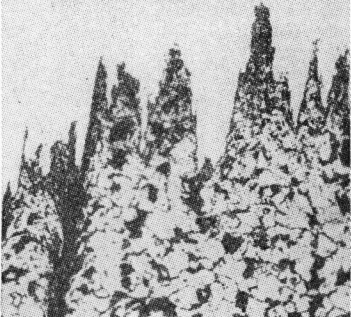

Dun's Review & Modern Industry

FIG. 35–5. The gears at the left appear to have smooth surfaces. Above right is a magnified view of the surface of the gear hub and (lower right) a greatly magnified view of its edge. When extreme smoothness is necessary, such magnifiers are needed for inspection.

widths of indentations made, the wider the indentation, the softer the material.

Electronic processes are nearly always used today to detect minute surface defects, flaws inside material, even internal strains, which make products fail too soon. Some of these methods use magnetism. In one method (the magnaflux method) the product being inspected is magnetized and dipped into a liquid solution containing iron filings or similar material which adheres loosely to the product along any crack or irregularity which interrupts the magnetic field. The crack or flaw itself is often invisible to the eye (in fact, it may be covered over with paint or electroplating), but the line of magnetic particles is visible and reveals the flaw.

Ultrasonics (extremely high vibration) is also used to detect hidden flaws. Faulty products take the vibrations differently from good products. X-ray pictures, taken just like a dentist takes pictures of teeth, are used sometimes to detect hidden flaws. Polarized light and polarized X rays are used to detect internal strain which might cause a product to fail when put to use. Since internal strain exists in nearly all metal

Field failures in drive shaft occurred at junction of weld and shaft; were not always stopped by thickening part.

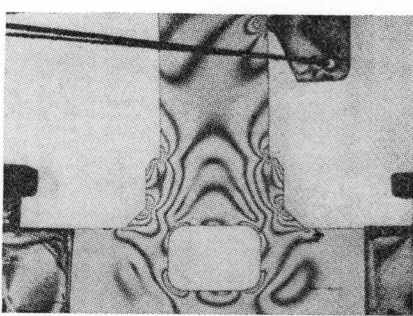

Stress analysis of original design shows concentration of strain at shoulder and weld junction.

Removing metal, not adding it, solved breakage problem. At right is the new design.

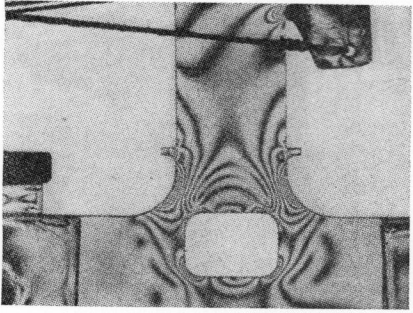

International Harvester Co.

Smooth curve, machined in new design, removes dangerous spots at weld junction and collar.

FIG. 35–6.

and glass products which are formed from molten material, extreme care must be taken to insure uniformity. The thin parts of the products cool, harden, and shrink before the thick parts; when the thick parts finally do cool and shrink, an internal strain is set up. Some day (maybe soon) this strain will cause the product to crack or break unless the product is "annealed" or reheated to high temperatures and cooled slowly so that all parts cool together.

Strain also appears in stamped material which is stamped by main force into various shapes or is sheared off into various shapes. An automobile fender, for example, is pressed into shape from a flat sheet of steel. Unless the material is soft, an internal strain may be set up by any such stamping process.

Internal strain in transparent material can be detected if polarized light is shown through it. If strain exists, the light will show rainbow colors around the points of strain. Figure 35–6 shows X-ray pictures taken of a part that was redesigned after the pictures showed that strain was extreme at a joint where there had been trouble with the item breaking.

In another application of science to inspection, the steel industry uses pictures of the spectrum of light to show the chemical makeup of steel in the making. A photograph is taken of the spectrum of light coming from a heat of molten steel. The lines that appear in the spectrum show the chemical elements present, and their width shows the amount of each present. The pictures can be taken and developed quickly, thus permitting corrections to be made in the chemical composition of the heat before it is poured. TV cameras also are used to show operations impossible to watch—as inside a furnace or vat or machine.

GAGE CHECKING

Factory men who have to turn out the product need gages so that they can tell whether they are doing good work. But gages wear and get out of adjustment just like production tools. Then what? If you don't find out about it, you will be making bad products and not know it.

You need sets of master gages—set just as perfectly as you can set them—and used just to check other gages. They ought to be set to ten times the accuracy of the gages that are checked against them. If work in the factory has to be accurate to the thousandth of an inch, the worker's gage ought itself to be accurate to $\frac{1}{10,000}$ of an inch, and it ought now and then be checked against a gage accurate to $\frac{1}{100,000}$ of an inch. Maybe you won't do quite that well, but it is important that master gages be set as accurately as can reasonably be done.

Some testing equipment needs a professional's look to see if it is still in adjustment. Perhaps men from your own laboratory can check it (they may even have designed it in the first place). If the equipment was bought outside, the manufacturer may send around someone to check it now and then. Or you may have to send it back to the maker for overhaul and resetting. However you do it, you should check even the master gages and testing equipment ever so often.

Making better gages—making them so they wear almost not at all—helps this problem. Some companies have tried gages made out of glass or gages with carbide tips. Both wear very little and keep down your gage checking problems.

Aren't we making a lot out of a little problem? No. Metalworking companies often own more gages than they have employees. And the gages are in use all day long every day. They do get worn and out of adjustment. One small company owning 3,000 gages won't allow any gage to be used more than one shift by an operator or inspector without its being checked against a master gage. Plug thread gages, in particular, are checked carefully. Gages returned after use are never reissued without being cleaned, inspected, and checked.

Gage checking may have to be done in a room under carefully controlled temperature and humidity conditions to insure uniform comparison. All adjustable gages should be set in a gage laboratory and adjustment screws covered with sealing wax or taped over to help keep operators or inspectors from readjusting them.

DISPOSITION OF REJECTED MATERIAL

Rejected parts and rejected material is rarely thrown out. Sometimes you can, by some rework operations, make them right. If that can't be done or if it is too expensive, maybe you can make them into other items, perhaps smaller-sized ones. Or maybe you can sell the rejected material as seconds, as they do with dishes or nylon stockings. Or if nothing else works, maybe you will have to scrap them.

There is (illogical though it may be) still another way to get rid of rejected parts and material. Go right ahead and use them up just as if they had passed to start with!—and do it with engineering's approval! Some companies have "material review boards" to pass on such cases. Material review boards include everyone who will be affected, the superintendent, the chief engineer, and, in the case of airplanes, the customer (the government). This often happens where parts aren't quite as perfect as they should be but where the product's operation will be affected little if at all.

But why set standards and then pay no attention to them? You do it because your policy of carrying practically no inventory of parts gets you in a jam if there is any holdup in parts supply. If you do hold up very many parts, you will soon close down the assembly department (and then all other parts departments). Here is a case of a top management policy (to hold inventories down) having an effect (loosening up on quality) that it probably does not want, in fact, probably doesn't even know about.

Rather than close down the plant, engineering gives in and says O.K. —pass them just this once but don't do it again. Same thing happens with purchased parts. The assembly department is screaming for the parts that the inspector wants to reject (and, on purchased items, it may take weeks to get a new supply). So the question becomes: are the defectives bad enough to justify closing down operations or can we let them go by? And, again, the choice is often: we'll pass them this time but don't let it happen again. But, of course, it does happen again. Sometimes you don't go ahead and use the bad items themselves, you use 100 per cent inspection (look at every piece) and throw out the defects. The inspection costs are extra. But in other cases you go ahead and use things you would not normally pass. Actually these temporary relaxations rarely seem to cause any trouble—the products still work and work well. It makes one wonder if the standards weren't too high in the first place.

Generally, rejects are clearly either scrap or reworkable, and the inspector decides which. But he should consult with the engineering department and the foreman in borderline cases. To rework materials additional and often different operations are needed, depending on the nature of the defects. Defective items are sorted according to the kind of defect, and rework operations for each group are decided upon. The inspector himself, in some companies, decides what rework operations are necessary and makes out a work order to cover their performance. In other companies, particularly where a whole series of rework operations may be required, the engineering department decides upon the operations and production control makes out the rework orders.

Reworking and repairing rejected items is nuisance work. It is always one or two of an item, and the work is partly handwork. Putting such jobs back into regular production often upsets regular operations and regular schedules. Maybe you'll have to do it that way if there are no other machines that can do the work. But many companies take all rework to a separate rework shop and do the work there.

Rework is all extra cost. Whose budget do you charge? The man whose department did the poor work. But it isn't always easy to tell. Suppose that a coat of paint tends to flake off. Is it purchasing's fault for buying wrong paint for the job? Or did engineering not specify the right kind of paint? Or the right kind of material under the paint? Or did the shop not get the right surface finish on the piece? Or did the cleaning department fail to get every bit of oil off the surface?

Inspectors who reject work must always indicate, on their report, *what* is the matter and *what department* is responsible. If there is any doubt it is settled by a committee.

Work-Away.   In some industries it is possible to "work-away" unacceptable materials by mixing them a little at a time into future mixtures. Off-colored material, for example, can be put into mixtures of dark materials in the rubber, glass, paint, and chemical industries, thus saving the full value of the raw material. If chemical mixtures contain too much of certain chemicals, they can be mixed into new batches intentionally made up with too few of those chemicals.

"Work-away" as a way of getting rid of rejects is sometimes used by vendors in a way that irritates customer companies no end. You, the customer, reject a certain lot of materials—say it is nuts or bolts—because you find it to contain 3 per cent defectives when your contract said no more than 2 per cent. You send the lot back. The vendor merely mixes the defectives up with some more and back they come as part of the next shipment.

This may not be so bad as it sounds. If the next lot started with only 1 per cent bad, the new mixture will be 2 per cent bad, which is the quality you're paying for. But some vendors are not above putting the old rejected lot of products into some new boxes and sending them to you again—one or two boxes in each shipment until they are all gone. You're not too likely to catch them.

Scrap Disposition.   When sold, scrap materials rarely bring more than a small fraction of their total cost. Of course you lose all of the money you have spent working on them and you even lose part of what you paid for the material. You don't get as much per pound for scrap as you paid per pound for it when you bought it as raw material. But, even so, scrap has some value, so it should be sorted and packed, or baled, in whatever way will bring the highest price. If, for example, you have different kinds of metal scrap, such as steel, brass, bronze, and other metals, sort them out and keep them apart. You'll get more per pound than if you mix them up.

STUDY QUESTIONS

1. "A manufacturer should always try to make the best quality products that he can." Discuss.
2. Why inspect? Discuss.
3. Who really is responsible for quality?
4. Why do foremen nearly always think that engineering sets tolerances too tightly? Is there any merit to their position? Discuss.
5. How can you tell when to inspect? Before or after what jobs?
6. Why not just inspect *all* the products whenever you inspect any of them? Isn't that what you have to do if you really want to do the job?
7. The book says to always inspect incoming purchased goods. Why?
8. Should inspectors work for foremen? Give arguments for and against. Which way do you think it ought to be? Justify your position.
9. What are (*a*) patrolling inspection, (*b*) roving inspectors, (*c*) first-piece inspectors? What do they do? How is their work alike? Different?
10. Tell when you would use central inspection. What are its good and bad points?
11. Tell when you would use floor inspection. What are its good and bad points?
12. Explain the part judgment ought to play in inspection.
13. How would you go about putting inspectors on incentives?
14. Can you mechanize inspection? Justify your answer.
15. What is selective inspection? What, if anything, does it do to interchangeability of parts?
16. How often should gages be checked? How is it done?
17. What happens to a lot of rejected products?
18. What is work-away? Is it good? Bad? Discuss.

CASE 35–1.   THE RICHMOND MANUFACTURING COMPANY

Owing to the variety of products manufactured at the Richmond Manufacturing Company plant, departmental inspection has been in existence for some time. This method of inspection involves the following procedure: When raw material is received in a department, it is inspected by the assistant foreman as to size, shape, quality, etc. After the first operation has been finished on a machine or on the bench, it is inspected by the section "straw boss" in charge of the respective departmental section. When the order is about one-half completed, the workman is supposed to present one of the parts or subassemblies to the assistant foreman for inspection. The third and final inspection is given by the foreman of the department before the complete order is delivered to the next department, or to the stock room.

It has happened, from time to time, that the above procedure did not function perfectly. The initial inspection has always been carried through as rigidly as the straw bosses could enforce it, but laxity existed in complying with the second and third stages of inspection. Thus, it often happened that the parts of subassemblies delivered to an assembly department by the main parts stock room were not up to standard. The established procedure called for the return of defective parts to the stock room. The stock room keeper, in turn, returned the material to the department from which he originally received it, with the request that the parts be repaired, reworked, or replaced.

The management felt that considerable time and money was being lost on account of improper inspection. The suggestion was made to set up a special Inspection Department whose inspectors would inspect the raw materials, single parts, and subassemblies, as well as the completely assembled products.

You have been requested to make a thorough investigation as to whether a special Inspection Department is needed, and to make recommendations and to answer the following questions: Do you agree that a special Inspection Department should be introduced? Why? To whom should the chief inspector report and why? How, where, when, how much, and by whom should the raw materials, single parts, subassemblies, and completed assemblies be inspected?

What steps do you recommend in order to obtain the best possible quality in production without a loss in quantity? Should the inspectors be paid the same hourly rates as the workmen, or should they receive higher or lower rates? Should they be compensated on a piece rate or by bonuses? If you recommend a bonus, on what basis should it be paid?

Chapter 36

STATISTICAL QUALITY CONTROL

STATISTICAL quality control applies the theory of probability to sample testing, or inspection. A great deal of inspection work has always been done by sampling; a small part of a certain lot of products is inspected, and its quality is assumed to be the quality of the lot. Doing this is a little risky, because it is always possible for a sample not to have exactly the same characteristics as the lot. Years ago, before statistical quality control, no one knew how much risk was involved. Sometimes larger samples than necessary were inspected. Other times more risk of bad work getting through was taken than anyone realized. With statistical quality control, inspection is more reliable and less costly.

Statistical quality control deals with *samples* and their reliability as indicators of lot characteristics. Sample inspection, where it can be used satisfactorily, eliminates most of the cost of 100 per cent inspection. It is the only possible method for products which must be tested until they fail or break, as in tests of length of life or tensile strength. Sampling is also the only way you can test the chemical or physical characteristics of liquids and powdered or granulated material, or the thickness of "gage" of sheet metal, paper, and cloth. Sampling is therefore desirable in many cases because it saves money. And it is a must in other cases because no other method of inspection can be used.

It is important to see that statistical quality control does not *make* risks nor does it *get rid of risks*. With or without statistical quality control there is a chance that any sample is not exactly like the rest of a lot. What statistical quality control does is to tell you how reliable the sample is. And it lets you decide the risks you are willing to take (that bad products will slip by). You can decide whether it will cost more to catch the bad products or to let them go and save inspection costs. You can make a conscious decision about how much risk you want to assume. SQC also helps during processing by warning you if machines are getting out of adjustment so that you can reset them *before* bad products are made.

Very small samples sometimes give quite dependable results. This happens when all the items in a sample are consistently much better (or much worse) than just passable. When this is so, you don't need to spend much money on testing and inspecting big samples. But, without SQC, large and unnecessary risks are sometimes taken when very small samples are used. That would happen if the sample pieces averaged just barely passable. SQC permits known risks to be taken and yet keeps inspection costs at a minimum.

Most of what we have said about SQC applies to checking products already made—that is called "acceptance" sampling. And that is where most of this matter of controlling risks applies. But SQC (still using samples and still dealing in risks) can also be used to *control* processes *while things are being made.* Here you get an even more direct benefit. Not only does it tell you when the process is out of adjustment and turning out bad work but it warns you ahead that the machine is getting out of adjustment. It catches and shows the drift toward defectives. This keeps you from making bad work in the first place and so cuts your scrap losses.

Curiously, control charts improve nonautomatic jobs too—the kind where quality depends on the man more than the machine. Keeping the charts right at the operation and letting the workers do their own measuring and plotting of points gets them interested. They become more quality conscious and try harder.

AREAS OF USE

Statistical quality control has three general uses: (1) to control the quality of work done on individual factory operations while the work is being done; (2) to decide whether to accept or reject lots of products already produced (whether bought or made within the company); and (3) to furnish to management a quality audit of the company's products. A fourth result—checking the reasonableness of the quality standards and specifications set up—is generally accomplished more or less as a by-product of SQC in operation.

When statistical quality control is used to control operations, "control" charts kept right at the job are used. Sample products are checked from time to time, and their *measurements* plotted on the control charts. Since it is impossible to make even two absolutely identical products, some minor variations in measurement are expected even when the machines are in adjustment. The machine will even produce an unacceptable item once in a long time when it is in adjustment. Control charts show when operations are making too many unacceptable products and so tell you when you need to reset the machine.

Statistical quality control for accepting or rejecting whole lots of products ("acceptance" sampling) usually deals with the *proportion* of rejects found in a sample. When a lot contains considerably more or considerably less than the allowable proportion of rejects, that fact will almost surely be revealed even by a small sample. Additional samples need be taken only when the small initial sample provides borderline or near-borderline results.

Statistical quality control as a quality audit also operates on a sample basis. Faults in samples of completed products are classified according to their seriousness, and demerits are assigned. Major defects, those which

DEMERIT LIST - STEP-BY-STEP SWITCH MECHANISMS

Item	Dem.	Defect Description	Item	Dem.	Defect Description
		1. ELECTRICAL			Rotary pawl springs:
			2010C	10	opening in loop exceeds specified limit
101B	50	Breakdown between (parts) on (specified) voltage			Rotary pawl play:
		Cross or ground between (parts):	2011C	10	rotary pawl binds
102A	100	affecting circuit, not readily corrected			Vertical position of rotary armature:
102B	50	affecting circuit, readily corrected	2012B	50	no overlap
			2012C	10	overlap not as specified
102C	10	may affect circuit	2013C	10	Rotary pawl position not as specified
103C	10	Clearance between insulated parts insufficient			Rotary magnet position:
		Open circuit:	2014C	10	rotary dog and ratchet tooth clearance not as specified
104A	100	not readily corrected			
104B	50	readily corrected	2015C	10	armature does not strike both magnet cores
		Current flow; release magnet coil:			Rotary pawl front stop position:
105B	50	more than 10% outside of specified value	2016C	10	clearance between rotary pawl and front stop not as specified
105C	10	10% or less outside of specified value			Rotary pawl guide position:
106C	10	armature does not release after operation on specified current	2017C	10	rotary pawl tip does not strike tooth as specified
107B	50	Contacts dirty; breaking continuity			Normal pin position:
			2018C	10	rotary pawl does not strike first tooth in same relative position as other teeth
		2. MECHANICAL			Rotary armat̶ posit̶
2001C	10	Bank or wiper contacts not cleaned or treated			
2002C	10	Lubrication not as specified			
		Position of adjusting screws:			
2003C	10	unused threads less t̶ specified			
		Straightnes̶ sp̶			
2004B	50				

Western Electric Co.

FIG. 36–1. Portion of a "demerit" list for rating the quality of finished products.

will interfere with the operation of the product or which might be dangerous, may, for example, be assigned 50 demerits. Minor defects which will shorten the life of the product or increase its maintenance costs may be assigned 10 demerits. Incidental defects, such as appearance blemishes, may be given five or even only one demerit, depending on their seriousness. Ratios of the number of demerits found, per unit of product inspected, are computed. The demerit ratio for products produced at one time can be compared with the ratio of those produced at another time, or the ratios may be combined to give department—or even plantwide—averages which can be used in further comparisons.

An SQC by-product is the check on the reasonableness of tolerances and specifications that they give. SQC may reveal that the standards can't be met satisfactorily with the men and machines you now have. If so, the standards ought to be relaxed, or if you don't want to do that, you will have to train your men to do better work, or get them some better machines, or resign yourself to a high scrap rate. Statistical quality control may also reveal that the products are so much better than the standards require that you can tighten up the standards without adding anything to costs.

Some companies using SQC for purchased materials have been able to cut their receiving inspection costs by rating their vendors. A vendor who uses statistical control procedures to check his outgoing product usually keeps his quality so high that you don't have to inspect his product all over again when it arrives in your plant. His using SQC doesn't guarantee that his product will be good, but if he uses it rightly, it does. So you check the incoming product carefully for a while. Then, if you find that his system really does give you a good product all the time, you cut your own inspection down to an occasional check.

The American Society for Quality Control has been working on setting up a nation-wide "vendor-certification" plan which would allow dependable quality companies to certify that the products they ship will pass your inspection. That would let you cut out the cost of receiving inspection. This is very important to government prime contractors because they can't let up on inspecting incoming products no matter how reliable the vendor unless the government lets them do so.

Most of the time you will not save a great deal if you cut down on your receiving inspection because all it amounts to is unpacking and looking at and counting items. You have to unpack them and count them anyway, and it is easy to look at them too. But sometimes the savings is big money. Items come in, specially wrapped, packaged, and cushioned against breakage, or covered by protection coatings. If you check these, you have to undo them all and clean them off and then afterwards recoat and repack them before you can put them on stockroom shelves. Having a reliable vendor saves you real money here.

ATTRIBUTES AND VARIABLES

When you look at a product and say "it passes" or "it is a reject," you are dealing with "attributes." But if you measure "how much," "how big," "how thick," "how round," etc., you are dealing with "variables."

You need to make this distinction because attributes and variables require different statistical procedures. Attributes deal with *percentages* of products rejected. Variables deal with *averages of measurements* and with the *extent of the deviation*. Attribute inspection is most important in "acceptance" sampling—inspecting products away from the operation and after considerable quantities have been made—as in the case of purchased items. Variable inspection is more important in controlling operations—mostly it is done at the job as products are turned out.

Attribute inspection is used (1) when items are obviously good or bad (as in ceramics, a dinner plate has a chip out of it or it doesn't); (2) when the characteristic can't be measured thus forcing an inspector to judge (as in the degree of shine on a polished surface or when deciding whether a solderal electrical connection is good enough); (3) when the characteristic can be measured but you don't care about the exact measurement (as when you use go-no-go gages to inspect for size). Most inspections of metal, glass, cloth, or painted surfaces, for cracks, scratches, or surface irregularities and most inspections of color finish are attribute inspections. So are inspections using go-no-go gages, or thread gages, because the purpose is simply to accept or reject, not to determine the exact measurement.

Most measurements of dimensions, however, and tests of hardness, as well as all types of length-of-life tests, are inspection of variables. Many kinds of variables can be measured only by tests which end up destroying the sample items tested. Destructive tests are necessary, for example, to measure tensile strength, resistance to abrasion, chemical content, blowing load of electric fuses, the heat content of gas, oil, or coal, flash point of gasoline, bursting strength of boxboard, or the length of time a product stands up under extreme test conditions. These tests are all examples of inspecting variables. The items tested always differ somewhat, and it is necessary to tabulate and analyze the frequency of each measurement.

"REPRESENTATIVE" SAMPLES

If statistical quality control is to operate successfully, samples *must* be "representative," meaning that they *must* have the same characteristics as the whole lots from which they are taken. A sample which does not have such characteristics is not a representative sample. Unfortunately, the only way that you can be absolutely sure that a sample is like the rest is to test them all, and you can't do that and still be sampling. But you can be pretty sure of that if your samples are representative.

In statistical quality control the whole lot from which a sample is taken is called the "inspection lot," "total population," the "parent population," or the "universe." In SQC the word "sample" always refers to a representative sample. It does *not* mean a nonrepresentative, nontypical, or poor sample. When samples are referred to as "random" samples, the intent has been to get a *representative* sample. A random sample from a barrel of material would include materials taken from the top, middle, bottom, outside, and inside of the barrel. A random sample of automatic machine products should include a few taken from the start of the run, a few periodically during the run, and a few at the end.

Products being sampled ought to be, and usually are, homogeneous (the same throughout). If they aren't—if some tote pans of parts have more bad items in them than other pans—the inspector must be very careful to see that he gets a representative sample. He should, for example, take a few items from every tote box. In fact, the inspector should always do that anyway, whether he suspects that the various boxfuls are of equal quality or not.

In factory inspection ordinarily only one universe, such as a shipment of products received from one vendor, or one run of products from an automatic machine needs to be considered at a time. It is desirable, however, to deal with each day's output of automatic machines as a separate lot. A random sample of each day's, or each hour's, output should be inspected separately, in order to catch gradual changes in the products which might be caused by tool wear or by the machine gradually getting out of adjustment.

SIZE OF SAMPLE

Some people think that big samples are better—give more reliable results—than small samples and that a sample twice as big as another sample is twice as reliable. They are right about their being better but wrong about how much better. A sample twice as big as another sample is *not* twice as reliable. We can't say exactly how much better a big sample is because, whereas a sample of 20 is considerably more reliable than 10, you gain much less reliability if you increase a sample of 1,000 to 2,000 —yet in each case you doubled the sample size. In fact, the gain in reliability from inspecting a sample of 300 instead of 200 is rarely worth the added inspection costs. Samples up in the hundreds are all pretty reliable. From there on you add little to reliability if you inspect more.

Even small samples are almost completely reliable except where they turn out to be of borderline quality. When inspecting variables, a 25-piece sample will produce virtually conclusive results if it is found to be *much better* or *much worse* than the limit of acceptability, because it is very unlikely that a sample will be very good or very bad when the whole lot is not also at least pretty good or pretty bad too. A sample of 100 pieces would, in such a case, add little to the reliability of the results found in the smaller sample. But if the 25-piece sample turns out to be of borderline quality, you are not so sure whether the whole lot should pass or not. If you inspect a 100-piece sample, you will find out almost certainly that the lot is borderline good or that it is borderline bad.

Another common misconception concerns the size of the sample as it relates to the universe. Some people think that the reliability of the sample depends on its *proportion* to the universe; that any sample of 10 per cent of the inspection lot, regardless of the size of that lot, is equal in reliability to any other 10 per cent sample. Actually, a sample's reliability is almost entirely dependent on its own *numerical* size. The size of the whole lot has little effect on the sample's reliability. A sample of 200 taken from a lot of 5,000 is almost as reliable an indicator of the whole 5,000 as is a sample of 200 taken from a lot of 1,000. Yet in the first case it is a 4 per cent sample as against 20 per cent in the second case. This fact is used in sampling inspection and permits considerable inspection cost savings by confining the sample to the smallest practicable quantity. Only very small samples, proportionally, from large lots, need be inspected.

Eastman Kodak sets the sample size for much of its inspection by the following formula:

$$n = \sqrt{2N},$$
$$n = \text{The sample size,}$$
$$N = \text{The whole lot.}$$

Using this formula, a sample of 200 would suffice for a lot of 20,000. Eastman inspects larger samples for products which it thinks might not be of even quality, but the biggest samples even if the items are of uneven quality are limited to 2.5 times the usual sample size, or 500 in the case of a 20,000 lot.

THE NORMAL CURVE AND THE STANDARD DEVIATION

Statistical quality control is based on the idea that no two things are exactly alike but that, when either man or nature tries to make identical products, their actual sizes will vary from small to large with most items hitting pretty close to middle. The most frequent size will be the middle size; the least frequent sizes will be the two extremes, larger and smaller than the middle size.

A large number of such items can be measured and tallied according to size. The count of items by size when plotted on a chart nearly always approximates a "normal" or "bell-shaped" curve. Most items, when measured closely, show a normal distribution. Occasionally the curve is pulled off to one side ("skewed"), showing that there are more items larger than the norm or more items smaller than the norm. If there is a pronounced variation from the normal distribution, ordinary statistical procedures are invalid, and statistical quality control should not be used.

In a normal distribution there is a progressive tapering off of the number of items above and below the point of greatest frequency, which itself is the highest point on the curve and is in the middle of the curve. This highest point is the average measurement (the "arithmetic mean") of the series. Expected variations in measurement of individual items from the mean can be figured on the basis of this normal curve.

But in SQC you deal with samples, not whole lots. So you measure each item of your sample and make a tabulation of the frequency of each measurement. Then you plot your tabulation on a chart. Almost always your chart turns out to be a miniature bell-shaped curve (miniature in the sense that it is based on 50 to 100 cases rather than 10,000). But your spread of measurements between big and little in the sample will be about the same as in the parent population. You could prove this by measuring the whole lot, but you know that it will happen so we don't need to measure every item. One sample tells you just about how the whole population measures up too.

In statistical quality control you have to figure the "standard deviation."[1] It is a measure of variation of individual item measurements from the sample's average. In all normal distributions the mean plus and minus one standard deviation gives values between which 68.3 per cent of the measures of the sampled products fall. The mean plus and minus two standard deviations gives limits between which 95.5 per cent of the cases fall. Three standard deviations each way set limits which include 99.7 per cent of the cases. These mathematical relationships are the bases on which statistical quality control rests.

Here's how it works. If a part 4 inches long is being manufactured, close measurement will show that the parts vary in size, most of them being close to but not exactly 4 inches long. The *average* size of the pieces in our sample, however, ought to be almost exactly 4 inches. Let's say that the average length of the parts in our sample is actually 4,000 inches and our standard deviation is .002 inches. 4.000 inches + and − one standard deviation is 4.002 and 3.998 inches, respectively; 68.3 per cent (or very close to it) of the sample measurements are between these limits. Go out 2 standard deviations to 4.004 and 3.996, and we find that 95.5 per cent of the cases fall within these limits. Or go on to 3 standard deviations, 4.006 and 3.994; 99.7 per cent of the cases fall between these limits.

But, you say, we are still dealing with the sample. How do we know that the parent population is like that? What are the chances that it is? We have to lead up to the answers to those questions. Let's first admit that *both the mean and the standard deviation of our sample may not be identical to the mean and the standard deviation of the whole lot.* And if more samples were taken and the mean for each sample computed, they would probably differ a little from the mean that we already have and would also differ a little from each other. We could take quite a few samples and compute each one's mean.

Then we could make up a table showing how often each *mean* turned up. Then the grand mean for all the samples combined could be figured. We could even calculate a standard deviation of the spread of the sample means, showing the limits beyond which there would be no sample means. (This would be the grand mean + or − three standard deviations

---

[1] To compute the standard deviation, it is necessary to find the amount of difference (of deviation) between the value or measure of each item and the value of the arithmetic mean. These deviations are expressed as numerical quantities. The procedure for arriving at the standard deviation is as follows: square each deviation (that is, multiply it by itself), add the squared numbers, divide the sum by the number of items, and take the square root of the quotient. The square root so obtained is the standard deviation. It is expressed in the same measure as are the values of the individual items and the mean. If the values are inches, the arithmetic mean and the standard deviation are both expressed in inches.

of our sample means.) After we did all of this we would have a little range within which practically all means of other samples—if we took some more samples—would fall. *We would also have the range within which it is practically certain that the mean of the whole parent population falls.* So we would have learned, from our samples, something about the whole population.

We can also go through a similar calculation for the standard deviation and find about how big the standard deviation for the parent population is. That would let us figure the probable distribution and maximum range of the total parent population.

We *could* do all of this, but fortunately it is possible to figure from one or a few small samples—knowing their averages and standard deviations—just about what the whole population's mean and standard deviations are. Just how to do it is in statistics books. In fact, statisticians have figured out how to do away with nearly all of the computing. On page 687 we give an example showing how to short cut the long method that we have been talking about. Here we are interested in showing that it can be done from a few small samples.

SQC is also helpful to you in the few cases where extremes are important, as for example with the weakest link in a chain. It is all very good for the average strength of each link to be well above minimum, but if even *one* link is too weak the chain breaks. You can set up our charts so that attention is focused on such extremes.

In other cases consistency is the important thing. Suppose that you bought two lots of one-eighth inch diameter ball bearings. And suppose that lot A averaged .1248 inches but lot B averaged a perfect .1250 inches. *But,* within lot A, the individual balls ranged between .1247 and .1251 inches each, while in lot B the sizes ranged from .1240 to .1260 inches. Which lot would you rather have? You'd pick lot A because no ball bearing varies more than 3 ten-thousandths of an inch from perfect, while in lot B some are off 10 ten-thousandths of an inch. Many SQC applications deal with this matter of consistency.

Whether the interest is in averages, extremes, standard deviations, or percentages, statistical quality control is directed first at getting the measurements, test scores, or per cent defectives for the items in the sample; second, at computing the combined measures for the sample; and, third, at comparing the combined sample measures to preset scales showing the limits of acceptability. Lastly, if the measures exceed the limits of acceptability, some action must be taken to remedy the situation. The statistical procedures used for these purposes are all based on the idea of the normal curve and the standard deviation.

CONTROL CHARTS FOR OPERATIONS

Books on statistical quality control do not furnish control charts. They tell you how to set up and use control charts. That is all that books can do because every control chart has to fit the operation it serves.

Look at Figure 36–2 to see the steps to go through. Your tool, the control chart, is the end product that comes out of a little preliminary research job. First you have to collect and analyze certain figures about your production. And you have to do it separately for *every* job where you plan to use control charts.

In Figure 36–2, step 1 shows the kinds of figures you might get if you were making a part that was supposed to be 4 inches long. Measuring them to the nearest thousandth of an inch you'd get a list like that in step 1. Next, see step 2, make a tally count (or a "frequency distribution") of the measures. In step 3, make a chart of the tally count.

In step 4 you remove the actual measurement scale along the bottom of the chart and put in markers for plus and minus 1, 2, and 3 standard deviations. You have to spot these in, of course, before you remove the actual measurement scale. Next, step 5, turn the chart around sideways, so that the standard deviation scale is on the side.

Then remove the chart itself and draw in upper and lower control limit lines at the +3 and −3 standard deviation marks—and get step 6. Now reinsert the actual measurement scale along the left. The bottom horizontal line becomes a time scale of hours or half-hours.

You now have a control chart set up for the job. But before using it you need to check to see that the control limits are within specification limits. If the specification says 4 inches ±.01, then you can go ahead because all of your production is well within the 4.01 and 3.99 inch limits. But if the specification says 4 inches ±.002, then you'd better try to improve your quality right away because only 68 per cent of present products will pass.

Now that you have the control chart set up, you use it by having the inspector measure a very small sample of products (maybe as few as 3 to 5) every half-hour or so and plot the average measurement on the chart as is done in Figure 36–3. If a point falls outside the control limits, something is the matter with the job. The chart has done its work—it tells you to stop the machine and get it back into adjustment.

Statisticians have figured out a short-cut method for setting up control limits for making control charts. You still have to get a set of figures to start with (step 1 in Fig. 36–2).

Suppose that you plan to inspect a sample of 4 every half-hour after you get your chart set up. Take a sample of 40 items and separate it into 10 subsamples of 4 each. But *don't sort them* into any order (as from large to small); *take them just as they come.*

For *each* set of 4, figure its average measurement, also its range (the difference between the largest and smallest item in the set). This gives you 10 averages and 10 ranges. Now figure the grand average (add the 10 averages together and divide by 10) and the average range (add the 10 ranges together and divide by 10).

Now look at Table 36–1. Read down to 4, the number in your subsamples, and find the factor .73.

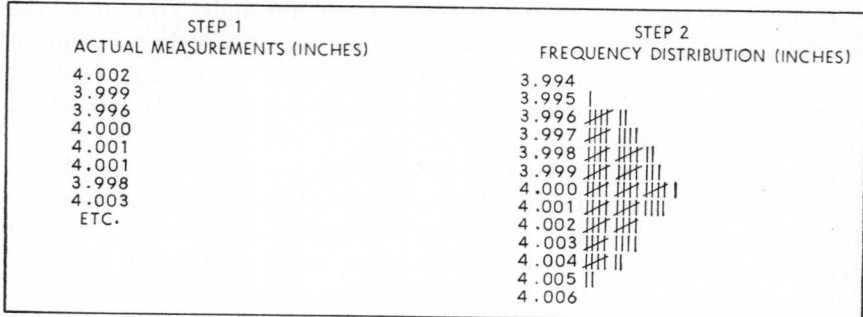

STEP 1
ACTUAL MEASUREMENTS (INCHES)
4.002
3.999
3.996
4.000
4.001
4.001
3.998
4.003
ETC.

STEP 2
FREQUENCY DISTRIBUTION (INCHES)
3.994
3.995 |
3.996 J┼┼ ||
3.997 J┼┼ ||||
3.998 J┼┼ J┼┼||
3.999 J┼┼ J┼┼ |||
4.000 J┼┼ J┼┼ J┼┼ |
4.001 J┼┼ J┼┼ ||||
4.002 J┼┼ J┼┼
4.003 J┼┼ ||||
4.004 J┼┼ ||
4.005 ||
4.006

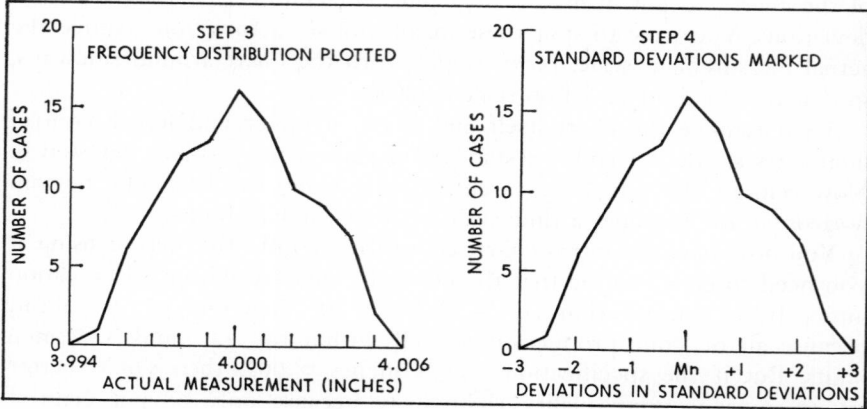

STEP 3
FREQUENCY DISTRIBUTION PLOTTED

STEP 4
STANDARD DEVIATIONS MARKED

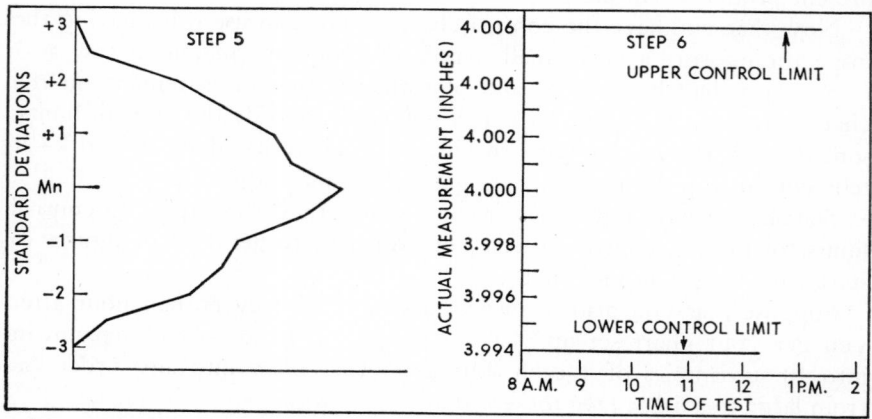

STEP 5

STEP 6
UPPER CONTROL LIMIT

LOWER CONTROL LIMIT

FIG. 36-2. Method of setting up "control limits" for a control chart. Step 1 shows the original measurements; step 2 the frequency distribution of the original measurements; step 3 is a
chart of the figures in step 2. Step 4 is the same chart as the step 3 chart, except that the bottom
scale is in standard deviations from the mean. Step 6 transfers the standard deviation scale back
to the terms of the original measurements.

You get your upper control limit by multiplying the average range by .73 and adding the result to the grand mean. To get the lower control limit, subtract the same amount from the grand mean. Assume that your pieces are supposed to average 1 inch long and that you find that the grand average is 1.000 inches and the average range of your 10 samples of 4 is .013 inches. Multiplying .013 by .73 gives you .009. Adding this and subtracting it from 1.000 gives you control limits of 1.009 and .991 inches. Does the statistician's short-cut method still sound long? It isn't. Once you get your 40 measurements, you can set up a control chart in just a few minutes. It takes lots longer to go through all the steps shown in Figure 36–2.

Also don't get concerned about the multiplying factors given in Table 36–1. Maybe you noticed that had you used subsamples of 5 instead of

TABLE 36–1

Number in Each Small Sample	Factor
2	1.88
3	1.02
4	.73
5	.58
6	.48
7	.42
8	.37
9	.34
10	.31

4 you would use .58 instead of .73. Doesn't that give you different control limits? No, they may differ a little, but they'll be about the same. Because with samples of 5 you will have bigger ranges, so our average range will be larger. If it turned out to be .015 (it was .013 with sub-sample of 4), you'd still get .009 to add and subtract to get your limits (because you'd multiply .015 × .58, instead of .013 × .73).

We have been talking about controlling the *average*, but nearly always you want to control reliability as well. Two pieces, one 4 inches long and one 6 inches long, average 5 inches long. But that isn't much comfort to you when you want two pieces 5 inches long.

Variability is controlled by paying attention to the *range* (the difference between the largest and smallest items in your samples). Control charts to keep track of the range are made up in almost exactly the same way as charts to control averages. And, here too, a short-cut method is available to let you set up the limits in a matter of minutes.[2]

---

[2] You'll find all of these explained in many statistics books. See Eugene L. Grant, *Statistical Quality Control* (2d ed.; McGraw-Hill Book Co., Inc., 1952), pages 137 and 513.

CONTROL CHARTS FOR VARIABLES

The example we just used to show how to set up a control chart dealt with a dimension. It required *measuring* the samples, so it dealt with a *variable*. It also dealt with the *average* size. Sometimes you want control charts that put the emphasis on the extremes, the largest or the smallest; and sometimes you are much more concerned about your product's *consistency*—the usual variation between extremes.

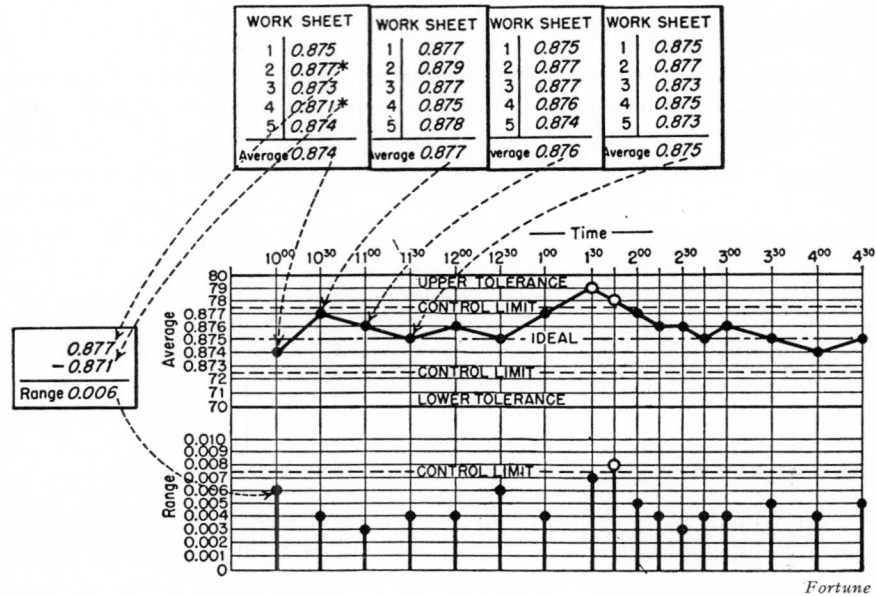

Fortune

FIG. 36–3. A control chart used to control a lathe operation making cylinders. Every half-hour five specimens are measured, their average size plotted on the average chart, and the spread between the largest and smallest plotted on the range chart. A reading beyond the dotted control limits on either chart means that the process has gone out of control. Note that the out-of-control reading at 1:30 brought remedial action, followed by more frequent sampling to insure that the process was back in control.

You can make up charts to control any or all of these. Sometimes you want to watch two or more of them at once. If so, don't make up two separate charts, just put them, one below the other, on the same chart, as is done in Figure 36–3. Not only does this make charting more simple but it ties together all the results from each sample. They are all charted on the same vertical line. Notice, in Figure 36–3, that the 10:30 A.M. sample of five items averaged 0.877 inches in diameter and that the largest item in that lot was 0.004 inches larger than the smaller.

Control charts are usually kept right at the machine. A worker or an inspector checks a small sample of the product periodically and plots its size on the chart. If the variable to be controlled is a dimension, the average of the dimensions of the sampled pieces will be posted. The minimum or maximum measurement, the difference between the two, or possibly the standard deviation may also be posted. If any of the measures is beyond the permissible limit, the products are unacceptable and the operation should be stopped. If they are still within limits but are steadily getting closer to one limit or the other, the operation will soon be turning out bad work. Maybe the tools are wearing down or the machine may be getting out of adjustment.

CONTROL CHARTS FOR ATTRIBUTES

Attributes, you recall, are the yes or no characteristics. Products pass or they don't pass. These things you don't measure. Sometimes you can't measure them (as the shininess of a polished surface or the amount of excess solder on an electrical connection) so you just decide. Sometimes you don't need to measure them, a glass tumbler has a crack in it or it doesn't, so you have no problem deciding. Instead of *measuring* every item in a sample, you just look at it and decide.

Control charts for attribute inspection are based on the *percentages* of products rejected by the inspector. Making control charts for attributes usually costs less than for variables because the inspection work itself is generally less expensive and the information required for attribute charts is available whether charts are made or not.

To make a control chart for attributes, you use the past performance record. Get figures for a dozen or so samples. Use big samples—up in the hundreds of items in each sample. Each sample is 100 per cent inspected, and the percentage of rejects for each is figured. It is the percentages that you work with.

They are used just as were the measurement figures in step 1 of Figure 36–2. After you get quite a few percentage figures for successive samples, the next thing to do is to make up a frequency distribution (step 2, Fig. 36–2), then figure the grand average percentage of rejects and the standard deviation and set up control limits.

Attribute charts show both upper and lower control limits. If 2 per cent rejects are normal for an operation, you might find that your control limits are 1 and 3 per cent. But why the lower limit? Isn't it good to get rejects down to as near zero as possible? Yes. But, if you go below 1 per cent, the job isn't being run the way it used to be. Going outside the low limit tells you that.

If you could be sure that your good record came from good reasons, you would look no farther into the matter and just set new control limits to cover the new performance. You'd do that if rejects were down because the worker was doing a better job. But your record could be improving because of bad reasons, so going below the lower control limit means that you check into why. Are inspectors passing too many bad items? Or are you actually getting better but fewer products? Maybe the men are now working slowly and carefully (but upping your costs). If either of these things is happening, you want to stop it. Lower control limits warns you to check.

Not all attribute control charts deal with percentages. Some deal with *ratios*, perhaps the number of defects per 100 items. These charts are

QUALITY CONTROL					LOT SIZE	SAMPLE SIZE	50% AN	1% AN	2% AN	3% AN	4% AN	5% AN	
LOT BY LOT RECORD OF STATISTICAL SAMPLING INSPECTION SINGLE SAMPLING					500– 799	75	1	2	3	4	5	6	
					800– 1299	115	2	3	4	6	8	9	
					1300– 3199	150	3	4	5	8	10	12	
					3200– 7999	225	4	5	8	11	14	17	
					8000–21999	300	5	7	10	14	18	22	

ITEM_____
INSPECTION FOLLOWS_____
DEPT._____DATE_____SHIFT_____
ACCEPTABLE QUALITY LEVEL_____
B/P_____

INSPECT FOR

OPERATOR CLOCK NO.

INSPECTOR	LOT NO.	LOT SIZE	NO. SAMPLES	NO. DEF.	LOT DISPOSITION																

FIG. 36–4. Form for recording results of sample inspection. The "plan" is at the upper right. In the columns headed "AN" (acceptable number) are shown the number of defectives that can be found and still allow the lot to be accepted.

set up the same way as other attribute control charts. You need defect ratio control charts for surface defects in metal, wood or paper, insulation defects on wire, air bubbles in glass, imperfections in a bolt of cloth or in rolls of film. In most of these cases, you don't fix a defect when you find it. You just accept it as a fact of life that a few defects will turn up. Then you decide further that a certain ratio is enough and that all products having more are rejects. You do, of course, try to improve so that there will be fewer rejects in the future.

In the case of defect-per-unit ratios, you can have ratios way above 100. One kind of "black box" part of a radar set made by the Lear Corporation has 1,800 possible trouble points. Picture yourself checking an assembly of electronic tubes, transistors, diodes, resistors, printed circuits, wires, and so on for the following possible defects (this is Lear's list on this particular assembly):

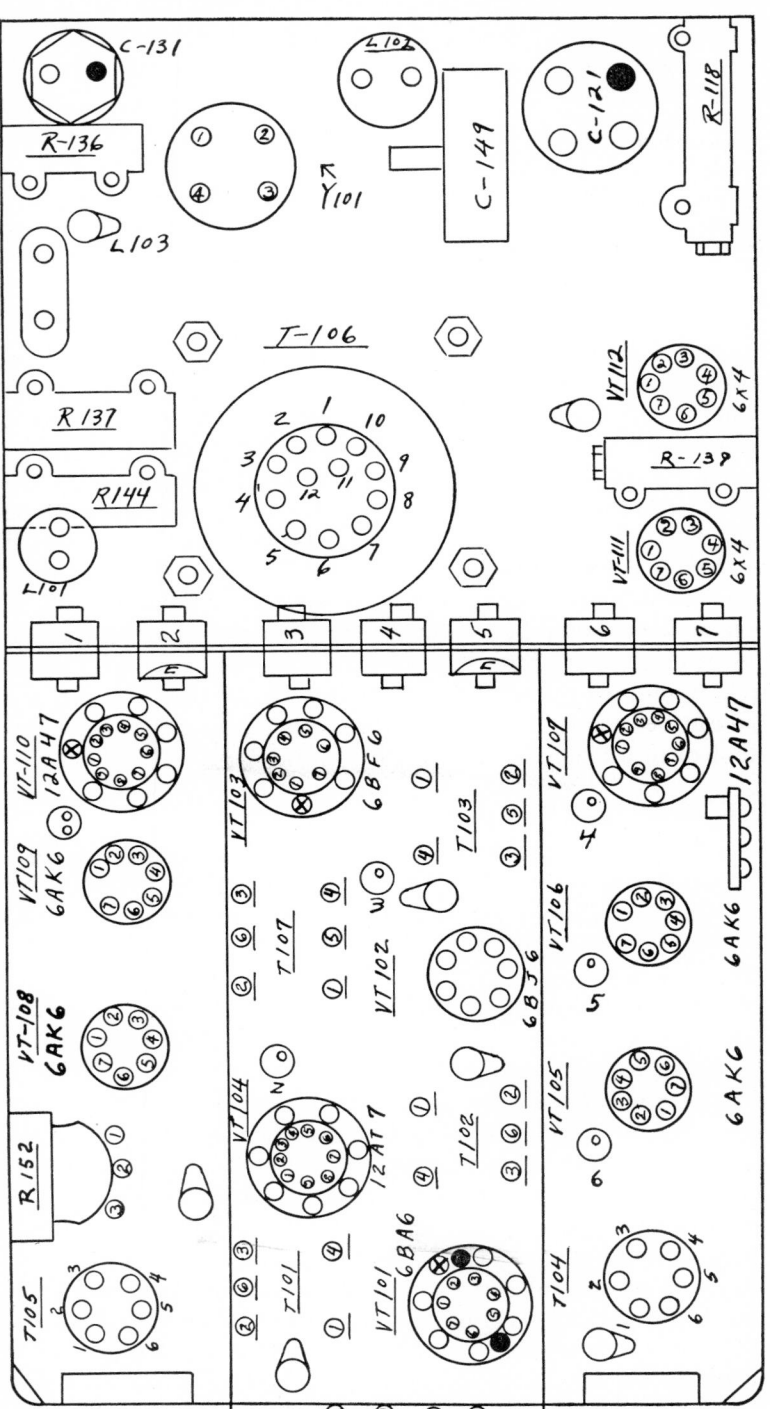

FIG. 36–5. An inspector's check sheet for an electronic component. There could be something wrong (usually poorly soldered connections) at every little circle in this diagram. Each and every one must be checked. This sheet identifies each point being checked. Each unit of product has such a check sheet on which the inspector indicates the defects he finds. Besides this, he keeps a tally count of how many of each kind of defect and where it occurred. The tally count shows up places that are causing trouble most often.

1. Improper solder
2. Burnt wires
3. Wrong component
4. Improperly installed
5. Probable shorts
6. Loose or burned screws
7. Riveting
8. Missing part
9. Defective part
10. Improperly sleeved
11. Broken wires or strands

You don't really have to go so far afield as radar to picture the inspector's problem and the possibility of having more defects than products. Think of an automobile dashboard with its gages and meters. There are hundreds of kinds of defects that could turn up.

Either of these examples would be good places to use charts of defects-per-unit. Also either of these situations is ideal for the auditing kind of quality control. Back on page 678 we described how different kinds of defects were classified and a demerit point scale set up. Serious defects mean 50 demerits, lesser defects mean fewer demerits, and so on. New demerit ratios are figured every day, so before long you could set up a control chart of these ratios. You need that kind of a chart when checking finished products or assemblies, where there are so many things that can be wrong that you have no other way to get an overall picture of quality changes.

ACCEPTANCE SAMPLING

Acceptance sampling means accepting or rejecting whole lots of completed products on the basis of what the sample shows. You work it by telling your inspectors how many pieces to inspect and how many bad items to allow: that many or less, and the lot passes; more than that many, and the lot is rejected.

Most often you find acceptance sampling in the receiving inspection department where you look over the things that you buy. You use acceptance sampling less in your own plant because you use control charts right at the operations in so many places. You never produce large lots of products which are made complete first and then inspected. You inspect a few at a time as they are being made.

Acceptance sampling is nearly always attribute inspection rather than variable inspection. And even more than in the case of operation control charts, acceptance sampling is a matter of calculated risks, because it deals with large quantities of already finished products. There is always a slight chance that bad lots will be passed or that good lots will be rejected.

Always, when you have large quantities of products, there are going to be at least a few defective pieces in every lot. Both buyer and seller understand that there will be some defectives, and contracts are drawn accordingly.[3] In fact, the number of expected defectives will be reflected in the price. If the buyer wants the products he buys to have a very low percentage of defectives, he pays more than if he is less demanding.

When the products arrive at the buyer's plant, he inspects them and accepts or rejects them depending on whether the rejects in the sample he looks at are above or below the ratio allowed. Both buyer and seller (SQC calls them the "consumer" and "producer") take some risks—the consumer runs the risk that now and then he will accept a lot with too many defectives (the sample might not have its share of defectives). The producer runs the risk that now and then a good lot will not pass inspection (if the sample happens to contain more than its share of defectives).

Acceptance sampling *does not* get rid of these risks, but it does let you decide how much risk you want to run and to inspect accordingly. The more certain you want to be, the bigger samples you must inspect (and pay more for inspection costs).

For acceptance sampling you have to decide first on the level of quality that you are willing to pay for, the per cent defectives that you'd like to hold to. This is the AQL, the "Acceptable Quality Level." You then set up your sampling plan so that it accepts lots that are that good almost all of the time.

This means that you will have to accept lots whose samples contain even a little more than the AQL ratio of defectives. If you don't set acceptance numbers this way, you'll reject too many lots which really ought to pass but whose samples happen to contain a few too many bad items. But doing this lays you open to accepting a considerable number of lots having too high a ratio of defectives. Normally this makes no problem because some lots will be considerably better than the AQL and they will offset any bad lots that get by.

On the other hand you should set up your plan so that very few really bad lots will pass. To protect yourself you need to set a high limit, the "Lot Tolerance Per Cent Defective" (LTPD), which used in conjunction with the AQL will give you the protection that you need.

When setting up standard tables of quantities to inspect and how many rejects to allow, the men setting them up generally put in a producer's risk of 5 per cent, which means that the plan will accept lots with the minimum proportion of defectives (the AQL), 95 times out of every 100 such lots. The consumer's risk is generally set at 10 per cent, which means that the plan should reject lots with the maximum proportion of defectives (the LTPD) 90 times out of every 100 such lots. You end up accepting lots that have, on the average, a proportion of defec-

---

[3] Actually the buyer and seller relationship is unimportant. The problem of accepting or rejecting complete products exists regardless of whether you buy or make the items.

tives about halfway between the AQL and the LTPD limits. If the AQL is 1 per cent and the LTPD 3 per cent and if the lots submitted are of varying quality, the lots accepted would average about 2 per cent defectives.

With acceptance sampling and *unlike* control charts you don't have to make up your own tables of sample sizes and rejection numbers for your inspectors. Statisticians have them all figured out, and there are sets of published tables. There are two main sets of published tables, the Dodge-Romig tables and Military Standard 105A. The procedure described above is the Dodge-Romig procedure. Military Standard 105A is a little different.

First, its AQL is *not* the *best* quality that you might get but is the actual average quality level that you are likely to get. Second, MS 105A never mentions the LTPD. But the LTPD lies behind the rejection numbers given in its published tables. MS 105A also gives figures for several "levels" of inspection. You inspect normally until a vendor has sent you several satisfactory lots. Then you cut out part of it and inspect only now and then. But if a lot is rejected, you go back to more frequent inspection for a while.

SINGLE, DOUBLE, AND SEQUENTIAL SAMPLING

For very good lots or very poor lots, relatively small samples are all that you need because the samples too will be so good or bad that there is little doubt about whether the whole lots are good enough to pass. You can take advantage of that in SQC by first inspecting only a very small sample to see whether it is clearly good or bad. True, doing this leaves you with a good many in-between cases where you don't know. If the answer is, you don't know, then inspect another sample and add it to the first. Having a larger sample allows you to be more sure whether a borderline lot is just good enough to pass or not quite good enough.

Some people, though, prefer to use just one sample and no more. This is "single sampling." Here you use just one fairly large sample and pass judgment after inspecting it. The lot passes or not without any more samples.

"Double sampling" means using a medium-sized sample first. With it alone you accept or reject all but borderline lots. With borderline lots you inspect a second sample, add it to the first one, and then decide. Figure 36–6 shows how that works.

"Sequential sampling" means starting out with quite small samples. Even such small samples tell you about the very good or very bad lots, so you accept or reject them right away. But there will be more doubtful lots because of the uncertainty of the small sample. So you take another sample and add it to the first. Putting the two samples together gives you a larger-sized sample and this gives you more certainty, so you can now pass or reject more of the borderline lots. But you still

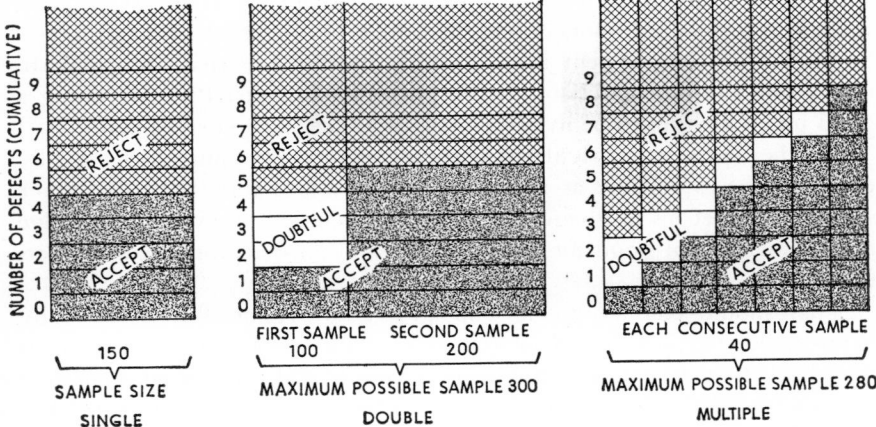

FIG. 36–6. Single, double, and sequential sampling. The three plans are designed for the same result on a lot of 3,200. Under single sampling, the lot would be accepted if a sample of 150 showed four or fewer defects, rejected for five or more. Double sampling would first use a sample of 100, with an "acceptance number" of one and a "rejection number" of five. If two to four defects appear, a second sample of 200 is taken. Multiple sampling is but a further extension of double sampling. For a succession of large lots, double and sequential sampling will often reduce the total amount of inspecting.

have a few remaining borderline lots—not yet passed or rejected. Take a third sample and add it to the first two. Now you have more certainty and can decide more cases. If there are still close borderline lots, just go on to a fourth sample (or more). Figure 36–6 shows how the successive samples work.

THE AVERAGE OUTGOING QUALITY LEVEL

If rejected lots were always scrapped, then your average quality of products used would probably be about halfway between the AQL and the LTPD.

But bad lots of *parts* can be 100 per cent inspected and the lot's quality improved just by taking out the bad items. This means that you end up getting good quality—and the *worse* the quality of lots first submitted, the *better* the quality you end up with. If most lots come through pretty bad, SQC will catch nearly all of them, and, after 100 per cent inspection, they will end up nearly perfect. Average these in with the good lots that passed plus the few bad lots that got through, and you'll have a better quality than if most lots were just good enough to pass.

SQC IN OPERATION

SQC doesn't work out in practice quite the way it is supposed to. On the good side is an extra degree of reliability from samples being inspected thoroughly. Because they are only samples they are usually checked carefully, whereas your inspectors on 100 per cent inspection jobs get careless. Western Electric says that sampling tells you more about how many bad electrical connections there are on a switchboard with 10,000 soldered connections than does 100 per cent inspection.

Also some 100 per cent inspectors get to thinking that they have to throw out a few products or the boss won't think that they are doing a good job. They get to be hypercritical. SQC seems to correct that.

On the bad side, particularly with acceptance sampling, SQC usually ends up *not* as reliable as it is supposed to be. Tables for acceptance sampling are set up to give certain average qualities, but with knowledge that an occasional good lot gets rejected and an occasional bad lot gets through.

That should end up giving you an average result. But what really happens when you reject a lot that is actually good enough to pass? It goes back to the vendor who checks a sample and finds it good enough to pass, so back the lot comes as your next regular shipment and it probably passes this time. The result is that no good lot ever stays rejected. In fact, even medium good lots all end up passing.

You can't criticize the vendor too much for shipping medium good lots back to you, but when you add these to the few bad lots that get by, your over-all average is a little poorer than the plan calls for. Worse yet —lots that should fail to pass (and did fail the first time) also are often sent back for a second try by the vendor. Maybe there is only one chance in four that they will pass. But one fourth of such lots got by the first time. Another one fourth of the remaining bad lots will get by if the vendor tries again. If he tries two or three times, he'll get quite a bit of bad work accepted. Of course, the vendor isn't supposed to do this, and he certainly doesn't tell you that he is doing it.

Another thing (and this may happen with control charts too, but it is more common in acceptance sampling) is the tendency for inspectors not to follow your rules. An inspector dips into a lot and finds enough rejects in his sample to make him reject the lot. But does he? No, he throws his sample back in and takes another sample. Maybe this time he gets a sample that passes, so he accepts the lot. If this sample, too, fails he may even try another. Once he finds one that passes, he accepts the lot. Inspectors will do things like this, so you end up with poorer quality than you'd planned.

Another problem is instructions. The SQC department writes up inspection manuals—sometimes of 300 or 400 pages. If you were an inspector, would you read it? Or remember it if you read it? No, and neither does a factory inspector. Giving him a 300-page instruction manual is like giving no instructions at all. Give him only what he needs and keep it simple.

PRESENT-DAY USE AND ADMINISTRATION OF STATISTICAL QUALITY CONTROL

Today most large companies and many small companies use statistical inspection procedures for some of their operations. Indeed, in a few companies the term "quality control" has come to mean "statistical quality control." Most quality control work done in industry, however, is still nonstatistical, and even in companies using statistical quality control it is only a small part of the total quality control work done.

Statistical quality control is, in most companies using it, administered by a separate department. At the Western Electric Company's Hawthorne plant in Chicago, it is actually a product final inspection department, the main purpose of which is to "audit" the quality of products being turned out and report to management. When it is asked to do so, it also helps out in improving factory operations. At the Hawthorne plant some statistical quality control work is also done by factory inspectors and machine operators in the factory departments under the direction of the various major department superintendents.

In some companies the quality control department does the final inspection of completed products and also directs sampling inspection wherever it is used at individual operations in the factory. But factory inspection on operations in the factory where 100 per cent inspection is carried on is still in the hands of the regular factory inspectors, who are not a part of the "quality control" department. In only a few companies has the quality control department completely replaced the old inspection department.

STUDY QUESTIONS

1. How does statistical quality control get rid of the risks involved in inspecting samples? Explain.
2. Tell how SQC can serve as a quality "audit."
3. Distinguish between attribute inspection and variable inspection. Show why the distinction is important.
4. Why must a sample be "representative" to be usable in SQC? Explain fully.
5. How is the size of sample related to its reliability? Discuss.
6. Explain how the normal curve is related to SQC.
7. What are the differences between control charts for attributes and control charts for variables? Explain.
8. If you had to start from scratch, how would you set up a control chart? What steps do you go through?
9. How can SQC *prevent* making bad parts? Explain.
10. Would you want a lower limit or a control chart for per cent defectives? Why?
11. What is meant by a "consumer's risk"? A "producer's risk"? Explain.
12. When would you favor sequential sampling over single sampling? Why?
13. "SQC doesn't work out in practice quite the way it is supposed to." How does it work? Is what happens good? Explain.

CASE 36–1. PULLEY HUB PROBLEM

You are to set up a control chart for hubs for a pulley. They are to be one inch in length. You plan to inspect a sample of four every half hour.

Here are the actual measurements you get in each of twenty sets of four that you measure for the purpose of setting up a control chart:

Group	Measurement in Inches			
1....................	1.011	1.008	.995	.991
2....................	.991	.988	.986	.989
3....................	.987	.996	1.007	1.013
4....................	.999	.990	1.002	.991
5....................	1.004	1.008	.991	.998
6....................	1.009	.990	1.008	.993
7....................	1.013	.988	.996	.993
8....................	.987	.994	.999	.990
9....................	.995	1.001	.988	1.012
10....................	1.001	.999	1.010	1.007
11....................	.988	1.008	1.006	1.004
12....................	1.001	1.007	.999	.990
13....................	1.004	.997	.993	.998
14....................	.996	.999	.987	1.001
15....................	.987	.990	1.010	.990
16....................	.996	1.004	.994	1.008
17....................	1.007	.989	1.013	1.010
18....................	.987	.991	1.006	1.009
19....................	.990	.997	.993	1.011
20....................	1.005	1.015	1.012	.995

(a) *Set up control limits for this operation.* (b) *Suppose that you had already set these limits from other measurements and that these measurements are those you got by measuring samples of four every half-hour from 8* A.M. *to 6* P.M. *Was the operation ever out of control? When?*

Chapter 37

PURCHASING

MOST manufacturing companies spend more than half of the money they take in for materials or already made up component parts. Chrysler spent $1.7 billion for materials in 1956. That comes to $8 million in a day. Ford spends $10 million a day. So does GE. GM spends $25 million daily for materials.

But does spending so much money make the work of purchasing important? Isn't it easy to *spend* money? Yes, and it *is* easier to *buy* well than it is to sell well. It is easier to pay out the dollars than it is to bring them in.

Purchasing is more, though, than just placing orders. You can spend wisely and pay less for what you buy. If you sell one billion dollars worth of products, you are selling products that probably contain purchased materials that cost some $600 million. The difference between a good and a bad job of buying is nearly always more than 5 per cent. But even at 5 per cent, it would come to $30 million in our example. Maybe purchasing is easier than selling, but it is still very important.

In extreme cases what you make (or lose) on inventory can outweigh what you do in regular operations. In 1957, for example, brass prices fell to $0.30 a pound from its 1956 peak of $0.48. The price of raw cotton and wool varies so much that textile companies can lose their shirts by poor buying. Meat packers and flour millers have the same headaches.

Purchasing's main job is to get the things that the factory needs when it needs it and to pay as little as possible considering the quality that you need. But this looks at the job too narrowly. Today many companies say that the purchasing department is responsible for "outside manufacture." This puts a different slant—a managerial slant—on the job. Vendor companies are thought of almost as departments of your own company—and subject to the same controls.

With this view purchasing is not so passive—it is more than just a matter of placing orders properly. Purchasing gets more into make-or-buy decisions, and the purchasing agent becomes almost a factory manager. He is interested in the efficiency of your suppliers. If they can't get their costs down, he may ask your own industrial engineers to go into the vendor's plant and help out.

The purchasing agent is interested in the tooling and the vendor plant uses, since you pay for all the special tooling he uses on your order. The P.A. is interested in the vendor plant's quality control procedures too. If they are good enough, you can save on inspection costs when its products arrive as your raw materials. More important, if its quality is all right, you'll have fewer troubles in your own manufacturing when you use the products.

But aren't we overlooking the vendor? Won't he resent your prying? You are not his only customer, and he probably has some ideas of his own about how to run his own company. What if all his customers try to tell him how to run his business?

He doesn't oppose your interferences as much as you might at first think. Of course he objects to your trying to whittle down his profit margin. But he wants to get your order and to have you as a satisfied customer. He doesn't even care who owns the special tooling needed for your job. You can pay him for it as part of the price or pay for it separately. You pay for it in either case. And as for your industrial engineers or quality control engineers going into a vendor's plant and telling him how to do his work better, he should be all for it, that is what he should be trying to do himself. The vendor is usually happy to have some free help from your men.

Purchasing men ("buyers") should always go beyond their bare order-placing responsibilities. Of course they must know and abide by all laws about purchasing and shipping of products. Besides, buyers should keep up on new materials and tell engineering about them. Engineering will probably know already about new materials but not about their price. Sometimes both the engineering and manufacturing departments are too busy to keep up with new materials. Purchasing is in a better position to do it.

Purchasing should always be on the lookout to see if less costly materials can be used. Naturally, purchasing can't tell whether the cheaper materials will do the job (engineering has to decide that) but it ought to tell the others about the prices.

Most companies making products (airplanes, tanks, etc.) for the government do not make every major part. They buy whole sections—such as engines or landing gear. The government's contract with the prime contractor (who makes the finished product) makes him responsible for seeing that all subcontractors live up to government laws and contract requirements. Often this means auditing the subcontractor's records to see that he has not charged too much overhead or added other wrong costs into his total (the price is often set on a cost-plus basis). The prime contractor's purchasing department is responsible for all of this.

THE PURCHASING DEPARTMENT ORGANIZATION

The purchasing department is headed by a "purchasing agent" or "director of purchases." He may be a vice-president. More often he is not, in which case he usually reports to the executive vice-president of the company. Except in small companies the purchasing agent does little buying himself. His duties deal more with administration, studying market trends, and policy making, although he is actively concerned in all large contracts.

No two purchasing departments are alike, but all of them buy thousands of different things, usually from thousands of suppliers. General Electric buys from 42,000 suppliers. Chevrolet counted its suppliers once and found that it had bought from 24,000 firms in one year. Having to buy so much material and from so many sources means that your buyers get a chance to specialize.

Besides buying materials and manufactured parts for the company's products, the purchasing department must buy supplies, containers for products, power (or coal), equipment, repair parts, and printed material for dealer displays. In most companies the purchasing department also operates the salvage department and sells or disposes of scrap and low-valued by-products.

Here are the men that General Electric's Apparatus Division purchasing agent (he is a vice-president) has reporting to him:

Buyer and assistant buyer—Fabricated copper, brass, bronze, nickel, silver (except ingot), lumber (including poles, ties, etc.), packages and packing materials (wood, cleated, corrugated, bobbins, reels, etc.), woodwork (turned or contracted), patterns.

Buyer—Refrigerator hardware and accessories, asbestos, rubber and rubber parts, molded parts, glass (including globes and lenses), hose, pipe covering, name plates, nonferrous metals except copper.

Buyer—Mica, mercury, polishing and grinding supplies, textiles, rope and twine, springs, leather and leather products (including all kinds of belting).

Assistant buyer—Paper and paper products (except carbon and abrasive papers), transmission appliances (including bearings, gears, etc.), hardware (except refrigerator items), refrigerator insulation gaskets, packing and fiber.

Buyer—Large tools and machinery, automobiles, jewels, coal.

Assistant buyer—Steam, gas and water supplies (except hose, gaskets, packing, and pipe covering), oilers and lubricators, small tools, brushes and brooms.

Assistant buyer—Oils, greases, and petroleum products, furniture (including typewriters, comptometers, tabulating machines, etc.), roofing materials (except paper), steel shelving and racks, partitions.

Assistant buyer—Electrical supplies (including clocks and meters), instruments, carbon brushes, and painters' supplies.

Assistant buyer—Screw machine products, stampings, bolts, nuts, washers, rivets and screws, hospital supplies, stationery and printing, and office supplies.

Buyer—Steel (sheet, strip, and stainless), aluminum (including wire and all forms except ingot), monel metal, and nickel.

Buyer—Pig iron, castings, ferro-alloys, chemicals, foundry supplies, factory supplies (except coal, oils, greases, and petroleum products), sand, gravel, and clay.

Buyer—Iron and steel (except sheet, strip, stainless, pig iron, and castings), nails, forgings, railway supplies, iron and steel wire, packages and packing (except wood and corrugated material), and tanks.[1]

It makes quite a list, but even so it describes the work only of the main men in the department.

Purchasing departments are not large, rarely going as high as one half of 1 per cent of the employees. But small numbers only high light what the buyers do. Buyers spend from $2 to $4 million each in a year— or from $1,000 to $2,000 an hour! It costs anywhere from one fourth of a cent up to over 1 cent to spend $1. And it costs $3 on the average to handle an order. Clerical help outnumbers buyers in all companies, sometimes as much as 4 to 1.

PURCHASING PROCEDURES

No one procedure will do for all of the 10,000 items or so that big companies buy. Some items (like sheet steel for a tin can maker) are shipped in steadily and, over a period of time, cost millions of dollars. Other items (like the equipment to make automobile motor blocks automatically in a new factory) are one-shot orders that cost millions. Between these extremes, steady high demand or giant one-shot contracts, you find every possible combination of volume, repetition, and variety clear down to 5-and-10-cent-store items bought once a year.

Besides the variety in kind and quantity, you deal with bulk items (liquids, powders), packaged items, standard items, special items, items always bought, items sometimes bought and sometimes made, and items where you make some and buy some more at the same time.

Big, Steady-Use Items. For the big, important items that you keep buying all the time, the purchasing department needs no requisitions from either production control or from the stores department. Purchasing gets its authority to go ahead and make purchase commitments directly from the approved production schedules for the months ahead. Purchasing has, in its files, lists of all of the things to buy and how much to buy in order to make one unit of all of your major products. All it has to do is to look at the scheduled quantities and multiply to get the amount of material needed.

You buy most of the big steady items on blanket contracts that cover a whole year's supply. Blanket contracts leave quantities and times of delivery (and sometimes price) to be set as you need materials. You send

---

[1] Stuart F. Heinritz, *Purchasing Principles and Practices* (2d ed.; New York: Prentice-Hall, Inc., 1951), pages 65–66.

ALUMINUM COMPANY OF AMERICA
RALPH O. KEEFER, General Purchasing Agent
PITTSBURGH 19, PA.

REQUEST
FOR
QUOTATION

A-B-C Box Company
2345 Main Street
Pittsburgh 5, Pa.

REQ'N NO. 510444
AUTH. NO.   DEL'Y REQ'D

SHIP VIA Motor Freight

Aluminum Company of America
Building 242
New Kensington, Pa.

SELLER PLEASE INSERT

F. O. B.

TERMS OF PAYMENT   (INCL. CASH DISCOUNT)

EST. SHIPPING WEIGHT

Please quote itemized prices for items listed below and insert information requested in space provided.

SHIPMENT PROMISED   DAYS AFTER RECEIPT OF ORDER

ITEM NO.	QUANTITY	DESCRIPTION AND SPECIFICATIONS	NET UNIT PRICE (INCL. DISCOUNT)
1	50,000	No. 3383-24 Alcoa Wrap Cartons, size 12-3/8 inch x 8-3/8 inch x 12-1/2 inch, 175 lb. test, R.S.C., printed 1C - 4 P.	

NOTES

A Cartons must be manufactured with extreme care since they will be filled and sealed by automatic equipment.

B Cartons must be palletized 400 per pallet, with protective cover on corners to prevent top layers of cartons from becoming distorted.

C Each pallet to be marked with quantity and item number.

REQUEST DATE   QUOTATION DUE DATE

Please return your quotation on one copy of this form to:
K.R.GRIMM:mrw

We offer to sell to you the above material at the price and terms specified hereon and upon the conditions printed on the back hereof. Alternative materials or specifications, if any, have been clearly indicated.

SIGNED _____ DATED _____

BY _____ DATED _____

THIS IS NOT AN ORDER

Aluminum Company of America

FIG. 37-1. Request for quotation.

out monthly (or even weekly) new "release" orders telling the vendor how many or how much to deliver and when and where.

Contracts for these steady-use, high-volume items are not really open to competition in the wide-open sense, except that you may buy from *two* sources instead of one, just for safety. The buyer-seller relation is much like that of one company department with a sister department. Supplying companies often keep certain contracts for years. Electric Auto-lite, for example, has made most of Chrysler Company's auto ignition systems since the mid-30's. Goodyear Tire has never failed to get a good chunk of GM's business since World War I.

Mostly the big contracts do not travel around because the seller takes as good care (price, quality, and service) of the customers as any one else could. Also these contracts are so big that no competitor could take one on and deliver overnight. He'd have to build one or several new factories, tool up, and line up a whole new work force for his new factory.

One exception to the big contracts traveling around is basic raw materials (materials of nature: cotton, wool, rubber, lumber, wheat, and so on). There are a good many suppliers of such items, and the price goes up and down. Here you don't always stick to one vendor but go where you can get the best deal each time that you let a new contract. Don't forget, however, that dependable service is important in such items. It is best not to switch your whole volume to unknowns, though you might give an unknown a trial order now and then.

Big One-Shot Jobs. Big, one-shot propositions are different. They usually are machinery for a newly built factory, for an electric power dam, or some other construction, or even for a warship. On these projects months go into planning. Discussions are held with several machinery makers. Alternative designs are considered. Sometimes the advance work takes so many man-hours that the customer pays an engineering fee to prospective bidders. Otherwise a vendor may be unwilling to spend $50,-000 on engineering for a job that he might not get.

Sometimes the one-shot propositions are so special that only one vendor can really do the job. But nearly always there are at least two or three. Each will be given a chance to bid on the job. The point is that vendors have to bid separately for every one of these big jobs.

Middle-Sized Orders. Here you are nearly always buying only after someone else inside the organization has asked you to. You get a purchase "requisition" from the production control department or from the stores department.

Production control sends you requisitions for items needed for making the products on the factory's production schedule (except for the heavy and steadily used items that we talked about above). Using the list of parts made up by engineering, production control figures out how many to make of made parts, how much and what kind of material to buy to make them, and how many to buy of bought items. It also figures out *when* it will need these things and asks you in purchasing to get them.

The raw materials stores department is often under production control's direction, in which case its requests cover new supplies of raw materials needed. Otherwise, production control tells raw stores what it will need in the weeks ahead and stores writes the purchase requisitions.

Middle-sized orders are almost always for the same things that you have bought before. That lets you cut down some on paper work. Use a "traveling" requisition card. Keep it with the store's record cards until you want to reorder. Then write in the new quantity you want this time and send it to purchasing. After placing the order, purchasing sends the card back to stores to be held till the next time.

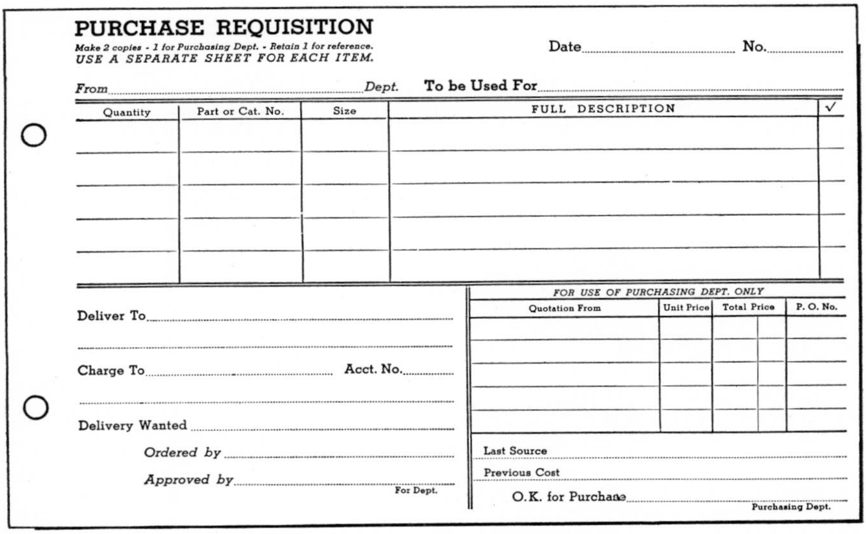

PURCHASE REQUISITION

Make 2 copies - 1 for Purchasing Dept. - Retain 1 for reference.
USE A SEPARATE SHEET FOR EACH ITEM.

Date ______ No. ______

From ______ *Dept.* To be Used For ______

Quantity	Part or Cat. No.	Size	FULL DESCRIPTION	✓

Deliver To ______

Charge To ______ Acct. No. ______

Delivery Wanted ______

Ordered by ______

Approved by ______ For Dept.

FOR USE OF PURCHASING DEPT. ONLY

Quotation From	Unit Price	Total Price	P. O. No.

Last Source ______

Previous Cost ______

O.K. for Purchase ______ Purchasing Dept.

FIG. 37–2. Purchase requisition form.

Middle-sized repeat orders are usually with the same vendors. But they don't work like releases against blanket orders. Vendors get specific purchase orders from purchasing for every order. Every new order again describes the product and orders a certain quantity to be delivered by a certain date.

But whether middle-sized orders are for old or new things, it is common to ask two or three vendors to bid. Generally you give the contract to the low bidder if he is dependable. Sometimes middle-sized orders are for standard catalogue items. If so (and particularly if you don't have much time), you may not shop around to try to get the best price but just order the material wherever you can get a reasonable price with an agreement to deliver soon.

Small Orders. Small orders are one of the headaches of purchasing. It costs anywhere from \$1 to \$10 to handle a purchase requisition and to place a purchase order, so you'd like to cut out all the little orders for

ALUMINUM COMPANY OF AMERICA
PITTSBURGH 19, PA.

PURCHASE ORDER

A-B-C Box Company
2345 Main Street
Pittsburgh 5, Pa.

REQ'N NO.	P.O. DATE	P.O. NO.
510444		657508
AUTH. NO.	DEL'Y REQ'D	SHIPM'T PROMISE
		As Req'd

SHIP TO:
Aluminum Company of America
Building 242
New Kensington, Pa.

SHIP VIA
Motor Freight

F.O.B.
New Kensington, Pa.

TERMS OF PAYMENT
1% 10 days - Net 30 days

Please ship the following items as instructed above.

ITEM NO.	QUANTITY	DESCRIPTION AND SPECIFICATIONS	PRICE
1	50,000 -	No. 3383-24 Alcoa Wrap Cartons, size 12-3/8 inch x 8-3/8 inch x 12-1/2 inch, 175 lb. test, R.S.C., printed 1C - 4 P.	$91.50 per M
2		Set-Up Charge for Each Release	9.75

NOTES

A | Cartons must be manufactured with extreme care since they will be filled and sealed by automatic equipment.

B | Cartons must be palletized 400 per pallet, with protective cover on corners to prevent top layers of cartons from becoming distorted.

C | Each pallet to be marked with quantity and item number.

KRG:mrw

NOTE: In accepting this order it is understood the Seller agrees to the terms and conditions shown above and printed on the back hereof. The Buyer hereby objects to any conflicting or additional terms or conditions.

ALUMINUM COMPANY OF AMERICA
RALPH O. KEEFER, General Purchasing Agent

BY_____

Aluminum Company of America

FIG. 37–3. A purchase order. Notice that it has been duplicated from the same master copy that gave us the request for quotation. Price and other information have been added.

one or two items or for 50 cents or $1 worth of materials. You have to have such things, though—worse yet, some of them are rush orders.

Most companies let these orders go through the regular procedure, cost what they may. Some, however, try to cut the cost down. Here

ALCOA ALUMINUM

ALUMINUM COMPANY OF AMERICA
PITTSBURGH 19, PA.

**REQUEST FOR
SHIPPING INFORMATION**

DATE_____

A-B-C Box Company
2345 Main Street
Pittsburgh 5, Pa.

Aluminum Company of America
Building 242
New Kensington, Pa.

SHIP TO

REQ'N NO. 510444	P.O. DATE	P.O. NO. 657508
AUTH. NO.	DEL'Y REQ'D	SHIPM'T PROMISE As Req'd

SHIP VIA
Motor Freight

F.O.B.
New Kensington, Pa.

TERMS OF PAYMENT
1% 10 days - Net 30 days

This is an important request for information concerning shipment of the item No.(s) circled below. Please return one copy of this form showing the current shipping schedule and other information requested.

ITEM NO.	QUANTITY	DESCRIPTION AND SPECIFICATIONS	PRICE
1	50,000 -	No. 3383-24 Alcoa Wrap Cartons, size 12-3/8 inch x 8-3/8 inch x 12-1/2 inch, 175 lb. test, R.S.C., printed 1C - 4 P.	$91.50 per M
2		Set-Up Charge for Each Release	9.75

NOTES

A   Cartons must be manufactured with extreme care since they will be filled and sealed by automatic equipment.

B   Cartons must be palletized 400 per pallet, with protective cover on corners to prevent top layers of cartons from becoming distorted.

C   Each pallet to be marked with quantity and item number.

KRG:mrw

REQUEST FOR SHIPPING INFORMATION

If material has been shipped, please show below complete tracing references for each shipment, including date shipped, bill of lading and waybill numbers, carrier, number of packages and gross weight.

_____

_____

_____

                                                    Mail Reply To

Aluminum Company of America

FIG. 37–4. A "follow-up" form asking when an order will be shipped. Notice that this is duplicated from the same master that made out the purchase order.

are American Can's policies: (1) Don't reorder little things often. Go ahead and order 2 or 3 years' supply. What if some day part of the supply of some item does get thrown out? It is still cheaper than buying little dribbles all the time. (2) Let departments buy directly all things costing less than $25. Don't bother the purchasing department about them. (3) Place blanket orders with suppliers, then just order what is wanted now and then by telephone without making out a purchase order every time. Cut out the paper work.

Follow-up.   Keeping large supplies of materials on hand is so costly that no one wants to do it. That means that you don't buy things (or at least don't get them delivered) until shortly before you need them. But that means also that if anything goes wrong and the vendor doesn't deliver on time, you are in trouble. So you "follow-up" orders for things that are on tight schedule. Call the vendor or write him a letter; ask him whether your order is coming along all right; remind him that you are counting on getting it on time. All of this helps. Not only do you get more things on time but you find out sooner about the orders that you are delayed. It gives you time to change your own plans.

Wouldn't it be cheaper just to carry a few more items in stock? Then not every delay would catch you short. No, you'd have to carry so much more that it would be very costly. Besides, vendors would still let you down sometimes and not deliver on time. You'd have to do some follow-up anyway or still be out of some material now and then.

Receiving Inspection.   Purchasing is not complete until you have the material in hand. Receiving usually is not under the purchasing department, but purchasing has to be told (it gets a copy of the "receiving report") when materials come in as ordered so that it can clear the orders out of its file and tell accounting to pay the bill. The bill (or "invoice") has by this time come in by mail to the accounting department. So has the freight bill covering shipping costs. If the material is not right in any way, purchasing has to handle all dealings with the vendor about what to do about it.

HOW MUCH CENTRALIZATION?

When you have several (or many) plants scattered around the country, should you have one central office do all of the buying or only some of it? There is no pat answer. Nearly all companies end up doing some of it centrally and some locally. General Motors decentralizes its buying to 52 divisions which in turn decentralize the actual buying to over 100 purchasing offices.

Do it centrally and you deal in larger volumes and sometimes get better prices. How much better? You'll save anywhere up to 10 per cent. Remember, though, that your total volume of any item is not increased by central buying. But the volume you talk about on a single contract will be the whole company's volume, not just one plant's volume, so you will probably get a better price.

You can have more specialized men doing the buying, too, when you buy centrally. No one has to be so all-purpose as do buyers in small divisions of a company. Also, central buying cuts out duplication of orders and so saves clerical costs. It gives top management a tighter control over the whole company's inventory policies. It forces more standardization into designs.

Bad things are that centralization is slow and too cumbersome for minor items. The thousands of little things can better be bought by separate purchasing departments at the plant level. Also you can't control plant inventories very well from a central office. The controls are likely to become too rigid. Central people just can't know local needs.

Also, even with central buying, you don't like to risk buying *all* of any important item from one supplier. Just for insurance against strikes and other holdups you should divide up the orders for most important items and place orders with at least two suppliers. But when you do, you lose part of the possible quantity discount that you expected to get from centralized purchasing.

Freight is another item. If you place your high volume orders with only one or two suppliers, and if they ship to all of your plants, long freight hauls may cancel out any quantity discount that you get from volume buying. This doesn't apply, however, if the vendor is also a multiplant company and can ship to your Midwest plant from his Midwest plant, and to your Pacific Northwest plant from his Pacific Northwest plant, and so on. But if the vendor of any item does not have close-by plants, it will probably pay to give up central buying of that item and let each plant order its needs from a nearby plant just to save freight.

Bad materials and short shipments also turn up at times. These can be much better handled locally then centrally. Local buying also creates community good will. And it gives plant managers more responsibility. They nearly always want to have some control over buying the materials they work on.

Big companies usually end up centralizing all buying: (1) where big amounts of money are involved, (2) when highly technical knowledge is required, (3) for purchases where reciprocity (see page 718) enters the picture, and (4) for all capital expenditures. All other things are bought by producing departments in the separate divisions. Often some dollar limit is set for local purchasing. All contracts for more money must clear through central purchasing. The central purchasing department also sets up policies and procedures for the decentralized groups to use.

Centralization in One-Plant Companies.   One-plant companies usually centralize *all* purchasing—even every minor item. Sometimes, however, department heads are allowed to buy directly items that don't cost over $10 or $20.

There are problems, though. Department heads will buy things anyway (and not just in small companies either). The first thing that purchasing knows about it is a telephone call from the receiving department asking: What is this? Who is it for? Where does it go? Purchasing then has to ask all around to see who ordered the item. This happens most often with small special machines, tools, and such items where purchasing never does have much to say about what is bought. Men using these items sometimes just bypass purchasing and go ahead and order the item directly from a vendor. It is bad practice, but it sometimes happens.

MAKE-OR-BUY

We talked about make-or-buy decisions in Chapter 6. Most of them are top management decisions, but the purchasing agent is nearly always in on them because he has to get the cost figures for buying. And, if you end up buying, he has to place the contracts.

But that isn't all there is to make-or-buy. Some items are made when work is slow, but subcontracted out in boom times. And some items you make part of and buy part of, as a regular practice. Also some half-manufactured items are sometimes sent out for certain work (such as heat-treating or electroplating) and then brought back for finishing. There are matters of scheduling, of sending out and getting back tooling, and of all the paper work. Purchasing and production control have to work closely together in all such mixed-up cases.

Make-buy decisions are often fairly permanent, but purchasing ought to be ever alert to changed situations that ought to make you change your decision. Maybe you have been buying certain items but now the volume is up to where you ought to go into making them. Or maybe the reverse. If suppliers can make things for less than you can, you ought to consider buying instead of making. Management will never know about these opportunities unless purchasing watches out for them.

VALUE ANALYSIS

Purchasing departments in giant companies today all carry on "value analysis." Value analysis means that you regard everything that you buy as being bought to serve a purpose. Before going out and buying the item or materials asked for, purchasing studies the purpose. Could another less costly item fill the need? Will less expensive material do the job? Are the vendor's costs as low as they ought to be? Would other lower cost designs work as well?

Purchasing doesn't decide answers. It raises questions and consults with its own engineering department and with its cost accounting department. It does the same with vendor company departments. Sometimes purchasing's fresh look unearths gold mines. Here are a few results of value analysis at General Electric.

A screw of special design cost 15 cents. Value analysis turned up a way to make it for 1½ cents. Annual saving $20,000. A handmade gasket (cost $4.15 each) made at GE was found to cost 15 cents from an outside gasket maker. A die-cast cover cost 60 cents. Changed to a stamping, it proved better and cost only 20 cents. Annual saving, $39,000.

General Motors' Frigidaire division points to these savings: An aluminum door to an evaporator, 3 vendor quotations ranging from $2.40 to $2.70. Frigidaire's estimate of what it should pay, $2.05. Final price, $2.10. Annual savings, $27,000. Food compartment door quotations ranged from $3.30 to $3.50. Frigidaire's estimate, $3.05. Final price, $3.05. Savings, $49,000. An escutcheon made from 0.032″ brass, changed to 0.025″ steel. Savings, $12,000.

Purchasing should also watch the specifications your own engineers are writing. In one plant the purchasing agent found that its own engineers had specified parts to be made to close fits—but then they were enameled before they were used! That destroyed any close fit. Loosening the tolerance cut the purchase price. Before that the company wasn't getting value for its money. It was paying for a close fit that it didn't need.

Of course you don't get those savings free of cost. It takes time and effort to cut such costs. And it is possible to spend dollars where only pennies can be saved. But value analysis, intelligently done, should produce savings of many times its cost.

MASS-PRODUCTION PURCHASING

General Motors spends over *half a billion dollars a month* for materials: Chevrolet, in a year, uses some 150,000 tons of steel costing over $2 million just for bumpers and springs alone! But you don't have to be a General Motors to find yourself buying many items in million-dollar quantities in a year.

Almost always these contracts are so big that neither buyer nor seller wants to take any chances on price, yet each wants to be sure of the contract. So the contracts are often written, leaving the price to be settled every now and then during a year. Quantities are also left open and to be as the customer orders week by week. The price, if the item is a manufactured product, is often set at cost plus a fee. If steel prices go up, Chevrolet pays more for its bumper steel, or the reverse if steel goes down. That way no one gets hurt when prices change. Often, but not always, there are penalty premiums for the vendor not delivering or if the buyer cancels.

Quantities, in mass production, are so big that neither buyer nor seller wants to carry enough inventory to last more than a few days, so both try to mesh their schedules together exactly. Supplier *dependability* is even more important than price. In busy times Chevrolet eats up steel for bumpers and springs at the rate of 800 tons a day. At 50 tons to a freight carload that means 16 freight carloads a day! Chevrolet would rarely carry more than a day or two's supply on hand. In fact, it would want the cars to come in at regular intervals all day long and not all at once. Both the vendor and the railroad know this and try to deliver on that kind of schedule.

On the other hand, lead time is very important. To get steel in July, it needs to be rolled in the steel mills in June. Steel mills plan June's production in May, so Chevrolet has to place its order in April. *But* in April, Chevrolet's July car-making schedule has not yet been firmed up. Of course it knows that it will make cars in July but not how many or exactly what kinds. Purchasing has to go ahead anyway and place the order, then in May or even June ask the vendor to change quantities to correct for any mis-guesses. All of this schedule changing makes young men grow old fast in the purchasing department and in the vendor plant's production control department, but it is what you have to do.

Chevrolet's bumper steel is, however, a simple example. Suppose that your bought item is an airplane engine that takes weeks to make and that it is made partly out of products bought from someone else who uses steel (special steel of course, not the kind you can get from a jobber) bought from someone else. Also suppose that these suppliers are loaded up with work and have to tell you to wait 3 to 6 months for your order, and that they will sell you only part of what you want. Steel was just that tight in 1955. You had to order some kinds of steel up to a year ahead in order to get it when you needed it.

HOW MANY TO BUY AT ONE TIME?

Very few purchases are one-shot items. Nearly everything you buy, you buy again and again, so there is the question of whether to buy few and often or more at a time and less often. For your big day-to-day, bread-and-butter items we have already given the answer: use blanket contracts covering perhaps a year's needs and then get frequent shipments as needed. For the bulk of other items—those bought repetitively but not on blanket contracts—the purchasing department usually does what someone else says. We talked about that on page 704.

Purchasing shouldn't be too passive, though. Remember, it costs anywhere from $1 to over $10 to process an order. That makes it expensive to order little items in little dribbles. Also there is the matter of price. Since small quantities always come in at higher unit prices, purchasing would naturally like to buy large quantities less often. But carrying inventory is expensive, so you ought to try to balance out. Inventory control men and purchasing men should work together on problems of how many to order at a time. In order to be sure that they do work together, a few (but only a few) companies put inventory control under the purchasing department.

FORECASTING IN PURCHASING

Forecasting for purchasing is a little different from sales forecasting and production forecasting. For purchasing you want to know about future prices and supply conditions.

Price forecasting is important because you don't want to get stuck with using high-priced materials if prices go down. Of course you can avoid most of that risk by buying from hand to mouth, but then your small quantity buying makes you pay more right along. Price forecasting is also important because if prices are going up you might make a tidy sum by doing a little stockpiling.

Most companies (presidents and boards of directors as well as purchasing agents) try their best to avoid risks of losing money, so they don't do much stockpiling, nor do they sign long-range contracts with fixed prices. No one criticizes you for missing a profit for failure to stockpile, but men lose their jobs when big stockpiling goes wrong.

When you feel that you must enter into long-term purchasing contracts, keep the price open—to be decided when the goods are delivered. But by no means does that mean that the price is vague. Spell it out in the contract, exactly how the price will be set. Doing this of course cuts out the chances to profit from price rises, but most companies are willing to pass up that chance if they can be sure of no losses.

Sometimes, though, you can find a vendor anxious enough to get a contract to agree to no price increase on the contract if prices go up but a cut if they go down. If he is a reliable vendor, that is ideal from the purchasing agent's point of view.

Forecasting *supply* conditions is unimportant when things are available. But just let anything get in short supply (as always happens in war and sometimes in peace), and it suddenly is very, very important. In 1955 you had to wait 6 and 8 months for plate glass and some kinds of steel. If you wait to order these things until you know just what the factory is going to ask for, you've waited too long. Yet look what it does if you do go ahead and order before you know exactly what you want. Your best way-ahead guess can't be wholly right, so you end up with too much of some things and not enough of something else.

Where does purchasing get all its information about the future? It gets it from vendor company salesmen, from its own sales department, and from reading. Forecasts are made and published regularly in trade magazines and in releases of trade associations. Basic commodity supply and demand relationships are also written up in many publications. Public sources of forecasts and basic information include newspaper financial pages, weekly national magazines, and governmental statistical sources. Private sources include various trade associations, trade magazines, and professional forecasting services such as Babson's, Brookmire's, McGill's and Fairchild Publications. Perhaps the various Washington "news letters," such as Kiplinger's, should also be mentioned here, since they sometimes contain advance information on federal laws and governmental buying.

BUYING IN A TIGHT MARKET

We have already said that you have to allow much more lead time when buying in a tight market—when things are hard to get.

Tight markets make other changes in purchasing. In a seller's market the seller can be choosy about whom he does business with and whose orders he will accept. That is when tough buyers get their come-uppance. During normal times some companies are very demanding: they try to whittle down prices, they are fussy and reject everything but perfect products, they want all kinds of service, special variations in products, unusual delivery and packing conditions, and so on. These companies go to the bottom of the seller's hit-parade list. Sellers take care of their best customers first. On the other hand, vendors don't cut off demanding customers completely. After all, the shoe will be on the other foot again sometime, and having demanding customers is better than having no customers. Those you take good care of don't always stay with you; maybe you'll want those fussy customers.

Of course, during the tightest markets of all, during a war, the government sets up controls and priority systems to fix prices and allocate materials. Hard bargainers get their share, but when you can't serve everyone you'll probably try harder to give your best service to your best customers.

In tight markets buyers have to put economy second to getting supplies at almost any cost. Price is not very important, neither are freight rates—never mind about the extra costs of less-than-carload shipments, express, or even air express. Getting materials *soon* is important, but getting them at all is urgent. Instead of salesmen calling on customers, the customers' "expeditors" call on the vendors to try to get them to accept orders and to deliver materials.

Vendors respond to all of this by parceling out their production, some here and some there. They send you part of your order so that you can keep going, but they can't fill it all or someone else is left out. When that starts, you as a customer start doing two things: (1) you overorder —order more than you want, then your share will be bigger—and (2) you advance your ordering. Normally you order in November what you want in January. So you just order it in September and say that you want it in November. Then if it comes two months later you are all right.

Of course doing both of these things just makes conditions worse. Vendors' order backlogs grow, and cuts and delays grow too. Everyone knows that some of this is going on, but no one knows how much; nor do they know what to do about it. But sometimes a tight market disappears overnight when buyers find that they can get what they want. Then they cut their orders and ask for later deliveries. Vendors' backlogs can melt away very quickly.

RUSH ORDERS

Rush orders to buy in a hurry should not exist. But they do, and purchasing has to make the best of it. In most companies maybe one order out of every five is rush. Rush orders cost money because there is no time to shop around for the best buy. You also have to spend four or five times more follow-up effort on a rush order than on a regular one. And, to top it off, you have to have things sent in express or even air express.

Perhaps other departments would cut these orders some if they realized the costliness of turning in orders at the last minute. Purchasing ought to be sure that the others realize what their lack of planning is costing in extras.

A real trouble with rush orders is that often they aren't genuinely rush. One company found that a vice-president always had to have things in a rush—"ship it by express!" Doing that saved two or three days, then the material lay around for two months before it was used. Purchasing should watch for such practices and try to get other departments to plan farther ahead and not to ask for quick delivery unless they need it.

SETTING THE QUALITY

This is engineering's job, so why talk about it as part of purchasing? We talk about it here because engineers are not so well acquainted with prices and price changes as is purchasing. Besides engineers don't always know how much money you spend for this or that item *in total*.

Engineers don't talk to salesmen coming into your company nearly so often as do your buyers. Buyers can ask salesmen to point out places where slight design changes will lower prices. These and other suggestions from salesmen can be passed on by the buyer to engineering. Actually, important quality decisions should be made by a committee on which both purchasing and engineering are represented.

Maybe the engineers are unknowingly asking for off-standard materials (which cost extra). Or maybe they are asking for features that they don't know cost extra. Or maybe they ask for something they do know costs extra but they don't realize how much. Or maybe their drawings have dimensions and tolerances all over them, but only certain of them are really important. Perhaps the others can be relaxed and save money. Purchasing can save money if it works with engineering, finds out which tolerances are musts and which are not, and then tells the vendor the places where he doesn't have to be so fussy.

PRODUCT DESCRIPTIONS

Purchasing is a matter of buying what you want. But when you are here and the vendor is 500 miles away, he has to figure out what you want from a piece of paper (your purchase order). Besides, if he has several things which are almost alike, you don't get to choose except as you choose from his catalogue where he described the differences.

It isn't like going into a paint store for a paint brush. There you can see and feel the brushes. You can ask about them. You can tell the clerk what you want the brush for and ask for his recommendations. And you come away with the brush that suits you. Now compare buying a brush this way with telling someone else that you need a brush. How many times have you tried to help someone out by buying something for him only to find that he doesn't like what you picked out for him?

What we are saying is that describing products is not easy. Sometimes, though, you don't have to write out lengthy specifications. Often you can order using standards generally understood by the trade, or you can specify an item's catalogue number, or a trade-mark name, or maybe you can furnish a drawing or a sample.

PURCHASING SPECIFICATION   2010890

RADIO CORPORATION OF AMERICA
PRODUCT ENGINEERING   STANDARDIZING DIVISION   CAMDEN, N.J.

PAGE-1 OF 3

DATE- AUGUST 1, 1957

(Formerly PS-890, File No. 100-1-890)

SUBJECT   LAMINATE, PHENOLIC, PAPER-BASE, COPPER-CLAD
(ROOM TEMPERATURE PUNCHING GRADE)

Commodity Code 1602

OF RADIO CORPORATION OF AMERICA, AND SHALL NOT BE MANUFACTURE OR SALE OF APPARATUS WITHOUT PERMISSION.

1. **Scope** - This specification applies to paper-base phenolic laminate with a copper foil facing bonded on one or both sides. This material is intended for use in the manufacture of etched copper circuits for applications subject to approval by Underwriters' Laboratories for continuous operation at 105C. It may be used where fine-line etching is a requirement.

2. **Material** -

*2.1 **Laminate** - The paper-base phenolic laminate shall conform to the requirements for Type PBE-P in Military Specification MIL-P-3115, and to the requirements of this specification. The color shall be natural.

2.2 **Copper Foil** - The copper foil shall be 99.5 percent pure and shall be uniform in quality and condition. It shall be clean, sound, smooth, and free from internal and external defects detrimental to fabrication and uniform etching.

There shall be no pin-holes larger than .015 inch average diameter nor more than one pin-hole larger than .005 inch average diameter per square foot of sheet area or fraction thereof. There shall be no more than three pin-holes less than .005 inch average diameter in any two-inch square area when the sheet is laid out in a grid pattern.

2.3 **RCA Part Numbers** - The material will be specified in accordance with the RCA part numbers listed in Table I, based on the thickness of the composite sheet.

3.1 **Composite Sheet** -

3.1.1 **Squareness** - The sheets as received from the vendor shall have the edges straight and the corners square within the limits of 90 degrees plus or minus 0.25 degree.

3.1.2 **Warp or Twist** - The warp or twist of the sheet as received from the vendor shall be measured within one hour after the shipping package is opened and shall not exceed 0.5 inch on sheets 18.25 inches square to 18.25 inches by 21.25 inches. The measurement shall be made at the highest point on the sheet when it is placed on a flat surface with the convex side up, deducting the thickness of the sheet. Permissible warp or twist for other sizes of sheets shall be negotiated with the vendor at the time of ordering.

The direction of warp, if any, on a single copper surfaced sheet shall be such that the copper surface is on the convex side of the sheet.

3.1.3 **Copper Foil Adhesion** - The minimum average value for the force required to separate the copper foil from the plastic laminate base shall be five pounds per inch of width with no individual test value less than four pounds.

The tests shall be made on one-inch wide specimens of the material approximately six inches long after a starting tab of the copper foil one or two inches long has been separated from the plastic laminate. A Hunter Spring Force indicator or other suitable equipment is attached to the starting tab and the minimum force

Radio Corporation of America

FIG. 37-5. A purchasing specification.

Written descriptions of materials are called "specifications" and must be used for many items that you can't describe any other way. Specifications describe the item in some detail and list certain requirements, such as chemical content, surface hardness, tensile strength, moisture content, or heat content. Usually the requirements are stated as test scores which will have to be met when the material is put to certain tests.

Sometimes specifications have to describe characteristics not easy to describe. A surface may be required to be "reasonably free from surface defects." A finish may be a "smooth satin finish." A specially made product may have to be "of good and workmanlike quality." These seem to be rather vague instructions, but sometimes it is hard to do any better.

Materials specifications are usually written either by the engineering or the purchasing department, or you use standards published by some recognized outside agency, such as the American Standards Association, the Society of Automotive Engineers, or the United States Bureau of Standards. Reference to standard specifications from outside sources are generally made simply by putting down the issuing agency's name and its specification number—not by quoting the whole thing.

Sometimes, in purchasing, you have the choice of using a brand-name item or of ordering practically its equivalent by specification. Which to do is a moot question. You might have this problem with wire, chemicals, cement, flour, tool steel, cutting oils, grinding wheels, cleaning compounds, and paints. You can buy all of these just by using the vendor's trade-mark, or you can forget trade-marked and catalogue items and write out your own specifications, stating what you want in the way of chemical composition, size, performance requirements, and so on.

If you buy all large quantities by specification, you'll usually save money. You get exactly what you want. Trade-marked items may not be just right for your job—maybe they are too good, or not good enough. Also, remember that trade-marked items are advertised and that people who buy those items pay for the advertising.

On the other hand, specification buying may cost more than buying trade-marked materials, particularly on small orders. If the vendor has to make a special run of materials for you, the cost of your special item may be more than trade-marked items. In general, for small quantities of anything, buy trade-marked items.

If you buy by specification, who should write out the specifications? Engineering or purchasing? Probably the engineers should, but with the help of purchasing. That will keep out costly frills. The specifications will be written so that vendors can understand them, yet you will get what you want. Incidentally, specifications should always include how the product is to be packaged as well as what it itself is to be like. Remember, too, that when you write your own specification you have to comply with all safety laws and all laws covering packaging products for shipment.

Quite often you don't have to worry about trade-marked items because you want something special anyway. If you make refrigerators and buy compressor units, yours are a little different from those of anyone else. You *must* write your own specifications.

VENDOR CHOICE

The purchasing department nearly always decides what company to buy from. Equipment buying is an exception; so are some trade-marked items that engineering or someone else insists on; so are reciprocity deals, where top management tells you the vendor to buy from.

To choose vendors intelligently you ought to know which things are sold by which companies. How do you find out? You learn from salesmen who call on you, from advertisements in technical and trade magazines, from trade directories and buyers' guides. Also, you need to keep a file catalogue of vendor companies and their price and discount lists.

Some companies keep a detailed card file of vendors. They write on each vendor's card notes about what orders were sent to him, and any price, service, delivery, and quality notes that will help them to decide whether to choose him the next time.

Just how do you decide who gets an order? Better look at it in the over-all. Price, important though it is, is only one thing to consider when picking vendors. Freight costs, for another thing, enter in; they affect delivered costs. And reliability outweighs small price differences. Can and will company deliver your order? Will it be on time? Will the materials pass inspection after they get here? If they don't, will the vendor you picked fix things up right away without argument?

How about schedule changes? If you want to put through a rush order or to cut your order, can he and will he take care of you? How about service if something goes wrong? Or maybe you need money and want credit extended. Will the vendor give you 30 or 60 days? Price is never forgotten in all of this, but these other factors influence the choice of vendors.

It is desirable to place orders for unusual or tricky products with big companies. As a rule they can handle tricky jobs, and they will make good on anything that is not right. But you can expect to pay a little extra when you give orders for unusual products to big companies. Their prices are usually a little higher than small company prices.

RECIPROCITY

Reciprocity is industry's version of "You scratch my back and I'll scratch yours." You buy from me and I'll buy from you. Back in the old days, when Henry Ford and Harvey Firestone were alive, Henry put Firestone tires on most new Fords and Harvey used Ford cars and trucks in his tire company.

Buying from each other sounds reasonable, although most people— particularly purchasing agents—condemn it. Most companies even deny that they practice it, but, on the other hand, they don't give customers a cold shoulder when they place purchase contracts. That would be a fine way to lose customers. Customers are not at all above asking, "If we buy from you, are you going to buy from us?" And, of course, you do have to buy from someone. You end up with reciprocity as a common practice.

Purchasing agents regard it as a necessary evil. But what is so bad about it? Purchasing agents don't like it because they have to buy some items where they're told and so don't get to shop around. They are afraid that they might have to take inferior materials, or pay higher prices, or get poorer services.

True, all of these things *may* occur—and some of them will occur once in a while. But purchasing agents look at only one side of the coin. Just as sure as you lose a little on buying sometimes, you gain on the selling end. Surely you get some sales where your product isn't the very best or least costly. Probably reciprocity balances out. And in time of materials shortage it even helps purchasing. Then reciprocity puts a lot of pressure on a vendor to take care of your needs.

If reciprocity hurts anyone, it is small companies. They don't buy enough to command much attention. Big companies have to buy from their *big* customers to keep them. Their big customers demand it. Small customers, demanding a share of what a big company buys, don't always get far with their threat to buy elsewhere. Actually, though, even small customers often get a share of a big company's purchases. Big companies try to satisfy *all* their customers by dividing up their ordering at least a little.

BIDDING VERSUS NEGOTIATED CONTRACTS

When the government lets contracts, it is supposed to ask for bids and to take the lowest price. Private industry has no such rules. Sometimes private companies don't even ask for bids but just dicker with their main supplier and agree on a contract, price and all.

At first that doesn't sound very smart. How can you tell that you are getting a good buy? Usually you know because either you make some of the same things yourself and know your own costs, or you do ask occasionally for bids from other companies, or you have your engineers go over the vendor's expected cost figures to be sure that he is pretty efficient and that his price is reasonable. In the end, some of the biggest buying contracts are negotiated and not bid.

On the other hand, most middle-sized orders and most large one-shot contracts are bid for. And if you don't give the contract to the lowest bidder, at least the one who gets it has to be near low. You always choose the lowest one from among those who you think can serve you well.

But the thousands of little things that you buy are neither negotiated nor bid. They are just ordered from the catalogue at list price less the usual discount. About all that you do is to look in two or three vendors' catalogues and order from the one quoting the lowest price. The money involved doesn't justify much effort in trying to save a few pennies.

PURCHASE CONTRACTS

Purchase orders, after acceptance by the vendor, become legal contracts that bind both parties. If either one doesn't live up to the contract, the other can sue. Almost never is there any trouble, though, because both parties do what they agree to. And if one side violates a small part of the contract (as when delivery of the materials is a few days late), the matter is rarely of such importance as to make any difference. Or if a small part of the shipment is rejected, the customer accepts the balance and pays accordingly. Or if it is all rejected, either the vendor replaces it or the contract is dropped and the order is placed elsewhere. Even if a customer cancels an order or wants to return materials, the vendor is usually willing to do what the customer wants just to keep him satisfied.

It is easy for each side to be agreeable in case of most minor contract violations, because no one is going to lose much. Often, though, the contracting parties aren't quite so agreeable if someone has to take a big loss. That might happen, for example, if a company orders a large quantity of special materials and then finds before it gets delivery that its business had fallen off so that it doesn't want the material. It may try to cancel the order, which by that time is almost ready in the vendor's plant. If the material is special, the vendor may not be able to sell it anywhere else except at a big loss. Some buying companies aren't above trying to get out of their obligation, not by canceling the order but by rejecting it when it arrives, saying that it is of poor quality when it really isn't.

Vendors, too, violate contracts sometimes. They ship (knowingly or unknowingly) substandard material or (and this is a common failure) they don't deliver your order when they promised to. Broken delivery dates always cause inconvenience and sometimes cause loss to the buyer.

If the prospective loss is great, the two parties sometimes submit their differences to arbitration or even to court. The aggrieved party sues the other for the damages he claims he has suffered. In court the *contract as written* is the basis for the decision as to whether an actual breach of contract has occurred. Whichever party is judged to have breached the contract will be liable for damages.

Standard printed contracts are used as the order form when the amount of money is small, but on large orders special contracts are written up almost every time. Once in a while, though, you don't even have a written contract with an often-used supplier. Mostly you do, however. Such things as the possible return of goods, contract cancellation, price adjustments, and provision for the arbitration of disputes between buyer and seller are all written into the contract. If there is any doubt about contract wording or interpretation, the purchasing department should consult with the legal department before contracts are signed.

DISCOUNTS

In the United States we are used to a one-price system. The seller sets a price, and we either pay it or don't buy. Discount houses flourish, though, in all of our big cities, proving that we do haggle about prices sometimes—and most of us shop around to get the best deal when it comes to buying a new car.

Company purchasing agents almost never buy at retail prices. As we have seen, they ask for bids or negotiate prices on all big and even all middle-sized contracts, and in all small contracts for special items. On smaller orders for catalogue items they expect, and get, discounts from list prices. Sometimes they get two or three discounts (like 20 per cent off, then 10 per cent off the balance, and maybe another 5 per cent off that) on the same order. Catalogue items have "list" prices. That is supposed to be a retail price, and it is the one a manufacturer almost never pays.

Regular discounts are of three kinds: trade, quantity, and cash. Trade discounts are supposed to be a certain per cent for retailers and a bigger per cent for wholesalers, jobbers, or other manufacturers. Manufacturers of items sold finally at retail sometimes get only as little as one third of the retail list price. Trade discounts are supposed (even required by the Robinson-Patman Act, a federal law) to be the same for all buyers in the same class (as, for example, wholesalers). The law is not too effective in the case of manufacturers buying from other manufacturers, because they ask for slightly different items—items not sold to others at all. So there can be no direct comparison between what they pay and what someone else pays.

Quantity discounts are generally offered to customers who buy big quantities. They are usually quite small compared with trade discounts. Quantity discounts are in addition to trade discounts and are supposed to be available equally to all customers. Large buyers have, in past years, often coaxed still bigger discounts (for themselves only) out of vendors by threatening them with buying elsewhere. Under present laws vendors are allowed to pass on, in the form of lower prices, the savings in cost that large orders make possible, but *no more* than that. The difficulty of figuring the exact savings keeps this law from being much good.

Cash discounts are often offered as inducements to pay up fast. Most bills are due in 30 days, but vendors don't want to wait that long for their money. Cash discounts of 2 per cent off if the bill is paid in 10 days (instead of 30) brings in most of the money sooner. Besides, it also cuts bad debt losses. Two per cent off for paying sooner is a fine windfall for the customer. If you work it out, you'll find that it is equivalent to 36 per cent a year. Most customers will pay up fast even if they have to borrow money from the bank to do so. You might wonder why the vendor wouldn't rather have 100 cents in 30 days than 98 cents in 10 days. Probably he would rather wait and get more, but he has to meet industry customs.

Competition has brought other kinds of concessions that amount to discounts. "Freight equalization" is common when competing vendors are not located the same distance away from the customer. A far-away vendor offers to pay the difference between the freight cost from his plant to the customer's plant and the freight cost from a competitor nearer to the company's plant. Other practices amounting, in effect, to discount include postdating the bill, thus extending credit for longer times, offering to pay part of the customer's advertising costs on the assumption that he will advertise the vendor's product, and offering free engineering or other help.

PURCHASING PROBLEMS

How Much Price Pressure?   Although the same prices are supposed to be quoted to all customers in each class (manufacturers, jobber, wholesaler, retailer), it doesn't always work that way. A very big customer in any class can chisel down the price he pays until it is not far above an item's cost to manufacture. All he has to do is to threaten to place his order somewhere else. Sometimes the threat isn't to go elsewhere. The customer says that he is thinking of making his own items and not buying them at all. Little customers can play at that game, too, although not quite so effectively.

Here is what one mail-order house used to do. If you ran a textile mill, it would offer to buy enough material from you to keep your mill operating through a normal seasonal closed-down period. The price it would offer was, however, only a little more than the cost of materials and labor. If you accepted the order, you got back only a small part of your overhead costs for the closed-down period. If you accepted, you would, therefore, be selling your product considerably below its total costs.

But look at your dilemma! If you refused the offer, you got back *none* of your overhead expenses for the closed-down period. You would be better off, in the short run, to accept the offer rather than to close down. But, in the long run, your low-priced items offered for sale by the chain store cut the throats of your regular customers. And you can't get out of this trouble just by holding your head high and turning down the order. There are too many textile mills. If you turn it down, someone else will take the order.

Years ago one automobile company would contract to buy the whole output of an accessory manufacturer. Then, after the supplier had lost his sales organization and dealers, the next contract prices were dictated on a take-it or leave-it basis.

Faultfinding Customers.   Distant customers can sometimes take advantage of vendors in ways which nearby customers cannot. A customer buying a carload of lumber or sheet steel, for example, may have his receiving inspector be overmeticulous and reject the shipment, when in fact the materials are satisfactory and should be accepted. The customer then offers to buy the rejected material at a lower price. If he is located far from the vendor plant and some distance from other markets, the vendor company will probably feel it has to agree to the lower price, particularly if it is special material that can't be sold elsewhere.

One auto company has had the reputation of being overfussy on receiving inspection. One supplier once was rather surprised to get a contract that others had had before. Upon inquiry among the former suppliers, the new one learned that it could expect 20 per cent rejections no matter how good its quality. And, at the price quoted, this would lose money.

Sure enough 20 per cent of its first month's products came back as rejects. The company just repacked them and sent them back as part of the next month's shipment. Again 20 per cent were returned. The vendor repacked and reshipped them along with the rest of the next month's shipment. This went on for the whole year until the model changed. The company ended up with only 20 per cent of its *last shipment* rejected, but that averaged out to less than 2 per cent of the year's production—a figure at which the supplier made money. Purchasing departments ought to know that their company's practices get aired around.

Unearned Discounts.   Some customers abuse the cash-discount privilege. They send in a check 15 or 20 days after they get material, yet they deduct the 10-day discount. Most vendors put up with this, but it is an abuse.

Costly Estimates.   Some companies, in the market for complex machinery made especially for them, ask several companies to prepare extensive drawings and nearly complete designs, all of which cost a lot of money to make up. Yet only one vendor can get the order. Vendors, having had this experience once or twice, soon learn to protect themselves by asking for an engineering fee.

Gifts.   Should an appreciative vendor show his appreciation for getting a contract? That is, should he show it by giving the man who sent him the order (your buyer) a gift? It is so easy to answer "no" that we seem to dispose of the problem. Any other answer opens the door to kickbacks, rebates, and outright bribery—to the detriment of the buying company—because bribed buyers will place orders where *they* get the most out of it, not where the company benefits the most.

But the problem won't down so easily. Vendors are appreciative, and most of us like to be appreciated. We corrupt easily on the receiving end of gifts. Spending money just seems to breed graft. Most companies have hard and fast rules against their buyers accepting gifts, but most of them wink at, say, free meals, a box of cigars, a cigarette lighter, or a few bottles of liquor at Christmas time. But a TV set or an automobile—no. Lavish entertainment during big city visits is also out.

Actually, industry seems to have controlled the problem of gifts and bribery very well indeed, but it should be said that sometimes the buyer is anxious to be so influenced and may perhaps have suggested the plan himself.

Most of the purchasing problems discussed above are matters of ethics, although some border on being illegal also. You might ask: Why should we do business with companies that do such things? Why not refuse orders from customers who try to drive a sharp bargain? The answer would be easy if you could get all the business you need from other customers. When business is very good, maybe you can afford to turn up your nose at customers who try to take advantage of you, but when business is bad you are glad to do business even with a hard bargainer. Competition is keen, and many companies, on the buying side, would discharge a purchasing agent who was not a hard bargainer.

BUYING MACHINES

The purchasing department usually places all orders for new equipment, but it doesn't have much to say about what is bought. Engineering and manufacturing recommend these purchases. They have to prepare reports proving that the new machines will pay off and to get top administration approval (see pages 149–51) before purchasing gets an order to go ahead.

Purchasing is, of course, in on some of the early planning and has, along with engineering, talked the whole thing over with the equipment company. Purchasing's part in all of this is to protect the company and to watch for jokers that will cost money that you don't think about.

Purchasing should ask: Will the vendor guarantee output? Will he supervise the installation of the equipment at no extra cost? Will he train your operators to use the equipment? Do you have to have any extras not included in the price quoted for the equipment? How expensive are repair parts? What kind of service will you get on repair parts? For how long will the vendor guarantee to carry repair parts? Is there a guarantee that you, the purchaser, will be protected against possible claims that the machine infringes on a patent? Is there a guarantee that it meets the safety regulations of the state in which it is to be used? The purchasing department should also be sure that the maintenance department is consulted to find out how similar equipment has held up in the past.

Besides raising these questions, which should help prevent unwise purchases, the purchasing department is directly concerned if there is a possibility of trading in an old machine on a new one. Sometimes the purchasing department may be able to get a better price for an old machine by selling it to a used machinery dealer or to another company than by turning it in on a new machine. Occasionally, for example, very good prices can be obtained for old machines in foreign markets.

How far should the purchasing department go in trying to influence other departments in choosing the kind of machines? The engineer or the manufacturing department head is often strongly prejudiced in favor of certain equipment, *which sometimes is not the best buy*. The purchasing department should try to find out what make of machine really is the best for the purpose and try to see that the others at least consider it, although engineering and manufacturing departments should have the final say.

THE SALVAGE DEPARTMENT

In many companies the purchasing department runs the salvage department and sells salvaged material which cannot be used in any way in production. Often this responsibility extends to collecting scrap materials and to sorting, cutting, and baling them for sale as scrap. Discarded

Dun's Review & Modern Industry

FIG. 37–6. It doesn't look like it here but the salvage department can usually recover a good bit of money from your junk.

and replaced machinery, if it is to be sold, generally is gotten rid of by the purchasing department.

But why purchasing? Why not sales? It goes to purchasing because the materials you are getting rid of are similar to the things purchasing buys. It knows market conditions, prices, and the companies dealing in such products. This gain outweighs the slight disadvantage in assigning such different work to purchasing.

MISCELLANEOUS FUNCTIONS OF THE PURCHASING DEPARTMENT

In trying to get others in the organization to use less costly materials, purchasing may get permission to try out new materials. That means sample runs in the factory and performance tests to see how the new materials work. Purchasing should follow all such trials, reporting on their success or failure.

Another duty of purchasing is to handle all matters relating to re- jected purchased materials—whether they are rejected right away in re- ceiving or later in processing. All correspondence having to do with disposing, reworking, or returning of anything is handled by the pur- chasing department.

In most companies the traffic department is either an independent de- partment directing both incoming and outgoing traffic matters or is under the direction of the sales department. Occasionally, however, it is a part of the purchasing department. Why there? Because for everything you buy you pay inbound freight charges. It doesn't matter whether you pay a low price for the materials and then pay the freight extra, or whether the vendor ups his price enough for him to pay the freight bill. Never fear, you, the customer, pay the bill. But if you have a good traffic man, he will save the company a lot of money by picking the lowest-cost way to ship things.

The purchasing department also sees that all returnable containers, such as wire cable reels, oil drums, etc., and returnable pallets are shipped back to the vendor.

Years ago many industrial purchasing departments bought products for company employees. The items purchased were ordered by the com- pany's purchasing department so that it got the company's usual dis- count. The products bought were passed on to the employees at cost. Officially not much of this goes on today, but the problem won't stay down. A 1955 study by *Purchasing* magazine found one third of the companies buying for employees as a regular thing, and more doing it sometimes. Probably most of it is done only for officials.

Most companies require the purchasing department to make various statistical reports periodically. The idea is to get some notion of how efficiently the department is running. Such reports analyze the dollar value of purchases by divisions or locations, summarize cash and other discounts, summarize waste, scrap, and salvage operations, show relation- ships of purchases to sales, report on the number of purchase orders handled and the size of the purchasing department. From the compari- sons, management gets an idea of whether purchasing is being efficiently done.

STUDY QUESTIONS

1. Suppose that you regard purchasing as "outside manufacture." In what way will that viewpoint affect you, the purchasing agent?
2. Contrast the purchasing procedures used for buying big steady-use items with the procedure for buying middle-sized orders.
3. Discuss centralized purchasing. When and what would you centralize? What is good and bad about it?

4. Who, in the company, should carry on "value analysis"? What is value analysis? When would you use it? When not?

5. Discuss the problems of purchase "lead time." What do you do about it?

6. How important is forecasting in purchasing? What things would you forecast? Why is it important to forecast them?

7. What do tight supply conditions do to your purchasing practices? Explain.

8. Do you recommend buying by specification or brand name? When and why?

9. Why all the emphasis on vendor reliability? Discuss.

10. If you were a purchasing agent would you engage in reciprocity? Explain and justify your answer.

11. "The exact wording of purchase contracts is relatively unimportant." Is it? Discuss.

12. Write out a policy instructing your purchasing agent about how much price pressure he should put on vendors.

13. What part does purchasing play in equipment purchasing? What part should purchasing play? Discuss.

CASE 37–1. THE BIGELOW SPRING COMPANY

The Bigelow Spring Company, manufacturer of bed springs, is considering buying band iron in carload lots. Assume that its requirements of 1 inch, No. 12 gage (gage refers to thickness) mild band steel, 16-foot lengths, will be 6,000 pounds per month.

This material may be bought F.O.B. Pittsburgh in carload lots for $12.00 per 100 pounds, freight $1.71 per 100 pounds. In less than carload (L.C.L.) shipments, an extra charge of $0.067 per 100 pounds is added by the manufacturer, and the freight is $2.16. A minimum carload is 36,-000 pounds. Mill orders must be placed 90 days before delivery; and to equalize irregularities in shipment, a resesrve stock of 45 days' supply is carried. Unloading from car to factory adds $0.09 per 100 pounds to the price.

If obtained from a nearby jobber, the warehouse price F.O.B. the Bigelow factory is $16.10, and a 2-ton order can be filled on a day's notice, practically no reserve stock being necessary.

The market may be assumed to be steady. The firm is able to earn 12 per cent on all the capital it has or can borrow. Prepare a schedule or stock limit plan for this item of material and find the comparative costs of the item per month under each of the three plans (mill carload, mill L.C.L., warehouse) of supply.

What conditions in addition to those here named might influence your choice between mill and warehouse buying? Which plan would you favor, and why? NOTE: In estimating the cost of purchasing by the carload or the L.C.L. method a charge for the inventory tied up must be included.

CASE 37–2. THE DETROIT MILLING MACHINE COMPANY

The Detroit Milling Machine Company produces, in its own foundry, all of the iron castings used in the company's products. Several grades of gray cast iron are used, ranging from regular gray cast iron to semisteel. Three types of pig iron, silvery, low silicon and high silicon, are used in making the different kinds of castings.

The foundry office orders its own pig iron. Orders are sent out once a month and 5 months in advance of the need for the iron. The company's usage of the three types of pig iron in the recent past is as follows:

MONTH	POUNDS					
	Low Silicon		High Silicon		Silvery	
	Last Year	This Year	Last Year	This Year	Last Year	This Year
Jan.........	37,000	47,000	400	200	21,000	8,000
Feb.........	36,000	17,000	1,000	3,000	7,000	16,000
Mar........	17,000	27,000	2,000	2,000	400	33,000
Apr........	19,000	27,000	0	1,000	6,000	41,000
May.......	7,000	....	0	....	7,000	....
June........	15,000	....	1,000	....	600	....
July........	10,000	....	0	....	8,000	....
Aug........	700	....	0	....	32,000	....
Sept........	33,000	....	2,000	....	8,000	....
Oct........	32,000	....	3,000	....	25,000	....
Nov.........	36,000	....	1,000	....	3,000	....
Dec........	41,000	....	700	....	7,000	....

The present stock and quantities on order are as follows:

	Low Silicon	High Silicon	Silvery	
Pig iron on hand..................	46,000	10,000		9,000
On order: Due			Due	
6/1.....................	100,000	0	4/1	40,000
9/1.....................	100,000		8/1	120,000
			9/1	80,000
Other information needed:				
Most economical purchase quantity.	100,000	6,000		40,000
Excess of iron on hand and on order over known future requirements..	....	9,000		....
Excess of known requirements over iron on hand and on order.......	30,000	....		80,000

Analyze and evaluate the company's pig iron purchasing practices. Recommend policies for the future, and show what orders you would place on May 1 and the delivery dates you would specify.

Chapter 38

INVENTORY CONTROL

Dᴜʀɪɴɢ 1956 General Electric sold $4.1 billion's worth of products. At the end of the year it owned $770 million's worth of inventories—stocks of materials and products. General Foods sold $1.0 billion's worth of products and ended the year owning $140 million's worth of inventories. RCA sold $1.1 billion's worth and finished the year owning inventory of $150 million. In these three companies (and they are typical) inventories tie up more than one fourth of all the money invested in the company.

Some inventories are in the form of *raw materials* and *purchased items* to be used in making products. Some inventories are *supplies* to be used up. Some are *half-manufactured* items in factory departments. Some are finished *parts* ready to be put into assembled products. Some are *finished products* in shipping rooms and warehouses.

Inventory is *money* temporarily in the form of a bar of brass, a sheet of steel, an iron casting, a bag of chemicals, a bolt of cloth, a spare grinding wheel. But it isn't at all like money in the bank. It is money on which you *pay* interest instead of earn interest. After a year, $100 in the bank may be worth $103. After a year on the shelf, $100 worth of inventory is worth nearer to $90 *and* it has cost you $10 *expenses* to carry it.

Inventory "control" keeps track of all of these things. But there is more to it than record keeping. Inventory control tries (1) never to run out of anything, while (2) never having much of anything on hand, and (3) never paying high prices because of buying in small quantities.

It isn't easy to make and sell big volumes of products while owning almost nothing "in-transit" and at the same time never run out of anything nor pay high prices from hand-to-mouth buying or making. Yet look at the money involved. If GE through poor control let its inventories go up 10 per cent, it would have to put $77 million more into the inventories it owns. But if good control were able to cut 10 per cent off its present investment, it would have $77 million extra money. Besides that, GE would save some more millions from not having to store all of the extra inventory.

Ten per cent means $14 million to General Foods and $15 million to RCA. Ten per cent of its inventory investment would mean a whopping $172 million to General Motors. All companies have to try their best to carry nothing on hand, never run out, yet never pay high prices.

An uncontrolled inventory is usually too much inventory. It is particularly bad because it is painless—even pleasant. No harm is done if new supplies don't come in on time. Production never runs out of anything.

Double Seal Piston Ring Co.

FIG. 38–1.   A scrap pile of over 100,000 obsolete diesel engine piston rings. These rings, mostly small over-runs on special orders over a ten-year period, show the losses that can come from overstocking and obsolescence.

Nor does a customer ever have to wait for a finished product. Everyone is happy, but the money tied up in inventory is enormous, as are all the costs that big inventories entail.

It wouldn't be quite so bad if you got to use up all the things you carry. But uncontrolled inventories always seem to contain 100 years' supply of some things and to have too many buggy whip items that you finally have to throw away. Their investment goes down the drain.

Now we need to back up a little. Inventory control that looks only at holding down the inventory is poor control. You run a *whole* company and must look at the whole picture. Suppose, for example, that you make products for the Christmas trade or for the building trades (with their spring-of-the-year sales peaks). Are you to jump production up and down with every up and down in sales? No, doing that would multiply production costs.

The point is that we sometimes intentionally build up inventories (of finished products) during periods of low sales. Inventory control is more a matter of planning and holding inventories at planned levels than it is of keeping them down. *Good* inventory control is control that fits the whole picture. It even means big inventories sometimes.

HOW MUCH CONTROL?

Big companies may have to keep track of 50,000 different kinds of stocked items. You don't control such inventories with one or two clerks. Probably, for a big company, controlling inventories takes 50 or 100 clerks, whose salaries run into hundreds of thousands of dollars.

Isn't there any way to avoid spending all of that money? Some of it, yes. Some factory items are like paper clips and rubber bands for the office. They aren't worth keeping records for. You're better off not keeping records. Just keep a supply of such items on hand and let people help themselves. When the supply gets low, order more. One purpose of inventory control is to control *with the least paper work cost.*

But you know that uncontrolled materials will be used wastefully. No matter for little things; it is cheaper to stand the loss than to keep the records. On the other hand, you can't just carry plenty of *everything* and let people help themselves to everything.

How do you decide which items to control tightly and which loosely? Start by looking over your stock records, item by item. Classify items into "A," "B," and "C." "A" items are the big investment items. General Electric, in one division, found that 8 per cent of the items tied up 75 per cent of the money. "A" items get the full record-keeping treatment. They are important. You forecast their use, plan purchases or manufacture carefully, and watch their use and replacement orders closely.

"B" items are less important but are worth keeping card records of their use. You are less fussy here about when and how many to reorder. But you still keep most of the records.

"C" items are the wasters. GE found that 67 per cent of the items it carried totaled only 5 per cent of the investment. For such items, you'd be better off to cut out all the record keeping possible. It's better to be overstocked than to waste valuable man-hours figuring out exactly how many you'll need and when. It's better just to carry plenty of these items and let men help themselves as they need them than it is to write out requisitions authorizing their use. Don't keep card records of what comes in, what is used, and what is left over for "C" items. Just watch your stock room bins. When the supply gets down, order more.

Loose controls on "C" items will boost your investment and your "shelf-wear" and even obsolescence costs some; but not nearly so much as to offset the savings in record-keeping costs. You'll end up ahead with loose controls on "C" items.

SALES FORECASTING IN INVENTORY CONTROL

As far as finished products inventory control is concerned, manufacturing to sales orders cuts out the need for forecasting because you don't have any finished products inventory. You ship products as soon as they are finished. But you still need to forecast because you have to have supplies of raw materials and bought parts. Many purchased items have to be ordered before you know exactly what products you will make, so you have to forecast the future level of sales.

Selling out of stock is, however, another matter. Here you *must* forecast, product by product, and month by month, the sales of every important product and of groups and classes of minor products. You must forecast in order to tell the factory what to make. The problem is to foresee what customers will buy, and they are a pretty unpredictable lot.

You might ask, why should you ever make products to stock? Why not let the customer put in his order and let him wait? That would be fine if he'd wait, but mostly he will go somewhere else and get what he wants. So, makers of nuts and bolts, electric light bulbs, cans of soup, and thousands of other things make to stock and fill orders out of stock.

They try, however, to carry very small quantities of each item in stock and to have new supplies coming in at about the same rate as sales is withdrawing finished products. That is where the forecasting comes in.

But forecasting alone isn't enough. Suppose that your forecast shows that product A's sales for the next 3 months will be 15,000, 25,000, and 10,000? You can't jump production up and down like that and keep costs within reason. At 25,000, maybe you'd be on a 10-hour, 6-day week. But at 10,000 you'd be on short hours, have some men laid off, and your plant half idle. You just *must* try to operate more steadily than that. But if you do operate more steadily you'll produce too much sometime and too little at other times. This means that besides forecasting sales peaks and valleys you have to plan to build up inventories during slow periods and then use them up in peak periods.

Making a sales forecast is quite a job, and it is never perfectly done. Some companies use a "top-down" method. They start with a general forecast of business conditions and then refine it into forecasts of sales of items. Some companies do the reverse and use a "bottom-up" method. They start with forecasts of sales of each product and build up to a total forecast.

"Top-down" Forecasting.   Here's how the "top-down" method works. Start with forecasts of general business conditions (you can get lots of them from the experts, some of whom were listed on page 713). Suppose that the experts say that next year's national income will be $500 billion, and suppose that you make kitchen appliances, stoves, refrigerators, disposals, dishwashers, and the like. Ask yourself how the new building industry will be affected by this $500 billion figure. Also, how many new houses will have these electrical appliances? And, how many will the industry sell to people living in old houses?

Then refine another degree: How much of the probable total market will your company get? How much for each appliance? Then, finally, how many of each appliance month by month. This is the top-down method.

"Bottom-up" Forecasting. The "bottom-up" method starts with product sale records. How many of each product does it look like you'll sell next year? Also, get estimates from salesmen and dealers. Finally, add them up and get a total which is your forecast.

Actually most companies use both the top-down and the bottom-up methods and then put them together and arrive at the best guess at what sales will be. Maybe you shouldn't dignify the answer as a forecast— there is so much guesswork in it. But whatever you call it, and in spite of its not being too good, you have to forecast the best you can so that you can make up production schedules.

THE FACTORY'S EFFECT ON ORDERING QUANTITIES

Stock piling during slack periods ahead of sales peaks is something that everyone says is good. It helps level production and lets you operate efficiently. When you reorder items that you really don't want right now, you are letting the factory's need for work set the ordering quantity, rather than letting today's sales needs rule.

Trouble is that seasonal sales patterns get all mixed up with general business conditions and with how much business you get and how much your competitors get and so on. Almost always when you go ahead and make products that aren't selling right now, you are running scared. You do it with mixed feelings—glad to keep the factory going and glad to have a supply on hand to take care of tomorrow's hoped-for sales pickup. But you don't like the costs of carrying stock, and you can't be sure when the sales pickup will come, or how big it will be, or for what products. You don't like to look at a big pile of unsold products.

At the top of sales peaks the factory again has much to do with re-order quantities. This time because it sets limits. You set reorder quantities at numbers you can get from the factory, not at numbers sales really wants.

INVENTORY FORECASTING

How do inventories fit into all of this? They cushion the difference between irregular sales and steady production. Here's one company's procedure, and it is typical: We'll call it the Jones Company. The Jones Company makes toys—mostly of the music box type but with rubber belts with bumps molded on to play the tunes. The music boxes are put into all kinds of toys and play tunes when a handle is cranked. It is a highly seasonal business, with Christmas being the big selling peak. For Jones this means a May and June production peak. Retail stores do most of their Christmas buying way ahead.

Jones' problem is how not to lose sales at its peak period yet to level out production as much as it can without carrying terrific inventories.

Also it doesn't want to get caught with Davy Crockett guitars after Davy's year. (Most toys have only a 1-year sale, then they are as dead as a dodo.)

Jones first makes a sales forecast for an item month by month for 12 months. For an example, we will take a toy banjo, Model "A," with a

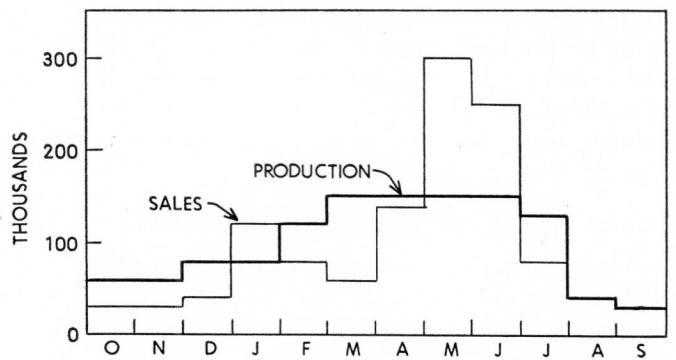

FIG. 38–2.   Forecasted sales and planned production of Model "A" toy banjos.

cranked music box inside. Table 38–1 and Figure 38–2 show its expected sales and cumulative sales for a year beginning with October and going through September of the next year. The 12 months' total comes out to 1,200,000 toy banjos, but the sales *peak* month has ten times the volume of the poorest months. The thin line in Figure 38–2 is the expected sales line.

Now look at the production schedule (it is the heavy line on Fig.

TABLE 38–1

EXPECTED SALES OF MODEL "A" TOY BANJO
(Thousands)

Month	Sales	Accumulated Sales	Production	Accumulated Production	Inventory at End of Month
Oct.............	30	30	60	60	30
Nov.............	30	60	60	120	60
Dec.............	40	100	80	200	100
Jan.............	120	220	80	280	60
Feb.............	80	300	120	400	100
Mar.............	60	360	150	550	190
Apr.............	140	500	150	700	200
May.............	300	800	150	850	50
June.............	250	1,050	150	1,000	− 50
July.............	80	1,130	130	1,130	0
Aug.............	40	1,170	40	1,170	0
Sept.............	30	1,200	30	1,200	0

38–2). It is much flatter than the sales line. The top production of 150,-000 banjos is only half of the sales peak. This is a big improvement from the factory's point of view. *But* it can be done only by building up inventories.

Look at Figure 38–3 showing Jones' forecasted inventory of the toy banjo. It shows that the inventory will reach a peak of 200,000 banjos on May 1. Also the average inventory for the whole year is only about 65,-000, or less than 3 weeks of average sales.

Figure 38–3 shows a negative inventory on July 1. How can that be? It just means that for a week or so at the end of June, Jones can't fill all the expected orders right on time. They hope that they won't lose

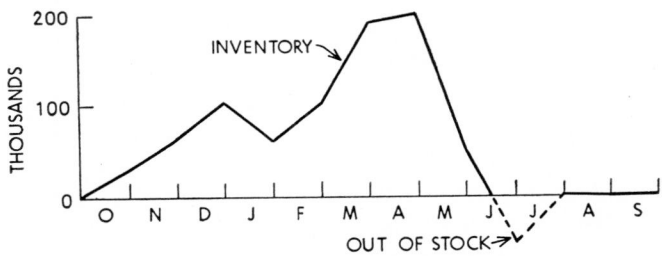

FIG. 38–3.   Planned inventory of Model "A" toy banjos.

any sales if they get those orders filled early in July. Early July orders they'll push back to the last half of the month. By then they'll be caught up.

Our example uses only one item—Model "A" banjos. Jones has to do the same thing for *all its main* items, one by one. For lesser items, Jones will probably forecast for groups at a time—perhaps using only sales dollar figures. After making forecasts, production schedules and inventory projections for the items separately Jones will combine them into over-all figures—probably just in dollars since they can't add Wyatt Earp pistols to Model "A" banjos.

In this chapter we are not concerned with the factory's schedule so much as we are with the planned inventory fluctuations. If you plan poorly, you have too much or too little inventory. Being off either way costs you money; carrying costs if you have too much, lost sales if you have too little.

EVALUATING SALES

As the year goes along you find out what your actual sales are. Almost never do they hit the forecast. Does it matter? Yes—it changes your inventories and maybe you ought to change your production rate. Let's go back to the Model A banjos. It is February 1, and here is the record:

(All Figures Are Thousands)

	SALES		INVENTORY (END OF MONTH)	
	Forecast	Actual	Forecast	Actual
Oct...............	30	10	30	50
Nov...............	30	25	60	85
Dec...............	40	55	100	110
Jan...............	120	160	60	30
Total.........	220	250		

You have the problem of figuring out what to do next. How do you interpret the January sales running way over the forecast? Did customers just buy earlier than usual this year? If that is it, you don't want to change production schedules. Or have you underguessed the market? If so, you ought to revise your production schedules upward right away. Already your inventory is down 30,000 below the plan. You'll be way behind if the top sales months, too, run ahead of the original forecast.

What to do is both a factory scheduling problem and an inventory problem. Up to now you let the first production schedule stand and let the inventory be different from the plan. Now, though, with sales catching fire and your best months still coming, maybe you should up production to your limit (150,000) right now. Otherwise you'll soon be out of stock.

We won't decide the answer here, but this is one of the problems of controlling inventories. To appreciate the problem, however, remember that you have this problem with *all of your hundreds or thousands of finished product items*. Also its effects reach clear back to raw materials stores. If you raise or lower production schedules, you upset all the raw materials inventory plans and even purchase order delivery schedules and vendor plant production schedules.

"COVERAGE" VERSUS ON-HAND

Your first protection against running out of anything is the supply on hand. But your real stock "available" is what you have on hand plus what is on order. If you have placed orders for replenishment stocks when you should have placed them, new supplies will arrive before the on-hand stock runs out. At any time, therefore, your future needs are "covered" up to the limit of the quantities on-hand plus on-order. This way you get the protection of a big inventory but without its investment.

On long lead time items you will sometimes have two or three orders out at the same time. Suppose, for example, that it takes 90 days to get an item, but you don't want to carry much on hand. All you do is to place small orders way ahead. If today is March 1, you might find this: on-hand equals 1½ month's supply; on-order, one order for a month's supply. You placed this order January 1 and expect it in about April 1. On-order also, a second order (placed February 1) for a month's supply expected about May 1. And it is time today to place a third order for a month's supply that you will hope to get on June 1. Doing it this way takes care of your needs without your carrying much stock even on long lead time items.

Don't forget though that long lead times are uncertain lead times. Sometimes it takes a long time to get things because it takes the vendor a long time to make them. In other cases you have to wait only because the vendor is busy. In either case you can't count on delivery in 90 days. The material might come in 80 days, but it might be 120.

Your own usage is also hard to predict so far ahead. What you think (on March 1) is a month's supply (for the month of May) may be used up in 2 or 3 weeks. You ought not skate on such thin ice as in our example. It would be better to boost your planned safety stock a little higher than if you were dealing with short lead time items.

IN-PROCESS INVENTORIES

Materials on-the-go make up most (in Westinghouse Electric they are 80 per cent) of all inventories in companies that have manufacturing cycles of weeks or months. Controlling inventory in process is a matter of moving products through production as fast as you can. It is a scheduling problem and is production control's responsibility. But even companies which count their manufacturing cycle in days instead of weeks have substantial amounts of money tied up in inventory in process. They, too, need to keep production moving.

RAW MATERIALS

Heavily used raw materials are usually bought on blanket contracts with deliveries scheduled to match the factory's need. Almost no reserve supply is carried—incoming shipments are scheduled to arrive daily or even at specific times during the day. You can do this if the items are made locally. But for shipped-in items you have to allow more leeway. Rarely is it safe to carry less than two or three days' supply. Release orders to suppliers telling them exactly how much and when to ship are given to the vendors by production control. In effect, production control controls such small inventories as you carry of heavily used raw materials.

Less heavily used raw materials are controlled by dollar limits, time limits, or other methods discussed in the following pages.

One minor problem in raw materials control is shrinkage—not the petty thieving kind (that too is a minor annoyance). Shrinkage comes from buying in one unit and issuing in another. For example, you buy sheet steel by the ton and issue it by the sheet. If the sheets are a little thicker than usual, you don't have as many sheets in a ton as you figured.

Also, some things are measured out as they are issued—wire (bought by the pound, issued by length), liquids, pipe, lumber, and so on. Issuers nearly always give liberal measure, so you end up short. Or, as in sheet metal, pipe, lumber, or glass, the lengths or sizes bought are standard, but there is some wastage in cutting to size. Experience will tell you what shrinkage to expect, but be sure to expect it.

SUPPLIES

Supplies are materials used up in running the plant or in making the company's products but which do not themselves go into the product. Normally their cost, over a year, is low compared to that of materials going into products, but it is still much too high to neglect. Supplies need control. Unfortunately, in many companies, particularly small ones, supplies are handled carelessly and wastefully. They are handed out without requisitions, and no check is made on their use. Since supplies are all expendable, except perhaps for complicated tooling, jigs, and fixtures for machines, it is difficult to check on their proper issuance and use.

You might wonder if the saving from controlling supplies' use would justify the paper work. On some items (like "C" items) it won't pay, but some supply items run into money. If they are not controlled, they will be wastefully used. Besides, every department head will build up his own little personal inventory of every supply item. Put them all together and you are very likely to find ten times as much lying around as you ought to carry. Normally you never know about these little private hoards because the materials are all charged out as if they had been used. You'll have to hunt out these little private caches.

To control supplies, you need several separate supplies' stock rooms: one for maintenance department supplies and materials, another for tools and tooling, another for cutting oils and lubricants, another for stationery supplies, and so on. Materials (except for very little things) should be issued from them only upon presentation of written requisitions, properly authorized and showing the account to be charged. Budgets can be established limiting departments in their use of supplies in order to discourage numerous little private inventories besides that of the stock rooms.

REORDERING POINTS

When and *how many* to reorder of regularly stocked items is the perennial inventory control question. Reordering points are the "when." It is easy to lay down a rule but hard to apply it. The rule: reorder far enough ahead so that the new supply comes in just as the last of the old stock is used.

Trouble is, you never know exactly how long it will take to get a new supply. And it doesn't matter whether you are talking about raw materials, bought finished parts, or finished products that you make. Also, you don't know exactly how fast you'll use up the stock you already have.

You can look to the past, and you do. If, on a particular item, you've used 50 per month lately, that will be your guess for the near future unless you have a pretty good idea that it will be different. Same with how long it takes to get more. How long did it take in the past? Usually 6 weeks? Then that is your lead time.

The *reorder point is a quantity*, and if you use reorder points, each item has its own quantity. It is the number of units that you'll use in

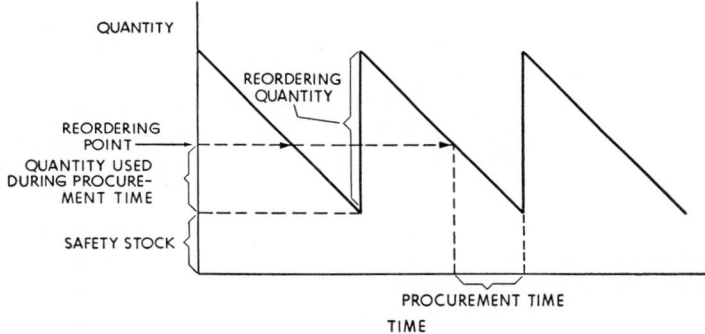

FIG. 38–4. When the use of any item is regular, it is possible to set a "reordering" point which the stock clerk must observe in originating reorders.

the replenishment lead time. In our example it could be 75—the number you normally use up in 6 weeks. But no, that is skating on too thin ice. Sometimes you use more than 50 a month. Sometimes it takes more than 6 weeks to get more. Either way you'd be out of stock too often. You had better boost the reorder point by, say, 25 to add a little safety. This puts it, the reorder point, up to 100 in the example. We call the extra amount added (the 25) a "reserve" or "safety factor," but it isn't exactly a reserve. It isn't held back or set aside. Normally, it is the amount that you still have on hand when a new order comes in.

Notice that your *need to have a safety stock boosts your inventory*. That costs money. But so does being out of stock. Today some companies are using mathematical formulas to tell them where to draw the line between the cost of carrying more inventory and the cost of "outage." They decide how costly it is to run out, and what are the chances of running out with different safety stocks, and how much it costs to carry extra amounts in safety stock. They find that on some items it pays to carry very little and to run out now and then rather than carry too much safety stock. In other cases they find that the cost of carrying a little extra safety stock is cheap insurance against irregular lead time and irregular use.

Notice that as you carry more and more safety stock, each added item gives you *less* added protection against outage. If a certain safety stock lets you fill orders from stock 90 per cent of the time, you may have to boost the safety stock by 25 per cent to get up to where you can fill 95 per cent of all orders right out of stock. Here is where the formulas are helpful. Which costs less, 10 per cent outage, in place of 5 per cent, or 25 per cent more inventory?

Although using formulas to tell you when to reorder seems to be gaining popularity, lots of people think that they aren't much good. They ask: what is the cost of being out of something? You can't answer that question very exactly. They say that the cost of being out of stock is different for every item and being out hurts worse at some times than it does at others. They ask, also, what are the chances that an order normally received in 6 weeks will not arrive until 8 weeks? Remember, that lead times are always somewhat irregular and unpredictable. What number will you use in your formula? They say, too, that your inventory policy also changes—sometimes you are willing to carry more on hand.

Using a formula, they say, gives you no better answer than the reliability of the figures used. Also all the figures used in formulas change so often that it is too costly to pay for all the calculation that must go on forever.

Formula users say, "We grant that our figures are our best guesses, but with the formulas we get *some* idea of when to reorder. Without formulas we're *really* just guessing." The cost of calculating and recalculating answers was always a stumbling block in the past, but now the new electronic computers will take care of changes so fast and calculate new answers so quickly that this objection to formulas, in companies having computers, no longer counts. Giant companies with their tens of thousands of items are using formulas more than they used to. You hear claims made that they give better service while cutting inventory investment by 10, 20, or even 40 per cent. If the stories are only half true, formulas will be more commonly used in the future.

Most companies do *not* use reorder points. Several reasons for this. One is that they reorder many items—particularly finished parts for assembled products—on the basis of known future need for the parts. We talk about ordering for known needs on page 745.

But some companies that use the reorder point idea don't calculate reorder points for every item and write the number on its stock card. They don't do it because there are so many changes in their usage and replenishment lead times. For changeable items these companies use the time-limit method instead.

It is a good idea to separate, physically, the reorder quantity if it can be done. Put the reorder quantity in a sack in the bin, or, if the material is stored in layers, put a cardboard over the bottom layers. When the stock issue clerk has to start using the reorder quantity he tells the card clerk. This gives a double check on being sure to order more on time.

INVENTORY TURNOVER

Inventory turnover is the cycle of using and replacing materials. You usually talk about it as a ratio—the number of turns a year. If you sell $100,000 worth of products a year and have an average inventory of $50,000, you have two turnovers a year. But, if you could get by with $25,000 worth and still not run out of things too often, you'd have four turns a year.

You'd like as many turns a year as possible—first, because you get by with less investment, $25,000 in our example. Besides, at 20 per cent annual carrying cost (most companies think that it costs that much or more to carry inventories) you would, in our example, save $5,000 expense a year.

Some companies use the turnover ratio along with other controls to set limits to inventory investment. They insist on a certain number of turns a year. Be careful though about using this for control. You may force the men doing the reordering to order too few too often. You'll get good turnover but high unit purchase or manufacturing cost.

DOLLAR LIMITS

Most companies set dollar limits or budgets to the amount that they will allow you to invest in each class of materials. Each class of materials has its account in the accounting department showing its investment at all times. The inventory control manager is responsible for seeing that the amounts stay within the allowed budgets.

Dollar limits don't often apply to specific items (except for the big items), nor do they tell you when or how much to reorder. All that they do is to say don't go too high in total. The inventory control supervisor has to figure out how much of each individual item he can have in each class of materials while keeping the investment within the limit.

TIME LIMITS

"Time limits" in inventory control are like dollar limits. Time limits are the common way to put dollar limits into effect. Dollar limits can be used directly to control only a few big use items, but time limits can easily be applied to every item. If you wanted to use dollar limits for every item, you would have to figure out separate dollar limits for every one of the thousands of items you carry. But one time limit can apply to as many items as you want.

How do you convert dollar limits into time limits? Let's use an example. Suppose that you use $10,000 worth of a certain class of material in a month and that your dollar limit is $10,000. That is about one month's supply, so one month's supply is your time limit.

Time limits don't say exactly when to reorder or how much. They merely say: don't at any time have more than, say, 30 days' supply on hand. Indirectly, though, time limits set top limits on how much you can order at one time. In order to hold your investment down to a month's usage, you can't order much more than a month's supply. Even so you'll have more than a month's stock of an item on hand when the new supply comes in because of the safety stock. Notice that time limits allow you to go over one month's supply on individual items, but for every item over the limit some other item must be below.

For long lead time items, time limits control when you reorder as well as how much. If it takes three months to get an item and you can order but one month's supply at once, you will need, every month, to place a new order for one month's needs, but it will be for three months ahead. You'll always have several orders out. Items on order don't count in your inventory as far as investment is concerned.

Time limits are easy to set, easy to change, and easy to operate, although, of course, some items will always be exceptions. Time limits can also be different for different classes of items. Or if an item's *use* changes, the time limit can stay put and the reordering quantity be changed.

PERIODIC REORDERING

Many, perhaps most, companies do not send requests to buy more materials to purchasing every day. Instead they do it once a month for everything that is running low. Warehouses commonly order more stock this way. Ordering everything all together saves clerical work because your whole order is just one long list.

Common though this method is, it is probably wasteful and makes you carry too much inventory. At the end of any month, you must look ahead and see if the stock might get down to the reorder point at *any time during the month*. If it might, you have to reorder more right now because you can't order more in between. So you do order now, and then the new supply comes in and gets here long before you really need it.

Although periodic reordering will usually keep you overstocked, it doesn't have to. You can place an order and tell the vendor not to deliver it right away. That is exactly what you do with blanket contracts. Then you send him, periodically, releases telling him exactly how much and when to deliver. You can get by with very little stock.

STANDARD QUANTITIES

Particularly with purchased items you have to watch for standard packages, full barrels, whole bundles. Nearly always if you order part of a package, you will have to pay more per unit. So you boost or cut your quantities so that they figure out to full standard units.

On many small items you can just set a fixed quantity to reorder every time. Supplies are often ordered that way. So are minor "free issue" items such as nuts and bolts. Ordering fixed quantities saves time.

You order standard quantities on big items too sometimes. If you wanted 25,000 pounds of steel, you'd have to pay a higher *per pound* freight rate than if you went on up to, say, 30,000. If you shipped 30,-000 pounds, the railroad would give you the lower full car rate per pound. The freight cost saving would almost surely more than offset the extra carrying cost of having the extra 5,000 pounds of steel on hand two or three weeks before you needed it.

ECONOMIC LOTS

The *best* number to order at a time is called the "economic" lot. That is the quantity that gives you the lowest cost per unit. The economic lot idea works both for purchased and manufactured items. Its

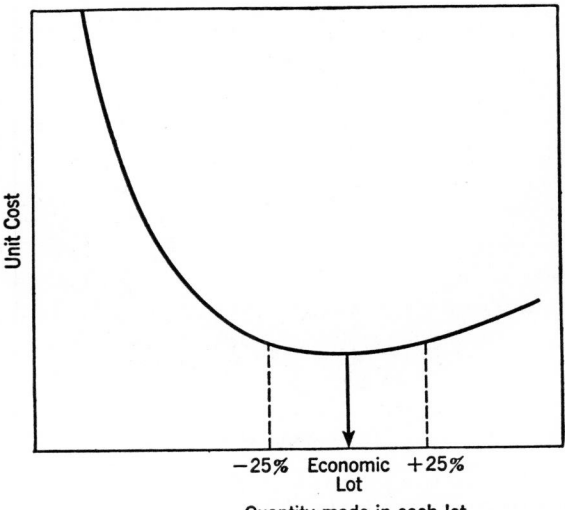

FIG. 38–5. Although the economic lot can be computed as a reasonably specific quantity, the unit cost curve is relatively flat over a range of 25 per cent above or 25 per cent below the economic lot.

theory is simple. It costs money for all the paper work needed for an order. And, in the factory, it costs money to set up machines and get ready to run the order. Some people call these "acquisition" costs. They are the same for big or little orders. So, the more you make at a time, the less they cost *per unit* of product. So far you make big lots.

But, the bigger the lot, the higher are inventory carrying costs. At some point—some quantity—the two will balance. That is the economic lot size. Any larger lot runs carrying costs per unit up faster than the cut in setup costs. Any smaller lot doesn't spread setup costs enough.

Figure 38–5 shows these relationships in chart form. Notice that the total cost curve is almost flat for some distance. That means that you don't have to hit the economic lot exactly to get low costs. In fact, you

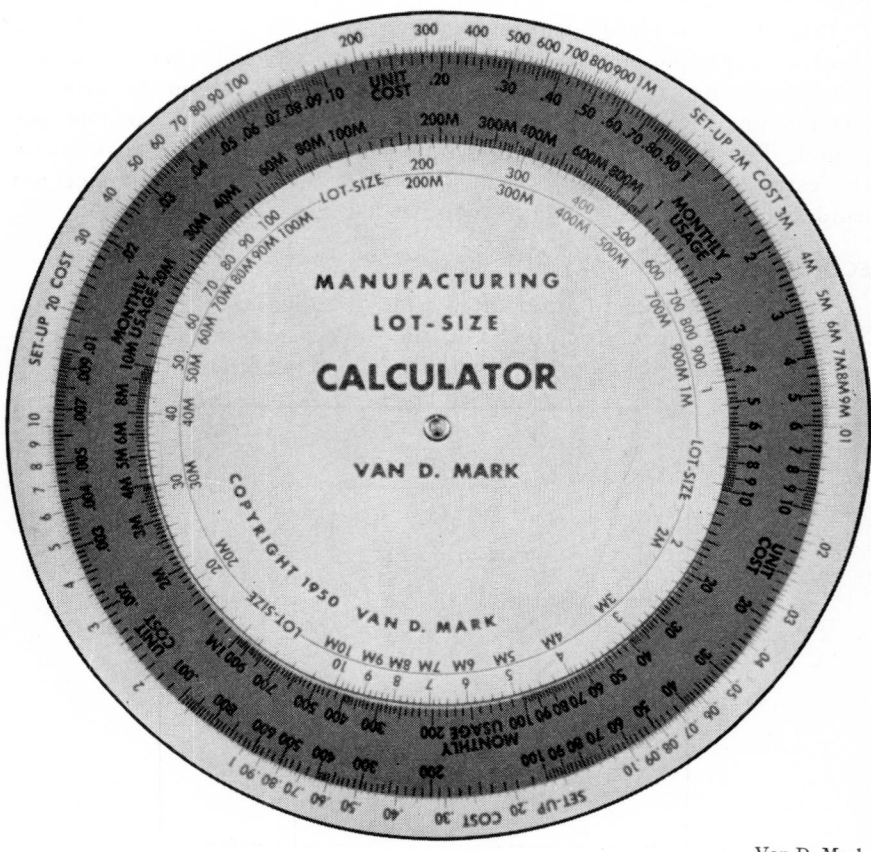

Van D. Mark

FIG. 38–6. An economic lot-size slide rule. This rule is made of two parts. The part extending out through the dark portion in the picture rotates and can be set at any point on the bottom piece, depending on the numbers you are working with.

usually get just about as low unit costs if you order 25 per cent more (or less) than the economic lot.

Since you don't have to hit it exactly to do pretty well, most companies that calculate economic lots (and by no means all do) use simple formulas that leave out such minor factors as the likelihood of obsolescence. Here is a common formula:

$$\text{Economic lot} = \sqrt{\frac{2 \times \text{the number of pieces per year} \times \text{the setup cost for an order}}{\text{Labor, material, and overhead cost per piece} \times \text{interest rate}}}$$

Some companies set up nomographs (a logarithmic kind of chart) and some use circular slide rules, like that shown in Figure 38–6, to figure economic lots easily.

Some companies say that they use economic lots yet never do any calculation of the economic lot size. Such companies look at every order's setup cost. If its setup cost is high, these companies run off several months' supply rather than one or two months' supply. This common practice is a rough application of the economic lot idea.

You won't find companies using economic lots too often largely because they have to use figures that are costly to get. Besides the figures keep changing, and that keeps the economic lots changing. Also the economic lot for operation 1 is not the economic lot for operation 2. Operation 3 is still different. The problem gets very mixed up, and it can easily cost more to get the answer than you can save.

Another reason for not using economic lots is that they are hard to start. Maybe the economic lot of an item would be a year's supply, and running it off all at once would tie up your machines so long that other orders would get behind schedule. So you run less at a time and give other orders a share of the machine time. Of course, once started, the plan could work because the long run would come only once a year.

The main reason, though, for not using economic lots is the common use of dollar limits and time limits as methods of control. They just rule out all long-time-ahead stocks of anything. More than one company is, today, wondering if that is smart. Economic lots seem to be gaining popularity.

REPLACING FOR KNOWN FUTURE DEMAND

The inventory control man in a job-lot shop has to contend with ups and downs and shifts back and forth in the use of his items. But he still has to try not to run out of anything and do it while carrying very little stock.

He can do a pretty good job of doing both at once if he is willing to do a little extra record work. The procedure starts in the production control department. As soon as production control gets an order to make a product, it figures the materials needed. It also looks at the schedule to find out when the materials will be needed. Production control then checks with the inventory control manager who checks his stock record card for each item and *allocates* enough of the "available" material (on-hand plus on-order minus any supplies reserved for other future orders) to take care of the order. If there is not enough available, he orders more right away so that it will be on hand when needed.

To do this, your stock record card needs two extra columns for figures. The first, called "allocated," "apportioned," or "reserved," shows the order numbers and quantities needed for all future orders for which material has been reserved. The allocation is purely a card record. You don't need actually to set aside the reserved materials.

The second extra column is the "available" column. It shows the sum of: the present stock, plus the quantities on order, minus the quantities reserved. Reserving stock doesn't always get new supplies in as soon as you need them, but you are warned ahead that a shortage is in sight and, usually, in time to get more stock.

ORDERING FOR ASSEMBLY'S NEEDS

This might be called a separate method of inventory control, although it is a variety of time limit control. It starts with the schedules for assembling finished products. They are issued months ahead to allow time to buy materials and make parts.

When ordering parts (and materials for parts you make yourself), you calculate the kinds and quantities needed for one month's assembled products—say August's. (You are doing this, say, in March.) To assemble in August means that you want most of the parts finished in July. Some of the parts go into subassemblies that will be put together in July, so you need to get these parts finished in June.

Having set completion dates for parts, you next look at how long it takes to make a finished lot of each one. That gives you a starting date for making each part. Notice that this start date depends on (1) when you want the part, and (2) how long it takes to make it. Different parts will have different start dates. You will start some items into production in April, some in May, and some not until June.

The date when you start to make a part is the date by which you need raw materials for it. So you work back through the time it takes to get raw materials to get a date for ordering.

So far this sounds like a scheduling matter and so belongs in our production control chapters not in our discussion of inventory control. It is a scheduling matter but it is also an inventory control matter. August's assembly needs tell you the quantities of some items that you have to order in June, in May, in April, or even earlier.

Mostly the only quantity figure that you pay any attention to is August's requirements. You order whatever quantities are needed to take care of August. Then, a month later, you order enough to meet September's requirements. When and how much to order depends on assembly requirements—and not much else. You order as late as you can to get the materials in time, and you rarely order more than one month's needs of anything at a time. Sometimes, though, you cut the month's requirements into parts and send through several small orders.

RECEIVING

Every bought item has to be "received." Bought items come in by rail or truck to a receiving department. There, each package is opened to see what the item is. There is a packing slip inside that tells what it is supposed to be, and usually it gives the purchase order number. A clerk makes out a receiving notice and sends the materials to the appropriate stock room. He sends copies of the receiving notice to purchasing (so it can close the order), accounting (so it can pay the bill and can charge the proper stores' account), stores (so it gets a record of what it is getting), and material control (so it knows what has come in).

Sometimes the packing slip gives too little information to tell what the material really is. Receiving gets a copy of all purchase orders (but with money figures marked out), so it can usually match the materials with some order. Some companies don't send a copy of the purchase order to receiving though for fear that it will make the men there careless when checking incoming shipments.

All incoming items are supposed to be inspected not only to be sure what they are but to check the quantity and to see that nothing is broken. Most receiving inspection goes no further. But sometimes you can't tell if incoming products pass inspection without some rather elaborate tests—chemical, electronic, or other. Could you, for example, tell if a shipment of thermostats for stoves was all right? Or picture tubes for television sets? Sometimes you need to call on engineering or the laboratory to pass final judgment.

ENCLOSED STOCK ROOMS

Most materials, particularly infrequently used items, are kept in enclosed stock rooms, from which they are issued only when a man presents a requisition. Materials in enclosed stock rooms are generally better cared for than things left out in the open. Also you get good records of what you have and what comes in and goes out. You need stock rooms (usually separate stock rooms) for raw materials, semifinished items, finished parts (including finished subassemblies), finished products, and supplies. Usually you will need more than one stock room for each kind of material, so that each will be near the point of use.

Individual stock rooms often stock several thousand items, so that you have some real problems with receiving materials, identifying them, knowing where they are kept, and putting them away. Besides that there are record-keeping problems.

There are several possible ways to arrange stock rooms, but in practice you have to combine them. You can arrange a stock room according to (1) the identification number of the materials; (2) the use of the item; (3) the frequency of use of the item; or (4) the nature, size, and shape of the item. In practice, however, no one of these can set the complete pattern of your stock room arrangement. Except for the last arrangement (the nature, size, and shape of the item) all arrangements have a common main trouble, that of storage bins. You just can't mix up large and small bins, and racks, indiscriminately.

Suppose that you wanted to arrange the storeroom by product identification numbers. Consecutive numbers have nothing to do with an item's size or shape. You'd have all kinds of awkward combinations of big bins, little bins, and racks next to each other. You'd be putting pieces of sheet metal, roller bearings, shafts, gears, nuts and bolts, springs, pieces of pipe, and rolls of wire next to each other.

Or suppose that you try arranging things according to the use of the item. That means that you would try to group all materials used in certain products. This method has all of the difficulties of arrangement by identification number and one more: where would you put items used in two or more products?

How about arranging according to the frequency of use of items? Put the fastest moving items nearest to the doors to cut handling costs. Here again the most frequently used items are of all kinds. No perfect answer here either.

That leaves arranging by the nature, size, and shape of the materials. This is the best from the stock room viewpoint. One area can be set up with racks for long pieces of material, another for buckets or bottles of liquids, another for bins or sacks of powdered material, another with large bins for large items and small bins for small items. You can furnish each area with the kind of materials handling equipment it needs, you can find things pretty easily, and it lets you make best use of stock room space.

But, even here, you will need to compromise some—certainly you will try not to have frequently used things in far corners. Also, you can set aside whole sections of the storeroom solely for the parts of certain finished products that don't have to have unusual bins. So you can, to some extent, arrange things by their use.

Because you end up with a mixed arrangment, you will have to make up an index so that people can find things. The index can be arranged by product description. And you may need a second index by identification number.

Don't forget, in arranging any stock room, that you will need some spare bins because you are always adding new items. Of course you are canceling old ones too, but nearly always you add more than you cancel. Also, don't forget the need for overflow bins—bins to take care of what won't go into the regular bin when the new supply of an item comes in. Now and then you will have to rearrange and reassign bins, but do it only now and then. The stock room clerks should know where things are without always having to look them up in the index.

OPEN STOCK ROOMS

A great deal of paper work and handling of materials can be saved by storing materials right next to the operation where they are needed. You can do that in most cases when the same kinds of material are used day after day and where the materials are not likely to be stolen. It can also be done with parts along assembly lines. As parts are made, or as bought parts arrive, they are checked in and taken directly to their point of use and left there rather than in stock rooms. The operators just help themselves to whatever they need. In the accounts of the company, the value of the materials used is charged to the products made on a standard cost basis. Neither reports of materials used nor requisitions are necessary.

When open stores are used, the supply (or "bank") of materials stored at the operation is relatively small, rarely (for big items) is it more than enough to carry on an hour or so. New supplies must be continually added. Of course you keep more of little items.

What happens, however, when parts are made in lots and not continuously? Lots go into finished stores (enclosed stores) from which the assemblers' supply bins are kept filled. Assemblers work from open bins.

Open stores don't work so well, though, where *assembly* is by lot. Before you assemble even one finished product you have to accumulate *all* the different parts you need and in the right quantity. Then the total supply of *all* the parts is issued and the products are put together one after the other.

PHYSICAL INVENTORIES

Records never stay wholly accurate, so you must make an actual count (take a "physical inventory") of what you have on hand from time to time. Companies used to close down for a week at the end of the year to count everything. This is still common, but now it is more popular to count all the time. That is, count what you have in one section this week, another section next week, and so on. This periodic checking usually costs very little because you let regular stock room clerks do it in their spare time. Maybe they get all the way around two or three times a year, and so you get a check that often on what your cards say that you have on hand.

Actually you have to count at least once a year whether you want to or not. The government insists on it. But why? Because profits taxes depend on profits, and profits are the difference between sales income and the cost of sales. And the cost of sales equals: your January 1 inventory value, plus the cost of things bought and made in the year, minus your December 31 inventory. It is kind of around Robin Hood's barn, but the amount you say that the inventory is worth affects your profits and that affects Uncle Sam's taxes, and so he says: be sure it's right—count.

Besides federal taxes, you pay local taxes. You pay personal property taxes on inventories. Local authorities too are interested in your having a proper value put on your inventories.

IDENTIFICATION SYSTEMS

Can you imagine a supermarket where the cans had no labels! You'd never know what you were getting. Factory stores items are more

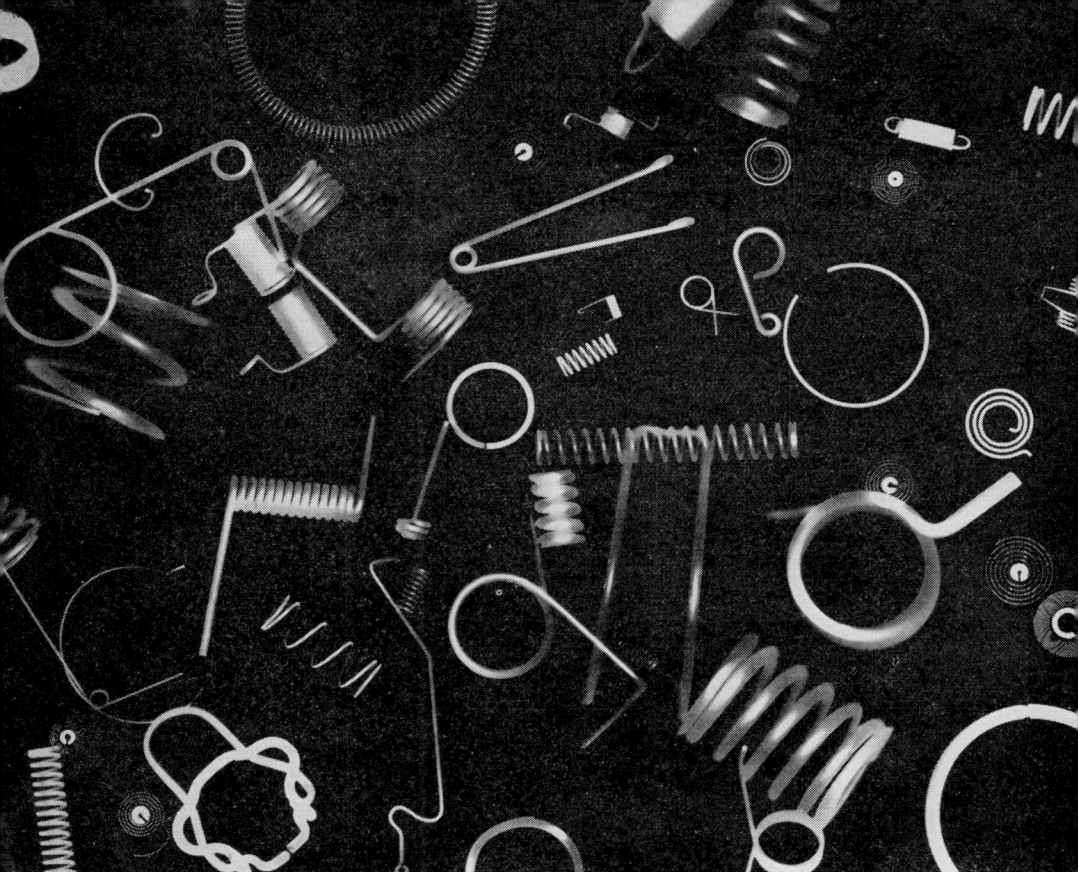

FIG. 38-7. Word descriptions alone will hardly do the job of identifying items such as these springs.

varied in looks than tin cans but are, without identification, just about as hard to identify. Look at Figure 38-7. You can tell that the items are springs, but they are different. How would you ever tell what they are for and, if you worked in the stock room, which one to hand out to an assembler to put in a certain product?

An identification system is a must. First, you need word descriptions of each item—descriptions that tell what every item is and descriptions that set every item apart from other items. But word descriptions that clearly set apart every item from every other item are too long and cumbersome for most uses, so you need, second, a number system. Numbers are shorter and easier to tell apart. Coded number systems (or number and letter systems) are used for all but the least important items.

Coded number systems try to give similar numbers to similar items. This helps let people who have to work with the records recognize the items more readily.

For *raw materials*, the code usually shows the kind of material. Groups of numbers are reserved for sheet steel, steel bars, tool steel, steel wire, steel castings, malleable iron castings, and so on. Other groups of numbers stand for brass items. Paints and varnishes would have a totally different number set.

The coded part of coded numbers is on the left. The left-hand digits in a product's number tell its general class. If this item's whole number has 6 or 8 digits, the first two or three mean its general class. The next one or two show its subclass. Only the last 3 digits are probably uncoded. You'd have to go to an index to find out exactly what the item is. There you would find the full word description.

Finished parts can't use the same base for coding that is suitable for raw materials. Often a finished part is itself a whole assembled product. It might be a pump, a set of gears, an electric motor. You can't classify a motor by what it is made of. Besides, trying to classify finished parts by what they are made of doesn't help people tie the product and its number together in their minds.

Using kind of materials would give different numbers to steel, brass, nylon, and fiber gears. But since they are all gears and serve the same purposes, it would seem better to have groups of similar numbers for the *kinds of items*. Then all gears of all kinds would have similar numbers. Some companies do that. But, this is not a perfect arrangement either, because it gives the parts of any finished product unlike numbers.

For finished parts it seems best to class things on a basis of *use*. Separate groups of numbers are set aside for parts for each finished product or each kind of finished product. That is the way most number codes for finished parts are set up, although you can't escape having many exceptions.

Using related use, you'd put electric motors, gears, roller bearings, and oil cups into the number system of the product they go in. But that would make you have unlike numbers for electric motors. Gears, bearings, and oil cups too would bear unlike numbers.

Common parts also upset all orderly numbering schemes. They are used in several products, and so their number is always out of series in all lists for a product's parts except one. Some companies give common parts a separate series of numbers, but then of course that tells you nothing about the item except that it has several uses.

You also have problems, in all numbering systems, because design changes cancel some old parts and their numbers, and add others. And you'd better not use old part numbers for new parts (at least not for years) or you'll have no end of confusion.

Airplane companies use a double numbering system. Every part on an airplane has a regular number, but besides, it has an "indent" number. The indent number tells at what point the part enters the airplane. That information is needed to schedule its manufacture at the right time. Think, for example, of a part that goes into the left wing flap, which goes into the left wing, which goes into the airplane. Some items go into one subassembly, which goes into another subassembly, which goes into another, and so on for seven or eight "generations." It gets to be quite complex, but there is no other way to get a quarter of a million parts of a bomber plane together at the right time and in the right order. Indent numbers help you get the parts and subassemblies ready at the right time.

The government may also upset your system. If you sell products to the government, it may give you its own parts numbers to use. Sometimes the government furnishes you with some parts (identical to others you use regularly in other products) but with its numbers attached. You may have to use a double numbering system in your own records.

Engineering drawings both help and confuse identification problems. Most parts for assembled products have drawings showing their size, dimensions, and other information. In the engineering department the drawings must be numbered. So, many companies just use the drawing number as all or part of the part's identification number. But some parts, as, for example, pieces of wire in a radio set, and materials such as welding rods and paint, need identification numbers, but have no drawing numbers. Their numbers are usually part of the raw materials series, so drawing numbers do not solve all problems.

In fact they make one new one. Drawings come big and little, and they are filed in the engineering department by size of the sheet of paper they are on. Each size has its own number series (as A-722 or B-1461 and so on). This is fine for filing and finding drawings, but using the drawing number as an item's number gives no clue as to what the item is.

IDENTIFYING MATERIALS

An identification system that suits the records is fine, but we also have to identify the items. There are two easy ways to do it as far as items in stock are concerned. For packaged items, put the item's description on the package. And for all items, packaged and unpackaged, put a tag on the storage bin. For materials-in-process, keep the material or its container tagged. This is important because the material is changed in form a little after every operation, making it even harder to tell by looking what an item is.

Tags and labels take care of most of the problem. But tags get lost, and materials get separated. And you can't run tags through heat-treating furnaces or degreasing tanks. Also some items, steel sheets, castings, and others are often not suitable for tagging, and they are often not kept in bins. Better stamp, mold, paint, or etch some kind of identification on every item. Castings nearly always have their numbers molded on. Bars and sheets of metal are stacked and painted with coded colors on the end.

A few companies have a curious identification problem. To prevent employees stealing parts that they can sell, the companies intentionally put wrong numbers on them. TV and radio manufacturers sometimes put false numbers on popular kinds of radio tubes so that they won't be stolen.

MATERIALS REQUISITIONS

A materials requisition is a request to the stock room to issue materials. It shows the kind and quantity of materials wanted, the use to be made of them (or the account number to be charged), and the signature of the authorizing person. Figure 38–8 shows a typical requisition. This one is made out and ready to present to the stock room in exchange for materials. When the stock clerk hands out the material, he

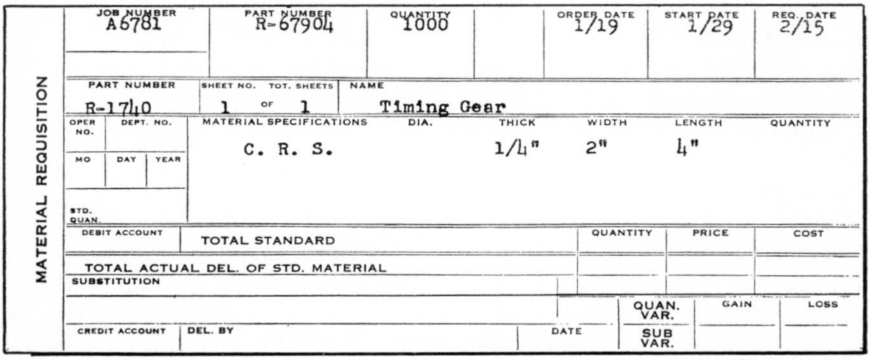

	JOB NUMBER A6781	PART NUMBER R-67904	QUANTITY 1000		ORDER DATE 1/19	START DATE 1/29	REQ. DATE 2/15

MATERIAL REQUISITION							
PART NUMBER R-1740	SHEET NO. 1	TOT. SHEETS OF 1	NAME Timing Gear				
OPER. NO.	DEPT. NO.	MATERIAL SPECIFICATIONS C. R. S.	DIA.	THICK 1/4"	WIDTH 2"	LENGTH 4"	QUANTITY
MO	DAY	YEAR					
STD. QUAN.							
DEBIT ACCOUNT	TOTAL STANDARD				QUANTITY	PRICE	COST
TOTAL ACTUAL DEL. OF STD. MATERIAL SUBSTITUTION							
					QUAN. VAR.	GAIN	LOSS
CREDIT ACCOUNT	DEL. BY			DATE	SUB VAR.		

Van W. Evans & Co.

FIG. 38–8. A materials requisition.

writes down the material identification number on the requisition and sends it to the stock record clerk. He, the record clerk, subtracts the quantity issued from his record card, writes in the amount he has left, puts the price per unit on the requisition, and sends it to the accounting department. There they multiply the unit price times quantity and get the value of the material issued. They subtract that amount of money from the materials account and add it to the account for which the material was withdrawn.

Requisitions for *supplies* are generally made out by foremen for quantities that will last the department for some time. Requisitions for *materials to make into products* may be made out by the foreman of the department doing the first operation. More often this is done ahead by production control. The requisitions are either given to the foreman of the first department for him to use when he wants the material or they are held in the production control's dispatch office until shortly before the first operation is to start. Then they are sent to the stock room, from which the materials are delivered to the first operation just before they are needed.

Requisitions for *parts for assembled products* are often copies of the assembly manufacturing order. This order lists the parts and quantities of each part needed. A copy goes to the finished goods stock room and serves as the stock room clerk's authority to issue all of the parts listed.

Materials requisitions are just so much extra paper work *if* you can do without them. But how can you? Isn't it necessary to know what materials you use for orders, and how much you issued, and how much is left? Yes. But on regular day-to-day use items you can figure that every product made takes its certain items and amounts of material. If you make 1,000 electric irons, you know that you have used 1,000 handles, 1,000 heating units, and so on. You don't need requisitions for issuing handles and heating elements. Let the men pick handles and heating units right out of bins without paper records of every part issued. Often you can cut out materials requisitions. Just count the items made, multiply by the amount needed for each one, and get the total amount used.

But isn't this dangerous? Won't things disappear? In most cases, no. Men don't try to steal very many kinds of parts, and if they don't steal parts, not many disappear. It is true that occasionally men throw rejects into the trash can and don't report them. And it is also true that small, valuable, salable items (like gold in a jewelry factory or even clocks for stoves) need to be kept in enclosed stock rooms. Some companies make workers installing valuable small items responsible for them by giving the men "meal-ticket" requisitions. Standard quantities are issued from time to time to the man, and a hole is punched in his card. Then he must see that those items go into the products. Except for the possibility of theft, requisitionless issuing of materials is the best way for regular use items.

PRICING THE MATERIALS ISSUED

When materials are made into products, their money value is taken out of the raw materials account and added into the account showing the value of materials in process. Later their investment is taken out of the materials in process account and added into the finished products account.

Sounds simple. But there is a troublesome problem here that won't be downed. Here is what happens: You have a bin full of an item, say, 125 in all. Suppose that you acquired them (whether by purchase or manufacture is immaterial) as follows: 25 units at $5 each, 50 units at $6, and 50 units at $7. These figures are extreme, but they'll illustrate the point. Your actual investment is $775 (although buying them all at today's price would cost you $875). Now suppose that you issue 100 pieces, what price do you put on the requisition? $5? $6? $7? or some combination?

You have 5 choices: "FIFO," "LIFO," average cost, last cost, standard cost.

FIFO.   FIFO means: "First-in, First-out." So you say 25 items at $5, 50 items at $6, and 25 items at $7, giving you a total of 100 items issued and reported as costing $600. You have left 25 items shown to be worth $175.

LIFO.   LIFO means "Last-in, First-out." So you say 50 items at $7, 50 items at $6, total 100 items costing $650. You have left 25 items shown to be worth $125.

Average Cost.   Your 125 items cost you $775 or $6.20 each on the average. So you say that you issued 100 items costing $620. You have left 25 items shown to be worth $155.

Last Cost.   Your last price was $7 each so you say that you issued 100 items costing $700. You have left 25 items shown to be worth $75. Accountants like this method *least* of all because your remaining inventory is hardly ever really worth what your books say.

Standard Cost.   Here you pick some standard figure that items ought to cost. It is commonly used for items you make yourself because no two lots ever cost exactly the same. Suppose you say that the standard cost in our example is $5.75. Then you would say that you had issued 100 items costing $575. Your 25 leftover items would be shown to be worth $200. This method lets you have just as wrong inventory values as does the last cost method, yet accountants think that it is all right.

Isn't all this picayunish? And isn't all of this just a play on numbers? Aren't your costs the same and aren't your selling prices the same no matter how we handle it? No, it is not picayunish, because the problem goes on forever (prices and manufacturing costs are always changing), and it affects nearly every item you use in making products. It also affects the income taxes you pay, and while things may come out about the same in the long run, you certainly can't be sure that they will.

You get different figures, depending on the method you use, for what your products cost. This means that your calculated profits are different, and that affects your income taxes. Also, if you set prices based on your calculated costs, you affect your income and maybe the sales volume too. No, you can't be sure that the different methods will ever work out the same.

We can say though that FIFO gives lower cost figures during the periods of price increases. FIFO shows more apparent profit and makes you pay more taxes. Also your inventories will be shown as worth today's higher prices. LIFO is the reverse. As prices go up you say that you use the last bought and most costly materials. LIFO boosts apparent costs, holds down profits and taxes, but values inventories too low. The other three methods fall between LIFO and FIFO. On price downswings, everything is reversed. Here FIFO shows high costs, lower profits, and cuts taxes. LIFO shows lower costs, high profits, and makes you pay more.

STUDY QUESTIONS

1. What does good inventory control try to do? What problems are there? Discuss.
2. Why might you want to classify the items you carry in stock into "A," "B," and "C" groups? What use would you make of these classes? Explain.
3. Do you have to forecast in order to control inventory? Explain your answer.
4. Compare the "top-down" and the "bottom-up" methods of forecasting. Which would you use? Why?
5. What has the problem of evaluating sales to do with inventory control? Explain.
6. How do you figure a reorder point? Explain. When would you use reorder points? When not?
7. How do you set the size of your safety stock? Discuss fully.
8. If you were the inventory controller, would you prefer to use dollar limits or time limits? Why?
9. What is the economic lot size? How do you figure it?
10. How do you set reorder quantities when you follow a policy of reordering to take care of specific known future demands? Explain.
11. What do you do when you "receive" incoming products? Why must you do the several things that you do?
12. Compare enclosed and open stock rooms. When is each better?
13. How ought an enclosed stock room be arranged? Why? What other ways could you use?
14. Are physical inventories necessary? Why?
15. What kind of an identification system seems best for raw materials? Why? What kind is best for finished parts? Why?
16. Why are materials requisitions used? Can you ever do without them? When?
17. What methods could you use for pricing materials requisitions? Compare them.

CASE 38–1.   THE EQUIPMENT MANUFACTURING COMPANY

The Equipment Manufacturing Company has decided to purchase a certain type of rheostat required in the operation of a machine which it manufactures. The company uses 2,000 rheostats per year: the average use is 8 per working day; the minimum use is 5 per working day; and the maximum is 10 per working day. It takes 30 working days to receive delivery on the rheostats after the ordering point is reached. The costs are $0.15 per unit per year for storage. The cost of putting through each order is $10. The inventory carrying charges are 20 per cent of the average investment inventory, not including space charges. The purchase prices are as follows:

$4.60 each on orders of 200 or less
4.50 each on orders of 201 to 400
4.40 each on orders of 401 to 600
4.35 each on orders of 601 to 800
4.30 each on orders of 801 to 2,000

Determine the safety reserve, the ordering point, the ordering quantity, and the normal maximum inventory.

CASE 38–2. THE STEVENS COMPANY

The inventory card for the oil bearing G-2357 of the Stevens Company reads as follows:

Date	Quantity Ordered	Received	Used	On Hand
1–15		300		300
1–16			75	225
2–16			75	150
3–16			75	75
3–17	300			
4–16			75	0
7–19		300		300
8–25			75	225

On August 28 the stock clerk checks the inventory card and sees that the bin has 225 bearings left. A check of the past 8 months shows that the average monthly use of the bearings is 47. This means that the bin has about 5 months' supply left and that no order need be placed until next month.

What reordering policy should be followed in the case of item G-2357?

Chapter 39

PRODUCTION CONTROL

Production control is the factory's nervous system. In a very real sense very little of a factory's work is making *products.* Most products are made of *parts;* most of a factory's activities have to do with making *parts.* Until you assemble the parts you have no product, just parts. Production control tells the factory what kinds of parts to make, how many, when. And it tells the factory what assembled products to make, and when, and out of what parts.

But parts are not made complete in single operations. Picture making a chair leg. To make it you saw, plane, sandpaper, drill holes, or do other things to a piece of wood. It ends up the right size, shape, and finish to be a chair leg, but you didn't make the whole change all at once. You did it bit by bit, operation by operation. So it is in a factory. Production control doesn't just tell the factory to make chair legs. It has to give the factory detailed directions telling the men to do certain operations to certain lots of materials. Making parts is all a directed process with production control giving the directions.

Manufacturing is just as varied as the products we buy—only more so because lots of products are made and used that we consumers never see. Production control is also very different in different companies and different industries. Certainly you would use different kinds of directions to tell the men what to make in a shoe factory, a nut and bolt factory, and an airplane factory.

The hardest production control job is in factories making assembled products out of metal parts, and the most difficult production control of all is in the airplane industry. In no other industry do you have to get a quarter of a million parts made, all on a schedule, so that they can be put together into one product. Production control is difficult, though, even with products simpler than airplanes. Even a typewriter has 2,000 parts. Remember too that each part requires several operations. A metal part that you can make in as few as ten operations is a simple part. When making assembled products made from metal parts, production

758

control must direct thousands and thousands of operations to be done.

In talking about production control we will spend most of our time on assembled metal products. No can of beans, no glass jar, no pair of shoes is as hard to make as almost any assembled metal product.

PRODUCTION CONTROL FUNCTIONS

Exactly what does production control do? Different things in different companies. Also jobs are split up among departments differently. But there are certain things that, taken collectively, make up the whole of the job of production control. Here's what it includes:

1. Help make up master production schedules.
2. Make plans for the men needed to meet schedules.
3. Receive orders to manufacture products.
4. "Explode" the orders for assembled products, thus determining the parts and operations needed.
5. Determine the raw materials requirements.
6. Operate the raw materials stock room and maintain the stocks.
7. Do original "routing" (determine, the first time a product is made, the operations and machines required to make products and parts).
8. Make up production orders directing the performance of the operations that make parts and products.
9. Make up schedules for the performance of operations and the use of machines.
10. Make sure that everything needed for production will be ready.
11. Decide and assign jobs to particular men and machines.
12. Direct the transportation of materials in process.
13. Receive reports of work done and compare them with that scheduled.
14. Help remove reasons for delays in production.
15. Remake plans when original plans are not carried out and when there are changes in the size of the order or its wanted completion date.
16. Operate the finished parts stock room and control the stock of parts.
17. Operate the finished products stock room and control the stock of finished products.
18. Answer inquiries concerning the progress of orders in process.
19. Help make cost estimates for prospective new orders.

Most of these basic functions are assigned to the production control department in most companies. Sometimes a few of them are assigned to other departments. Sometimes one or more nonproduction control duties, such as operating the plant mail service, operating the tool storeroom, or setting time standards for incentive purposes, are assigned to the production control department.

Have you wondered about *men?* Only number 2 and 11 in our list even mention men. Production control has very little to do with manning the factory and nothing at all to do with training men. In some companies production control figures out how many men the factory will need, and in some companies it assigns work to men. But it is the foreman's job to provide men. Except during extreme ups and downs of production, production control does most of its work just as if it were sure that the right number of men would be on the job.

TERMS

If only industry would settle on words and definitions, it would be easier to talk about production control. But industry hasn't, so we have to do with terms as custom has set them and that means that we can't set exact definitions.

For example, the name of the main department doing most of the production control work may be the "production department," "production control department," "production planning department," "production planning and control department," or some other title. In metal-working industries, more companies probably use the term "production department" than any other term. Notice that the "production" department is *not* a factory department working on the product. It is the department that makes up and issues directives to the factory and controls production.

Various parts of production control work also have different names in different companies. A list of parts for an assembled product may be called a "bill of materials," a "materials list," a "parts list," or a "requirements list." A list of operations for making a part may be a "route sheet," a "process sheet," a "layout," or an "operation list." "Scheduling" may mean: (1) setting wanted dates for the completion of orders, (2) setting wanted dates for the completion of individual operations, (3) setting specific starting and stopping times for operation performance, or (4) making up lists of jobs ahead of machines. There is no part of production control where words mean the same everywhere. The student should know that this is so and not be confused when, out on the job, he runs into usage different from that he has learned.

THE PRODUCTION CONTROL DEPARTMENT

Production control is usually headed by a "production manager" who reports to the plant manager.

In middle-sized companies the production control department may be told to do all the things in our list of functions above. In small companies some jobs, such as forecasting manpower needs, are not done at all or are done by someone else. At the other extreme, giant companies separate out some of the work, particularly raw materials control, and take it away from production control. Original routing, deciding how things are to be made, also is often done by production engineering, not production control.

Also production control's work in continuous production differs from its work in job-lot manufacturing. In continuous manufacture, production control's work is to keep production inside the plant flowing, to see that the *rates* of *making* and *using* of items match up, and that is about all it does. Its work is still very important, but there is only a fraction as much paper work and plant directions as you find in job-lot work.

The point we are getting at is that how you set up the department depends on the work you give it to do. And although the things you give to a production control department to administer depend in part on your kind of manufacture, they also depend some on your own views. Some companies say, "engineering *designs* the product, production control (with the help of the factory) decides how to make them." Others say, "No, the engineers design the product and also tell you how to make it."

Also, who tells the man in the shop what job to work on next? Production control does in some companies. But in others, production control just sets dates by which jobs are to be done, and the foreman assigns jobs to his men.

Sometimes too you find odd combinations that go so far back that no one knows why they are together. Allis-Chalmers' production control department has charge of plant maintenance as well as time study. In another company production control reports to the personnel director!

But aren't there any organization patterns inside the production control department? Yes. Almost always there are two main divisions: one, often called the "planning" department, handles all of the way-ahead details. It takes schedules for weeks and months ahead and figures out parts, materials, and even tools needed. Then it checks to see what you will have and orders whatever you will need.

The other main division of production control deals with the near future and the here and now. Often called the "scheduling" department, it makes up the factory orders to go ahead and do work, and it sets times by which things are to be done. It keeps track of what *is* done and, whenever things don't go right, keeps after them and tries to see that production comes out on schedule.

Curiously, this scheduling section of production control is sometimes called the "production control" department. This doesn't happen, of course, if you call the whole department by that name. You find it often, however, in companies that call the main department, the "production department."

ORIGINAL AUTHORITY TO MAKE PRODUCTS

We try never to make anything that we can't sell, and we try to make as many of everything as we can sell. This means that *all* production must be authorized. Don't allow the factory to make anything without an authorization.

Production control gives the factory its authorizations, but almost never does production control get to decide what the factory should make. Production control, in turn, has to get authorizations.

But from whom? Someone, somewhere, has to start things. Generally, production control gets its marching orders in the form of a master schedule covering the next several months. Sometimes master schedules are made out by a master scheduling department. But both production control and sales get in on the schedule making.

Master Schedules: Manufacture to Order. When you make products to customers' orders, the job of master schedule making is largely one of looking at your future plant work load of orders already on hand and seeing when you can promise delivery of new orders. This means that you must know about how many man-hours (or tons) of work your future orders will amount to in each major department. That tells you how soon you will have some open capacity in each department. Then you must estimate, for the orders that sales is bidding on, how much capacity they will need, department by department.

Be sure to pay attention to the *sequence*. You'll have to design the item first (that will take engineering man-hours), then some time later you'll need capacity in the foundry or forge or sheet metal shop, still later in the machine shop, and so on. See how soon the work load for design can be handled, and how soon after that there will be any open time in the foundry, and then in the next department, and so on. Finally you end up with a promise date. And if you get the order, you add in the work load for the appropriate departments and times.

Notice that production control's authority to tell the factory to go ahead comes from *sales orders,* not from the master schedule itself. All that the master schedule is in this case is a summation, at the end of each month, of the booked but unfinished jobs for future months. It extends as far ahead as the last delivery date on the last order you have on hand so far. And it shows month by month the orders that will be finished and shipped.

Notice too that production control has an active part in the setting of the schedule. Often, when you manufacture to order, there is no other master scheduling department.

Making to order is not without its headaches as far as schedules are concerned. Maybe you set promise dates on several possible contracts expecting to get only one, and so you plan to use the same open time for them all as far as bidding goes. Then you get two or three of the orders. Or you set a promise date and the customer says O.K. to everything except that he wants delivery sooner. What do you do? Maybe the president will tell you to figure out some way to get it out sooner. Also there are matters of cancellations, and of the factory not getting things done on time, or even of customers dallying overlong about signing the contract and then still wanting you to make good on your first promises about delivery.

When sales are directly to customers' orders, a copy of the sales order (or an abstract of it) is production control's authority to prepare the factory directives and to see that the products are made. One important exception to this occurs where the sales order is a blanket order (usually from another manufacturer or a chain store or mail-order company) for a large quantity of a product to be delivered in frequent small shipments from time to time as directed by the customer's production control department. Such orders constitute a large part of many manufacturers' business. In this situation new releases of authority to make more products must come from the various customers and not from anyone inside the company. Separate releases will come from each customer, and they will come at different times. The production control department in these companies gets many authorizations from many sources and at different times, instead of one long list of products every week or month. Similarly, in manufacturing directly to sales orders the orders probably come to production control day by day as they are received rather than all at one time, but in this case they come to production control from the sales department and not directly from the customer.

Master Schedules: Making to Stock.   Makers of almost all consumers products—the things you and I buy—manufacture to stock. They must try to forecast what and how many of everything we are going to buy and then make those things in those quantities. We discussed forecasting on page 731 along with inventory control.

You start with a sales forecast, but you will nearly always find that it has too many ups and downs to use it directly as a production schedule. You have to level out peaks and valleys some, building up inventories sometimes and cutting them down other times. After some juggling around, you get a master schedule that goes to production.

Production control takes part in the juggling around before the schedule beds down. It, production control, has to figure out whether the factory can handle the tentative schedule and how the ups and downs will work. Will there be enough machines? How about factory men? Will you need more? Or will you have to lay off some? These and other questions, production control must answer. After getting answers it shifts the schedule around some and gets one that suits both sales and the factory as well as possible. Notice that, in this process, production control helps set up the master schedule that becomes its authority to produce.

Production Programs.   Many companies make things that can be made complete in a very short time (hours or days), but they are made out of materials that take more time to get. And because of the high volume (as in automobile upholstery fabrics and automobile tires) you use so much material that you have to plan for and order materials months ahead.

You must forecast your sales not only so that purchasing can go ahead but also so that you can plan to level out sales peaks and valleys as much as you can. Also you need, as in the case of tires, to forecast your product mix pretty well because some of your equipment is special for certain tire sizes.

Production programs differ from other master schedules, though, in that an approved program does *not* give production control itself authority to do anything. It gets its authority to go ahead in the form of weekly "releases" against the problem. And it gets the releases only two or three weeks ahead of when the products are wanted! You can do this only when the manufacturing cycle is short. It gives you considerable flexibility to shift from one product to another (as from one tire size to another or, in a shoe factory, from one size or style of shoe to another) and to follow market trends. It only requires that your total volume forecast be reasonably accurate.

The total volume forecast has to be pretty good because you have raw materials coming in on a schedule to meet that volume. Notice that, with production program releases, production control has *nothing* to do with getting raw materials. Materials control, a separate department, controls the raw materials stock room. Materials control orders materials from the authority of the program, not from the weekly releases. Production control has no concern about there being raw material when it gets a weekly production release. The materials are supposed to be here.

Master Schedules: The Time Period.   Master schedules often cover production for a year ahead. They need to if it takes a long time to make products. Not many things, though, need a year's lead time for manufacturing.

But *forecasts* (on which master schedules are based) need to extend a year or more ahead most of the time—particularly when you make annual models. You have to do that so that you can tell how much mechanization (the "depth" of tooling) you should go in for. Big volume will make heavy mechanization pay off well.

Companies making annual models do forecast the whole year's sales to help them decide on mechanization. But they don't make production schedules nearly so far ahead. Mostly they use production programs and releases. Only the releases authorize production.

But some companies (makers of machinery, locomotives, etc.) make long lead time items. It takes months to make their products. If you were in that kind of work, you'd have to have master schedules that actually authorized production months ahead. You need to be far ahead for two reasons: first, because the products take a long time to make and, second, because raw materials control is likely to be production control's job too. It has to know what products you are going to make at least 6 months ahead in order to figure what materials to get. Then it has to go ahead and order the materials, and when they arrive, start making the parts.

You find two different kinds of way-ahead master schedules. One kind always covers the next 5 or 6 months. When one month ends, you add on the sixth month ahead. That is the way General Motors does it in its Electro Motive division which makes diesel locomotives.

The other way goes more in jumps. You add 6 months at a time. In May you have a schedule clear through December. But you don't extend it any farther in June and July. Then in August you issue a schedule for the whole 6 months, January to June, of the next year. Then nothing more until February, and so on. The Union Special Company (sewing machine makers) does it this way. So does the Cincinnati Milling Machine Company. So do many other machinery makers.

Why the difference? It is a matter of volume and standardization. Use the first method wherever you don't have many kinds of products and where you keep on making at least a few of them all the time. But when your products are more varied, the second method is likely to be better.

It is better because you will want to make some products in lots. Suppose that you sell twelve a year of one kind of machine. Making them at the rate of one a month sounds good until you think of making the parts. How will you make them? Make enough in January for all twelve and keep them in bins, some until December? Or will you set up machinery to make enough parts for one product in January, do it again in February, and so on every month, twelve times?

No, it will almost certainly be much cheaper to make the twelve machines in, say two lots of six. Make (assemble) one lot of six in March and another lot of six in September. That will let you manufacture at reasonable cost and will let you give customers pretty good service. Tell a customer who orders in January to wait until March. Same with February customers. The March customer gets his right away. Then you'll have to carry in stock the other three machines but not for long. They'll be gone before July.

But, you may ask, why can't we do this just by adding one month at a time to the schedule? Why must we move our schedule forward several months at a time? It is because some products will be made (assembled) over a 2- or 3-month period, rather than one.

Here's the trouble. Suppose that at the end of February, you "firm up" July's assembly schedule and add it to March-June. In July, we'll say you find that you are to make ten of product X, which has been off the schedule for a while. You start right away to order the material and start making long lead time parts.

At the end of March, you add August. August's schedule has ten more product X's on it. And later when you add September, you find ten more product X's on that schedule. But, you see, you find out about the parts requirements a little at a time. And, on the long lead time items, you went ahead in March and ordered parts lots with quantities to suit July's assemblies. Had you but known about August and September you could have made some of the parts in big enough quantities to take care of them all—and at much lower costs. In April and May it is too late to boost the lot sizes of the parts orders for July's products because they are halfway through production.

But what if the parts can be made in a short time? It doesn't take months to make every little part. True. What we have said doesn't count for short lead time items. For them you don't start making July's parts until June anyway. By that time you know all about August and September and can raise the lot quantities to cover them all if you want to. This whole matter of scheduling far ahead is to take care of *long lead time items*.

Master Schedules: Classes of Products.   Some companies make thousands of kinds of products, very few of which by themselves amount to much in dollars. Picture yourself making plumbing fittings, pipe connections, tees, ells, and so on, or nuts and bolts, or even medicines of hundreds of kinds and in all sizes of packages.

Some companies with thousands of items use approved master schedules only for whole classes or groups of products. Quantities are shown in dollars, tons, pounds, gallons, or some other unit common to all items in the class. So are planned inventories shown only for classes of products.

It is up to production control to decide when and how many to make for individual items. But it must meet the planned inventory size, must keep the factory working as planned, and must not run out of any items. Production control itself sets its own finished products schedule. To do this, of course, it must have charge of the finished goods inventory and of the records, item by item, of past manufacture and sales.

PARTS

Production control's authority to make things almost always comes to it as orders or schedules for whole products. In highly repetitive manufacture, it has little to do with bought items whether they are raw materials or bought finished parts or components.

But production control has to see to the making of all made parts. Authority to go ahead and make parts is always covered in the authorization to make finished products. Production control will have to figure out what parts will have to be made, how many, and when. In fact, for some general use parts (like nuts and bolts), production control doesn't even have to pay much attention to assembly orders. When such parts get low, production control just orders more of them. It doesn't bother calculating how many of them the schedule will call for. Nor does it need any direct authorization to order more.

When you get away from highly repetitive manufacture and more into varied end-products with varied parts, it is different. Here you will find production control figuring the parts needed for the assembled products already scheduled and ordering just the right number. ("Just the right number" of course means ordering enough extra to allow for the normal number of rejects in production.)

SERVICE PARTS

Customers need repair parts sometimes. For wearing parts, such as bearings or cutting tools, you'll end up selling lots of repair parts. But even nonwearing parts (automobile fenders) also get banged up and need replacement.

The need for service parts means that you make more parts than your products need. Past experience will tell you about how many extra parts of each kind to make. Sales and production control together work out the numbers. Notice that you will need to make a few extra parts right away so that you can give service to customers with new products.

Also notice that you'll have to keep on making some parts long after you have quit making a product. If you made products in 1900, someone, somewhere, is still using your 1900 model and now and then wants repair parts. Hunting up the old blueprints and the old tooling and making one or two is a real headache to production control, but it has to be done sometimes.

CAPACITY IN SCHEDULE MAKING

We said, on page 763, that master schedules and production programs try to level out sales peaks and valleys. Actually we don't get to do too much of that because it costs so much to carry inventories. Also seasonal peaks and valleys are all mixed up with business getting better or worse, and with your company getting more or less of the market, and with some of your products selling well—better than you thought—and others lagging behind.

You end up having to be pretty fast on your feet and doing a lot of adjusting up and down as you go along. You adjust your capacity. You do a lot of it by changing work hours. You do some of it by hiring men or laying them off. You add shifts or cut them off. You add or cut off workdays.

Often, too, you go in for more permanent changes, particularly on the upside. If business picks up and you can't handle it with your present machines, you buy more machines. Build an addition to the present factory, or build a new one somewhere else. Production control's part in such decisions is to tell management whether or not the factory can handle a proposed schedule, and to tell the top men how many ups and downs there will have to be in work hours. Then they, the top brass, can decide if they want to get more equipment or just how they want the final schedule to be set up.

Regardless of the method by which production control gets the authority to make products, there should be a check on the over-all quantities ordered. The factory's normal capacity is usually relatively fixed. It can be expressed, for control purposes, in terms of the number of tons, dollar value of product, or other appropriate measures that can be produced in a period of time. The capacity requirements of the orders sent to the production control department should be in accord with the plant's capacity to produce.

In the last analysis, however, the orders sent to production control depend upon sales, and sales are not wholly dependent on the company's desire to operate steadily. If the orders available require less than the plant's capacity, you will have to go on short hours or lay off men. If orders exceed present capacity, customers' orders must be delayed or the capacity expanded.

Within reasonable limits, steady operations override other considerations. If your backlog of orders begins to build up a little, you just give customers more distant promise dates. But you increase capacity if backlogs build up very much—you don't want to lose customers. And if the backlog shrinks, you don't, at first, cut capacity. You just give earlier promise dates on new orders. If it shrinks some more, you'll cut capacity.

"PRODUCING" AUTHORITY

Now we go to how production control passes out, to the factory, authority to make products. Nearly always production control tells the factory four things: (1) what to make, (2) how many, (3) when, and (4) how. The first three give the factory "producing" authority to go ahead and make products. The fourth gives the factory "processing" authority.

Producing authority tells the factory: (1) to assemble parts into finished products, (2) to make individual piece products (as a casting sold as such), (3) to make individual piece parts, or (4) to process bulk materials (liquids, powders) and pack them into big and little packages.

Assembly orders tell the factory's assembly department what finished products, and how many, to make and give a list of the subassemblies and parts needed for each assembly order. The manufacture of parts and individual piece products requires more detailed producing directives. In most companies *every operation* done on parts and integral products must be separately planned for and must be *individually authorized*.

Producing Authority Is One-Time Authority. When the factory finishes what you have told it to do, it needs more directions. You have to forever keep issuing new authorizations. Notice, too, that although we call it "authority," the factory has no discretion. Your directions are also *orders*. Your "authority" tells the factory to make the products the schedules call for, and not something else, and it must try to hit the quantity ordered too and not go very far over or under, and it must try to get things done on schedule.

"PROCESSING" AUTHORITY

Processing authority is the *how* to make products. Little companies leave it up the foreman. They let the engineers figure out the product's shape, size, and materials, but let the factory figure out how to make it. You see no sign of processing authority in small companies because the foreman has it.

But, in big companies, leaving it up to the foreman leaves too many things to chance. Engineers design parts and products, then other engineers decide how to make them. Some of these men are called product engineers, and sometimes they work in the production control department. Industrial engineers and methods men also help decide how workers are to perform operations—not only in parts making but also in assembly.

Production control is much concerned with processing authority in the big in-between area—things made neither in ones and twos nor in millions. But even in the in-between area, production control is more like a forwarding agent than it is an originator.

Engineering puts out "master bills of material" (lists of subassemblies and parts) for assembled products. And it puts out for each part a "master route sheet" showing the operations needed to make it. Production control gets both of these masters, both bills and route sheets.

When production control gets an order to make a certain number of products, it makes out individual bills and, for the parts, individual route sheets. Both are actually orders for the factory to go to work. Both tell the factory what to make and so constitute producing authority. We'll call the orders to assemble, "order" bills; and the orders to make parts, "shop orders."

Order bills differ from master bills by showing what you want *this* time. If you want fifty products, multiply all of the items on the master by fifty (it shows how many of every part you need for one product). Also put on the order number (its identification) and the schedule (when you want the products made). Next send copies of the order bill to the assembly department, the finished parts stock room, and wherever else they need one.

But how is an order bill of materials processing authority? If all it is is a list of parts and an order to assemble them, it is producing authority. Actually, processing authority is not too much in evidence on order bills. Mostly you don't tell the assembly department foreman how to assemble a product. But you do in a limited way, so there is some processing authority given when he gets an order bill. You can arrange the parts on the list in the order that the parts are assembled. This is sometimes done. Or, your engineers may have made up certain instructions for assembling. If they did, you send those along too.

The order bill also shows which items go together first into sub-assemblies rather than directly into the product. Engineering usually decides this, but in airplane companies production control can switch things around. You can't always tell, on a drawing board, which way is best. Would you, for example, assemble automobile door locks, then put them into the door latch, then put the latch into the door, then put the door into the body, and then put the body onto the chassis? Or would you put the door on the car, then put the frame for the latch on the door, and then assemble the latch and lock?

Shop orders are more directly processing authority. Their list of operations tells the factory just how to make an item. Look at Figure 39–1. It is a shop order. Look at the list of operations. They tell you what to do but they are so brief (the words "clean," "paint," "broach," and so on are actually the names of operations to be done) that the factory isn't getting too much instructing. Of course an engineering drawing goes along with the shop order, so there are some more instructions.

ROUTING SHEET

PART NAME			PART NO. 8638p			NO. OF SHEETS 1		
DATE 10/20		DATE DUE 1/20	ORDER NO. 1624			ORDER QUANTITY 200		

OPER.	OPERATION DESCRIPTION	MACH CENTER	TOOL NUMBER	C_END	PROCESSING TIME	START DATE	DEPT.
	CR STEEL SAFE 1020						
10	CLEAN	1		1	32.0	57.2	25
20	PAINT	2		3	10.0	58.1	25
30	FACE SHORT HUB SWEEP 1 IN DIA FORM HAND GRIP	30	3687	2	33.4	58.4	34
40	FACE FIN TURN AND RAD HUB. FORM RAD ON GRIP CTR DR AND REAM	30	6211	7	30.6	59.4	34
50	DR AND REAM	21		5	8.6	58.7	31
80	BROACH	53	6329	8	18.0	60.3	33
90	BURR	3		9	16.0	60.8	33
110	POLISH	47		4	6.0	61.0	33
120	INSPECT	4					44

Remington-Rand Division, Sperry Rand Corp.

FIG. 39–1. A shop order. All of the information except the order number, quantity, processing times, and start dates comes from the master route sheet.

Notice, too, the right-hand columns on Figure 39–1. The order calls for 200 of the item. Cleaning time will take 32.0 hours, painting 10.0 hours, and so on. The "start date" column may be confusing. This company is using a "thousand-day" calendar. Cleaning is to start on day number 572, painting on day number 581. With thousand-day calendars, you give consecutive numbers to every workday for about 4 years and use them on all work schedules instead of regular dates. At the end of 4 years, start in again. You give everyone in the company a copy of a regular calendar with your day numbers printed in. Purchase orders and items going outside use regular calendar dates.

Master bills of materials and master route sheets *confer continuing processing authority;* they can be used again and again for repeat orders for the same product. Processing authority is actually not really permanent, though, because you change products and processes all the time.

COST ESTIMATING

Before you make any product, you'd better estimate its cost. Production control doesn't make cost estimates very often, but it works with engineering, accounting, and sales as they make estimates.

In job-lot manufacturing, when most manufacturing is to customer's order, cost estimating is very important because the prices quoted to customers are determined largely by the expected cost of producing the orders. Competition for orders is generally keen enough so that you won't get very much business if you quote prices much over your costs. At the same time, you don't want to quote such low prices that you get the business, but lose money on it.

In cost estimating you try to do cost accounting in advance. So you have to figure your expected costs of materials, labor, overhead, and any extras. Calculating these ahead is a lot of work, almost as much, in fact, as you would have to do if you already had the order and were planning its production. For assembled products here's what you have to do: first, make up a parts list; second, decide the kind and quality of raw material required for each part; third, figure out, for each part, the operations needed and the special tooling required, if any, for every operation; and, fourth, figure the costs of all of these materials, operations, tools, and extras. Then add up, add in overhead, and you have your cost.

Job-lot shops have to bid for so many orders that they don't get, that the cost of making estimates has to be held down. Customers often ask several companies to submit bids, but only one gets the job. Some job-lot shops have to bid on five to ten or more jobs for every one they get. So they don't go through all of this work in making up most of their estimates.

They just have to use short-cut estimating methods even though that sacrifices some accuracy. Here are some short cuts. From past jobs, get the cost per pound or ton of the job. Use that on new jobs. How much will a new job weigh? Multiply by the old cost per pound and you have a rough cost estimate. Or on sheet metal jobs: How much per square foot of metal used have past jobs cost? How many square feet will the new job take? Multiply and get your cost estimate. House builders do that. They figure the cost per square foot of floor space, or even per cubic foot, in houses they build. With these figures they can look at plans for a new house and guess pretty closely what it will cost to build.

Rough estimates don't necessarily lose you any money. Some will be a little low and you may lose money on them, but others will be a

Form 377-8 Rev. TPM

COST ESTIMATE SUMMARY

DIVISION _____

Customer's Name _____   Date Completed _____

Customer's Part No. _____ Part Name _____
Date Required _____ Delivery Promised _____

Customer Quantity Requirements _____
Total Quantity this Order _____ Tool Design Flow Time _____ Tool Design $ _____
Quantity for Tool Recovery * _____ Tool Mfg. Flow Time _____ Tool Mfg. $ _____
Quantity per Set-Up _____ Production Flow Time _____ Tool Purch's. $ _____
Material - Purchased ( ) Furnished ( )   TOTAL FLOW TIME _____ TOTAL $ _____
MATERIAL _____ Add ___% _____
_____ TOTAL TOOL $ _____

No.	DEPARTMENT NAME	STD. D.P.L. Hrs. PER 100	STD. D.P.L. $ PER 100	DEPT. COST PER 100 PCS.	SET-UP HRS.	SET-UP COST	SET-UP CHARGE SUMMARY
301	Automatics						Set-Up Cost (without Scrap) _____
302	Turret Lathes						___ Pcs. Set-Up Scrap - Mat'l. _____
303	Milling Etc.						___ Pcs. Set-Up Scrap - ½ Labor _____
304	Drill Presses						SUB - TOTAL _____
305	Surface Grinding						Add ___% G and A, Div. Adm. _____
306	Cylinder Grinding						
307	Bench Work						TOTAL _____
308	Punch Presses						
309	Comp. Machining						
310	Assembly						
311	Flex. Rotor Pump						
312							COST ESTIMATE SUMMARY
313	Nene Machining						Manufacturing Cost /100 _____
314	Inspection						Add ___% G and A, Div. Adm. _____
315	Packaging						SUB - TOTAL _____
316	Pre-Production						Royalties _____ _____
319	Hydraulic Coupling						_____ _____
320	Comp. Mach'g. Exp.						_____ _____
321	Tumbling						SUB - TOTAL _____
322	Rubber Lab.						Profit ___% _____
323	Repairs						
324	Heat Treat-Plating						
							SALES PRICE _____
	TOTALS						

Add ___% Variance _____
Add Material Cost per 100 _____   QUOTATIONS TO CUSTOMER:
Add ___% Scrap Allowance _____   Date _____
SUB - TOTAL _____   Price per _____ Pieces $ _____ $ _____
Add Tooling Recovery per 100 _____   Separate Tooling Charge _____ _____
Manufacturing Cost (without Set-up _____   Set - Up Charge _____ _____
Notes on Quotation _____

* Total Quantity of Sales expected before Major Design Change OR Total Quantity which Tools will Produce whichever is smaller is to be used.

Thompson Products, Inc.

FIG. 39-2. Cost estimate summary showing the many items which must be included.

little high and you'll make extra on them. It will average out. But will it? Don't count on it. Smart customers will give you all the jobs when you are low and give your competitor all the jobs when he is low. You don't get so many of the jobs when you are high. Make your estimates as carefully and accurately as you can afford to. Remember though that you can't afford to spend too much time on them.

On big jobs, cost estimates, even if carefully worked out, are often just starting points for more talks. The customer may want you to come up with lower figures, so he will let you cut a corner here and there. After you've done that he might want a still lower figure. Remember the "value analysis" discussion on page 710? Customer company buyers often tell you what *their* estimators say that *your* costs ought to be and so insist on your getting your price near that figure—but without any further design changes.

You of course try to whittle costs all you can to meet the figure. But if business is bad or if the contract is big, you may just cut your price and take the contract even at a slight loss. Get the contract and you recover your overhead or most of it. Besides, as you keep making products to fill the contract, your own people will figure out ways to save a little here and there. Also you can ask the customer to send over his estimators to your plant to tell your men how they figure that you can make the product at such a low cost.

Cost estimates should always be tied in with volume. Volume lets you use greater depth of tooling (more mechanization). Remember that with big volume your high tooling cost turns into low product costs. But for little orders you can afford to sink only small amounts in special tooling, so your costs will never be very low. The point is that your costs and bid prices depend on how many products the customer wants to buy. You must know that before you can quote a price.

How about companies that make products to stock and not to customers' orders? Do they have to estimate costs? Mostly yes, but not always. If you make thousands of items and are thinking about making another item that requires no new machines, it is almost as simple just to make some of the new items and see what they cost. Also this way you can try selling them. If they sell you keep on. If they don't sell, or if in too small volume, or at too low a price, quit making them.

Not often can make-to-stock companies escape estimating so easily. In fact, cost estimating for stock items is *very* important on high volume. It ties in with good market forecasting and depth of tooling. Know your future volume and you can choose the right depth of tooling and so get the lowest possible cost for that volume.

But don't overlook price. Can you sell the volume you started with (in your calculations) at a *price* that will cover the costs and more? If the answer is yes, you are in pretty good shape. But if the answer is no, you start in all over again on the merry-go-round of trying to cut costs some more at the expense of product frills. This makes you ask again at what price and in what volume will the customer buy the "frill-less" product. All of this is of utmost importance because you sink so much money into costly production lines that losses can be ruinous if you guess wrong.

What part does production control play in all of this? In mass-production shops, not too much. But in job shops delivery time is very important. Production control figures that out. Sometimes, too, quick deliveries are possible only if you work overtime on some machines or if you put jobs on poorly suited machines (because the best suited are busy). These things affect costs, so production control is sometimes in on cost estimating.

STUDY QUESTIONS

1. What justification does the text give for discussing production control largely from the point of view of makers of assembled metal products? Give the supporting arguments.
2. Outline, as briefly as you can, the main jobs of production control.
3. "Engineers design products, but they should let the factory decide how to make them." Discuss.
4. Compare master schedules when you make-to-order with master schedules when you make-to-stock. Explain fully.
5. How do production programs differ from master schedules? Discuss.
6. How far ahead should master schedules extend? How do you keep them ahead? Discuss.
7. When would you use master schedules for classes of products instead of specific products? Discuss.
8. How does production control get its authority to order parts made? Explain fully.
9. How does your manufacturing capacity affect your schedules? Discuss fully.
10. Compare producing and processing authority. What do the terms mean? When would you use each one?
11. Is a shop order for a certain lot of parts an example of producing authority or processing authority? Explain.
12. How accurately should you try to estimate costs before you make products? Why not more accuracy or less accuracy?

CASE 39–1. THE SAGINAW COMPANY

The Saginaw Company, which manufactures parts for the automobile industry, has, in recent months, experienced serious scheduling problems caused by the sales department's changing specifications on orders after the order has been scheduled or partially fabricated. This has been a source of serious irritation, because it greatly increases the difficulty of completing, on schedule, all the orders in the plant. The company's production is all to customer orders; so the product design is determined mainly by the whims of the customers. In order to get orders, the sales department often makes concessions with respect to installing special features on its products. Customers in the industry have come to expect parts manufacturers, such as the Saginaw Company, to allow design changes after the order has been entered on a fixed schedule.

This practice greatly increases the problems of the manufacturing and the production control departments and likewise adds to their costs of operation. The foremen are conscious of these costs: their bonuses are based on the economy of production in their respective departments. The heads of the manufacturing departments, therefore, often resist making these design changes. The relations between the manufacturing and sales departments have become strained on numerous occasions.

The production control department also finds the design changes costly to make. In the past the production control department has operated on a budget based upon the number of orders which are scheduled and produced each budget period. The design changes received from the sales department are not regarded as additional orders and so are not computed in the production control department's budget; but it has become evident that, although these changes are not officially considered new orders, they often take more man-hours than original orders because of the last-minute rescheduling that is required. Naturally, they are concerned over unnecessary charges to their cost records. Both the manufacturing and production control departments have insisted that something be done to reduce these extra cost orders. Management has experimented with various plans aimed at solving the problem.

Should design changes be permitted after production has started? If so, should the customer be charged extra? What do you think of the way the production control department budget operates? How would you reconcile the differences between the sales department and the manufacturing and production control departments?

Chapter 40

ORDER CONTROL

PRODUCTION control methods differ so much that we can't describe them all. But we can describe some commonly used types even while admitting that few companies fit the picture perfectly. A good many companies fit the patterns fairly well.

We start with job-lot shops. Everything that they make, they make to order. True, sometimes they get repeat orders for the same thing, but they make very few things, or even nothing, to stock. Manufacture is in lots; nothing is made continuously.

Job-lot shops use "order control." You give every lot or order a number and plan its production individually. You make out separate directives to cover every lot's production and usually keep a separate cost record for every lot.

Order control is expensive because you have to do all your production control work over again for every order. Paper work costs are high. Sometimes you can cut out some paper work by controlling operations only loosely. But loose control means that things will go wrong (orders will get lost, or not get finished on time) more often. Even with loose control, you still have to do most of the paper work. You can't cut out very much of it.

Look at Figure 40–1 for a preview of order control. Notice all the departments listed across the top, and all of the steps you go through listed down along the side. Notice, too, the arrows connecting the steps in the right-hand columns. Every step means papers (instructions and reports) going from one department to another.

PLANNING

All the "way-ahead" production control work is called planning. For an assembled product it starts with an order to assemble certain products. Planning has to "explode" the order into the hundreds of orders to do individual things that the factory needs.

Requirements Lists. Start by getting out from your file the master bill of materials (the parts list that engineering made out when you first made that product). It shows how many of each part you need; multiply by the number of products wanted. That gives you a parts "requirements" list.

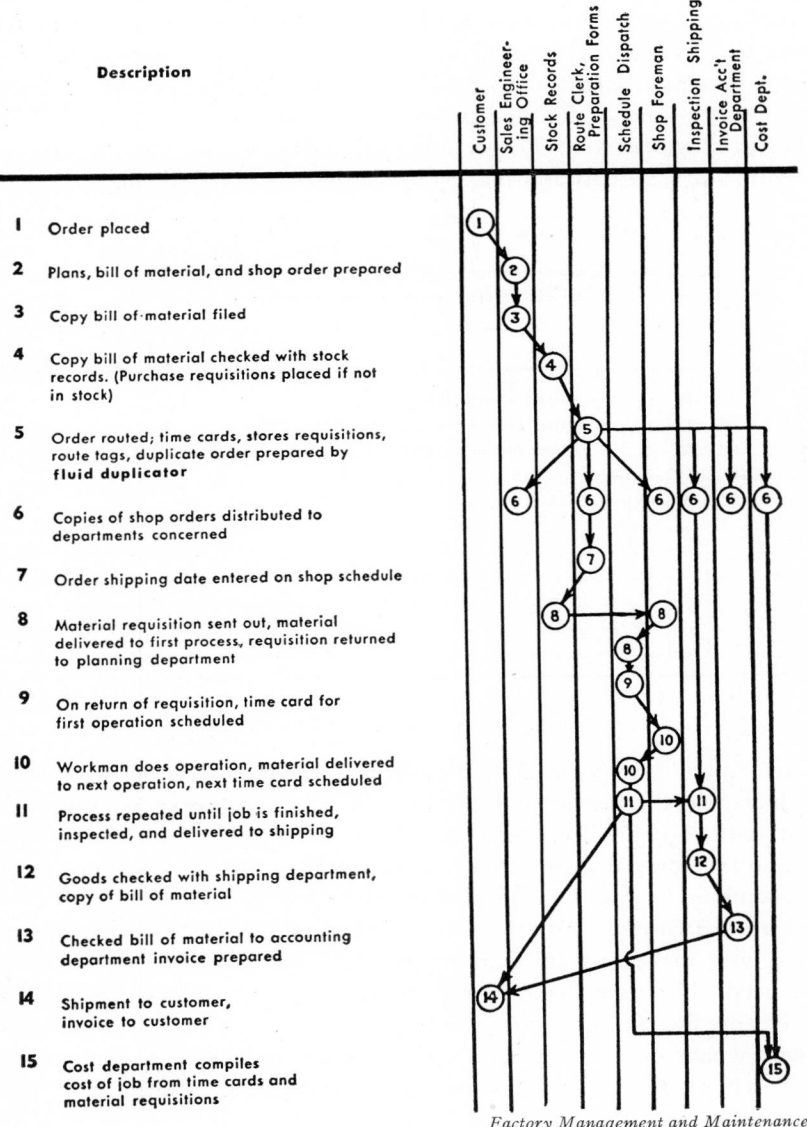

	Description	Customer	Sales Engineering Office	Stock Records	Route Clerk, Preparation Forms	Schedule Dispatch	Shop Foreman	Inspection Shipping	Invoice Acc't Department	Cost Dept.
1	Order placed	①								
2	Plans, bill of material, and shop order prepared		②							
3	Copy bill of·material filed		③							
4	Copy bill of material checked with stock records. (Purchase requisitions placed if not in stock)			④						
5	Order routed; time cards, stores requisitions, route tags, duplicate order prepared by **fluid duplicator**				⑤					
6	Copies of shop orders distributed to departments concerned	⑥		⑥		⑥	⑥	⑥		⑥
7	Order shipping date entered on shop schedule					⑦				
8	Material requisition sent out, material delivered to first process, requisition returned to planning department		⑧		⑧	⑧				
9	On return of requisition, time card for first operation scheduled					⑨				
10	Workman does operation, material delivered to next operation, next time card scheduled				⑩	⑩				
11	Process repeated until job is finished, inspected, and delivered to shipping					⑪	⑪			
12	Goods checked with shipping department, copy of bill of material							⑫		
13	Checked bill of material to accounting department invoice prepared								⑬	
14	Shipment to customer, invoice to customer	⑭								
15	Cost department compiles cost of job from time cards and material requisitions									⑮

Factory Management and Maintenance

FIG. 40–1. Steps in a typical order control procedure.

Put on the order number and assembly period (the week or month) dates, and you have an assembly order. Send a copy to the assembly department and another to the finished parts stock room. The first tells the assembly foreman what his men are to make, how many, out of what, and when. The second tells the stock room foreman that he has to gather together the list of parts by a certain date and deliver them to the assembly floor.

Parts Orders. But this is not all that planning does. It checks the requirements list against records of parts on hand and orders more of the items that you make yourself and asks purchasing to get more of the things you buy. Remember, too, that some items are made or bought for this one kind of finished product only, and some items are used in other products as well. To get low costs you combine the requirements of common use items and make out single orders for them.

EMPL. NO. & DATE COMP.	OPER. NO.	MACH. OR DEPT. NO.	OPER. STD	SET UP STD	TOTAL STD	TOOLS	DESCRIPTION	AMT. O.K.	INSPECTOR
	1	86	.05	.50	.56	Shear Die R-1740-1-P	Shear		
	2	13	.11	.25	.36	Rotary Fixture R-1740	Drill 3/16 Hole		
	3	13	.12	.25	.37	Rotary Fixture R-1740	Tap per B/P		
	4	160	.06	.00	.06	--	Grind		
	5	90	.05	.00	.05	--	Degrease		

Shop order header: JOB NUMBER A6781 · PART NUMBER R-67904 · QUANTITY 1000 · ORDER DATE 1/19 · START DATE 1/29 · REQ. DATE 2/15 · PART NUMBER R-1740 · SHEET NO. 1 OF 1 · NAME Timing Gear · MATERIAL SPECIFICATIONS C. R. S. · THICK. 1/4" · WIDTH 2" · LENGTH 4"

Van W. Evans & Co.

FIG. 40–2. A shop order for 1,000 timing gears.

Remember lead time also. You are planning today, in March, for products that the factory will assemble in August. Some items you won't want until August, but others will have to be ready by the middle of June so that they can be put into subassemblies that later go into bigger subassemblies before they go into the final product.

Materials Orders. So far we have talked about finished parts. But for things you make you have to figure, item by item, the raw materials you need. This gives you a new requirements list, a raw materials requirements list. So, for each raw material item, you check what you need against what you have on hand and on order, and ask purchasing to get more whenever you need more. And, again, don't forget lead time. Those parts that have to be ready by June 15 take time to process into parts. Maybe you'll have to start making some of them by May 1. And if it takes a month to get more raw materials, you have to get your order out to the supplier by April 1, which is only tomorrow.

Manufacturing Facilities. Planning also has to check to see if you have the tools and machines needed to make the product and its parts.

Normally you have them already, but you sometimes make new products that require new machines, or you start making something a new way and need new tools or jigs. Planning has to keep checking on such things because, without some prodding of the toolroom, some tools are sure not to be ready on time. In some companies planning itself has to order the new tools and jigs. And that, of course, has to be done still farther ahead. Some companies call that pre-planning work.

Shop Orders. Planning makes up all of the shop orders to make parts, materials requisitions, job tickets, and move orders that the factory will need. Sometimes, though, the planning section of the production control department *leaves off* all dates. It turns all of these papers over to the scheduling section of production control. Schedulers in that section fill in all the dates telling the factory when to do things.

ORDER SCHEDULING

Assembled products schedules show certain quantities to be made (assembled) in a month or week. Some are actually assembled early in the month, others late. In job-lot work you normally *finish* making *all* the parts and subassemblies *before* you assemble the first finished product in a lot. You can see, though, that you have some big piles of parts around on the first day of a month. To keep the pile down within reason you sometimes cut up the parts lots into several smaller lots and schedule them to be finished one after the other during the month.

But whether you process a month's supply as one lot (or more or less) and whether the assembled products are customers' orders or whether they are just items on your master schedule and as yet unsold, you start, when setting schedules, with the assembly schedule. You start there and figure the time needed for putting together subassemblies. That gives you the dates by which parts need to be finished. Then you figure the parts manufacturing time, allowing for time between operations, and finally get a start date. All of this, of course, for each different part.

That tells you when to *start* an order into production. This date you put on the shop order. Nearly always you put the wanted *completion date for every operation* on the order too. Then it will always be easy for foremen to tell which jobs to do first and also you can find out quickly if an order falls behind schedule anywhere along the line.

When an order falls behind, it is usually not too hard to get it back on schedule if the cause for its delay is fixed quickly. The total time allowed to make the order usually has a lot of "fat" in it. You allow more time between operations than is really needed. Also you almost never "overlap" operations (start operation 2 on some products before all of them get through operation 1). If you are in a jam you can squeeze out some of the fat or overlap operations or work overtime.

Sometimes though you have more trouble, trouble from having too many orders to get out in too short a time. Changes in the product mix make a little trouble because some departments end up with unplanned overloads. But rush orders make much more trouble. Some customers send in their order today and want their orders *now*, so sales wants you to add on a few extra orders for rush production; all in addition to the regular schedule of course—not in place of anything else. So you end up overloaded. Sometimes you can get out of trouble by delaying orders for stock items; you let them get finished at a later date. If they get done before you run out, no harm will be done.

But why always be in a jam when rush orders come in? Why not allow a little space in the schedule for them? That is just what you can do. Don't plan, at first, to operate at full schedule. Allow say 5 to 10 per cent for last-minute rush jobs. Often this works out very well, although not perfectly. It is not quite perfect because you don't allow very much space in the schedule for rush jobs for fear that they might not come in. If only a few come in, you'll still be busy. But if a good many come in, you are overloaded.

"LOADS"

The factory's "load" is its work ahead. We can express it in tons, in dollar value, in time, or in other ways. Mostly, for production control use, we talk about time. A plant, department, or machine has so many hours', days', weeks', or months' work ahead already authorized and scheduled.

Master schedules are never approved until you match their load against the factory's capacity. Generally that is done only in over-all terms such as tons, dollars, or, if you make only a few kinds of products, product units. If you manufacture to stock, the approved master schedule gives the factory its load (a full load when business is good) for a given period of time in the future.

But if you manufacture to order, you just add the load of new orders to your present load, not as an increase in today's load, but as an extension of your load into future months. You accept orders, giving early delivery promise dates up to your capacity. Then you keep on accepting orders, but you add the load to future months and give more distant promise dates.

A plant with a load that matches its over-all capacity usually has all departments loaded about equally. But not wholly so. Product mix variations throw unequal loads onto departments. Also, *within* departments, individual machine loads vary. When you think that you have approved a schedule that will give you nice smooth operation, it doesn't always work out quite so smoothly down at the machines.

The point that we are making is that you can schedule orders the way we described on page 779 (working back from assembly dates to get start dates for shop orders) and think that you are sure to have enough time on machines to carry out all the operations, and then find that you have overscheduled some machines.

Remember that in talking about scheduling orders we paid attention only to when you wanted to get things done. We paid *no attention* to whether or not your machines would prove to be overloaded. Most of the time it is safe to set schedules that way (paying no attention to machine loads) because you have enough machines to turn out the total plant work load that was approved in the form of a master schedule.

SCRAP TICKET		
N.º 13333	**Total Prod. Feb. 13-Feb. 19: 14,525**	
	F.O. NO. 260185	

PART NAME......Coil................................ PART NO...**711-127-20**.......

DATE **2-20-53**......... DEPT. **46**...............QUAN. .....**1048**..........

REASON ....Coils damaged in winding and cutting....................

.........(Breaking in new operator)..................................

SIGNED .... APPROVED........................
AUTHORIZED
BY ....
                                        CHIEF INSPECTOR

COST DEPARTMENT

TOTAL QUANTITY THIS MONTH

TOTAL COST		COST PER 1000	
MAT'L:	LABOR:	MAT'L:	LABOR:

The Lionel Corp.

FIG. 40-3. A scrap report.

But now and then scheduling that way gets you into jams because of the ups and downs of individual machine time needed. And of course the problem is at its worst when business is best—when you are pushing the factory to turn out all it can and when you just can't find any extra machine to relieve a bottleneck.

Some companies keep an individual machine "load" record for every likely bottleneck machine. Here's how you keep it. Every time that a new order comes out, see how many hours of machine time it will take on such a machine. Add these hours to the machine's load. Every time a job is finished, subtract its time. This will give you an up-to-the-minute record of work scheduled but not yet done on the machine.

One minor point: you'll probably want to keep the load record in terms of *standard* hours of work ahead of the machine. Also, when a job is done, subtract its standard-hour time—not the actual time it took. That gets rid of your total being affected by how fast a man works. On the other hand, if men work at 125 per cent efficiency, they'll do

10 hours work in 8. A work load of 200 standard hours is about 160 hours (4 weeks) actual work.

Suppose that a new order comes out with a due date of April 15 for work on a machine that is already loaded till May 1? Using load records you find this out right away, today, a month or so ahead of April 15, and can do something about it in time. Maybe you can work overtime, or send the job outside. Or maybe you can't get it out, in which case you'll have to get the schedule changed.

MACHINE SCHEDULING

Rarely do you make up individual *machine* schedules except for big important machines. You could, though, for any machine, go through the orders ahead and find out not only its total load of work but also decide *when* each order should start and *when* it ought to finish. Then you'd have a machine schedule.

Normally you don't do that because it serves no useful purpose. You can stack up the orders in sequence and let these be the machine's schedule. Then, if some order gets held up and is not ready for the machine when it is supposed to be ready, you merely select the next order in the pile (provided that job has arrived in the department and is ready to work on). You don't have to re-do a whole plan for the machine's use. And when the held-up order is ready to go, you just put it on top of the pile ahead of other orders. Again no change in a plan.

The same is true if the machine gets behind. If orders are running several hours behind schedule, no records need changing. If you get very far behind, you can work overtime and catch up, but again record changes are few.

It is different, however, on your big machines or on bottleneck operations. For them you may want to plan a machine's use. You may even make a chart and see how things are shaping up. We talk about charts on page 787.

TOOL CONTROL

The controlling of orders, materials, and machines isn't enough. Factory machines are incomplete without all kinds of attachments. Generally production control just figures that all the tools, jigs, fixtures, and foundry patterns needed will be ready when they are needed and usually they are. But all that this means is that someone else controls tools; production control's work is mostly to check up on special tools and see that they will be ready.

The tool department keeps all the accessories in storage until they are needed. Normally it issues them to the man on the job when he is ready for them in exchange for one of his tool tags. Big accessories are of course delivered to the job ahead, and tool tags are not used.

Tools that wear out (cutting tools) are issued on requisitions that the foreman makes out.

Copies of shop orders always show the identification number of all special tools that a man will need for every operation. The orders tell him what tools to use and also tell the tool department (you send it a copy of the shop order) what tools will be wanted and when. It is up to the tool department to get them on time.

Don't forget, too, the need to control tools to cut expenses. Careless tool control always leads to wasteful tool use and high tool expense.

HOW MUCH CENTRALIZATION?

The production control department makes out the factory's assembly orders and shop orders for parts; it orders materials; and it tells each foreman what jobs are coming to him, what work to do, when it ought to be finished, and where next to send the job.

These directions finally have to go to the man on the job. He has to be told what to do. Here, at the firing line, you have a choice. Production control can put in its own men in all departments to pass out orders to the men, or you can let the foreman do it. If the foreman does it, you call it *decentralized* control. You let him, the foreman, decide *who* works on each job, and if there is a choice, you let him decide which machine to use, and you let him decide *when* to do the job (as long as he meets the due date).

Centralized Control. If you choose centralized production control, you put your own dispatch offices in every department. Of course you usually give the foreman copies of all the shop orders his men are, or will be, working on, but they are only to tell him what his men are doing. With tightly centralized control you make up all directives (including materials requisition, individual job tickets for every operation, and move orders to tell truckers where to take jobs) in the central office. These you send to dispatch offices in the various departments, where they hold them until the job comes along. Then the dispatch clerk issues them directly to the men when that job's turn comes.

Usually, with tight centralization, you get copies, after the work is done, of the man's job ticket (showing when he finished the job), inspectors' reports, and move tickets. These keep you informed. You almost always know exactly where everything is all the time. Job progress reports come through the dispatch offices to the central office, where you post them to a record that keeps you up to date on the progress of every order. The record that you keep there is put on a copy of the shop order. As the men's job tickets come in you check off the operations.

Decentralized Control. Decentralized control does two things. First, it transfers part of the work away from the production control department to the foremen, and, second, it cuts out part of the paper work. It works this way. Production control still makes up assembly orders and parts orders. And parts orders still list all operations and their wanted finish dates. Copies of these work orders go to all foremen of departments that will have anything to do on the order.

From here on it is up to the foreman. The foreman of the first department writes out a requisition for raw materials. He decides when to do the job and who does it. He (or his department clerk) writes out the man's job ticket. After the operation is done, he sends the job to the next department where the next foreman takes over. Each job has a "traveler" copy of the shop order that stays right with it. That identifies it and tells truckers where it goes next. There are no written move orders for truckers.

Some companies don't go quite so far with decentralizing. Production control makes out requisitions and job tickets ahead and sends them in an envelope along with the traveler copy of the shop order. This makes sure that they are made out right. Besides, it costs less to make them on the same office machines that make the shop order copies than it does to make them out in the shop.

Cutting Out Paper Work.   The paper work saving in decentralized control comes in cutting out written move orders to truckers and in cutting out reporting and posting the operations finished on a central production control record. But don't you lose all control if you cut that out? No, you lose only a little.

First, nearly all orders come along as scheduled. They have to just because the factory is working. It turns out work hour by hour and day by day. There is a *"pull"* there that pulls work through the plant. You don't always have to *"push"* jobs through. As long as you don't give the factory more orders than it can handle, and as long as your foremen pass out first jobs first, orders will come through and on time too.

Trouble is that troubles, big and little, interfere. Men are absent, a machine gets out of order for a day or two, you spoil more materials half way through than you expected, an order gets lost, and so on. Usually none of these things happen and most orders do come through on time, but you can't assemble a refrigerator without door hinges. You need *all* the parts. If a few items get held up, you are in trouble.

If you cut out the reporting system, you don't find out about delays until you want the finished item. By then you need the item badly. Is there any way to cut down on the paper work without losing control over individual operations? Yes, but you have to put in a little paper work again.

Here's what airplane companies do (and the big ones have maybe 20,000 parts orders in the shop all the time). Foremen make *no* reports of what they *do*, only of what they *don't do*. They make daily reports of jobs in their departments that are *behind schedule*, and why, and what is being done. If a job is not reported to production control as behind schedule, then it is on schedule. No news is good news. Some companies don't go quite so far in cutting out reports. They have foremen send in a jobs-completed report too.

The streamlined method (reporting only jobs behind) isn't quite so good as it sounds because you don't know if an operation is not *started* on time; you don't hear about it until it isn't *finished* on time. Also you need to know the "attrition" (how many items are rejected and thrown out after each operation). The number of items in a lot goes down a little after most operations. This affects operating time for future operations, and it gets to be vitally important if very many pieces get scrapped. If you end up with too few pieces, you'll have to send through a small rush order for enough more to bring the lot back up to size— and orders like that are very expensive.

False counts and disappearing orders also give you trouble. Piece-workers sometimes report that they turned out more than they did. Sometimes men spoil items and throw them away without reporting them. If you believe their job card report, you may be wrong and not know about the loss until several operations later. Better have inspectors count production when they inspect the products.

Orders get lost, too. There are so many trays, racks, or tote pans of materials of jobs ahead, jobs done, or jobs held up lying around that jobs just get lost now and then. Sometimes traveler copies of the shop order get lost, so no one knows what the half-made parts are. Or a lot is held up until some of its rejects are reworked, or it is held up because it is rejected or because the next operation's tools aren't ready.

Every company and every department has its nooks and corners where such things pile up with no one interested in them until some day when a wild-eyed expediter comes desperately looking for them.

Expediters. "Expediters" ("stock chasers") are a necessary evil in order control. They father fussy or "rush" jobs through the plant, find lost orders, get rid of reasons for holdups, and push orders through in a hurry. They are necessary because things will go wrong, and they help get them straightened out. They are an evil because the only way that they can rush things through is to get foremen to disregard regular schedules and even to tear down machine setups to do the rush job. It is all very costly and irritating, but there seems to be no other way to do the work that they do.

DISPATCHING

"Dispatching" means handing out work orders to the men. You don't hear much about dispatching in decentralized control where the foreman passes out the jobs. Instead it is a term used where the production control's branch office (the dispatch office) in each department tells men what jobs to work on. And you have such branch offices only with centralized control. Dispatching also includes getting reports back from the men when they finish jobs.

REPLANNING AND RESCHEDULING

You can never get all of the output out of a plant that ideally it should put out. That you know and allow for in master scheduling. You approve only a total load that you really expect to get.

But you have to handle individual orders differently. You must always plan and schedule them *as if nothing ever went wrong*. Why? Because, nothing does go wrong on most orders most of the time. You know, for example, that tools sometimes won't be on hand or that men will be absent, and you know about all the other holdups that always happen. But you can't tell ahead where they will happen, or when, or *what order* will be held up. You can't plan an extra day of machine time for an order to go on a radial drill next Tuesday because Joe Blow, the operator, will be absent that day. No, except for scrap, you have to plan for everything going well. For scrap, you raise the quantity a few extra pieces to allow for attrition.

Notice what planning and scheduling for everything going well does to you. It throws you out of gear every time something goes wrong. You have to change schedule dates and rearrange machine schedules every time. But can't you avoid most of the replanning and rescheduling by starting jobs a little earlier, so that the time allowed has more slack in it? Yes, that will help, and it does take care of most delays. Also sometimes (but not often) things go the other way. A man does a job faster than you expect.

But there are other plan upsets that aren't just scheduling matters. How about an inspector throwing out way more than the usual number of rejects (or even throwing out much less than you allowed for)? Now you don't have enough pieces in the lot (or you have too many). Or some pieces just disappear? Or a whole order gets lost? Or engineering (or the customer) changes the design so we have to do some operations over again. Or the customer wants to raise the quantity—or to cut it. Or he decides that he has to have his order now instead of next month.

All of these changes ruin production control's plans and schedules. If you were in a production control department, you'd probably spend more time remaking plans and schedules than you spent making them up the first time.

Here are the kinds of things you do. Customer wants quick delivery? You change the wanted completion dates for all remaining operations on his order. Or split it in two parts and "send-ahead" one part. That way you can send him part of his order fast. Customer wants to up the quantity? Hold up his first order wherever it is, and start a rush second order for the added quantity through until it catches up with the first. By then you'll probably have to rush the whole order through the rest of the operations, but at least you save double setups for the rest of the operations. Customer wants to cut the quantity? Cut it right where it is. Change quantities shown on the orders for remaining operations. Decide what to do with cut-off quantity. Issue orders for reworking it into something else. Have sales charge the customer for the loss.

What if an order gets lost? Put an expediter on it. If he finds it, it will probably be behind schedule and will need top priority through remaining operations. If it stays lost, make out a new order and rush it through. That may upset your materials inventories (you have drawn out twice as much materials as you planned), so you may be in trouble.

What if an inspector rejects too many? Have them reinspected right away. Must you reject them? Maybe (suppose the flaw is just looks and won't hurt the product's operation) you can get permission from engineering to go ahead and use them. But if not, then how about repairing them? Often that is possible (as, for example, with poor soldered connections in a TV set). So make up work orders covering the rework operations. Meanwhile hold up the rest of the lot. Then put the repaired items back and rush the whole lot along until it gets back on schedule.

Do you get an idea of what replanning and rescheduling is? It is lots of little things, and it goes on all the time and in total is one of production control's big jobs.

GRAPHIC CONTROLS

Over the years people have tried to picture machine schedules on charts. Henry Gantt did it 50 years ago, and for a while his charts were sometimes used. Today you'd look a long time before you'd find anyone using a Gantt chart regularly in production control. Gantt charts aren't so bad for showing your planned machine use before a period starts. But they get all mixed up after production starts when you try to show changes and replans and reschedules on them.

Today you can buy any one of several kinds of commercial variations of Gantt charts. Productrol boards and Schedugraphs are the most common. Both use a time scale across the top, and both use lines down the side for your machines or orders, whichever you are picturing. They are most often kept in the central production control office and not out in the shop.

Productrol boards have two rows of small holes across the board for each line along the left. To show the use of a machine you put pegs, with strings attached, in holes for the time that jobs will start and stop. The lower row of holes shows the plan for the machine's use. Production, day by day, can be shown by putting other pegs in the upper row of holes for each machine. Colored and numbered pegs give you ways to show quite a bit of information. A string, placed vertically and moved daily, is used to show you where you are, to let you see where production is lagging.

Schedugraphs (see Fig. 40–4) are a little different. Each machine has its line, but the lines that you see are really just the bottom edges of a series of overlapping flaps that extend clear across the horizontal space. Each flap is set below the other by one-half inch, so that normally only

FIG. 40–4.   A Schedugraph production control board.

the bottom half-inch of each one is visible, the rest of it being covered by the flap above. The bottom half-inch of each flap is a transparent pocket, so that anything inserted in it shows the bottom half-inch when the flap above covers it.

To use Schedugraphs for machine schedules, you have to make out a card for each operation to be done on the machine. This is not a man's job card. It is special, made out just to use in the Schedugraph. The left side of the card shows everything about a job, including the time it will keep the machine busy. The card is then cut to length, depending on how long the job will tie up the machine. A 1-day job card could be, say, 2 inches long, and a 5-day job card, 10 inches long. Then you put the cards for jobs ahead for a machine into the transparent pocket of the flap for that machine one after the other from left to right. The bottom half-inch of these cards is colored red, so that when the flaps are all flat down, the red shows the time the machine is to be busy. Production against the orders is shown by colored inserts put into the pocket to show how much work is done. A vertical colored strip, moved daily, tells you where you stand all the time.

There are other commercial devices, but none is used as widely as Productrol boards and Schedugraphs. Both of these devices give a better picture of production and are easier to use than Gantt charts. Best thing about them is that they high-light trouble spots and often will show up prospective trouble before it occurs. Worst thing is that they are extras. All the work of keeping them up is extra. With or without them, you keep the same records. During slack times they are of little value to most companies because there is no difficulty then in getting orders out. But, get swamped with orders, and Productrol boards and Schedugraphs help.

Both devices, Productrol boards in particular, are good in inventory control. In fact, Productrol boards are probably better for inventory control than they are for scheduling orders or for scheduling machines.

TABULATING MACHINES

Electronic computers make the headlines today. We talked about them in Chapter 32. They are the last word in tabulating machines.

There is so much detail work to do in production control that all companies try to mechanize it all they can. Nearly everyone, big and little, uses tabulating equipment (the kind that uses punched cards). But electronic computers cost so much that only big companies can make them pay.

You can use tabulating machines (made by International Business Machines or Sperry Rand) to keep your inventory records. They will post quantities ordered, add quantities received, figure average prices, subtract quantities issued, put prices on requisitions, figure new quantities on hand, and print lists of any or all of these things.

They will multiply quantities of items needed (item by item) to make an assembly by the number of assemblies you want and get the number of each part that you need. They will add in a safety quantity to cover production losses. Then they will compare what you need with what you have on hand and on order, and tell you which items need ordering and how many.

Same with shop orders to make parts. They will compute operation times and print up a shop order complete. Look at Fig. 40–7. All the information on it was put there by machine.

Leaving out electronic computers, regular tabulating machines use $3\frac{1}{4} \times 7\frac{3}{8}$ inch cards. Figure 40–5 shows a Sperry Rand card. Figure 40–6 is an IBM card. The punched holes carry coded information. Notice on each card, at the top, the printed letters and numbers. They tell you

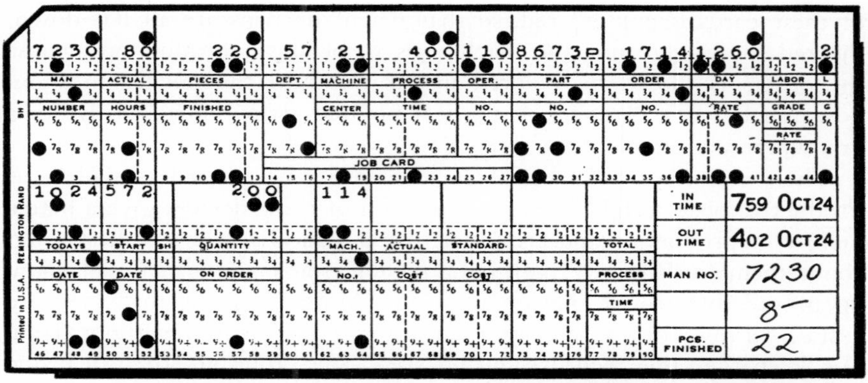

FIG. 40–5. A job ticket. This ticket has been used in the shop, the work time reported, and the information punched into the card so that it can be used in a tabulating machine or a data computer.

what the punched holes mean. The machine doesn't need anything but the holes, but you and I can tell what the card says only if it is "interpreted."

To use tabulating machines in production control work you need to prepare several packs or "decks" of basic data cards. For every finished product you need one deck as a parts list. That means one card for every kind of part. Figure 40–6 is a card out of a master parts deck.

When you get an order to make certain assembled products, the order shows order number, quantity, and the schedule period when they will be assembled. You punch up one card with that information. Call that an assembly order card. Hold it for a moment. Put your master deck of parts cards through your card duplicator and make a duplicate deck. Put away the master deck. Now put the new parts card deck into your calculator unit along with the assembly order card. The calculator will

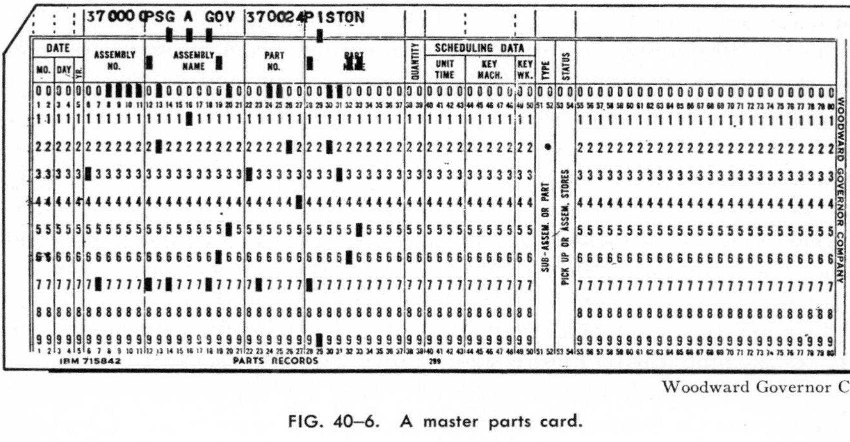

FIG. 40–6. A master parts card.

FORM 93-1874-5 **INTERNATIONAL BUSINESS MACHINES CORPORATION**
ENDICOTT, NEW YORK

MANUFACTURING ORDER—FACTORY COPY

ACCOUNT CONTROL NO. — PART NO.	PROD. SEQ. OR ACCOUNT NO.	ZONE NO.	QUANTITY	SHEET NO.
120615	0115		500	

GEAR STUD

CERTIFIED ROUTING

DESCRIPTION OF OPERATION	√	OPER. NO.	DEPT. NO.	TOOL NO.	MACH. GROUP	SCHED. DATE
RAW STORE 061971699		1	500	2560	32	312
TURN FORM LEAVE TWO SHOULDERS .007 PLUS .002 MINUS .000 OVER SIZE THIRD CUTOFF AND SLOT		5	150	55270	91	113
GRD LARGE SHLDR		25	070		120	313
GRD SMALL SHLDR		30	070		120	413
INSPECT		35	401			014
CLEAN AND OIL		40	401			314
STOCK			830			115
EC 3698						
EC 270						
EC 14223 091048 17 01 10	49					

ON DETAIL PARTS ENGINEERING CHANGE ON PRINT AND MANUFACTURING ORDER MUST AGREE.

International Business Machines Corp.

FIG. 40–7. An assembly order. This assembly order was prepared automatically on tabulating equipment.

calculate, card by card, how many in total of each part will be needed and will punch that into the new parts cards. It also puts in the order number. You end up with a parts requirements pack of cards. Put it through the printer unit, and you get a bill of materials (up to twenty copies if you want them) for the order. Figure 40–7 is a copy of a mechanically prepared assembly order.

Each card in the new pack of cards shows the *requirements* of a subassembly or part. Subassemblies are, however, also made of lesser assemblies and individual parts. You use their master decks of parts cards just the same way to make new sets of their parts requirements cards. If a major subassembly contains minor subassemblies, you do it over again for the minor subassemblies until you get the requirements of all individual parts.

Next you check what you need against what you have—all automatically, of course. Here you use a second file of cards—cards that tell you what you have on hand and on order. These cards are called "stock status" cards. You keep a "stock status" card for every item. Each status card shows the item's identification number, name, whether it is bought or made, and if made, the kind of raw material and amount required for one unit of product, the amount on hand, the amount on order, the known future demands for assembly orders already issued, and *the projected future balance*. The status card is not the item's stock record card but is in addition to regular stock cards on which all receipts and issues of the item are recorded.

Put the requirements cards and the status cards into the machine and it will subtract the new requirements from the old balance and will punch a new status card for every part. Then you can print up a materials status list and look over it to see what items will be low or even out of stock. The list will show up every item whose new balance is below its safety reserve.

The stock control supervisor then decides what parts to order made or asks purchasing to buy. Sometimes, in mechanical tabulation, the typical lead time that must be allowed for getting new supplies is punched into the card and printed on the status reports. If your cards show lead times, the machines will tell you when you'd better get the order started.

Manufacturing orders for parts can also be made mechanically. There is on file for every *part* a master pack of individual operation cards for every operation. Each of these master cards shows most or all of the following: the part identification number; the operation name, number, and sequence; drawing number, if any; special tooling required; class of labor, setup time, teardown time, running time per hundred pieces, and piece rate.

A shop order card showing the order number, quantity ordered, and wanted finishing date is put into the card duplicating machine along with the master pack of operation cards, and *a new set of operation cards for that shop order* is made out. The operating time per unit of product for each operation is multiplied by the quantity on the order, and the total time required for each operation is punched into its card.

These cards can be put through the printing machine to print the shop order for the making of the part. If the wanted operation completion date for every operation must be shown so that the shop order can be used as a schedule, that, too, can be done mechanically. The master card would have to show the normal time between each operation and the finishing time of the preceding operation.

The equipment can then be set to punch operation completion dates into every operation card by working backwards from the completion date for the last operation, and subtracting the sum of the last operation time plus the normal time between the last two operations to give the wanted completion date for the next to the last operation. Repeat this process setting completion dates, operation by operation, back to the first, and you get the order's proper start date. Don't forget, though, that doing it this way gives no consideration to the load of work ahead of any operation, so that you can't be positive that, during periods of high production, the dates can be met.

It is possible mechanically to keep records of the load of work ahead of machines and to avoid the weakness named above. It is also possible mechanically to make out job tickets, materials requisitions, inspection tags, tool orders, move orders, etc. Design changes, materials changes, and the addition or subtraction of parts or changes in the number of places where common parts are used can all be done mechanically, once the system is set up.

REPRODUCING SHOP DIRECTIVES

Two or more copies are needed of most shop directives. The fluid duplicator ("Ditto") process is probably the most widely used method of duplicating shop orders and other instructions. But you'll find companies using mimeographs, multiliths, and occasionally addressographs. Tabulators too can make close to twenty legible carbon copies at one printing, or they can make a Ditto master.

Fluid duplicators are especially useful in production control because you can take an old master copy from which old orders have been run and use it for new orders. Just put the new order number on a separate piece of paper cut to size so that it will cover the old information that you don't want. Fasten both sheets on the machine, and it will run off new orders as if you had prepared all the information especially for the new order. It not only saves work and expense but cuts out mistakes. If all the parts lists or operation lists on the old order were originally typed right, they are bound to be right on the new order.

Multiliths are occasionally used. This is offset printing, uses fairly expensive equipment, and requires a skilled operator. You type, print, or draw on a heavy paper "duplimat," and then put it in the machine and run off as many copies as you want. Duplimat masters are more expensive than Ditto masters and harder to correct if you make a mistake. But they are clearer, so there is less chance to misread a number.

In most companies the production control department must prepare hundreds and thousands of identification tags for orders in production. All the methods described above are used for tag making. Besides them, special tag-printing machines are available. Large companies often operate a print shop for making forms and for printing tags. Nearly all companies buy blank tags and print them up to suit themselves.

PLANT TRANSPORTATION

Order control is used when the orders are numerous and varied. They follow any number of different paths through the plant, so you can't use conveyors. You have to use trucks, pulled or driven by truckers, and you have to give them a steady flow of directions telling them where to go, what to pick up, and where to take it.

You can use written "move" orders. That means separate pieces of paper for every move giving the trucker his instructions. Move orders, if you use them (they are most common in highly centralized control), are made up by the production control department and passed out to truckers by the production control department's departmental dispatchers. The truckers are employees of the production control department.

A simpler arrangement is to have the truckers work regular routes. Each producing department has a delivery and pickup area. As he makes his rounds, the trucker picks up all orders set out at the pickup area and takes them to the department shown next on the traveler copy of the shop order. At that department he leaves the order in the receiving area. The truckers work for a centralized transportation department, usually under production control's direction. Materials are moved *within* departments from the receiving area to machines and to the pickup area by machine operators or by laborers who work for the foreman in his department only.

Still another arrangement is to have no materials transportation department and no truckers following routes. Each department is responsible for moving materials from its receiving area to the machines and, after the work is complete, to the next department's receiving area. Truckers, in this case, work for individual factory department foremen.

COMMUNICATION SYSTEMS

So much information has to flow back and forth from the production control department and its dispatch offices that it usually needs its own private "intercom" system. You will find Tel-Autographs and Tele-Type-writers, too, wherever written messages have to go back and forth.

All the various "production papers" discussed above (shop orders, operation tickets, and so on) must be sent to the dispatch offices or to the various shop departments. The regular in-plant mail service is usually too slow, so production control runs an in-plant mail service of its own. Some companies (it is uncommon) use pneumatic tubes for sending orders around, but not if they have to send bulky drawings, too.

Many companies send $8\frac{1}{2} \times 11$ cellophane envelopes along with all shop orders. They put identification tags for tote pans, the traveler copy of the shop order, materials requisitions, move orders, job tickets, and drawings all in the envelope and let it travel along with the order through the plant.

Motorola, Inc.

FIG. 40–8. A "handi-talkie" used to report production to the central production control office.

A few companies use radio in their production control. The production control department of the Weatherhead Company, Cleveland, has for years used "roving" radiomen who check how jobs are going at machines and, using their "handi-talkie," report job progress continually to the central office. Truck drivers, too, have two-way radios and get their directions that way. Weatherhead says that radio-directed trucks not only cut inventory-in-process materially but that they need fewer truckers and fewer production control people.

STUDY QUESTIONS

1. What is the "planning" part of production control? How does it differ from any other part?
2. What is the difference between order scheduling and department "loads"? Explain.

3. When would you keep "load" records? Why? Explain how to do it.
4. What is the difference between machine schedules and "loads"? Explain.
5. Explain the difference between centralized and decentralized control. What is good and bad about each?
6. What is the "pull" of the factory? What has it to do with production control?
7. How much replanning and rescheduling would you expect to do in production control? Why?
8. What kinds of graphic controls are there for use in production control work? What are their good and bad points? When would you use them?
9. Why do you need decks of "master" cards if you use tabulating equipment in production control? Explain.
10. Fluid duplicators (of the "Ditto" type) are among the best for making up copies of production control directives. Tell how they work and why they are better than other methods.

CASE 40–1. THE BROWN AND BUCKINGHAM ENGINE COMPANY

The Brown and Buckingham Engine Company, manufacturers of small gasoline engines for lawn mowers, etc., has decided to centralize most of the details of its production control work in a single office.

In the past the foremen have worked from drawings and notices telling them how many of each type of finished product to make. The foremen decided how to make parts and what machines to use. They also decided when each job would be run and assigned jobs to the workers, seeing to it that the jobs in process were moved through the plant.

Assume that you are to be put in charge of a new production control department to which most of these responsibilities are to be transferred. The new arrangement is to be explained to the foremen at a meeting. The works manager is to tell them of the change but expects you to explain to them how the new arrangement will work and how it will help them.

What will you tell them?

CASE 40–2. WILLIAMS CORPORATION

The Production Control Department of the Williams Corporation was having trouble with the quantities of items being finished on production orders for stampings made from sheet steel. Ample quantities were always started into production, but shortages of finished stampings were frequent.

The steel, in large sheets, was ordered from the steel storage yard. It was placed on a conveyor and sent to the pickling room, where it was pickled; then sent to the shear department, where it was cut to size; and finally moved to the press departments, where it was blanked, pierced, and drawn. No records were kept from the time a given number of pieces were dispersed from the steel yards until the first operation, "blank," was completed. Thus, if there were shortages, they were not caught until the completion of the blanking operation on the order. When shortages were found, it was necessary to (a) hold the press until additional steel could be pickled and sheared (often quite a while) or (b) pull the die out and come up short on the run. Both "holding the press" (letting it stand idle) with the die in it or "pulling the run short" (setting the press up for another job although the first order was short) and later having to make an additional setup to finish the short order involved considerable money, to say nothing of the damage done to customer relations because of a broken delivery promise to a customer.

When an attempt was made to determine whether (a) the steel storage group had sent in the proper number of sheets, (b) the shearing department had made a mistake in shearing and had wasted a few pieces before the mistake was caught, or (c) the blanking department had made a lot of scrap, each foreman passed the buck to the other two.

Set up a procedure for determining which department was responsible for the shortages; and if it is not possible to correct the condition entirely, establish a method for catching the shortages as early as possible in the manufacturing process so that additional material can be brought up to the same stage of completion and then carried along with the rest of the material with little additional expense.

Chapter 41

OTHER KINDS OF PRODUCTION CONTROL

Aᴌᴍᴏꜱᴛ all companies use order control somewhere in their production. But very few companies use only order control. Just as soon as you get repeat orders on anything or get long runs, you begin to think of cutting out part of the paper work. Most of the short cuts that volume lets you take don't have names, but people writing about production control call one common method "flow" control. Besides that, there are less common methods such as "load" control and "block" control.

LINE ASSEMBLED PRODUCTS

Big manufacturing's bread-and-butter items are all made on production lines—stoves, automobiles, farm tractors, televisions, and many more. Here is where you use "flow" control.

A product is put together one part at a time as it moves down the line. The men stay put at separate work stations (only 5 or 6 feet apart). As soon as a man puts on his part the product moves on and another product comes to him for its part.

The first thing you need to get is the "flow" idea. Products *flow* off the end of the line minute by minute all day, all week, and all month long. Products *flow* past the men on the line. *Parts* and *subassemblies* must *flow* to the men along the line at a *rate* equal to their use. Flow production control must match up the rates of flow of parts, subassemblies, and final assemblies.

So far it doesn't seem too hard. Now you reach the second important thing about flow control. Not only do you have to control the flow *rate* but you have to control *variety* in finished products as well. Think of autos. They come in different models, colors, number of cylinders, with or without power brakes and power steering, and with all kinds of different trim and accessories. Ford cars have so many possible combinations of different things that Ford could run all year and never make two cars exactly alike. You still want cars to flow off the assembly lines, but you have to make sure that red cars don't get blue wheels and that a four-door car ends up with four doors, not two. Also, if you want 50 cars to have 8-cylinder motors, not only do you want 50 8-cylinder motors but that is 50, 6-cylinder motors that you *don't* want. Not every manufacturer has as much variety as autos, but most line production companies have some variety.

The third thing is to get the flow of parts to match their use. Perhaps you use automobile wheels at the rate of 5 per car, and each assembly line makes a car every 2½ minutes. Forgetting for the moment that you probably run several lines, you need wheels at the rate of 1 every 30 seconds.

Making one wheel every 30 seconds may not be exactly the most economical rate. Maybe the wheel making assembly line works best when it turns out wheels 1 every 20 seconds, 3 a minute instead of the 2 a minute that the final assembly line needs. Then what? Should you slow down the wheel line? Almost never would you do that because the men would be idle one third of their time, and paying for all that idle time would make the wheels cost lots more. No, you'd better go ahead and turn out the wheels at 3 a minute and pile up the excess. By mid-afternoon each day you'd have enough extra to keep the final assembly busy the rest of the day, so the wheel line would shut down and the men go on other jobs or go home.

What happens if the wheel assembly line can make only 1 wheel a minute when you need 2? Then you: (*a*) buy some wheels outside, or (*b*) work two shifts on the wheel line to one for final assembly, or (*c*) put in a second wheel assembly line.

Lack of perfect balance between production rates of parts and sub-assemblies and final assembly use is the rule, not the exception—yet *production per day or per week must balance* and without carrying big inventories. Flow production control must cope with this.

The problem of matching production and use without carrying big inventories and without running out of anything (if you run out you stop the assembly line and that stops everything else) is even greater for most individual piece parts. Many parts are made in lots; if you made them continuously you'd have a year's supply in a week or two. These items you usually make in an unending series of successive lots a week or a month apart. But you don't use order control for them because you make new lots so often that everyone knows what the items are and what operations to perform.

Items bought outside also come in as successive lots. Kelsey-Hayes makes auto wheels, but it can't deliver them to you one every 30 seconds. The best that it can do is to send you truck loads or freight-car loads, so many a day or a week.

So sum up what flow control has to do: It has to keep products flowing off the assembly line; it has to keep subassemblies and parts flowing to the assembly line; it has to control variety; it has to cope with lack of balance in production rates of parts and their use; and it has to deal with parts coming in in lots instead of in a steady stream.

FINISHED ASSEMBLY LINE CONTROL

Controlling finished assembly is almost altogether a matter of controlling the *variety*—seeing that each separate product gets the combination of parts and accessories that you want. We omit here the work of telling men *what* to do because industrial engineers figure out every-

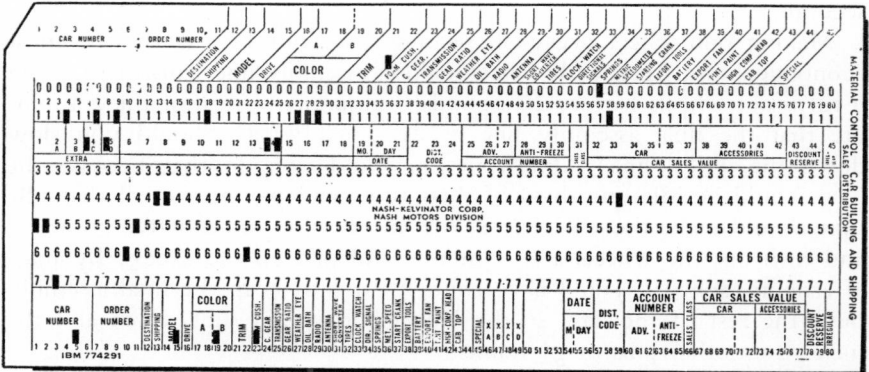

American Motors Co.

FIG. 41–1. A tabulating card providing spaces for showing attachments and accessories for an automobile, information used by the final assembly line.

one's work assignment when the line is set up. And we omit almost all instructions about *moving* materials. At the start we might need a few instructions telling men how to do their jobs or telling truckers where to move things, but instructions are few. And along the line itself—no instructions at all. Products being assembled move right along the conveyor.

Instructions covering *variety* are more complicated for making automobiles than for making almost anything else. You'll find simpler instructions elsewhere. For auto assembly you need an "order-of-run" or "building sequence" list for the assembly line. It lists every car to be made in a day and its sequence. For each one, it lists the kind of car, motor, steering, brakes, tires, accessories, trim, and all other details.

Copies of this list go to several points along the line to tell assemblers what items to put on and to tell parts supply men what parts to line up for cars coming along. Some companies don't send such lists to the shop at all because they would have to change it sometimes. Instead, they use Tele-Typewriters and Tel-Autographs to send written directions to key points just before the cars come along the line. Of course more instructions come along all day long. Also, by way of a check, every car carries a tag listing the parts and accessories it is to have.

Most line-assembly products are easier to schedule than automobiles. Much of the work in making clothing, shoes, radios, televisions, auto speedometers, typewriters, cash registers, and telephones is bench work. Except in the cases of clothing and shoes, all you need are simple tools— bolt tighteners, soldering irons, and so on. Most of the people along the line do almost the same kind of work. They put parts in place, screw them down, or bolt, rivet, or solder them.

This gives production control considerable freedom to raise or lower schedules without changing shift hours. You just put some more men (or more likely women) at extra work spaces along the line and send more work down the line. Normally, production control doesn't have to concern itself with the effects of minor production ups and downs on manpower. The burden of getting more men (or cutting some off) falls on the foreman, and so does the job of redividing the work so that everyone can keep busy. Better warn the foreman, though, of coming ups and downs of schedules so that he can plan his work force.

CENTRAL PRODUCTION CONTROL

Most companies big enough to use flow control are also multiplant companies. Some of the production control work is done in the company's central production control department. Some is done in each plant's own production control department. The company's central production control department starts from sales forecasts and such customer orders as you already have for special products. It, the central production control department, makes up weekly and daily final assembly schedules for each factory. It also makes up, for each factory, lists of the subassemblies and parts each factory will need. Central production control also sets up schedules for subassemblies and parts production or purchase.

But isn't it unwise to try to make up, in Detroit, production schedules for Atlanta, Dallas, Seattle, and elsewhere? Why not let each factory's own production control department make up its own lists of subassemblies and parts? It is, of course, better to let each plant make up its own schedules wherever you can. Also you can let them make schedules for items that they make for themselves. But it is different where components come in from outside—whether from sister plants or from outside suppliers. Supplier plants have to ship to a dozen or more of your plants. They, the suppliers, have to know your total requirements so that they can plan their production. A maker of fabric for automobile seats, for example, has to plan his runs of each fabric. He can work out his production and shipping schedule much better if he gets one list from your central production control department instead of a dozen lists from your dozen factories.

Your lists always show delivery schedules day by day or week by week, and they also show cumulative figures—how many in total you have released (ordered) since the start of the year. That lets you see how you stand. If *total deliveries* are below *total releases*, the supplier has to catch up. Underruns in any period have to be made up in the next. Deliveries not keeping up with releases means that your supply banks are running low. Or still worse, it means that you run completely out of this item every now and then and so lose production in final assembly.

The central production control department makes up all of these schedules and lists (and there are thousands of them) every week or month. Every month the Ford division of Ford Motor Company sends out schedules to 800 suppliers giving them schedules for sending 11,000 parts to 16 plants.

Besides, you have to re-do all of these schedules when there are changes. Suppose that you don't guess the market perfectly (and you never can). You have to cancel all of the lists already out in various plants and supplier companies and give them new lists. Or suppose that you have to make an urgent design change. Change, change, change; you have to make and remake schedules all the time.

FACTORY PRODUCTION CONTROL

Each *plant* has its own production control department. It takes the weekly schedules sent out from central production control and makes up order-of-run lists for final assembly. It also makes up specific "loading sheets" to tell men loading supply conveyors what to put on the supply conveyors. The supply conveyors bring assemblies and parts to the assemblers along the line. A loading sheet tells the supply men to load a blue dashboard onto the supply conveyor for car number 20, a red one for car 21, and so on.

Back in the supply area, the plant's production control watches the size of the banks all the time. Materials supply men tell production control when banks build up or shrink. To production control, either one means trouble somewhere. If the bank goes up, final assembly is behind schedule. If it goes down, something is wrong in subassembly production. Production control also gets hourly reports of final assembly's production, so it knows the final line's use. But with the thousands of things that it must watch, watching the banks (instead of relying on production reports) is a quick way to detect trouble.

SUBASSEMBLIES

Always make final products out of subassemblies wherever you can. Can you imagine putting, one by one, the separate pieces of an automobile speedometer (we saw a picture of them back on page 332) onto a car going down the assembly line? The assembly line is no place to handle eighth-inch-long parts. Put the speedometer together as a unit, then fasten the whole thing onto the assembly as a unit. In fact, don't even do that. Put the speedometer into the dashboard first. Then fasten on the whole dashboard.

You make most subassemblies continuously along assembly lines of their own at a rate that matches the final assembly line's needs. Production control's work with subassembly lines is like controlling final assembly. You still have some variety, and you still have to match up

Western Electric Co.

FIG. 41–2. A subassembly production line. Operators are making an electronic part for a guided missile.

rates of parts production and their use. But controlling any one sub-assembly line is simpler than controlling the final assembly line. There are fewer parts and less variety.

Three things about subassemblies are different. First, the quantities you make are always greater than the final line uses, because you have to make some extras to allow for a few rejects and for customers' repair service. Both mean raising the subassembly quantities. Second, your main user is final assembly. If your subassembly production rate per hour doesn't match final assembly's needs (as well as take care of the two extras), you operate the subassembly line different hours. Operate it longer hours if its rate is slower, shorter hours if its rate is faster. Third, at your main factory you make some subassemblies for all the other plants. So your quantities go way up and your delivery schedules get more complicated.

Because of different production rates between final assembly and sub-assemblies and because of the extras for customer repairs and for sister plants, you have to reconcile yourself to having some inventories around. Subassembly lines usually feed their output into temporary storage areas from which final assembly is supplied. Subassembly production and final assembly needs don't have to mesh perfectly. Don't make a mistake, though; the supply, or "bank," of items carried is small. If subassembly stops, final assembly, too, stops before long. Or if final assembly stops, subassembling soon has to halt for lack of space to store its output.

Bought items or items shipped in from sister plants are a little different. If they come from nearby, maybe you can get by with a few hours' supply in the bank. But if they come from farther away, you have to try to schedule freight cars in on the days you want them. However, rail service from distant points is not too dependable. You can't count on getting things exactly when you want them, so you will have to carry more on hand to be sure of not running out if a freight car gets delayed. On the other hand, giant companies have to watch their freight-car schedules very closely. Ford Motors receives over 1,000 freight cars of materials every day.

PARTS CONTROL

Assembly lines are the showy parts of manufacturing. Here you see the product take form. All of the parts are ready—they are the right shape, size, color—and they are ready on time. Behind all the smooth flow of assembly lines lies the still bigger job—making parts. All of their production schedules must mesh in with assembly line use.

Controlling their production is much like controlling subassembly production, except that there are thousands of parts to make or buy and only dozens of subassemblies. All of their production schedules must tie to assembly line needs.

Most parts differ from subassemblies, too, in that they are made in lots and not continuously. Only big parts are made continuously. But making parts in lots does not mean using order control. Here they are repetitive lots. With repetitive lots you set lot quantities to suit the line and send through, say, a new lot every week. Repetitive lots have no lot numbers and use no move orders, route sheets, or drawings. You also cut out individual job tickets and job-lot cost collecting since standard costs are used.

If it takes a week to process a lot of a part, you put, on Monday, a lot into production. By some time Tuesday the whole lot will be past operation 1 and some of the items will be past operation 2. Some may be even past operation 3. By the second Monday the first of the lot will be coming off the last operation and the whole lot of that part will be finished by, say, the second Tuesday evening. Suppose that your lot was for enough pieces to last 2 weeks. If so, you won't have to start the next lot through until the third Monday. Then you'll go through it all again. By the fourth Tuesday you'll have a new supply on hand. Production control decides how big the lots are to be. And it figures out ahead of time when you will need a new lot finished and when it must start into production. It also watches the banks of parts being used up as new supplies near completion and makes sure that you never run out.

Production control has to watch, too, to see that it doesn't overload machines. The machines are used all the time, but for successive lots of *different* parts. If you plan to start a lot of one part in on a machine on Monday morning, that machine will have to be free on Monday morning. It can't still be working on some other part that should have been finished last Friday.

Some people call making repetitive lots "cycling." Cycling allows you to cut out most of the shop papers that go with order control. You don't need any directions of any kind because everyone recognizes the part each time another lot comes along and everyone knows what operations to perform, what tools to use, where to move products, and so on.

Notice that cycling means lots of machine setups. That will be costly unless your engineers design tooling so that the men can put tooling on and take it off machines in a hurry. Note also that cycling lets you use machines for several parts and so keep the machines busy.

Some companies don't go quite so far in cutting out shop paper. Sometimes different parts look so much alike that you do need to identify them. And on some minor parts, you might even go to regular order control. Here's what GM's Electro-Motive division (makes diesel-electric railroad engines) does:

When a lot of parts is needed, a scheduler assigns it a "sequence" number and makes out a raw materials requisition for enough materials for the lot. He sends the requisition to the foreman whose department has to do the first operation. The foreman, when his man is ready to work on the job, draws the material from the stock room. Sequence numbers are a little like job order numbers in order control in that they identify the job. But they are also job priority numbers. Foremen must process low numbers first.

But since there is no regular shop order, how does the foreman know what operations to perform? Usually he knows without any instructions at all because he has made so many lots of the same item before. Actually, he has in his office a list of every part regularly coming through his department, and for every part he has an operation list (or "route" sheet). He can turn to his book of route sheets if he is in doubt. But what if the item is not a regular item? Then he'll get a regular shop order as in order control; it will tell him what to do.

Electro-Motive's method also tells the factory's central production control office how the lot is moving through production—but only as it moves from one department to the next—not as it moves within a department. Products going out of a department pass a final inspector who not only inspects what goes out but reports to production control which lots and how many have gone on to the next department. Foremen always tell production control, though, when any lots are held up in their departments, so production control knows right away about holdups.

LEAD TIMES

Lead time is the time between ordering an item and getting it. Production control has to know the usual lead times on all items and particularly on all items made in lots or items shipped in (all items coming in come in in lots). If you are wrong about lead time, you may run out of an item before the next lot comes in.

Lead times make trouble because you can't count on them, especially on the shipped-in items. Rail freight from distant suppliers is something like letters in the mail. Sometimes they come through fast, and other times not so fast.

Production control sets all start dates for making parts and assemblies with the usual lead times in mind. Same with vendors; the schedules of shipments that production control sends them allow for the usual lead times.

It is so easy to say "allow for the usual lead times" that it makes it sound simple. Buick is only one GM division, and not its biggest, but its production control department has to make up over 10,000 schedules every month just for assembly work alone. How many more schedules its eight separate factory production control departments make for piece parts Buick has never counted.

Lead times vary from 0 to 10 days for items coming in to Buick's main plant. How long depends mostly on where they come from, but partly the time allowed is to take care of irregularities in shipping. It takes from 0 to 30 days to make parts and subassemblies. It takes 5 to 8 days to ship home-plant-supplied parts to the other plants. Then it takes from 0 to 10 days in the other plants. Notice that these lead times follow one another, chain fashion. First you must allow lead time to get bought materials or parts, then time to make parts and subassemblies, then time to ship to other plants, then time for final assembly. Finally it adds up to anywhere from 5 to 58 days. Production control has to know what the right lead time is for every item.

Besides this, there are such matters as scheduling things to arrive on different days of the week so that you won't have whole freight trains waiting to be unloaded on Monday morning and then nothing coming in on Thursday. You can see that schedulers in continuous manufacturing can keep busy. And remember, too, that every time your forecasters miss the market a little you have to change all the schedules as you frantically try to bring production back into line with sales. And don't forget that strikes in supplier plants, or a snow storm or flood along a railroad, also upset your production schedules and make you do them all over again.

"LOAD" CONTROL

Back on page 780 we talked about how a factory doing job-lot work set schedules and paid attention to the "load" of work ahead. Sometimes you hear a man say that his company uses "load" control. This is a little different from what we talked about on page 780. Anyone talking about load control usually refers to schedule making for one or more big important machines.

It, the big key machine, is used for many sizes and varieties of products, and the load control idea is to apportion its time to jobs. Usually the key machine is a fast producer, such as a printing press that prints magazines, telephone books, seed catalogues, books, and so on. Some of these printing presses turn out as many as 10,000 magazines an hour.

But in one sense even such a fast machine is a bottleneck. It is a bottleneck compared with the minor operations before it and after it. The point is that you don't have to schedule the minor jobs at all. There is plenty of capacity to handle all the big machines turn out. Its schedule is everything.

Note, though, that you do need order numbers so that you can control quantities and so that you get the right pages into the right magazines or books.

The rubber industry has a different situation with its calenders (large machines for rolling rubber mixtures into sheets of exact thicknesses). They are kept busy all the time on certain material. The only schedule they need is the amount of the product to run each day. Small increases or decreases in the quantity can be cared for by varying the number of hours worked daily. And if you run a little over or under in one day, you even it out the next. (Note: you can't do that in printing. You can't run extra pages of one book to make up for a shortage of pages for another book.)

You don't need load control for the calenders which can be kept busy on one product. But you do need it for calenders doing varied work. Small-volume products are assigned to one or two calenders, which get new schedules daily. Generally the same products are made daily, and they are run in the same sequence but in varying quantity.

Materials in the rubber industry need no order number, but they do need identification tags. Tags are attached to the rolls of sheet rubber, but they show only the material's identification number and the date the operation was done. There are no route tags and no operation lists. Calender operators know what to do to all materials that come to them;

they also have materials specification books to refer to if they are in doubt.

PROCESS MANUFACTURING

Processing industries change the physical or chemical form of large quantities of materials. Included are companies making gasoline, chemicals, paints, flour, glass, rayon, nylon, cement, asphalt tile, plaster, and even paper. "Production" takes place inside tanks, retorts, vessels, and furnaces as materials are mixed or heated and as changes go on. Equipment is connected by pipes and ducts which move the material around.

Equipment runs at full capacity or not at all. Changing quantities means changing work hours. Normally, however, big companies have several processing lines so they can vary production by changing either work hours or the number of lines they operate.

Production is usually to stock or to large sales orders, but even if it is to stock, not much stock is carried. Volume is so great that a few days' production would fill all the storage tanks or warehouses.

Process companies use flow production control, but it is a little different from the automobile kind. You give the factory weekly lists of products, quantities, and sequences of running different products, but you don't send such lists to very many places—just to men in charge at key points, where the equipment has to be reset to make different products. When you have duplicate lines, production control makes up schedules for each one.

Production control gives out no processing instructions telling the factory how to make products. All processing instructions are in the foreman's specification books. And of course there are no move orders or cost collection reports since you use standard costs. Production control does get, however, reports, perhaps hourly, of production, and at the end of each day it gets reports of the exact quantities run. And it gets a telephone report right away if anything goes wrong during the day.

As in automobile flow control, production control in processing companies has to send out vendor release schedules. And the tremendous volume (one or more whole freight trains a day) makes necessary carefully worked out incoming materials schedules.

Same thing on the going-out side. It takes just as many freight cars to haul products away as it did to get raw materials in. Production control is, however, usually not concerned with the going-out freight cars—only with having the material ready to go out.

Production control in processing companies has two problems that differ from other flow control. One occurs early in production, the other, late in production.

Processing industries usually start with products of nature. Nature's products are never quite consistent; they aren't the same throughout.

The laboratory has to be ever watchful in inspecting the material for chemical or physical characteristics. You nearly always find some variation. What can you do about it? One thing you can do is to mix and blend together materials from different shipments. That helps make the material you work with pretty even throughout. Or you can change your mixing formulas, or processing temperatures, or processing times and rates of output. The production control department is concerned with the last of these—the processing times and rates of output. It may have to change the production schedules because you are turning out processed materials faster or slower than normal.

Production control in processing industries also often has special work to do for the last stages of production, particularly with packaging and labeling. The production control department has to issue specific directions for the packaging operations, so that the right number of each size of package or brand name or the right cuts to size are made.

"BATCH" MANUFACTURING

In early stages of manufacture it is often necessary to mix and process "batches" of materials. You find batches in many branches of the food processing and canning industry where materials must be mixed and then cooked. In the paint industry, paints and coloring materials are made in batches. Same with rubber. It is mixed with its ingredients in batches. Drugs and pharmaceuticals are processed in batches. Glass is often made by melting fixed quantities at a time. Iron, steel, and other metals are made in "heats."

The size of the batch is usually dependent on the size of the equipment. Several hundreds of pounds of ingredients are brought together into batches and put into masticators or mixers. Sometimes, as in the case of extracting metal from ore, the process is heating rather than mixing. Sometimes chemical reactions are involved.

In batch manufacturing the production control department has to schedule the mixing or heating equipment in accord with the time cycle for each batch as specified by the laboratory. Also production control has to set finished product quantities to use up whole batches. Batch sizes are usually fixed, and only full batches can be made. You always go ahead and make up all batch-mixed material into finished products. You do this to hold down inventories in process and, in the case of foods and rubber, to save loss because mixed but unfinished material is perishable. The control most commonly used in "batch" manufacturing is "load" control. Order numbers, operation job tickets, and move orders are not needed.

BLOCK CONTROL

"Block" control is a variation of order control used in the men's clothing industry. Before men's suits are manufactured, styles and cloth patterns are decided upon, and pictures and samples sent out to the retailers. Retailers make their selections and order the suits they want, distributed as they see fit among sizes, styles, and patterns.

The factory's ability to turn out suits is relatively fixed at so many suits per day. Production control groups the orders by cloth pattern and by style. Then it adds together groups into "blocks." A block is the number of suits the factory can turn out in half a day. All orders in the block will be issued to the plant at once. A new block is issued each half day. Within a block, *every suit has its own individual suit number*, so that sleeves, pockets, etc., for the suit will be brought together into the right coat. All suits belonging to the same order carry the order number also, and all suits in the block carry the block number.

Each suit is inspected several times during its manufacture, and its individual suit number is checked off as it passes the inspection station. Any suit in process can be located readily by looking over the books at the inspection stations. Departments are required to finish a ·whole block before clearing the next block. If any suit gets behind, you know it right away because the block isn't cleared on production control's record. When the delayed suit is found, it is finished right away or that suit is replaced in the block by one from the next block.

Block control is both a method of releasing identical amounts of work to the factory at half-day intervals and a method of pushing orders through. It does not make you get any more suits out, but it makes sure that no suit gets pushed aside and forgotten.

The ladies' shoe industry uses a method quite similar to block control except that no block numbers are used and no individual pairs of shoes are given individual numbers.

Ladies' shoes aren't so standard as men's suits, so you can't just figure that the plant should turn out the same number of pairs of shoes every day or half day. Instead, production control looks at the piecework cost of cutting the upper leather part of the shoes on each order. You know how much money the cutters in the cutting department earn every day, and that is a relatively fixed amount of money. So you add up, order by order, the cutting cost for each pair of shoes, until the total equals what the cutters earn in a day. You then issue that many orders and no more to the factory for the day.

Once started into production, the shoes go through checking points, where the progress of each order is recorded. A report is also made to the production control department, where you note the date the operation is completed in a "book" showing the progress of all orders.

In both men's clothing and the ladies' shoe industries, shop orders are made out showing the number and kind of products to make. Operations are so standard, however, that printed operation lists are used. The list is printed on lightweight cardboard, on which each operation is represented by a detachable stub. When an operation is performed, the pieceworker detaches the stub for the operation he has completed, puts it with the others he has accumulated, and turns them in as his report of the work he has done.

Block control uses no schedules in the usual sense of the term. What starts in at one end of the factory has to come out the other end and in about the usual time too. If it slows down, you'll find it out when it fails to pass the checking stations.

Nor is there any concern over the ability of all departments to get out the work. How can you be sure that there will be no bottlenecks? There could be bottlenecks sometimes but not often because the size of successive departments is in balance. The sewing department is just the right size to handle all that the cutting department turns out, and so on with other departments. Fortunately, differences in product mix have little effect on the work loads of different departments.

TRANSPORTATION COMPANY REPAIR SHOPS

All companies must maintain their equipment, but transportation companies, airlines, railroads, taxi, truck, and bus fleet operators are in a peculiar situation in this respect. Their equipment is scattered all over a wide area. Breakdowns in operation can be serious, and can occur anywhere. In fact, they usually do occur everywhere except in the company's repair shop.

Preventive maintenance is a must. Ordinarily, transportation companies follow set schedules for lubrication, inspection of wearing parts, and periodic overhaul or replacement of major component units of the equipment. Airplane motors, for example, are replaced regularly with new or rebuilt motors. Records have to be kept of the dates when various kinds of overhaul were last done, so that they will be done again when they should be. Operating schedules must be watched, too. Equipment must not be on the road, far from the repair shop, when the scheduled time for its overhaul is reached.

Transportation company repair shops and, on a far greater scale, the United States Armed Forces repair shops for airplanes and naval ships are large-scale factories. They disassemble and assemble products, test them, and buy, make, and repair parts. Their operations are in many ways similar to those of all manufacturers of assembled products, but they are more complex. They are more complex because disassembly is extra and because you never know, until you get the product apart, what new parts you will need or what you will have to do to repair the old parts. The parts you take out are in various stages of wear. Some are too worn to put back in, others are repairable, and still others can be cleaned and then reused as they are.

Running repair shops is also more complex because you have so many types and models of equipment in use. Some are old, some very old, and some are new. Some came from one manufacturer, some from another, but one thing they all have in common: except for the occasional one that has to be scrapped, they must all be kept in use. You just can't stock all the parts that you might need, and maybe you won't even be able to buy some of the parts by the time you need them.

Repair problems are often made more difficult because emergency and rush jobs are common. You can't even set up a very fixed schedule of repair and overhaul so that you can operate at an even keel.

Production control in a repair shop has to be order control; frequently you'll have to make up separate orders for the repair of every part. That means making new operation lists individually, and you can't do this until the product is disassembled because only then can you see what repair operations the part needs. Big parts you try to repair and put back into the same product from which they were taken, so they must all be identified by the product number. During all of the time that parts are repaired, the disassembled product lies around idle, taking up space on the assembly floor.

You can avoid some of these difficulties by maintaining a stock of rebuilt subassemblies to install when occasion arises. Taxicab companies, for example, can put a whole rebuilt engine or rear end into a car with little confusion. The engines removed are then rebuilt by regular line assembly methods. Railroads do this with diesel engine motors and generators.

REPAIR PARTS

All manufacturers of assembled products must supply repair parts (some people call them "service" parts) to customers. For current product models there is no trouble making the parts, whether flow control or order control is used. All you have to do is to manufacture larger quantities of parts than you need for assembly purposes. Store the extras for future sale as repair parts.

Parts for old models make problems, however. For last year's models, you can make up and carry in stock all the parts the customers will need. But it doesn't pay to carry stocks of parts for very old products. You make up those on special order when customers want them.

Most large companies separate repair parts manufacture from regular production. Repair parts are made in a repair parts department on a job-lot basis, using order control. If the company has no repair parts department, then orders usually go through regular production.

STUDY QUESTIONS

1. Explain the "flow" idea. When and why is it important? What effect does it have on production control?
2. How do you reconcile the steady use of parts with their being produced or received in lots? How do you handle this?

3. What problems are there in scheduling work along an assembly line? Explain.

4. What does a multiplant's central production control department do? Explain fully.

5. Subassembly production is said to be different from final assembly line work. How? How does this affect production control?

6. How does parts manufacture for volume production differ from final assembly as far as production control is concerned? What problems are peculiar to parts production? What do you do about them?

7. Are "lead" times more important in flow control than they are in order control? Explain and justify your answer.

8. Explain "load" control. How is it different from "flow" control?

9. How does manufacture by "batches" affect production control? Explain.

10. Could you use "block" control for an automobile assembly line? Tell why or why not.

11. Why do transportation company repair shops have a particularly difficult production control situation? What can they do to lessen it?

Chapter 42

OFFICE WORK

Personnel, engineering, purchasing, production control, accounting, and all the other staff departments we have been talking about—all are white-collar departments. They don't work on the product. Neither do line employees beginning with the foreman and going up. And everywhere—in line and staff work alike—you find typists, clerks, and other office employees.

All white-collar men are knee-deep in paper. Someone has said that it takes two tons of paper to produce one ton of product. Maybe that exaggerates, but desk work and paper work do go hand in hand. There is no escaping having a steady flow of paper—so much that it takes quite a staff of typists, stenographers, and clerks to make out reports and file them. You put out work directives, get reports of work done, write letters and memoranda, and fill in printed forms in duplicate, triplicate, and quadruplicate.

The worst thing about office work is that it grows and grows and grows. In a 1900 factory only 1 out of every 40 employees worked in an office. By 1935, it was 1 out of 10. Now it is 1 out of 4! Where will it be by 1975? Manufacturing, over the years, has become more and more efficient, but office work grows less efficient. Ben Graham, an office management authority, says that office people usually work at only 50 per cent of their capacity. Not only that but, Graham says, one third of what they do is waste work anyway. And still worse, he says that management doesn't get all the information that it needs even with big office staffs.

Why does management put up with it all? Why doesn't it cut office work down to size? Some people say that all the government rules, regulations, and required reports make you have more office people. And, of course, that is one thing that makes more office work, and you can't avoid it. Management can't cut that work down.

Another reason is the growth of staff departments. Fifty years ago you had a handful of them, but now you have all kinds of staff departments: sales promotion, public relations, education and training, and on and on. Why not cut them out? But no, management wants them. Top management created them and approved setting them up as departments so it must be that top managers feel that they pay for themselves.

Big manufacturing companies today are so big and so complex that you can't run them without staff departments. In 1957, there were, in the United States, 30 industrial companies with more than 50,000 employees each. They are too big to run without lots of staff departments. And there were 200 companies with over 10,000 employees. They, too, are so big that they have to have a good many staff departments—and that means lots of office workers.

But don't mistake: all that we are saying is that you have to have more white-collar workers; we are not justifying their growth uncritically. Staff departments probably grow as much from the operation of Parkinson's Law as from real need.[1] But regardless of how the growth occurs, a company with 50,000 employees of whom 10 to 15 thousand are office people just *must* try to control their work and their cost. General Motors has 150,000 office workers whose payroll costs is over a half billion dollars a year. General Electric's office payroll probably exceeds $200 million a year. Even a little giant company of 10,000 employees has 2,500 office workers whose salaries come to $10 million a year. Is it any wonder that office work cost is the new frontier for cost reduction?

Controlling office costs is harder than controlling factory costs because the work doesn't lend itself well to setting standards and budgeting. Since it is hard to do, most companies, in the past, slighted it. But not now. It is still hard to do, but it is no longer overlooked. Standards, budgets, charts, reports, even mechanization—every device used in the factory to cut costs is now being tried on office costs.

PROCEDURES

An office procedure is an established method for conveying information, or authorizing work, or getting reports of work done. The usual way of developing office procedures is just to let them grow—let the men who have to pass information around figure out how to do it. It is a poor way. Office supervisors are not efficiency experts and don't think of trying to do things in simple ways. Even if they did think of it, they wouldn't know how to go about it. And, besides, they don't know

---

[1] "Parkinson's Law" means that staffs grow in size at an annual rate of from 5 to 6 per cent a year even if the work load stands still. The idea comes from *Parkinson's Law*, written by C. Northcote Parkinson and published by Houghton Mifflin Co. (Boston, 1957). He writes somewhat with tongue in cheek basing his conclusions on the growth of the staffs in the English Admiralty and in the English Colonial Office. At least two American company presidents have checked their companies' experiences and found that their companies fit the pattern. One of them relabeled it Parkinson's disease as he ruefully decided that it was no joke.

anything about how other departments operate and what can be done to save money when a procedure touches several departments.

Maybe the idea of a procedure is vague. We can use making out an invoice (a bill) as an example. Here's what has to go on an invoice: the customer's name and address, his purchase order number, how the products were shipped to him (by rail or truck), credit terms, the products you shipped, their prices, discounts, and the amount the customer owes you.

You start the invoice-making procedure with the customer's order. You copy from this order his name and address, the purchase order number, the products he wants, and any shipping instructions he may have given. At this point the invoice is incomplete, but that is all you do to it for the moment.

Several people in your company need the information you have just typed out. So, make several copies, not just one, of your typed form. If the products are kept in stock, one copy goes to the finished goods stock room to tell the men there to ship the order. If some of the products have to be made up special, a copy goes to production control so that it can get them made. A copy goes, too, to the packing and shipping room for the packer to put inside the package when it is shipped. Another copy, with glue on the back, is the address label that goes on the package.

Besides these copies of the invoice, you have several more copies which you fill in when the order is shipped. You fill in the exact quantity of each product shipped, its price, the discounts, the amount of money the customer owes, and the way you shipped the order. One copy you send to accounting so that it can subtract the value of the products shipped from its record of finished goods inventory and add it on to accounts receivable. One copy goes to accounts receivable. A copy stays in the order department. The original goes to the customer as his bill for the order.

We won't follow it farther. There is more when the customer pays his bill and when production control has the factory make products for an order, but they are really other related procedures, not parts of the invoice procedure.

How do you simplify procedures? Just about the same way that a motion study man improves factory jobs. You must dig down into details. Remember back in Chapter 29, the charts that motion study men use? To improve an office procedure, the best way is to first make a chart. Look at Figures 42–1 and 42–2. They show "before" and "after" charts. Use charts to help you try to cut out steps. Cut out the copying and recopying of figures. Design forms to serve several purposes. Try to cut down on the number of copies of reports made. What are they used for? Send copies only where they are needed.

You may have to resort to trickery to cut down on copies of reports.

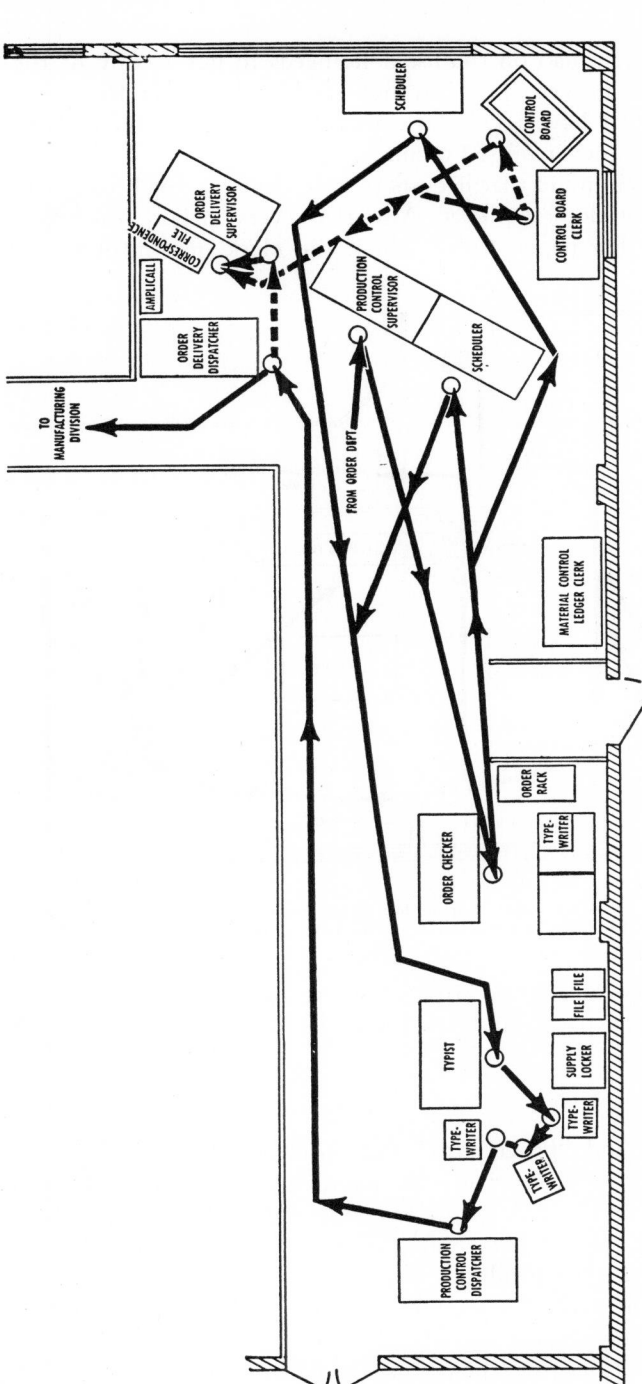

FIG. 42—1. Before: This arrangement wasted steps, wasted time, wasted energy, wasted money. Solid lines show that each order traveled 162 feet. Broken lines show that auxiliary forms traveled 80 feet.

If you ask each man on the list if he needs to get a copy of the report, he'll always say yes. Try just not sending him one for a few times. Companies that have tried this say that some of the men who just had to have copies never missed them.

Also keep in mind that it costs twenty times as much to create a piece of paper as it does to file it. Also that every paper you create has to have supporting papers from which the clerk gets information to put

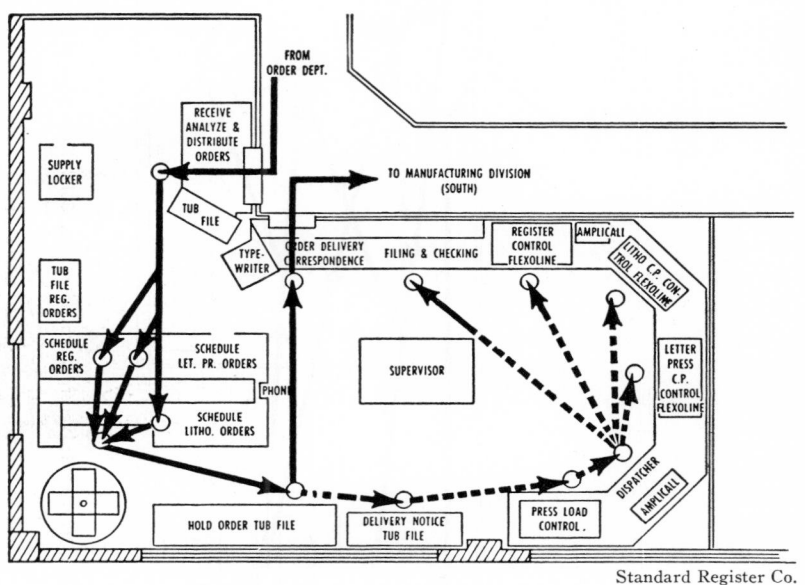

Standard Register Co.

FIG. 42–2.   After: After rearranging desks. Floor space was cut from 960 to 460 square feet. The order now travels 35 feet and the auxiliary forms another 35 feet.

on it. And the supporting papers have to be propped up by still others. Cut out *making* paper, and you'll save far more than you ever can from efficient filing.

SYSTEMS

"Systems" and "procedures" aren't quite the same thing. "Systems" cover more ground. Our invoice handling procedure is an example of a procedure. It is restricted; it is concerned only with the invoice. But it ties in with sales orders coming in, with factory manufacturing orders needed to make the products, with accounts receivable, and with other areas. You can make some gains only if you study *all* the related areas at the same time.

Studies of *procedures* help you see when to cut corners *within* part of the whole picture. But you need to study the whole picture. What does production control need to know about an order? What does accounts receivable need to know? Studying invoice handling by itself won't answer these questions. Study the whole system and you will be paying attention to the needs of all areas together. You may very well end up with different forms, different information on the forms, different arrangements of information from what you'd arrive at studying procedures separately. You'll end up with an integrated system that allows each procedure to work well and economically within itself and also helps related procedures do the same.

You get into such matters as designing printed forms and deciding how many copies to make. You ask: Who gets them? Why? Can you cut some names off the list? Does the receiver have to copy from the form that he gets to a record? Or to a report that he sends out? Can you have it come in in a form that cuts out the copying?

One company found that its production control department had tabulating equipment that used cards punched with round holes. Its accounting department's tabulating machines used rectangular holes. Factory workers' job tickets had round holes because that was the kind production control made. But, when these tickets got into accounting, new rectangular hole duplicates had to be made. Systems analysis will help you straighten out this kind of waste.

Systems analysis usually shows that too many kinds of reports are made and too much unused information is put on them. Copies are sent to too many places and to too many persons who don't need them. Sometimes a whole report can be eliminated; if not, certain steps in its preparation can be omitted. One report can, perhaps with slight modifications, be made to serve two purposes.

Sometimes the form or shape of the report or instruction sheet can be changed so that it can be prepared more easily or along with something else you have to prepare anyway. Material receiving report forms, for example, can be filled in almost completely when purchase orders are made out. One carbon copy of the purchase order is made on a form printed up to serve as the receiving report. Space is provided on that copy for the receiving clerk's notation, to be made later, that the material has arrived.

Sets of forms, several copies of which need to be made, can be bought already preassembled in order and with single-use carbon papers already inserted. The whole set of forms is typed at one time, after which the binder edge is torn off and the single-use carbons discarded. This method costs less than having the typist spend the time assembling the copies, inserting the carbons, and then carefully removing them and saving them for future use.

Most forms must be filled in by copying certain information onto them. Frequently this information is copied off later onto some permanent record. Design the form to make such copying easy. Copying is easier if you design the form so that figure columns are near the edge of the

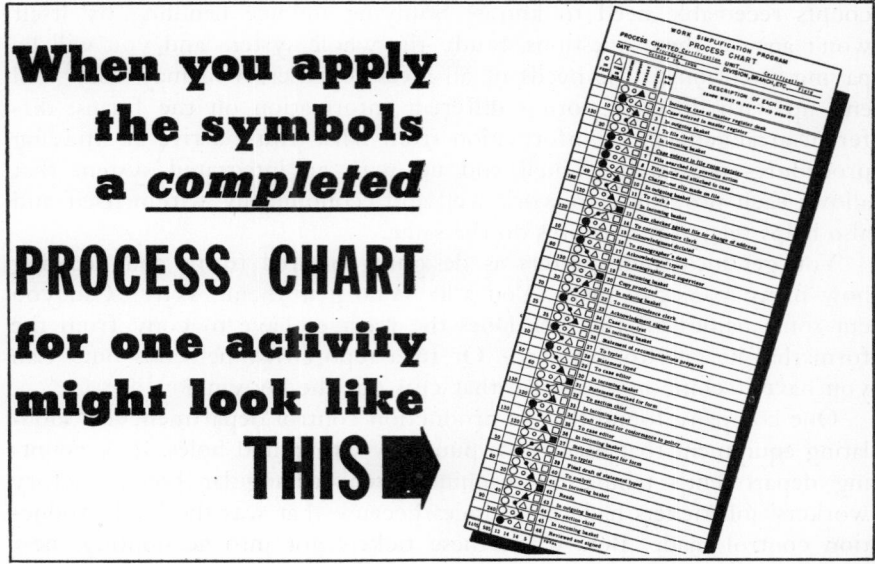

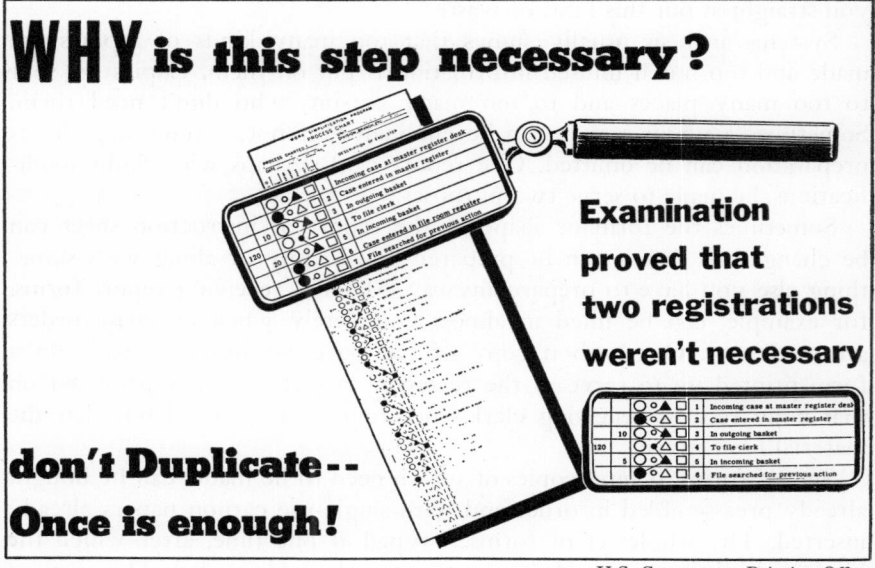

FIG. 42–3. A process chart used to analyze an office procedure.

paper. Use the same arrangement of columns or lines on both forms—the one being copied from and the one being copied on.

It may be possible to economize by changing the method of reproduction of forms or reports. Fluid duplicators may replace mimeographs, or vice versa; which way is best depends on quantity. Tabulating machines can often take over the job of preparing reports if the forms are designed for them. In many companies pay checks and payroll deduction slips are now prepared on tabulating machines.

In large companies substantial savings in the cost of stationery are made possible by the use of half-size stationery for short letters, memoranda, etc., and of obsolete or spoiled paper forms for scratch pads, and by the careful control of the number of copies of duplicated material run. One company found that employees sometimes ran 1,000 copies, "just in case," when 100 would have been enough.

For internal correspondence, extra file copies of correspondence can often be eliminated. Answers to letters and memoranda should, when possible, be written on the original letter rather than on a separate sheet. Internal communications can be put in "repeat use" envelopes.

Process charts can be employed to advantage in analyzing office procedures for improvement purposes. Each step in the procedure—the entering of information, its transfer to other departments, its transcription to other records, etc.—can all be depicted on process charts. Such charts, described for use in factory work in Chapter 29, help the analyst visualize unnecessary steps and develop improved procedures.

Caterpillar Tractor Company has a forms review department. Some companies set up special "procedures" departments. The office manager can also act in this capacity because in most cases he is responsible for purchasing forms and for operating the company's reproducing equipment on which forms made within the company are processed.

FORMS

You don't have to be big to have hundreds of printed forms. Giant companies have thousands. Olin Mathieson has 14,000 forms in its central forms control files.

People using forms usually design them. At first this sounds logical. After all they know what information they need. But again you find that amateurs do amateur jobs. Big companies now turn much of their forms designing over to a forms design man. He works in the procedures department. Remember, though, that before he does any work on a form, you should try to cut it out altogether. Failing in that, confine it to necessary information. Then, and only then, let him go ahead with improving the arrangement of the form.

What does a forms design man do? He arranges information in locations to cut eye travel. Don't have a man look five different places for related information. Design forms so that men using them don't have to turn them back and forth. If they are to be filled in by typewriter, the forms designer tries to arrange the spaces to be filled in to save typist time. He even pays attention to the kind and size of paper, trying always to use the least costly paper that will serve and to make the form only as big as it has to be. He tries, too, to cut out large off-size forms because they cost more than standard sizes.

It sounds like picayunish work. How can it save enough to pay for the analyst's time? Remember Olin Mathieson's 14,000 forms? Remember General Motors half-billion-dollars-a-year office payroll? There is no grand over-all way to hold these costs down. You have to dig—get down into details, cut a corner here, cut a corner there. Cut a thousand corners a thousand times and you save big money. Forms study usually cuts 15 to 20 per cent off the costs of forms. That alone pays well, but the big payoff comes from systems and procedures analysis; forms analysis is part of the big picture.

PRODUCTION STANDARDS IN THE OFFICE

Nearly everyone agrees that office work is done less efficiently than most factory work. It is easier for office workers to produce less, if they feel like doing so, than it is for factory employees. Office workers have more opportunities to dawdle over their work, to visit with fellow workers, and to "kill" time in washrooms and over a cup of coffee. Office worker productivity depends a great deal upon the quality of supervision they receive.

Office workers on strictly routine work sometimes become restless in the late hours of the day and are inclined to waste time because of boredom. Some companies have them do their assorted odds and ends of tasks during that part of the day, or assign them to different work just for variation.

There is an inherent tendency toward inefficiency in the offices of staff departments caused by their use of specialists. The specialists sometimes cannot keep busy working at their specialty and so work at less highly skilled work to fill in their time. It is, of course, better for them to do this than to do no work, but to use a highly paid man on routine work is just as wasteful in the office as in the factory.

Perhaps the most important reason for office inefficiency is the lack of standards. Usually there is no unit of work that you can measure and say how long it will take. Another reason is the variety of things done. In spite of the difficulty of setting standards and the variety of work, some companies use office standards. Here are a few of one company's office standards:

Kind of Work	Standard Quantity (per Hour)
Type addresses or labels (from typewritten copy).....	141
Straight typing (keystroke count)..................	13,786
Copying from printed copy.........................	200 lines
Copying from fairly legible printed copy............	175 lines
Copying from stenographic notes...................	125 lines
File correspondence..............................	130
Print and insert index cards.......................	242
Tab addressograph plates..........................	678
Emboss addressograph plates with name and address...	61
Post accounts on bookkeeping machine..............	242

Let's look at another office task: inventory control. You'd have to set standards for entering stock issues on the cards, making subtractions, writing in the quantities still on hand, and putting the item's unit price on the requisition slip. Other standards would cover posting records of materials ordered and of materials received. Also, you'd need standards covering making out requests for more stock of items that run low. And there would be some other standards too.

These standards would not, in contrast to those for many office jobs, be hard to make up. And having them would help you set up budgets telling you how many men you will need to work on inventory record cards. But notice that you need to know, in order to set up a budget, how many times each bit of work will happen in the week or month ahead.

Can you tell that? No, not very accurately, so your budget won't be too good. But *without standards you have even less control*. You hardly know anything about the future work load for inventory controllers. But making manpower budgets costs some money too. There are so many kinds of little jobs that you need hundreds of standards, and it will take hours of study of future manufacturing schedules to decide how many times each minor task will need to be done.

After a period is over, comparing actual costs to the budget is not just a matter of comparing total dollars because there is so much variation in how often the work bits were done. You need to find out how often each little job was done, multiply by its standard time, and add up to get the standard hours of work done. Then compare standard to actual. Actual will practically always be more than standard. If it comes to 200 hours extra in a month, you have a little over one too many men in the department.

How about piecework in offices? It works well in the factory, and it produces lower costs there. Piecework in offices is uncommon but not unknown. In the first place, office standards can rarely be accurate enough to be true and exact measures of a man's effort. In the second place, you must be able to verify the worker's report of quantity. How many times did he do this? How many times did he do that? Item by item, all the things he claims to have done need to be verified. Sometimes that can't be done or can be done only at high cost.

Perhaps with the ever-increasing emphasis on cost saving in offices we'll see more piecework in offices. Some companies that have tried it say that piecework in offices pays well. Pitney-Bowes has these jobs on piecework: transcribing, order and traffic, duplicating, addressograph, mail, payroll, mail receivers of customers' checks, accounts receivable, billing, sales records, and branch accounts. Pitney-Bowes has netted a saving of over $120,000 in these departments from using standards.

FILING

Filing isn't just putting papers away. You must classify the papers and put them away under certain headings so that you can later find them. You can file correspondence alphabetically, or by number, or date, or product, or customer, or district, or subject—any number of ways. That is why sometimes you have a hard time finding things.

Suppose, for example, that John Brown of the Apex Company wrote in asking the prices of can openers and meat grinders. How do you file his letter and the carbon of your answer? Under A for Apex Company, B for Brown, C for can openers, M for meat grinders? You could even make copies of his letter and file one each place. Not often would you go to that expense, but companies do sometimes make index cards for important correspondence so that they can have a cross-reference file to help them find things.

It would be nice if you didn't have to file anything, but you do. Experts say that if you actually refer later to as much as 20 per cent of what you file that you are doing all right. But if you refer to no more than 10 per cent of the papers you file, that you are filing too many. You'd better throw more papers away. Also you'd better throw nearly everything away after a year. In fact, only about 1 per cent of requests for information make you go back to last year or earlier.

Filing costs much too much for you to keep everything. Some people say that it costs $40 a year to keep up a four-drawer file. Every now and then you'd better clean out your files. Most of us keep too much filed too long. Of course you can't let the file clerks decide what to throw out and that makes part of the trouble. Higher-ups won't take time to decide, and lower-downs aren't allowed to. But higher-ups can decide *what kinds* of things to throw out and tell the clerks to do it. Westinghouse once threw out *120 freight carloads* of old office papers at once. Sun Oil threw out *500 tons* in 3 years.

Actually, why should you keep old papers and records at all? You can't get away from it. Customers of years ago sometimes want repair parts for old products, so you need to keep enough drawings to be able to give them good service. But far more important are legal reasons. You need to keep patent records, property title records, and so on just in case someone sues you.

Worse than that the law compels you to keep some records. You have to keep employee timecards two years to comply with the wage-hour law. Companies with government contracts have to keep timecards for four years. Social security and unemployment compensation laws make you keep employee pay records for four years. Interstate Commerce Commission regulations make you keep freight cost papers for two years.

To save storage costs companies are turning more and more to microfilming the old records that they have to keep. Microfilming saves 99 per cent of the space. It isn't a perfect solution to the problem though. First, it costs $100 to microfilm a file drawer's contents. Then you have to index what is on the film. Then you need an enlargement viewer so that you can read the microfilmed sheets when you have to refer to them. If you want something on the film, it is probably way down on the inside end of the roll, and you have to run the whole roll through to get the picture you want. If you really want to use an old micro-filmed document, you'll have to get an enlarged copy made. Remember, however, that rarely do you ever refer to your dead files, so microfilming is pretty good after all.

HOW MUCH CENTRALIZATION?

Centralization between Plants. Giant companies have plants all over the country. Individual plants do most of their own office work. Orders come in to district sales offices and are sent by them to the nearest factory. There the jobs are scheduled, made and shipped, or shipped from stock. And from there the bills go out to customers. The home office gets general reports, but has little to do with each plant's internal paper work.

Some companies do centralize certain records though. The Aluminum Company of America, a giant company, has all sales orders come to its home office in Pittsburgh, from which they are parcelled out to the factories. And, after shipment, the home office mails out all the bills. Doing that lets the home office balance out work loads of factories and lets it divide up big customer company orders so that its closest factories will ship to the closest customer factories. Sometimes, however, orders are not shipped as soon as they could be because of delays in getting shipping instructions from the home office. Most companies also keep some other records, such as employee pension records, centrally.

Centralization in Single Plants. Sales records, customer orders, inventory records, payroll, cost accounting, and general accounting are all fairly big office jobs. Within individual plants, most of these are centralized.

But typing, stenographic service, filing, and duplication (mimeographing) can be centralized or not. Neither choice is perfect. Some of both usually works best.

Centralize and you get better use of people. They work under specialized supervisors, and they work most the time at the thing they are best at (statistical typists, accounting statement typists, legal typists, patent typists). You get excellent work. You cut waste because you can balance out work (typists can cut stencils or type, stenographers can be given routine typing to fill in lulls). Individual rush jobs can be handled easily, just put several people on them. You cut office machine idleness and so get by with fewer machines. And because of volume you can use expensive machines (varitypers and multiliths) economically.

Absences and vacations don't upset things so much in centralized offices. It is easy to work new people in. Salaries are easier to administer, and you can even use production standards and incentives.

But centralization is not all good. Services are slower—usually much slower. If you want to send a letter, you have to dictate to a dictaphone, and send discs or tapes to central stenographic, and then get letters back hours or days later. Corrections take still longer. It is hard to explain anything unusual. Also nothing is private in a central pool. Everyone's business is truly everyone's business.

Having a private secretary is a mark of distinction to men having them, so not having them takes that away. Probably you'd be better off not to centralize the secretarial work of middle-level or top offices. The loss in the use of secretaries is more than offset by saving the time of $10-an-hour officials.

The case for centralized filing of records and letters is different. Centralize them and you know where they are, and also can probably find them because you have well-trained filing clerks. But if individual departments must refer very often to filed papers, or if you have confidential papers, financial records, legal correspondence, patent material, and so on, you'd better let individual departments keep their own files. On the other hand, if two or three departments need the same files sometimes, central filing may be better. Of course you could make duplicates of letters, one for each file, but that multiplies your paper and you don't want to do this if you can help it.

OFFICE EQUIPMENT

Except for electronic data-processing machines and tabulating equipment, office machines are relatively simple. They include files, typewriters, intercom systems, dictating and transcribing machines, calculators, adding machines, bookkeeping machines, mimeographs, multiliths, and microfilming equipment. All these machines and the desk they set on are made especially for speed and ease of operation.

Office machines, like factory machines, cost money, but not nearly so much as factory machines. In most offices the furniture and machines combined cost less than $200 per employee per year. Office machines, too, need maintenance. If you have few of them it usually pays to let the company that sold you the machine keep it in working order. You can get regular inspections, cleaning, and minor repairs for a nominal service fee. In big offices, though, you have enough servicing to make it pay to have your own repairman.

OFFICE LAYOUT

Many office people work in scattered factory departments in ones and twos. How they arrange their desks is unimportant. But when you get into accounting, order receiving, and even engineering, production control, and personnel—you get into tens and twelves or even hundreds of workers.

Here, space and arrangements are important. Probably you can get by on as little as 50 square feet per clerk, but that is only a space 7 feet by 7 feet. Seventy-five feet per worker is still not overly generous.

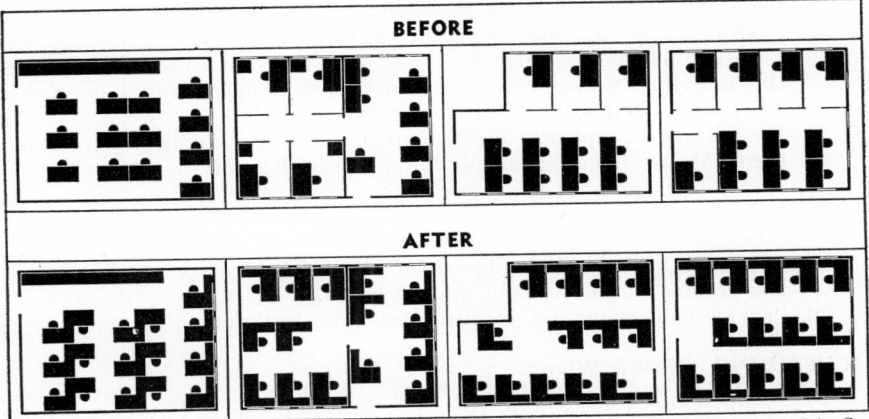

BEFORE

AFTER

The Globe-Wernicke Co.

FIG. 42–4. Various before and after arrangements of desks in offices. The new arrangement actually provides *more* work space per office worker than the old and allows more desk spaces to be provided at the same time.

Private offices run from 100 to 300 square feet. Back in Chapter 12 we talked about how to lay out the factory. Same ideas apply in offices, but here are some more guides just for offices:[2]

1. Utilize one large area in preference to an equivalent area of small parcels. The single large area permits better lighting, ventilating, supervising, and communicating.
2. Use uniform size desks in any one area. This gives better appearance and promotes the feeling of equality among employees.
3. Keep filing cabinets and other cabinets at uniform height in any one area to improve general appearance.
4. Use straight symmetry in layout. Avoid offsets, jogs, and angle arrangements.
5. Provide for work to flow in straight lines as nearly as possible. Avoid backtracking, crisscrossing, and unnecessary movement of papers. Give major preference to the dominant flows of work.
6. Provide for maximum work loads.
7. Have the work come to the employee, not the employee go to the work. Keep employee flow to a minimum.
8. Place related departments adjacent and keep jobs of a similar nature in close relationship.
9. Anticipate and provide for future changes. Keep the layout flexible.
10. Locate supervisors at rear of their work groups so that they can easily observe what goes on in the work area.
11. Place all employees so that they face in the same direction. Do not have employees facing one another.
12. Arrange desks so that ample natural light comes over the left shoulder. Do not have the employee facing a window.
13. Avoid private office locations which cut off natural light to the adjacent general office area.

---

[2] Reprinted from George R. Terry, *Office Management and Control* (3d ed.; Homewood, Ill.: Richard D. Irwin, Inc., 1958), pages 354–55.

14. Place units requiring noisy equipment and machines in an area with soundproofing to avoid disturbance to others.
15. Locate departments which normally have many visitors from the outside near the entrance or, if this is not feasible, make provisions so that this traffic will not disturb other departments.
16. Put files and frequently used equipment near the employees who use them. Abstain from putting all files at deadwall space.
17. Place filing cabinets back to back.
18. If a corner is required, consider the possibility of providing it with filing cabinets.
19. If possible, provide lounging areas where employees can relax during rest periods, talk informally, and eat lunch.
20. Provide convenient and adequate rest-room facilities.

SCHEDULING OFFICE WORK

Peaks and valleys are bound to occur in office work. Pay-check time in the payroll department and extra end-of-the month work for sending out bills to customers in the billing department are typical. You don't have to staff up for peak loads in each department, however. You can dovetail some of the different department peaks together by shifting clerks back and forth. You'll need to schedule and plan work loads and to train clerks for two or three jobs.

STUDY QUESTIONS

1. Why does office work tend to grow? Explain. Why doesn't management cut it back?
2. What is the difference between an office procedure and a system? Of what importance is the distinction?
3. How would you go about simplifying office work? Explain.
4. Who should design forms? Why? How?
5. Can production standards be used in offices? If so, why aren't they common?
6. When would you centralize filing of papers? When not? Justify your answer.
7. How many reports and papers should you keep? How long? Where? In what form?
8. What differences are there between layout techniques as they apply to offices and factories? What similarities? Discuss.

BIBLIOGRAPHY

Accident Facts. National Safety Council. (Annual.)

Advanced Management. Society for the Advancement of Management, Inc. (Monthly.)

American Standard Practice for Industrial Lighting. Illuminating Engineering Society, 1953.

American Standards Yearbook. American Standards Association. (Annual.)

AMRINE, HAROLD T.; RITCHEY, JOHN A.; and HULLEY, OLIVER S. *Manufacturing Organization and Management.* Prentice-Hall, Inc., 1957.

ANTHONY, ROBERT N. *Management Accounting.* Richard D. Irwin, Inc., 1956.

———. *Management Controls in Industrial Research Organizations.* Harvard Press, 1952.

APPLE, JAMES M. *Plant Layout and Materials Handling.* The Ronald Press Co., 1950.

BEEMAN, DONALD (ed.). *Industrial Power Systems Handbook.* McGraw-Hill Book Co., Inc.

BETHEL, LAWRENCE L.; ATWATER, FRANKLIN S.; SMITH, GEORGE H. E.; and STACKMAN, HARVEY A., JR. *Industrial Organization and Management.* 5th ed. McGraw-Hill Book Co., Inc., 1954.

BLAKE, ROLAND T. (ed.). *Industrial Safety.* 2d ed. Prentice-Hall, Inc., 1953.

BOWMAN, EDWARD H., and FETTER, ROBERT B. *Analysis for Production Management.* Richard D. Irwin, Inc., 1957.

CANNING, RICHARD G. *Electronic Data Processing for Business and Industry.* John Wiley & Sons, Inc., 1956.

CARLSON, ALBERT (ed.). *Economic Geography of Industrial Materials.* Reinhold Publishing Co.

CARROLL, PHIL. *How Foremen Can Control Costs.* McGraw-Hill Book Co., Inc., 1955.

———. *How to Control Production Costs.* McGraw-Hill Book Co., Inc., 1955.

———. *Time Study for Cost Control.* 3d ed. McGraw-Hill Book Co., Inc., 1954.

CHARNES, A.; COOPER, W. W.; and HENDERSON, A. A. *An Introduction to Linear Programming.* John Wiley & Sons, Inc., 1953.

CHURCHMAN, C. WEST; ACKOFF, RUSSELL L.; and ARNOTT, E. LEONARD. *Introduction to Operations Research.* John Wiley & Sons, Inc., 1957.

COPLEY, FRANK BARKLEY. *Frederick W. Taylor.* 2 vols. Harper & Bros., 1923.

COWDEN, DUDLEY J. *Statistical Methods in Quality Control.* Prentice-Hall, Inc., 1957.

DALE, ERNEST. *Planning and Developing the Company Organization Structure.* (Research Report No. 20.) American Management Association, 1952.

DAVIS, RALPH CURRIER. *The Fundamentals of Top Management.* Harper & Bros., 1952.

———. *Industrial Organization and Management.* 3d ed. Harper & Bros., 1957.

DE TOQUEVILLE, ALEXIS. *Democracy in America* (1840). Vol. II. Colonial Press, 1900.

DEAN, JOEL. *Managerial Economics.* Prentice-Hall, Inc., 1951.

DIEBOLD, JOHN, and TERBORGH, GEORGE. *Automation: The Advent of the Automatic Factory.* D. Van Nostrand Co., Inc., 1953.

DRUCKER, PETER F. *The Practice of Management.* Harper & Bros., 1954.

DUNCAN, ACHESON J. *Quality Control and Industrial Statistics.* Richard D. Irwin, Inc., 1952.

Electronics in Action. American Management Association, 1957.

Essentials of Machinery Procurement and Development. American Management Association, 1956.

Factory Management and Maintenance. McGraw-Hill Publishing Co. Inc. (Monthly.)

GARDNER, FRED V. *Profit Management and Control.* McGraw-Hill Book Co., Inc., 1955.

GARDNER, GLEN, and GARDNER, ROBERT L. *Vitalizing the Foreman's Role in Management.* McGraw-Hill Book Co., Inc., 1949.

GILLESPIE, CECIL. *Cost Accounting and Control.* The Ronald Press Co., 1957.

GILMOUR, ROBERT W. *Wage and Salary Control.* John Wiley & Sons, Inc., 1956.

GOETZ, BILLY E. *Management Planning and Control.* McGraw-Hill Book Co., Inc., 1949.

GOMBERG, WILLIAM. *A Trade Union Analysis of Time Study.* Prentice-Hall, Inc., 1955.

GRANT, EUGENE L. *Statistical Quality Control.* 2d ed. McGraw-Hill Book Co., Inc., 1952.

GRANT, EUGENE L., and NORTON, PAUL T. *Depreciation.* The Ronald Press Co., 1955.

GREENWALD, DAKOTA U. *Linear Programming, An Explanation of the Simplex Algorithm.* The Ronald Press Co., 1957.

HALSEY, GEORGE D. *Selecting and Developing First-Line Supervisions.* Harper & Bros., 1955.

Heating, Ventilating, and Air Conditioning Guide. American Society of Heating and Ventilating Engineers, 1952.

HEINRITZ, STUART F. *Purchasing Principles and Practices.* 2d ed. Prentice-Hall, Inc., 1951.

HENRICI, STANLEY B. *Standard Costs for Manufacturing.* 2d ed. McGraw-Hill Book Co., Inc., 1953.

HERSEY, REXFORD. *Better Foremanship.* 2d ed. Clinton Press, 1955.

HERTZ, DAVID B. *The Theory and Practice of Industrial Research.* McGraw-Hill Book Co., Inc., 1950.

HEYEL, CARL. *Foreman's Handbook.* 3d ed. McGraw-Hill Book Co., Inc., 1955.

HICKS, CHARLES B., and PLACE, IRENE. *Office Management.* Allyn & Bacon, 1956.

HOAR, ROGER S. *Patent Tactics and Law.* 3d ed. The Ronald Press Co., 1950.

HOLDEN, PAUL E.; FISH, LOUNSBURY S.; and SMITH, HUBERT L. *Top-Management Organization and Control.* McGraw-Hill Book Co., Inc., 1949.

How to Reduce Production Costs. American Management Association, 1956.

IMMER, JOHN R. *Layout Planning Techniques.* McGraw-Hill Book Co., Inc., 1950.

———. *Materials Handling.* McGraw-Hill Book Co., Inc., 1953.

Industrial Engineering, report of the British Specialist Team on Industrial Engineering. British Productivity Council, 1954.

IRESON, WILLIAM G. *Factory Planning and Plant Layout.* Prentice-Hall, Inc., 1952.

IRESON, W. GRANT, and GRANT, EUGENE L. *Handbook of Industrial Engineering and Management.* Prentice-Hall, Inc., 1955.

JAMISON, CHARLES L. *Business Policy.* Prentice-Hall, Inc., 1953.

Journal of the Franklin Institute. Annual issues a century ago.

Journal of the Royal Arts Society. Annual issues a century ago.

JUCIUS, MICHAEL J. *Personnel Management.* 3d ed. Richard D. Irwin, Inc., 1955.

JURAN, J. M. *Quality Control Handbook.* McGraw-Hill Book Co., Inc., 1950.

KELLER, L. WAYNE. *Management Accounting for Profit Control.* McGraw-Hill Co., Inc., 1957.

KIPERS, RICHARD F. *Manufacturing Analysis.* McGraw-Hill Book Co., Inc., 1949.

KOEPKE, CHARLES A. *Plant Production Control.* 2d ed. John Wiley & Sons, Inc., 1949.

KOONTZ, HAROLD O., and O'DONNELL, CYRIL. *Principles of Management.* McGraw-Hill Book Co., Inc., 1955.

KOZMETZKY, GEORGE, and KIRCHER, PAUL. *Electronic Computers and Management Control,* McGraw-Hill Book Co., Inc., 1956.

LANDY, THOMAS M. *Production Planning and Control.* McGraw-Hill Book Co., Inc., 1950.

LANHAM, E. *Job Evaluation.* McGraw-Hill Book Co., Inc., 1955.

LAWSHE, CHARLES H., JR. *Psychology of Industrial Relations.* McGraw-Hill Book Co., Inc., 1953.

LEARNED, E. P.; ULRICH, D. N.; and BOOZ, D. R. *Executive Action.* Harvard University, 1951.

LEWIS, HOWARD T., and ENGLAND, WILBUR B. *Procurement: Principles and Cases.* 3d ed. Richard D. Irwin, Inc., 1957.

LUNDY, JAMES L. *Effective Industrial Management.* The Macmillan Co., 1957.

MACNIECE, E. H. *Production Forecasting, Planning and Control.* John Wiley & Sons, Inc., 1957.

MAIER, NORMAN R. F. *Principles of Human Relations.* John Wiley & Sons, Inc., 1952.

Making Effective Use of Research and Development. American Management Association, 1956.

Management News. American Management Association. (Monthly.)

Management Review. American Management Association. (Monthly.)

MAPI Replacement Manual. Machinery & Allied Products Institute, 1950.

MATERIALS HANDLING INSTITUTE, INC. *Modern Methods of Materials Handling.* Prentice-Hall, Inc., 1951.

MAYNARD, H. B. (ed.). *Industrial Engineering Handbook.* McGraw-Hill Book Co., Inc., 1956.

MEES, KENNETH C. E., and LEERMAKERS, JOHN A. *The Organization of Industrial Scientific Research.* McGraw-Hill Book Co., Inc., 1950.

MELNITSKY, BENJAMIN. *Industrial Stores Keeping Manual.* Chilton Co., 1956.

———. *Management of Industrial Inventory.* Conover-Mast Publications, Inc., 1951.

———. *Profiting From Industrial Standardization.* Conover-Mast Publications, Inc., 1953.

MICHELON, LENO C. *Industrial Inspection Methods.* Harper & Bros., 1950.

Mill and Factory. Conover-Mast Publications, Inc. (Monthly.)

MOORE, FRANKLIN G. *Production Control.* McGraw-Hill Book Co., Inc., 1951.

MORROW, L. C. (ed.). *Maintenance Engineering Handbook.* McGraw-Hill Book Co., Inc., 1956.

MORROW, ROBERT L. 2d ed. *Motion Economy and Work Measurement.* The Ronald Press Co., 1957.

MORSE, PHILIP M., and KIMBALL, GEORGE E. *Methods of Operations Research.* John Wiley & Sons, Inc., 1951.

MUNDEL, MARVIN E. *Motion and Time Study Principles and Practices.* 2d ed. Prentice-Hall, Inc., 1955.

MUTHER, RICHARD. *Practical Plant Layout.* McGraw-Hill Book Co., Inc., 1955.

NADLER, GERALD. *Motion and Time Study.* McGraw-Hill Book Co., Inc., 1955.

NATIONAL SAFETY COUNCIL. *Handbook of Accident Prevention for Business and Industry.* 1953.

———. *Supervisor's Safety Manual.* 1956.

NEWMAN, WILLIAM H. *Administrative Action.* Prentice-Hall, Inc., 1951.

NIEBEL, BENJAMIN W. *Motion and Time Study.* Richard D. Irwin, Inc., 1955.

NIEBEL, BENJAMIN, and BALDWIN, EDWARD N. *Designing for Production.* Richard D. Irwin, Inc., 1957.

Operations Research. Journal of Operations Research Society of America. (Bimonthly.)

Operations Research Applied; New Uses and Extensions. American Management Association, 1957.

Organizing for Effective Systems Planning and Control. American Management Association, 1956.

Organizing the Research Function for Profit. American Management Association, 1957.

OTIS, JAY L., and LEUKART, RICHARD H. *Job Evaluation.* 2d ed. Prentice-Hall, Inc., 1956.

OWENS, RICHARD N. *Management of Industrial Enterprises.* 3d ed. Richard D. Irwin, Inc., 1957.

OXENFELDT, ALFRED R., and WATKINS, MYRON W. *Make or Buy.* McGraw-Hill Book Co., Inc., 1957.

Parkinson, C. Northcote. *Parkinson's Law.* Houghton Mifflin Co., 1957.

Personnel. American Management Association. (Bimonthly.)

PETERSEN, E., and PLOWMAN, E. G. *Business Organization and Management.* 3d ed. Richard D. Irwin, Inc., 1953.

Principles and Applications of Job Evaluation. (Studies in Personnel Policy, No. 62.) National Industrial Conference Board.

RITCHIE, WILLIAM E. *Production and Inventory Control.* The Ronald Press Co., 1951.

ROETHLISBERGER, F. J.; DICKSON, WILLIAM J.; and WRIGHT, H. A. *Management and the Worker.* Harvard University Press, 1947.

ROSCOE, EDWIN S. *Organization for Production.* Richard D. Irwin, Inc., 1955.

Sampling Procedures and Tables for Inspection of Attributes. Military Standard 105 A. Government Printing Office, 1950.

SCHALLER, GILBERT S. *Engineering Manufacturing Methods.* McGraw-Hill Book Co., Inc., 1953.

SCHIFF, ERIC. *Business Investment Policy.* Machinery and Allied Products Institute, 1956.

SCOTT, W. D.; CLOTHIER, R. C.; and SPRIEGEL, W. R. *Personnel Management.* 5th ed. McGraw-Hill Book Co., Inc., 1954.

SIMON, H. A. *Administrative Behavior*. Macmillan Co., 1957.
SIMONDS, ROLLIN, and GRIMALDI, JOHN V. *Safety Management*. Richard D. Irwin, Inc., 1956.
SPRIEGEL, W. R., and LANSBURGH, R. H. *Industrial Management*. 5th ed. John Wiley & Sons, Inc., 1955.
STANIER, WILLIAM. *Plant Engineering Handbook*. McGraw-Hill Book Co., Inc., 1950.
State Workmen's Compensation Laws (Supplement to Bull. No. 161.) U.S. Department of Labor, Bureau of Labor Statistics, 1955.
Successful Production Planning and Control. American Management Association, 1955.
TAYLOR, FREDERICK WINSLOW. *Scientific Management*, collection of the works of Taylor. Harper & Bros., 1947.
TERBORGH, GEORGE W. *Equipment Policy*. Machinery & Allied Products Institute, 1954.
TERRY, GEORGE R. *Office Management and Control*. 3d ed. Richard D. Irwin, Inc., 1958.
———. *Principles of Management*. Rev. ed. Richard D. Irwin, Inc., 1956.
THUESEN, H. G. *Engineering Economy*. Prentice-Hall, Inc., 1957.
URE, ANDREW. *Philosophy of Manufactures*. C. Knight, 1835.
VAN DOREN, HAROLD L. *Industrial Design*. 2d ed. McGraw-Hill Book Co., Inc., 1954.
VILLERS, RAYMOND. *The Dynamics of Industrial Management*. Funk & Wagnalls Co., 1954.
VORIS, WILLIAM. *Production Control*. Richard D. Irwin, Inc., 1956.
WESTING, JOHN H., and FINE, I. V. (eds.). *Industrial Purchasing*. John Wiley & Sons, Inc., 1955.
WHITIN, THOMSON N. *The Theory of Inventory Management*. Princeton University Press, 1953.
WHITWORTH, SIR JOSEPH, and WALLIS, GEORGE. *The Industry of the United States*. George Routledge & Co., 1854.
YASEEN, LEONARD C. *Plant Location*. American Research Council, 1956.
YODER, DALE. *Personnel Management and Industrial Relations*. 4th ed. Prentice-Hall, Inc., 1956.
———. *Personnel Principles and Policies*. Prentice-Hall, Inc., 1952.

INDEX

This book has been set on the Linotype in 10 point Janson leaded 2 points. Chapter numbers are in 18 point Lydian Bold italics and chapter titles in 18 point Lydian Bold caps. The size of the type page is 27 by 47 picas.